Sec.4.1 Exponential properties

If $b > 0$ and u and v are any real numbers, then

$$b^u b^v = b^{u+v} \qquad b^0 = 1$$

$$b^u/b^v = b^{u-v} \qquad b^1 = b$$

$$(b^u)^v = b^{uv}$$

Sec. 4.3 Logarithm properties

If b, u, and v are positive ($b \neq 1$) and p is any real number, then

$$\log_b(uv) = \log_b u + \log_b v \qquad \log_b 1 = 0$$

$$\log_b(u/v) = \log_b u - \log_b v \qquad \log_b b = 1$$

$$\log_b(u^p) = p \log_b u$$

Sec. 4.4 Natural exponential and logarithmic functions

The base of the natural exponential function (e^x) and the natural logarithmic function ($\ln x$) is the number $e \approx 2.718281828$. These functions are related:

$$\ln x = y \text{ if and only if } e^y = x$$

$$\begin{cases} e^{\ln x} = x & \text{for all po} \\ \ln e^x = x & \text{for all re} \end{cases}$$

Sec. 5.1 Circular sector

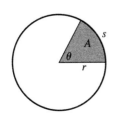

Arc length: $s = r\theta$

Area of sector: $A = \frac{1}{2}r^2\theta = \frac{1}{2}rs$

$\left.\right\}$ where θ must be measured in radians

Sec. 5.2 Trigonom

Unit Circle

For any $P(t)$ on the unit circle, $\begin{cases} \text{the } x\text{-coordinate is } \cos t \\ \text{the } y\text{-coordinate is } \sin t \end{cases}$

Sec. 5.3 Trigonometric functions

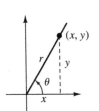

Angles in Standard Position

$$\cos \theta = x/r$$

$$\sin \theta = y/r$$

$$\tan \theta = y/x$$

Angles in Right Triangle

$$\cos \alpha = \text{adj/hyp}$$

$$\sin \alpha = \text{opp/hyp}$$

$$\tan \alpha = \text{opp/adj}$$

Sec. 5.4 Graphs

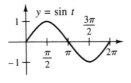

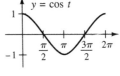

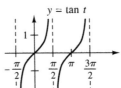

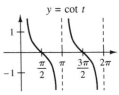

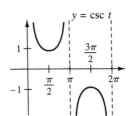

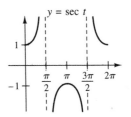

PRECALCULUS

PRECALCULUS
Second Edition

Lawrence O. Cannon
Utah State University

Joseph Elich
Utah State University

HarperCollins*College*Publishers

Sponsoring Editors: **Anne Kelly and George Duda**
Development Editor: **Laurie Golson**
Cover Design: **Jeanne Calabrese**
Project Coordination and Text Design: **Elm Street Publishing Services, Inc.**
Compositor: **Interactive Composition Corporation**
Printer and Binder: **R. R. Donnelley & Sons Company**
Cover Printer: **R. R. Donnelley & Sons Company**

Precalculus, Second Edition

Library of Congress Cataloging-in-Publication Data
Cannon, Lawrence O.
    Precalculus / Lawrence O. Cannon, Joseph Elich.—2nd ed.
        p.   cm.
    Elich's name appears first on the earlier ed.
    Includes bibliographical references and index.
    ISBN 0-673-46728-7
    1. Mathematics. I. Elich, Joseph, 1918– . II. Title.
QA39.2.C345   1993
512′.1—dc20   93–15109

        95 96 9 8 7 6 5 4 3

TABLE OF CONTENTS

CHAPTER 10   **ANALYTIC GEOMETRY**   **532**

![HISTORICAL NOTES]

HISTORICAL NOTES

████████████████ **FOR GRAPHERS**

Precalculus, second edition, is intended for any calculus preparatory course. We have revised the book to make it more responsive to the challenges of a new century while remaining mindful of two critical areas precalculus students need to develop: (1) an understanding of basic concepts, and (2) the mathematical skills for problem solving.

In this edition, we continue to stress the importance of graphs and pictures to visualize and understand functions, as we did in the first edition.

We assume that every student has convenient access to a scientific calculator, and we include graphing calculator exercises in an optional feature called **For Graphers**.

New Content Highlights

Chapter 1 is rewritten to focus on the role of mathematics as a model, tool, and language for problem solving. The algebra review is streamlined to give more coverage of significant digits and approximation. The advantages and limitations of calculators are also outlined.

We moved some of the geometry material to Chapter 2 to emphasize graphing and the relation of core graphs to more complicated ones obtained by translating, stretching, and compressing.

Chapter 3 takes better advantage of technology for visualizing and understanding functional behavior and includes finding both exact and approximate zeros for polynomial functions.

New sections on harmonic motion, vectors, matrix algebra, and linear programming are added to the material in Chapters 6, 7, and 9.

New and Enhanced Features

New problem-solving strategies accompany many of the solutions to examples. The strategies help students to examine ways they might think about and attack the problems posed in the examples. We hope the strategies get students to make estimates, to think about the results of their calculations, and to get into the habit of asking themselves if their solutions are reasonable. The strategies also alert students to common errors to avoid.

Many more *examples and figures* have been added to this edition. The examples include more applications, more conceptual material, and more calculus-related applications. We not only have more figures and graphs to aid student conceptualization, but we also urge students to draw their own graphs to analyze functional behavior and to determine relationships when solving problems.

For Graphers is an optional feature that allows instructors to incorporate the graphing calculator into the course as much or as little as they wish. Each is contained on one page and usually includes an example and related exercises. More than 250 exercises help students to understand their graphing calculator in order to make it a more effective learning tool.

Historical Notes appear in new and revised forms in the second edition. They engage students by helping them realize that mathematics is a very human endeavor that continues by the efforts of ordinary mortals as much as by geniuses.

New, *first-person anecdotes* are brief, autobiographical quotes from contemporary mathematicians that inspire and entertain students. An appendix, "How They Came to Mathematics," gives capsule biographies of the individuals quoted.

More than 5,000 *exercises* appear in the second edition. Several types of nontraditional exercises are added to the regular mix of drill and conceptual exercises for new ways of learning:

- *Check Your Understanding* exercises at the end of each section go beyond the typical skill-based exercises. They give the students a chance to find out how well they understand the key ideas of the section.

- *Test Your Understanding* exercises at the end of each chapter allow students to integrate the important ideas in the chapter.

- *Explore and Discover* exercises are expanded from the previous edition. These open-response questions include writing assignments and topics that the instructor can use for group discussion and class projects.

  Writing exercises help students examine their own learning processes as well as understand mathematics more thoroughly and develop communication skills.

  Classroom projects help instructors to incorporate collaborative learning in the course. Students sometimes learn more effectively when they work together, and they can often make difficult ideas more understandable to their peers.

- *Review Exercises* at the end of each chapter help students to assess their concept mastery and progress, to synthesize ideas from several sections, and to consolidate larger topics.

Supplement Package to Accompany the Text

This text is accompanied by the following supplements:

For the Instructor

The *Instructor's Guide* includes solutions to all of the text exercises. A collection of problems for each chapter can be used for tests.

The *HarperCollins Test Generator for Mathematics* is one of the top testing programs on the market for IBM and Macintosh computers. It enables instructors to select questions for any section in the text or to use a ready-made test for each chapter. Instructors may generate tests in multiple-choice or open-response formats, scramble the order of questions while printing, and produce up to 25 versions of each test. The system features printed graphics and accurate mathematical symbols. The program also allows instructors to choose problems randomly from a section or problem type, or to choose problems manually while viewing them on the screen with the option to regenerate variables. The editing feature allows instructors to customize the chapter disks by adding their own problems.

The *QuizMaster On-Line Testing System,* available in both IBM and Macintosh formats, coordinates with the HarperCollins Test Generator and allows instructors to create tests for students to take at the computer. The test results are stored on disk so the instructor can view or print test results for a student, a class section, or an entire course.

With *GraphExplorer software,* available in IBM and Macintosh versions, students can graph rectangular, conic, polar, and parametric equations; zoom; transform functions; and experiment with the families of equations quickly and easily.

For the Student

The *Student's Solution Manual* contains detailed solutions to the odd-numbered exercises. It is available for student purchase; ask your college bookstore manager to order ISBN 0-673-46729-5.

College Algebra and Trigonometry: Graphing Calculator Investigations by Dennis Ebersole of Northampton County Area Community College provides investigations that help students to visualize and explore key concepts, to generalize and apply concepts, and to identify patterns. To order, use ISBN 0-06-500888-X.

Precalculus Investigations Using DERIVE by David Mathews of Longwood College will help you to integrate technology with DERIVE software into either an algebra and trigonometry or precalculus course. Twelve lab exercises provide carefully structured, interactive learning environments for students. The manual includes real-world applications, concept overviews, and lab reports. To order, use ISBN 0-673-99097-4.

Acknowledgments

We are very appreciative to the reviewers who read substantial portions of the manuscript for this and the previous edition. They generously shared their ideas and suggestions, for which we are grateful. They include the following:

Richard Armstrong, St. Louis Community College at Florissant Valley
Holly J. Ashton, Brevard Community College
Kathleen J. Bavelas, Manchester Community College
Lewis Blake, Duke University
Paul W. Britt, Louisiana State University—Baton Rouge
Alan S. Chesen, Miami University—Hamilton
Douglas B. Crawford, College at San Mateo
Bettyann Daley, University of Delaware
Margaret D. Dolgas, University of Delaware
Thomas Farmer, Miami University
Richard Flint, University of Minnesota—Duluth
Ray Glenn, Tallahassee Community College
Lyman Holden, Southern Illinois University
Patrick A. Hughes, Cuesta College
Giles Wilson Maloof, Boise State University
Eldon L. Miller, University of Mississippi
Theodore F. Moore, Mohawk Valley Community College
John F. Moseley, Kentucky State University

Henry Osner, Modesto Junior College
Reed Parr, Salt Lake Community College
Donna Fields Rochon, Western Washington University
Jean E. Rubin, Purdue University
Steven Terry, Ricks College
David G. Wright, Brigham Young University

Thanks also go to George Duda and Anne Kelly, our editors at HarperCollins, to Laurie Golson, our developmental editor, and to Michele Heinz of Elm Street Publishing Services.

Finally, to our families, we are deeply indebted for their patience, understanding, and support during the countless hours we devoted to the project.

Lawrence O. Cannon
Joseph Elich

If you have a graphing calculator in your hand, you hold more computing power than entire universities had 25 years ago. And your access to that power is much more convenient. A generation ago no computer scientist could have imagined how easily you can now get your calculator to do complex calculations.

In this brief introduction, we only touch on its capabilities, but there is enough information for you to use your calculator as a helpful tool in your study of mathematics. With the techniques we talk about here, you can do everything required for the graphing calculator exercises in this text. More important, as you become more comfortable with your calculator, you can explore additional capabilities on your own.

To build more skill and confidence with your calculator, we suggest that you take advantage of several resources:

- Go through this section carefully, calculator in hand, and make sure that your display matches any display the book shows.

- Work with friends; talk with each other. Together you can be your own best teachers.

- Share problems and successes with your instructor. Sometimes your teacher will know how to do something you've missed, and sometimes you will discover something that will help others in the class. The technology of graphing calculators is changing so rapidly that all of us are learning together.

- Come back to this introduction regularly, especially when you encounter something new in your work or when you want to refresh some particular calculator skill.

- The headings in the margins identify particular calculator capabilities as an index when you want a reminder about how to do something you need for an exercise or exploration.

What Calculators?

Our discussion refers specifically to the Texas Instruments TI-81 and TI-82, and the Casio fx7700G. Other calculators are available, but if you learn to use one of these, you will have little difficulty learning to use comparable features on similar machines. Throughout our discussion, we refer to the machines as TI and Casio. Machine-specific instructions appear in two columns: TI on the left, and Casio on the right.

All calculations are done on the home or text screen.

TI	Casio
You are on the home screen when you press `ON`, and you can always return to the home screen from any other display screen by `2nd` `QUIT`.	You get a status display when you press `ON` (the same as the clear key, `AC`). You want to be in computation mode, so if the top line does not read RUN/COMP, press `MODE` `+`. Then `AC` clears the screen for computing.

Multiple Key Use

Most keys perform at least three different operations (usually color coded): one as marked on the key itself and two others as marked above the key.

TI

2nd activates the functions and menus in light blue above most keys. ALPHA activates the letter keys and functions in grey (such as the comma above the decimal point).

Casio

SHIFT activates the functions in orange above most keys, as well as some menus in green (as MATH). ALPHA activates the letter keys and functions in pink (such as the bracket above the decimal point).

Doing Compu-tations

Graphing calculators take instruction differently than earlier scientific calculators. To evaluate $\sqrt{2^2 + 3^2}$, for example, most calculators perform (and display) the operations in sequence, so that you square 2 (4), add the square of 3 (9), add by pressing = (13), and then $\sqrt{}$ (3.6 . . .). On a graphing calculator, we type in the entire operation before evaluating:

$\sqrt{}$ (2 x² + 3 x²), and the display reads $\sqrt{(2^2+3^2)}$.

When we press ENTER or EXE , the result is displayed on the next line, 3.605551275.

WARNING: Parentheses are essential; without parentheses, $\sqrt{2^2 + 3^2} = \sqrt{4 + 9} = 11$.

Making Correc-tions

An extremely useful feature of the graphing calculators we are using is their capacity to replay the most recent calculation, either to repeat with some modification, or to correct errors. Suppose, for instance, that you forgot parentheses. Press ↑ (on the TI-81) or ← (on the Casio), or 2nd ENTRY (on the TI-82) and the previous display appears again:

$$\sqrt{2^2 + 3^2}.$$

Move the cursor with the arrow keys to the 2 and insert (INS on TI, SHIFT INS on Casio) (. Then move the cursor to the right end of the expression and type) . Now the display reads $\sqrt{(2^2 + 3^2)}$. When you press ENTER or EXE to execute the corrected instruction, the proper result appears on the next line. After pressing the replay arrow, you can insert, delete, or write over to make changes.

Graphs and Windows

Of all the features of graphing calculators, our most immediate concern is drawing graphs. It is a simple matter to graph any of the functions we study in precalculus; it is sometimes more difficult to get a picture that shows what we need. To get an appropriate picture, we must know a little about how the calculator works and the effect of changing the viewing window.

The calculator screen has nearly 6000 pixels that can be turned on individually. Each pixel has coordinates that depend on the range values we set. For a given function, no matter how large or how small an x-range we choose, the calculator splits the range into 95 pieces and calculates a y-value for each column of pixels. If the y-value fits into the specified y-range, then the appropriate pixel is turned on, and when y-values differ for adjacent x-values, the machine is programmed to connect the dots visually by lighting several pixels in the same column. The result is the graph displayed on the graphics screen. By changing the x- and y-range values we determine the viewing window and, accordingly, what we see.

Here are several simple examples. First we set the ranges with some values to give nice pixel coordinates.

	TI	Casio
Set Range / **Familiar Window**	Press RANGE (TI-81) or WINDOW (TI-82). We get a new screen and can set maximum and minimum values for both variables. Enter the following values (ENTER after each): -4.7, 4.8, 1, -3.1, 3.2, 1 or (TI-82) ZOOM 4. Because this window has such convenient pixel addresses, we will call this the "Familiar Window." The scale ("scl") determines the tick marks on the axes and can be set as you wish.	Press RANGE. We get a new screen and can set maximum and minimum values for both variables. Enter the following values (EXE after each): -4.7, 4.7, 1, -3.1, 3.1, 1. This window has such convenient pixel addresses that we will call it the "Familiar Window." You can set this window by pressing F1 (for INITial values). The scale ("scl") determines the tick marks on the axes and can be set as you wish.
Choose Function	Press Y= to get the function screen. If there are any functions showing, CLEAR each one. Then go to the first line and enter "X" with the X|T key. To get the graph, press GRAPH. We go to the graphics screen and the calculator displays the graph, the familiar line $y = x$.	Press GRAPH and the screen displays "Graph Y=" so that we need only enter the function to be graphed. Press X,θ,T to enter "X". To get the graph, press EXE. We go to the graphics screen and the calculator displays the graph, the familiar line $y = x$.

We want to explore the effect of changing the viewing window. The function remains the same; only our view changes.

	TI	Casio
Change Window	Return to RANGE and change the x-values to -10 to 10. (Note that we must use the "change-sign" key, the grey key on the bottom line; the blue "subtract" key won't work.) Then press GRAPH to see the graph in this new window.	Return to RANGE and change the x-values to -10 to 10. We need to get back to the home screen, so after entering the new range values, press RANGE twice. The home screen should show "Graph Y=X" and "done". Press the replay key ← and "done" disappears. Press EXE to regraph the function in the new window.

We still see a line, but the line does not bisect the first quadrant as we expect the line $y = x$ to do. The slope is much steeper, and the y-values are out of range for much of the window. Now repeat the above instructions to get an x-range of $[-2, 2]$ and regraph the function. The result is a line with a much flatter slope that doesn't reach the top or bottom of the screen. To re-emphasize, the function has not changed; our view has.

Now change the x-range again to $[-0.1, 0.1]$ and regraph. The screen shows us an essentially horizontal line. Press the $\boxed{\text{TRACE}}$ key (above $\boxed{\text{F1}}$ on Casio) and move the cursor along the graph with the right or left arrow keys. The coordinates of the points are displayed. Notice that the y-coordinates match the x-coordinates (as they should for the graph $y = x$), but they are so small relative to the 6.2 unit y-range that for much of the screen, no new pixels are turned on above or below the x-axis, and even at the ends of the screen, the graph is at most one pixel away from the x-axis. To go to the other extreme, set an x-range of $[-100, 100]$ and regraph. Now the graph is limited to two or three vertical columns of pixels and is almost indistinguishable from the y-axis.

| Equal Scale Window |

The graphs that look most familiar to us are those with the same size unit on each axis. With unequal units, slopes are off and circles don't look round. We don't want to be bound to the same scale, but it is handy to be able to "square-up" a graph at times. Graphing calculator screens have about $\frac{2}{3}$ as many vertical pixels as horizontal ($\approx\frac{64}{96}$). If a viewing window is $[a, b] \times [c, d]$, we call it an Equal Scale window if the ratio $(d - c)/(b - a)$ is about $\frac{2}{3}$. Thus the Familiar Window is an Equal Scale window. To equalize the scale on a window, either make the y-range $\frac{2}{3}$ of your x-range, or make the x-range $\frac{3}{2}$ as large as your y-range. On the TI ZOOM menu, option #5 is titled Square. It equalizes the scale by making the y-range $\frac{2}{3}$ of the current x-range.

| Zoom: In/Out Box |

One of the most powerful features of graphing calculators is the capacity to zoom in or out on a graph. Zooming in lets us examine a graph as if we had a microscope of variable magnification; zooming out lets us step back to view the graph from afar to see the general shape. We can zoom in or out with our focus on a particular point, or we can select a box, which has the effect of visually setting a window. Comparing graphs before and after you select a box illustrates dramatically how the calculator stretches or squeezes part of a graph to fit a window.

We illustrate by looking at a graph that will become very familiar in Chapter 5, $y = \sin x$, and we will also discover more range and window features. Both of our calculators have special automatic windows for trigonometric functions, but first we must be in radian mode.

| | TI | Casio |

Setting Radian Mode

TI

Press MODE. The third line shows "Rad" and "Deg". If "Rad" is not already highlighted, move the cursor down to "Rad" and ENTER.

Casio

Press SHIFT DRG (above 1). We see a menu at the bottom of the screen, beginning "Deg" "Rad." Press F2 EXE to put the calculator in radian mode.

Trig Window

TI

Press Y=, clear Y1, and press SIN X|T. We get the "Trig" window from the ZOOM menu, #7. Pressing 7 sets the Trig Window and the graph appears immediately. If we wish, we can see the range values by pressing RANGE.

Casio

Press GRAPH SIN. Do *not* put in "X". Without the X, when we press EXE, the calculator automatically sets the Trig Window, and the graph appears immediately. If we wish, we can see the range values by pressing RANGE.

We now want to use this graph to experiment with some zoom features, starting with Box to draw a box around something we wish to examine. The calculator then stretches or squeezes the contents of the box to fill the entire screen. The diagram shows the curve $y = \sin x$ as it appears in the Trig Window, with three different boxes we want you to duplicate in turn.

TI

To draw a box, press ZOOM. Option #1, "Box," is already highlighted, so ENTER. We return to the graph, but now a cursor is blinking near the origin. Use the arrow keys to move the cursor up to one corner of the first box in the diagram, and ENTER. This fixes a corner of the box. Now moving the arrow keys will produce a line, and then a box whose size changes with the cursor. When we have a box we want, press EXE again, and the box is blown up to fill the screen. Trace along the curve to find the coordinates of the highest point on the graph.

Return to the original graph by ZOOM 7 (TI-81), ZOOM MEM 1 (TI-82), and draw a box like our second box in the diagram. This second box is not one we would ordinarily choose; it shows how the machine squeezes and stretches the contents of a box to fit the screen.

Finally, return to the original graph and draw a box like our third box in the diagram. Use trace to find out where the graph crosses the x-axis. Zoom in again, if needed, to verify that the crossing is very near $(\pi, 0)$.

Casio

To draw a box, press F2 for the Zoom menu. The first option is BOX, so press F1. We return to the graph, but now a cursor is blinking near the origin. Use the arrow keys to move the cursor up to one corner of the first box in the diagram, and EXE. This fixes a corner of the box. Now moving the arrow keys will produce a line and then a box whose size changes with the cursor. When we have a box we want, press EXE again, and the box is blown up to fill the screen. Trace along the curve to find the coordinates of the highest point on the graph.

Return to the original graph by ZOOM and then F5 (for "Original"). Then draw a box like our second box in the diagram. This second box is not one we would ordinarily choose, but it shows how the machine squeezes and stretches the contents of a box to fit the screen. Finally, return to the original graph and draw a box like our third box in the diagram. Use trace to find out where the graph crosses the x-axis. Zoom in again, if needed, to verify that the crossing is very near $(\pi, 0)$.

Second Graph	A common use of the graphing calculator is to look at several graphs together and to find points of intersection, so we first consider how to graph more than one function in the same window. First clear the graphics screen by 2ND DRAW 1 ENTER on the TI, or from the graph on the Casio, F5 EXE.

TI

Go to the Y= menu and with Y1 = sin X, move the cursor to the second line and let Y2 = X/8. Set a range of [−6.28, 6.28] × [−1.5, 1.5] and then graph. The sine curve appears first, followed by the line $y = x/8$.

Casio

On the home screen (G↔T toggles between the graph screen and home), enter "Graph Y = sin X." To add a second instruction, insert a line feed, SHIFT EXE, and enter "Graph Y = X/8." Set a range of [−6.28, 6.28] × [−1.5, 1.5] and then graph. The sine curve appears first, followed by the line $y = x/8$.

Power Scroll	Trace along the line clear to the right edge of the screen and beyond; the screen scrolls to show more of the graph. This allows us to see more of a graph extending off-screen to the right or to the left. The automatic power scroll only works to the right and the left, not up and down.
Find Inter- sections	We want to see if the line $y = \frac{x}{8}$ meets the sine curve further to the right than our original window shows. Scrolling to the right, it appears that there is another intersection near the top of the next hump of the sine. If we zoom into a box around the intersection, we see that the curves meet at two points, near (7.5, 0.94) and 7.95, 0.994).

Graphing in Parametric Mode

The use of parametric equations is an important topic in Chapter 10 and in several areas of calculus, but graphing in parametric mode on a graphing calculator need not wait until we have studied parametric equations. Basically, to graph the function $y = f(x)$ in parametric mode, we graph the number pairs (x, y), where both x and y are expressed in terms of a common variable t. When the calculator is in parametric mode, pressing the X|T key (TI) or the X,θ,T key (Casio) automatically puts "T" on the screen rather than "X," and the calculator is set to accept function pairs for x and y. Begin by changing to parametric mode.

TI

Casio

Set Parametric Mode	Press MODE. The fourth line of the screen shows "Function Param." Move the cursor until it is blinking on "Param" and ENTER. Then 2ND QUIT returns the home screen.	Press SHIFT MODE. Under "Graph type" we want "X:PARAM," so press ×. We return to the home screen and are ready to enter our function in parametric form.

Enter Parametric Equations	We begin by plotting $y = \sqrt{x}$, and then we will add the line $y = x$.

TI

On the Y= menu enter $X_{1T} = T$, $Y_{1T} = \sqrt{T}$. The machine plots pairs (x, y) where $y = \sqrt{x}$.

Casio

Press GRAPH and "Graph (X,Y)=" appears. Enter (T,√T). The machine plots pairs (x, y), where $y = \sqrt{x}$.

In parametric mode, we must set range values for three variables; t, x, and y. For most of our applications, we simply set $x = t$ or $y = t$ so choose a suitable xy-window and set the same range for t as for x or y. "Tstep" (TI) or "ptch" (Casio) determines the t-intervals for plotting. Unless the t-range is very large, we set a fairly small value, say 0.1.

	TI	Casio
Set Range for T, X, Y	For the RANGE we set values of T, X, and Y. Use [0,4.7] for T and X and Tstep = .1, and [0,3.2] for Y. Then GRAPH . The graph of $y = \sqrt{x}$ is one we have seen.	Press RANGE , set X and Y values as before. Press RANGE again to set values for T. Use [0,4.7] × [0,3.1] for the xy-window, and [0,4.7] for T, with ptch: 0.1. Then GRAPH . The graph of $y = \sqrt{x}$ is one we have seen.

Now return to Y= and enter $X_{2T} = \sqrt{T}$, $Y_{2T} = T$. This has the effect of interchanging the x- and y-coordinates from the graph of $y = \sqrt{x}$.

G↔T returns the home screen. Replay (with left arrow), and add a second function, Graph $(X,Y)=(\sqrt{T},T)$. This has the effect of interchanging the x- and y-coordinates from the graph of $y = \sqrt{x}$.

When we GRAPH , we see two graphs. The first is $y = \sqrt{x}$; the other is a reflection in the line $y = x$. Now Trace. The cursor moves along one curve. The up and down arrows switch from one curve to the other. The X- and Y-values switch while the T-value remains the same.

When we GRAPH , we see two graphs. One is $y = \sqrt{x}$ and the other is a reflection in the line $y = x$. Now Trace. The cursor moves along one of the curves. The up and down arrows switch us from one curve to another. The X- and Y-values switch while the T-value remains the same.

Matrix Operations

These calculators have outstanding routines for matrix operations. Both calculators will store at least three matrices (of any size up to 6 × 6), calculate determinants and inverses, and compute matrix products. We illustrate the steps to compute $A^{-1}B$ for the matrix solution of the matrix equation $AX = B$, where $A = \begin{bmatrix} 5 & 3 \\ 4 & 2 \end{bmatrix}$ and $B = \begin{bmatrix} 1 \\ 2 \end{bmatrix}$.

TI | Casio

Enter or Edit Matrix

The $\boxed{\text{MATRX}}$ key takes us to a pair of menus. Move to the EDIT screen with the right arrow key and choose the matrix to edit, say A. On the new screen, set the size 2×2 and move down to the entries. Enter 5, 3, 4, 2, using the arrow keys if needed to make corrections. For matrix B, $\boxed{\text{MATRX}}$ EDIT 2, set size 2×1 and enter 1, 2. Now the matrices A and B are stored and we must return to the home screen ($\boxed{\text{2ND}}$ QUIT) to

Matrix Product

work. $\boxed{\text{2ND}}$ [A] (above 1) puts [A] on the screen of the TI-81; $\boxed{\text{MATRX}}$ 1 on the TI-82. For the matrix product AB, [B] $\boxed{\text{ENT}}$ and the product is displayed. For $A^{-1}B$, the solution to $AX = B$, [A] $\boxed{x^{-1}}$ [B] $\boxed{\text{ENT}}$ displays the product, the column matrix with entries 2 and -3.

We first get into MATRIX mode by pressing $\boxed{\text{MODE}}$ 0. The menu at the bottom of the screen allows us to choose the matrix to edit, say A ($\boxed{\text{F1}}$). To set size, $\boxed{\text{F6}}$ $\boxed{\text{F1}}$ (DIM) and enter 2×2; the resized matrix A appears. Enter 5, 3, 4, 2 in turn, using the arrow keys if needed to make corrections. To enter matrix B, $\boxed{\text{PRE}}$ takes us back to the PREvious screen, where $\boxed{\text{F2}}$ gives B. Set size ($\boxed{\text{F6}}$ $\boxed{\text{F1}}$ 2×1) and put in entries 1, 2. Now A and B are stored. $\boxed{\text{PRE}}$ returns the menu where we can operate. If we want the matrix product AB, we just press $\boxed{\text{F5}}$ ($\times$) and the product appears as matrix C. For $A^{-1}B$, the solution to $AX = B$, $\boxed{\text{F1}}$ gives A, and $\boxed{\text{F4}}$ shows A^{-1} as matrix C. $\boxed{\text{F1}}$ puts A^{-1} into the A register. Then $\boxed{\text{PRE}}$ $\boxed{\text{F5}}$ ($\times$) shows the product $A^{-1}B$ in C. The solution is the column matrix with entries 2, -3.

Wrong Size Product

Try to multiply matrices of the wrong size. Attempting to compute BA will give an "Error" message.

Try to multiply matrices of the wrong size. Attempting to compute BA (first interchange A and B by $\boxed{\text{F5}}$ (A↔B), then $\boxed{\text{PRE}}$ $\boxed{\times}$) gives "Dim ERROR."

Determinants

For the square matrix A, to calculate $|A|$, on the home screen, $\boxed{\text{MATRX}}$ 5 or $\boxed{\text{MATRX}}$ MATH 1 displays "det". Then [A] $\boxed{\text{ENT}}$ gives det[A] $= -2$.

For the square matrix A, to calculate $|A|$, on the A screen, $\boxed{\text{F3}}$ ($|A|$) displays detA $= -2$.

1

BASIC CONCEPTS: REVIEW AND PREVIEW

In Chapter 1 we consider the nature of mathematics, where it comes from, and how it is used. This chapter lays a foundation for the entire book. Section 1.1 describes how mathematical models represent real-world problems, including calculator use and approximations. Sections 1.2 and 1.3 review terminology and the properties of real numbers related to ordering and absolute values. Section 1.4 discusses the language of mathematics and the need for careful, precise use of words and symbols. Section 1.5 reviews some of the techniques and notions from elementary algebra that must be mastered before going on to study the rest of the book. Section 1.6 emphasizes the importance of graphs in representing sets both on a number line and in a plane. The final section demonstrates how to approach and formulate problems, displaying techniques that are useful throughout the study of mathematics.

Understanding Mathematics

Mathematics compares the most diverse phenomena and discovers the secret analogies that unite them.
   Joseph Fourier

What Is Mathematics?

Consider these situations and note what they have in common:

1. At the edge of the Beaufort Sea, north of the Arctic Circle, a dozen adults of the Inuit people are tossing a young boy aloft on a human-powered trampoline made of a blanket.

2. From the observation deck of the Sears Tower (the world's tallest building at 1454 feet) a visitor can see nearly six miles further out into Lake Michigan than someone at the top of the John Hancock Center (1127 feet tall).

3. A pilot of a Goodyear blimp heading south over Lake Okeechobee at 5300 feet wants to estimate the time remaining before visual contact with the Orange Bowl, where a football game is to be televised.

Each of these situations deals with the curvature of the earth's surface and the fact that it is possible to see farther from a higher elevation. The Inuits want to get an observer high enough to see whether the pack ice is breaking up in the spring; the Sears Tower is 327 feet taller than the Hancock Center; at an elevation just over a mile, how far can the blimp pilot see?

   Mathematics strips away the differences in these situations and finds one simple model to describe common key features. Figure 1.1 shows a cross section of the earth as a circle with center at O and radius r. Our model assumes a

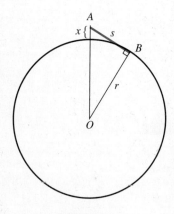

FIGURE 1.1

How far can you see from x miles above the earth?

2

spherical earth, a fairly good approximation of the truth. From point A located x feet above the earth, the line of sight extends to B. (Line AB is tangent to the circle and hence perpendicular to radius OB.)

All of the situations listed above fit in this structure. The Inuit boy, the visitor to the top of a skyscraper, and the blimp pilot could each be seen as located at point A for different values of x. For any given x, applying the Pythagorean theorem (discussed in Section 1.6) to the right triangle AOB gives the corresponding distance s to the horizon.

$$r^2 + s^2 = (r + x)^2, \text{ where } x, r, \text{ and } s \text{ are in miles.}$$
$$r^2 + s^2 = r^2 + 2rx + x^2$$
$$s^2 = 2rx + x^2$$
$$s = \sqrt{2rx + x^2}.$$

Part of the power of mathematics comes from its capacity to express in a single sentence truths about several seemingly diverse situations. The solution to one equation automatically applies to any other application that gives rise to the same equation. The expression for s can be used to solve any of the problems listed above. See Exercises 33–38.

Mathematics and the Real World

Much of the importance and vitality of mathematics comes from its relationship with the world around us. Humans invented numbers to count our sheep; we created rules for addition and multiplication as we needed to barter or compare land holdings. As human understanding of the world grew more sophisticated, mathematical tools grew as well. Sometimes mathematical curiosity led people in unexpected directions and their explorations became important for their own sake.

Mathematics is a lively part of our intellectual heritage. Some of the most intriguing and challenging mathematical investigations grew out of attempts to answer seemingly innocuous questions or understand simple observations. The most lasting and significant human achievements are direct consequences of our desire to understand and control the world.

Mathematics and Mathematical Models

When we encounter a problem whose solution involves the use of mathematics, we must decide how much detail is essential. In the line-of-sight examples the solution assumed the earth as a perfect sphere. The differences between that mathematician's earth and the actual globe are substantial. The equation for the distance to the horizon (s miles) implies that someone could see more than 40 miles from the top of either the Sears Tower or the Hancock Center; on a clear day someone in Chicago might want to check that conclusion.

In a mountain valley ringed by peaks that rise several thousand feet, it isn't possible to see 40 miles in any direction, even from 1500 feet up. Does that invalidate our mathematical model? Of course not; we must know something about particulars when we interpret a result. Questions about the way the world works frequently require simplifying assumptions to make the problems more tractable. See the Historical Note, Mathematical Models and Gravity (p. 142).

Geometry really turned me on. My father taught me by giving me problems to solve. He gave me thousands of geometry problems while I was still in high school. After he gave me one and I came back with a solution, he would say, "Well, I'll give you another one." The solving of thousands of problems during my high school days—at the time when my brain was growing—did more than anything else to develop my analytic power.

George Dantzig

Calculators

A calculator is an indispensable piece of equipment for this course. Virtually any calculator with keys for the trigonometric functions (⎡Sin⎤, ⎡Cos⎤) or logarithmic functions (⎡Log⎤ or ⎡Ln⎤) will be adequate. Since we use calculators regularly, we will discuss calculator use from time to time throughout the course, especially when we encounter new functions.

The calculator is an incredibly powerful device, but limited. While a calculator can do wonders, it might be called a "Smart-Stupid," a name coined by Douglas Hofstadter. A calculator is a machine capable of amazing feats of computation, but not smart enough to know that you meant to press ⎡+⎤ instead of ⎡÷⎤ .

Approximate Numbers and Significant Digits

When we use mathematics to model the real world, we have to realize that measurements of physical quantities can be only approximations. A biologist may be able to count exactly the number of eggs in a bird's nest, but comparing the volume or weight of two eggs requires *approximate numbers,* since any number we use is only as good as our measuring device. We also use approximate numbers when we need a decimal form for a number such as $\sqrt{3}$.

Questions involving approximations entail decisions about the tolerable degree of error. Error tolerance decisions usually hinge on concerns other than mathematics, but all of us must make such decisions in working problems that involve measurements or when we use calculators. We need guidelines.

Perhaps the greatest problem in working with calculators is interpreting displayed results. When we enter data, the calculator returns so many digits so quickly and easily that we may think we have gained more information than we really have. This difficulty can be illustrated by an example from a recent calculus text. The book derives an equation for the volume of a pyramid, as shown in Figure 1.2, and then applies the formula to find the volume of the Great Pyramid of Cheops. The original dimensions are given (approximately) as

$$s = 754 \text{ feet} \qquad \text{and} \qquad h = 482 \text{ feet.}$$

When we substitute these numbers into the formula, a calculator immediately displays 91341570.67, from which the authors conclude that the volume is "approximately 91,341,571 cubic feet." In the following example, we illustrate why we are not justified in rounding to the nearest cubic foot, even if the values for s and h are measured to the nearest foot.

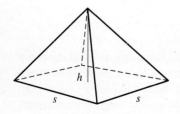

FIGURE 1.2

The volume of a pyramid of height h and sides s: $V = \frac{1}{3}s^2h$.

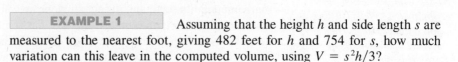 **EXAMPLE 1**   Assuming that the height h and side length s are measured to the nearest foot, giving 482 feet for h and 754 for s, how much variation can this leave in the computed volume, using $V = s^2h/3$?

Solution

To say the linear measurements are correct to the nearest foot means that they satisfy the inequalities

$$753.5 < s < 754.5 \qquad \text{and} \qquad 481.5 < h < 482.5.$$

Strategy: Let V_0 be the volume using the smaller values of s and h, while V_1 is the volume using the larger values of s and h. Compute V_0 and V_1, and then compare the results.

Using the smaller values for s and h gives

$$V_0 = \frac{(753.5)^2(481.5)}{3} \approx 91,125,841.12.$$

The upper values for s and h yield

$$V_1 = \frac{(754.5)^2(482.5)}{3} \approx 91,557,631.87.$$

The difference between V_1 and V_0 is

$$V_1 - V_0 \approx 431,790.75.$$

The computed and actual volumes could differ by nearly *half a million cubic feet!* See Example 3. ▲

The world of mathematics is an *ideal* world, dealing with exact numbers and precise relationships, but mathematics also says much about the inexactitude and fuzziness of the physical world. In applying mathematics, we create a precise model to mirror an imprecise reality. Whenever mathematics delivers an answer for an applied problem, we must ask what the numbers mean and what degree of significance they have for the original problem.

As a simple case in point, we may ask for the diagonal distance across a piece of land which a surveyor has measured as a square one mile on a side. The mathematical model for the diagonal of a square tells us that the diagonal is approximately $\sqrt{2}$ miles. The number of decimal places we can legitimately use from our calculator display depends on the accuracy of the measurement of the sides of the lot. If the sides are measured to the nearest 10 feet, then it makes no sense to represent the diagonal as a six-place approximation for $\sqrt{2}$; such accuracy would be close enough to measure the thickness of a single blade of grass!

Significant Digits, Precision, and Scientific Notation

When multiplying and dividing approximate numbers, we consider **significant digits,** the digits that indicate measured accuracy. Normally zeros that serve only to locate the decimal point are not significant. These numbers each have four significant digits:

400.5 ft.   0.002596 mm.   1.032 km.   93,410,000 mi.

In scientific applications, special notation makes it easy to identify the significant digits. By moving the decimal point as needed, any positive real number can be written as a product of a number between 1 and 10 and some power of 10. A number written as such a product is said to be in **scientific notation.** We would write the four numbers above in scientific notation as follows.

4.005×10^2 2.596×10^{-3} 1.032 9.341×10^7

Usually we do not write 10^0 for a number that is already between 1 and 10.

In addition and subtraction, our concern is *precision,* the *question of which decimal places have meaning.* If we are told that an ancient tree is 3000 years old, we consider that 3000 as a less precise number than the age of a 17 year old.

> **Guidelines for Computation with Approximate Numbers**
>
> In multiplication and division with approximate numbers, round off final results to the *least number of significant digits* in the data used. Results are no more accurate than the least accurate data; *record no more significant digits than occur in* any *of the given data.*
>
> In addition and subtraction with approximate numbers, round off final results to the *least level of precision* in the data used.

EXAMPLE 2   Determine which digits are significant, and write the number in scientific notation.

(a)   325.6   (b)   28.40   (c)   205,000   (d)   0.00640

Solution

(a)   All digits are significant: $325.6 = 3.256 \times 10^2$.

(b)   The last 0 does not locate the decimal point; all digits are significant: $28.40 = 2.480 \times 10$.

(c)   Without additional information, we can only assume that the first three digits are significant: $205,000 = 2.05 \times 10^5$. If we had some reason to believe that 205,000 represented a measurement accurate to the nearest hundred, then four digits would be significant and we would write $205,000 = 2.050 \times 10^5$.

(d)   The first three zeros just locate the decimal point, but the last zero is significant: $0.00640 = 6.40 \times 10^{-3}$.   ▲

Strategy: Since both s and h are given to three significant digits, use the formula and round off the result to the same accuracy.

EXAMPLE 3   Use the formula $V = s^2h/3$ to calculate the volume of the Great Pyramid of Cheops, where $s = 754$ feet and $h = 482$ feet.

Solution

Follow the strategy.

$$V = \frac{(754)^2(482)}{3} \approx 91,341,570.67 \approx 91,300,000.$$

Hence the volume is approximately 91,300,000 cubic feet. As we would expect, the result lies well between the extreme values of V_0 and V_1 in Example 1.   ▲

EXAMPLE 4   Simplify, assuming that the numbers are approximate measurements:

(a) $2.483 + 15.4$ (b) $7200 - 1720 + 32$

Solution

(a) Since 15.4 (measured to the nearest tenth) is less precise than 2.483 (measured to the nearest thousandth), round off the sum to the precision of the less precise number.

$$2.483 + 15.4 = 17.883 \approx 17.9.$$

(b) The least precise of these numbers is 7200, so round off the sum to the same level of precision, to the nearest 100:

$$7200 - 1720 + 32 = 5512 \approx 5500. \quad \blacktriangle$$

The Number Pi

The number pi, denoted by the Greek letter π, pops up in the most unexpected places in mathematics, several of which we will encounter in this book. See the Historical Note, The Number π. Most of us first meet pi in connection with circles through its historical definition as the ratio of the circumference to the diameter of a circle. Scientific calculators have a key labeled $\boxed{\pi}$ which approximates π:

$$\pi \approx 3.141592654.$$

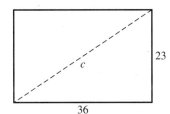

FIGURE 1.3

Find the distance between opposite corners.

EXAMPLE 5   A rectangular garden measures 23 feet by 36 feet (to the nearest foot). What is the distance c between its opposite corners? (See Figure 1.3.)

Solution

Using the Pythagorean theorem,

$$c = \sqrt{23^2 + 36^2} \approx 42.72001873.$$

Our rule suggests stating the result to two significant digits, so the diagonal distance is 43. $\blacktriangle$

EXAMPLE 6   The radius of a circle measures 24.5 cm. What is its area?

Solution

The equation for the area A of a circle in terms of the radius is $A = \pi r^2$. Replacing r with 24.5, and rounding off to three significant digits,

$$A = \pi(24.5)^2 \approx 1890.$$

The area is approximately 1890 cm^2. $\blacktriangle$

THE NUMBER π

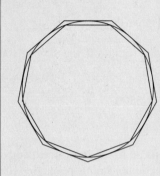

The number π (which represents the ratio of the circumference to the diameter of a circle) has fascinated people since antiquity. The Babylonians, Chinese, and Hebrews all knew that the value of π was near 3. The Egyptians computed the area of a circle by squaring $\frac{8}{9}$ of the diameter, implying a value for π of $\frac{256}{81} = 3.16$. In about 200 B.C., Archimedes used inscribed and circumscribed polygons (see figure) to get the bounds $3\frac{10}{71} < \pi < 3\frac{1}{7}$. We still use $\frac{22}{7}$ as a convenient (and fairly good) approximation.

More than 1700 years passed before a Frenchman, Viète, significantly improved on the efforts of the Greeks. Real progress accompanied the invention of calculus. Sir Isaac Newton calculated π to 15 decimal places and confessed to a colleague, "I am ashamed to tell you to how many figures I carried these calculations, having no other business at the time." By 1706 Machin in England correctly computed π to 100 digits.

Through all this time, people were looking for a repeating pattern of digits. It wasn't until 1761 (2000 years after the Pythagoreans proved that $\sqrt{2}$ is not rational) that Lambert (from Germany) finally proved that π is *irrational,* so the pattern of digits will never repeat.

EXERCISES 1.1

Check Your Understanding

Exercises 1–5   True or False. Give reasons for your conclusion.

1. If x is any real number, then x^2 is positive.

2. If x is a number such that $\frac{1}{x} < 1$, then x must be greater than 1.

3. For all nonnegative numbers x and y, $\sqrt{x + y} \geq \sqrt{x} + \sqrt{y}$.

4. Without additional information, we must assume that the zeros in the numbers 45,000 and 0.0045 are not significant digits.

5. All of the zeros in the numbers 3.005 and 4.720 are significant digits.

Exercises 6–10   Complete the sentence by selecting from the list below *all choices* that make the statement true.

(a) 1   **(b)** 2   **(c)** 3

(d) 4   **(e)** 6   **(f)** 8

6. In the decimal representation of the quotient $\frac{5}{7}$, the digit in the fourth decimal place is _____ .

7. The number of significant digits in
 (a) 10.2 is _____   **(b)** 1200 is _____
 (c) 0.12 is _____ .

8. If the dimensions (in inches) of a cereal box are measured to be $3.1 \times 7.2 \times 8.0$, then the diagonal of the box can be calculated and the number of meaningful significant digits is _____ .

9. If the two legs of a right triangle are 2 and 5, then the length of the hypotenuse is less than _____ .

10. If the radius of a circle is doubled, then its area increases by a factor of _____ .

Explore and Discover

1. Describe how you might determine the number of revolutions made by a wheel on your car in traveling one mile. Your description should indicate what measurements you would need to take and what kind of assumptions you would make about the shape of the wheel and tire.

2. From your computations in Exercise 1, what is the outside diameter of a wheel measured vertically? Horizontally? If the measurements differ, how does that difference affect your model? If you assumed a perfect circle, how accurate do you think your conclusions are?

Develop Mastery

Exercises 1–15 The purpose of these exercises is to give you practice with your calculator. Many of the exercises are simple enough to solve in your head. Their real value comes from the effort to make your calculator do all the necessary steps and agree with the result in brackets. Some answers are rounded off to three decimal places.

1. $(6 + 3) \cdot 8$ [72]

2. $6 \cdot 3 + 3 \cdot 8$ [42]

3. $2 \cdot 3^2 + 3 \cdot 4^2$ [66]

4. $\frac{1/2 - 3}{4}$ [−0.625]

5. $\frac{2/3 + 3/4}{7/8}$ [1.619]

6. $(2 \cdot 3)^2 + (3 \cdot 4)^2$ [180]

7. $\frac{(4.5 - 3.1)^2}{5.6}$ [0.35]

8. $4.5^2 - \frac{(3.1)^2}{5.6}$ [18.534]

9. $\frac{(4.5)^2 - (3.1)^2}{5.6}$ [1.9]

10. $\sqrt{2 + 3}$ [2.236]

11. $\sqrt{2} + \sqrt{3}$ [3.146]

12. $\frac{1}{\sqrt{2}} + \frac{1}{\sqrt{3}}$ [1.284]

13. $\frac{1}{\sqrt{2} + \sqrt{3}}$ [0.318]

14. $\frac{1 + \sqrt{3^2 - 1}}{3}$ [1.276]

15. $\sqrt{\frac{4 - \sqrt{2}}{2}}$ [1.137]

16. Write each number in scientific notation and tell which digits are significant.

    (a) 406   (b) 40,600   (c) 406.0
    (d) 0.0406   (e) 0.004060

17. Tell which digits are significant, and then express in standard decimal notation.

    (a) 3.2×10^3 (b) 5.06×10^{-3}
    (c) 8.400×10^{-2}

18. Round off to two significant digits.

    (a) 3254   (b) 4.32   (c) 0.05642
    (d) 357894   (e) 80.5   (f) 0.35501

19. Give decimal approximations rounded off to three significant digits.

    (a) $\sqrt{3}$ (b) $\frac{\pi}{5}$ (c) $\sqrt{25\pi}$
    (d) $\sqrt{17 + \sqrt{47}}$

Exercises 20–26 Consider all data as measured numbers. Round off each computation to an appropriate number of significant digits.

20. $x = 33.7$, $y = 2.35$, $z = 0.431$. Find (a) xy
    (b) yz (c) $\frac{y}{z}$.

21. Evaluate
    (a) $32.51 + 63.2$ (b) $65.1 - 23.18 + 2.407$
    (c) $\sqrt{3.82^2 + 2.63^2}$.

22. Find the length of a diagonal of a rectangle with sides of 31.4 feet and 16.3 feet.

23. The radius of a circle is 3.64 feet. What is its (a) circumference? (b) area?

24. The legs of a right triangle measure 2.4 meters and 5.8 meters. Find the (a) hypotenuse (b) perimeter (c) area.

25. What is the volume of a sphere whose radius measures 31.4 inches? See inside cover.

26. The length of a side of a square is 2.4 yards and the radius of a circle is 4.1 feet. Which has the greater area, the square or the circle? By how much?

Exercises 27–32 Consider the following.

(a) Nicole rides the Sky Scraper, a gigantic Ferris wheel at Lagoon.

(b) The Galapagos islands, located near the equator, rotate with the earth.

(c) Minneapolis, located near 45° latitude, rotates with the earth.

(d) A space capsule orbits the earth.

(e) The earth orbits the sun.

Each situation can be modeled mathematically as an object traveling in a circular orbit of radius r at a fixed speed. The distance traveled in one revolution is $2\pi r$ (the circumference of the circle). The time T for one rotation and the rotational speed V are related by the equation $VT = 2\pi r$. (*Hint:* If N is the number of rotations per unit of time, then $T = \frac{1}{N}$.)

27. The Sky Scraper carries its riders to a height of nearly 150 feet, has a wheel diameter of 137 feet, and has

two speeds, 1.30 or 1.60 rotations per minute. At the slower speed, determine Nicole's speed in **(a)** feet per second   **(b)** feet per minute   **(c)** miles per hour.

28. Determine Nicole's speed, as in Exercise 27, when the Sky Scraper rotates 1.60 times per minute.

29. How fast are the giant tortoises of the Galapagos islands moving about the center of the earth (in miles per hour)? Take the radius of the earth to be 3960 miles.

30. How fast is a baseball player standing at first base in Minneapolis moving about the axis of the earth (in miles per hour)? See the diagram.

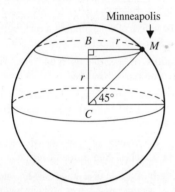

31. If the space capsule is 270 miles above the surface of the earth and makes a complete orbit in 1.70 hours, how fast is it traveling due to its rotation? The radius of the earth is 3960 miles.

32. How fast are Nicole, the Galapagos tortoises, and the entire baseball team in Minneapolis traveling (in

miles per hour) about the sun? Use 93 million miles as the distance from the earth to the sun.

Exercises 33–38   Use the model discussed at the beginning of this section (Figure 1.1), with the radius of the earth as 3.960×10^3 miles. If h is the height in feet, then $x = \frac{h}{5280}$ miles.

33. How far can the Inuit boy see if he is tossed 15 feet high?

34. Compare the distances that can be seen from **(a)** the Sears Tower ($h = 1454$ feet)   **(b)** John Hancock Center ($h = 1127$ feet).

35. If the air is clear, how far should the pilot of the Goodyear blimp be able to see from an elevation of 5300 feet?

36. From the top of Lagoon's Sky Scraper ride (see Exercise 27), how far should Nicole be able to see over the Great Salt Lake?

37. Sailors follow a rule of thumb that they can see as many miles to the horizon as the square root of their height above the waterline, so a lookout in a crow's nest 64 feet up should be able to see about 8 miles. How does this estimate compare with the figure given by the model in this section? Which do you think is more accurate? Why? See Develop Mastery Exercise 53, Section 7.1.

38. If $s = \sqrt{2rx + x^2}$, as in this section, write an equation giving x in terms of s. A lighthouse is to be built on Cape Cod on the shore of the Atlantic Ocean. How high above the ocean must the observation platform be to allow the operator to see a ship 12 miles from shore?

SECTION 1.2   **Real Numbers**

....

The complexities of modern science and modern society have created a need for scientific generalists, for men (and women as well) trained in many fields of science. The habits of mind and not the subject matter are what distinguish the sciences.
                    Mosteller, Bode, Tukey, Winsor

Numbers occur in every phase of life. It is impossible to imagine how anyone could function in a civilized society without having some familiarity with numbers. We recognize that you have had considerable experience working with numbers, and we also assume that you know something about the language and notation of sets.

Subsets of Real Numbers

We denote the set of real numbers by R. We make no attempt to develop the properties and operations of R; this is reserved for more advanced courses. Several subsets of the set of real numbers are used so frequently that we give them names. Most of these sets are familiar. The set of **natural numbers** is also called the set of **positive integers** or **counting numbers.** A **prime** is a positive integer greater than 1 that is divisible only by 1 and itself. The table lists the most commonly encountered subsets of R.

Subsets of R	
Subset	*Symbol and Elements*
Natural numbers	$N = \{1, 2, 3, \cdots\}$
Whole numbers	$W = \{0, 1, 2, 3, \cdots\}$
Integers	$I = \{\cdots, -1, 0, 1, 2, 3, \cdots\}$
Even integers	$E = \{\cdots, -2, 0, 2, 4, 6, \cdots\}$
Odd integers	$O = \{\cdots, -3, -1, 1, 3, 5, \cdots\}$
Prime numbers	$P = \{2, 3, 5, 7, 11, 13, \cdots\}$
Rationals	$Q = \{\frac{p}{q} \mid p, q \in I, q \neq 0\}$
Irrationals	$H = \{x \mid x \in R \text{ and } x \notin Q\}$

I had such an amazingly deprived high school education. There wasn't a useful math book in the library.

Bill Gosper

Figure 1.4 indicates schematically that some of the sets listed are subsets of others. For example, $P \subset N$, $N \subset W$, and $W \subset I$. The sets E and O together make up I, so we can write $E \cup O = I$. Further, for any $p \in I$, since $p = \frac{p}{1}$, every integer is also a rational number, so $I \subset Q$.

The existence of some irrational numbers has been known since at least the time of the ancient Greeks, who discovered that the length of the diagonal of a

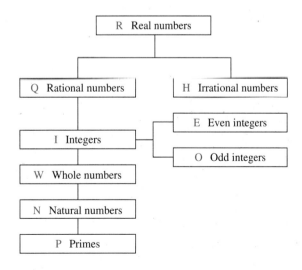

FIGURE 1.4

Subsets of the real numbers.

square is not a rational multiple of the length of the sides (see Develop Mastery Exercise 38). The length of the diagonal of a unit square is the irrational number $\sqrt{2}$, and we recognize many others such as $\sqrt{3} - 1$ and $2 + \sqrt[3]{7}$ and π. The ratio of the circumference of any circle to its diameter is the number π (pi), approximately 3.1416. (See the earlier Historical Note, "The Number Pi.")

Although most of this book (and most of calculus as well) involves only real numbers, we also make use of the set of *complex numbers* (see Section 1.3), especially in Chapters 3 and 7.

EXAMPLE 1   Determine whether the statement is true.

(a) $N \subset Q$ **(b)** $I \cap H = \emptyset$ **(c)** $\sqrt{5} \in Q$
(d) $\sqrt{64} \in H$ **(e)** $41 \in P$ **(f)** $87 \notin P$

Solution

Strategy: Think about the meaning of each set (in words). For given numbers, decide if each fits the description of the indicated set.

(a) True; every natural number is rational.
(b) True; every integer is rational and hence not in H.
(c) False; $\sqrt{5}$ is an irrational number.
(d) False; $\sqrt{64} = 8$ and is not irrational.
(e) True; 41 is a prime number.
(f) True; $87 = 3 \cdot 29$, so 87 is not a prime number.   ▲

EXAMPLE 2   Simplify:

(a) $P \cap N$ **(b)** $W \cap Q$ **(c)** $Q \cup H$

Solution

(a) $P \cap N = P$; every prime number is also a natural number.
(b) $W \cap Q = W$; every whole number is also a rational number.
(c) $Q \cup H = R$; every real number is rational or irrational.   ▲

Decimal Representation of Numbers

Every real number also has a decimal "name." For instance the rational number $\frac{3}{4}$ can also be written as 0.75, which is called a **terminating decimal.** To get the decimal representation for the rational number $\frac{5}{11}$, we divide 5 by 11 and get the **repeating** (nonterminating) decimal 0.454545. . . , which we write as $0.\overline{45}$. The bar notation indicates that the block under the bar, in this instance 45, repeats forever. A terminating decimal can also be considered as repeating. For instance, $\frac{3}{4}$ can be named by 0.75, or by $0.75\overline{0}$, or even by $0.74\overline{9}$ (see Example 3).

An irrational number such as $\sqrt{2}$ has a **nonterminating** and **nonrepeating** decimal representation. The distinction between repeating and nonrepeating decimals distinguishes the rational numbers from the irrationals.

Approximating Pi

As indicated in Section 1.1, the important number π occurs in problem-solving applications as well as theoretical mathematics. In recent years sophisticated techniques have allowed computer evaluation of π to *billions* of decimal places,

Approximating the Number π

π = 3.14159 26535 89793 23846 26433
83279 50288 41971 69399 37510
58209 74944 59230 78164 06286
20899 86280 34825 34211 70679
82148 08651 32823 06647 09384
46095 50582 23172 53594 08128
48111 74502 84102 70193 85211
05559 64462 29489 54930 38196
44288 10975 66593 34461 28475
64823 37867 83165 27120 19091
45648 56692 34603 48610 45432
66482 13393 60726 02491 41273

A computer can calculate these first 300 digits of π in minutes. The same calculation by hand requires months of work.

People continued to be fascinated by π even after it was shown to be irrational. In 1844 Johann Dase, who could multiply 100 digit numbers in his head, took months to compute π to 205 digits. The champion at hand calculating must be William Shanks, who spent 20 years to grind out 707 digits. His record stood until 1945, when D. W. Ferguson used a mechanical calculator to find an error in Shanks' 528th digit.

No further search for accuracy can be justified for practical purposes of distance or area computation. An approximation to 45 digits would measure the circumference of a circle encompassing the entire universe with an error less than the radius of a single electron. People have found many other reasons, in addition to the sheer fascination of knowing, for computing the digits of π, though.

Computers brought a new era. In 1949, a machine called ENIAC, composed of rooms full of vacuum tubes and wires, in 70 hours computed 2037 digits of π.

More recent milestones are listed below. Remarkably, the last record was achieved on a *home-built* super computer. You can read more in "Ramanujan and Pi," *Scientific American* (Feb. 1988), and in "The Mountains of Pi," *The New Yorker* (Mar. 12, 1992).

1973	Jean Guilloud, M. Bouyer	CDC7600	1 million digits
1985	R. William Gosper	Symbolics	17 million digits
1986	David H. Bailey	Cray-2	29 million digits
1987	Yasumasa Kanada	NEC SX-2	134 million digits
1989	D. and G. Chudnovsky		480 million digits
1990	Yasumasa Kanada	NEC SX-2	1 billion digits
1991	D. and G. Chudnovsky	M Zero	2.26 billion digits

but there is still no way to express the decimal representation of π exactly. See the Historical Note, "Approximating the Number π."

The rational number $\frac{22}{7}$ is sometimes used as an approximation of π, but it is important to understand that π is not equal to $\frac{22}{7}$. Other rational number approximations of π include $\frac{333}{106}, \frac{355}{113}$, and $\frac{208,341}{66,317}$ (see Develop Mastery Exercises 39 and 40).

Characterizing Real Numbers

A real number is **rational** if and only if its decimal representation repeats or terminates.

A real number is **irrational** if and only if its decimal representation is nonterminating and nonrepeating.

From Decimal Representation to Quotient Form

Finding a decimal representation for a given rational number is simply a matter of division; going the other way is more involved, but not too difficult. Given a number x with a repeating representation, these steps will yield the desired rational number:

1. Multiply x by an appropriate power of 10 to move the decimal point to the beginning of the repeating block.

2. Multiply x by another power of 10 to move the decimal point to the beginning of the next block.

3. The difference between these two multiples of x is an integer, which allows us to solve for x.

EXAMPLE 3   Express each number as a quotient of integers in lowest terms.

(a) 0.74 **(b)** $0.\overline{74}$ **(c)** $0.74\overline{9}$

Solution

(a) From the meaning of decimal notation, $0.74 = \frac{74}{100}$, which reduces to $\frac{37}{50}$. Thus 0.74 represents the rational number $\frac{37}{50}$.

(b) With a repeating block, we follow the procedure outlined above. Let $x = 0.\overline{74}$. The decimal point is already at the beginning of the block, so multiply by 100 to move the decimal point to the beginning of the next block.

$$\begin{array}{r} 100x = 74.\overline{74} \\ x = 0.\overline{74} \\ \hline 99x = 74, \text{ from which } x = \dfrac{74}{99}. \end{array}$$

Thus $0.\overline{74}$ represents the rational number $\frac{74}{99}$. You may wish to verify this by dividing 74 by 99.

(c) Let $y = 0.74\overline{9}$, multiply by 1000, then by 100, and take the difference:

$$\begin{array}{r} 1000y = 749.\overline{9} \\ 100y = 74.\overline{9} \\ \hline 900y = 675, \text{ from which } y = \dfrac{675}{900} = \dfrac{3}{4}. \end{array}$$

Hence $0.74\overline{9}$ represents the rational number $\frac{3}{4}$, which says that $\frac{3}{4}$ has *two different* decimal names, $0.74\overline{9}$ and 0.75. Actually, every rational number that can be written as a terminating decimal has two representations. ▲

Note that the procedure outlined above involves subtracting repeating decimals as if they were finite decimals. We will justify such operations in Section 8.2.

Exact Answers and Decimal Approximations

When we use a calculator to evaluate a numerical expression, in most cases the answer is a **decimal approximation** of the exact answer. When we ask for a four decimal place approximation, we mean round off the calculator display to four decimal places.

> **EXAMPLE 4** Use a calculator to get a four decimal place value. Is the value exact or an approximation?
>
> **(a)** $\frac{3}{4} + \frac{1}{8}$ **(b)** $\frac{1}{5} + \frac{2}{3}$ **(c)** $\sqrt{2}$

Solution

(a) $\frac{3}{4} + \frac{1}{8} = 0.8750$; exact decimal value.

(b) $\frac{1}{5} + \frac{2}{3} \approx 0.866666667 \approx 0.8667$; approximation.

(c) $\sqrt{2} \approx 1.414213562 \approx 1.4142$; approximation. ▲

Square Roots and the Square Root Symbol

There are two numbers whose square is 2. That is, the equation $x^2 = 2$ has two roots. We reserve the symbol $\sqrt{2}$ for the **positive root,** so the roots of the equation are $\sqrt{2}$ and $-\sqrt{2}$, which we often write as $\pm\sqrt{2}$. For every positive x, the calculator will display a positive number when we press $\boxed{\sqrt{x}}$, and we use $\sqrt{x}$ to denote the positive number whose square is x.

> **EXAMPLE 5** Find an approximation rounded off to four decimal places.
>
> **(a)** $1 + \sqrt{3}$ **(b)** $\sqrt{1 + \sqrt{3}}$

Solution

(a) Using a calculator, we get $1 + \sqrt{3} \approx 2.7321$.

(b) After evaluating $1 + \sqrt{3}$, and with the full decimal capacity of your calculator in the display, press $\boxed{\sqrt{x}}$ to get

$$\sqrt{1 + \sqrt{3}} \approx 1.6529. \quad ▲$$

EXERCISES 1.2

Check Your Understanding

Exercises 1–4 True or False. Give reasons for your conclusion.

1. The number π is equal to $\frac{22}{7}$.
2. The integer 119 is a prime number.
3. The intersection of the set of rational numbers and the set of irrational numbers is the empty set.
4. The set of prime numbers is a subset of the set of odd numbers.

Exercises 5–10 Complete the sentence by selecting from the list below *all choices* that make the statement true.

(a) a real **(b)** an even **(c)** an odd

(d) a rational

5. Every integer is also _____ number.
6. The product of two odd numbers is _____ number.

7. Every prime number is also _____ number.

8. The sum of two odd numbers is _____ number.

9. Every prime number greater than 2 is _____ number.

10. The integer 1 is _____ number.

Explore and Discover

1. Explain why you cannot identify a largest real number. Why can't ∞ be treated as a real number? What would happen if we tried to use ∞ with operations like addition or subtraction?

2. What rational numbers have terminating decimal representations? Consider the fractions in the following two sets and find their decimal representations.

   (a) $\frac{1}{2}, \frac{1}{4}, \frac{1}{5}, \frac{1}{8}, \frac{1}{16}, \frac{1}{20}, \frac{1}{25}, \frac{1}{40}, \frac{1}{80}$

   (b) $\frac{1}{3}, \frac{1}{6}, \frac{1}{9}, \frac{1}{11}, \frac{1}{15}, \frac{1}{18}$

   From your observations in these particular cases, make a conjecture about the positive integers n for which $\frac{1}{n}$ will have a terminating decimal representation.

3. The decimal representation for $\frac{1}{7}$ is $0.\overline{142857}$, so we say that $\frac{1}{7}$ has a repeating decimal expansion with a cycle of length 6.

   (a) Find the decimal representation of $\frac{2}{7}, \frac{3}{7}, \frac{4}{7}, \frac{5}{7}$, and $\frac{6}{7}$. Compare the cycle for each with the cycle for $\frac{1}{7}$. Explain the relationships between these cycles and the cycle for $\frac{1}{7}$ by dividing 7 into 1 and looking at the remainder.

   (b) What is the 185th digit after the decimal point in the decimal representation of $\frac{1}{7}$?

   What is the sum of

   (c) the first 6 digits?

   (d) the first 20 digits after the decimal point?

4. The repeating decimal for $\frac{8}{17}$ has a repeating cycle of 16 digits. Find a way to use your calculator to find the cycle of 16 digits. Can you use your method to find the repeating cycle for $\frac{4}{19}$?

Develop Mastery

Exercises 1–8   Determine whether each statement is true or false. Refer to the subsets of R listed in this section.

1. (a) $0 \in N$ (b) $17 \notin P$

2. (a) $-5 \notin N$ (b) $-5 \in I$

3. (a) $\{-4, 3\} \subseteq I$ (b) $\{7, 81\} \subset P$

4. (a) $\{\sqrt{4}, \sqrt{5}\} \subset H$ (b) $\{0.5, 0.7\} \subset Q$

5. (a) $I \cup N = I$ (b) $I \cap W = W$

6. (a) $P \cap I = P$ (b) $Q \cup I = Q$

7. (a) $Q \subseteq H$ (b) $H \cup I = H$

8. (a) $P \cup Q = Q$ (b) $I \cap Q = I$

Exercises 9–10   Indicate which of the subsets $P, N, I, O, E, Q,$ and H contain each number. For instance, 17 belongs to $P, N, I, O,$ and Q.

9. (a) $\frac{29}{3}$ (b) $\sqrt{16}$ (c) $\sqrt{32}$ (d) $\frac{2^5}{2^3}$

10. (a) $3.\overline{27}$ (b) 29   (c) $\frac{0.13}{1.27}$ (d) $2\pi - 1$

Exercises 11–14   Express each as a terminating decimal, or as a repeating decimal using the bar notation.

11. (a) $\frac{5}{8}$ (b) $\frac{5}{12}$

12. (a) $\frac{73}{40}$ (b) $\frac{25}{33}$

13. (a) $\frac{37}{45}$ (b) $\frac{10}{13}$

14. (a) $\frac{16}{35}$ (b) $\frac{48}{65}$

Exercises 15–18   Express each as a fraction (quotient of integers) in lowest terms.

15. (a) 0.63   (b) $0.\overline{63}$

16. (a) 1.45   (b) $1.\overline{45}$

17. (a) $0.8\overline{3}$ (b) $0.\overline{83}$

18. (a) $1.3\overline{6}$ (b) $0.\overline{621}$

Exercises 19–21   Give a decimal approximation rounded off to three decimal places.

19. (a) $\frac{67}{195}$ (b) $\frac{\sqrt{17}}{12}$

20. (a) $\frac{1142}{735}$ (b) $\sqrt{1 + \sqrt{2}}$

21. (a) $\frac{343}{110}$ (b) $\frac{11(4 - \sqrt{3})}{8}$

Exercises 22–30   Give decimal approximations rounded off to six decimal places. Do the numbers appear to be equal?

22. $\sqrt{8}; 2\sqrt{2}$

23. $\sqrt{48}; 4\sqrt{3}$

24. $1 + \sqrt{2}; \frac{1}{\sqrt{2} - 1}$

25. $\frac{\sqrt{3} + 1}{2}; \frac{1}{\sqrt{3} - 1}$

26. $\sqrt{6} + \sqrt{2}; 2\sqrt{2 + \sqrt{3}}$

27. $\sqrt{3 + \sqrt{5}} + \sqrt{3 - \sqrt{5}}; \sqrt{10}$

28. $\sqrt{6 + 4\sqrt{2}}; 2 + \sqrt{2}$

29. $\sqrt{8 + 2\sqrt{15}}; \sqrt{5} + \sqrt{3}$

30. $\sqrt{6 - 2\sqrt{5}}; 1 - \sqrt{5}$

31. What is the smallest nonprime positive integer greater than 1 that has no factors less than 12?

32. What is the smallest prime number that divides $3^7 + 7^{11}$?

Exercises 33–34 Determine whether each statement is true or false.

33. (a) The sum of any two odd numbers is an odd number.

(b) The product of any two odd numbers is an odd number.

(c) The product of any two consecutive positive integers is an even number.

34. (a) The sum of three consecutive even numbers is an odd number.

(b) If a positive even integer is a perfect square, then it is the square of an even number.

(c) If the sum of two integers is even, then both must be even.

35. Give an example of irrational numbers for x and y that satisfy the given condition.

(a) $x + y$ is irrational.   (b) $x + y$ is rational.

(c) $x \cdot y$ is rational.   (d) $\frac{x}{y}$ is rational.

36. If $x = \sqrt{1.5 + \sqrt{2}} + \sqrt{1.5 - \sqrt{2}}$, determine whether x is rational or irrational. (*Hint:* Evaluate x^2.)

37. If $x = \sqrt{2 + \sqrt{3}} + \sqrt{2 - \sqrt{3}}$, determine whether x is rational or irrational. (*Hint:* Evaluate x^2.)

38. Prove that $\sqrt{2}$ is not a rational number. (*Hint:* Suppose $\sqrt{2} = \frac{b}{c}$, where $b, c \in N$ and $\frac{b}{c}$ is in lowest terms. Then $b^2 = 2c^2$. Explain why b must be even. Then also argue that c must be even. This would contradict the assumption that $\frac{b}{c}$ is in lowest terms.)

Exercises 39–40 Refer to the number π, whose decimal form is nonterminating and nonrepeating. Rounded off to 24 decimal places,
$$\pi \approx 3.1415\ 92653\ 58979\ 32384\ 62643.$$

39. The following rational numbers are used as approximations of π. Use your calculator to evaluate and compare each result with the given decimal approximation of π.

(a) $\frac{22}{7}$ (b) $\frac{333}{106}$ (c) $\frac{355}{113}$

40. The rational number $\frac{208,341}{66,317}$ is an excellent approximation of π. Evaluate it to at least 12 decimal places and compare the result with the approximation given above.

41. In 1991 the Chudnovsky brothers used a supercomputer they built to compute more than 2.26 billion digits of π. Count the number of symbols in an average line of this book and estimate how long a line of type (measured in miles) the Chudnovsky result would give. (See the Historical Note, "Approximating the Number π.")

Real Number Properties; Complex Numbers

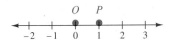

(a) Integers on a number line.

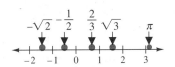

(b) Real numbers on a number line.

FIGURE 1.5

. . . one of the central themes of science [is] the mysterious power of mathematics to prepare the ground for physical discoveries which could not have been foreseen by the mathematicians who gave the concepts birth.

Freeman Dyson

Real Number Line

One of the great ideas in the history of mathematics is that the set of real numbers can be associated with the set of points on a line. We assume a one-to-one correspondence that associates each real number with exactly one point on a line, and every point on the line corresponds to exactly one real number.

We frequently identify a number with its point, and vice versa, speaking of "the point 2" rather than "the point that corresponds to 2." Figure 1.5 shows a few numbers and the corresponding points on a number line.

Order Relations and Intervals

The number line also represents the ordering of the real numbers. We assume that the ideas of less than and greater than, and the following notation are familiar:

Order Relations for Real Numbers

Notation	Terminology	Meaning
$b < c$	b is less than c.	$c = b + d$, for some positive number d
$c > b$	c is greater than b	$b < c$
$b \leq c$	b is less than or equal to c.	$b < c$ or $b = c$
$c \geq b$	c is greater than or equal to b.	$b \leq c$

The mathematics course at San Diego High School was standard for that time: plane geometry in the tenth grade, advanced algebra in the eleventh, and trigonometry and solid geometry in the twelfth. . . . After plane geometry, I was the only girl still taking mathematics.

Julia Robinson

We also need notation for sets of all numbers between two given numbers, or all numbers less than or greater than a given number. Such sets are called **intervals.**

Definition: Intervals

Suppose b and c are real numbers and $b < c$:

Name	Notation	Number-line Diagram
Open interval	$(b, c) = \{x \mid b < x < c\}$	
Closed interval	$[b, c] = \{x \mid b \leq x \leq c\}$	
Half-open interval	$[b, c) = \{x \mid b \leq x < c\}$	
Half-open interval	$(b, c] = \{x \mid b < x \leq c\}$	
Infinite intervals	$(b, \infty) = \{x \mid x > b\}$	
	$[b, \infty) = \{x \mid x \geq b\}$	
	$(-\infty, b) = \{x \mid x < b\}$	
	$(-\infty, b] = \{x \mid x \leq b\}$	

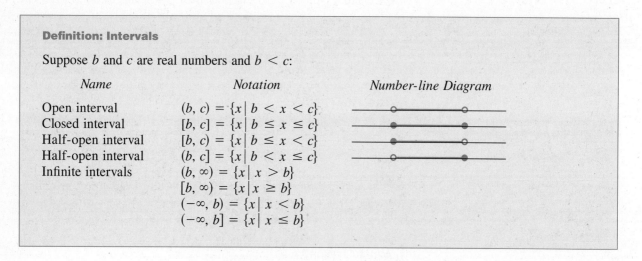

In these definitions, the symbol ∞ (infinity) *does not represent a number,* and we never use a closed bracket to indicate that ∞ is included in an infinite interval.

Absolute Value and Distance

It is a simple matter to find the absolute value of specific numbers. For example,

$$|2| = 2 \qquad |0| = 0 \qquad |-1.375| = 1.375.$$

For much of our work, however, we need a more general definition. We give this in two forms, one in terms of distance and one in algebraic notation.

> ### Definition: Absolute Value
>
> Suppose x is any real number. Then the **absolute value** of x, denoted by $|x|$, is defined either by
>
> **(a)** $|x|$ is the distance between 0 and the point x, or by
>
> **(b)** $|x| = \begin{cases} x, & \text{if } x \geq 0 \\ -x, & \text{if } x < 0 \end{cases}$

Definition (b) follows from (a) because, for any given positive distance, there are always two numbers (with opposite signs) that far away from 0.

EXAMPLE 1   If t is $1 - \sqrt{3}$, show both t and $-t$ on a number line and express $|t|$ in exact form without using absolute values.

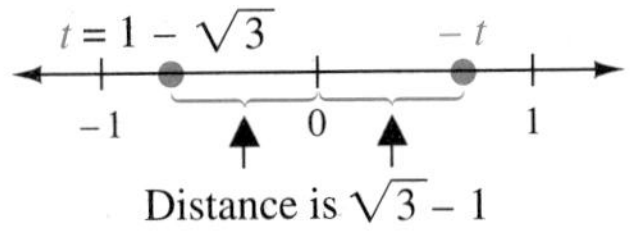

$t = 1 - \sqrt{3}$

$-1 \qquad 0 \qquad 1$

Distance is $\sqrt{3} - 1$

FIGURE 1.6

Solution

Since t is negative ($t \approx -0.732$), $-t$ is positive. Both t and $-t$ are the same distance from 0, as shown in Figure 1.6.

By definition (b), since $t < 0$, $|t| = -t = -(1 - \sqrt{3}) = \sqrt{3} - 1$. Thus $|1 - \sqrt{3}| = \sqrt{3} - 1$. ▲

> ### Some Useful Properties of Absolute Values
>
> Suppose x and y are any real numbers.
>
> 1. $|x| \geq 0$ 2. $|x| = |-x|$
> 3. $|x \cdot y| = |x| \cdot |y|$ 4. $\sqrt{x^2} = |x|$
> 5. $\left| \dfrac{x}{y} \right| = \dfrac{|x|}{|y|}$ if $y \neq 0$ 6. $|x + y| \leq |x| + |y|$

EXAMPLE 2   Let $x = -3$, $y = 2$, and $z = 1 - \sqrt{3}$. Evaluate the expressions. Are the values in each pair equal or not?

(a) $\sqrt{x^2}, x$ **(b)** $|x \cdot y|, |x| \cdot |y|$ **(c)** $|y + z|, |y| + |z|$
(d) $|x + z|, |x| + |z|$

Strategy: Identify each number as positive or negative before applying a definition of absolute value.

Solution

(a) $\sqrt{x^2} = \sqrt{(-3)^2} = \sqrt{9} = 3$; $x = -3$.

(b) $|x \cdot y| = |(-3) \cdot 2| = |-6| = 6$; $|x| \cdot |y| = |-3| \cdot |2| = 3 \cdot 2 = 6$.

(c) $|y + z| = |2 + (1 - \sqrt{3})| = |3 - \sqrt{3}| = 3 - \sqrt{3} \approx 1.27$.
$|y| + |z| = |2| + |1 - \sqrt{3}| = 2 + (\sqrt{3} - 1) = 1 + \sqrt{3} \approx 2.73$.

(d) $|x + z| = |-3 + (1 - \sqrt{3})| = |-2 - \sqrt{3}| = 2 + \sqrt{3} \approx 3.73$.
$|x| + |z| = |-3| + |1 - \sqrt{3}| = 3 + (\sqrt{3} - 1) = 2 + \sqrt{3}$.

The pairs in parts (b) and (d) are equal; those in (a) and (c) are not. ▲

Complex Numbers

Although most of our work deals exclusively with real numbers, sometimes we must expand to a larger set, the set of **complex numbers.** For any real number c, c^2 is nonnegative, so the equation $x^2 = -1$ has no solution in R.

Accordingly, we introduce a new type of number, one that is not a real number, called the **imaginary unit i,** such that $i^2 = -1$. That is, i is a solution to the equation $x^2 = -1$. See the Historical Note, "Growth of the Number System." We then define the set C of complex numbers as:

$$C = \{c + di \mid c \text{ and } d \text{ are real numbers, and } i^2 = -1\}$$

Note that if we take c to be any real number and d to be 0, then $c + di$ is simply c. This leads to an important conclusion:

Every real number is also a complex number.

That is, R is a subset of C.

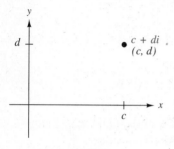

FIGURE 1.7

The complex number $c + di$ is identified with the point (c, d).

The Complex Plane

Just as we identify each real number with a point on a number line, we identify each complex number $c + di$ with a point in the plane having coordinates (c, d). See Figure 1.7. In this correspondence, the x-axis is the real number line and all real multiples of i are located on the y-axis.

The **standard form** for a complex number is $c + di$, where c and d are real numbers. The number c is called the **real part** and d is the **imaginary part.** If the imaginary part is nonzero, then we call the complex number $c + di$ an **imaginary number.** If z is the complex number $c + di$, then the **conjugate** of z, denoted by $\bar{z}$, is the number $c - di$. That is, if $z = c + di$, then $\bar{z} = c - di$.

Complex Number Arithmetic

When are two complex numbers equal? How do we add, subtract, multiply, and divide complex numbers? Given complex numbers z and w in standard form, say $z = a + bi$ and $w = c + di$, we treat these numbers as we would any algebraic expressions, combining like terms in the usual fashion, with one exception. In multiplication we replace i^2 by -1 wherever it occurs. For division, $\frac{z}{w}$ $(w \neq 0)$, we multiply numerator and denominator by $\bar{w}$ as follows:

$$\frac{z}{w} = \frac{a + bi}{c + di} = \frac{a + bi}{c + di} \cdot \frac{c - di}{c - di}$$

$$= \frac{ac - adi + bci - bdi^2}{c^2 - d^2i^2} = \frac{(ac + bd) + (bc - ad)i}{c^2 + d^2}$$

Definitions: Complex Number Arithmetic

Suppose $z = a + bi$, $w = c + di$, where a, b, c, and d are real numbers.

Equality: $z = w$ if and only if $a = c$ and $b = d$.

Addition: $z + w = (a + bi) + (c + di) = (a + c) + (b + d)i$

Subtraction: $z - w = (a + bi) - (c + di) = (a - c) + (b - d)i$

Multiplication: $z \cdot w = (a + bi)(c + di) = ac + adi + bci + bdi^2 = (ac - bd) + (ad + bc)i$

Division: $\dfrac{z}{w} = \dfrac{(ac + bd) + (bc - ad)i}{c^2 + d^2} = \dfrac{ac + bd}{c^2 + d^2} + \dfrac{bc - ad}{c^2 + d^2}i$, where $c^2 + d^2 \neq 0$.

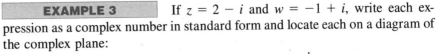

EXAMPLE 3   If $z = 2 - i$ and $w = -1 + i$, write each expression as a complex number in standard form and locate each on a diagram of the complex plane:

(a) $z + w$ **(b)** $\bar{z}$ and $-z$ **(c)** zw **(d)** $\frac{1}{w}$

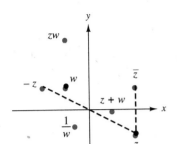

FIGURE 1.8

Points in the complex plane.

Solution

(a) $z + w = (2 - i) + (-1 + i) = 1 + 0i = 1$.

(b) $\bar{z} = 2 + i$, and $-z = -2 + i$.

(c) $zw = (2 - i)(-1 + i) = -2 + 2i + i - i^2 = -2 + 3i - (-1)$
$= -1 + 3i$.

(d) $\dfrac{1}{w} = \dfrac{1\bar{w}}{w\bar{w}} = \dfrac{1(-1 - i)}{(-1 + i)(-1 - i)} = \dfrac{-1 - i}{1 - i^2} = \dfrac{-1 - i}{1 - (-1)} = -\dfrac{1}{2} - \dfrac{1}{2}i$.

The points are shown in Figure 1.8. ▲

Absolute Value of a Complex Number

We define the absolute value of a real number x as the *distance* between the point x and the origin 0. In a similar manner, we define the absolute value of $a + bi$ as the distance in the plane between (a, b) and the origin $(0, 0)$. The diagram in Figure 1.9 and the Pythagorean theorem give a distance of $\sqrt{a^2 + b^2}$.

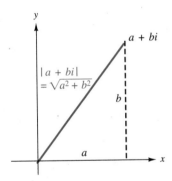

FIGURE 1.9

The absolute value of a complex number is the distance to the origin in the complex plane.

Definition: Absolute Value of a Complex Number

Suppose z is the complex number $a + bi$. The *absolute value of z,* denoted by $|z|$, is $\sqrt{a^2 + b^2}$, and we write $|z| = \sqrt{a^2 + b^2}$.

Many of the properties of absolute values of complex numbers are the same as those for real numbers.

Properties of Absolute Value of a Complex Number

If z and w are any complex numbers, then:

1. $|z| \geq 0$ 2. $|\bar{z}| = |-z| = |z|$

3. $|z \cdot w| = |z| \cdot |w|$ 4. $\sqrt{z \cdot \bar{z}} = |z|$

5. $\left| \dfrac{z}{w} \right| = \dfrac{|z|}{|w|}$ if $w \neq 0$ 6. $|z + w| \leq |z| + |w|$

EXAMPLE 4   Suppose $z = 2 - i$ and $w = -1 + i$ (the complex numbers of Example 3). Verify that the properties of absolute values hold for each pair.

(a) $|z| + |w|, |z + w|$ **(b)** $|\bar{z}|, |-z|$ **(c)** $|zw|, |z| \cdot |w|$

Solution

(a) $|z| + |w| = |2 - i| + |-1 + i| = \sqrt{2^2 + (-1)^2} + \sqrt{(-1)^2 + 1^2}$
$= \sqrt{5} + \sqrt{2}.$
$|z + w| = |1 + 0i| = \sqrt{1^2 + 0^2} = 1.$
Since $1 < \sqrt{5} + \sqrt{2}, |z + w| < |z| + |w|$ (Property 6).

(b) $|\bar{z}| = |2 + i| = \sqrt{2^2 + 1^2} = \sqrt{5};$
$|-z| = |-2 + i| = \sqrt{(-2)^2 + 1^2} = \sqrt{5}.$
Thus $|\bar{z}| = |-z|$ (Property 2).

(c) $zw = -1 + 3i,$ and so $|zw| = |-1 + 3i| = \sqrt{10}.$
$|z| \cdot |w| = \sqrt{5} \cdot \sqrt{2} = \sqrt{10}.$ Therefore $|zw| = |z| \cdot |w|$
(Property 3). ▲

Principal Square Roots

In Section 1.2 we defined $\sqrt{b}$ for any nonnegative number b. Complex numbers allow us to extend this definition to include square roots of negative numbers.

Definition: Principal Square Roots

Suppose b is a positive real number. The **principal square roots** of b and $-b$ are:

$\sqrt{b}$ is the nonnegative number whose square is b, as $\sqrt{4} = 2.$
$\sqrt{-b}$ is the imaginary number $\sqrt{b}\,i$, as $\sqrt{-9} = 3i.$

Ordering of the Complex Numbers

Real numbers are ordered by the less than relation, so that if b is any real number, then exactly one of the following is true:

$$b = 0 \quad \text{or} \quad b < 0 \quad \text{or} \quad b > 0.$$

Since R is a subset of C, any ordering of the complex numbers should be consistent with the ordering of R. Consider the nonzero complex number i. If we could extend the ordering of R to C, then we would have to have

$$i < 0 \quad \text{or} \quad i > 0.$$

If $i > 0$, then we can multiply both sides by the positive number i and get

$$i \cdot i > i \cdot 0 \quad \text{or} \quad -1 > 0,$$

which is not a true statement in R. That leaves only the possibility that i is negative, $i < 0$. If we multiply both sides by the negative number i, we must reverse the direction of the inequality, and we get the same contradiction:

$$i \cdot i > i \cdot 0 \quad \text{or} \quad -1 > 0.$$

We are forced to conclude that *there is no consistent way to order the set of complex numbers using the less than relation*. Thus, for example, we cannot say that one of the two numbers $3 - 4i$ and $-1 + 2i$ is less than the other.

╔══════════════════════════════════════╗

Historical Note

GROWTH OF THE NUMBER SYSTEM

Boethius (left), using written Arabic numerals, triumphs over Pythagoras and his abacus in a mathematical contest. The goddess Arithmetica presides over the competition.

The ancient Greeks believed numbers expressed the essence of the whole world. Numbers to the Pythagorean philosophers meant whole numbers and their ratios—what we would call the *positive rational numbers*. It was extremely distressing to some when they discovered that something as simple as the diagonal of a square cannot be expressed rationally in terms of the length of the side of the square. Pythagoras (ca. 550 B.C.) is said to have sacrificed 100 oxen in honor of the discovery of irrational numbers. Nonetheless, irrational numbers were called *alogos* in Greek, carrying the double meaning that such numbers were not ratios and also that they were not to be spoken.

Hundreds of years passed before mathematicians became comfortable with the use of numbers like $\sqrt{2}$. Even we are reluctant to accept new numbers, as our language reflects. We equate rational with reasonable, and dislike irrational or negative concepts.

Not until the Middle Ages did mathematicians become secure with fractions and negative numbers. Also at that time, they recognized that irrationals have negatives, so two numbers have the square 2, namely $\sqrt{2}$ and $-\sqrt{2}$.

Complex numbers have a history somewhat shorter than that of irrational numbers. Cardan made the first public use of complex numbers in 1545 when he showed how to find two numbers with a sum of 10 and a product of 40, giving the result as $5 + \sqrt{-15}$ and $5 - \sqrt{-15}$. Although he observed that the product equals $5^2 - (-15)$ or 40, he considered such expressions no more real than negative numbers describing lengths of line segments. In 1777 Euler first used the symbol i to denote $\sqrt{-1}$. As with $\sqrt{2}$, people first considered only one root of -1, but then recognized that i and $-i$ both satisfy the equation $x^2 + 1 = 0$.

We have come gradually to recognize that our number system is much larger and richer than childhood experience conceives. We extend our counting numbers to accommodate subtraction and division and then to solve simple equations such as $x^2 = 2$ and $x^2 = 1$. Other extensions are possible, and we hope to be open to accepting whatever is useful for solving new problems.

╚══════════════════════════════════════╝

EXERCISES 1.3

Check Your Understanding

Exercises 1–5   True or False. Give reasons for your conclusions.

1. If both b and d are negative real numbers, then $\sqrt{-b}\sqrt{-d} = \sqrt{bd}$.

2. $|3 - \sqrt{10}| = \sqrt{10} - 3$.

3. $1 - \sqrt{10} > 1 - \pi$

4. In the complex plane, $3 + 4i$ is farther from the origin than $5i$.

5. If $0 < b < 1$ and $-1 < c < 0$, then
$-1 < b - c < 1$.

Exercises 6–10   Complete the sentence by selecting from the list below *all choices* that make the statement true.

(a) -1 **(b)** 0 **(c)** 1 **(d)** a real number
(e) an imaginary number   **(f)** a positive number
(g) a negative number

6. For every positive integer k, $\frac{3+k}{6+k}$ is less than _____.

7. If k is any positive integer, then i^{4k} is equal to _____.

8. The smallest integer that is greater than $3 - \sqrt{10}$ is _____.

9. If $\bar{z} = z$, then z must be _____.

10. The greatest integer less than $\frac{3-\pi}{4}$ is _____.

Explore and Discover

1. Make a table for various values x (positive and negative) comparing x and $\frac{1}{x}$. Make a guess about the intervals on which $\frac{1}{x} \geq x$ and the intervals on which $\frac{1}{x} < x$.

2. Repeat Exercise 1, comparing x and $\sqrt{x}$. Where is $\sqrt{x} = x$? $\sqrt{x} < x$? $\sqrt{x} > x$?

3. Some people would like to use the symbol $\sqrt{4}$ to represent two different numbers, 2 and -2, because the squares of both 2 and -2 equal 4. Explain why it is important that every mathematical symbol have an unambiguous meaning. You might consider the kind of difficulties we would have if a calculator sometimes displayed 2 and sometimes -2 when we pressed $\boxed{4}$ then $\boxed{\sqrt{}}$.

4. **(a)** There are exactly two real numbers having an absolute value of 1, namely 1 and -1. In contrast, many complex numbers have the absolute value 1, including ± 1, $\pm i$, $\frac{(1 \pm i)}{\sqrt{2}}$, etc. Thinking about absolute values and distances, what property appears to characterize all complex numbers that have an absolute value of 1?
(b) Do you think that it makes sense to use the same absolute value symbol for real numbers and complex numbers? Explain why or why not.

Develop Mastery

Exercises 1–6   Show the subset of R on a number line.

1. $\{x \mid x > -2 \text{ and } x < 2\}$

2. $\{x \mid x \geq -1 \text{ and } x \leq 1\}$

3. $\{x \mid x < 1 \text{ or } x > 3\}$

4. $\{x \mid x \leq -1\} \cup \{x \mid x > 4\}$

5. $\{x \mid x > 0\} \cap \{x \mid x < 3\}$

6. $\{x \mid 1 \leq x < \sqrt{7}\}$

Exercises 7–9   Simplify. Express each in exact form without using absolute values, and as a decimal approximation rounded off to four decimal places.

7. **(a)** $\left| \frac{1}{4} - \frac{3}{2} \right|$ **(b)** $\left| 3 - \frac{9}{2} \right|$

8. **(a)** $\left| 1 - \frac{4}{7} \right|$ **(b)** $\left| 3 - \sqrt{17} \right|$

9. **(a)** $\left| \pi - 3 \right|$ **(b)** $\left| \pi - \frac{22}{7} \right|$

Exercises 10–13   Enter one of the three symbols $<$, $>$, or $=$ in each blank space to make the resulting statement true.

10. **(a)** -4 _____ -6
(b) $-\pi$ _____ $-\sqrt{10}$

11. **(a)** $\frac{5}{11}$ _____ 0.45
(b) $1 + \sqrt{2}$ _____ 2.9

12. **(a)** $\frac{47}{3}$ _____ 16
(b) $0.\overline{63}$ _____ $\frac{7}{11}$

13. **(a)** $\left| 1 - \sqrt{3} \right|$ _____ $\sqrt{3} - 1$
(b) $\left| -5 \right|$ _____ 4

Exercises 14–17   Order the set of three numbers from smallest to largest. Express the result using the symbol $<$, as, for instance, $y < z < x$.

14. $x = 5$, $y = -7$, $z = -3$

15. $x = \frac{16}{23}$, $y = \frac{5}{12}$, $z = \frac{7}{15}$

16. $x = 1 - \sqrt{3}$, $y = \sqrt{3} - 1$, $z = -1$

17. $x = \left| 1 - \frac{7}{5} \right|$, $y = \left| 1 - \frac{6}{5} \right|$, $z = \left| 1 - \frac{1}{5} \right|$

Exercises 18–19   Determine whether each statement is true or false.

18. **(a)** $\pi^2 < 10$ **(b)** $\frac{1}{\sqrt{2} - 1} > 2.28$

19. **(a)** $1.33 < 1.\overline{3}$ **(b)** $0.54 > \frac{6}{11}$

Exercises 20–25   Show the intervals on a number line.

20. $(-1, 4)$ **21.** $(-\infty, 2)$

22. $[-2, \infty)$ **23.** $[1, 4] \cap (0, 5)$

24. $(-\infty, 3) \cup (3, 4]$ **25.** $[-3, 2] \cap [2, 5]$

Exercises 26–27   Show the described set on a number line.

26. The set of all negative real numbers greater than -5

27. The set of all real numbers greater than -2 and less than 3

28. What is the largest integer that is **(a)** less than or equal to -5?   **(b)** less than -5?

29. What is the largest integer that is less than $1 + \sqrt{17}$?

30. What is the smallest integer that is greater than $\frac{348}{37}$?

31. What is the smallest even integer that is greater than $12 + \sqrt{5}$?

32. What is the largest prime number that is less than $\frac{23}{0.23}$?

Exercises 33–46 Perform the indicated operations. Express the result as a complex number in standard form.

33. $(5 + 2i) + (3 - 6i)$ **34.** $(3 - i) + (-1 + 5i)$

35. $(6 - i) - (3 - 4i)$ **36.** $8 - (3 + 5i) + 2i$

37. $(2 + i)(3 - i)$ **38.** $(-1 + i)(2 + 3i)$

39. $(1 + 3i)(1 - 3i)$ **40.** $(7 - 2i)(7 + 2i)$

41. $\frac{1 + 3i}{i}$ **42.** $\frac{1 + i}{1 - i}$

43. $(1 + \sqrt{3}i)^2$ **44.** $\frac{2i}{(1 - i)(2 - i)}$

45. (a) i^2 (b) i^6 (c) i^{12} (d) i^{18}

46. (a) i^5 (b) i^9 (c) i^{15} (d) i^{21}

Exercises 47–51 If z is $1 - i$ and w is $-2 + i$, express in standard form.

47. $z + 3w$ **48.** $zw - 4$ **49.** $\bar{z} \cdot \bar{w}$

50. $|z + w|$ **51.** $\frac{z - \bar{w}}{w}$

Exercises 52–55 For the given z and w, show in the complex plane: **(a)** z **(b)** w **(c)** $\bar{z}$ **(d)** $z + w$ **(e)** $z \cdot w$

52. $z = 2 - 2i;\ w = 3 + 4i$

53. $z = -3 + 2i;\ w = -2 - i$

54. $z = -1 + 2i;\ w = 3i$

55. $z = 5 - i;\ w = -1 + i$

56. **(a)** If $z = \frac{1}{2} + \frac{\sqrt{3}}{2}i$, find z^2, z^3, z^4, z^5, z^6.
   (b) Evaluate each of $|z|, |z^2|, |z^3|, \ldots, |z^6|$.

57. From Exercise 56 draw a diagram showing $z, z^2, z^3, z^4, z^5,$ and z^6 in the complex plane. Note the distance from each of these points to the origin. On what circle do these points lie?

SECTION 1.4   ## The Language of Mathematics

Formal logic is an impoverished way of describing human thought, and the practice of mathematics goes far beyond a set of algorithmic rules. . . . Mathematics may indeed reflect the operations of the brain, but both brain and mind are far richer in their nature than is suggested by any structure of algorithms and logical operations.
     F. David Peat

[At thirteen] it was hard for me to imagine original mathematics, thinking of something that no one else had thought of before. When I went to college. . .I thought I might become a biologist. I was interested in many different things. I studied psychology and philosophy, for instance. We didn't have grades, but we did have written evaluations. And I kept getting the message that my true talents didn't lie in subject X but in mathematics.
     William Thurston

In mathematics, language is the key to understanding while problem solving is the key to learning. The two are closely related since it is impossible to solve a problem without first understanding it. Learning to communicate is fundamental to all education. People express ideas in words, which they combine to form meaningful sentences. Sentences are the basic elements of communication.

The language of mathematics is both precise and concise, often making use of symbols. However, mathematical symbols are combined together to form sentences having similar grammatical structures, including subjects and predicates, as sentences in our more familiar daily language.

The use of symbols allows us to write sentences in very compact form. For instance, in place of "The sum of 2 and 3 is 5," we write "$2 + 3 = 5$." Similarly, the symbolic sentence "$x \le 4$" in everyday language means "x is less than or equal to 4," which is a complete sentence.

This section concentrates on those sentences we can label either true or false. One goal here is for you to be able to determine which statements are true, and to be able to change the forms of sentences into equivalent sentences that may be easier to analyze.

> **Definition: Statement**
>
> A **statement** is a sentence that has a truth value, either true or false.

Consider the following sentences and their truth values.

1. Boston is the capital of Massachusetts.   T
2. René Descartes was born in the eighteenth century.   F
3. Wolfgang Amadeus Mozart was born in 1756.   T
4. Some basketball players are taller than seven feet.   T
5. Either $4 > 6$ or $7 \leq 0$.   F
6. There are infinitely many prime numbers.   T
7. The smallest positive rational number is $\frac{1}{100}$.   F
8. Every even integer greater than 2 is the sum of two primes.   ?
9. $x + 3 = 7$ Not defined
10. $n^2 - n + 17$ is a prime number.   Not defined

The first seven sentences are clearly statements because each is either true or false. Sentence 8 is either true or false, and hence is a statement, but no one yet has been able to prove its truth value. This famous unsolved problem of mathematics is known as Goldbach's conjecture (see Historical Note).

Sentences 9 and 10 are not statements; neither is true or false until we replace the variable by a number. Replacing the variables by any specific number, say 5, yields statements:

$$5 + 3 = 7 \quad \text{F} \quad \text{and} \quad 5^2 - 5 + 17 \text{ is a prime number.} \quad \text{T}$$

A sentence that includes a variable, and whose truth depends on the value of that variable, is called an **open sentence.** (The = functions as the verb.) Finding the values of a variable that make an open sentence a true statement is often called "solving" an equation. For sentence 9 the only number that makes the sentence true is 4. We invite you to verify that open sentence 10 is true for many positive integers such as when n is 1, 2, 3, 5, and 10, but is not true when n is 34, as well as many other values.

Connectives and Assignment of Truth Values

Simple statements together can make more complex statements. Suppose P and Q are two given statements, each having a truth value T or F. Consider how to combine P and Q to get other statements whose truth value depends on the truth values of P and Q. These new statements involve the use of key words *not, and, or,* and *if . . . then.* These key words, called *connectives,* have formal names and symbols from logic.

> **Connectives**
>
> Not (negation)   ~   And (conjunction)   ∧
> Or (disjunction)   ∨   If . . . then (conditional)   ⇒

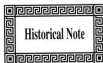

GOLDBACH, COUNTEREXAMPLES, AND UNSOLVED PROBLEMS

Historical Note

Four colors suffice to color even complicated maps.

Note: At a Cambridge University seminar in June, 1993, Professor Andrew Wiles of Princeton announced the proof of a conjecture about elliptic curves. His proof establishes that Fermat's Last Theorem is true.

On page 26 we mentioned Goldbach's conjecture that "Every even integer greater than 2 is the sum of two primes." Goldbach made this assertion in 1742 in a letter to Euler. A quick look at the first cases shows how reasonable the conjecture seems:

$$4 = 2 + 2, \quad 6 = 3 + 3,$$
$$8 = 5 + 3, \quad 10 = 7 + 3.$$

The question, of course, is how long this continues. Could we use computers to check?

Computer searches support Goldbach's assertion for *all even numbers up to a hundred million,* but forever? Who knows? A single *counterexample,* one even number that is not the sum of two primes, would prove Goldbach's conjecture false. Computers could conceivably show that Goldbach was wrong; no blind search process can ever prove him right.

An unsolved problem in mathematics does not necessarily mean there is no solution; it means that we cannot yet prove or disprove an assertion.

Each year, some long-standing questions are answered, and each answer raises more questions. Some recent milestones:

Four Color Theorem Four colors are enough to color any map; part of the proof required 1200 hours of computer time.

Classification of Simple Groups There are exactly 26 simple groups of a special type; the proof requires thousands of pages contributed by many mathematicians. The biggest group, called "The Monster," has more than 10^{53} elements.

Fermat's Last Theorem The equation $x^n + y^n = z^n$ has no solutions in integers if $n > 2$. (For $n = 2$ there are lots; see Explore and Discover in Section 5.2.) A major step was taken by a German mathematician in 1983, marking the most progress in more than a hundred years. The problem is over three hundred years old.

What makes such progress exciting is more than just the solution of an unsolved problem. Work on one problem can help us understand others, and light shed in one corner of mathematics often lights up whole new vistas whose existence we may not even have suspected previously.

Negation

The word *not* is used in mathematics much as it is in everyday language. It denies or negates the statement to which it is applied. Thus not P, denoted $\sim P$, is false when P is true and true when P is false. For instance, if P is the statement $2 < 5$, then $\sim P$ is the statement $2 \not< 5$ (or $2 \geq 5$). In this case P is true and $\sim P$ is false. Similarly, if Q is the false statement $2 + 3 \cdot 5 = 25$, then $\sim Q$ is the true statement $2 + 3 \cdot 5 \neq 25$.

> **Definition: Truth Values for Negation**
>
> Suppose P is any statement.
>
> If P is true, then $\sim P$ is false; if P is false, then $\sim P$ is true.

Negations are frequently needed to think through mathematical arguments. It is important to recognize different forms of statements that say the same thing. For example, consider these equivalent true statements:

> All integers are rational numbers.
>
> Each integer is a rational number.

The negation of the same idea may also be expressed in a variety of forms:

> Not every integer is a rational number.
>
> Some integer is not a rational number.
>
> There is at least one integer which is not a rational number.

Conjunction

When we connect statements P and Q by the word *and,* we get a new statement called **conjunction** of P and Q, denoted by $P \wedge Q$, or more simply, by P *and* Q. The truth value of the statement $P \wedge Q$ is defined as follows.

> **Definition: Truth Values for Conjunction**
>
> Suppose P and Q are any statements.
>
> $P \wedge Q$ is true only when *both* P and Q are true;
>
> $P \wedge Q$ is false when either P or Q is false (or both are false).

Disjunction

When P and Q are connected by the word *or,* the new statement is called the **disjunction** of P and Q, denoted by $P \vee Q$, or by P *or* Q. Common conversation is sometimes ambiguous in the use of *or*, but in mathematics we must define the truth value of $P \vee Q$ with no ambiguity. The truth value of the statement $P \vee Q$ is defined as follows.

> **Definition: Truth Values for Disjunction**
>
> Suppose P and Q are any statements.
>
> $P \vee Q$ is false only when *both* P and Q are false;
>
> $P \vee Q$ is true when either P or Q is true (or both are true).

Strategy: In **(a)** $-3 < x < 3$ means $-3 < x$ *and* $x < 3$, so we need the truth value of the conjunction $-3 < 4$ *and* $4 < 3$. For **(b)** we need the truth value of the disjunction $4 < -3$ *or* $4 > 3$.

| EXAMPLE 1 | Determine the truth value of

(a) $4 \in \{x \mid -3 < x < 3\}$ **(b)** $4 \in \{x \mid x < -3 \text{ or } x > 3\}$

Solution

Follow the strategy.

(a) Since $-3 < 4$ is a true statement and $4 < 3$ is false, the conjunction is false. Therefore the given statement is false.

(b) At least one of the statements $4 < -3$ and $4 > 3$ is true, so the disjunction is also true. Thus the given statement is true. ▲

Conditional or Implication

Many important mathematical statements have the form "if P then Q" where P and Q are statements. Essentially all mathematical theorems can be stated in such a form, which makes them **conditional** statements. The conditional if P, then Q can be written "$P \Rightarrow Q$," which is sometimes read "P implies Q," hence the alternative name **implication.** The truth value of $P \Rightarrow Q$ is defined as follows.

Definition: Truth Values for Conditionals

Suppose P and Q are statements.

$P \Rightarrow Q$ is false when P *is true and Q is false.*

$P \Rightarrow Q$ is true when P *is true* and Q *is true,* or when P *is false* and Q *is either true or false.*

| EXAMPLE 2 | P is the statement $-1 \leq 2$ and Q is the statement $2 + 5 = 8$. Find the truth value of **(a)** P **(b)** Q **(c)** $P \Rightarrow Q$ **(d)** $P \wedge (\sim Q)$.

Solution

(a) P is true.

(b) Q is false.

(c) The implication is false only when P is true and Q is false, which is the case here. Thus $P \Rightarrow Q$ is false.

(d) An *and* statement is true only when both parts are true. P is true and $\sim Q$ is also true, so $P \wedge (\sim Q)$ is true. ▲

Statements with Quantifiers

Words that give information about quantities such as *all, for every, some,* or *none* are called **quantifiers.** Statements with quantifiers are used all the time in mathematics. We need such statements, as well as their negations.

Take a homely, nonmathematical analogy. Suppose you want to rent the video "When the Turtles Ate Miami," and the clerk tells you, "All our copies are checked out." You can't believe such a vital movie is unavailable; you hope he is wrong, that his statement is false. What would it take to prove the negation?

The negation requires not that *all* copies are back, but that *one* has been returned and is hiding on the shelf.

For a mathematical example, let *P* be the statement:

If *x* is any positive real number, then $\sqrt{x} \leq x$.

How would we prove that *P* is false? *P* asserts something about *all* positive real number replacements for *x*. If *x* is replaced by 1 or 4 or 25, we get true statements. Do we always get a true statement when *x* is replaced by any positive number? At the video store, you didn't care how many videos are out, and we don't care how many positive *x*-values satisfy $\sqrt{x} \leq x$. If we can find *one* positive number that doesn't work, one number "hiding on the shelf," then *P* is false. We leave you to verify that $\frac{1}{4}$ is such a number and therefore statement *P* is false.

A number, such as $\frac{1}{4}$, that proves a statement false is called a **counterexample.** For statement *P* above, any number between 0 and 1 would serve as a counterexample to prove *P* false. What the counterexample actually shows is that the negation of *P* is true:

There is at least one positive real number *x* for which $\sqrt{x} > x$.

Often when we want to prove something about a particular statement, it may be easier to prove the opposite about the negation.

EXAMPLE 3   Determine the truth value of the statement:

P: $n^2 - n + 17$ is a prime number for every positive integer *n*.

Solution

This is related to open sentence 10 at the beginning of this section. While $n^2 - n + 17$ is prime for the first several positive integers (how many?), we know that *P* is false if we can produce one counterexample. Replacing *n* by 17, we get $17^2 - 17 + 17$, which is equal to 17^2, certainly not prime. Thus *P* is a false statement.   ▲

EXAMPLE 4   Let *P* be the statement:

If *x* is any positive number, then $\frac{1}{x} \leq x$.

(a)   State the negation of *P*.   **(b)** Determine the truth value of *P*.

Solution

(a)   ~*P* is the statement: There is at least one positive number for which $\frac{1}{x} > x$.

(b)   First, try a few values of *x* in *P*.

When *x* is 1, $\frac{1}{1} \leq 1$ (True).   When *x* is 2, $\frac{1}{2} \leq 2$ (True).

When *x* is 5, $\frac{1}{5} \leq 5$ (True).   When *x* is $\frac{1}{2}$, $\frac{1}{1/2} \leq \frac{1}{2}$, or $2 \leq \frac{1}{2}$ (False).

Since we have found one value of *x*, namely $\frac{1}{2}$, that yields a false statement, $\frac{1}{2}$ is a counterexample and we conclude that statement *P* is false.   ▲

> **EXAMPLE 5** Let Q be the statement:
>
> If b is any positive number, then $b + \dfrac{1}{b} \geq 2$.
>
> Determine the truth value of Q.

Solution

First, check a few values of b in the expression $b + \frac{1}{b}$.

When b is 1, $1 + \dfrac{1}{1} \geq 2$ (True)   When b is 2, $2 + \dfrac{1}{2} \geq 2$ (True)

When b is 6, $6 + \dfrac{1}{6} \geq 2$ (True)   When b is $\frac{1}{2}$, $\dfrac{1}{2} + \dfrac{1}{1/2} \geq 2$ (True)

It appears that Q may be true, but examples are not enough to prove it.

Looking more closely at the inequality $b + \frac{1}{b} \geq 2$, we can try equivalent forms. For example, we are interested only in positive numbers for b, so we could multiply both sides of the inequality by b and get rid of the fraction:

$$b^2 + 1 \geq 2b, \qquad b^2 - 2b + 1 \geq 0, \qquad \text{or } (b - 1)^2 \geq 0.$$

The last inequality is true for every positive b, and it is *equivalent to the original inequality*. Therefore we conclude that statement Q is true. ▲

EXERCISES 1.4

Check Your Understanding

Exercises 1–5 True or False. Give reasons for your conclusion.

1. The smallest integer greater than $3 + \sqrt{2}$ is 5.
2. The largest integer less than $1 - \sqrt{10}$ is -3.
3. $-\pi$ is less than $-\sqrt{10}$.
4. $\sqrt{(2 - \sqrt{5})^2} = 2 - \sqrt{5}$.
5. If $0 < x < 2$, then $0 < \frac{1}{x} < 4$.

Exercises 6–10 Complete the sentence by selecting from the list below *all choices* that make the statement true.

(a) even   (b) odd   (c) greater
(d) less   (e) positive   (f) negative

6. If x is between 0 and 1, then $\frac{1}{x}$ is _____ than 1.
7. If x is between 0 and 1, then $x + \frac{1}{x}$ is _____ than 2.
8. If x is an _____ integer, then x^2 is an odd integer.
9. If b is a negative number and c is a positive number, then $c - b$ is _____.
10. If x is any number between 0 and 1, then $\sqrt{x}$ is _____ than x.

Explore and Discover

1. Perform the sequence of operations listed below using several different starting numbers in Step 1; try 8, 15, 36, 142, 217, and so on. From your results in Step 5, observe where your starting number appears in the final result.

   Step 1. Take any positive integer.
   Step 2. Double your number.
   Step 3. Subtract 4 from the result.
   Step 4. Multiply the result by 5.
   Step 5. Add 25 to the result.

2. Describe the processes in Exercise 1 in terms of algebraic notation and show why the results you observed must occur. Make up a similar sequence of operations of your own.

Exercises 3–5 Write a brief paragraph comparing the sentences (a), (b), and (c) below. For instance, is each sentence a statement? Give the truth value of each statement with a justification.

3. (a) $x^2 - 4 = (x + 2)(x - 2)$.
   (b) For every x, $x^2 - 4 = (x + 2)(x - 2)$.
   (c) For every negative number x, $x^2 - 4 = (x + 2)(x - 2)$.

4. (a) $\sqrt{x^2} = x$.
   (b) For every real number x, $\sqrt{x^2} = x$.
   (c) For every negative number x, $\sqrt{x^2} = x$.

5. (a) $\sqrt{x} \le x$.
   (b) For every positive number x, $\sqrt{x} \le x$.
   (c) For every number x greater than 1, $\sqrt{x} \le x$.

Develop Mastery

Exercises 1–6 Determine whether or not the sentence is a statement. Give the truth value for each statement.

1. 57 is a prime number.   2. $x + 3 < 5$
3. $x^2 - 2x - 3 = 0$ 4. $2 + 3 \cdot 5 = 25$
5. He is president of the United States.
6. San Francisco is the capital of California.

Exercises 7–18 Determine the truth value.

7. $4 \in \{x \mid x^2 - 16 = 0\}$
8. $-3 \notin \{x \mid |x| < 1\}$
9. $-4 \in \{x \mid -5 < x < 1\}$
10. $-4 \notin \{x \mid x < -5 \text{ or } x > 1\}$
11. $5 \in \{x \mid x \text{ is an odd positive integer}\}$.
12. There is a smallest positive rational number.
13. There is a largest negative integer.
14. There is a largest negative real number.
15. The product of two odd integers is an odd integer.
16. The sum of any two irrational numbers is an irrational number.
17. The product of any two irrational numbers is an irrational number.
18. The set $\{n^2 - n + 47 \mid n \text{ is a positive integer}\}$ contains only prime numbers.

Exercises 19–22 Determine the truth value of:
(a) $P \wedge Q$ (b) $P \vee Q$ (c) $\sim P \vee \sim Q$.

19. P: $3 < 8$ 20. P: $1 - \sqrt{3} < 0$
    Q: $4 = 5$ Q: $\sqrt{5} - 1 > 0$
21. P: 7 is a prime number.
    Q: 3 is a rational number.
22. P: $\sqrt{2}$ is not a rational number.
    Q: $\sqrt{16}$ is not an integer.

Exercises 23–24 Determine the truth value of the conditional statements:
(a) $P \Rightarrow Q$ (b) $Q \Rightarrow P$ (c) $\sim Q \Rightarrow \sim P$.

23. P: $|2 - \sqrt{5}| = 2 - \sqrt{5}$
    Q: $2 - \sqrt{5}$ is positive.

24. P: $(5 - 3 \cdot 4)$ is positive.
    Q: $(4 + 8 \cdot 17)$ is even.

Exercises 25–29 Give a verbal statement that describes the negation of P and give the truth value of $\sim P$.

25. P: $n(n + 1)$ is an even number for every positive integer n.
26. P: $2n + 1$ is an odd number for every positive integer n.
27. P: $4n - 1$ is a prime number for every positive integer n.
28. P: For some positive integer n, $n^2 - n + 17 < 17$.
29. P: There is at least one rational number between 1 and 2.

Exercises 30–35 Determine the truth value of the statement obtained when the variable is replaced by the given value.

30. $x^2 - 4x < 0$; x is 4
31. $x^2 + 5x - 14 = 0$; x is -2
32. If $x^2 - 4x = 0$, then $x = 0$; x is 4
33. If $x = 0$, then $x^2 - 4x = 0$; x is 4
34. $x(x - 2)$ is negative; x is -2
35. $x - \sqrt{5}$ is an irrational number; x is $3 + \sqrt{5}$

Exercises 36–39 Find a value of x that will prove the statement false; that is, find a counterexample.

36. $x^2 \ge x$ for every positive real number x.
37. $\sqrt{x^2} = x$ for every real number x.
38. $|x + 4| = |x| + 4$ for every real number x.
39. $x^2 - x + 41$ is a prime for every positive integer x.

Exercises 40–41 From the diagram showing $m, n, p,$ and q on the number line, determine the truth value of each statement.

40. (a) $mn > 0$ (b) $\sqrt{p} < p$ (c) $\frac{1}{p} < q$
    (d) $n - m < 0$ (e) $pq < p$

41. (a) $|m - n| = n - m$ (b) $\frac{1}{m} > -1$
    (c) $mn > m$ (d) $0 < \frac{1}{q} < 1$ (e) $-m > n$

Exercises 42–45   If x is replaced in the open sentence by the given number, determine the truth value of the resulting conditional statement.

42. If $x^2 - 4x = 0$, then $x = 4$.
   (a) 4   **(b)** 0   **(c)** 1

43. If $x^2 - 4x = 0$, then $x = 0$ or $x = 4$.
   (a) 0   **(b)** 4   **(c)** -4

44. If $x^2 > 4$, then $x < -2$ or $x > 2$.
   (a) 3   **(b)** -3 **(c)** 1

45. If $0 < x < 4$, then $x^2 - 4x < 0$.
   (a) 1   **(b)** 2   **(c)** 5

Exercises 46–50   Find a value of x to show that the sentence is *not* an identity. That is, find a number such that, when substituted into the open sentence, makes the resulting conditional statement false.

46. If $x < 2$, then $x^2 < 4$

47. If $x > 0$, then $x^2 > x$.

48. If $x > 0$, then $x > \frac{1}{x}$.

49. If $x^2 - 2x > 0$, then $x > 2$.

50. If $x > 0$, then $\sqrt{x} < x$.

SECTION 1.5   Open Sentences in One Variable

There is something very funny here. We can teach a computer to decide whether a mathematical formula is well formed or not. That's very easy. But we cannot teach a computer to talk, to form sentences. It is obviously a million times as hard. But take any kid who learns how to speak. If, as a kid, he hears two languages, he learns two languages. If he is mentally retarded, he still becomes bilingual. He will know fewer words, but he will know those words in both languages. He will form sentences. Now try to explain to him what is a well formed algebraic formula!
        Lipman Bers

The traditional view of algebra, by those who know no algebra, is that it consists of solving equations. While we know that we must do much more than this, we do, nonetheless, need to develop such skills.

Equations and inequalities share many properties, including the methods to solve them, so we treat them together. Both equations and inequalities are mathematical sentences in which the verb is $=$ (for an equality), or one of $<$, $>$, $\leq$, or $\geq$ (for an inequality). As we discussed in Section 1.4, we deal with open sentences, sentences containing variables or place holders, usually letters such as x, y, or z. When we replace a variable with a number, we get a statement, which is either true or false. The **domain** or **replacement set** of a variable is the set of numbers that the problem allows as replacements for the variable. Restrictions on domains should be clearly stated; otherwise we adopt the following domain convention.

> **Domain Convention**
>
> If no restrictions are stated, the domain of a variable is assumed to be the set of all real numbers that give meaningful real number statements. This excludes any division by zero or square roots of negative numbers.

EXAMPLE 1   Find the domain of the variable x in the open sentence:

$$\sqrt{x + 1} \geq \frac{1}{x - 3}.$$

Solution

Assuming the domain convention, we require $x - 3 \neq 0$ or $x \neq 3$, and we must have $x + 1 \geq 0$, or $x \geq -1$. Taking the conditions together, the domain D of the variable consists of all real numbers greater than or equal to -1, except for 3. In interval notation, D is $[-1, 3) \cup (3, \infty)$.   ▲

The **solution set** for an open sentence is the set of all numbers in the domain that yield true statements. To solve an equation or inequality means to find the solution set, and the *roots* of an equation are the numbers in the solution set.

Solving equations and inequalities is not always easy, but to simplify this work we most generally perform operations that give us equivalent open sentences, hoping to reach a sentence whose solution set is obvious. Thus, for example, $2x - 3 = 5$ is equivalent to $2x = 8$, which is equivalent to $x = 4$. The solution to $2x - 3 = 5$ is 4. Equivalent open sentences have the same solution set. The following equivalence operations on open sentences yield equivalent open sentences.

Equivalence Operations

1. *Replace* any expression in the sentence by another expression identically equal to it.

2. *Add* or *subtract* the same quantity on both sides.

3. For an equation, *multiply* or *divide* both sides by the same nonzero quantity.

4. For an inequality, *multiply* or *divide* both sides by the same positive quantity, or multiply or divide both sides by the same negative quantity and reverse the direction of the inequality.

The last equivalence operation for inequalities points up one of the major differences between equations and inequalities: multiplication by a negative number reverses the direction of an inequality. To avoid the necessity of treating separate cases, we suggest that you *never* multiply an inequality by an expression involving a variable.

Linear Equations and Inequalities

A **linear open sentence** is one that is equivalent to

$$ax + b \;\boxed{}\; 0, \text{ with } \boxed{} \text{ replaced by } =, <, >, \leq, \text{ or } \geq,$$

where a and b are constants and a is not zero.

The equivalence operations allow us to find the solution set for any linear open sentence.

Strategy: (a) First use Equivalence Operation 2 to get all x-terms on one side and the constants on the other (i.e., subtract x and 4 from both sides).
(b) Similarly, use Operation 2 to collect the x-terms on one side and constants on the other.

EXAMPLE 2

Find the solution set.

(a) $3x + 4 = x - 1$
(b) $2 - 3x \le 4$

Solution

Follow the strategy.

(a) $3x - x = -1 - 4,$ or $2x = -5.$

Divide both sides by 2 (Equivalence Operation 3), giving $x = -\frac{5}{2}$. The solution set is $\{-\frac{5}{2}\}$.

(b) $-3x \le 4 - 2,$ or $-3x \le 2.$

By Equivalence Operation 4, we can divide both sides by -3 if we reverse the direction of the inequality, getting $x \ge -\frac{2}{3}$. The solution set is $\{x \mid x \ge -\frac{2}{3}\}$, or in interval notation, $[-\frac{2}{3}, \infty)$. ▲

Quadratic Equations and Inequalities

A **quadratic open sentence** is one that is equivalent to

$$ax^2 + bx + c \;\square\; 0, \text{ with } \square \text{ replaced by } =, <, >, \le, \text{ or } \ge,$$

where a, b, and c are constants and a is not zero.

If we can factor $ax^2 + bx + c$, then we can use signed-product principles to find solution sets.

Signed-Product Principles

Zero-product principle. A product of two factors *equals zero* if and only if *at least one is zero.*

Positive-product principle. A product of two factors is *positive* if and only if they have the *same sign* (that is, both are positive or both are negative).

Negative-product principle. A product of two factors is *negative* if and only if they have *opposite signs* (that is, one is positive and one is negative).

EXAMPLE 3

Find the solution set.

(a) $2x^2 - 3x - 2 = 0$ **(b)** $2x^2 - 3x - 2 < 0$

Solution

(a) $2x^2 - 3x - 2 = (2x + 1)(x - 2)$, and so by Equivalence Operation 1 the given equation is equivalent to

$$(2x + 1)(x - 2) = 0.$$

By the zero-product principle,

$$2x + 1 = 0 \quad \text{or} \quad x - 2 = 0.$$

Each of these equations yields a root of the original equation (*Check!*), so the solution set is $\{-\frac{1}{2}, 2\}$.

(b)   Equivalence Operation 1 says that the inequality is equivalent to

$$(2x + 1)(x - 2) < 0.$$

The product can be negative only when the factors have opposite signs, one positive and one negative. This leaves two possibilities:

      (i) $2x + 1 > 0$ and $x - 2 < 0$

or

      (ii) $2x + 1 < 0$ and $x - 2 > 0$.

These, in turn, are equivalent to:

    (i) $x > -\frac{1}{2}$ and $x < 2$ or   **(ii)** $x < -\frac{1}{2}$ and $x > 2$.

In **(ii)** x must be both less than $-\frac{1}{2}$ *and* greater than 2, which cannot happen. From **(i)** we get the open interval $(-\frac{1}{2}, 2)$. For each number in this interval the factor $(2x + 1)$ is positive and the factor $(x - 2)$ is negative, so the product is negative. Hence, the solution set is $(-\frac{1}{2}, 2)$. ▲

For quadratic expressions that cannot be factored readily, we can use another familiar tool from introductory algebra, the **quadratic formula,** in conjunction with the zero-product principle.

Quadratic Formula

The equation $ax^2 + bx + c = 0$, where a is not zero, is equivalent to

$$x = \frac{-b \pm \sqrt{b^2 - 4ac}}{2a}.$$

This equation is called the *quadratic formula.*

Nature of the Roots of a Quadratic Equation   The nature of the roots of a quadratic equation depends on the sign of the expression under the square root.

The expression $b^2 - 4ac$ is called the **discriminant** and determines the nature of the roots of a quadratic equation.

    If $b^2 - 4ac = 0$, there is only one real root, $x - -\frac{b}{2a}$.

    If $b^2 - 4ac > 0$, there are two real roots.

    If $b^2 - 4ac < 0$, there are no real roots. Two are imaginary.

Strategy: Use the quadratic formula and determine whether or not the solutions are real numbers.

EXAMPLE 4 Apply the quadratic formula to solve $2x^2 + 4x + 3 = 0$, where the domain set is

(a) the set of real numbers **(b)** the set of complex numbers.

Solution

Substituting 2 for a, 4 for b, and 3 for c in the quadratic formula gives

$$x = \frac{-4 \pm \sqrt{4^2 - 4(2)(3)}}{2 \cdot 2} = \frac{-4 \pm \sqrt{-8}}{4} = \frac{-2 \pm \sqrt{2}i}{2}.$$

Since the solutions are imaginary numbers, we conclude that:

(a) The given equation has no solutions in R.

(b) In C the solutions are:

$$\frac{-2 + \sqrt{2}i}{2} \quad \text{and} \quad \frac{-2 - \sqrt{2}i}{2}. \quad \blacktriangle$$

More on Quadratic Inequalities

The solution sets for the inequality and the equation in Example 3 illustrate a general relationship that applies to a broad class of quadratic inequalities. Given an inequality $ax^2 + bx + c \ \square \ 0$, we speak of the **related equation,** $ax^2 + bx + c = 0$. If the related equation has two distinct real roots, say $r_1 < r_2$, then the solution set for the inequality consists either of

all points *between* r_1 and r_2, or all points *outside* the interval (r_1, r_2).

The numbers r_1 and r_2 are included if the inequality sign is either $\leq$ or $\geq$. Points where the expression $ax^2 + bx + c$ can change sign are called *cut points* for the expression.

Cut points "cut" the number line into intervals in each of which the expression does not change sign. If we have cut points for an inequality, we can substitute a **test number** from each interval into the inequality. If we get a true statement, the whole interval belongs to the solution set; if not, no part of the interval is in the solution set.

Strategy: Find the roots of the equation $-x^2 + 2\sqrt{2}\,x + 2 = 0$ by using the quadratic formula, with $a = -1$, $b = 2\sqrt{2}$, $c = 2$ to find r_1 and r_2. Pick a test number to see whether the solution set is inside or outside the interval (r_1, r_2).

EXAMPLE 5 Find the solution set for $-x^2 + 2\sqrt{2}x + 2 \leq 0$.

Solution

Follow the strategy.

$$x = \frac{-2\sqrt{2} \pm \sqrt{(2\sqrt{2})^2 - 4(-1)(2)}}{-2}$$

$$= \frac{-2\sqrt{2} \pm 4}{-2}$$

$$= \sqrt{2} \pm 2.$$

This gives r_1 as $\sqrt{2} - 2 (\approx -0.59)$ and r_2 as $\sqrt{2} + 2 (\approx 3.41)$, both of which belong to the solution set S of the inequality. The rest of the solution set consists of all numbers inside or outside (r_1, r_2).

A convenient test number in this case is 0. Replacing x by 0 in the original inequality gives:

$$-0^2 + 2\sqrt{2}(0) + 2 \leq 0 \qquad \text{or} \qquad 2 \leq 0.$$

Since $2 \leq 0$ is a false statement, 0 is not in S. The solution set is therefore outside the interval (r_1, r_2), namely

$$(-\infty, \sqrt{2} - 2] \cup [\sqrt{2} + 2, \infty). \quad \blacktriangle$$

More Applications of the Zero-Product Principle

We can use the zero-product principle whenever we have a product equal to zero. The next example illustrates some typical uses.

Strategy: Use Equivalence Operation 2 to get a zero on one side of the open sentence, then factor as far as possible and apply the zero-product principle.

EXAMPLE 6   Find the solution set.

(a) $x^3 = x^2 + 4x$ **(b)** $1 < \dfrac{3}{x + 1}$

Solution

(a) Subtract $x^2 + 4x$ from both sides to get zero on one side and factor.

$$x^3 - x^2 - 4x = 0 \qquad \text{or} \qquad x(x^2 - x - 4) = 0$$

By the zero-product principle, either $x = 0$ or $x^2 - x - 4 = 0$. We can use the quadratic formula to find the roots of the second equation:

$$x = \frac{1 \pm \sqrt{1 - 4(1)(-4)}}{2} = \frac{1 \pm \sqrt{17}}{2}.$$

The solution set is

$$\left\{ 0, \frac{1 + \sqrt{17}}{2}, \frac{1 - \sqrt{17}}{2} \right\}.$$

(b) First, we get a 0 on one side by subtraction.

$$1 - \frac{3}{x + 1} < 0.$$

Combining fractions we get $1 - \frac{3}{x + 1} = \frac{x - 2}{x + 1}$. Therefore, by Equivalence Operation 1, the given inequality is equivalent to

$$\frac{x - 2}{x + 1} < 0.$$

The sign properties for quotients are the same as for products; to be negative, the two factors, $x - 2$ and $x + 1$, must have opposite signs. Thus -1 and 2 are *cut points*. Choose a test number in each of the three intervals, $(-\infty, -1)$, $(-1, 2)$, or $(2, \infty)$, say -2, 1, and 5. Go back to the original inequality and replace x by each test number. The results are, respectively, $1 < -3$ (false), $1 < \frac{3}{2}$ (true), and $1 < \frac{3}{6}$ (false). The solution set is the interval $(-1, 2)$.

$\blacktriangle$

WARNING: Multiplying both sides of the inequality in Example 6 **(b)** by $x + 1$ would not give an equivalent inequality. See Explore and Discover Exercise 1. It is sometimes tempting to clear fractions, but in Equivalence Operation 4, we must keep or reverse the inequality, depending on the sign of the multiplier.

Equations and Inequalities Involving Absolute Values

When working with open sentences that involve absolute values, it is often useful to replace them with equivalent open sentences without absolute values. Because the definition of absolute value depends on sign, it is often necessary to consider cases. The following table gives replacements that yield equivalent open sentences.

Absolute Value Equivalents

Suppose c is any positive number and u any expression involving a variable.

Equivalent Replacement

$\lvert u \rvert = c$	$u = c$ or $u = -c$
$\lvert u \rvert < c$	$-c < u < c$
$\lvert u \rvert > c$	$u < -c$ or $u > c$

EXAMPLE 7   Find the solution set.

(a) $\lvert 2x + 3 \rvert = 5$ **(b)** $\lvert 2x + 3 \rvert \leq 5$ **(c)** $\lvert 2x + 3 \rvert > 5$

Solution

(a) From the list above, replace the given equation by:

$$2x + 3 = 5 \quad \text{or} \quad 2x + 3 = -5$$
$$2x = 2 \quad \text{or} \quad 2x = -8$$

The solution set is $\{1, -4\}$.

(b) We can replace $\lvert 2x + 3 \rvert \leq 5$ with two inequalities,

$$-5 \leq 2x + 3 \quad \text{and} \quad 2x + 3 \leq 5$$
$$-8 \leq 2x \quad \text{and} \quad 2x \leq 2$$
$$-4 \leq x \quad \text{and} \quad x \leq 1.$$

The final two inequalities together name the interval $[-4, 1]$ as the solution set.

(c) We could use the last replacement from the table above and proceed as in part **(b)**, but it is easier to recognize that the solution set for $\lvert 2x + 3 \rvert > 5$ consists of all numbers that do *not* satisfy part **(b)**. Therefore the solution set is $(-\infty, -4) \cup (1, \infty)$.   ▲

EXAMPLE 8   What integers satisfy the inequality

$x^2 + 2\lvert x \rvert - 8 < 0$?

Strategy: Consider two cases: **(a)** for $x \geq 0$, replace $|x|$ by x; **(b)** for $x < 0$, replace $|x|$ by $-x$. In each case solve the resulting inequality.

Solution

Follow the strategy.

(a) $x \geq 0$: $x^2 + 2x - 8 < 0$,   or $(x + 4)(x - 2) < 0$.

We have two cut points, -4 and 2, but only 2 satisfies $x \geq 0$.

(b) $x < 0$: $x^2 - 2x - 8 < 0$ or $(x - 4)(x + 2) < 0$.

Again, there are two cut points, 4 and -2, but only -2 satisfies $x < 0$. The cut points for the original inequality are 2 and -2. Checking test points in the original, we find that the solution set is the interval $(-2, 2)$. The integers in the interval $(-2, 2)$ are -1, 0, and 1.   ▲

EXAMPLE 9   A water tank can be filled by two hoses (A and B) of different sizes. When hose B is used alone, it takes twice as long to fill the tank as when hose A is used alone. When both hoses are used together, it takes 4 hours to fill the tank. How much time does it take to fill the tank when only hose A is used?

Strategy: If x is the number of hours it takes to fill the tank when A is used alone, then $2x$ is the number of hours for B to fill the tank alone. In 1 hour A fills $\frac{1}{x}$, and B fills $\frac{1}{2x}$, and together they fill $\frac{1}{4}$ of the tank.

Solution

Following the strategy,

$$\frac{1}{x} + \frac{1}{2x} = \frac{1}{4}.$$

Multiply both sides by $4x$:

$$4 + 2 = x, \qquad \text{or} \qquad x = 6.$$

Therefore it takes 6 hours to fill the tank with hose A alone. (*Check!*) Does this answer make sense? If it takes 6 hours to fill the tank with hose A alone, then it must take 12 hours to fill the tank with hose B alone. As in the strategy, in 1 hour, hose A fills $\frac{1}{6}$ of the tank and hose B fills $\frac{1}{12}$. Used together, in one hour they fill $\frac{1}{6} + \frac{1}{12}$, or $\frac{1}{4}$, of the tank.   ▲

EXERCISES 1.5

Check Your Understanding

Exercises 1–6   True or False. Give reasons for your conclusion.

1. The two equations $x^3 - 2x^2 - 5x = 0$ and $x^2 - 2x - 5 = 0$ have the same solution set.

2. The sum of all the integers in the set $\{x \mid -7 < 3x - 1 < 14\}$ is 14.

3. The number -2 is in the solution set for $x^2 - 3x - 5 > |x|$.

4. The solution set for $(x + 3)^2 = 1$ is the same as the solution set for $x + 3 = 1$.

5. The solution set for $x < \frac{4}{x}$ is the same as the solution set for $x^2 < 4$.

6. The solution set for $x < |x|$ is the set of negative numbers.

Exercises 7–10   Complete the sentence by selecting from the list below *all choices* that make the statement true.

(a) 0   (b) -1 (c) 1   (d) -2 (e) 2
(f) more than 2

7. The set $\{x \mid x^2 - 16 < 1\}$ contains _____ prime numbers.

8. The solution set for $\sqrt{x^2} = 1$ contains _____ elements.

9. The largest negative integer x for which $|3x - 1| \geq 2$ is _____.

10. If k is any positive number, then $x^2 + 2x - k = 0$ has _____ real root(s).

Explore and Discover

1. If both sides of the inequality in Example 6(b) are multiplied by $x + 1$, the resulting inequality is $x + 1 < 3$, which has the solution set $(-\infty, 2)$. Find some numbers in $(-\infty, 2)$ that do not satisfy the original inequality. Write a paragraph explaining why multiplying both sides of an inequality by $x + 1$ is not an equivalence operation.

2. If x_1 and x_2 are the roots (real or imaginary) of the equation, evaluate $x_1 + x_2$ and $x_1 \cdot x_2$
   (a) $x^2 - 3x - 4 = 0$
   (b) $2x^2 - 5x - 12 = 0$
   (c) $3x^2 + 2x - 8 = 0$
   (d) $x^2 - 2x + 5 = 0$

   From your results, speculate about formulas that will give the sum and product of the two roots of the quadratic equation $ax^2 + bx + c = 0$ in terms of the coefficients a, b, and c.

3. The quadratic equation $ax^2 + bx + c = 0$ is equivalent to the quadratic equation $x^2 + \frac{b}{a}x + \frac{c}{a} = 0$ $(a \neq 0)$. If x_1 and x_2 are the two roots, then

   $$x^2 + \frac{b}{a}x + \frac{c}{a} = (x - x_1)(x - x_2)$$

   is an identity. Expand the right side and use the result to get formulas for the sum and the product of the roots in terms of the coefficients a, b, and c. Compare with your guess in Exercise 2.

4. Continuing Exercise 3, find formulas for
   (a) $x_1^2 + x_2^2$ (b) $x_1^3 + x_2^3$. (*Hint:* Use the identities $(x_1 + x_2)^2 = x_1^2 + 2x_1x_2 + x_2^2$ and $(x_1 + x_2)^3 = x_1^3 + x_2^3 + 3x_1x_2(x_1 + x_2)$.

Develop Mastery

If not specified, the domain of the variable is assumed to be R.

Exercises 1–8 Solve. Simplify the result.

1. $5 - 3x = 7 + x$
2. $5x - 1 = \sqrt{3}$
3. $(x - 2)^2 = x^2 - 2$
4. $(1 - 2x)^2 = 4x^2 - x$
5. $3x^2 + 2x - 1 = 0$
6. $2x^2 + x = 10$
7. $6x + 5 = 9x^2 - 3$
8. $\sqrt{3x} - 4 = x$

Exercises 9–10 Assume the replacement set is the set of complex numbers. Solve. Simplify the result.

9. $4x^2 + 4x - 15 = 0$
10. $2x^2 + 4x + 5 = 0$

Exercises 11–26 Solve.

11. $3x - 1 > 5$
12. $\frac{1 - 2x}{-3} > \frac{1}{2}$
13. $-0.1 \leq 2x + 1 \leq 0.1$
14. $-1 \leq \frac{x + 3}{-2} \leq 1$
15. $(2 - x)(1 + x) \geq 0$
16. $2x^2 - x - 3 > 0$
17. $\frac{4 - x^2}{x + 3} \geq 0$
18. $x + 1 > \frac{2}{x}$
19. $2 \leq 3x - 1 \leq 8$
20. $0 \leq x^2 - 1 \leq 8$
21. $|x| > x$
22. $x^4 + 4x^3 \geq 12x^2$
23. $|2x - 3| > 5$
24. $|x - 4| + x \leq 6$
25. $|x - 2| + 2x \leq 4$
26. $x^2 - 71x - 10{,}296 < 0$

Exercises 27–30 Find the solution set and show it on a number line.

27. $5x - 1 > 3 + 7x$
28. $x^2 - x > 12$
29. $\frac{x + 2}{x^2 - 9} > 0$
30. $2x + 1 > \frac{2}{x}$

Exercises 31–34 Find the solution set and express it in interval notation.

31. $|x - 1| < 2$
32. $|2x + 1| > 3$
33. $|x| + 1 < \sqrt{2}$
34. $|1 - x| \leq 0.1$

Exercises 35–36 Use the discriminant to determine the number of real roots.

35. $x^2 - 15x + 8 = 0$
36. $4x^2 + 4\sqrt{3}x + 3 = 0$

Exercises 37–46 Solve.

37. $x^4 + 3x^2 - 10 = 0$
38. $2|x + 3| - 1 = 5$
39. $|5 - x| - 5 = 3$
40. $(\sqrt{x})^2 - 2\sqrt{x} - 3 = 0$
41. $|x|^2 - 2|x| = 3$
42. $\sqrt{2x + 3} = 1$
43. $\sqrt{x^2 + 4x} = x + 2$
44. $\frac{1}{x} - \frac{3}{x} = \frac{1}{2} + \frac{1}{4}$

45. $\sqrt{x^4 - 5x^2 - 35} = 1$

46. $x - 2\sqrt{x} - 8 = 0$

Exercises 47–50   Find the solution set. Assume that the replacement set is the set of integers.

47. $-4 \le 3x - 2 \le 4$ **48.** $|2 - 3x| < 4$

49. $2x^2 + x < 15$ **50.** $\sqrt{(x-2)^2} \le 3$

Exercises 51–52   Determine the values of x for which the expression yields a real number.

51. $\sqrt{-x^2 - 4x - 3}$ **52.** $\sqrt{x - \frac{4}{x}}$

Exercises 53–54   Determine the values of x for which the expression yields and imaginary number.

53. $\sqrt{-x^2 - 5x - 6}$ **54.** $\sqrt{4 - 2|x|}$

Exercises 55–56   Find the solution set. (*Hint:* Recall $\sqrt{u^2} = |u|$).

55. $\sqrt{(2x - 1)^2} = 5$ **56.** $\sqrt{x^2} = -x$

Exercises 57–58   Find the solution set.

57. $x + 2 < 3$ and $x + 2 > -3$

58. $2x - 3 \le -1$ and $2x - 3 > -4$

Exercises 59–62   Use the zero-product principle to find a quadratic equation with the pair of roots.

59. $-2, -4$ **60.** $-2, \dfrac{1}{2}$

61. $1 + \sqrt{2}, 1 - \sqrt{2}$ **62.** $1 + i, 1 - i$

Exercises 63–64   Determine the number of *integers* in the set.

63. $\{x \mid 2x + 5 > 0$ and $-3x + 16 > 3\}$

64. $\{x \mid |x - 3| < \sqrt{5}\}$

Exercises 65–66   Use the zero-product principle to find the solution set.

65. $(x^2 - 9)(x^2 + x - 6) = 0$

66. $(|x| - 1)(3 - |x + 1|) = 0$

67. How many prime numbers are contained in the set $\{x \mid x^2 - 15x \le 0\}$?

68. Find the largest integer k for which the equation $kx^2 + 10x + 3 = 0$ will have real roots.

69. Find the smallest integer c for which the equation $x^2 + 5x - c = 0$ will have real roots.

70. What is the sum of all the positive integers x for which $x^2 - 2x - 17$ is negative?

71. What is the smallest integer k such that $3x(kx - 4) - x^2 + 4 = 0$ has no real roots?

72. What is the largest integer x such that the reciprocal of $x + 4$ is greater than $x - 4$?

73. What is the sum of all prime numbers in the set $\{x \mid 3x + 4 < 5x + 7 < 4x + 15\}$?

74. In the right triangle in the diagram, $c = b + 1$, and the perimeter is 12. Find a, b, and c.

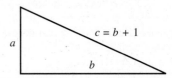

75. In a triangle having sides a, b, and c, if $a = 10$, $b = 12$, and $b^2 = a^2 + c^2 - ac$, find all possible values for c.

76. (a) If $x + y = 8$ and $x^2 + 4xy + 3y^2 = 48$, find $2x + 6y$. (*Hint:* Factor the left-hand side.)

   (b) If $a^2b + ab^2 + a + b = 72$ and $a \cdot b = 8$, then find the sum $a + b$ and the sum $a^2 + b^2$. (*Hint:* First factor the left side, and then use $(a + b)^2 = a^2 + 2ab + b^2$.)

77. A certain chemical reaction takes place when the temperature is between 5° and 20° Celsius. What is the corresponding temperature on the Farhrenheit scale? (*Hint:* $F = \frac{9}{5}C + 32$.)

78. In 1990 the population of Newbury increased by 1600 people. During 1991 the population decreased by 12 percent and the town ended up with 56 fewer people than had lived there before the 1600 increase. What was the original population?

79. Two pumps, A and B, can be used to empty a large tank by operating one at a time or together. Pump A alone takes four hours to empty the tank; pump B alone can empty the tank in six hours. How long does it take when both are used together?

80. In Exercise 79 if pump A alone takes 8 hours to empty the tank, and together the two pumps can empty the tank in 3 hours, how long does it take for pump B to do the job alone?

81. A boy walking to school averages 90 steps per minute, each step 3 feet in length. It takes him 15 minutes to reach school. His friend walks to school along the same route averaging 100 steps per minute, each step covering 2.5 feet. How long does it take for the friend to walk to school?

82. A beaker contains 100 cc of water. Suppose x cc of water are removed and replaced by x cc of pure acid.

From the resulting mixture, another x cc are removed and replaced by x cc of acid. In the final mixture the ratio of water to acid is 16 to 9. Find x, and the final volume of acid.

83. A farmer has 200 feet of fencing to enclose a rectangular garden. If the width of the garden is x feet, find an equation that gives the area A of the garden in terms of x. For what values of x is the equation meaningful?

84. A rectangle is inscribed in a circle of diameter 10 inches, as shown.
  (a) Using the information shown in the diagram, find an equation that gives the area A of the rectangle in terms of x.
  (b) For what values of x is the equation meaningful?

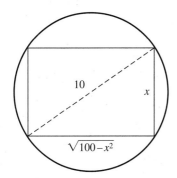

85. A box with an open top is to be made from a rectangular piece of tin 8 inches by 12 inches, by cutting a square from each corner and bending up the sides as shown in the diagram. Let x be the length of the sides of each square.
  (a) Show that the volume V of the box is given by $V = 4x^3 - 40x^2 + 96x$.
  (b) For what values of x is $V > 0$?

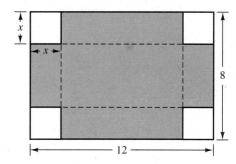

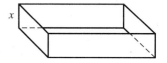

| SECTION 1.6 | **Rectangular Coordinates and Graphs** |

Creative people live in two worlds. One is the ordinary world which they share with others and in which they are not in any special way set apart from their fellow men. The other is private and it is in this world that the creative acts take place. It is a world with its own passions, elations and despairs, and it is here that, if one is as great as Einstein, one may even hear the voice of God.
  Mark Kac

Rectangular Coordinates

Few intellectual discoveries have had more far-reaching consequences than coordinatizing the plane by René Descartes nearly 400 years ago. We speak of **Cartesian** or rectangular coordinates in his honor.

A rectangular coordinate system uses two perpendicular number lines in the plane, which we call coordinate axes. The more common orientation is a horizontal **x-axis** and a vertical **y-axis,** but other variable names and orientations are sometimes useful.

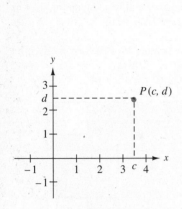

FIGURE 1.10

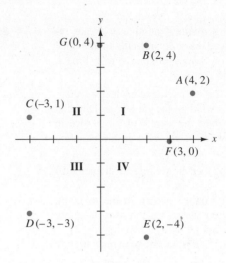

FIGURE 1.11

Each point P in the plane is identified by an ordered pair of real numbers (c, d), called the **coordinates** of P, where c and d are numbers on the respective axes as shown in Figure 1.10. Conversely, every pair of real numbers names a unique point on the plane.

> A rectangular system of coordinates provides a one-to-one correspondence between the set of ordered pairs of real numbers and the points in the plane.

The axes divide the plane into four quadrants labeled I, II, III, IV, as shown in Figure 1.11. In the figure, points A and B are in Quadrant I, C is in II, D is in III, and E is in IV. Point F is on the x-axis while G is on the y-axis; points on the coordinate axes are not in any quadrant.

The distance $d(r, s)$ between points r and s on a number line is expressed in terms of absolute value.

$$d(r, s) = |r - s|$$

We extend the idea of distance to the coordinate plane by means of the familiar Pythagorean Theorem.

> **Pythagorean Theorem**
>
> Suppose a and b are the lengths of the legs of a right triangle and c is the hypotenuse. Then
>
> $$a^2 + b^2 = c^2.$$

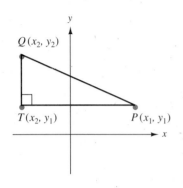

FIGURE 1.12

Conversely, suppose $a^2 + b^2 = c^2$. Then the triangle must be a right triangle with hypotenuse c.

Distance Between Points in a Plane

Suppose $P(x_1, y_1)$ and $Q(x_2, y_2)$ are any two points in the plane. The distance between P and Q, denoted $d(P, Q)$ or $|\overline{PQ}|$, is defined to be the length of the line segment between P and Q. ($\overline{PQ}$ denotes the line segment from P to Q.) Figure 1.12 shows a right triangle PTQ whose legs are given in terms of absolute values.

$$|\overline{PT}| = |x_1 - x_2| \qquad \text{and} \qquad |\overline{TQ}| = |y_1 - y_2|$$

Applying the Pythagorean theorem gives

$$|\overline{PQ}|^2 = |\overline{PT}|^2 + |\overline{TQ}|^2 = |x_1 - x_2|^2 + |y_1 - y_2|^2.$$

Since $|x_1 - x_2|^2 = (x_1 - x_2)^2$ and $|y_1 - y_2|^2 = (y_1 - y_2)^2$, we have the following.

Distance Formula

Suppose $P(x_1, y_1)$ and $Q(x_2, y_2)$ are any two points in the plane. If $d(P, Q)$ denotes the distance between P and Q, then

$$d(P, Q) = \sqrt{(x_1 - x_2)^2 + (y_1 - y_2)^2}.$$

We can also write $d(P, Q)$ as $|\overline{PQ}|$.

Midpoint of a Line Segment

Suppose $P(x_1, y_1)$ and $Q(x_2, y_2)$ are any two points in the plane. To get the midpoint M of the line segment $\overline{PQ}$, we take the average of the two x-values and the average of the two y-values. M is the point

$$M\left(\frac{x_1 + x_2}{2}, \frac{y_1 + y_2}{2}\right).$$

It is easy to show that $d(P, M) = d(Q, M)$ and that $d(P, Q) = 2 \cdot d(P, M)$.

EXAMPLE 1 Given points $A(-4, -1)$ and $B(2, 3)$, find the coordinates of the midpoint M of the segment $\overline{AB}$ and locate all three points on a diagram. In which quadrant is A? B? M? Find $d(A, B)$ and $d(A, M)$.

I had lots of exams at school. At sixteen I took [a nationwide exam] in mathematics, physics, and chemistry, and was told that if I passed chemistry I could then drop it and do just pure math, applied math, and physics. So I did. . . . I now realize that I quite enjoyed organic chemistry because that ties in somewhat with graph theory.

Robin Wilson

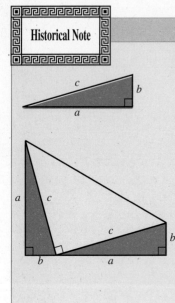

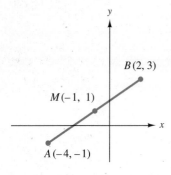

A PROOF OF THE PYTHAGOREAN THEOREM

How many United States presidents have made an original contribution to mathematics? There is at least one. In 1876 while a member of Congress, four years before he became president, James A. Garfield discovered an original proof for the Pythagorean theorem, one of dozens of proofs given after Euclid's (ca. 300 B.C.).

President Garfield's proof uses two facts. First, the area of a right triangle is half the product of the legs (base × altitude). Second, the area of a trapezoid equals its base times its average height. Given any right triangle, two copies and an isosceles right triangle can be put together to form a trapezoid, as shown in the figure. The sum of the areas of the triangles is $2\frac{ab}{2} + \frac{c^2}{2}$; the area of the trapezoid is $(a + b)(\frac{a + b}{2})$. Equating these expressions and multiplying by 2 gives

$$2ab + c^2 = a^2 + 2ab + b^2$$

or

$$c^2 = a^2 + b^2.$$

Solution

The coordinates of M are $[(-4 + 2)/2, (-1 + 3)/2]$, or $(-1, 1)$. Point A is in Quadrant III, M is in Quadrant II, and B is in Quadrant I, as shown in Figure 1.13.

$$d(A, B) = |\overline{AB}| = \sqrt{[2 - (-4)]^2 + [3 - (-1)]^2} = \sqrt{52} = 2\sqrt{13}.$$

$$d(A, M) = |\overline{AM}| = \sqrt{[-1 - (-4)]^2 + [1 - (-1)]^2} = \sqrt{13}.$$

Graphs

A coordinate plane allows us to make an algebraic relation visible in the form of a graph. We can then apply visual and geometric tools to reveal analytic properties.

> ### Definition: Graph of an Equation in Two Variables
>
> The graph of an equation in variables x and y is the set of points whose coordinates (x, y) satisfy the equation.

Technically, there is a difference between a graph as a set of points and as a sketch or picture of a set, but in practice we will use *graph* to refer to either the set or a pictorial representation of the set.

We find a specific point on a graph by substituting a value for one variable into the equation, then solving for the other variable. With time and patience, we can get enough points for a reasonable picture. Without the help of technology, however, the process is tedious at best. We need to develop some familiarity with certain kinds of equations and their graphs. We start with two simple and important graphs: lines and circles.

Linear Equations and Lines

> **Linear Equation**
>
> A **linear equation** in x and y is an equation equivalent to
>
> $$ax + by + c = 0 \tag{1}$$
>
> where a, b, and c are real numbers and at least one of a and b is nonzero.

We find points on the graph of a linear equation by substituting values into the equation. If you plot several points that satisfy a given linear equation, you will readily see why we call the graph of a linear equation a *line*. Since any two points determine a line, we can graph a linear equation by drawing the line through any pair of points whose coordinates satisfy the equation. It is less obvious that every line in the coordinate plane can be described by a linear equation, but we address that question in Section 2.3.

Intercept Points and Slope

Any point where a line crosses a coordinate axis is called an **intercept point.** If the line crosses the y-axis, we find the **y-intercept** point by substituting 0 for x and solving for y. Similarly for the **x-intercept** point, substitute 0 for y and solve for x. We often speak of the line $ax + by + c = 0$ when we mean the line whose coordinates satisfy the equation.

The intuitive idea of direction of a line becomes more specific in the concept of *slope.*

> **Definition: Slope of a Line**
>
> Suppose $P(x_1, y_1)$ and $Q(x_2, y_2)$ are two points on a nonvertical line L. The slope m of L is given by
>
> $$m = \frac{y_2 - y_1}{x_2 - x_1}. \tag{2}$$
>
> If L is vertical, then $x_2 = x_1$ and the slope of L is undefined (since Equation 2 would involve division by zero).

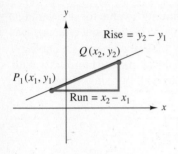

FIGURE 1.14

Slope: $m = \dfrac{y_2 - y_1}{x_2 - x_1}$

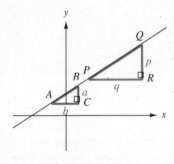

FIGURE 1.15

Slope: $m = \dfrac{a}{b} = \dfrac{p}{q}$

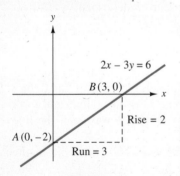

FIGURE 1.16

The slope is $\frac{2}{3}$.

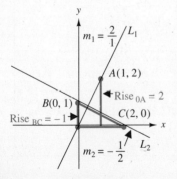

FIGURE 1.17

There are several ways to think of slope, as Figure 1.14 illustrates. As we move along the line to the right, the change in x-coordinates is sometimes called the *run,* and the change in y is the *rise,* which can be either positive or negative. For a nonvertical line, we can restate the slope equation as:

$$m = \frac{\text{rise}}{\text{run}} = \frac{\text{change in } y}{\text{change in } x}.$$

The slope of a line is independent of the two points we choose, as Figure 1.15 shows. The slope from Equation 2 is the ratio of two sides of a triangle. Triangles ABC and PQR are similar, so ratios of corresponding sides are the same. The slope of L is either $\frac{a}{b}$ or $\frac{p}{q}$.

| EXAMPLE 2 | Given the line $2x - 3y = 6$. |

(a) Find the intercept points and draw a graph.

(b) Use the intercept points to find the slope of the line.

Solution

(a) Substituting 0 for x, $-3y = 6$ or $y = -2$. Substituting 0 for y, $2x = 6$ or $x = 3$. This gives a y-intercept point of $A(0, -2)$ and an x-intercept point of $B(3, 0)$. Plot A and B and draw the graph as in Figure 1.16.

(b) Using the coordinates of A and B in Equation 2, determine the slope.

$$m = \frac{-2 - 0}{0 - 3} = \frac{2}{3} \quad \blacktriangle$$

The slope of a line is very handy in drawing a graph. Express the slope m as a fraction (with denominator 1 if needed). The denominator is the run and the numerator is the corresponding rise. From any point on the line, move to the right for the run and up or down for the rise, to get the coordinates of another point on the line.

| EXAMPLE 3 | Line L_1 passes through the origin, and the y-intercept point of line L_2 is $B(0, 1)$. Their slopes are given respectively by $m_1 = 2$ and $m_2 = -\frac{1}{2}$. Draw both lines on the same set of coordinate axes. |

Solution

Express m_1 as a fraction, $m_1 = \frac{2}{1}$. To locate another point on L_1, from $O(0, 0)$ plot a run of 1 unit to the right and a rise of 2, giving point $A(1, 2)$. Similarly, since $m_2 = -\frac{1}{2}$, a run of 2 corresponds to a rise of -1 (so the line drops as it moves rightward). From the y-intercept point, 2 units right and 1 down gives point $C(2, 0)$. Line L_1 is determined by O and A; L_2 contains B and C. Both lines are shown in Figure 1.17. $\blacktriangle$

Circles

A circle is defined as the set of points that are a fixed distance, called the *radius,* from a fixed point, called the *center.* If the center is point $C(h, k)$, then $P(x, y)$ is on the circle with radius r precisely when the distance $d(P, C)$ equals r (see

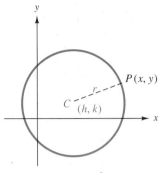

FIGURE 1.18

Circle with center $C(h, k)$
and radius r

Figure 1.18). Using the distance formula,

$$d(P, C) = \sqrt{(x - h)^2 + (y - k)^2} = r.$$

Since the radius r is a positive number, we may square both sides to get the standard form for an equation of a circle.

Standard Form for Equation of a Circle

Suppose h, k, and r are given real numbers ($r > 0$). Point (x, y) lies on a circle of radius r and center (h, k) if and only if (x, y) satisfies

$$(x - h)^2 + (y - k)^2 = r^2 \qquad \text{(3)}$$

> ### EXAMPLE 4

(a) Write an equation for the circle with center $C(2, -3)$ and radius 3. Sketch the graph.

(b) Determine which of the points $O(0, 0)$, $A(2, 0)$, and $B(4, -1)$ are inside the circle.

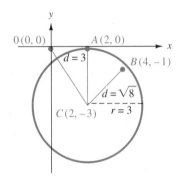

FIGURE 1.19

Solution

(a) Given the coordinates of the center, $h = 2$ and $k = -3$, replace h by 2, k by -3, and r by 3 in Equation 3 to get

$$(x - 2)^2 + [y - (-3)]^2 = 3^2 \qquad \text{or} \qquad (x - 2)^2 + (y + 3)^2 = 9.$$

The graph, with points O, A, and B, is shown in Figure 1.19.

(b) From the graph, it appears that O is outside the circle, but it is not as clear whether A and B are inside or outside. Using the distance formula,

$$d(A, C) = \sqrt{(2 - 2)^2 + (0 + 3)^2} = \sqrt{9} = 3,$$

$$d(B, C) = \sqrt{(4 - 2)^2 + (-1 + 3)^2} = \sqrt{8}.$$

From the definition of a circle, A is on the circle and B is inside because $\sqrt{8} < 3$. ▲

The standard form for an equation of a circle identifies the center and the radius. If we expand the squared terms on the left side of Equation 3 and collect the constants, we get a general form for an equation of a circle.

General Form for the Equation of a Circle

For any real numbers A, B, and C, the graph of the equation

$$x^2 + y^2 + Ax + By + C = 0 \qquad \text{(4)}$$

is either a circle, a point, or no points.

We can show that Equation 4 is equivalent to Equation 3 by completing the square on $x^2 + Ax$ and on $y^2 + By$, as illustrated in Example 5.

EXAMPLE 5

Strategy: Write in the form of Equation 4 and then complete the squares. Remember to add to both sides of the equation.

Find the center and radius. Draw a graph.

(a) $x^2 + y^2 = 4x$ **(b)** $2x^2 + 2y^2 - 4x + 6y + \dfrac{1}{2} = 0$

Solution

(a) Follow the strategy.

$$(x^2 - 4x) + y^2 = 0$$

$$(x^2 - 4x + 4) + y^2 = 4 \quad \text{or} \quad (x - 2)^2 + (y - 0)^2 = 2^2$$

The center is $(2, 0)$ and the radius is 2.

(b) Divide by 2 and collect x- and y-terms. Complete the squares.

$$x^2 + y^2 - 2x + 3y + \frac{1}{4} = 0$$

$$(x^2 - 2x) + (y^2 + 3y) = -\frac{1}{4}$$

$$(x^2 - 2x + 1) + \left(y^2 + 3y + \frac{9}{4}\right) = -\frac{1}{4} + 1 + \frac{9}{4}$$

$$(x - 1)^2 + \left(y + \frac{3}{2}\right)^2 = 3.$$

The center is $(1, -\frac{3}{2})$ and the radius is $\sqrt{3}$. Both circles are shown in Figure 1.20. ▲

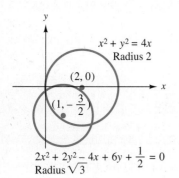

$x^2 + y^2 = 4x$
Radius 2

$2x^2 + 2y^2 - 4x + 6y + \dfrac{1}{2} = 0$
Radius $\sqrt{3}$

FIGURE 1.20

EXAMPLE 6

Find the coordinates of the highest and the lowest points on the graph of $x^2 + y^2 - 4x + 6y - 3 = 0$.

Solution

Looking at the equation, our first observation is that the graph appears to be a circle. From the graph we should be able to locate the high and low points. Find the center and radius by completing the squares on $x^2 - 4x$ and $y^2 + 6y$.

$$(x - 2)^2 + (y + 3)^2 = 16.$$

The center of the circle is at $(2, -3)$ and the radius is 4. The graph is shown in Figure 1.21. The graph shows the highest point 4 units above the center, at $(2, 1)$, and the lowest point 4 units below the center, at $(2, -7)$. ▲

EXAMPLE 7

Find the distance between the x-intercept points on the graph of $x^2 + y^2 - 4x + 6y - 3 = 0$.

Solution

This is the equation from Example 6, with the graph in Figure 1.21. Find the distance between points A and B. To find the x-intercept points, replace y by 0

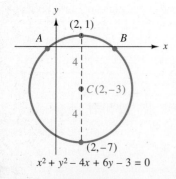

$x^2 + y^2 - 4x + 6y - 3 = 0$

FIGURE 1.21

For Graphers 1.6

DRAWING LINES AND CIRCLES

Graphing calculators are programmed to draw graphs of *functions*, not equations. The calculator will accept only Graph $Y = f(X)$. If needed, solve for y, as in the following example.

EXAMPLE Draw a graph and find the coordinates of the intercept points of

(a) the line $3x - 2y = 4$ **(b)** the circle $x^2 + y^2 = 4$.

Strategy: Solve each equation for y. For (b), graph two functions.

Solution **(a)** Solving for y, we get $y = 1.5x - 2$. Set the Familiar Window. Then enter the function $Y = 1.5X - 2$ and $\boxed{\text{EXE}}$ or $\boxed{\text{ENTER}}$ to see the graph, which should be a line with slope 1.5 and y-intercept -2.

Using the Trace function, we can read the y-intercept point as $(0, -2)$, but we cannot read the exact coordinates of the x-intercept point. The best we can do is locate points near the intercept point: $(1.3, -0.05)$ and $(1.4, 0.1)$. Algebra will reveal the x-intercept point: set $y = 0$ and solve for x, giving $(\frac{4}{3}, 0)$. Since x-coordinates of pixels in the Familiar Window are all multiples of 0.1, the calculator cannot show the exact point.

(b) Two functions are required to define the circle: $Y = \boxed{\sqrt{}}(4 - X^2)$, and $Y = -\boxed{\sqrt{}}(4 - x^2)$ *(Don't forget parentheses.)* Set the Familiar Window, and enter two separate functions (see "Using a Graphing Calculator" at the front of this book). You should see the upper semicircle, which is a graph of $y = \sqrt{4 - x^2}$, followed by the lower semicircle $y = -\sqrt{4 - x^2}$. The Trace function identifies the intercept points as $(-2, 0)$, $(2, 0)$, $(0, 2)$, and $(0, -2)$. (Remember that up or down arrows move the cursor from one semicircle to the other.) ▲

Warning Without pixel addresses for critical points, the calculator will not show them. For **(b)** above, changing the range by a single tenth (say to $X\text{min} = -4.8$) will produce a graph with two properties:

1. The top and bottom functions do not meet [that is, the circle is not complete because there is no $(2, 0)$ or $(-2, 0)$ pixel].

2. We cannot read the y-intercept coordinate exactly because no pixel has an x-coordinate of 0.

Exercises

Exercises 1–4: Linear Equations Draw a graph of the given equation in the Familiar Window and find the coordinates of the intercept points. If the portion of the graph that appears in the Familiar Window is inappropriate for your purposes, adjust your viewing window.

1. $y = 2x - 3$ **2.** $y = 3x + 4$

3. $3x - 2y = 5$ **4.** $4x - y + 3 = 0$

Exercises 5–8: Circles Graph the given equation and find the coordinates of the intercept points. To get a good picture, you may need to write the equation in the form $(x - h)^2 + (y - k)^2 = r^2$, and graph the functions $Y = k \pm \boxed{\sqrt{}}(r^2 - (X - h)^2)$ in a translated window, $(h - 4.7, h + 4.8) \times (k - 3.1, k + 3.2)$ on the TI-81, and $(h - 4.7, h + 4.7) \times (k - 3.1, k + 3.1)$ on the Casio fx7700G.

5. $x^2 + y^2 = 9$ **6.** $(x + 2)^2 + y^2 = 4$

7. $x^2 + y^2 - 2x = 5$

8. $x^2 + y^2 - 2x + 4y = 5$

9. Draw the graph of the circle $x^2 + y^2 = 8$. Can you read the coordinates of the y-intercept points? Do the semicircles meet? Try a different viewing window. Explain why you cannot get the two semicircles to meet even in an adjusted window.

and get

$$x^2 - 4x - 3 = 0.$$

Using the quadratic formula, the roots are $2 \pm \sqrt{7}$.

Here we have two different values of x. The graph makes it clear that the x-coordinate of A is negative, namely $2 - \sqrt{7} (\approx -0.65)$, and the x-coordinate of B is $2 + \sqrt{7}$ (≈ 4.65), so A and B are the points $(2 - \sqrt{7}, 0)$ and $(2 + \sqrt{7}, 0)$, respectively. Since A and B lie on the same horizontal line, the distance between them is given by the difference in their x-coordinates:

$$d(A, B) = |(2 + \sqrt{7}) - (2 - \sqrt{7})| = 2\sqrt{7} \approx 5.29. \quad \blacktriangle$$

EXAMPLE 8   Describe the graphs of

(a) $x^2 + y^2 - 2x + 4y + 5 = 0.$ **(b)** $x^2 + y^2 - 2x + 4y + 6 = 0.$

Solution

(a)   Completing the squares on $x^2 - 2x$ and $y^2 + 4y$ gives

$$(x - 1)^2 + (y + 2)^2 = 0.$$

This equation has the appearance of the equation of a circle with center at $(1, -2)$ and radius $0!$ We want the set of points whose coordinates satisfy the equation. The sum of two squares can be 0 only if both terms are 0. The graph is a single point, $(1, -2)$. This is sometimes called a *point circle*.

(b)   Completing the squares on the x and y terms, we get

$$(x - 1)^2 + (y + 2)^2 = -1.$$

This is even worse; there are no points whose coordinates satisfy the given equation. No graph is associated with the equation, but, by analogy with the point circle of part **(a)**, the equation in part **(b)** is sometimes called an *imaginary circle*. $\blacktriangle$

EXERCISES 1.6

Check Your Understanding

Exercises 1–7   True or False. Give reasons for your conclusion.

1. The graph of $x^2 + y^2 + 2x + 1 = 0$ is a single point.

2. The point $(1, \sqrt{3})$ is inside the circle whose equation is $x^2 + y^2 = 4$.

3. The point $(1, -2)$ is the center of the circle whose equation is $x^2 + y^2 + 2x - 4y = 0$.

4. The graph of $x^2 + y^2 - 2x = 0$ is a circle with diameter 2.

5. There is no real number c such that the point $(1, c)$ is 1 unit from $(-1, 2)$. (*Hint:* Think geometrically.)

6. There are two numbers c for which the point $(1, c)$ is 4 units from $(-1, 2)$ (*Hint:* Think geometrically.)

7. The graph of $x^2 + y^2 - 2x + 4y - 5 = 0$ is a circle whose center is in the second quadrant.

Exercises 8–10   Complete the sentence by selecting from the list below *all choices* that make the statement true.

(a) first   **(b)** second   **(c)** third   **(d)** fourth

8. If (a, b) is any point in the second quadrant, then (b, a) is in the _____ quadrant.

9. The graph of $x + y - 1 = 0$ does not contain any points in the _____ quadrant.

10. The graph of $x - \sqrt{3}y = 0$ is a line passing through the _____ quadrant.

Explore and Discover

1. Triangle ABC has vertices $A(3, 2)$, $B(5, 6)$, and $C(1, 8)$.
   (a) Find the perimeter P_1 of $\triangle ABC$.
   (b) Let D, E, and F be the midpoints of the sides of $\triangle ABC$. Find the perimeter P_2 of $\triangle DEF$.
   (c) What is the ratio $\frac{P_2}{P_1}$?

2. **(a)** Repeat Exercise 1, with new vertices $A(0, 0)$, $B(2, 0)$, and $C(6, 6)$.
   (b) Repeat again with a triangle of your choice.
   (c) What is your guess about the ratio of $\frac{P_2}{P_1}$ for an arbitrary triangle? Why?

Develop Mastery

Exercises 1–5 **(a)** Draw a diagram showing points A and B and find the distance between them. **(b)** Find the coordinates of the midpoint M of the line segment $\overline{AB}$. **(c)** Verify that $d(A, M) = \frac{1}{2}d(A, B)$.

1. $A(1, 3)$, $B(-2, 4)$ **2.** $A(-2, 3)$, $B(4, -1)$
3. $A(-\frac{1}{2}, 2)$, $B(1, -\frac{1}{3})$ **4.** $A(1, -2)$, $B(-\frac{1}{3}, -\frac{1}{3})$
5. $A(2\sqrt{2}, -3\sqrt{2})$, $B(-2\sqrt{2}, \sqrt{2})$

Exercises 6–11 Determine whether the three points are vertices of a right triangle, an equilateral triangle, an isosceles triangle, or none of these.

6. $A(-1, 2)$, $B(4, -2)$, $C(8, 3)$
7. $A(4, -2)$, $B(-4, 2)$, $C(7, 4)$
8. $A(0, 0)$ $B(2\sqrt{3}, 2)$, $C(0, 4)$
9. $A(0, 0)$, $B(4, 2)$, $C(0, 4)$
10. $A(-1, -1)$, $B(4, 1)$, $C(1, 4)$
11. $A(-2, -3)$, $B(4, 6)$, $C(-6, -\frac{1}{3})$

Exercises 12–21 Write an equation for the circle that satisfies the given conditions. First draw a diagram showing the circle. Give the result in expanded form.

12. Center $(0, 0)$; radius 3
13. Center $(1, 1)$; radius $\sqrt{3}$
14. Center $(2, -1)$; radius $\sqrt{5}$
15. Center $(-1, 5)$; diameter 1
16. Center $(-2, -1)$; tangent to the x-axis
17. Center $(-2, -1)$; tangent to the y-axis
18. The segment from $A(-3, 4)$ to $B(1, 1)$ is a diameter.
19. The segment from $A(3, -2)$ to $B(5, 4)$ is a diameter.

20. The circle is circumscribed about the triangle having vertices $A(0, 0)$, $B(8, 0)$ and $C(8, 6)$. (*Hint:* Triangle ABC is a right triangle.)

21. The circle passes through the three points $A(2, 1)$, $B(6, 1)$ and $C(6, 4)$. (*Hint:* $\angle ABC$ is a right angle.)

Exercises 22–23 An equation of a circle is given. Find **(a)** the highest and lowest points and **(b)** the points furthest to the right and left. See Example 6.

22. $x^2 + y^2 + 4x - 4y - 8 = 0$
23. $x^2 + y^2 - 6x - 2y + 1 = 0$

Exercises 24–25 An equation of a circle is given. Find **(a)** the x- and y-intercept points, **(b)** the distance between the x-intercept points, and **(c)** the distance between the y-intercept points. See Example 7.

24. $x^2 + y^2 + 2x - 2y - 8 = 0$
25. $x^2 + y^2 - 6x - 2y + 1 = 0$

Exercises 26–27 An equation of a line is given. Find **(a)** the x- and y-intercept points and **(b)** the distance between the intercept points.

26. $2x - 3y = 6$ **27.** $3x - 4y + 12 = 0$

Exercises 28–39 **(a)** Identify the graph of the equation as a line or a circle. **(b)** For a line, find the coordinates of the intercept points. For a circle, find the radius and the coordinates of the center. **(c)** Sketch the graph.

28. $2x + 3y = 6$ **29.** $x + y = 4$
30. $x^2 + y^2 = 4$ **31.** $y = 3x - 2$
32. $2y = x^2 + y^2$ **33.** $3x^2 + 3y^2 = 21$
34. $7x + 7y = 21$ **35.** $x^2 + 2x + y^2 = 0$
36. $x^2 + y^2 = 2x + 4y$
37. $x^2 - 4x + y^2 + 2y + 1 = 0$
38. $2x^2 + 2y^2 + 4y = 12x + 15$
39. $x^2 + 4x + y^2 + 4y = 4$
40. Which of the points $A(3, 4)$ or $B(-4, 2)$ is nearer point $C(2, -3)$?

Exercises 41–43 For these exercises, remember that point (x, y) is a lattice point if both x and y are integers.

41. Give an example of two lattice points in Quadrant 1 that define a line segment whose midpoint is not a lattice point.

42. Give an example of two lattice points in Quadrant I that define a line segment whose midpoint is also a lattice point.

43. Find a pair of lattice points, A and B, with A in Quadrant II and B in Quadrant IV for which the midpoint of segment $\overline{AB}$ is **(a)** in Quadrant I, **(b)** in Quadrant II, **(c)** in Quadrant III, **(d)** not in any quadrant.

Exercises 44–48 Find all lattice points in Quadrant I on the graph of the equation.

44. $2x + y = 6$

45. $x + 3y = 13$

46. $2x + 3y = 12$

47. $x^2 + y^2 = 5$

48. $x^2 + y^2 = 25$

49. If $A(0, 3)$, $B(-1, -1)$, and $C(4, 1)$ are three vertices of a parallelogram, what are the coordinates of the fourth vertex? Draw a diagram. Is the answer unique?

Exercises 50–51 Find the point P that is equidistant from the three points A, B, and C, that is, find P such that $|\overline{PA}| = |\overline{PB}| = |\overline{PC}|$. (*Hint:* First show that the three points are vertices of a right triangle and consider the circle circumscribing $\triangle ABC$.)

50. $A(8, 3)$, $B(4, 10)$, $C(2, 6)$

51. $A(2, 3)$, $B(8, 0)$, $C(5, 9)$

52. A rectangle has sides parallel to the coordinate axes. Two of its vertices are at $(-5, -7)$ and $(4, -2)$. Find the coordinates of the other two vertices and the length of a diagonal.

53. A rectangle has sides parallel to the coordinate axes and its upper left corner at $A(-3, 2)$ as shown in the diagram (which is not drawn to scale). The length (horizontal side) is twice the width, and the perimeter is 30. Find the coordinates of the other three vertices.

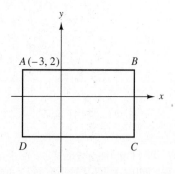

54. A 90° rotation of a plane counterclockwise about the origin moves point $(3, 0)$ to $(0, 3)$ and point $(0, 5)$ to $(-5, 0)$ (see the diagram). What is the image of each point under the same rotation? Draw diagrams.
(a) $(-4, 0)$ **(b)** $(0, -3)$
(c) $(3, 4)$ **(d)** $(-3, -4)$

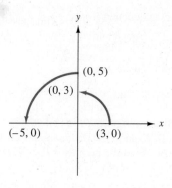

55. Repeat Exercise 54 with a rotation of 180° counterclockwise.

56. The diagram shows $ABCD$ as a square with sides of length 8. Circular arcs with centers at B, and D, have radii equal to 8. Find the area of the shaded region.

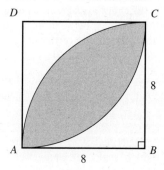

57. Find the area of the region that is inside the circle $x^2 + y^2 - 2x - 3 = 0$ and outside the circle $x^3 + y^2 = 1$. (*Hint:* First draw a diagram.)

58. What is the area of a circle if the reciprocal of its circumference equals the length of its radius?

59. The line $x + y = 3$ divides the interior of the circle $x^2 + y^2 = 9$ into two regions. If A_1 and A_2 are the areas of the larger and smaller of the two regions, respectively, find the ratio $\frac{A_1}{A_2}$.

60. Given points $A(1, 4)$ and $B(4, 1)$, describe the set of all points C such that A, B, and C are vertices of an isosceles triangle where
(a) $\overline{AB}$ is the base.
(b) $\overline{AC}$ is the base.
(c) $\overline{BC}$ is the base.
(d) Find the coordinates of all points C such that A, B, and C are vertices of an equilateral triangle. (*Hint:* Think geometrically.)

61. If $(2, -1)$ is the center of a circle, the origin $(0, 0)$ is inside the circle, and $(4, 1)$ is outside the circle, how large can the radius be? How small?

62. **(a)** Find an equation for the circle that is tangent to the *x*-axis at (2, 0) and tangent to the *y*-axis at (0, 2). (*Hint:* First draw a graph.)
   (b) Is the lattice point (3, 1) inside or outside the circle in **(a)?** Is (4, 1) inside or outside? Give reasons.
   (c) Find all lattice points inside the circle in **(a)**.

| SECTION 1.7 | 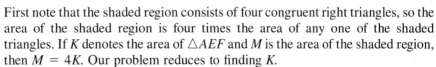 |

One cadet, who had a private airplane pilot's license, was failing mathematics. When he was asked how much gas he would need to carry if he were going to fly two hundred miles at so many miles per gallon, he didn't know whether to multiply or divide. How, the officers asked, was he able to get the right answer? He replied that he did it both ways and took the reasonable answer. They felt that anybody who knew what was a reasonable answer had promise, so they gave him a second chance.

Ralph P. Boas, Jr.

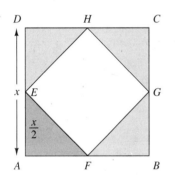

FIGURE 1.22

Problem solving is the key to learning mathematics. In this section we consider problems that are somewhat different from some you may have met earlier. Here we try to draw on what you already know, and to develop reasoning and strategy to attack a given problem. Always try your own approach; do not just follow an example in the book or mimic a solution from someone else. Genuine learning takes place when you think for yourself.

No single strategy applies to all problems. Here we look at several examples and then outline a few general guidelines. We begin with an example illustrating two different methods of solution.

> **EXAMPLE 1**   The area of the square *ABCD*, shown in Figure 1.22 is 64. Points *E*, *F*, *G*, and *H* are midpoints of the sides, as shown. Find the area of the shaded region.

Solution 1

First note that the shaded region consists of four congruent right triangles, so the area of the shaded region is four times the area of any one of the shaded triangles. If *K* denotes the area of $\triangle AEF$ and *M* is the area of the shaded region, then $M = 4K$. Our problem reduces to finding *K*.

Triangle *AEF* is an isosceles right triangle with legs half as long as *x*, the side of the square. Since the area of the square is 64, $x^2 = 64$ so $x = 8$. (Why not ± 8?) Thus $K = \frac{1}{2}(4)(4) = 8$, and $M = 4(8) = 32$. Hence the area of the shaded region is 32.

Solution 2

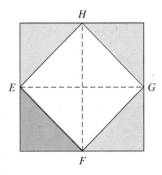

FIGURE 1.23

Draw line segments $\overline{EG}$ and $\overline{FH}$ (see Figure 1.23). We have four more unshaded right triangles, each congruent to the shaded triangles. (Why?) Therefore, the area of the shaded region is half of the area of the square. The area of the shaded region is $\frac{64}{2}$, or 32. ▲

EXAMPLE 2   Inichi and Maria share an apartment 2 miles from campus, where they have the same 8:45 class. Inichi leaves home at 8:00, walking at her usual 3 mph pace, while Maria is still in the shower. Maria, who has missed class three days in a row, knows that she can jog all the way at a 5 mph pace. If she gets out the door by 8:20, will that pace allow Maria to **(a)** catch up with Inichi on the way or **(b)** get to class on time?

Strategy: The ready-made model for such problems is $d = r \cdot t$. Let T be the time it would take for Maria to catch up, when the distances would have to be equal. We know their rates; equate distances and solve for T.

Solution

(a) Suppose Maria can catch Inichi in T minutes. Maria's speed, 5 mph, is equal to 1 mile in $\frac{1}{5}$ of an hour (12 minutes), so in T minutes she travels $(\frac{1}{12})T$ miles. By the time Maria has jogged T minutes, Inichi has walked for $T + 20$ minutes at 3 mph (1 mile in 20 minutes), for a distance of $(\frac{1}{20})(T + 20)$ miles. Therefore T must satisfy the equation

$$\frac{1}{12}T = \frac{1}{20}(T + 20), \text{ so}$$

$$20T = 12T + 240 \qquad T = 30.$$

Maria could catch Inichi in 30 minutes, or at 8:50. However, it takes Inichi only 40 minutes ($\frac{2}{3}$ of an hour) to get to school, so she arrives at 8:40; Maria cannot catch her.

(b) It takes Maria $\frac{2}{5}$ of an hour (24 minutes) to jog 2 miles, so if she leaves home at 8:20 and doesn't have to wait for a streetlight, she can make it to class with 1 minute to spare. ▲

EXAMPLE 3   You are offered a job as a sales representative for a cosmetics firm. You can choose between two compensation arrangements: a straight 10 percent commission on total sales, or $100 per week plus a 5 percent commission on your total weekly sales.

(a) How much money would you earn under each option if you sell $1500 a week?

(b) At what weekly sales level would you earn more on straight commission?

Strategy: Let x be the dollar amount of sales in a week, and let A and B be the amounts earned per week with the given options. **(a)** Evaluate both when you sell 1500. **(b)** Express as an inequality to be solved for x.

Solution

Follow the strategy. From the given information we have

$$A = (0.10)x \qquad B = 100 + (0.05)x.$$

(a) When $x = 1500$, then $A = 150$ and $B = 175$. The salary plus commission option pays $25 more.

(b) We want to find out when $A > B$, or the values of x for which

$$(0.10)x > 100 + (0.05)x.$$

Solving the inequality we get $(0.05)x > 100$ or $x > 2000$. If you can sell more than $2000 worth of cosmetics per week, you will earn more on straight commission. ▲

In the next example we first show an indirect approach in solving a problem and then suggest an alternate method.

EXAMPLE 4   In the isosceles triangle ABC shown in Figure 1.24(a), we are given

$$|\overline{AB}| = 169, |\overline{AC}| = 169, \text{ and } |\overline{BC}| = 130.$$

Find the length of the altitude h to side $|\overline{AB}|$.

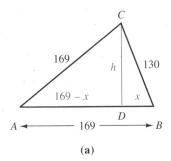

(a)

Solution 1

If we had the area K of $\triangle ABC$, we could use the relation area $= (\frac{1}{2})(\text{base} \times \text{altitude})$ and find h from $K = (\frac{1}{2})(169)h$. Let k be the altitude to side $\overline{BC}$ (Figure 1.24(**b**)). We can use the Pythagorean theorem to find k and then the area.

$$k^2 = 169^2 - 65^2 = 24{,}336 \quad \text{or} \quad k = 156.$$

Therefore the area of $\triangle ABC$ is $K = \frac{1}{2}(130)(156) = 10{,}140$. Since we also know that $K = \frac{1}{2}(169)h$, we can solve for h.

$$h = \frac{2(10{,}140)}{169} = 120.$$

Thus the length of the altitude to side $\overline{AB}$ is 120.

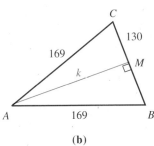

(b)

FIGURE 1.24

Solution 2

While Solution 1 is straightforward, try the following approach. In Figure 1.24(**a**), let x be the length of $\overline{BD}$ and $\overline{AD} = 169 - x$. Apply the Pythagorean theorem to the right triangles ADC and BCD, and get two expressions for h^2 in terms of x. Set these equal to each other, solve the resulting equation for x and then find h. See Exercise 17. ▲

EXAMPLE 5   Figure 1.25(**a**) shows an equilateral triangle ABC in which the length of each side is 4 and a circle with center C that passes through A and B. What is the area of the shaded region?

Solution

Strategy: If K_1 is the area of the circular sector and K_2 is the area of the triangle, then the area K of the shaded region is $K_1 - K_2$.

Follow the strategy. The area K_1 of the circular sector is one-sixth of the area of a circle of radius 4. (Why?) Thus

$$K_1 = \frac{1}{6}(\pi r^2) = \frac{1}{6}(\pi \cdot 4^2) = \frac{8\pi}{3}.$$

| For Graphers 1.7 | **PROBLEM SOLVING WITH GRAPHS** |

For many applied problems, the Familiar Window shows us nothing of value. We must read carefully, perhaps check some values by doing some computing on the home screen, and then select a useful window. The procedure is illustrated by a return to Example 3 of this section.

EXAMPLE   Example 3 asks about the relative values of two functions, A and B. Draw graphs of $Y1 = 0.1X$ (for A, straight commission) and $Y2 = 100 + 0.05X$ (for B) and then use the Trace function to find where the graphs intersect and hence answer the questions in the example.

Strategy: Read the problem carefully. Evaluate Y_1 and Y_2 at $x = 1500$ and 2500 and choose a y-range to fit, then graph and trace.

Solution   Set $X\text{min} = 1500$. When $x = 1500$, $Y1 = 150$ and $Y2 = 175$. Try $Y\text{min} = 150$. For weekly sales of 2500, $Y1 = 250$ and $Y2 = 225$. This suggests $X\text{max} = 2500$ and $Y\text{max} = 250$. Try $Y\text{scl} = 50$ and $X\text{scl} = 100$.

When we enter the functions and $\boxed{\text{EXE}}$, we see two straight lines: $Y1$ first and then $Y2$. Trace shows the intersection very near the point $(2000, 200)$. Thus the graph shows that straight commission ($Y1$) pays less money for sales less than $2000 a week, but that sales above $2000 a week would boost salary plus commission higher.   ▲

Exercises

1. A clothing store has a policy that the retail price of any item is determined as a 60 percent markup over the wholesale price. For a promotion all items in the store are put on sale at 25 percent off their retail prices. Denote the wholesale price of an item by x and let y be the corresponding price during the sale. Write an equation expressing y in terms of x. Draw a graph and use it to determine the sale price of items whose wholesale prices are $60, $150, and $200. Find the wholesale price of an item whose sale price is $90. (*Hint:* First determine the usual retail price; y is 75 percent of retail.)

2. In the preceding exercise, let p denote the profit over the wholesale price. Find an equation giving p in terms of x. Draw a graph and use it to find the profit on items whose wholesale prices are $60, $120, and $200. What wholesale price will give a profit of at least $36?

3. An auto repair shop has a fixed shop charge of $25, plus a charge of $30 per hour for labor (plus parts, of course). Let y denote the cost of a repair job that requires x hours of labor. Find an equa-

    tion giving y in terms of x. Draw a graph and use it to determine the number of labor hours for a repair job with **(a)** $35 for parts and total bill of $155, and **(b)** $75 for parts and a total bill for $375. **(c)** For what value of x is the total cost (excluding parts) less than $400?

4. If you drive 200 miles at a speed of 50 mph and then return along the same route at a speed of x mph, find an equation that gives the average speed y for the round trip. Draw a graph and use it to determine what value of x will give an average speed y of **(a)** 40 mph, **(b)** 60 mph. **(c)** If circumstances allowed you to return at 120 mph, the top speed of your car, what would be your maximum average speed for the round trip? **(d)** What speed would you have to attain on the return trip to achieve an average round-trip speed of 90 mph? (*Hint:* The average speed is given by the total distance divided by the total time; first figure the time for each part of the trip separately. To get nice x-coordinate pixels, try an x-range of [30, 125] for the T1 and [30, 124] for the Casio. For part (d), you may have to change your window or scroll horizontally several times.)

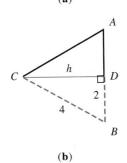

(a)

To get the area K_2 of $\triangle ABC$, draw a separate diagram (Figure 1.25(**b**)) and determine the length h of an altitude. Applying the Pythagorean theorem to $\triangle BCD$ gives

$$h^2 + 2^2 = 4^2, \quad \text{or} \quad h = \sqrt{12} = 2\sqrt{3}.$$

Therefore, for K_2 we have

$$K_2 = \frac{1}{2}|\overline{AB}|\, h = \frac{1}{2}\cdot 4 \cdot 2\sqrt{3} = 4\sqrt{3}.$$

Finally, the area K of the shaded region is equal to $K_1 - K_2$, so the area of the shaded region is $\frac{8\pi}{3} - 4\sqrt{3}$ (exact form), or approximately 1.45 square units. ▲

(b)

FIGURE 1.25

Strategy: Let u and v denote the two numbers, so $u + v = 8$ and $u \cdot v = 5$. Find $u^2 + v^2$ and $u^3 + v^3$. If we try to find u and v, the solution gets messy, but identities for $(u + v)^2$ and for $(u + v)^3$ involve the product and sum of u and v.

| EXAMPLE 6 | The sum of two numbers is 8 and their product is 5. What is the sum (**a**) of their squares? (**b**) of their cubes?

Solution

Follow the strategy.

(**a**) From the identity $(u + v)^2 = u^2 + 2uv + v^2$ subtract $2uv$ from both sides to express $u^2 + v^2$ in terms of the sum and product of u and v:

$$u^2 + v^2 = (u + v)^2 - 2uv = 8^2 - 2\cdot 5 = 64 - 10 = 54.$$

The sum of the squares is 54.

(**b**) For the sum of the cubes we try a similar approach.

$$(u + v)^3 = u^3 + 3u^2v + 3uv^2 + v^3 = u^3 + v^3 + 3uv(u + v)$$

$$u^3 + v^3 = (u + v)^3 - 3uv(u + v) = 8^3 - 3\cdot 5\cdot 8 = 392.$$

The sum of the cubes of the two numbers is 392. It is instructive to compare the work we have done in this example with the work it takes to find the two numbers u and v, and then to square each and cube each, to find the sums of the squares and the cubes. See Exercise 18. ▲

As should be clear from the diverse problems we have considered and the variety of approaches illustrated, no single set of methods is sufficient to solve any particular problem, but some consistent guidelines can help.

Problem Solving Guidelines

1. **Be certain that you understand the problem.** You may need to read it several times.

2. **Concentrate on what the problem calls for** and identify all the information given.

3. **Draw diagrams or graphs whenever appropriate.** This is extremely important in planning your solution strategy.

4. **Introduce variables** to name the quantities involved and label diagrams.

5. **Use what you have learned earlier.** For instance, if you need the area of a figure, review pertinent formulas. Be aware that many useful formulas and relations appear in this book, many of them on the inside front and back covers.

6. **Always check your results.** Don't just plug a number into a formula, but ask yourself if your results makes sense in terms of the original statement of the problem. Whenever possible begin with some kind of reasonable estimate of what the result should be.

7. **Work in terms of complete sentences.** Use clearly readable sentences and precise mathematical notation to identify variables, state relationships, etc. Write your conclusion as a sentence, as well. This care will pay great dividends in clarity of thinking, in understanding how to approach a problem, and in knowing what the result means.

EXERCISES 1.7

Check Your Understanding

Exercises 1–6   True or False. Give reasons for your conclusion.

1. The three line segments joining the midpoints of the sides of an equilateral triangle form an equilateral triangle.

2. When 31^{64} is expanded and written in usual base-10 form, the units digit is 4.

3. The isosceles triangle having sides of lengths 6, 6, and 4 has an altitude (drawn to the short side) of length $4\sqrt{2}$.

4. The area of the triangle described in Exercise 3 is equal to $16\sqrt{2}$.

5. Points $(-2, 3)$ and $(4, 1)$ lie on a circle whose center is at $(-1, -4)$.

6. When x is replaced by $\frac{-2}{3}$ in the open sentence $|3x + 1| - 2x = 1$, the resulting statement is true.

Exercises 7–10   Complete the sentence by selecting from the list below *all choices* that make the statement true.
(a) greater than   **(b)** less than   **(c)** equal to
(d) more   **(e)** less

7. The area of a square having sides of length k is _____ the area of a circle with diameter of length k.

8. It takes _____ time to walk 2 miles at the rate of 4 mph than it does to walk 3 miles at the rate of 5 mph.

9. The distance from point $A(-1, -4)$ to point $B(-2, 3)$ is _____ the distance from A to point $C(4, 1)$.

10. If the sum of two numbers is 5 and their product is 3, then the sum of their squares is _____ 19.

Explore and Discover

1. Read the marginal quotation from George Dantzig in Section 1.1 and write a paragraph expressing your feelings about the importance of working many problems to learn mathematics. Use specific examples from your own experience.

2. If x_1 and x_2 denote the roots of the equation $x^2 - 2x - 5 = 0$, find $x_1 + x_2$, $x_1 \cdot x_2$, and $x_1^2 + x_2^2$.

3. If x_1 and x_2 are the roots given by the quadratic formula for the equation $ax^2 + bx + c = 0$, find formulas in terms of a, b, and c:
   (a) $x_1 + x_2$ **(b)** $x_1 \cdot x_2$
   (c) $x_1^2 + x_2^2$ (*Hint:* See Example 6.)

Develop Mastery

1. If the reciprocal of b is 12, and $\frac{b}{c} = 1$, then find c.

2. Find all values of x (if any) for which the reciprocal of $x + 1$ equals $x - 1$.

3. When a meatball mixture is molded into a spherical shape, the radius of the sphere is 4 inches. How many meatballs of radius 1 inch each can be made from the mixture?

4. (a) Find five consecutive integers whose sum is 100.
   (b) Find eight consecutive integers whose sum is 100.
   (c) Are there six consecutive integers whose sum is 100? Explain.

5. An auto repair shop charges a $20 shop charge plus $25 per hour for labor. If the total charge for a repair job is $80 plus parts, how many hours of labor did the job require?

6. Robin and Bart are 0.7 miles apart when they begin walking in a straight path toward each other. Robin walks at the rate of 3 mph and Bart at the rate of 4 mph.
   (a) How long (in minutes) will it take for the two to meet?
   (b) How far will each walk?

7. Anna enters a walkathon that covers a total distance of 20 miles. She runs part of the distance at the rate of 6 mph and walks the remaining distance at a rate of 4 mph, completing the course in 4 hours and 30 minutes.
   (a) How far did Anna run? How far did she walk?
   (b) How many hours did she run? How many did she walk?

8. Two insurance companies, Arliss and Bailey, pay sales representatives every month. Arliss pays a fixed 12 percent commission on the total amount of insurance sold, while Bailey pays $250 per month plus 7 percent commission on the total sold. For a month's sales of x dollars, let A denote the amount Arliss pays, and let B denote the amount Bailey pays for the same sales.
   (a) Find formulas for A and B in terms of x.
   (b) For what volume of sales will Arliss pay more than Bailey?

9. The diameter of a circle is 6 times the reciprocal of the circumference. Find the area of the circle.

10. Find the area of a circle if the reciprocal of the circumference equals the length of the radius.

11. If $\frac{1}{a} - \frac{1}{c} = \frac{1}{a+c}$ then find the value of the ratio $\frac{a}{c}$.

12. The radiator of a car has a capacity of 6 quarts and is filled with a 30 percent mixture of antifreeze.
    (a) How many quarts of antifreeze are in the radiator?

(b) If you drain a quarter of the mixture in the radiator and replace it with pure antifreeze, what is the percentage of antifreeze in the resulting mixture?

(c) How many quarts of the original mixture should you drain and replace with pure antifreeze to get a mixture that is 51 percent antifreeze?

13. Is the expression $\frac{1 + x^2}{\sqrt{1 + x^2}} - \sqrt{1 + x^2}$ equal to zero for every real number x? Explain your answer.

14. A square is inscribed in a circle and then a circle is inscribed in the square.
    (a) What is the ratio of the area of the larger circle to the area of the smaller circle?
    (b) If the larger circle has a radius of 16 cm, what is the area of the ring-shaped region between the two circles, and what is the area of the square?

15. A chord of a circle is the perpendicular bisector of a radius of length 4. How long is the chord?

16. Two triangles are inscribed in a semicircle as shown in the diagram, where $|\overline{AB}| = 12$ and $\angle BAC = \angle ABD = 30°$. What is the area of the shaded triangular region common to triangles ABC and ABD?

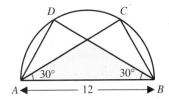

17. Carry out the details suggested in Solution 2 of Example 4.

18. (a) If $u = 4 + \sqrt{11}$ and $v = 4 - \sqrt{11}$, show that $u + v = 8$ and $u \cdot v = 5$.
    (b) Evaluate $u^2 + v^2$ and $u^3 + v^3$. Compare with Example 6.

19. Given that the side of one square is the diagonal of a second square. If A_1 is the area of the first square and A_2 is the area of the second square, then find the value of the ratio $\frac{A_1}{A_2}$.

20. If you drive 160 miles at an average speed of 50 miles per hour, and then return along the same route at a more leisurely speed of 30 miles per hour, what is your average speed for the round trip?

21. If you drive d miles at an average speed of 50 mph and return along the same route at an average speed of 30 mph, what is your average speed for the round trip?

22. If you drive d miles at an average speed of v_1 mph and return along the same route at an average speed of

v_2 mph, what is your average speed for the round trip?

23. A race car driver must average 150 mph for four separate laps to qualify for a race. Because of a minor engine problem the car averages only 120 mph for the first two laps. What average speed is required on the final two laps to qualify for the race?

24. How many ounces of a 60 percent solution of acid must be added to 20 ounces of a 30 percent solution to get a 40 percent solution?

25. A circle is inscribed in an equilateral triangle of side length 4. Find the area of the circle.

26. A rectangle intersects a circle as shown in the diagram. $|\overline{AB}| = 6$, $|\overline{DE}| = 7$, and $|\overline{EF}| = 8$. What is the length of $\overline{BC}$?

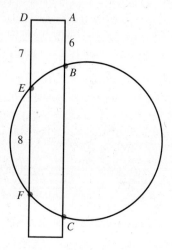

27. In rectangle $ABCD$ shown in the diagram $|\overline{AE}|$ is $\frac{3}{4}$ of $|\overline{AB}|$, and the area of triangle BEC is 24 cm². What is the area of the rectangle?

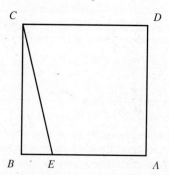

28. Find the area of the shaded region in the diagram, where the circle is inscribed in a square having length of side equal to 8.

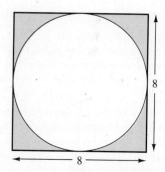

29. Denote the two x-intercept points of the graph of $x^2 + y^2 = 16$ by A and B, and the two y-intercept points by C and D. What is the area of the quadrilateral with vertices A, B, C, and D?

30. Two candles of the same length are made of different materials and hence burn at different rates. One burns down completely at a uniform rate in 4 hours while it takes the other 5 hours. If both candles are lit at 2:00 P.M., at what time will one be half as long as the other?

31. Given points $A(-2, 0)$ and $B(4, 0)$, find a point C with both coordinates positive integers and such that the area of $\triangle ABC$ is a minimum. Is the answer unique? What is the area of $\triangle ABC$?

32. Point P is 6 units from the center of a circle of radius 10. How many chords having integer length can be drawn through P? (*Hint:* First draw a diagram.) The longest chord is a diameter. What is the shortest chord?

33. A particle moves along the line in the diagram at a uniform speed. The distance d moved in t seconds is given by the equation $d = 2t$. In the diagram, the point A_k shows the position of the particle at the end of k seconds, so the distance between successive A_k's is 2. If the perpendicular distance from the origin to the line is 12, find the area of each of the triangles OA_0A_1, OA_1A_2, OA_2A_3, ...

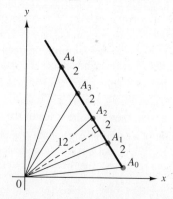

34. A square has sides of length 4. The shaded region inside the square is bounded by circular arcs as shown in the diagram. Find the area of the shaded region.

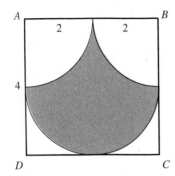

35. Three mirrors, each of length 4 feet, are placed to form an equilateral triangle ABC. A light source is placed at the midpoint M of side $\overline{AB}$, as shown in the diagram, and is aimed at an angle of $60°$ so that the light will be reflected to follow the dotted line. How far does the light travel before returning to M?

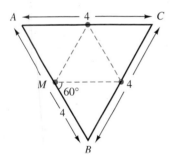

36. In the diagram square $ABCD$ has an area of 16. The vertices of each inscribed square are midpoints of the sides of the square in which it is inscribed. Find the area of the shaded square.

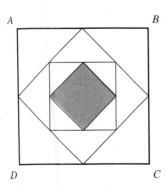

37. The diagram starts with an isosceles right triangle with legs of length 2 and hypotenuse of length a, then adds successive right triangles each having one leg of length 2 and the other leg as the hypotenuse of the preceding triangle.
   (a) Find lengths a, b, c, and d.
   (b) If we continue constructing right triangles and labeling the length of each hypotenuse with successive letters of the alphabet, what letter corresponds to the hypotenuse of length 6?

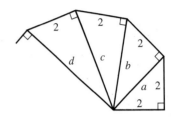

38. For the patio in the diagram, where vertical walls $\overline{AD}$ and $\overline{CE}$ are 7 and 11 feet high, respectively, how far apart must the walls be to allow the lower vertex of an equilateral triangle ($\triangle ABC$) to touch the floor? (*Hint:* First find x, then find y and z.)

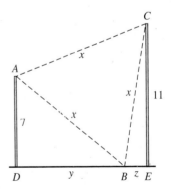

39. Given three distinct lines l_1, l_2, and l_3 in a plane, if l_1 intersects the parallel lines l_3 and l_2, how many points in the plane are equidistant from all three lines? (*Hint:* Draw a diagram.)

40. *Working with Large Numbers* The Andromeda galaxy is approaching our galaxy at a speed of about 100 kilometers per second.
   (a) How fast is Andromeda approaching us in miles per hour? (1 mile = 1.609 km)

(b) How far does Andromeda travel toward us each year?

(c) How long would it take an object moving at Andromeda's speed to travel from the sun to the earth (93 million miles)?

(d) How long would it take an object moving at Andromeda's speed to travel 1 light year (the distance light, moving at 186,000 miles per second, travels in a year)?

(e) The estimated distance between the Milky Way (our galaxy) and Andromeda is 2 million light years. Assuming Andromeda continues to approach us at its current speed, when will our galaxies meet?

CHAPTER 1 REVIEW

Test Your Understanding

Exercises 1–36 Determine the truth value (T or F). Give reasons for your conclusion.

1. The largest real number is ∞.

2. There is only one even prime number.

3. There is no smallest positive real number.

4. There is no greatest negative integer.

5. There is no smallest positive rational number.

6. $2^{16} + 3^{65}$ is an odd number.

7. $3^{17} + 7^{27}$ is an odd number.

8. The imaginary number $3i$ is greater than $2i$.

9. There is no real number x for which $\sqrt{-x} > 0$.

10. $x \geq \frac{1}{x}$ for every positive real number x.

11. No real number x satisfies the equation $\sqrt{-x} = \sqrt{x}$.

12. For every real number x, $|x - 4| + 3 > 0$.

13. It is not true that the solution set for the equation $|x - 1| + 1 = 0$ is the empty set.

14. $\sqrt{x^2} + |x| = 2|x|$ for every real number x.

15. The inequalities $x^2 < 4$ and $x < \frac{4}{x}$ have the same solution set.

16. If $\frac{a}{b} = x$, where $b \neq 0$ and $a \neq b$, then $\frac{a+b}{a-b} = \frac{x+1}{x-1}$.

17. If x is any positive real number, then $\sqrt{x} < x$.

18. There is no positive real number x for which $\sqrt{-x^2 - x}$ will be a real number.

19. If $x = \frac{1}{\sqrt{2} - 1}$ and $y = \sqrt{2} + 1$, then $x = y$.

20. The intervals $(-2, 2]$ and $(2, 3]$ are disjoint.

21. The intersection of the intervals $(0, 1.\overline{3})$ and $(1.3, 2)$ is the empty set.

22. The sum of any two irrational numbers is an irrational number.

23. The product of any two irrational numbers is an irrational number.

24. If n is any positive integer, then $n(n + 1)$ will be an even positive integer.

25. The product of any two imaginary numbers is an imaginary number.

26. There is no point (x, y) in Quadrant I that is on the line $x + y + 1 = 0$.

27. The graph of $x - y = 1$ does not pass through Quadrant II.

28. The graph of $x^2 + y^2 = 2x$ passes through the point $(1, 1)$.

29. For every real number x, $\sqrt{x^2 + 1} = x + 1$.

30. The solution set for the equation $(x + 1)^2 - 1 = x^2 + 2x$ is the set of real numbers.

31. If x and y are real numbers where $x < y$, then $|x - y| = y - x$.

32. If both x and y are negative numbers, then $|x + y| = -x - y$.

33. If x and y are any real numbers, then $|x + y| = |x| + |y|$.

34. If x is positive and y is negative, then $|x - y| = x - y$.

35. A triangle with sides 3, 4, and 5 is a right triangle.

36. A triangle with sides 1, 2, and $\sqrt{3}$ is a right triangle.

Exercises 37–39 From the diagram showing m, n, p, and q on the number line, determine the truth value.

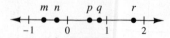

37. (a) $mr < 0$ (b) $\frac{1}{r} < 1$ (c) $pq < q$

38. (a) $|m + n| = n + m$ (b) $|n - p| = n - p$
    (c) $|p - q| = p - q$

39. (a) $\frac{m}{n} < 0$ (b) $\frac{m}{n} > 1$ (c) $r - p > r - q$

Review for Mastery

1. Is $\sqrt{9 - 4\sqrt{5}}$ equal to $2 - \sqrt{5}$?

2. Is $\sqrt{23 - 8\sqrt{7}}$ equal to $\sqrt{7} - 4$?

3. Is $0.\overline{54}$ equal to $\frac{5}{11}$?

4. Which number, π, $\frac{22}{7}$, or $\frac{355}{113}$, is the smallest? Which is the largest?

5. Express each of the following in exact form without using absolute value.
   (a) $\left| 3 - \frac{22}{7} \right|$ (b) $\left| \sqrt{8} - 3 \right|$
   (c) $\left| 0.36 - 0.\overline{36} \right|$

6. Express as a fraction of two integers in lowest terms.
   (a) 1.36 (b) $1.\overline{36}$ (c) $0.\overline{45} - 0.45$

7. Enter one of the symbols $<$, $>$, or $=$ in the blank so that the resulting statement is true.
   (a) -5 ___ -7 (b) $\sqrt{3} - 1$ ___ 0.732
   (c) $\left| \sqrt{2} - \sqrt{8} \right|$ ___ $\sqrt{2}$

8. Subsets of real numbers are given in interval notation. Show each on a number line.
   (a) $(-1, 4)$ (b) $[-1, 0] \cup [2, 4]$
   (c) $[-3, 1) \cap (0, 3]$ (d) $(-\infty, -2] \cup [2, \infty)$

9. Show the subset of real numbers on a number line.
   (a) A is the set of all prime numbers less than 8.
   (b) B is the set of all real numbers greater than 2 and less than 5.
   (c) C is the set of all integers greater than -3 and less than 4.

10. For what values of x is $\left| x + 3 \right| = x + 3$?

11. For what values of x is $\left| x - 3 \right| = 3 - x$?

12. How many real numbers are in the set $\{x \mid x^2 - 2 = 0\}$?

Exercises 13–24   Find the solution set.

13. $3x - 5 = 3$
14. $2x^2 - 3x = 0$
15. $\left| x + 1 \right| - 1 = 0$
16. $2\left| x + 1 \right| - 3 = 0$
17. $2x^2 - 4x - 5 = 0$
18. $\sqrt{3}x = x + 1$
19. $3 - 2x - x^2 = 0$
20. $\sqrt{2x - 3} = 3$
21. $x - 3 = \frac{4}{x}$
22. $(3 - 2x)(x^2 - 5x) = 0$
23. $\sqrt{x^2} - 2\left| x \right| + 3 = 0$
24. $\sqrt{(x + 3)^2} = 4$

Exercises 25–28   Express in $a + bi$ form where a and b are real numbers.

25. $\frac{5 + 10i}{2 - i}$
26. $i^2 - i^3 + i^4$
27. $\sqrt{-3}\sqrt{-8}$
28. $(1 + i)^2 + 3i^2$

Exercises 29–32   Statements p and q are
$$p: 2 + 4 \cdot 5 = 30 \qquad q: \sqrt{3^2 + 5^2} < 8.$$

Determine the truth value of each of the following.

29. (a) p (b) $\sim p$ 30. (a) q (b) p and q
31. (a) $p \Rightarrow q$ (b) $q \Rightarrow p$
32. (a) $p \Rightarrow \sim q$ (b) $\sim p$ or q

Exercises 33–44   Determine the solution set.

33. $3x - 4 < 5$
34. $4x - 3 \leq x + 7$
35. $2x^2 > 2 - 3x$
36. $\frac{x^2 - 1}{x + 2} \geq 0$
37. $2x - 3 > \frac{5}{x}$
38. $x < \frac{1}{x}$
39. $\left| x + 1 \right| - 2 \leq 0$
40. $\left| x^2 - 1 \right| < 2$
41. (a) $\left| x \right| - x = 2$ (b) $\left| x \right| - x < 2$
42. (a) $x - 2 = \frac{8}{x}$ (b) $x - 2 \geq \frac{8}{x}$
43. (a) $\left| x \right| = x$ (b) $\left| x \right| > x$
44. (a) $x^2 - 1 = x + 1$ (b) $x^2 - 1 < x + 1$

45. For what values of x is $\sqrt{5 - 4x - x^2}$ a real number?

46. For what values of x is $\sqrt{x - \frac{4}{x}}$ an imaginary number?

47. Find an equation for the circle with center at $(-3, 2)$ and radius 1.

48. Find the center and radius of the circle given by $x^2 + y^2 - 2x + 4y + 1 = 0$.

Exercises 49–54   (a) Draw a graph. Give the coordinates of any   (b) x-intercept points,   (c) y-intercept points.

49. $3x - 2y = 6$
50. $4x + 3y + 6 = 0$
51. $(x - 3)^2 + (y + 1)^2 = 4$
52. $x^2 + y^2 + 2x + 4y + 1 = 0$
53. $\sqrt{3}x + y = 3$
54. $x^2 + y^2 = 4x$

55. (a) Draw a graph of the circle $(x - 3)^2 + (y - 2)^2 = 4$.
    (b) For points $A(5, 1)$, $B(2, 3)$, and $C(3, 0)$, determine which are inside the circle, outside the circle, or on the circle.

56. A ball is dropped from the top of a building 256 feet high. Its position at t seconds after being dropped is given by $s = 256 - 16t^2$, where s is its distance from the ground.

(a) How long will the ball take to drop halfway to the ground?

(b) What values of t are meaningful in the given formula?

57. You mix 2 quarts of antifreeze with 3 quarts of water.

(a) What percentage antifreeze is the mixture?

(b) How much more antifreeze should be added to get a mixture that is 60 percent antifreeze?

58. The campus bookstore is having a 25 percent off sale. Hilary purchases a book and, after a 5 percent sales tax is added, she pays a total of $28.98. What is the original price of the book?

59. A car and truck are traveling along a highway in the same direction. The car is 20 feet long and is traveling at a speed of 60 mph (88 feet per second), while the truck is 46 feet long and its speed is 45 mph (66 feet per second). How many seconds will elapse from the instant the car reaches the truck until the car is completely past the truck?

60. Suppose in Exercise 59 we are not given the speed of the truck, but we know that it takes 4 seconds for the car to pass it. How fast is the truck traveling?

61. An equilateral triangle is inscribed in a circle with a radius of length 8. Find the area of the region inside the circle and outside the triangle.

62. If $u + v = 10$ and $uv = 7$, find $u^2 + v^2$, $u^3 + v^3$, $u^4 + v^4$. (*Hint:* See Example 6 of Section 1.7.)

63. In an equilateral triangle ABC, where each side has length 16, let D be the foot of the perpendicular from A to $\overline{BC}$, and let M denote the midpoint of $\overline{AD}$. See the diagram. What is the length of $\overline{BM}$?

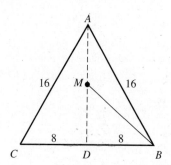

64. A ladder is resting vertically against a wall. When the bottom of the ladder is pulled horizontally out from the wall a distance of 15 feet, the top of the ladder slides down the wall a distance equal to $\frac{2}{5}$ of the length of the ladder. What is the length of the ladder?

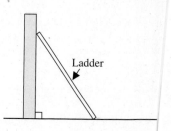

65. In the diagram, $ABCD$ is a square and point P is located on side $\overline{AB}$ so that $|\overline{PB}| = 2$ ft. and $|\overline{PC}| = 4$ ft.

(a) What is the perimeter of the square?

(b) What is the area of the square?

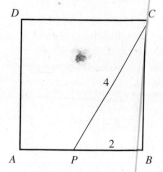

2

FUNCTIONS

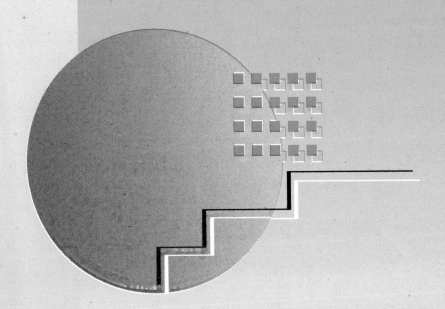

A common thread running through mathematics is the notion of *function*. This chapter introduces the basic ideas, notation, and terminology for functions, in general, and for some key classes of functions. Historically, functions have developed in different contexts. Each context has contributed a definition, and each definition can deepen understanding. In the first two sections of the chapter we give definitions and show how to visualize functions by means of graphs. Graphs will then become central to every aspect of our study, for both theoretical understanding and problem solving.

Lines are graphs of linear functions (Section 2.3) and parabolas are graphs of quadratic functions (Section 2.4). We use these two types of functions and their graphs to solve problems in Section 2.5. Section 2.6 shows how we combine functions in analysis, particularly composition, which is central to the study of calculus. Also vital for calculus (and for much of this book) is the study of inverse functions (Section 2.7). Section 2.8 gives just a taste of the incredible variety of ways mathematicians use functions to describe the world.

SECTION 2.1 | **The World of Functions**

This is a very common situation in mathematics; a required quantity is unknown to us, but we do know certain relationships in which it stands to other quantities. From these relationships we may be able to find out the value of the unknown quantity.
    Rózsa Péter

Definition of Function

We all make daily use of the idea of correspondences. We assign a number to a person, or a street address to a house, or a number to another number (as, 11 is the fifth prime). The area of a square depends on (is a function of) the side length. In words, the area is the square of the length of a side; in symbols, $A = s^2$.

The most common rules of mathematical correspondence are given by equations. For example, if $y = x^2 - 1$, for each selected x value, we get the corresponding y value by squaring the x value and then subtracting 1. If, however, for each x value we subtract 1 and then square the result, we have a very different correspondence, given by the equation $y = (x - 1)^2$.

Computer (or calculator) terminology provides rich language to describe functions. We think of x values as *input* values for the function, each with a corresponding *output*. The square root function, $y = \sqrt{x}$, is evaluated by pressing a single calculator key. When we enter 4, the output is 2. For the input 3, the display is something like 1.732050808; -2 is not an acceptable input and the calculator gives an error message. For any given function, the set of acceptable inputs is the **domain** of the function, and the set of outputs is the **range.**

> **Definition: Function, Domain, and Range**
>
> A function f is a correspondence between the elements of two non-empty sets D and R, established by a rule, that assigns to each element of D exactly one element of R. The set D is called the domain of f; the set R is called the range of f.

Functional Notation

For any element x in the domain of function f, the element that corresponds to x is denoted $f(x)$, which is read "f of x" or "the value of f at x." If the rule of correspondence is given by an equation such as $y = x^2 - 1$, then we may say "the function $f(x) = x^2 - 1$," or "the function f given by $f(x) = x^2 - 1$." Other letters can designate functions and variables, as for example,

$$g(u) = \sqrt{u^2 - 2u - 3} \qquad \text{or} \qquad h(x) = \frac{3x - 2}{4x}.$$

When we use notation such as $y = x^2 - 1$, we say that y depends on x, so y is a **dependent variable,** and in this case x is the **independent variable.** In general, the independent variable comes from the domain and the dependent variable comes from the range. In the equation defining the area of a square, $A = s^2$, the dependent variable is A and the side length s is the independent variable.

Many functions that mathematicians need frequently have standard names, including exponential, logarithmic, and trigonometric functions. Calculator keys often use these names as labels, as $\boxed{\texttt{log}}$, $\boxed{\sqrt{}}$, or $\boxed{\texttt{sin}}$.

The rule of correspondence for a given function may be specified by an equation, or it may be stated in words or presented graphically, or as a table of data. Since a function pairs a range element to each domain element, the function may be described as a set of ordered pairs.

> *I think I always had a fascination for numbers. When [my grandfather] drove along in a car, he would factorize every car number [three-digit license plate] coming along. He once actually drove into a brick wall while multiplying out car numbers in his head. When I was a teenager, I used to sing in our church choir and the sermons used to go on a bit, so I used to do things like multiply the numbers on the hymn board, or square all the numbers up to a hundred. I enjoyed playing with numbers and puzzles.*
>
> Robin Wilson

EXAMPLE 1 Suppose the domain D of function f is $\{-1, 3, 5\}$ and f assigns to each number in D its square. Evaluate $f(x)$ for each x in D and find the range of f.

Solution

$$f(-1) = (-1)^2 = 1 \qquad f(3) = 3^2 = 9 \qquad f(5) = 5^2 = 25$$

The range of f consists of the outputs, so $R = \{1, 9, 25\}$ ▲

Domain Convention

The definition of a function must include its domain. The domain can be given explicitly (as in Example 1), or it may be clear from context, as in the function for the area of a square where only positive side lengths have meaning.

Whenever the domain of a function is not explicitly stated, the following domain convention applies.

Domain Convention

If the domain D of a function f is not explicitly stated, assume D is the set of all real numbers x for which $f(x)$ is also a real number.

To determine the domain of a function f, begin by weeding out all unacceptable input numbers for f. The easiest things to look for are division by zero and square roots of negative numbers.

EXAMPLE 2   Find the domain of each function.

Strategy: Exclude values of x that would give negative numbers under a square root or zero denominators.

(a) $g(u) = \sqrt{u^2 - 2u - 3}$ (b) $h(x) = \dfrac{\sqrt{3x + 2}}{4x - 4}$

Solution

(a)   The acceptable values of u are those that satisfy the inequality

$$u^2 - 2x - 3 \geq 0 \quad \text{or} \quad (u + 1)(u - 3) \geq 0.$$

Using techniques from Section 1.5, the solution set, which is the domain of function g, is $\{u \mid u \leq -1 \text{ or } u \geq 3\}$.

(b)   We must have $3x + 2 \geq 0$, and since we cannot divide by 0, we also need $4x - 4 \neq 0$. Together,

$$x \geq -\frac{2}{3} \quad \text{and} \quad x \neq 1.$$

The domain of h is the set $\{x \mid x \geq -\frac{2}{3}, x \neq 1\}$, or $[-\frac{2}{3}, 1) \cup (1, \infty)$. ▲

Functions of Algebraic Expressions

We have so far applied function rules to input numbers to get output numbers. We often need to allow algebraic expressions as input, as well. If $f(x) = 2x + 4$, then f doubles the input and adds 4, whether the input is a number or an algebraic expression.

$$f(-3) = 2(-3) + 4 = -2 \quad \text{and} \quad f(x - 1) = 2(x - 1) + 4 = 2x + 2.$$

In calculus the definition of a derivative involves a *difference quotient* expressed in terms of a function of an expression, as illustrated in the next example.

EXAMPLE 3   If $f(x) = x^2 - 2x$, then evaluate or simplify:

(a) $f(2)$ (b) $f(0)$ (c) $f(a + 1)$ (d) $\dfrac{f(x + h) - f(x)}{h}$.

For Graphers 2.1

EXAMPLE   Draw a graph of $y = \sqrt{3 - x^2}$. Use the graph to determine the domain and range of the function. Check the domain by solving the inequality $3 - x^2 \geq 0$.

Strategy: First find a good viewing window. To start, try $[-10, 10] \times [-10, 10]$, and then adjust as needed.

Solution   Begin by entering the equation of the function. The $[-10, 10] \times [-10, 10]$ window shows a small half-oval, centered near the origin. We could zoom in, either at the origin or by enclosing the graph in a box. Since we want to read the domain and range, convenient coordinates may help. In the Familiar Window (which is an Equal Scale window), the graph appears to be the top half of a circle that doesn't hit the x-axis. Trace to see that the function is defined for all x values between -1.7 and 1.7, and y values range from about 0.332 to 1.732. Zoom in on the point $(1.7, 0)$, to see that the right end of the graph is nearer $(1.75, 0.025)$. Zoom in again, or set an Equal Scale window, say $[-1.73, 1.73] \times [0, 2.31]$, and see the domain to an accuracy of two decimal places. Solving the given inequality algebraically, we find $-\sqrt{3} \leq x \leq \sqrt{3}$. The range is $\{y \mid 0 \leq y \leq \sqrt{3}\}$. ▲

Exercises

1. Draw a graph of $f(x) = \sqrt{5 - 2x - x^2}$. Use the graph to determine the domain and range of f. Check the domain by solving the inequality $5 - 2x - x^2 \geq 0$.

2. Draw a graph of $f(x) = \frac{x^2}{x^2 + 4}$ and use it to answer the following questions.
   (a) Is $f(x) \geq 0$ for every x?
   (b) Is there an x for which $f(x) \geq 1$?
   (c) What is the range of f?

3. Repeat Exercise 2 for the functions $g(x) = \frac{x^2}{x^2 + 1}$ and $h(x) = \frac{x^2}{x^2 + 2}$.

4. Repeat Exercise 2 for the functions $G(x) = \frac{x^2}{x^2 - 4}$ and $H(x) = \frac{x^2}{x^2 - 1}$.

5. On the basis of your results in Exercises 2 through 4, write a paragraph describing the behavior of functions of the form $F(x) = \frac{x^2}{x^2 + c}$ and $G(x) = \frac{x^2}{x^2 - c}$ for positive numbers c.

6. A rectangle with one side of length x is inscribed in a circle of radius 5. Draw a diagram and write an equation that gives the area y of the rectangle as a function of x. Draw a graph of the function and use the graph to find the value of x that gives the rectangle with the largest area.

Solution

(a) $f(2) = 2^2 - 2 \cdot 2 = 0$.

(b) $f(0) = 0^2 - 2 \cdot 0 = 0$.

(c) $f(a + 1) = (a + 1)^2 - 2(a + 1) = (a^2 + 2a + 1) - 2a - 2$
$= a^2 - 1$.

(d) $\dfrac{f(x + h) - f(x)}{h} = \dfrac{[(x + h)^2 - 2(x + h)] - [x^2 - 2x]}{h}$

$= \dfrac{2xh + h^2 - 2h}{h} = 2x + h - 2$. ▲

In many cases, the rule for a function cannot be expressed by a single equation. When different equations apply for different portions of the domain, as in Example 4, the function is defined **piecewise** (in pieces). Other function rules are best given verbally, as in Example 5.

EXAMPLE 4   For the function

$$f(x) = \begin{cases} x^2 & \text{if } x \le 1 \\ 2 - x & \text{if } x > 1 \end{cases}$$

evaluate (a) $f(-3)$, (b) $f(1)$, and (c) $f(\sqrt{3})$.

Solution

(a) and (b)   Since $-3 < 1$ and $1 \le 1$, the top piece of the function definition applies:

$$f(-3) = (-3)^2 = 9 \qquad \text{and} \qquad f(1) = 1^2 = 1.$$

(c) $\sqrt{3} > 1$, so the bottom part of the definition gives $f(\sqrt{3}) = 2 - \sqrt{3}.$ ▲

Strategy: Follow the rule for the function and count the number of primes less than x.

EXAMPLE 5   Function f is stated "$f(x)$ is the number of prime numbers less than x." The domain of f is the set of positive numbers. Evaluate (a) $f(2)$, (b) $f(12)$, and (c) $f(5\sqrt{2})$.

Solution

(a)   The value of $f(2)$ is the number of prime numbers less than 2. Since there are no primes less than 2, $f(2) = 0$.

(b)   There are five primes less than 12, namely 2, 3, 5, 7, and 11, so $f(12) = 5$.

(c) $5\sqrt{2} \approx 7.071$, so there are four primes less than $5\sqrt{2}$; $f(5\sqrt{2}) = 4$. The function f is well-defined for every positive number, but to evaluate something like $f(14,732)$, we would need an extensive table of prime numbers. For the curious reader, $f(14,732) = 1,724$. ▲

The next function introduces some useful notation. First, $\min(a, b)$ denotes the *minimum* of the two numbers a and b. Similarly, $\max(a, b)$ is the *maximum* of a and b. If $a = b$, then $\min(a, b) = \max(a, b)$.

EXAMPLE 6   Let $g(x) = \min(x + 2, 6 - x)$. Evaluate (a) $g(-1)$, (b) $g(2)$, and (c) $g(\sqrt{5})$.

Solution

(a) $g(-1) = \min[-1 + 2, 6 - (-1)] = \min(1, 7) = 1$

(b) $g(2) = \min(2 + 2, 6 - 2) = \min(4, 4) = 4$

(c) $g(\sqrt{5}) = \min(\sqrt{5} + 2, 6 - \sqrt{5}) = 6 - \sqrt{5}$, since $\sqrt{5} + 2 \approx 4.236$ and $6 - \sqrt{5} \approx 3.764$. ▲

EXERCISES 2.1

Check Your Understanding

Exercises 1–5   True or False. Give reasons for your conclusion.

1. There is no function with domain $\{0, 1\}$ and range $\{3\}$.

2. If $F(x) = 2x^3 + 3x^2 - 2x$, then $F(\tfrac{1}{2}) = 0$.

3. If $f(x) = x + 1$, then $f(\sqrt{2} + \sqrt{3}) = f(\sqrt{2}) + f(\sqrt{3})$.

4. If f is any function, then for every x in the domain of f, $f(-x) = -f(x)$.

5. If $f(u) = \frac{1+u}{1-u}$ then $f(-u) = \frac{1}{f(u)}$.

Exercises 6–10 Complete the sentence by selecting from the list below *all choices* that make the statement true. D denotes the domain of f and R denotes the range of f.

(a) $f(0) > 1$
(b) $f(3) < 0$
(c) $f(1)$ is an integer.
(d) D is the set of real numbers.
(e) R contains only primes.
(f) $f(-x) = f(x)$ for every real x
(g) $f(-x) = -f(x)$ for every real x

6. If $f(x) = x^2 + 1$, then _____ .

7. If $f(x) = 4x - x^3$, then _____ .

8. If $f(x) = \frac{x}{x^2+1}$, then _____ .

9. If $f(x) = \sqrt{x+3}$, then _____ .

10. If $f(x)$ is the smallest prime number that is greater than x, then _____ .

Explore and Discover

1. The function f is given by $f(n) = \sqrt{24n+1}$, where the domain is the set of positive integers.
   (a) Evaluate $f(1), f(2), f(3), \ldots, f(15)$. Which of these values are integers?
   (b) Make an interesting guess about which integers belong to the range of f.
   (c) Test your guess. Pick a number p that you think should belong to the range and then solve the equation $f(n) = p$ for the value n. Is n an integer? What characteristic of p allows you to find an integer n for which $f(n) = p$?

2. It is a common error to think that the domain of the function $f(x) = \sqrt{-x}$ is either the empty set or $\{0\}$. Discuss why the error is a reasonable mistake and describe the correct domain.

3. Let $f(x) = \sqrt{x^2+1} - x$. Write a brief paragraph explaining why $f(x)$ must be positive for every real number x. (*Hint:* You may consider cases with x positive, and those with x negative.)

4. Let $f(x) = \sqrt{x^2+1} - x$. Explain why $f(x)$ must be a number between 0 and 1 for any positive number x. (*Hint:* Show that $\sqrt{x^2+1} - x$ is always equal to $\frac{1}{\sqrt{x^2+1}+x}$.)

Develop Mastery

Exercises 1–4 Write the range (in set notation) of the function f, where D is the domain.

1. $f(x) = 4x$
   $D = \{-1, 0, 1\}$

2. $f(x) = x^2 + 1$
   $D = \{-1, 0, 1, 2\}$

3. $f(x) = \frac{x^2}{x^2+2}$
   $D = \{-3, -2, 2, 3\}$

4. $f(x) = \sqrt{x^2+4x}$
   $D = \{-4, 0, 4\}$

Exercises 5–12 **(a)** Evaluate f at the indicated x value. **(b)** Write the domain of f in set notation using the Domain Convention.

5. $f(x) = 3x + 4; f(-1)$

6. $f(x) = \frac{x}{x-2}; f(-2)$

7. $f(x) = \frac{x+1}{x^2+1}; f(4)$

8. $f(x) = x + \sqrt{x+1}; f(3)$

9. $f(x) = \frac{\sqrt{1-x}}{x+2}; f(-3)$

10. $f(x) = \frac{\sqrt{x+1}}{\sqrt{4-x}}; f(1)$

11. $f(x) = \sqrt{x^2+3x-4}; f(-5)$

12. $f(x) = \sqrt{4-3x-x^2}; f(-4)$

Exercises 13–16 Evaluate the indicated expression.

13. $f(x) = \frac{x+1}{x^2-2x+1}; f(x+1)$

14. $f(x) = 1 + \sqrt{-x}; f(-4x^2)$

15. $g(x) = \frac{x}{\sqrt{x^2+4}}; g(-x)$

16. $g(x) = x^2 + x; g(x+1) - g(x)$

Exercises 17–20 Evaluate f at the indicated numbers. If the result is a rational number, leave it in exact form; otherwise approximate it to two decimal places.

17. $f(x) = 5x + \sqrt{3}; f(-4), f\left(\frac{-\sqrt{3}}{5}\right)$

18. $f(x) = \sqrt{x^2+4}; f(\sqrt{3}), f(\pi)$

19. $g(x) = \sqrt{25-x^2}; g(-4), g(1.3)$

20. $g(x) = \frac{x}{x+1}; g(-3), g(\sqrt{3})$

Exercises 21–26 Express the difference quotient, $\frac{f(x+h) - f(x)}{h}$, in simplest form.

21. $f(x) = 3x - 4$

22. $f(x) = 2 - 3x$

23. $f(x) = x^2 - 2x$

24. $f(x) = -x^2 + x + 3$

25. $f(x) = \frac{1}{x}$

26. $f(x) = 1 - \frac{3}{x}$

Exercises 27–30 Express the rule of correspondence for f as a verbal statement, that is, translate the rule into English.

27. $f(x) = 3x + 4$

28. $g(x) = 9 - x^2$

29. $f(x) = 4 - \sqrt{x}$

30. $f(x) = \sqrt{4+x^2}$

Exercises 31–33   Evaluate the function as indicated in exact form.

31. $f(x) = \begin{cases} x^2 & \text{if } x \geq 0 \\ -x & \text{if } x < 0 \end{cases}$ $f(3), f(-4), f(2 - \sqrt{5})$

32. $g(x) = \begin{cases} 1 & \text{if } x \geq 0 \\ -x^2 & \text{if } x < 0 \end{cases}$ $g(-\sqrt{2}), g(3), g(\sqrt{17} - 4)$

33. $f(x) = \begin{cases} 1 & \text{if } x \text{ is an integer} \\ -1 & \text{if } x \text{ is not an integer} \end{cases}$ $f(-3), f(\tfrac{3}{5}), f(\sqrt{7})$

Exercises 34–35   Evaluate. Then write the equation for g in piecewise form.

34. $g(x) = \min(2x - 3, 6 - x)$
   (a) $g(-2)$ **(b)** $g(0)$ **(c)** $g(3)$ **(d)** $g(5)$

35. $g(x) = \max(1 - 2x, 2x + 3)$
   (a) $g(-3)$ **(b)** $g(-1)$ **(c)** $g(0)$ **(d)** $g(\sqrt{2})$

Exercises 36–40   Evaluate as indicated.

36. The function $f(x)$ is the greatest integer that is less than x.
   (a) $f(3)$ **(b)** $f(4.3)$ **(c)** $f(-1.5)$
   (d) $f(2 - \sqrt{5})$

37. When f is applied to any quantity, it squares that quantity and then subtracts 4 from the result.
   (a) $f(3)$ **(b)** $f(-\sqrt{3})$ **(c)** $f(x^2)$
   (d) $f(1 - x)$

38. When g is applied to any quantity, it subtracts the square root of that quantity from 4 and then divides the result by 3.
   (a) $g(16)$ **(b)** $g(3)$ **(c)** $g(1.69)$
   (d) $g(x^2)$

39. The rule for the function f is: $f(x)$ is equal to the smallest prime number greater than or equal to x.
   (a) $f(0)$ **(b)** $f(3.4)$ **(c)** $f(2 + \sqrt{7})$
   (d) $f(43)$

40. The domain of f is the set of positive integers; $f(x)$ is the remainder when x is divided by 3.
   (a) $f(21)$ **(b)** $f(2)$ **(c)** $f(5)$
   (d) $f(4736)$ **(e)** What is the range of f?

41. Find all values of x (if any) for which $f(x) = 4$.
   (a) $f(x) = 3x + 2$
   (b) $f(x) = \frac{1}{2x - 1}$
   (c) $f(x) = \sqrt{x + 4}$
   (d) $f(x) = 2x^2 - x - 1$

Exercises 42–48   Write an equation that expresses the dependent variable as a function of the independent variable.

42. The area A of a circle depends upon its radius r.

43. The circumference C of a circle depends on its
   (a) radius r **(b)** diameter d.

44. The radius r of a circle depends upon its
   (a) diameter d **(b)** circumference C.

45. The perimeter P of a square depends upon its side length s.

46. The hypotenuse of a right triangle is 4 and one leg has length x. The area A of the triangle depends upon x. What is the domain of the area function?

47. The area of a square depends upon its perimeter P.

48. The area A of a circle depends upon its circumference C.

49. A rectangle having one side of length x is inscribed in a circle of radius 5.
   (a) Draw diagrams for $x = 1, 5, 9$. In each case compute the area of the rectangle.
   (b) Find a formula that gives the area A of the rectangle as a function of x.

50. Point $P(x, 0)$ is on the x-axis, and point $A(0, 1)$ is on the y-axis.
   (a) Draw a diagram showing point A and points P when x is 1, when x is -3, and for an arbitrary x.
   (b) What is the distance from A to P when x is 2?
   (c) Determine an equation giving the distance d from A to P as a function of x. What is the domain of this function?
   (d) Evaluate d when x is 0, 2, -4.

51. **(a)** Give an equation that describes the distance d between points $A(0, 1)$ and $Q(x, 1)$ as a function of x.
   (b) Evaluate the distance function when x is 1, -3.
   (c) What is the domain of the distance function?

52. Two cars leave at noon from the same point, one traveling east at 50 mph, the other traveling due north at 60 mph.
   (a) How far apart are they at 1 PM? at 1:30 PM?
   (b) If t is the number of hours after noon, find an equation expressing the distance between the cars as a function of t.

53. An auto mechanic is paid $18 per hour when he works no more than 40 hours a week. When he works more than 40 hours a week, he earns time-and-a-half for each additional hour.
   (a) How much does he earn in a 32-hour week? a 48-hour week?
   (b) Find an equation expressing his wages W as a function of the number of hours x in a work week.

54. A window has the shape indicated in the diagram. The perimeter of the window (total distance around) is fixed at 16 feet. Let x denote the radius of the semicircle and h the height of the rectangle.

(a) Find an equation giving h as a function of x. What is the domain of the function?

(b) Express the area A of the window as a function of x.

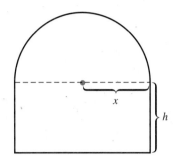

55. A man 6 feet tall is walking away from a streetlight 16 feet high so that his shadow is directly in front of him. Let x denote his distance from the base of the light as shown in the diagram.

(a) Express the length L of his shadow as a function of x.

(b) How far away from the lamp must he be to cast a shadow 6 feet long?

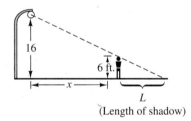

(Length of shadow)

56. A square is inscribed in an isosceles right triangle as shown in the diagram. Let x denote the length of each leg of the triangle. Express as a function of x:

(a) The perimeter P of the triangle.

(b) The area A of the triangle.

(c) The area K of the square.

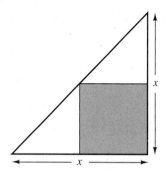

57. A rectangle is inscribed in a right triangle ABC as shown in the diagram, where $|\overline{AC}| = 15$, $|\overline{BC}| = 8$, and x is the length of one side of the rectangle. Express the area A of the rectangle as a function of x. What is the domain of this function?

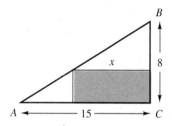

58. A square is inscribed in an isosceles triangle of base 12 as shown in the diagram. Let h denote the length of the altitude drawn to the base of the triangle. Express as a function of h:

(a) The perimeter P of the triangle.

(b) The perimeter S of the square.

(c) The area A of the square.

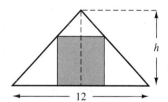

SECTION 2.2 | **Graphs of Functions**

One can envisage that mathematical theory will go on being elaborated and extended indefinitely. How strange that the results of just the first few centuries of mathematical endeavor are enough to achieve such enormously impressive results in physics.

P. W. C. Davies

Graph of a Function

A function f assigns a range element to each domain element, so it is often useful to think of the function as pairing numbers (if the domain and range are sets of numbers). The function is completely determined by these ordered pairs. In mathematical notation,

$$f = \{(x, f(x)) \mid x \in D\}, \text{ where } D \text{ is the domain of } f.$$

When the function is defined by an equation, $y = f(x)$, then

$$f = \{(x, y) \mid y = f(x), x \in D\}.$$

The ordered pairs that define f look like coordinates of points in the plane, and we can use this feature to define the graph of a function.

Definition: Graph of a Function

If f is a function with domain D, then the graph of f is the set of points with coordinates (x, y) such that $x \in D$ and $y = f(x)$.

An accurate graph of a function makes both the domain and the range of the function apparent. The domain is the set of x values of points on the graph, and the range is the set of y values.

Function Properties and Graphs

It is natural to think of drawing a graph by plotting points and connecting them in an appropriate way to get a curve. This is precisely how a computer or graphing calculator shows graphs on a screen. Without the capability to compute hundreds of function values quickly, however, pencil and paper techniques are time consuming and tedious. With or without access to the tools of technology, some additional tools can help us draw graphs and understand the properties of functions.

In this section, we examine symmetry properties of graphs and introduce the notion of even and odd functions. Also, certain core graphs are given. Knowing a single core graph and how it is affected by simple changes, we can draw graphs of a whole family of related functions.

I think that starting mathematics early had given me a certain self-reliance. I felt you didn't learn anything in class, you just figured it out yourself.

Paul Cohen

Intercept Points   We are usually interested in the points where a graph meets the coordinate axes. If 0 is the domain of f, then $f(0)$ is called the **y-intercept** and the point $(0, f(0))$ is the **y-intercept point.** If $f(c) = 0$, then c is called an **x-intercept** and the point $(c, 0)$ is an **x-intercept point.**

Symmetry Properties of Graphs; Even and Odd Functions

Given a point $A(a, b)$, three symmetrically located points can help in graphing. We can reflect A in the y-axis to the point $C(-a, b)$, in the x-axis to the point $D(a, -b)$ or in the origin to the point $E(-a, -b)$. Figure 2.1 shows a first-quadrant point A and its reflections. We apply reflections in graphing functions $f(x) = x^2$ and $g(x) = x^3$.

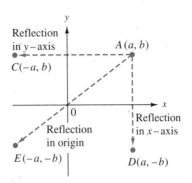

FIGURE 2.1

Reflecting point A in the axes and in the origin.

Suppose f is the function given by $f(x) = x^2$. Consider $f(-x)$.

$$f(-x) = (-x)^2 = x^2 = f(x).$$

This means that if (c, d) is any point on the graph of $y = f(x)$, then

$$d = f(c) = c^2 = (-c)^2 = f(-c),$$

so $(-c, d)$ is also a point on the graph. The point $(-c, d)$ is the reflection of (c, d) in the y-axis. Therefore, the graph of $y = x^2$ is **symmetric** about the y-axis, and the y-axis is an **axis of symmetry** for the graph. If we have the portion of the graph for $x \geq 0$, then the rest of the graph is a reflection of that portion through the y-axis. The resulting graph, called a **core parabola,** appears in Figure 2.2.

Now consider the function $g(x) = x^3$.

$$g(-x) = (-x)^3 = -x^3 = -g(x).$$

Thus $g(-x) = -g(x)$, for every x.

If (a, b) is a point on the graph of g, then $g(a) = b$ and $g(-a) = -g(a) = -b$. This means that the point $(-a, -b)$ is also on the graph. Reflect the point (a, b) in the origin and get the point $(-a, -b)$. Thus the graph of $y = x^3$ is symmetric about the origin. If we have the portion of the graph for $x \geq 0$, the rest of the graph is a reflection of that portion through the origin. See Figure 2.3.

The function $f(x) = x^2$ is an example of an **even function,** and $g(x) = x^3$ is an **odd function.**

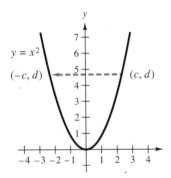

FIGURE 2.2

The graph of $y = x^2$ is symmetric about the y-axis.

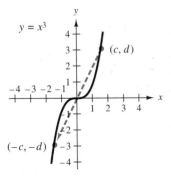

FIGURE 2.3

The graph of $y = x^3$ is symmetric about the origin.

Definition: Even and Odd Functions and Symmetry Properties of Graphs

Suppose f is a function with domain D.

If, for every x in D, $f(-x) = f(x)$, then f is called even; its graph is symmetric about the y-axis.

If, for every x in D, $f(-x) = -f(x)$, then f is called odd; its graph is symmetric about the origin.

EXAMPLE 1   Determine whether the function is odd or even, and sketch its graph.

(a) $f(x) = |x|$ (b) $g(x) = \dfrac{1}{x}$

Solution

(a) From Section 1.3,

$$|x| = x \text{ when } x \geq 0 \quad \text{and} \quad |x| = -x \text{ when } x < 0.$$

This implies that when $x \geq 0$, the graph is the same as the graph of $y = x$, the familiar line through the origin that bisects the first quadrant (the solid line in Figure 2.4a). Since

$$f(-x) = |-x| = |x| = f(x),$$

f is an even function. Complete the graph by reflecting the first-quadrant portion through the y-axis (the dotted line in Figure 2.4a).

(b) To determine whether g is odd or even, look at $g(-x)$:

$$g(-x) = \frac{1}{-x} = -\frac{1}{x} = -g(x).$$

Thus $g(-x) = -g(x)$ and so g is an odd function. To graph its graph, plot points for $x > 0$ (note that 0 is not in the domain of g) and reflect through the origin. Since the value of $g(x)$ is just the reciprocal of x, you can easily get a number of points in the first quadrant, as indicated in the table for Figure 2.4b. Connecting these points with a smooth curve (solid line) and taking the reflection through the origin (dotted line) gives the graph in Figure 2.4b. ▲

A function may be neither even nor odd, as the next example shows.

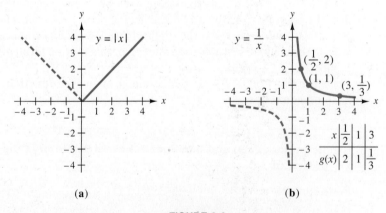

(a)   (b)

FIGURE 2.4

(a) The function $f(x) = |x|$ is an even function. The left half is a reflection in the y-axis.

(b) The function $g(x) = \frac{1}{x}$ is an odd function. The left half is a reflection in the origin.

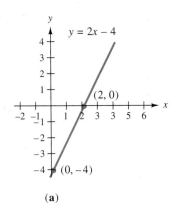

(a)

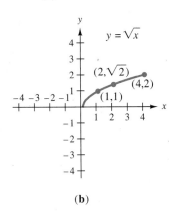

(b)

FIGURE 2.5

(a) $F(x) = 2x - 4$ is neither
even nor odd.
(b) $G(x) = \sqrt{x}$ is neither even
nor odd.

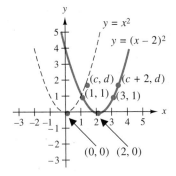

FIGURE 2.6

The graph of $g(x) = (x - 2)^2$
is a horizontal translation of
$y = x^2$.

| EXAMPLE 2 | Show that the function is neither even or odd,
and sketch its graph

(a) $F(x) = 2x - 4$ **(b)** $G(x) = \sqrt{x}$

Solution

Apply the definition of even and odd functions.

$$F(-x) = 2(-x) - 4 = -2x - 4 \qquad -F(x) = -2x + 4$$
$$G(-x) = \sqrt{-x} \qquad\qquad\qquad -G(x) = -\sqrt{x}$$

Since $F(-x) \neq F(x)$ and $F(-x) \neq -F(x)$, F is neither even nor odd, and similarly, G is neither even nor odd.

To graph the two functions, plot points as in Figure 2.5. ▲

Translations and Reflections; Stretching and Compressing Core Graphs

All the graphs in Figures 2.2, 2.3, 2.4, and 2.5b are core graphs. Using a core graph and a few simple tools, we can draw many other related graphs.

Horizontal Translations   First we illustrate how to translate the core parabola to draw other parabolas.

| EXAMPLE 3 | If $f(x) = x^2$, then use the graph of f to graph

(a) $g(x) = (x - 2)^2$ **(b)** $h(x) = (x + 1)^2$

Solution

(a) The graph of f is the core parabola in Figure 2.2. To see the relation between the graphs of f and g, suppose that (c, d) is a point on the graph of f, so that $d = f(c) = c^2$. There is a corresponding point on the graph of g:

$$g(c + 2) = [(c + 2) - 2]^2 = c^2 = d,$$

so the point $(c + 2, d)$ is on the graph of g. The point $(c + 2, d)$ is two units to the right of (c, d). It follows that the graph of $g(x) = (x - 2)^2$ is a parabola obtained by translating the core parabola two units to the right, as shown in Figure 2.6.

(b) By the same analysis, for each point (c, d) on the core parabola, the point $(c - 1, d)$ is on the graph of h, one unit to the left of (c, d), because

$$h(c - 1) = [(c - 1) + 1]^2 = c^2 = d.$$

Therefore graph $h(x) = (x + 1)^2$ by translating the core parabola one unit to the left, as shown in Figure 2.7. ▲

When we know a core graph, some clues make it easier to remember whether a translation moves a curve right or left. In the case of the core parabola, a distinctive feature is the vertex, the lowest point on the graph, which corresponds to squaring 0. The low point of $g(x) = (x - 2)^2$ obviously occurs when x is 2 (when we square 0), so the vertex is translated to the point $(2, 0)$, or two

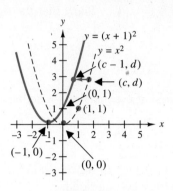

FIGURE 2.7

The graph of $h(x) = (x + 1)^2$
is a horizontal translation of
$y = x^2$.

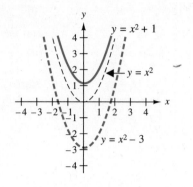

FIGURE 2.8

The graphs of $g(x) = x^2 + 1$ and
$h(x) = x^2 - 3$ are vertical
translations of $y = x^2$.

units right. Similarly, the vertex of $h(x) = (x + 1)^2$ is located where x is -1, one unit to the left of the vertex of the core parabola. See the Graphing Tips in Section 2.4.

Vertical Translations   The graphs of $g(x) = x^2 + 1$ and $h(x) = x^2 - 3$ (Figure 2.8) show fairly clearly that they are vertical translations of the core parabola (one unit up and three units down, respectively).

Guidelines for Horizontal and Vertical Translations

Suppose c is any positive number.

To graph $y = f(x - c)$, translate the graph of $y = f(x)$ horizontally c units to the right.

To graph $y = f(x + c)$, translate the graph of $y = f(x)$ horizontally c units to the left.

To graph $y = f(x) - c$, translate the graph of $y = f(x)$ vertically c units downward.

To graph $y = f(x) + c$, translate the graph of $y = f(x)$ vertically c units upward.

Core Graphs   Figure 2.9 shows a handy catalog of core graphs for your reference. Several examples illustrate how to use the core graphs. Keep the catalog handy, not just for the graphs you are asked to draw in this section, but for much of your subsequent work.

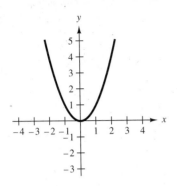

(a) $f(x) = x^2$

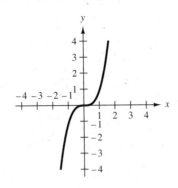

(b) $f(x) = x^3$

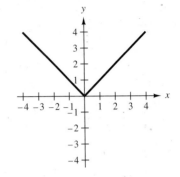

(c) $f(x) = |x|$

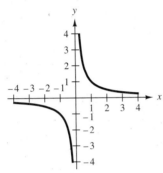

(d) $f(x) = \dfrac{1}{x}$

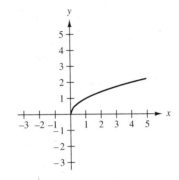

(e) $f(x) = \sqrt{x}$

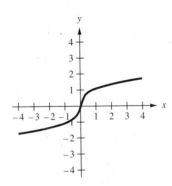

(f) $f(x) = \sqrt[3]{x}$

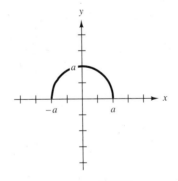

(g) $f(x) = \sqrt{a^2 - x^2}$

FIGURE 2.9

Catalog of core graphs

EXAMPLE 4   Use a core graph to sketch a graph of

(a) $g(x) = (x + 1)^3$ **(b)** $h(x) = x^3 + 1$.

Solution

Functions g and h are both cubics, so the core graph is b from Figure 2.9; $f(x) = x^3$. From the guidelines, identify the graph of $g(x) = (x + 1)^3$ as a

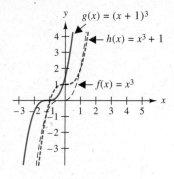

FIGURE 2.10

Translations of $y = x^3$

Strategy: a) Combine a horizontal and a vertical translation. b) The function does not match the form of any core graph. First complete the square under the radical and then use Core Graph g.

horizontal translation of core graph by one unit to the left. (The graph crosses the x-axis when x is -1.) The graph of $y = x^3 + 1$ is a vertical translation of Core Graph b one unit upward. See Figure 2.10. ▲

EXAMPLE 5   Sketch the graph of

(a) $p(x) = |x + 1| - \dfrac{1}{2}$ **(b)** $k(x) = \sqrt{3 - 2x - x^2}$.

Solution

(a)   Core Graph c is a graph of $f(x) = |x|$, and since $f(x + 1) = |x + 1|$, the graph of $y = |x + 1|$ is a translation of Core Graph c with the lowest point at $(-1, 0)$. Since $p(x) = f(x + 1) - \frac{1}{2}$, make a second translation one-half unit downward to get the graph of function p. See Figure 2.11a.

(b)   Follow the strategy:

$$3 - 2x - x^2 = 3 - (x^2 + 2x) = 4 - (x + 1)^2.$$

Thus $k(x) = \sqrt{4 - (x + 1)^2} = \sqrt{2^2 - (x + 1)^2}$; the graph of this function comes from Core Graph g. The graph of k is a semicircle of radius 2 translated one unit to the left. See Figure 2.11b. ▲

Stretching and Compressing   Now we want to compare the graphs of $y = f(x)$ and $y = 2f(x)$. For any point (c, d) on the graph of $y = f(x)$, the point $(c, 2d)$ lies on the graph of $y = 2f(x)$. This suggests that we draw a graph of $y = 2f(x)$ by stretching the graph of $y = f(x)$ vertically. Each point on the graph of $y = 2f(x)$ is *twice as far* from the x-axis as the corresponding point on the graph of $y = f(x)$.

Similarly, the graph of $y = \frac{1}{2}f(x)$ can be drawn by compressing the graph of $y = f(x)$. Each point on the graph of $y = \frac{1}{2}f(x)$ is only *half as far* from the x-axis as the corresponding point on the graph of $y = f(x)$.

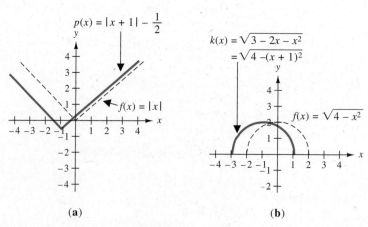

(a)   **(b)**

FIGURE 2.11

> **Guidelines for Stretching and Compressing**
>
> Suppose c is any positive number.
>
> If $c > 1$, to graph $y = cf(x)$ from the graph of $y = f(x)$, stretch vertically away from the x-axis by a factor of c.
>
> If $0 < c < 1$, to graph $y = cf(x)$ from the graph of $y = f(x)$, compress vertically toward the x-axis by a factor of c.

EXAMPLE 6   Draw graphs of **(a)** $p(x) = \frac{1}{2}x^2$ and **(b)** $q(x) = \frac{1}{2}x^2 - 1$.

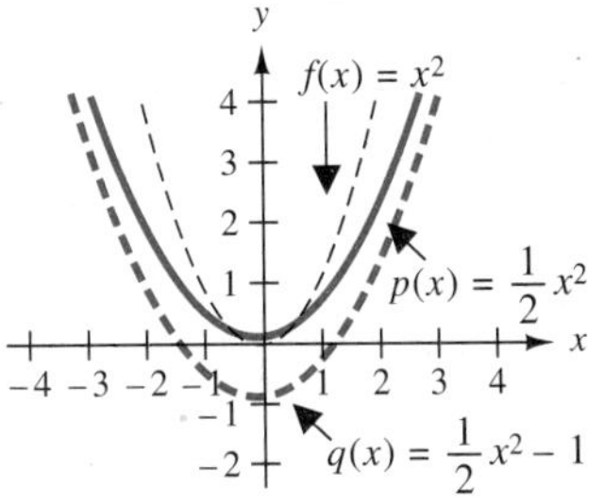

Solution

(a) Since $\frac{1}{2}$ is between 0 and 1, we get the graph of p by compressing Core Graph a. Points $(0, 0)$, $(\pm 1, 1)$ on the core graph correspond to points $(0, 0)$ and $(\pm 1, \frac{1}{2})$ on the graph of p. The graph of p has the same general shape as the core graph, but is compressed toward the x-axis as shown in Figure 2.12.

(b) The graph of $y = \frac{1}{2}x^2 - 1$ is a translation of the graph in part **(a)** downward one unit. See Figure 2.12. ▲

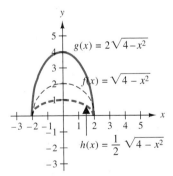

FIGURE 2.12

EXAMPLE 7   Draw graphs of **(a)** $g(x) = 2\sqrt{4 - x^2}$ and **(b)** $h(x) = \frac{1}{2}\sqrt{4 - x^2}$.

Solution

Both graphs come from the semicircle in Core Graph g. For part **(a)** stretch the graph vertically away from the x-axis by a factor of 2. For part **(b)** compress the same semicircle toward the x-axis. Both graphs are shown in Figure 2.13. ▲

When we stretch or compress a circle, the result is no longer a circle. The graphs of the two functions in Example 6 are both half-ellipses. We will become familiar with ellipses and their graphs in Chapter 10.

Reflecting a Graph   We have observed that the graph of an odd function is symmetric in the origin; the portion of the graph for negative values of x is a reflection in the origin of the portion of the graph for positive values of x.

We also noted that we can reflect a point $A(a, b)$ in the y-axis to $C(-a, b)$ and the reflection of A in the x-axis is the point $D(a, -b)$ (see Figure 2.1). Suppose f is a function and that $A(a, b)$ is on the graph of $y = f(x)$. This implies that $C(-a, b)$ is on the graph of $y = f(-x)$ and $D(c, -d)$ is on the graph of $y = -f(x)$. We can draw graphs of $y = -f(x)$ and $y = f(-x)$ by reflecting the graph of $y = f(x)$ in one of the coordinate axes.

FIGURE 2.13

Stretching and compressing
$y = \sqrt{4 - x^2}$

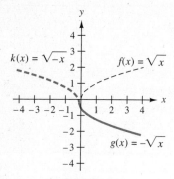

FIGURE 2.14

Reflections of $y = \sqrt{x}$

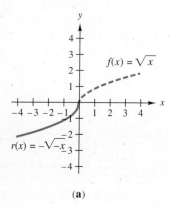

(a)

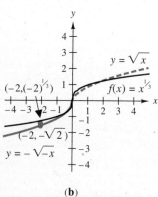

(b)

FIGURE 2.15

Guidelines for Reflection

To graph $y = -f(x)$, reflect the graph of f in the *x-axis*. (Tip the graph of f upside down.)

To graph $y = f(-x)$, reflect the graph $y = f(x)$ in the *y-axis*.

EXAMPLE 8 Draw graphs of $g(x) = -\sqrt{x}$, and $k(x) = \sqrt{-x}$.

Solution

If $f(x) = \sqrt{x}$, then $g(x) = -f(x)$ and $k(x) = f(-x)$. The graph of f is Core Graph e. Following the guidelines for reflection, the graph of g is the reflection of the core graph (the dashed black curve in Figure 2.14) in the *x*-axis (the solid curve). Similarly, the graph of k is a reflection of the core graph in the *y*-axis (the dashed curve in color in Figure 2.14). ▲

EXAMPLE 9 If $r(x) = -\sqrt{-x}$, **(a)** find the domain of r, **(b)** draw a graph of r, and **(c)** from the graph of r, find the range of r.

Solution

(a) Following the domain convention, we must have $-x \geq 0$, or $x \leq 0$, so the domain is $\{x \mid x \leq 0\}$.

(b) Draw the graph in one of several ways; each will give the same result. As in Example 8, if $f(x) = \sqrt{x}$, then $r(x) = -f(-x)$, which means that we can reflect Core Graph e in the *y*-axis and then in the *x*-axis (or in reverse order), which amounts to reflecting Core Graph e through the origin. The graph of r is the solid curve in Figure 2.15a.

(c) The graph of r is the bottom half of a parabola and the *y*-values in the graph include 0 and all negative numbers. The range is $\{y \mid y \leq 0.\}$ ▲

The two curves in Figure 2.15a together look much like Core Graph f, but there are differences. For example, point $(-2, -\sqrt{2}) \approx (-2, -1.414)$ is on the graph of r, but for $f(x) = \sqrt[3]{x}$, $f(-2) = (-2)^{1/3} \approx -1.260$. Figure 2.15b includes Core Graph f (the black curve) for comparison.

EXAMPLE 10 Draw the graph of $f(x) = x|x|$.

Solution

Strategy: Use the definition of $|x|$ to rewrite $f(x)$ in piecewise form.

The form of the function f does not match that of any function with a core graph in Figure 2.9. We know, however, that $|x|$ can be expressed as

$$|x| = \begin{cases} x, & \text{if } x \geq 0 \\ -x, & \text{if } x < 0 \end{cases},$$

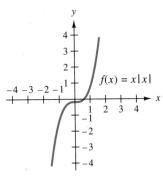

FIGURE 2.16

Accordingly, we can write

$$f(x) = x|x| = \begin{cases} x^2, & \text{if } x \geq 0 \\ -x^2, & \text{if } x < 0 \end{cases}$$

The first-quadrant portion of the graph (for $x \geq 0$) is the same as the first-quadrant portion of Core Graph a (the right half of the parabola). For negative values of x, we want to graph $y = -x^2$, an upside down parabola, so we reflect the left half of Core Graph a in the x-axis (see Figure 2.16). ▲

We could use symmetry to graph the function f in Example 10.

$$f(-x) = (-x)|-x| = -x|x| = -f(x),$$

so f is an odd function. For positive x, we have $|x| = x$, so $f(x) = x^2$, and the first-quadrant portion of our graph is Core Graph a. The remainder of the graph is obtained by reflection in the origin. The graph of f is similar to the core graph of a cubic (Core Graph b), but a comparison of values makes it clear that they are not identical. (See the comment following Example 9.)

Piecewise and Step Functions

In Section 2.1 (Example 4) we introduced functions defined piecewise (with different rules for different portions of their domains). An example of a familiar function defined piecewise comes from the postal system. In 1991 the United States Post Office set first-class postal rates as a piecewise function. The cost (in cents) C for mailing a letter to any address in the United States is 29 cents if the weight W is less than 1 ounce. For each additional ounce up to 11 ounces the cost increases in increments of 23 cents. In mathematical language

$$C = \begin{cases} 29 & \text{if } 0 < W < 1 \\ 29 + 23k & \text{if } k \leq W < k + 1 \end{cases} \quad \text{where } k = 1, 2, 3, \ldots$$

Mailing cost is a function of the weight of a letter. It remains constant for a while and then suddenly jumps to a new value. The graph looks like disconnected stair steps (see Example 11).

Another mathematical function is useful for describing functions such as that for postage cost. It is called the **greatest integer function** (or sometimes simply the **bracket function**) and is denoted by $[x]$.

Definition: Greatest Integer Function

$[x]$ is the greatest integer that is less than or equal to x.

Thus $[2] = 2$, and $[x] = x$ for every integer x, but $[\sqrt{2}] = 1$, $[\pi] = 3$. Since $-\pi$ is between -4 and -3, $[-\pi] = -4$. We can express the first-class postal cost function in terms of the greatest integer function (*check!*):

$$C(W) = 6 + 23[W + 1], \ 0 < W < 11.$$

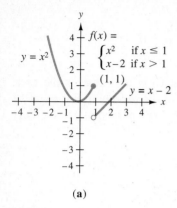

(a)

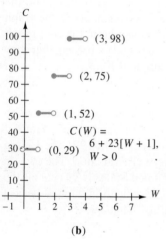

(b)

FIGURE 2.17

EXAMPLE 11   Draw a graph of

(a) $f(x) = \begin{cases} x^2 & \text{if } x \le 1 \\ x - 2 & \text{if } x > 1 \end{cases}$ **(b)** $C(W) = 6 + 23[W + 1]$.

Solution

(a) Since f is defined in two pieces, the graph consists of two pieces, as well. For the portion of the domain where $x \le 1$, the graph is the part of Core Parabola a to the left of point $(1, 1)$. For $x > 1$, part of line $y = x$ is translated down two units, as shown in Figure 2.17a. The two parts of the graph are not connected, and the point $(1, -1)$ is not on the graph, as indicated by the open dot in the figure.

(b) The cost function remains constant at 29 cents $(6 + 23 \cdot 1)$ on the interval $0 < W < 1$. At 1 ounce the cost jumps to 52 cents $(6 + 23 \cdot 2)$, and remains the same until the weight reaches 2 ounces, when it jumps by another increment of 23 cents. The graph is shown in Figure 2.17b. ▲

Graphs of Functions and Relations

Not all equations define functions, and some familiar graphs are not graphs of functions. A function assigns to each domain element exactly *one* element of the range. This implies that for any function f and any given domain number c, there is exactly one point, $(c, f(c))$, on the graph of f. A vertical line can meet the graph of f in at most *one* point, which is the basis for the following handy test.

Vertical Line Test

For a given graph, if at each number c of the domain, the vertical line $x = c$ intersects the graph in exactly one point, then the graph represents the graph of a function. If some vertical line meets a graph in more than a single point, then the graph is not the graph of a function.

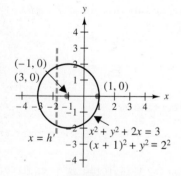

FIGURE 2.18

Vertical line $x = h$ meets the graph of the circle in two points.

EXAMPLE 12   Draw a graph of $x^2 + y^2 + 2x = 3$ and explain why this equation does not define y as a function of x.

Solution

From Section 1.6 we know that the graph of $x^2 + y^2 + 2x = 3$ is a circle. By completing the square on the x terms, we get

$$x^2 + 2x + 1 + y^2 = 3 + 1 \qquad \text{or} \qquad (x + 1)^2 + (y - 0)^2 = 2^2.$$

The center of the circle is at $(-1, 0)$ and the radius is 2. The graph is shown in Figure 2.18. It is clear from the graph that any vertical line $x = h$, where $-3 < h < 1$, will intersect the graph at two points; the graph fails the vertical line test. The circle is not the graph of a function. ▲

For Graphers 2.2

PROPERTIES OF GRAPHS

As we have seen, important functions are often defined in pieces; one rule applies to part of the domain and a different rule applies elsewhere. Graphing calculators handle such functions nicely.

Piecewise defined functions

TI

A function defined piecewise looks like

$$Y1 = (2 - X)(X < 1) + X^2(X \geq 1).$$

Add two pieces, each defined by its own formula, with the appropriate domain in parentheses.

Everything is easy to enter on the $\boxed{Y=}$ menu except the inequality signs, which are found on the $\boxed{TEST}$ menu. To get $<$, press $\boxed{2nd}$ $\boxed{TEST}$ (above MATH) 5. The inequality is entered on the $\boxed{Y=}$ screen.

Casio

A function defined piecewise looks like

Graph $Y = 2 - X$, $[-4.7, 1]$:
Graph $Y = X^2$, $[1, 4.7]$.

Each piece is defined by its formula as a separate function. The interval is given in brackets, following a comma.

The comma is necessary; it is located above the $\boxed{\rightarrow}$ key, in yellow, and hence is activated by the $\boxed{SHIFT}$ key. The brackets are in pink, on the bottom row, so press the pink $\boxed{ALPHA}$ key. Since we need two functions, use either a colon $\boxed{SHIFT}$ $\boxed{PRGM}$ $\boxed{F6}$ or line feed $\boxed{SHIFT}$ $\boxed{EXE}$.

Exercises

1. For each value of k, draw a graph of $y = k\sqrt{4 - x^2}$.

   (a) $k = 1$ (b) $k = 2$
   (c) $k = \frac{1}{2}$ (d) $k = -1$
   (e) $k = -3$ (f) $k = -\frac{1}{4}$

   Calculator hint: Use an Equal Scale window. TI: Enter $Y1 = \sqrt{(4 - X^2)}$; for $Y2$, use $2 \cdot Y1$ (where we get $Y2$ from the Y-VARS menu (above $\boxed{VARS}$. You can graph as many as four functions at once. Casio: Enter "Graph $Y = \sqrt{(4 - X^2)}$" and $\boxed{EXE}$, then toggle back to the home screen $\boxed{G\leftrightarrow T}$, INSert 2 before the radical, and $\boxed{EXE}$. The new graph is added to the first. You can overwrite as many times as you wish as long as you do not change the window.

2. Write a brief paragraph describing what happens to the graph of $y = k\sqrt{4 - x^2}$ for various values of k, as you have illustrated in Exercise 1.

3. Draw graphs of the functions (a) $y = \sqrt{x}$
   (b) $y = -\sqrt{x}$ (c) $y = \sqrt{-x}$
   (d) $y = -\sqrt{-x}$.

Exercises 4–7 Draw the graph. Determine what symmetry the graph has about the x-axis, the y-axis, the origin. Is the function even, odd, or neither? Explain.

4. $y = x|x|$ 5. $y = 4 - x^2$
6. $y = x(1 - x^2)$ 7. $y = \frac{x^2}{1 + x^2}$

Exercises 8–10 Draw a graph of the given function and determine the range.

8. $f(x) = \begin{cases} x^2, & \text{for } x \geq 0 \\ 2 - x, & \text{for } x < 0 \end{cases}$

9. $f(x) = \begin{cases} x^2, & \text{for } x < 1 \\ 2 - x, & \text{for } x \geq 1 \end{cases}$

10. $f(x) = \begin{cases} x^2, & \text{for } x \leq 0 \\ 2 - x, & \text{for } x > 1 \end{cases}$

Although a circle is a set of ordered pairs, it is not the graph of a function because there are two y values corresponding to some x values. Any collection of ordered pairs is a **relation.** Every function is a special kind of relation, but not every relation is a function, as Example 12 demonstrates. A point (x, y) belongs to the graph of a relation if and only if (x, y) is an ordered pair in the relation.

We define the domain and range of a relation as we do for a function: the domain consists of all the first elements (the x values) in the pairs of the relation; the range is all the second elements (the y values). An equation or inequality in two variables defines a relation. We know from Chapter 1 how to graph equations that define circles, and for some equations we can use techniques we have learned in this section, as illustrated in the next example.

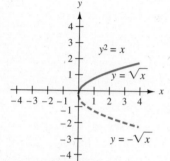

FIGURE 2.19

The horizontal parabola is not the graph of a function.

EXAMPLE 13   Sketch a graph of all points that satisfy the equation $y^2 = x$. Use the vertical line test to verify that the graph is not that of a function.

Solution

If we solve for y, we get $y = \pm\sqrt{x}$, and we must have $x \geq 0$. (Why?) The graph consists of two parts, $y = \sqrt{x}$, and $y = -\sqrt{x}$, both of which we have graphed earlier (Figure 2.14). The first is Core Graph e, and the second is the reflection of the core graph in the x-axis. Together, we get a horizontal parabola, as shown in Figure 2.19. Since any vertical line through the positive x-axis meets the graph twice, the vertical line test indicates that the graph is not the graph of a function. ▲

EXERCISES 2.2

Check Your Understanding

Exercises 1–6   True or False. Give reasons for your conclusion.

1. The graph of a function cannot have more than one y-intercept point.

2. The graph of $y = \frac{x}{|x|}$ is identical to the graph of $y = \frac{|x|}{x}$.

3. For the greatest integer function $f(x) = [x]$,
   (a) $f(-2.5) = -f(2.5)$ (b) $f(-3) = -f(3)$.

4. The distance between the x- and y-intercept points of the graph of $y = 1 - x$ is $\sqrt{2}$.

5. The graph of $y = x^2 - 2x$ can be obtained by translating the graph of $y = x^2$ one unit to the right and one unit downward.

6. If the graph of $y = \sqrt{x}$ is reflected in the y-axis, the result is the graph of $y = -\sqrt{x}$.

Exercises 7–10   Complete the sentence by selecting from the list below *all choices* that make the statement true.

(a) an even function   (b) an odd function
(c) neither even nor odd   (d) QI
(e) Q II   (f) Q III   (g) Q IV

7. If $f = \frac{2x}{x^2 + 1}$, then f is _____.

8. The function $f(x) = \frac{x^2}{|x|}$ is _____.

9. The graph of $f(x) = -x^2 - 2x - 5$ contains points in _____.

10. The graph of $f(x) = (x - 1)^2$ contains no points in _____ .

Explore and Discover

1. Using the greatest integer function, $[x]$,
   (a) find two numbers t for which $[-t] = -[t]$.
   (b) describe all numbers x for which $[-x] = -[x]$.

2. Figure 2.17b shows a graph involving the greatest integer function $[x]$. Explain the meaning of the solid dot at the left end of each horizontal segment and the open dot at the right end. What do the solid and open dots mean for someone mailing a letter?

3. Referring to Figure 2.17b, how could you define a function whose graph consisted of the same horizontal segments with an open dot at each left end and a solid dot at the right? Could there be a function whose graph has an open dot at both ends? Could there be a function whose graph has a solid dot at both ends? Write a coherent paragraph to discuss your answers.

Develop Mastery

Exercises 1–4 A function is given along with its domain. Draw a graph of the function. The graph consists of isolated points. State the range of the function.

1. $f(x) = 2x - 1; D = \{-1, 2, 3\}$
2. $f(x) = 4 - x^2; D = \{-1, 0, 1, 2\}$
3. $f(x) = x^3 - x; D = \{-2, -1, 0, 1, 2\}$
4. $f(x) = \sqrt{x}; D = \{1, 2, 4\}$

Exercises 5–8 Make a table of several (x, y) ordered pairs that satisfy the equation. Plot the points in your table and draw a graph.

5. $y = 2x - 4$
6. $y = 4 - 2x$
7. $y = x^2 - x$
8. $y = 2x^2 + 4x$

Exercises 9–12 Determine whether the function is odd, even, or neither.

9. $f(x) = x^4 - 3x^2$
10. $f(x) = x - x^3$
11. $f(x) = x^3 - 1$
12. $f(x) = (x + 1)(x - 1)$

Exercises 13–32 **(a)** Draw a graph of the function by using appropriate core graphs from Figure 2.9, along with translations, reflections, stretching, or compressing as needed.

13. $f(x) = (x + 2)^2$
14. $f(x) = x^3 - 2$
15. $g(x) = \sqrt{x + 2}$
16. $f(x) = \frac{1}{x - 2}$
17. $g(x) = \sqrt[3]{-x}$
18. $f(x) = |x - 1| - 1$

19. $g(x) = \frac{1}{2}\sqrt{16 - x^2}$
20. $g(x) = (x + 1)^2 - 2$
21. $g(x) = -2\sqrt{4 - x^2}$
22. $f(x) = -(x + 2)^2$
23. $g(x) = \sqrt{x + 2} + 1$
24. $g(x) = -|x| + 2$
25. $g(x) = 2 - x^3$
26. $f(x) = \frac{1}{x - 1}$
27. $g(x) = \frac{1}{1 - x}$ (*Hint:* See Exercise 26.)
28. $f(x) = x^2 - 4x + 7$ (*Hint:* First complete the square.)
29. $f(x) = \sqrt{8 + 2x - x^2}$ (*Hint:* First complete the square.)
30. $f(x) = 2x^2 - 4x - 1$ (*Hint:* Complete the square.)
31. $f(x) = \sqrt{2 - x}$ (*Hint:* If $g(x) = \sqrt{x - 2}$, then $f(x) = g(-x)$.)
32. $f(x) = \sqrt{-x}$

Exercises 33–39 Write an equation for the function whose graph is described, then draw a graph.

33. Core Graph a is translated 2 units left and 1 unit downward.
34. Core Graph b is reflected about the origin.
35. Core Graph d is reflected about the y-axis and then translated 1 unit upward.
36. Core Graph g is reflected about the y-axis.
37. Core Graph e is translated 1 unit right and then reflected about the x-axis.
38. Core Graph a is translated 1 unit downward and then reflected about the x-axis.
39. Core Graph c is translated 1 unit right and two units downward.

Exercises 40–43 **(a)** Draw a graph of f, with the indicated domain. **(b)** Find the range of f.

40. $D = \{x \mid x \geq 0\}; f(x) = 2x - 3$
41. $D = \{x \mid x < 0\}; f(x) = 1 - x$
42. $D = \{x \mid x > 1\}; f(x) = x^2$
43. $D = \{x \mid x \leq 2\}; f(x) = x^2$

Exercises 44–45 Draw a graph.

44. $f(x) = \begin{cases} x & \text{if } x \leq 0 \\ 1 + x & \text{if } x > 0 \end{cases}$
45. $f(x) = \begin{cases} x^2 + 2x & \text{if } x < 1 \\ 4 - x & \text{if } x \geq 1 \end{cases}$

Exercises 46–55   Match the graph with the appropriate function. Each graph is obtained from a core graph with translation, reflection, stretching, or compressing.

(a) $f(x) = |x + 1| + 1$ **(f)** $f(x) = 2 - |x|$

(b) $f(x) = 1 - \sqrt{-x}$ **(g)** $f(x) = 1 + \sqrt{4 - x^2}$

(c) $f(x) = (x - 2)^2$ **(h)** $f(x) = \sqrt{x - 1}$

(d) $f(x) = \dfrac{1}{x + 1}$ **(i)** $f(x) = \frac{3}{2}\sqrt{4 - x^2}$

(e) $f(x) = 1 - (x - 2)^2$ **(j)** $f(x) = \sqrt{4 - (x + 1)^2}$

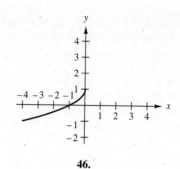

46.

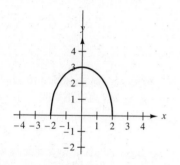

47.

48.

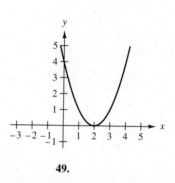

49.

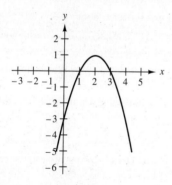

50.

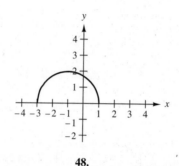

51.

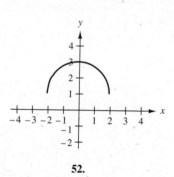

52.

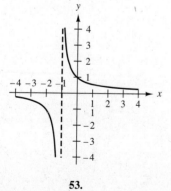

53.

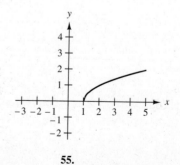

54.

55.

Exercises 56–62 Refer to the function f whose graph is shown in the diagram with domain $[-2, 6]$.

56. From the graph, give $f(-2)$, $f(0)$, and $f(4)$.

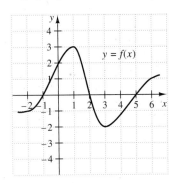

y = f(x)

57. Order the following numbers from smallest to largest: $f(-1), f(\frac{1}{2}), f(3), f(\frac{9}{2})$.

58. **(a)** What is the maximum value (the largest value) of $f(x)$?

(b) What is the minimum value (the smallest value) of $f(x)$?

(c) What is the range of f?

59. Give the coordinates of the highest and the lowest point on the graph.

60. Give the coordinates of the y-intercept point and the x-intercept points.

61. **(a)** For what values of x is $f(x)$ negative?
(b) For what values of x is $f(x)$ positive?

62. Determine the truth value (true or false) for each of the following.
(a) $f(-2)$ is less than $f(3)$.
(b) $f(4.3)$ is a negative number.
(c) $f(-1) - f(\sqrt{3})$ is a negative number.
(d) There are three x-intercept points for the graph of f.

63. Use the vertical line test to determine which of these graphs are graphs of functions that have x as the independent variable.

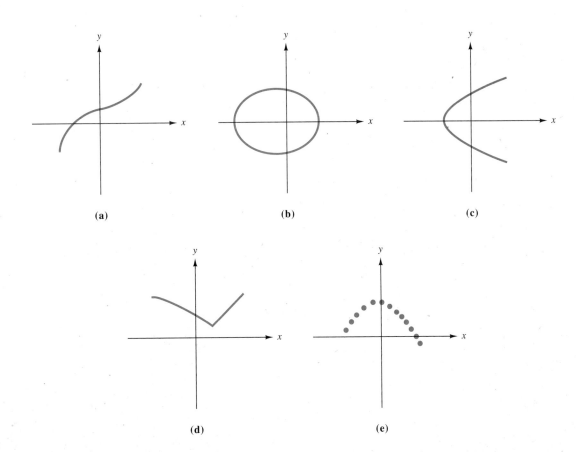

(a) (b) (c)

(d) (e)

64. Find the domain, and sketch the graph, of $f(x) = 3 + \sqrt{x} + \sqrt{-x}$.

65. $f(x) = \frac{x^2}{x^2 + 1}$

   (a) What is the domain of f?

   (b) Is f even, odd, or neither?

   (c) Make a table of some x and y values, including some large values of x. How large and how small can the y-values be?

   (d) Sketch a graph of the function.

Exercises 66–67   Make a table of values and sketch a graph of the function. Find domain and range.

66. $f(x) = \frac{x}{|x|}$ **67.** $f(x) = \frac{x - 1}{|x - 1|}$

68. Evaluate.   **(a)** $[-4]$ **(b)** $[-2.3]$
   (c) $[\sqrt{5}]$ **(d)** $[\pi + 2]$ **(e)** $[-\pi + 2]$

Exercises 69–72   Sketch a graph of f.

69. $f(x) = [x] - 1$ **70.** $f(x) = [x - 1]$

71. $f(x) = (-1)^{[x]}$ **72.** $f(x) = x - [x]$

Exercises 73–76   Find the solution set.

73. **(a)** $[x] - 2 = 0$ **74.** **(a)** $[2x] - 3 = 0$
   (b) $[x - 2] = 3$ **(b)** $2[x] - 3 = 0$

75. **(a)** $2[x] - 3 = 3[x]$
   (b) $2[x + 2] - 3 = 1$

76. $[\sqrt{p}] = 4$, where p is a prime number.

77. **(a)** Show that $[x - 2] = [x] - 2$ for every real number x.

   (b) Solve the equation $2[x] + 1 = 3[x - 2] + 3$.

   (c) Give several points (x, y) each of which belongs to both the graph of $y = 2[x] + 1$ and the graph of $y = 3[x - 2] + 3$.

78. Evaluate the function when x is 0, 1, 2, 3, 4, and 5.

   (a) $f(x) = \sqrt{x + 1 - 2\sqrt{x}} + \sqrt{x + 4 - 4\sqrt{x}}$

   (b) $g(x) = |\sqrt{x} - 1| + |\sqrt{x} - 2|$

   (c) $h(x) = \begin{cases} 3 - 2\sqrt{x} & \text{if } 0 \le x < 1 \\ 1 & \text{if } 1 \le x \le 4 \\ -3 + 2\sqrt{x} & \text{if } x > 4 \end{cases}$

   (d) Comparing the computed values of $f(x)$, $g(x)$, and $h(x)$, what can be concluded about functions f, g, and h? Justify your conclusion. (*Hint:* In part **(a)** note that $x + 1 - 2\sqrt{x} = (\sqrt{x} - 1)^2$ and $x + 4 - 4\sqrt{x} = (\sqrt{x} - 2)^2$.)

79. This section discussed postage charges. When a parcel or letter exceeds 11 ounces, a different rule applies for determining mailing cost as a function of weight. The rule depends upon mailing zones as well as weight and is given in tabular form. For example, when mailing from Zone 1 to Zone 8, the partial table below lists charges where w is the weight (not exceeding the number of pounds) and c is the cost in dollars.

w	c
1	2.90
2	2.90
3	4.10
4	4.65
5	5.45
6	8.60
7	9.65
8	10.70

Draw a graph of c as a function of w. Notice that the rate does not change from 1 to 2 pounds, and then there are abrupt jumps. You might wonder how anyone comes up with this kind of rule.

80. A bug starts at point $(1, 0)$ and travels along the line segment $\overline{AB}$ toward point $(0, 2)$ as shown in the diagram. If $P(x, y)$ denotes the location of the bug when it has traveled a distance d from $(1, 0)$, express the coordinates x and y as functions of the distance d.

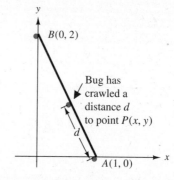

81. Factor $x^2 y - y^3 + 3x^2 - 3y^2$ and then use the zero-product principle from Section 1.5 to help you draw a graph of the equation $x^2 y - y^3 + 3x^2 - 3y^2 = 0$.

82. **(a)** Sketch a graph of $y = \sqrt{x}$.

   (b) Rotate the graph of $y = \sqrt{x}$ 180° counterclockwise about the origin and draw the resulting graph.

   (c) What is an equation for the new graph? (*Hint:* Under a 180° rotation about the origin, the point (x, y) is rotated to the point with coordinates $(-x, -y)$.)

Linear Functions and Lines

The concept of linearity has played a central role in the development of models in all the sciences.
B. J. West

> **Definition: Linear Function**
>
> A **linear function** is a function with an equation equivalent to
>
> $$f(x) = ax + b, \qquad (1)$$
>
> where a *and* b are real numbers.

And then [my father] showed me a proof of the Pythagorean theorem. He also taught me about Cartesian coordinates and showed me how to solve two linear equations by seeing where the lines intersect. And this seemed to me the most beautiful thing in the world.

Lipman Bers

Unless there is some restriction, the domain of a linear function is R, the set of all real numbers. For a linear function we may write $y = ax + b$, or $ax - y + b = 0$. This is an equation that in Section 1.6 we called a **linear equation.** Recall from Section 1.6 that the graph of a linear equation is a line, so it follows that the graph of a linear function is a line as well. Further, since $f(0) = b$ and $f(1) = a + b$, the y-intercept point of a linear function is $(0, b)$, and the line contains the point $(1, a + b)$. We can use these two points to determine the slope m of the line:

$$m = \frac{y_2 - y_1}{x_2 - x_1} = \frac{(a + b) - b}{1 - 0} = a.$$

Thus we immediately have considerable information about the graph of Equation 1.

> **Graph of a Linear Function**
>
> The graph of the linear function $f(x) = ax + b$ is a line with slope a and y-intercept b.

If a line has positive slope, then the function value increases with x and the graph slants upward as it moves to the right. The graph of a constant function, $f(x) = b = 0x + b$, has slope 0; it consists of all points of the form (x, b) and hence is a horizontal line (see Figure 2.20a). A line with negative slope slants downward as it moves to the right, as in Figure 2.20b. A vertical line consists of all points that have the same x-coordinate, and hence can be described by an equation of the form $x = c$. The definition of slope is meaningless for such a line;

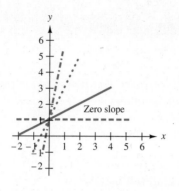

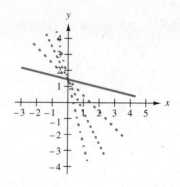

(a) Lines with nonnegative slope   **(b)** Lines with negative slope

FIGURE 2.20

the slope of a vertical line is undefined. By the vertical line test, a vertical line is not the graph of a function.

> **EXAMPLE 1**   For the point $P(-1, 1)$, sketch the line through P and the given point. Find the slope.
>
> **(a)** $A(2, -3)$ **(b)** $B(4, 1)$ **(c)** $C(0, 2)$ **(d)** $D(-1, 3)$

Solution

The lines are drawn in Figure 2.21. By the slope formula,

(a) $m_1 = \dfrac{-3 - 1}{2 + 1} = -\dfrac{4}{3}$ **(b)** $m_2 = \dfrac{1 - 1}{4 + 1} = 0$

(c) $m_3 = \dfrac{2 - 1}{0 + 1} = 1$ **(d)** $m_4 = \dfrac{3 - 1}{-1 + 1} = \dfrac{2}{0}$ (undefined slope)

The figure illustrates lines with negative, positive, and zero slope, and a vertical line, for which no slope can be defined. ▲

FIGURE 2.21

Equations of a Line

We can easily draw the graph of a linear function by plotting two points, but we want to be able to find the linear function associated with a given line as well. There are several convenient forms for equations of lines.

Equation 1 identifies the slope and y-intercept for the line, and hence is called the **slope-intercept equation** for the line. A line can be determined by either **(a)** a pair of points, or **(b)** a point and a slope. From the coordinates of two points that do not lie on a vertical line, we can immediately get the slope m:

$$m = \frac{y_2 - y_1}{x_2 - x_1},$$

so in either case **(a)** or case **(b)**, we can assume that we have the coordinates of a point on the line and its slope.

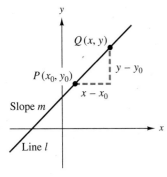

FIGURE 2.22

Q is on line l if and only if
$$\frac{y - y_0}{x - x_0} = m.$$

Let l be the line that contains the point $P(x_0, y_0)$ with slope m. Any other point $Q(x, y)$ belongs to line l if and only if the slope determined by P and Q is the number m (see Figure 2.22):

$$\frac{y - y_0}{x - x_0} = m, \qquad \text{or, multiplying by } x - x_0,$$

$$y - y_0 = m(x - x_0). \tag{2}$$

Equation (2) is called the **point-slope equation** for the line l.

A vertical line cannot be described by either the slope-intercept equation form or the point-slope form because a vertical line has an undefined slope. As we noted above, however, $x = x_0$ is an equation for the vertical line through the point $P(x_0, y_0)$.

Each of the equations above is equivalent to an equation of the form

$$Ax + By = C, \tag{3}$$

which is called a **standard equation** for a line. The box summarizes.

Equations of a Line

A nonvertical line l has an equation in any of the following forms:

1. Slope-intercept: $y = mx + b$ l has slope m and y-intercept b.
2. Point-slope: $y - y_0 = m(x - x_0)$ l has slope m and contains the point (x_0, y_0)
3. Standard: $Ax + By = C$ $B \neq 0$

A vertical line has an equation of the form $x = c$.

Strategy: First determine the slope of the line through P and Q, then use the point-slope form, taking either P or Q for (x_0, y_0).

EXAMPLE 2   Find an equation for the line l that contains points $P(-1, 2)$, and $Q(3, 4)$.

Solution

Following the strategy,

$$m = \frac{4 - 2}{3 - (-1)} = \frac{1}{2}.$$

Using the point-slope form with point P, l has equation

$$y - 2 = \frac{1}{2}[x - (-1)] \qquad \text{or} \qquad y = \frac{1}{2}x + \frac{5}{2}.$$

The last equation is in slope-intercept form, and we can obtain a standard form equation for l by multiplying by 2 and rearranging terms: $x - 2y = -5$. ▲

| EXAMPLE 3 | An equation for line l is $3x + 2y = 6$. Find **(a)**
the slope of l, **(b)** the intercept points.

Solution

Strategy: (a) Find the slope-intercept form.

(a)   To write the equation for l in slope-intercept form, solve for y:

$$y = -\frac{3}{2}x + 3.$$

This indicates that l has slope $-\frac{3}{2}$ and y-intercept point $(0, 3)$.

(b)   To find the x-intercept point, substitute 0 for y and solve for x. This gives x as 2, so the x-intercept point is $(2, 0)$.   ▲

Parallel Lines

Lines that do not intersect are **parallel.** Given a nonvertical line l, any vertical translation of l is parallel to l, and conversely, every line parallel to l can be obtained from l by vertical translation, up or down.

A line with slope m is a graph of a linear function

$$f(x) = mx + b,$$

and any vertical translation of f has the form

$$f(x) + k = (mx + b) + k = mx + (b + k),$$

which is still an equation of a line with slope m (see Figure 2.23). It is also true that all vertical lines are parallel to each other.

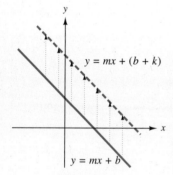

FIGURE 2.23

A vertical translation of a nonvertical line gives a parallel line.

Parallel lines

Two lines are parallel if and only if their slopes are equal, or both lines are vertical.

Perpendicular Lines

Perpendicular lines intersect at right angles. Suppose two lines l_1 (with slope m_1) and l_2 (with slope m_2) intersect at some point (h, k). Line l_1 with equation $y = m_1 x$ is parallel to l_1 and line l_2 with equation $y = m_2 x$ is parallel to m_2, and l_1 and l_2 intersect at the origin (see Figure 2.24).

Lines l_1 and l_2 are perpendicular to each other if and only if $\triangle OAB$ in Figure 2.24 is a right triangle, or, by the Pythagorean theorem if and only if $|\overline{OA}|^2 + |\overline{OB}|^2 = |\overline{AB}|^2$. By the distance formula,

$$|\overline{AB}|^2 = (m_1 - m_2)^2 = m_1{}^2 - 2m_1 m_2 + m_2{}^2, \text{ and}$$

$$|\overline{OA}|^2 + |\overline{OB}|^2 = 1^2 + m_1{}^2 + 1^2 + m_2{}^2 = 2 + m_1{}^2 + m_2{}^2.$$

Therefore l_1 and l_2 are perpendicular if and only if

$$m_1{}^2 - 2m_1 m_2 + m_2{}^2 = 2 + m_1{}^2 + m_2{}^2, \text{ or simplifying,}$$

$$m_1 m_2 = -1.$$

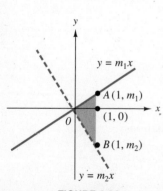

FIGURE 2.24

Perpendicular lines have slopes whose product is -1.

If either l_1 or l_2 has no slope, then one must be vertical; lines that are perpendicular to vertical lines are horizontal.

Perpendicular Lines

Two lines are perpendicular if and only if the product of their slopes is -1, or one line is vertical and the other is horizontal.

EXAMPLE 4   Find an equation for the line L that passes through the point $(1, -3)$ and is parallel to the line $3x - y = 5$.

Solution

To find the slope of the given line, solve for y to get $y = 3x - 5$. The slope of the given line is 3, the coefficient of x. Since L is parallel to the given line, its slope is also 3. Hence L has slope 3 and passes through $(1, -3)$. Substituting into the point slope form gives

$$y - (-3) = 3(x - 1).$$

Solving for y and simplifying gives the slope-intercept form for L:

$$y = 3x - 6. \quad \blacktriangle$$

EXAMPLE 5   Find an equation for the line L that is the perpendicular bisector of the line segment $\overline{AB}$, for the points $A(-1, 4)$, and $B(3, 2)$.

Solution

Strategy: First find the coordinates of the midpoint M of $\overline{AB}$ and the slope m of the line through A and B. The perpendicular bisector is the line with slope $\frac{-1}{m}$ that contains M.

Follow the strategy. The coordinates of the midpoint M of $\overline{AB}$ are given by

$$x = \frac{-1 + 3}{2} = 1 \quad \text{and} \quad y = \frac{4 + 2}{2} = 3.$$

Hence M is the point $(1, 3)$. The slope of the line through A and B is given by

$$m = \frac{4 - 2}{-1 - 3} = -\frac{1}{2}.$$

Therefore the slope of L is 2, the negative reciprocal of $-\frac{1}{2}$. L is the line that passes through $(1, 3)$ with slope 2. Substituting into the point-slope form gives

$$y - 3 = 2(x - 1) \quad \text{or} \quad y = 2x + 1. \quad \blacktriangle$$

Lines and Circles

In geometry some lines have significant relationships with certain circles. A line that meets a circle in just one point is called a **tangent line** and the point of intersection is a **tangent point.** Recall also from geometry that the line that contains the center of the circle and the tangent point is perpendicular to the tangent line, as illustrated in the next example.

For Graphers 2.3

LINEAR FUNCTIONS AND LINES

Looking at a Family of Related Graphs   To compare several graphs, it is handy to show them on the same set of axes. Remember Calculator Hint for Exercise 2 in For Graphers 2.2; we can see several graphs at the same time. On the TI, enter functions $Y1 - Y4$ on the $\boxed{y=}$ menu. On the Casio, enter several equations and graph all, or do one, toggle back to the home screen, replay (left arrow), make changes, and $\boxed{EXE}$. The new graph is added to the previous one(s).

Exercises

Exercises 1–3   On the same set of axes draw graphs of the given linear functions.

1. **(a)** $y = 2x - 3$ **(b)** $y = 2x - 1$
   (c) $y = 2x + 1$ **(d)** $y = 2x + 1.6$
   Based on these graphs, write a paragraph that describes graphs of functions of the form $y = 2x + c$, where c is any given number.

2. **(a)** $y = -2x + 3$ **(b)** $y = -x + 3$
   (c) $y = x + 3$ **(d)** $y = 1.5x + 3$
   Based on these graphs, write a paragraph that describes graphs of functions of the form $y = mx + 3$, where m is any given number.

3. **(a)** $y = -2x + 1$
   (b) $y = -0.5x + 3$
   (c) $y = -x + 1$ **(d)** $y = -3x + 1.4$
   Based on these graphs, write a paragraph that

describes graphs of functions of the form $y = -mx + b$, where m and b are any given positive numbers.

4. Draw a graph of $y = -2x + 7$. Use your graph to find all lattice points in the first quadrant that lie on the line. Calculator Hint: What kind of window do you need to make sure that the x-coordinates of pixels include the positive integers?

5. On the same set of axes draw graphs of $4x + 3y = 27$ and $x^2 + y^2 + 2x - 4y - 20 = 0$. Does it appear that the line is tangent to the circle? If so, what is the point of tangency? See Example 8. Calculator Hint: To draw the circle, first complete the squares and write the equation in the form $(x - h)^2 + (y - k)^2 = r^2$, and then solve for y.

EXAMPLE 6   A circle with center C has the equation $(x + 1)^2 + (y - 2)^2 = 25$.

(a) Show that point $P(3, 5)$ is on the circle.

(b) Find the slope m_1 and equation for the line l_1 that contains points P and C.

(c) Find an equation for the line l_2 that is perpendicular to l_1 and contains P.

(d) Show that the line l_2 intersects the circle at only one point.

Solution

Strategy: (a) Show that the coordinates of P satisfy the equation of the circle. **(b)** The slope of l_1 is $-\frac{1}{m_1}$.
(c) Substitute the value of y from the line into equation of circle, and solve for x.

Follow the strategy. It is always a good idea to draw a sketch to help visualize what is needed. The center of the circle is at $(-1, 2)$ and the radius is 5. See Figure 2.25.

(a) Substituting 3 for x and 5 for y, $(3 + 1)^2 + (5 - 2)^2 = 16 + 9 = 25$, so P is on the circle.

(b) $m_1 = \frac{5-2}{3+1} = \frac{3}{4}$. Using P as the point and $\frac{3}{4}$ as slope, l_1 has the equation

$$y - 5 = \frac{3}{4}(x - 3) \quad \text{or} \quad y = \frac{3}{4}x + \frac{11}{4}.$$

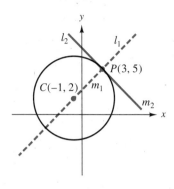

FIGURE 2.25

(c) As in the strategy, $m_2 = \frac{-4}{3}$, so using P again, line l_2 has equation

$$y - 5 = -\frac{4}{3}(x - 3) \qquad \text{or} \qquad y = -\frac{4}{3}x + 9.$$

(d) Substitute $\frac{-4}{3}x + 9$ for y in the equation of the circle, and simplify (check our algebra).

$$(x + 1)^2 + \left[\left(-\frac{4}{3}x + 9\right) - 2\right]^2 = 25 \qquad \text{or} \qquad x^2 - 6x + 9 = 0.$$

The only root of the last equation is 3, from which y is 5. The line l_2 intersects the circle only in the point $P(3, 5)$. ▲

Linear Depreciation

Linear functions are powerful models for many real-world phenomena. For instance, the value of business equipment decreases over time. The loss in value is called **depreciation** and is considered a tax-deductible business expense. A standard model of depreciation considers it a linear function of time. Suppose that some office furniture costs $1000 and the time allowed for complete depreciation is ten years; each year it loses one-tenth of its original value. For tax purposes, the value of the furniture four years after its purchase is

$$V(4) = 1000 - 4\left(\frac{1}{10} \cdot 1000\right) = 600.$$

> **Linear Depreciation Formula**
>
> Let C denote the original value of a piece of equipment. If the equipment depreciates linearly over a period of n years, its value $V(t)$ after t years is described by the equation
>
> $$V(t) = C - \frac{t}{n}C = C\left(1 - \frac{t}{n}\right).$$

EXAMPLE 7 The manager of a fish cannery has a large processing machine installed that costs $180,000. Assuming the machine depreciates linearly over 30 years, find its tax value after seven years.

Solution

Using the linear depreciation model with $C = 180{,}000$ and $n = 30$, $V(t) = 180{,}000(1 - \frac{t}{30})$. When $t = 7$, the value is

$$V(7) = 180{,}000\left(1 - \frac{7}{30}\right) = 138{,}000.$$

After seven years the machine is valued at $138,000 (for tax purposes only; the real value to the cannery or for resale purposes may be quite different). ▲

EXERCISES 2.3

Check Your Understanding

Exercises 1–5   True or False. Give reasons for your conclusion.

1. If $f(x) = 2|x| - 3$, then f is a linear function in x.

2. The slope of the line $3x - 6y = 2$ is 2.

3. The point $(2, -4)$ is on both the lines $2x + y = 0$ and $3x - y = 10$.

4. There is no linear function whose graph contains points in quadrants QI and QIII, but no points in QII or QIV.

5. The graph of the function $f(x) = \sqrt{2}x - 3$ is a line that passes through $(0, -3)$.

Exercises 6–12   Complete the sentence by selecting from the list below *all choices* that make the statement true.

(a) Quadrant I   (b) Quadrant II
(c) Quadrant III   (d) Quadrant IV
(e) positive   (f) negative
(g) zero   (h) undefined
(i) is   (j) is not

6. The slope of any line that is perpendicular to the line $3x - 6y = 5$ must be _____.

7. If two nonvertical lines are perpendicular to each other, then the slope of one of the lines must be _____.

8. The line passing through the two points $(2, -1)$ and $(1, -2)$ has _____ slope.

9. Any line that has a positive slope must contain points in _____.

10. The function $f(x) = \sqrt{x^2} + 4$ _____ a linear function.

Explore and Discover

1. Try various numbers m and b in $y = mx + b$ and draw the corresponding lines. Based on your observations, make guesses about what values of m and b give lines that pass through (a) exactly three quadrants (b) two quadrants. Do any lines pass through all quadrants? Through only one quadrant?

2. A point is called a lattice point if both coordinates are integers.
   (a) Given lines L_1: $2x + 3y = 5$ and L_2: $2x - 4y = 3$, find the coordinates of at least two lattice points on L_1. Explain why L_2 contains no lattice points.

(b) Try other equations of the form $ax + by = c$, where a, b, and c are integers. In each case determine whether or not the line contains lattice points.

(c) Make a guess about conditions on a, b, and c that will give a line with lattice points.

3. (a) Describe a sequence of steps that would lead to a solution of this problem:
   Find an equation for the line l that is perpendicular to the line $y = 2x - 3$ and such that the first quadrant triangular region bounded by the line l and the coordinate axes has an area of 8. Follow your steps to solve the problem.

Develop Mastery

Exercises 1–6   Find the slope of the line that contains the two points.

1. $P(-2, 4), Q(0, 1)$ 2. $P(3, 5), Q(-4, 1)$
3. $A(-4, -3), B(5, 2)$ 4. $A(2, -3), B(4, -5)$
5. $C(1, -2), D(4, -2)$ 6. $C(-3, 4), D(-3, 1)$

Exercises 7–12   Find an equation stated in slope-intercept form for the line with slope m that contains P.

7. $P(-3, 4); m = -2$ 8. $P(1, 0); m = -1$
9. $P(0, 0); m = -\frac{2}{3}$ 10. $P(-\frac{1}{2}, \frac{5}{4}); m = 3$
11. $P(\frac{3}{4}, -\frac{3}{2}); m = 0$ 12. $P(\sqrt{3}, 1); m = \sqrt{3}$

Exercises 13–18   Find the slope and intercept points.

13. $3x + 2y = 6$ 14. $x - 3y = 3$
15. $2x + y = 4$ 16. $3x - 3y = 4$
17. $6x + 2y = 12$ 18. $2x - 2y = 4$

Exercises 19–24   (a) Draw a graph showing P and the line l whose equation is given. (b) Find an equation for the line l_1 that contains P and is parallel to l. (c) Find an equation for the line l_2 that contains P and is perpendicular to l.

19. $P(-1, 3); x - 2y = 4$
20. $P(0, 0); 3x - 4y = 6$
21. $P(0, -2); 2x + 3y - 5 = 0$
22. $P(-2, 4); 3x - 4y = 8$
23. $P(-1, 2); y + 4 = 0$
24. $P(2, 4); x + 3 = 0$

Exercises 25–28   Determine whether or not points A, B, and C are collinear (lie on the same line). (*Hint:* Consider slopes.)

25. $A(0, 0)$, $B(1, 2)$, $C(-3, -5)$

26. $A(2, -2)$, $B(5, 2)$, $C(-1, -6)$

27. $A(0, -4)$, $B(6, 0)$, $C(3, -2)$

28. $A(0, 2)$, $B(4, 0)$, $C(5, -1)$

Exercises 29–32   Determine the quadrants through which the line passes. (*Hint:* Draw a graph.)

29. $2x - 3y = 6$ **30.** $x + 3y = 4$

31. $3x + 2y = 0$ **32.** $x - 2y = 0$

33. Draw a graph of a linear function that contains no points in **(a)** QII **(b)** QIII **(c)** QII or QIV.

34. Write an equation for a linear function whose graph contains no points in **(a)** QII **(b)** QI or QIII.

Exercises 35–38   **(a)** Draw a diagram showing points P and Q, and find the midpoint M of line segment $\overline{PQ}$. **(b)** Find an equation for the perpendicular bisector of segment $\overline{PQ}$ and draw it on your diagram.

35. $P(-2, 3)$, $Q(2, 5)$ **36.** $P(1, 4)$, $Q(-3, 2)$

37. $P(3, 0)$, $Q(-3, 4)$ **38.** $P(-3, -1)$, $Q(1, 4)$

Exercises 39–42   Let $P(x, y)$ be any point that is equidistant from points A and B. Find an equation that must be satisfied by x and y. (*Hint:* Draw a diagram.)

39. $A(1, -3)$, $B(3, 5)$ **40.** $A(-2, 3)$, $B(4, -1)$

41. $A(0, 0)$, $B(-2, 6)$ **42.** $A(1, -4)$, $B(1, 2)$

Exercises 43–44   For the three given values of $f(x)$, can f possibly be a linear function? Explain

43. $f(-1) = -2, f(0) = 0, f(3) = 6$

44. $f(-1) = -5, f(\frac{1}{2}) = -2, f(3) = 2$

Exercises 45–46   For the three given values of $f(x)$, can the graph of $y = f(x)$ be a line? Explain.

45. $f(1) = 1, f(3) = 5, f(-2) = -4$

46. $f(-1) = 5, f(0) = 3, f(3) = -3$

47. If k is a positive number and the line $x + y = k$ is tangent to the circle $x^2 + y^2 = k$, then find k.

48. **(a)** Show that the three points $A(8, 3)$, $B(4, 10)$, and $C(2, 6)$ are the vertices of a right triangle.
(b) Find the equation of the circle that contains points A, B, and C. (*Hint:* Use a theorem from geometry concerning a right triangle inscribed in a circle.)

49. Repeat Exercise 48 for three points $A(6, 6)$, $B(8, 8)$ and $C(0, 12)$.

50. **(a)** Is point $P(5, 6)$ inside, outside, or on the circle $x^2 + y^2 - 2x - 6y - 15 = 0$?
(b) If P is inside, find the distance between the x-intercept points; if P is outside, find the distance between the y-intercept points; if P is on the circle, find an equation for the line passing through P that is tangent to the circle.

51. The cost of renting a car is $15 a day, plus 20¢ per mile.
(a) If you rent a car for four days and drive x miles, express the total cost C as a function of x.
(b) If you cannot afford more than $100 for your four days, how many miles can you drive?

52. Assume that the Celsius and Fahrenheit temperature scales have a linear relationship and that $C = 0$ when $F = 32$ and $C = 100$ when $F = 212$.
(a) Express C as a linear function of F. (*Hint:* Let $C = aF + b$, and find values a and b.)
(b) Express F as a linear function of C.

53. A firm that manufactures calculators has a fixed daily cost for salaries and plant operation of $1200; in addition, it costs $10 to produce each calculator.
(a) Find an equation for the total daily cost C as a function of the daily production of x calculators.
(b) If the wholesale price of a calculator is $16, express the total daily revenue R as a function of x.
(c) If the daily profit P equals $R - C$, express P as a function of x. For what values of x is $P > 0$?

54. You are traveling at a speed of 88 feet per second (60 mph) along a highway that runs parallel to railroad tracks on which a train is traveling in the same direction at 73 feet per second ($\approx$50 mph). **(a)** If your car is 20 feet long and the length of the train is x feet, express the time T that it takes to pass the train as a function of x. **(b)** If the train is 400 feet long, how many seconds does it take the car to pass it?

55. Find b such that the graphs of $x + 2y = 3$ and $bx - 2y + 5 = 0$ intersect at right angles.

56. After being depreciated in a linear fashion for four years of a 12 year depreciation schedule, a car is valued at $5760. What was the initial cost of the car?

57. In starting a new business the manager has the office equipped with new furniture that costs $80,000. Assuming linear depreciation over a 20 year period,
(a) what is the value of the furniture after 4 years?
(b) how much can the firm deduct for tax purposes at the end of the first year?

58. If $f(x) = 2x + 3$ and the domain D of f is given by $D = \{x \mid x^2 + x - 2 \le 0\}$, then **(a)** draw a graph of f, and **(b)** find the range of f. (*Hint:* What values of y occur on the graph?)

59. The length L of a metal rod is a linear function of its temperature T, where L is measured in centimeters and T in degrees Celsius. The following measurements have been made: $L = 124.91$ when $T = 0$, and $L = 125.11$ when $T = 100$.
 (a) Find a formula that gives L as a function of T.
 (b) What is the length of the rod when its temperature is 20° Celsius?
 (c) To what temperature should the rod be heated to make it 125.17 cm long?

60. The owner of a grocery store finds that, on average, the store can sell 872 gallons of milk per week when the price per gallon is \$1.98. When the price per gallon is \$1.75, sales average 1125 gallons a week. Assume that the number N of gallons sold per week is a linear function of the price P per gallon.
 (a) Find a formula that gives N as a function of P.
 (b) If the price per gallon is \$1.64, how many gallons should the store owner expect to sell per week?
 (c) To sell 1400 gallons per week, what price should the store set per gallon?

61. For what value(s) of m will the triangle formed by the three lines $y = -2$, $y = mx + 4$, and $y = -mx + 4$ be equilateral?

62. Find m such that the three lines $y = mx + 6$, $y = -mx + 6$ and $y = 2$ form a triangle with a perimeter of 16.

63. Given the three lines $y = m(x + 4)$, $y = -m(x + 4)$, and $x = 2$, for what value of m will the three lines form a triangle with an area of 24?

64. (a) Is the point $(-1, 3)$ on the circle $x^2 + y^2 - 4x + 2y - 20 = 0$?
 (b) If the answer is yes, find an equation for the line that is tangent to the circle at $(-1, 3)$; if the answer is no, find the distance between the x-intercept points of the circle.

65. (a) Show that points $A(1, \sqrt{3})$ and $B(-\sqrt{3}, 1)$ are on the circle $x^2 + y^2 = 4$.
 (b) Find the area of the shaded region in the diagram. (*Hint:* Show that segments $\overline{OA}$ and $\overline{OB}$ are perpendicular to each other.)

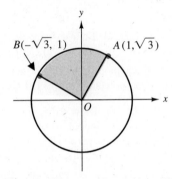

66. The horizontal line $y = 2$ divides $\triangle ABC$ into two regions. Find the area of the two regions for the triangle with these vertices:
 (a) $A(0, 0)$, $B(4, 0)$, $C(0, 4)$
 (b) $A(0, 0)$, $B(4, 0)$, $C(8, 4)$

67. The vertices of $\triangle ABC$ are $A(0, 0)$, $B(4, 0)$, $C(0, 4)$. If $0 < k < 4$, then the horizontal line $y = k$ will divide the triangle into two regions. Draw a diagram showing these regions for a typical k. Find the value of k for which the areas of the two regions are equal.

SECTION 2.4   Quadratic Functions and Parabolas

....

It is only fairly recently that the importance of nonlinearities has intruded itself into the world of the working scientist. Nonlinearity is one of those strange concepts that is defined by what it is not. As one physicist put it, "It is like having a zoo of nonelephants."
  B. J. West

Much of this course, and calculus courses to follow, deals with other inhabitants of the "zoo" of nonlinear functions, including families of polynomial, exponential, logarithmic, and trigonometric functions. All are important, but quadratic functions are among the simplest nonlinear functions mathematicians use to model the world.

Definition: Quadratic Function

A **quadratic function** is a function with an equation equivalent to

$$f(x) = ax^2 + bx + c, \qquad (1)$$

where a, b, and c are real numbers and a is not zero.

For example, $g(x) = 5 - 4x^2$ and $h(x) = (2x - 1)^2 - x^2$ are quadratic functions, but $F(x) = \sqrt{x^2 + x + 1}$ and $G(x) = (x - 3)^2 - x^2$ are not. (In fact, G is linear.)

Basic Information and Graphs of Quadratic Functions

The graphing techniques we introduced in Section 2.2, translations, reflections, and stretches, are collectively called **basic transformations.** The graph of any linear function is a line, and any two points determine the graph. Graphing a quadratic function is not quite so simple, but we want to show that the graph of any quadratic function can be obtained from the core parabola, $f(x) = x^2$, by applying basic transformations.

We will go through the pattern for a general quadratic function to justify our assertion, but to graph a particular quadratic, you may not need all of the steps. In general, we begin by factoring out the coefficient a. We then add and subtract the square of half of the resulting coefficient of x to complete the square on x.

$$f(x) = ax^2 + bx + c = a\left[\left(x^2 + \frac{b}{a}x\right) + \frac{c}{a}\right]$$

$$= a\left[\left(x^2 + \frac{b}{a}x + \frac{b^2}{4a^2}\right) - \frac{b^2}{4a^2} + \frac{c}{a}\right]$$

$$= a\left[\left(x + \frac{b}{2a}\right)^2 - \frac{b^2 - 4ac}{4a^2}\right].$$

The final equation has what we call the **transformation form** for $f(x)$:

$$f(x) = a[(x - h)^2 + k] \qquad (2)$$

The transformation form identifies the basic transformations needed to graph the function f: translate the vertex of the core parabola to the point (h, k) and reflect, stretch, or compress by the factor a. To illustrate consider the example in the Graphing Tips feature.

Graphing Tips

Use the core parabola to graph the quadratic function $f(x) = -2x^2 + 8x - 6$.

Step 0   Write the equation in transformation form:

$$f(x) = -2(x^2 - 4x + 3) = -2(x^2 - 4x + 4 - 4 + 3)$$
$$= -2[(x - 2)^2 - 1].$$

Step 1   Begin with some key points on the core parabola.

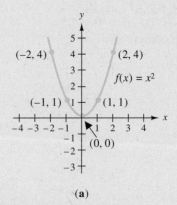

(a)

Step 2   Translate each key point 2 units right and 1 unit down, and sketch a parabola through the new key points.

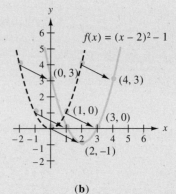

(b)

Step 3   Reflect and stretch; multiply the y-coordinate of each new key point by -2, and sketch a parabola through the resulting points.

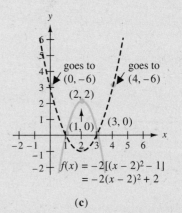

(c)

Parabola Features

From the core parabola and the transformation form of the equation of a quadratic function, we can identify some critical features.

Properties of Graphs of Quadratic Functions

Suppose f is a quadratic function with equation $f(x) = ax^2 + bx + c$.

The graph of f is a parabola with a vertex that is either the low point or the high point, depending on whether the parabola opens up or down.

The graph is symmetrical, about the vertical axis through the vertex.

The axis of symmetry is the line $x = \frac{-b}{2a}$, and the parabola opens up if $a > 0$, or down if $a < 0$.

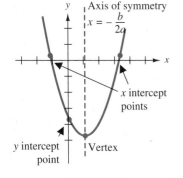

FIGURE 2.26

Not every parabola intersects the x-axis, but we can find any intercept points as we did for linear functions. The y-intercept point has coordinates $(0, f(0))$, and to find any x-intercepts, we solve the equation $f(x) = 0$. By the nature of a parabola, every quadratic function has either a **minimum** or a **maximum** (depending upon whether the parabola opens up or down), given by the y-coordinate of the vertex. To find the maximum or minimum, set $x = \frac{-b}{2a}$, and solve for y. See Figure 2.26.

EXAMPLE 1   Express the function in transformation form and identify the basic transformations required to sketch the graph.

(a) $f(x) = x^2 - 2x - 3$ **(b)** $f(x) = 2x^2 + 4x - 1$

Solution

(a) $f(x) = x^2 - 2x + 1 - 1 - 3$ Add and subtract $\left(-\frac{2}{2}\right)^2$ or 1.

$\qquad = (x - 1)^2 - 4$ Translate 1 unit right, 4 down.

(b) $f(x) = 2\left[(x^2 + 2x) - \dfrac{1}{2}\right]$

$\qquad = 2\left[(x^2 + 2x + 1) - 1 - \dfrac{1}{2}\right]$ Add and subtract $\left(-\frac{2}{2}\right)^2$ or 1.

$\qquad = 2\left[(x + 1)^2 - \dfrac{3}{2}\right]$ Translate 1 unit left, $\frac{3}{2}$ down, and stretch by a factor of 2. ▲

EXAMPLE 2   If $f(x) = x^2 - 2x - 3$, **(a)** sketch a graph, **(b)** find the maximum or minimum value f, and **(c)** find the intercept points.

Solution

(a)   From Example 1, $f(x) = (x - 1)^2 - 4$. Following strategy from Graphing Tips above, we get the graph in Figure 2.27.

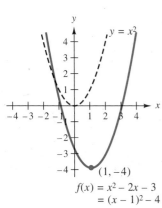

$f(x) = x^2 - 2x - 3$
$\qquad = (x - 1)^2 - 4$

FIGURE 2.27

(b)   The vertex is at $(1, -4)$, so the minimum value of f is -4.

(c) $f(0) = -3$, so the y-intercept point, as in the figure, is $(0, -3)$. Solving the equation $x^2 - 2x - 3 = 0$ we have $(x - 3)(x + 1) = 0$, so the x-intercept points are $(-1, 0)$ and $(3, 0)$.   ▲

EXAMPLE 3   Repeat Example 2 for the function $f(x) = 2x^2 + 4x - 1$.

Solution

(a)   Again from Example 1, $f(x) = 2[(x + 1)^2 - \frac{3}{2}] = 2(x + 1)^2 - 3$. The graph is shown in Figure 2.28.

(b)   The vertex is at $(-1, -3)$, so the minimum value of f is -3.

(c)   The value of $f(0)$ is -1, so the y-intercept point is $(0, -1)$. The equation $2x^2 + 4x - 1 = 0$ does not readily factor, so we use the quadratic formula and find the x-intercepts:

$$x = \frac{-2 \pm \sqrt{6}}{2}; \ x\text{-intercept points} \left(\frac{-2 + \sqrt{6}}{2}, 0\right) \text{ and } \left(\frac{-2 - \sqrt{6}}{2}, 0\right). \quad ▲$$

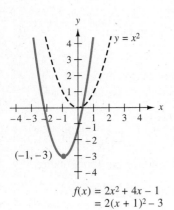

$f(x) = 2x^2 + 4x - 1$
$= 2(x + 1)^2 - 3$

FIGURE 2.28

Quadratic Functions with Limited Domain

According to the domain convention the domain of any quadratic function is the set of all real numbers unless there is some restriction. Many applications place natural restrictions on domains, as illustrated in the next two examples.

Strategy: (a) Draw a separate diagram (Figure 2.29b) to show a right triangle formed by altitude CD. $\triangle CDB$ is similar to $\triangle FEB$. Use ratios of the sides to relate h and x.

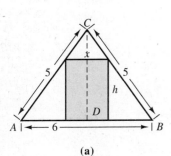

(a)

(b)

FIGURE 2.29

EXAMPLE 4   A rectangle is inscribed in an isosceles triangle ABC, as shown in Figure 2.29a, where $|\overline{AB}| = 6$ and $|\overline{AC}| = |\overline{BC}| = 5$. Let x denote the width, h the height, and K the area of the rectangle. Find an equation for **(a)** h as a function of x, **(b)** K as a function of x. **(c)** Find the domain of each.

Solution

(a)   Following the strategy, the ratios $\frac{|\overline{CD}|}{|\overline{DB}|}$ and $\frac{|\overline{FE}|}{|\overline{EB}|}$ are equal. $|\overline{DB}| = 3$, $|\overline{FE}| = h$, and $|\overline{EB}| = 3 - \frac{x}{2}$. For $|\overline{CD}|$ we can apply the Pythagorean theorem to $\triangle CDB$: $|\overline{CD}| = \sqrt{5^2 - 3^2} = 4$. Therefore

$$\frac{|\overline{CD}|}{|\overline{DB}|} = \frac{|\overline{FE}|}{|\overline{EB}|} \quad \text{or} \quad \frac{h}{3 - \frac{x}{2}} = \frac{4}{3} \quad \text{or} \quad h = 4 - \frac{2x}{3}.$$

(b)   The area K is the product of x and h:

$$K = x \cdot h = x\left(4 - \frac{2x}{3}\right) = 4x - \frac{2}{3}x^2.$$

(c)   From the nature of the problem, there is no rectangle unless x is a positive number less than 6. Hence the domain of both h and K is $\{x \mid 0 < x < 6\}$.   ▲

For Graphers 2.4

QUADRATIC FUNCTIONS

Looking Ahead to Calculus   It is shown in calculus that the tangent line to the graph of a quadratic function $f(x) = ax^2 + bx + c$ has slope $2ax + b$ at any point $(x, f(x))$ on the graph.

EXAMPLE   **(a)** Find an equation for the tangent line to the curve $y = x^2$ at point $(1, 1)$. **(b)** Graph both $y = x^2$ and the tangent line in the Familiar Window and then ZOOM in on point $(1, 1)$ to see how closely the tangent line approximates the curve.

Solution   **(a)** For $f(x) = x^2$, the coefficients are $a = 1, b = c = 0$, so the slope of the tangent line at any point (x, x^2) should be $2x$. At point $(1, 1)$ the slope is 2. Using the point-slope form for the tangent line, we have

$$y - 1 = 2(x - 1) \quad \text{or} \quad y = 2x - 1.$$

(b) Graphing $Y = X^2$ and $Y = 2X - 1$ in the Familiar Window, the graphs appear to run together near $(1, 1)$. Zooming in, either directly or with boxes, the two curves appear so close together that under high magnification, the curve is almost indistinguishable from the graph of the tangent line.   ▲

Exercises

1. At the beginning of this section we noted that $F(x) = \sqrt{x^2 + x + 1}$ is not a quadratic function.
    (a) In the Familiar Window, graph, in turn, each of the following:

    $$f(x) = \sqrt{x^2 + x - 1}$$
    $$F(x) = \sqrt{x^2 + x + 1}$$
    $$G(x) = \sqrt{x^2 + 2x + 1}$$

    (b) Write a paragraph to describe some of the differences between the graphs of f, F, and G. Note any symmetries and comment on domains and on ways each graph differs from a parabola.
    (c) The graph of G in part (a) should look familiar. Explain how G is related to one of the core graphs in Figure 2.9.

Exercises 2–5   Draw a graph of both linear and quadratic functions. If the line seems tangent to the parabola, determine the point of tangency. See the example above.

2. $y = x - 4, f(x) = x^2 - 3x$
3. $y = x + 3, f(x) = -x^2 + x + 2$
4. $y = -2x - 2, f(x) = 3x^2 - 2x - 2$
5. $y = -3x - 2, f(x) = 3x^2 - x - 2$

Exercises 6–9   Referring to the quadratic functions in Exercises 2 through 5, write an equation for the tangent line to the graph at the point where x is 1, and then graph both the function and the tangent line together in the Familiar Window. See the example above.

Strategy: Graph K and find the highest point on the graph (the vertex).

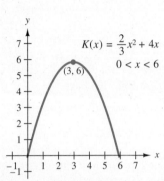

FIGURE 2.30

| EXAMPLE 5 | Find the dimensions (x and h) for the rectangle with the maximum area that can be inscribed in the isosceles triangle ABC in Figure 2.29a.

Solution

Follow the strategy. In Example 4, we found the area K as a quadratic function of x:

$$K(x) = -\frac{2}{3}x^2 + 4x, \; 0 < x < 6.$$

Graphing K as a function of x, we get *part* of a parabola that opens down. Writing the equation in factored form,

$$K(x) = -2x\left(\frac{x}{3} - 2\right),$$

we see that the x-intercepts are 0 and 6. The maximum value of K occurs at the vertex of the parabola, where

$$x = -\frac{b}{2a} = \frac{-4}{2(-2/3)} = 3.$$

The graph of K is shown in Figure 2.30. When $x = 3$, $h = 4 - (\frac{2}{3})3 = 2$, and $K(3) = 6$. Therefore the inscribed rectangle with the largest area has sides of lengths 3 and 2 and area 6. ▲

Lattice Points and Integer Domains

Many applied problems restrict the domain of a variable to integers, as in the following example.

Strategy: Graph P and find (a) the integers nearest the x-intercepts and (b) the point nearest the vertex for which x is an integer.

| EXAMPLE 6 | The profit P for a daily production of x grinders is a quadratic function x: $P(x) = -0.2x^2 + 25x - 350$. Find the values of x for which $P(x)$ is (a) positive (b) maximum.

Solution

(a) The graph of P is a parabola that opens down. $P(x) > 0$ between the x-intercepts:

$$x = \frac{-25 \pm \sqrt{25^2 - (0.8)(350)}}{-0.4} \approx 16.06 \text{ or } 108.9$$

Since we cannot make a fraction of a grinder, there is a positive profit by producing any whole number of grinders between 17 and 108, inclusive.

(b) To find the vertex of the graph, set $x = \frac{-b}{2a} = \frac{-25}{-0.4} = 62.5$. The maximum profit would be $P(62.5)$, or \$431.25, but this would require producing half a grinder. The profit for either 62 or 63 grinders is only a nickel less; $P(62) = P(63) = \$431.20$. ▲

In Example 6, only points with positive integer x values on the graph of P have physical meaning. At other times we may be interested only in points both of whose coordinates are integers. Such points are called lattice points. The points $(0, 0)$, $(1, 2)$, $(-4, 7)$, and $(-17, 0)$ are all lattice points, but $(\frac{1}{2}, 0)$, $(5, \sqrt{2})$, and $(-1, -\pi)$ are not.

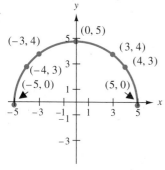

FIGURE 2.31

Lattice points on semicircle

EXAMPLE 7   Sketch a graph of $f(x) = \sqrt{25 - x^2}$ and find the set of all lattice points on the graph.

Solution

The graph of f is a semicircle (see Core Graph g, Figure 2.9), so the domain is the set $\{x \mid -5 \leq x \leq 5\}$. To find the lattice points of the graph, identify the points (x, y) with integers for both coordinates. By symmetry, it is sufficient to find the lattice points in Quadrant 1. Try each of $x = 0, 1, 2, 3, 4, 5$ in turn and find out which values yield integer y values. When $x = 0$, $y = 5$ (a lattice point); when $x = 1$, $y = \sqrt{24}$ (not a lattice point); when $x = 2$, $y = \sqrt{21}$ (not a lattice point); when $x = 3$, $y = 4$ (a lattice point); and so on. See Figure 2.31. The set of lattice points on the graph is

$$\{(0, 5), (3, 4), (4, 3), (5, 0)\} \cup \{(-5, 0), (-4, 3), (-3, 4)\}. \quad \blacktriangle$$

EXERCISES 2.4

Check Your Understanding

Exercises 1–5   True or False. Give reasons for your conclusion.

1. If we translate the graph of $y = x^2$ two units to the right and one unit down, the result will be the graph of $y = x^2 - 4x + 3$.

2. The y-intercept point for the graph of $y = x^2 + x - 3$ is above the x-axis.

3. There are no lattice points on the graph of $y = \sqrt{x}$.

4. There are no lattice points on the graph of $y = x^2 + \sqrt{3}x - 2\sqrt{3}$.

5. The graph of $y = x^2 - 4x + 1$ contains no points in the third quadrant.

Exercises 6–10   Complete the sentence by selecting from the list below *all choices* that make the statement true.
(a) is   (b) is not   (c) $(2, 3)$
(d) $(-1, -4)$ (e) $(1, 0)$ (f) $(-1, 0)$
(g) $(-1, 4)$ (h) $(-1, 2)$

6. If $f(x) = x(1 - x) + 3$, then f _____ a quadratic function.

7. If $f(x) = x^2 + x(1 - x)$, then f _____ a quadratic function.

8. Both of the x-intercept points of the graph of $y = x^2 - 5x + 6$ are horizontally to the right of _____

9. The graph of $y = x^2 - 1$ passes through the point _____.

10. The axis of symmetry for the parabola $y = x^2 + 2x - 3$ passes through the point _____.

Explore and Discover

1. (a) Draw parabolas for various values of a, b, c in $y = ax^2 + bx + c$.
(b) Which of your parabolas contain points in exactly two, three, or four quadrants?
(c) Determine conditions on $a, b,$ and c that will give parabolas that contain points in exactly two, three, or four quadrants. Is there a parabola that lies completely in one quadrant? Explain.

2. Each of the parabolas in *DM* Exercises 45–48 in this section contains lattice points. Must every parabola with an equation of the form $y = ax^2 + bx + c$, where $a, b,$ and c are integers, contain at least one lattice point? More than one lattice point? Explain why you think your answer is correct.

3. Is there an equation for a parabola that contains no lattice points? Explain your conclusion.

Develop Mastery

Exercises 1–8   The function is expressed in transformation form. Identify the basic transformations needed to sketch the graph. See Example 1.

1. $f(x) = x^2 - 3$ **2.** $f(x) = -x^2 + 3$

3. $g(x) = 2(x - 1)^2$ **4.** $g(x) = 2(x + 1)^2$

5. $f(x) = (x + 1)^2 - 3$ **6.** $f(x) = (x - 3)^2 + 1$

7. $f(x) = -(x + 1)^2$ **8.** $f(x) = -(x - 2)^2 + 3$

Exercises 9–20   **(a)** Express the function in transformation form and **(b)** find the coordinates of the vertex and intercept points. **(c)** Sketch the graph.

9. $f(x) = x^2 - 2x + 4$

10. $f(x) = -x^2 + 2x - 1$

11. $f(x) = -x^2 - 2x + 2$

12. $f(x) = x^2 + 4x + 1$

13. $f(x) = 2x^2 - 4x + 2$

14. $f(x) = -2x^2 + 8x - 5$

15. $f(x) = \frac{1}{2}x^2 + 2x$

16. $f(x) = -\frac{1}{2}x^2 - 2x - 1$

17. $f(x) = x^2 - 3x - 4$

18. $f(x) = x^2 - 4x + 4$

19. $f(x) = -2x^2 - 4x + 1$

20. $f(x) = -x^2 - 4x - 4$

Exercises 21–24   Find the equation (in slope-intercept form) for the line that contains the origin and the vertex of the graph of the function.

21. $f(x) = x^2 - 4x + 3$

22. $f(x) = 2x^2 + 4x - 1$

23. $g(x) = -2x^2 + 2x - 1$

24. $g(x) = 3x^2 - 6x - 5$

Exercises 25–28   Find the equation (in slope-intercept form) for the line containing the vertex and the y-intercept point of the graph f.

25. $f(x) = x^2 - 4x + 1$

26. $f(x) = x^2 - 3x$

27. $f(x) = -2x^2 - 8x + 3$

28. $f(x) = -3x^2 - 12x - 8$

Exercises 29–32   Find the coordinates of the vertex and, without further computation, tell whether or not the graph of the function will have any x-intercept points.

29. $y = 2x^2 - 4x + 3$ **30.** $y = -x^2 + 4x - 5$

31. $y = -2x^2 - 6x - 3$ **32.** $y = 3x^2 - 6x + 2$

Exercises 33–36   Determine the quadrants through which the graph of the function passes. Drawing a graph may help.

33. $y = x^2 - 4x + 3$ **34.** $y = 2x^2 + 7x + 3$

35. $y = x^2 + 4x + 5$ **36.** $y = -x^2 - 2x - 1$

Exercises 37–40   Find the distance between the x-intercept points for the graph of the function.

37. $f(x) = x^2 - 4x - 3$

38. $g(x) = x^2 + 2x - 8$

39. $g(x) = 2x^2 - 4x + 1$

40. $f(x) = -2x^2 + 4x + 3$

Exercises 41–44   Let A be the y-intercept point and B, C be the x-intercept points for the graph of the function. Draw a diagram and then find the area of $\triangle ABC$.

41. $f(x) = -x^2 - x + 6$

42. $f(x) = x^2 - 6x + 8$

43. $f(x) = -x^2 - 2x + 8$

44. $f(x) = -x^2 - 6x + 8$

Exercises 45–48   Each of the graphs shown began with the core parabola ($y = x^2$) followed by one or more basic transformations. **(a)** Give a verbal description of the transformation used. **(b)** Give an equation for the function.

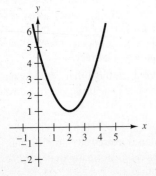

45.

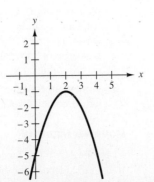

46.

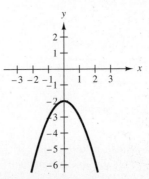

47.

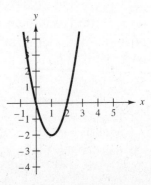

48.

Exercises 49–52 Determine the quadratic function whose graph satisfies the given conditions.

49. The axis of symmetry is $x = 2$, the point $(-1, 0)$ is on the graph, and $(0, 5)$ is the y-intercept point. (*Hint:* Use symmetry to find the other x-intercept point, and then express $f(x)$ in factored form.)

50. The vertex is $(3, -4)$ and one of the x-intercept points is $(1, 0)$. (See the hint in Exercise 49.)

51. The graph is obtained by translating the core parabola 3 units left and 2 units down.

52. The graph is obtained by reflecting the core parabola about the x-axis, then translating to the right 2 units.

53. The length of each of the two equal sides of an isosceles triangle is twice the length x of the base.
(a) Express the area of the triangle as a function of x.
(b) Express the area of the triangle as a function of the perimeter P of the triangle.

54. A piece of wire x units long is shaped into a circle. Express the area of the circle as a function of x.

55. (a) A wire 36 inches long is bent to form a rectangle. If x is the length of one side, find an equation that gives the area A of the rectangle as a function of x.
(b) For what values of x is the equation valid?

56. Find the coordinates of all lattice points in the first quadrant and also on the graph of $y = -x^2 - 2x + 14$. See Example 7.

57. Find the coordinates of all lattice points in the second quadrant and also on the graph of $y = -x^2 + 2x + 20$. See Example 7.

58. Find the coordinates of all lattice points that are below the x-axis and also on the graph of $y = x^2 - x - 12$.

59. How many lattice points are inside the region bounded above by the graph of $y = -x^2 - 2x + 4$ and below by the x-axis?

60. A gutter with an open top and rectangular cross section is made from a long sheet of tin that is 12 inches wide by bending up equal strips of width x (see the diagram). The carrying capacity of the gutter is determined by the area A of its cross section. Express A as a function f of x. What is the domain of f?

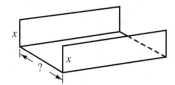

61. A farmer has 800 feet of fencing left over from an earlier job. He wants to use it to fence in a rectangular plot of land except for a 20-foot strip that will be used for a driveway (see the diagram, where x is the width of the plot). Express the area A of the plot as a function f of x. What is the domain of f?

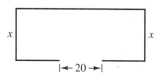

62. A toy rocket is fired vertically from the ground at an initial speed of 36 meters per second. Its position at any time t seconds after firing is given by $s = 36t - 4.9t^2$, where s is the distance in meters from the ground.
(a) Draw a graph of $s = 36t - 4.9t^2$. Keep in mind the graph does not represent the path of the rocket since the rocket goes straight up and down. However, the graph helps answer certain questions. Use the graph to read off approximate answers to the following.
(b) At what times t is the rocket on the ground?
(c) At what times t is the rocket 50 meters from the ground?
(d) At what time does the rocket reach its highest point?

63. A travel agent is proposing a tour in which a group will travel in a plane of capacity 150. The fare will be $1400 per person if 120 or fewer people go on the tour; the fare per person for the entire group will be decreased by $10 for each person in excess of 120. For instance, if 125 go, the fare for each will be $1400 - \$10(5) = \$1350$. Let x represent the number of people who go on the tour and T the total revenue (in dollars) collected by the agency. Express T as a function of x.

64. In the diagram the smaller circle is tangent to the x-axis at the origin and it is tangent to the larger circle, which has a radius of 1 and center at $(1, 1)$. What is the radius of the smaller circle?

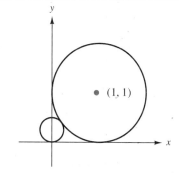

65. *Looking Ahead to Calculus*   A solid has as its base
the region in the *xy*-plane bounded by the circle
$x^2 + y^2 = 4$.
   (a) If every vertical cross section perpendicular to
   the *x*-axis is a semicircle, express the area *K* of
   the cross section at a distance *u* from the origin
   as a function of *u*.

   (b) Repeat part **(a)** if each vertical cross section is an
   isosceles triangle with an altitude half as long as its
   base (not a semicircle).

   (c) Repeat part **(a)** if each vertical cross section is an
   equilateral triangle.

   (d) Repeat part **(a)** if each vertical cross section is a
   rectangle whose base is twice its vertical height.

| SECTION 2.5 | **Using Graphs in Problem Solving** |

*In two and a half millenia of Western science, every conceivable
misconception about motion, velocity, and acceleration has cropped up,
[and] the errors that students make during their lightning trip through
mechanics are merely the echoes of all the errors made by the great
thinkers of the past.*
      H. C. von Baeyer

*I didn't hate high school, and
I did well eventually in
advanced placement classes.
What I didn't like was the
pace of school. If I became
interested in a subject,
biology or mathematics, I
found it unpleasant to have
to put everything aside after
an hour and go on to
something else.*

      William Thurston

This section explores the power of graphs to help solve problems.

Solving Quadratic Inequalities

In Section 1.5, we solved quadratic inequalities by factoring quadratic expressions. Here we look at the more general situation of solving quadratic inequalities with the use of graphs, as illustrated in the following example.

| **EXAMPLE 1** | Find the domain of the function $f(x) = \sqrt{x^2 - 2x - 4}$.

Solution

To avoid taking square roots of negative numbers, limit the domain of *f* to the set of numbers that satisfy the inequality $x^2 - 2x - 4 \ge 0$. What numbers belong to this set?

   Let $y = x^2 - 2x - 4$ and draw a graph. This gives a parabola that opens upward, with vertex at $(1, -5)$. To find the *x*-intercept points, solve the equation

$$x^2 - 2x - 4 = 0$$

by the quadratic formula to get $x = 1 \pm \sqrt{5}$. Thus the intercept points are $A(1 - \sqrt{5}, 0)$ and $B(1 + \sqrt{5}, 0)$, as shown in Figure 2.32. Use the graph to read off the solution set to the inequality that defines the domain of *f*:

$$D = \{x \mid x \le 1 - \sqrt{5} \text{ or } x \ge 1 + \sqrt{5}\}$$
$$= (-\infty, 1 - \sqrt{5}) \cup (1 + \sqrt{5}, \infty).$$ ▲

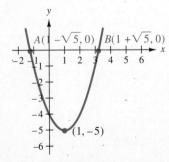

FIGURE 2.32

Range of a Function

It is not always a simple matter to determine the range of a function from an equation. Remember, though, that the range of f is the set of all y values that occur on the graph of $y = f(x)$. We can easily graph a quadratic function to find its range, as illustrated in the following examples.

Strategy: Graph $y = -x^2 + 2x - 2$. **(a)** Read the range from the y-values of the graph. **(b)** Find the x values for which the graph is below the x-axis, where y is negative.

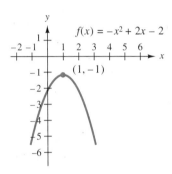

FIGURE 2.33

The graph is below the x-axis for all real numbers.

EXAMPLE 2   For $f(x) = -x^2 + 2x - 2$, find **(a)** the range of f and **(b)** the set of values for which $f(x) < 0$.

Solution

(a) Follow the strategy. The graph of f is a parabola that opens down. Its highest point is the vertex. For the x-coordinate of the vertex,

$$x = -\frac{b}{2a} = -\frac{2}{2(-1)} = 1.$$

When $x = 1$, $y = -1$, so the vertex is at $(1, -1)$. See Figure 2.33. The range of f is the set of all y values on the graph, $\{y \mid y \leq -1\}$ or $(-\infty, -1]$.

(b) The graph clearly shows that for every real number x, the corresponding y value is negative. Therefore $f(x)$ is negative for all real numbers. The solution set for the inequality $f(x) < 0$ is R, the set of real numbers. ▲

EXAMPLE 3   Find the range of the function $f(x) = x^2 - 4x + 2$, where the domain of f is $\{x \mid 0 < x \leq 3\}$.

Solution

The graph of f is the part of the parabola $y = x^2 - 4x + 2$ on the interval $(0, 3]$, as shown in Figure 2.34. When $x = 3$, $y = -1$. The point $(3, -1)$ is on the graph. If we could have $x = 0$, the corresponding y value would be 2, but since 0 is not in the domain of f, the point $(0, 2)$ is not on the graph, as indicated by the open dot in the diagram. The range of g is the set of all y values for points on the graph. The graph shows a range of $\{y \mid -2 \leq y < 2\}$, or $[-2, 2)$. ▲

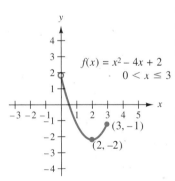

FIGURE 2.34

The range is $[-2, 2)$.

Strategy: Use the definition $|x| = x$ if $x \geq 0$, and $|x| = -x$ if $x < 0$, and rewrite f.

EXAMPLE 4   **(a)** Draw a graph of $f(x) = x^2 - 2|x| - 3$ and find the range of f. **(b)** Find the solution set for $x^2 - 2|x| - 3 > 0$.

Solution

Following the strategy, write f in piecewise form:

$$f(x) = \begin{cases} x^2 - 2x - 3 & \text{if } x \geq 0 \\ x^2 + 2x - 3 & \text{if } x < 0 \end{cases}$$

(a) To draw the graph of f, draw a graph of each of the pieces, which are parts of parabolas. When x is negative, $y = x^2 + 2x - 3$, draw a parabola

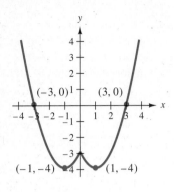

y

$(-3, 0)$ $(3, 0)$

$(-1, -4)$ $(1, -4)$

FIGURE 2.35

opening up with its vertex at

$$x = -\frac{b}{2a} = -\frac{2}{2 \cdot 1} = -1, y = (-1)^2 - 2 - 3 = -4.$$

The graph for $x < 0$ is the left portion of Figure 2.35.

Similarly, when $x \geq 0$, $y = x^2 - 2x - 3$. This describes a parabola with its vertex at $(1, -4)$, the right portion of the figure. Since the low point of each portion has the same y-coordinate, the graph shows clearly that the range is $\{y \mid y \geq -4\}$.

(b) Also from the graph, notice that y is positive when x is less than -3 or when x is greater than 3. Thus the solution set for $x^2 - 2|x| - 3 > 0$ is the union of two intervals: $(-\infty, -3) \cup (3, \infty)$. ▲

Maximum and Minimum Values of a Function

When we use mathematical models to answer questions about an applied problem, we frequently need to determine the maximum or minimum values of a function. The general problem can be very difficult, even using the tools of calculus, but when quadratic functions are involved one can simply read off a maximum or minimum value from a graph.

Definition: Maximum or Minimum Value of a Function

Suppose f is a function with domain D.

If there is a number k in D such that $f(k) \geq f(x)$ for every x in D, then $f(k)$ is the maximum value of f.

If there is a number k in D such that $f(k) \leq f(x)$ for every x in D, then $f(k)$ is the minimum value of f.

Strategy: In each case first draw a graph, being aware of the given domain. From the graph, read off the minimum or maximum values of y (if any). Do not give coordinates

EXAMPLE 5 Determine the maximum and minimum values of the function.

(a) $f(x) = x^2 - 4x$

(b) $g(x) = x^2 - 4x$, where $-1 \leq x \leq 3$

(c) $h(x) = x^2 - 4x$, where $-1 < x \leq 3$

Solution

Follow the strategy. A graph of each of the functions is shown in Figure 2.36 where we include key points. In parts **(b)** and **(c)** the domain is restricted, and so we have only portions of the parabola. The desired information can be read from the graphs.

(a) The minimum value of f is the smallest value of y that occurs on the graph. From Figure 2.36 **(a)** we see that the minimum value is -4 (when x is 2), and we see that f does not have a maximum value since the graph continues upward in both directions.

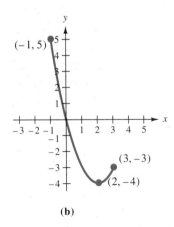

(a)

(b)

(c)

FIGURE 2.36

Maximum and minimum values (if any) depend on the
domain as well as the function.

(b) From Figure 36**(b)** we see that g has a minimum value of -4 (when x is 2)
and a maximum value of 5 (when x is -1).

(c) From Figure 2.36**(c)**, h has a minimum value of -4, but it has no maximum
value since there is no largest number less than 5. ▲

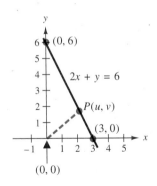

FIGURE 2.37

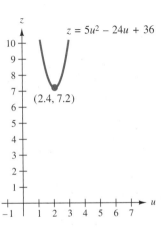

FIGURE 2.38

| **EXAMPLE 6** |

(a) Find the minimum distance from the origin to the line L given by
$2x + y = 6$.

(b) What are the coordinates of the point Q on L that is closest to the origin?

Solution

First draw a diagram that will help formulate the problem (Figure 2.37). Since
$P(u, v)$ is on L, then $2u + v = 6$, or $v = 6 - 2u$.

$$d = \sqrt{(u - 0)^2 + (v - 0)^2} = \sqrt{u^2 + v^2} = \sqrt{u^2 + (6 - 2u)^2}$$
$$= \sqrt{5u^2 - 24u + 36}.$$

(a) The minimum value of d will occur when the expression under the radical
is a minimum. Determine the minimum of the function

$$z = 5u^2 - 24u + 36,$$

whose graph is shown in Figure 2.38. The lowest point on the parabola
occurs where

$$u = -\frac{b}{2a} = -\frac{-24}{10} = 2.4$$

When $u = 2.4$, $z = 7.2$. Therefore, the minimum value of z is 7.2, so the
minimum distance from the origin to the line L is $\sqrt{7.2}$ (≈ 2.68).

(b) The point Q on L that is closest to the origin is given by $u = 2.4$ and
$v = 6 - 2(2.4) = 1.2$. Thus, Q is point $(2.4, 1.2)$. ▲

| For Graphers 2.5 | PROBLEM SOLVING WITH GRAPHS |

Exercises

Exercises 1–2 Draw a graph of the function and use the graph to find the domain and range.

1. $y = \sqrt{3 + 2x - x^2}$

2. $y = \sqrt{4 - 2x - x^2}$

3. A rectangle is inscribed in a circle of diameter 4.
    (a) If x denotes the length of one side of the rectangle, express the area and the perimeter in terms of x as functions $A(x)$ and $P(x)$, respectively.
    (b) Graph $A(x)$ and find the value of x that gives the largest value for the function $A(x)$.
    (c) Repeat part (b) for the perimeter function $P(x)$.
    (d) Calculus techniques can show that the same value of x maximizes both $A(x)$ and $P(x)$,

namely $2\sqrt{2}$. How close did you come to that value? Why shouldn't you expect the value 2.828427125?

4. It can be shown that the height of the bug in Develop Mastery Exercise 69 above the ground at time t is given by

$$y = \frac{t\sqrt{400 - t^2}}{20}, \text{ for } 0 \le t \le 20.$$

Graph the function and find (approximately) the maximum height reached by the bug.

Exercises 5–17 Use your graphing calculator to help you solve Develop Mastery Exercises 31 through 43.

| EXERCISES 2.5 |

Check Your Understanding

Exercises 1–5 True or False. Give reasons for your conclusion.

1. The graph of $y = x^2 - 2x - 5$ does not cross the x-axis.

2. The minimum value of the function $f(x) = x^2 - 2x - 3$ is $(1, -4)$.

3. The function $f(x) = 3 - 4x - x^2$ does not have a maximum value.

4. If $a > 0$ and $c < 0$, then the graph of $y = ax^2 + bx + c$ must have two x-intercept points.

5. If $a < 0$ and $c > 0$, then the graph of $y = ax^2 + bx + c$ will not cross the x-axis.

Exercises 5–10 Complete the sentence by selecting from the list below *all choices* that make the statement true.

  (a) 3   (b) −3   (c) 6   (d) −4   (e) 4

6. The minimum value of the function $f(x) = x^2 - 2x - 3$ is _____.

7. The maximum value of the function $f(x) = 2 - 4x - x^2$ is _____.

8. The solution set for $x^2 - 2x - 3 > 0$ contains the number _____.

9. The minimum value of the function $f(x) = \sqrt{x + 1} + 3$ is _____.

10. All points on the graph of $y = 1 - 4x + x^2$ are on or above the horizontal line $y =$ _____.

Explore and Discover

1. Try various numbers for b and c (zero, positive, and negative) in $f(x) = \sqrt{x^2 + bx + c}$. In each case, determine the domain of f. What condition or conditions on b and c will ensure that the domain is R? That the domain is a proper subset of R? Are there any values of b and c for which the domain of f contains no real numbers?

2. Try various numbers for b and c in $f(x) = \sqrt{-x^2 + bx + c}$. In each case, determine the domain of f. What condition or conditions on b and c will ensure that the domain is a proper subset of R? Are there any values of b and c for which the domain is all of R?

Develop Mastery

Exercises 1–8 Find the solution set for the given inequality. First sketch an appropriate graph from which you can read the answer.

1. $x^2 - 4x + 3 > 0$ **2.** $x^2 + 5x + 4 < 0$
3. $2x^2 - x - 3 < 0$ **4.** $3x^2 + 2x - 8 \geq 0$
5. $-x^2 + 2x + 4 \leq 0.$ **6.** $-2x^2 + 3x - 4 \leq 0$
7. $x^2 - 4x + 4 \leq 0$ **8.** $x^2 - 6x + 9 > 0$

Exercises 9–16 Determine the range of the function. State your answer using **(a)** set notation and **(b)** interval notation. A graph will be helpful.

9. $f(x) = x^2 - 2x - 3$
10. $f(x) = x^2 + 3x - 4$
11. $g(x) = -2x^2 + 4x + 1$
12. $g(x) = -3x^2 + 6x - 5$
13. $f(x) = (3x - 2)(3x + 2)$
14. $f(x) = (4 - x)(2 + x)$
15. $g(x) = x^2 - 2\sqrt{3}x$
16. $g(x) = 2x^2 + 4\sqrt{3}x$

Exercises 17–20 An equation for a function is given along with its domain D. Find the range of the function. An appropriate graph will allow you to read off the answer.

17. $f(x) = x^2 + 2x + 5;$
$D = \{x \mid -3 \leq x \leq 0\}$
18. $f(x) = x^2 + 2x + 5;$
$D = \{x \mid 0 \leq x \leq 2\}$
19. $g(x) = -x^2 - 4x + 4;$
$D = \{x \mid -3 < x < 1\}$
20. $g(x) = -x^2 + 2x + 4;$
$D = \{x \mid 0 \leq x \leq 3\}$

Exercises 21–30 Find the maximum and/or minimum value(s) of the function. A graph will be helpful.

21. $f(x) = x^2 - 3x - 4$
22. $f(x) = x^2 + 5x - 2$
23. $g(x) = -x^2 + 4x + 1$
24. $g(x) = -x^2 + 4x + 3$
25. $f(x) = (x - \sqrt{5})(x + \sqrt{5})$
26. $f(x) = (x - 2\sqrt{3})(x + 2\sqrt{3})$
27. $g(x) = x^2 - x, \quad -1 \leq x \leq 4$
28. $g(x) = 3x - x^2, \quad 0 < x < 4$
29. $f(x) = 6x - x^2, \quad x \geq 0$
30. $f(x) = 12x - 3x^2, \quad x \geq 0$

Exercises 31–34 **(a)** Draw a graph of f. Use the graph to help you find **(b)** the range of f and **(c)** the solution set for $f(x) < 0$.

31. $f(x) = x^2 - 2|x| - 3$
32. $f(x) = |x - 2|$
33. $f(x) = -x^2 + 2|x| + 3$
34. $f(x) = |x| + x - 3$

Exercises 35–38 Find the maximum and/or minimum value(s) of the function.

35. $f(x) = \sqrt{3 + 2x - x^2}$
36. $f(x) = \sqrt{5 + 4x - x^2}$
37. $g(x) = \sqrt{3 + 2x + x^2}$
38. $g(x) = \sqrt{4 - 2x + x^2}$

39. Determine whether or not f has a maximum or a minimum and then find the extreme value. First draw a graph.
   (a) $f(x) = |x - 1| + 2$
   (b) $f(x) = -|x - 1| - 2$
   (c) $f(x) = |x - 1| - x$

Exercises 40–43 Find the domain.

40. $f(x) = \sqrt{x^2 - 2x - 3}$
41. $f(x) = \sqrt{x^2 - 4x - 2}$
42. $f(x) = \sqrt{x^2 + x + 2}$
43. $g(x) = \sqrt{5 - x^2}$

Exercises 44–49 Find the minimum distance from point A to line l. First draw a diagram.

44. $A(0, 0); \ l: 2x + y = 10$
45. $A(0, 0); \ l: 3x - y = 10$
46. $A(0, 0); \ l: x - 2y = -5$
47. $A(1, 2); \ l: 2x + y = 9$
48. $A(3, 3); \ l: 2x + y = 4$
49. $A(-2, 3); \ l: 2x + y = 10$

Exercises 50–55 For point A and line l given in Exercises 44 through 49, find the point on l that is nearest to A. See Example 6(**b**).

56. Of all the rectangles of perimeter 15 centimeters, find the dimensions (length and width) of the one with greatest area.

57. At a fireworks display, a rocket is fired vertically upward from a point 3 feet above ground level at an initial speed of 96 feet per second. If s represents the distance (in feet) from ground level at time t seconds after launch, then s is given by the formula

$$s = -16t^2 + 96t + 3.$$

(a) How far from ground level will the rocket be 2 seconds after launch?

(b) At what time will the rocket reach its maximum distance from ground level? What is this maximum distance?

58. A piece of wire 30 inches long is bent into an L-shape. The distance d from the endpoints is a function of x. See diagram.

(a) Find a formula for d in terms of x.

(b) What value of x will give a minimum value of d?

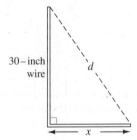

59. Function f is given by $f(x) = \min(x - 1, 5 - x)$.

(a) Draw a graph of $y = f(x)$. (*Hint*: First draw graphs of $y = x - 1$ and $y = 5 - x$ on the same set of coordinate axes, then use the information you see to draw the graph of $y = f(x)$.)

(b) What is the maximum value of $f(x)$?

60. Function f is given by $f(x) = \min(x + 2, 4 - x)$.

(a) What is the maximum value of $f(x)$?

(b) Give a piecewise formula for f. (*Hint*: See Exercise 59.)

61. Sketch the graph of the function $f(x) = \max(x^2 - 4, 4 - x^2)$. (*Hint*: See Exercise 59.)

62. Find the solution set for the inequality $2\sqrt{x} < x$. (*Hint*: Draw the graphs of $y = 2\sqrt{x}$ and $y = x$ on the same set of axes and use the graphs to help you see the answer.)

63. Point $P(u, v)$ is in the first quadrant on the graph of the line $x + y = 4$. A triangular region is shown in the diagram.

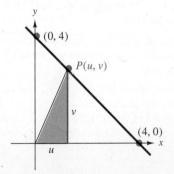

(a) Express the area A of the shaded region as a function of u.

(b) For what point P will the area of the region be a maximum?

(c) What is the maximum area?

64. Repeat Exercise 63 for point $P(u, v)$ on the line segment joining $(0, 3)$ and $(4, 0)$.

65. A long, rectangular sheet of galvanized tin, 10 inches wide, is to be made into a rain gutter. The two long edges will be bent at right angles to form a rectangular trough (see diagram, which shows a cross section of the gutter with height x inches).

(a) Find a formula that gives the area A of the cross section as a function of x. What is the domain of this function?

(b) What value of x will give a gutter with maximum cross sectional area?

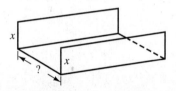

66. A piece of wire 100 centimeters long is to be cut into two pieces; one of length x centimeters, to be formed into a circle of circumference x, and the other to be formed into a square of perimeter $100 - x$ centimeters. Let A represent the sum of the areas of the circle and the square.

(a) Find an equation that gives A as a function of x.

(b) For what value of x will A be the smallest?

67. A travel agency is offering a two-week tour of the Orient, in which a group will travel in a plane of capacity 180. The fare is $2400 per person if 100 or fewer subscribe but the cost per person will be decreased by $15 for each person in excess of 100. For instance, if 125 go, then the cost for each is $2400 - 15(25) = $2025.

(a) Determine a formula (function) that will allow the travel agency to compute the total revenue T when x people go on the tour.

(b) What is the domain of this function?

(c) Draw a graph and use it to determine the number of people that will give the maximum revenue.

68. An oil field has 10 wells and each produces 200 barrels of oil a day. For each new well drilled in this field that produces oil, the daily production of each well decreases by 4 barrels.

(a) Express the total daily production P of oil as a function of x, where x is the number of new wells drilled.

(b) What is the domain of this function?

(c) How many new producing wells should be drilled to get the maximum daily production?

69. A 20-foot ladder rests vertically against a wall. A bug starts at the bottom of the ladder and climbs up at the rate of 1 foot per minute. At the same time, the foot of the ladder is being pulled along the ground at the rate of 1 foot per minute until the top reaches the ground. The position of the bug t minutes later is shown in the diagram. Let x denote the distance of the bug from the wall at time t. It can be shown that x is given by

$$x = t - \frac{t^2}{20} \quad \text{for} \quad 0 \le t \le 20.$$

Note that when $t = 0$ (at the start), $x = 0$. Also when $t = 20$ (the bug is at the other end of the ladder), then $x = 0$. What is the farthest the bug will be from the wall in its march up the ladder?

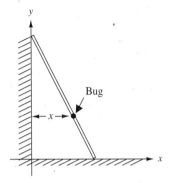

| **SECTION 2.6** | **Combining Functions** |

What is proved about numbers will be a fact in any universe.
    Julia Robinson

Just as we combine numbers to get other numbers, so we may combine functions to get other functions. The first four ways of combining functions give familiar sums, differences, products, or quotients, as we would expect. **Composition,** less familiar, is a key idea throughout much of what follows.

Definition: Sum, Difference, Product, Quotient Functions

Suppose f and g are given functions. Functions denoted by $f + g$, $f - g$, $f \cdot g$, and $\frac{f}{g}$ are given by:

Sum: $(f + g)(x) = f(x) + g(x)$

Difference: $(f - g)(x) = f(x) - g(x)$

Product: $(f \cdot g)(x) = f(x) \cdot g(x)$

Quotient: $\left(\dfrac{f}{g}\right)(x) = \dfrac{f(x)}{g(x)}$

The domain of each combined function is the set of all real numbers for which the right side of the equation is meaningful as a real number. Use parentheses as needed for clarity.

The definitions stated here are not mere formal manipulations of symbols. For instance, the plus sign in $f + g$ is part of the name of the function that assigns to each x the sum of two numbers, $f(x) + g(x)$.

> **EXAMPLE 1**   If $f(x) = 4x - 6$ and $g(x) = 2x^2 - 3x$, write an equation for **(a)** $f - g$ and **(b)** $\frac{f}{g}$, and give the domain of each.

Solution

(a) $(f - g)(x) = f(x) - g(x) = (4x - 6) - (2x^2 - 3x) = -2x^2 + 7x - 6$. The domain is the set of real numbers.

(b)
$$\left(\frac{f}{g}\right)(x) = \frac{f(x)}{g(x)} = \frac{4x - 6}{2x^2 - 3x} = \frac{2(2x - 3)}{x(2x - 3)},$$

which simplifies to $\frac{2}{x}$ for $x \neq \frac{3}{2}$. Therefore $(\frac{f}{g})(x) = \frac{2}{x}$, where the domain is $\{x \mid x \neq 0 \text{ and } x \neq \frac{3}{2}\}$. ▲

Composition of Functions

The other way to combine functions is used frequently and plays an important role in both precalculus and calculus.

Definition: Composition of Functions

Suppose f and g are given functions. The rule for the composition of g followed by f, denoted by $f \circ g$, is given by:

$$(f \circ g)(x) = f(g(x)).$$

The notation $f \circ g$ is frequently read as "f of g" because its value for a given number x is f of $g(x)$. The domain of the composition function $f \circ g$ is the set of real numbers for which $f(g(x))$ is meaningful; that is, x must be in the domain of g *and* $g(x)$ must be a number in the domain of f.

> **EXAMPLE 2**   If $f(x) = 4 - x^2$ and $g(x) = \sqrt{x}$, write an equation that gives the rule of correspondence for **(a)** $f \circ g$ **(b)** $g \circ f$.

Solution

(a) $(f \circ g)(x) = f(g(x)) = f(\sqrt{x}) = 4 - (\sqrt{x})^2$
Note that for $\sqrt{x}$ to be a real number, we must have $x \geq 0$. As long as we limit x to nonnegative numbers, we can simplify the equation for $f \circ g$:

$$(f \circ g)(x) = 4 - x, \text{ where } x \geq 0.$$

(b) $(g \circ f)(x) = g(f(x)) = g(4 - x^2) = \sqrt{4 - x^2}$.
Again, we must limit the domain; $\{x \mid -2 \leq x \leq 2\}$.

Alternate Solution   Sometimes it is easier to verbalize the rules that define functions. The rules for f and g state that, for any given input, f squares the input and subtracts the result from 4, while g takes the square root of its input. Thus, suppose $\sqrt{x}$ is the input. The function f squares $\sqrt{x}$ and subtracts the result from 4: $4 - (\sqrt{x})^2$. Similarly, when g is applied to $f(x)$, g takes the square root of $f(x)$. The output is: $g(f(x)) = \sqrt{f(x)} = \sqrt{4 - x^2}$. ▲

Neyman . . . interviewed me [for a job at Berkeley and] said he would let me know. . . . I didn't really expect anything to happen. I had already written 104 letters of application to black colleges. Eventually I got a letter from [Neyman] saying something like "In view of the war situation and the draft possibilities, they have decided to appoint a woman to this position." [My eventual appointment here came 12 years later.]

David Blackwell

Example 2 shows that $f \circ g$ and $g \circ f$ are not the same function. In general $f \circ g$ and $g \circ f$ are different, although there are important exceptions, as the next example demonstrates.

| EXAMPLE 3 | If $f(x) = 3x - 8$ and $g(x) = \frac{x+8}{3}$, write an

equation that gives the rule of correspondence for **(a)** $f \circ g$ **(b)** $g \circ f$.

Solution

Here the rule for f is triple the input and then subtract 8; for g it is add 8 to the input and then divide the sum by 3.

(a) $$(f \circ g)(x) = f(g(x)) = f\left(\frac{x+8}{3}\right) = 3\left(\frac{x+8}{3}\right) - 8 = x.$$

(b) $$(g \circ f)(x) = g(f(x)) = g(3x - 8) = \frac{(3x - 8) + 8}{3} = x.$$

Thus $(f \circ g)(x) = (g \circ f)(x)$ for every number x. We say that the two functions $f \circ g$ and $g \circ f$ are equal, $f \circ g = g \circ f$. ▲

| EXAMPLE 4 | If $f(x) = x^2 - 2x$ and $g(x) = 3 - x$, solve the

equations.

(a) $(f \circ g)(x) = 0$ **(b)** $(g \circ f)(x) + x^2 + 5 = 0$

Strategy: Write each equation in a more familiar form.

Solution

(a) $(f \circ g)(x) = f(g(x)) = f(3 - x) = (3 - x)^2 - 2(3 - x)$
   $= x^2 - 4x + 3$. Thus the given equation becomes

$$x^2 - 4x + 3 = 0 \quad \text{or} \quad (x - 1)(x - 3) = 0.$$

The solutions are 1 and 3.

(b) $(g \circ f)(x) = g(f(x)) = g(x^2 - 2x) = 3 - (x^2 - 2x)$
   $= -x^2 + 2x + 3$. Replacing $(g \circ f)(x)$ by $-x^2 + 2x + 3$, the given equation becomes

$$(-x^2 + 2x + 3) + x^2 + 5 = 0 \quad \text{or} \quad 2x + 8 = 0.$$

The solution is -4. ▲

| EXAMPLE 5 | If $f(x) = x^2 - 9$ and $g(x) = 2x - 5$, find the

solution for:

$$f(g(x)) < 0$$

Strategy: Get simpler expressions for the composition function, substitute, and solve.

Solution

$f(g(x)) = f(2x - 5) = (2x - 5)^2 - 9$.
Therefore the given inequality may be written as $(2x - 5)^2 - 9 < 0$. This is equivalent to:

$$(2x - 5)^2 < 9 \quad \text{or} \quad -3 < 2x - 5 < 3 \quad \text{or} \quad 1 < x < 4.$$

The solution set is $\{x \mid 1 < x < 4\}$. ▲

For Graphers 2.6	COMBINING FUNCTIONS

Exercises

1. If $f(x) = 4 - x^2$ and $g(x) = \sqrt{x}$, draw graphs of **(a)** $y = (f \circ g)(x)$ and **(b)** $y = (g \circ f)(x)$. Determine whether or not the functions $f \circ g$ and $g \circ f$ are identical. (*Calculator Hint:* Without a key for composition, first express $f \circ g$ in a form that the calculator can handle. Does the calculator show the same graph for $Y = 4 - (\sqrt{X})^2$ as for $Y = 4 - X$?)

2. If $f(x) = x^2 - 9$ and $g(x) = 2x - 5$, find the solution set for **(a)** $f(g(x)) < 0$ and **(b)** $g(f(x)) > -11 - 5x$. (*Calculator Hint:* Graph $y = f(g(x))$ and $y = g(f(x)) + 5x + 11$.)

3. Draw graphs of the functions:
   (a) $y = |x|$ **(b)** $y = |x - 2|$
   (c) $y = |x + 2| - 2$ **(d)** $y = -|x + 2|$
   Write a brief paragraph to describe how each graph relates to the graph in **(a)**. (*Calculator Hint:* $|x + 1|$ must be entered as Abs $(X + 1)$. On the TI, the absolute value is above the x^{-1} key: 2nd ABS. On the Casio, press SHIFT MATH F3 (for NUMerical functions) F1 (for Abs).)

4. What is the minimum value of $f(x)$, where $f(x) = x^2 + 2|x - 3|$? (*Calculator Hint:* Draw a graph of $y = x^2 + 2|x - 3|$.)

5. Find the solution set for **(a)** $x - |2x + 3| = 0$ and **(b)** $x - |2x + 3| < 0$. (*Calculator Hint:* Draw a graph of $y = x - |2x + 3|$.)

6. Find the solution set for $|x^2 - 2|x|| < 1$. (*Calculator Hint:* Draw a graph of $y = |(x^2 - 2|x||) - 1$.)

Exercises 7–8   Graph the functions f and g. Are these functions identical? Explain.

7. $f(x) = \sqrt{x^2 - 4x + 4}$ $g(x) = |x - 2|$
8. $f(x) = \sqrt{(x + 3)^2}$ $g(x) = x + 3$
9. Use your graphing calculator to help solve DM Exercise 68. (*Calculator Hint:* Graph $y = 10(2x + 3)^2 - 60(2x + 3) + 800$ in the window $[0, 4.75] \times [700, 2500]$.)

EXAMPLE 6	An oil spill on a lake assumes a circular shape with an expanding radius r given by $r = \sqrt{t + 1}$, where t is the number of minutes after measurements are started and r is measured in meters.

(a)   Find a formula that gives the area A of the circular region at any time t.

(b)   What is the area at the beginning measurement ($t = 0$)? What is the area 3 minutes later?

Strategy: (a) Since $r = \sqrt{t + 1}$ is a function of t and $A = \pi r^2$ is a function of r, then by composing functions we can express A as a function of t.

Solution

(a)   Follow the strategy.

$$A = \pi(\sqrt{t + 1})^2 = \pi(t + 1).$$

Thus A as a function of t is

$$A = \pi t + \pi.$$

When t *is* 0, $A = \pi \cdot 0 + \pi = \pi$ square meters. When t is 3, $A = 3\pi + \pi = 4\pi$ square meters.   ▲

Calculator Evaluations

Many function evaluations by calculator actually involve composition of functions. For instance, to evaluate $F(x) = \sqrt{x^2 + 1}$, when x is 3, we first evaluate $(3^2 + 1)$ and which gives 10, then we press $\boxed{\sqrt{x}}$ to get a decimal approximation to $\sqrt{3^2 + 1}$. This amounts to treating F as a composition $f \circ g$, where $g(x) = x^2 + 1$ and $f(x) = \sqrt{x}$.

EXAMPLE 7

If $F(x) = \frac{1}{x^2 + 1}$, express F as a composition of two functions.

Solution

Let $f(x) = \frac{1}{x}$ and $g(x) = x^2 + 1$. Then

$$f(g(x)) = f(x^2 + 1) = \frac{1}{x^2 + 1}.$$

Thus, $F(x)$ is given by $F(x) = (f \circ g)(x)$. This is probably the way you would evaluate $F(x)$ by calculator. First evaluate $x^2 + 1$, and then press the reciprocal key, $\boxed{1/x}$. ▲

In problems of the type discussed in Example 7, be aware that there are many different solutions. For example, we could have taken

$$f(x) = \frac{1}{x + 1} \qquad \text{and} \qquad g(x) = x^2.$$

Then

$$f(g(x)) = f(x^2) = \frac{1}{x^2 + 1}.$$

EXERCISES 2.6

Check Your Understanding

Exercises 1–5 True or False. Give reasons for your conclusion.

1. If $f(x) = x^2$ and $g(x) = x^2 - 1$, then $g \circ f$ is a quadratic function in x.

2. If $f(x) = x^2$ and g is any function for which the domain of $g \circ f$ is not the empty set, then the function $g \circ f$ must be an even function.

3. If $f(x) = 2x - 1$, then $f(a + b) = f(a) + f(b)$ for all real numbers a and b.

4. If $g(x) = 3x$, then $g(c + d) = g(c) + g(d)$ for all real numbers c and d.

5. If $f(x) = x^2 + 1$ and $g(x) = x + 3$, then the graph of $y = (f \circ g)(x)$ contains no points below the x-axis.

Exercises 6–10 Complete the sentence by selecting from the list below *all choices* that make the statement true.

(a) 0   (b) 1   (c) 3   (d) -3 (e) an odd
(f) an even   (g) a linear   (h) a quadratic
(i) $f(1)$ (j) $f(4)$

6. If $f(x) = 1 - x$ and $g(x) = 2x + 3$, then $f \circ g$ is _____ function.

7. If $f(x) = x^2 - 2x + 3$ and $g(x) = 2 - x^2$, then $f + g$ is _____ function.

8. If $f(x) = 2x + 1$ and $g(x) = x^2$, then $(f \circ g)(-1) = $ _____.

9. If $f(x) = x^2$ and $g(x) = \sqrt{x}$, then $g \circ f$ is _____ function.

10. If $f(x) = x^2 - 5x + 4$ and $g(x) = x^2$, then the sum of the roots of the equation $(f \circ g)(x) = 0$ is equal to _____.

Explore and Discover

1. The function f is said to be **additive** if $f(u + v) = f(u) + f(v)$ for all numbers in the domain of f. Determine which, if any, of the following functions are additive.

$$f(x) = x + 1 \qquad f(x) = x^2$$
$$f(x) = \sqrt{x} \qquad f(x) = 3x$$

2. Comparatively few functions are additive. Give three examples of additive functions. What conditions must the constants a and b satisfy to make the linear function $f(x) = ax + b$ additive? Are there any additive quadratic functions? If so, describe them.

3. Consider the functions $f(x) = \frac{1}{x-1}$ and $g(x) = \frac{1}{x}$. Find equations and domains that describe functions $f \circ g$ and $g \circ f$. Why is the domain of $g \circ f$ different from the domain of $h(x) = x - 1$? (*Hint:* Consider $h(1)$ and $g(f(1))$.)

Develop Mastery

Exercises 1–4 Evaluate **(a)** $(f - g)(-1)$ **(b)** $(f \cdot g)(0.5)$.

1. $f(x) = 2x$, $g(x) = 1 - 2x$

2. $f(x) = x^2 - 3$, $g(x) = \sqrt{x + 4}$

3. $f(x) = |x - 2|$, $g(x) = x + 1$

4. $f(x) = x^2 - x$, $g(x) = 3|1 - x|$

Exercises 5–8 Find formulas for **(a)** $(f + g)(x)$ and **(b)** $(\frac{f}{g})(x)$. In each case state the domain.

5. $f(x) = x - \dfrac{1}{x}$, $g(x) = x$

6. $f(x) = x^2 - 1$, $g(x) = 1 - x$

7. $f(x) = \sqrt{x} - 2$, $g(x) = 1 - \sqrt{x}$

8. $f(x) = x - 4$, $g(x) = \frac{1}{x}$

Exercises 9–10 Use $f(x) = x + 2$ and $g(x) = x^2 - 2x$.

9. Evaluate **(a)** $(f \circ g)(-1)$ **(b)** $(g \circ f)(3)$ **(c)** $(f \circ f)(4)$

10. Find an equation to describe **(a)** $(f \circ g)$ **(b)** $(g \circ f)$.

11. The domain of the function f is $\{-3, -1, 0, 1, 3\}$ and the domain of g is $\{-1, 0, 1, 3, 5\}$. The rules for f and g are given in tabular form:

x	-3	-1	0	1	3
$f(x)$	-1	0	2	3	5

x	-1	0	1	3	5
$g(x)$	-2	-1	2	3	4

(a) Complete the following table for $g \circ f$. If an entry is undefined write U.

x	-3	-1	0	1	3
$(g \circ f)(x)$	___	___	___	___	___

What is the domain of **(b)** $g \circ f$? **(c)** $f \circ g$?

Exercises 12–13 Use $f(x) = \sqrt{x}$ and $g(x) = x^2 - 4$.

12. Give an equation to describe $f \circ g$. State the domain.

13. Give an equation to describe $g \circ f$. State the domain.

Exercises 14–19 For functions f and g,

$$f(x) = x^2 - 2x - 3 \qquad \text{and} \qquad g(x) = 2x - 3,$$

solve the equation.

14. $(f + g)(x) = 10$

15. $(\frac{f}{g})(x) = x + 1$

16. $(f \cdot g)(x) = 0$

17. $(g \circ f)(x) = 3x$

18. $(f \circ g)(x) = 5$

19. $(g \circ f)(x) + x^2 = 0$

Exercises 20–25 For functions f and g,

$$f(x) = -x^2 - x + 1 \qquad \text{and} \qquad g(x) = 3 - x,$$

find the solution set.

20. $(f + g)(x) < 1$

21. $(f - g)(x) \geq -4$

22. $(f \circ g)(x) + x \leq 1$ **23.** $(f \circ g)(x) + x^2 \geq 0$

24. $(g \circ f)(x) + 1 > 0$ **25.** $(g \circ g)(x) \geq x - 1$

Exercises 26–29   **(a)** Draw a graph of the function $y = (f \circ g)(x)$. **(b)** Give the x and y intercept points.

26. $f(x) = x^2 - 1$, $g(x) = x + 1$

27. $f(x) = 3x - 4$, $g(x) = 1 - x$

28. $f(x) = 2x - 4$, $g(x) = x^2 + x$

29. $f(x) = 3 - x^2$, $g(x) = x + 2$

30. Graphs of the functions f and g are shown. Complete the following tables.

x	-3	0	1	2	4
$(g \circ f)(x)$					

x	-2	0	1	3	5
$(f \circ g)(x)$					

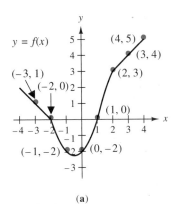

$y = f(x)$

(4, 5)

(3, 4)

(−3, 1)

(−2, 0) (2, 3)

(1, 0)

(−1, −2) (0, −2)

(a)

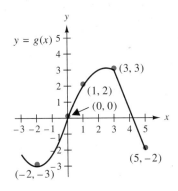

$y = g(x)$

(3, 3)

(1, 2)

(0, 0)

(−2, −3)

(5, −2)

(b)

Exercises 31–34   Given functions f and g, **(a)** find equations that describe the composition functions $f \circ g$ and $g \circ f$. **(b)** Are the functions $f \circ g$ and $g \circ f$ equal? That is, do they have the same domain D, and is $(f \circ g)(x) = (g \circ f)(x)$ true for every x in D?

31. $f(x) = 3x - 1$, $g(x) = \frac{x + 1}{3}$

32. $f(x) = 4 - 3x$, $g(x) = \frac{4 - x}{3}$

33. $f(x) = x^2 + 1$, $g(x) = \sqrt{x - 1}$

34. $f(x) = x^2 + 1$, $g(x) = \sqrt{x}$

Exercises 35–38   For the given function f, find a function g such that $f(g(x)) = x$ for every value of x. (*Hint:* In Exercise 35, $f(g(x)) = 2g(x) - 5$; solve the equation $2g(x) - 5 = x$ for $g(x)$.)

35. $f(x) = 2x - 5$ **36.** $f(x) = 3 - 4x$

37. $f(x) = \frac{2x}{x - 2}$ **38.** $f(x) = \frac{-3x}{2x + 3}$

Exercises 39–42   If $f(x) = \sqrt{x}$ and $g(x) = \frac{x}{x - 1}$, evaluate the expression and round off the result to two decimal places.

39. $(f + g)(\sqrt{3})$ **40.** $(f \circ g)(1.63)$

41. $(g \circ f)(5)$ **42.** $\left(\frac{f}{g}\right)(0.37)$

Exercises 43–50   Function F is given. Find two functions f and g so that $F(x) = (f \circ g)(x)$. Solutions to these problems are not unique.

43. $F(x) = \frac{1}{x^2 + 5}$

44. $F(x) = \sqrt{x^2 - 3x + 5}$

45. $F(x) = |5x + 3|$

46. $F(x) = \frac{4}{x^2} + 1$

47. $F(x) = [x^2 - 1]$

48. $F(x) = (x^2 - 1)^2$

49. $F(x) = \sqrt{x^2 + 1}$

50. $F(x) = \frac{1}{\sqrt{4x + 1}}$

Exercises 51–54   Express the given function as a composition of two of these four functions

$$f(x) = x - 4 \qquad g(x) = x^2 + 1$$

$$h(x) = \frac{1}{x} \qquad k(x) = |x|.$$

51. $F(x) = |x| - 4$

52. $G(x) = \frac{1}{|x|}$

53. $H(x) = \frac{1}{x^2} + 1$

54. $K(x) = x^2 - 3$

55. If $g(x) = 2x - 3$ and $f(g(x)) = 4x^2 - x$, find $f(-5)$.

56. If $g(x) = 4 - x^2$ and $f(g(x)) = \frac{3 - x^2}{x^2}$, find $f(3)$.

57. If $g(x) = x - 5$ and $f(g(x)) = \sqrt{x + 1}$, find $f(3)$.

58. If $g(x) = 2x + 5$ and $f(g(x)) = x^2 + 4$, find $f(-1)$.

Exercises 59–62 A function f is given. New functions denoted $f^{(1)}$, $f^{(2)}$, $f^{(3)}$, . . . , where $f^{(1)}(x) = f(x)$, $f^{(2)}(x) = f(f(x))$, $f^{(3)}(x) = f(f(f(x)))$, ... Observe that the notation $f^{(n)}$ indicates repeated composition of f, not multiplication; that is, $f^{(n)}(x)$ is not the same as $(f(x))^n$.

59. $f(x) = \frac{-3x}{2x + 3}$ **(a)** Evaluate $f^{(1)}(-1)$, $f^{(2)}(-1)$, $f^{(3)}(-1)$, $f^{(4)}(-1)$.   **(b)** Based on your observations, what is $f^{(16)}(-1)$? $f^{(23)}(-1)$?

60. $f(x) = \frac{2x}{x - 2}$ **(a)** Evaluate $f^{(1)}(3)$, $f^{(2)}(3)$, $f^{(3)}(3)$, $f^{(4)}(3)$.   **(b)** Based on your observations, what is $f^{(24)}(3)$? $f^{(47)}(3)$?

61. $f(x) = x^2 - 1$ **(a)** Evaluate $f^{(1)}(0)$, $f^{(2)}(0)$, $f^{(3)}(0)$, $f^{(4)}(0)$.   **(b)** Based on your observations, what is $f^{(32)}(0)$? $f^{(45)}(0)$?

62. $f(x) = 2 + \frac{3}{x}$ **(a)** Evaluate $f^{(1)}(1)$, $f^{(2)}(1)$, $f^{(3)}(1)$, $f^{(4)}(1)$, . . . and continue until you see something interesting in the display of your calculator. What number does the sequence appear to be approaching?   **(b)** You should eventually arrive at a number in the calculator display that does not change; call the number c. When you evaluate $f(c)$, you get c again, that is, $f(c) = c$. Show that the equation $f(c) = c$ is equivalent to the equation $c^2 - 2c - 3 = 0$. In other words, the number c is a root of the quadratic equation $x^2 - 2x - 3 = 0$.

63. A manufacturer determines that the cost C (in dollars) to build x graphing calculators is described by the equation

$$C = 80 + 48x - x^2 \qquad \text{for } 0 \le x \le 40.$$

Also, it is known that in t hours, the number x of calculators that can be produced is

$$x = 4t, \text{ where } 0 \le t \le 10.$$

(a) Express C as a function of t.
(b) What is the cost when the factory operates four hours?
(c) For what time t is the cost the greatest?

64. A rock is thrown into a lake causing a ripple in the shape of an expanding circle whose radius r is given by $r = \sqrt{t}$, where t is the number of seconds after the rock hits the water and r is measured in feet.

(a) What are the radius, circumference, and area of the circle when $t = 4$?
(b) Express the circumference C and area A as functions of t.
(c) At what time t is the circumference 8 feet?
(d) At what time t is the area 36 square feet?

65. A spherical balloon is being inflated in such a way that the diameter d is given by $d = \frac{t}{2}$, where t is measured in seconds and d in centimeters. **(a)** Express the volume V of the balloon as a function of t. **(b)** At what time t will the volume be 20 cubic centimeters?

66. A manufacturing company sells toasters to a retail store for $25 each plus a fixed handling charge of $15 on each order. The retailer applies a 30 percent markup to the total price it pays to the manufacturer.

(a) Suppose the order consists of 20 toasters. How much does the retailer pay for the order? What is the retailer's total revenue from the sale of the 20 toasters? How much profit per toaster does the retailer make?
(b) Suppose C is the cost to the retailer for an order of x toasters, R is the total revenue from the sale of x toasters, and P is the profit per toaster. Find formulas that give C, R, and P as functions of x.

67. A circle is shrinking in size in such a way that the radius r (in feet) is a function of time t (in minutes), given by the equation $r = f(t) = \frac{1}{t + 1}$. The area of the circle is given by $A(r) = \pi r^2$, so the area is also a function of time, given by $(A \circ f)(t)$.

(a) Write a formula for $(A \circ f)(t)$.
(b) What is the area at the end of one minute? Two minutes?
(c) For what value of t is the area $\frac{\pi}{25}$?

68. The number of bacteria in a certain food is a function of the food's temperature. When refrigerated, the number is $N(T)$ at a temperature T degrees Celsius, described by the equation

$$N(T) = 10\,T^2 - 60\,T + 800, \text{ for } 3 \le T \le 13.$$

When the food is removed from the refrigerator the temperature increases and t minutes later the temperature is $T = 2t + 3$, for $0 \le t \le 5$.

(a) Determine an equation that describes the number of bacteria t minutes after the food is removed from the refrigerator.

(b) How many bacteria are in the food three minutes after it is removed from the refrigerator?

(c) How many minutes after the food is taken out of the refrigerator will it contain 2150 bacteria?

69. A spherical weather balloon is being inflated in such a way that the radius is $r = f(t) = 0.25t + 3$, where t is in seconds and r is in feet. The volume V of the balloon is the function $V(r) = \frac{4\pi r^3}{3}$.

(a) What is the radius when the inflation process begins?

(b) Write an equation to describe the composition $V \circ f$ that gives the volume at t seconds after inflation begins.

(c) What is the volume of the balloon 10 seconds after inflation begins?

(d) In how many seconds will the volume be 400 cubic feet?

70. Given a right triangle ABC with medians $\overline{AN}$ and $\overline{CM}$ as shown in the diagram, the medians are perpendicular to each other and intersect at point K.

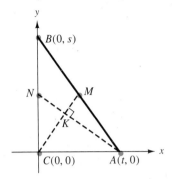

(a) Determine the y-coordinate s of B as a function of the x-coordinate t of A. (*Hint:* Consider the slopes of the two lines that contain the medians.)

(b) Find an equation that gives the length of the median $\overline{AN}$ as a function of t.

(c) Find the length of $\overline{CM}$ as a function of t.

71. *Looking Ahead to Calculus* Suppose $f(x) = 2x^3 + 1$, $g(x) = x^2 - 1$, and $F(x) = f(g(x))$. In calculus there are functions f', g', and F' given by $f'(x) = 6x^2$, $g'(x) = 2x$, $F'(x) = f'(g(x))g'(x)$.

(a) Find an equation describing F'.

(b) Evaluate $F'(-2)$.

SECTION 2.7   Inverse Functions

Is it not a miracle that the universe is so constructed that such a simple abstraction as a number is possible? To me this is one of the strongest examples of the unreasonable effectiveness of mathematics. Indeed, I find it both strange and unexplainable.
R. W. Hamming

In Section 2.2 we noted that a function can be considered as a set of ordered pairs in which no two different pairs have the same first component. For each first number, any ordered pair can have exactly one second number.

As an example, suppose function f is $f(x) = 2x$, where the domain is $D = \{-2, -1, 0, 1, 2\}$. In terms of ordered pairs, f may be written as

$$f = \{(-2, -4), (-1, -2), (0, 0), (1, 2), (2, 4)\}.$$

The range R of f is given by $R = \{-4, -2, 0, 2, 4\}$. Now suppose we interchange the two entries in each of the ordered pairs of f and get a new set of ordered pairs that we denote by g.

$$g = \{(-4, -2), (-2, -1), (0, 0), (2, 1), (4, 2)\}$$

We can make several observations concerning g:

1. Since no two pairs of g have the same first numbers, g is a function.

2. The domain of g is $D' = \{-4, -2, 0, 2, 4\}$ and the range is $R' = \{-2, -1, 0, 1, 2\}$.

3. Function g is $g(x) = \frac{x}{2}$, where $x \in D'$.

4. The domains and ranges of f and g are interchanged; $D' = R$ and $R' = D$.

Let us consider the composition function $g \circ f$ defined by $(g \circ f)(x) = g(f(x))$ for x in D. For instance,

$$\text{when } x \text{ is } -2, \ g(f(-2)) = g(-4) = -2$$
$$\text{when } x \text{ is } -1, \ g(f(-1)) = g(-2) = -1$$

and so on. In general,

$$g(f(x)) = g(2x) = \frac{2x}{2} = x.$$

We get a similar result for $f \circ g$:

$$(f \circ g)(x) = f(g(x)) = f\left(\frac{x}{2}\right) = 2\left(\frac{x}{2}\right) = x.$$

The functions f and g that we have been discussing are related in a special way—one is the **inverse** of the other. Since $f(g(x)) = x$ and $g(f(x)) = x$, we may say that each of the functions "undoes" or neutralizes the other. If we start with x, apply f and get $f(x)$, and then apply g to $f(x)$, we get back to x.

Schematically, think of a function as a map that sends each element in the domain to a corresponding range element. The inverse function sends each element of the range to the original element of the domain. A diagram like Figure 2.39 may help clarify the relationship. Observe that the diagram may be read in either direction so that applying f and then g, or g and then f, always yields the initial input.

Definition: Inverse Functions

Suppose f and g are functions that satisfy two conditions: $g(f(x)) = x$ for every x in the domain of f, and $f(g(x)) = x$ for every x in the domain of g. Then f and g are inverses of each other.

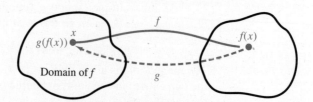

FIGURE 2.39

Inverse function: $g(f(x)) = x$ for every x in the domain of f.

Characterization of Inverse Functions

Suppose f is a function described as a set of ordered pairs such that no two pairs have the same second element, $f = \{(x, y) \mid y = f(x)\}$.

Let g be the set of ordered pairs obtained by interchanging the elements of each pair of f. If g is a function, then f and g are *inverses of each other*.

Notation for Inverse Functions

Suppose g is the inverse of function f. It is customary to denote g by f^{-1}. Replacing g by f^{-1} in the above definition gives an important pair of identities.

Inverse Function Identities

$$f^{-1}(f(x)) = x \text{ for each } x \text{ in the domain of } f.$$

$$f(f^{-1}(x)) = x \text{ for each } x \text{ in the domain of } f^{-1}.$$

EXAMPLE 1   **(a)** Verify that

$$f(x) = 2x + 3 \qquad \text{and} \qquad f^{-1}(x) = \frac{x - 3}{2}$$

are inverses of each other. **(b)** Draw graphs of $y = f(x)$ and $y = f^{-1}(x)$.

Strategy: (a) Simply verify that $f(f^{-1}(x)) = x$ and $f^{-1}(f(x)) = x$ for every real number x.

Solution

(a)   Follow the strategy. For every real number x,

$$f^{-1}(f(x)) = f^{-1}(2x + 3) = \frac{(2x + 3) - 3}{2} = \frac{2x}{2} = x.$$

$$f(f^{-1})(x)) = f\left(\frac{x - 3}{2}\right) = 2\left(\frac{x - 3}{2}\right) + 3 = (x - 3) + 3 = x.$$

Therefore, the given functions are inverses of each other.

(b)   The graphs of $y = 2x + 3$ and $y = \frac{x - 3}{2}$ are the lines shown in Figure 2.40.

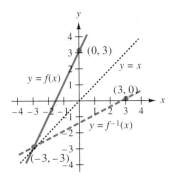

FIGURE 2.40

Graphs of Inverse Functions

For the two functions in Example 1 the graphs of $y = f(x)$ and $y = f^{-1}(x)$ in Figure 2.40 appear symmetric with respect to the line $y = x$. A definition of what we mean, in general, by symmetry with respect to a line may clarify this.

Definition: Symmetry with Respect to a Line

Two points P and Q are said to be symmetric with respect to the line L provided that the line through P and Q is perpendicular to L, and P and Q are equidistant from L. That is, L is the perpendicular bisector of the segment $\overline{PQ}$.

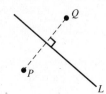

FIGURE 2.41

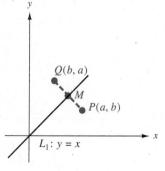

FIGURE 2.42

Figure 2.41 illustrates the definition of symmetry with respect to L.

We want to show that for any pair of inverse functions, the graphs of f and f^{-1} are symmetric with respect to the line $y = x$.

Suppose that (a, b) is any ordered pair in f. This implies that (b, a) is an ordered pair in f^{-1}. Let L_1 denote the line $y = x$, We can show that points $P(a, b)$ and $Q(b, a)$ are symmetric with respect to L_1 by showing that L_1 is the perpendicular bisector of the segment $\overline{PQ}$ (see Figure 2.42).

The slope m_1 of line L_1 is 1. The slope m_2 of line L_2 through P and Q is given by

$$m_2 = \frac{a - b}{b - a} = -1.$$

Since $m_1 \cdot m_2 = -1$, lines L_1 and L_2 are perpendicular.

Let M be the midpoint of P and Q. The coordinates of M are

$$\left(\frac{a + b}{2}, \frac{b + a}{2} \right),$$

Since the x- and y-coordinates are equal, the midpoint M is on line L_1. Hence, P and Q are equidistant from the line $y = x$.

We conclude that for every point (a, b) on the graph of $y = f(x)$, there is a corresponding point (b, a) on the graph of $y = f^{-1}(x)$ that is symmetric with respect to the line $y = x$, and conversely.

Graphs of Inverse Functions

The graphs of $y = f(x)$ and $y = f^{-1}(x)$ are symmetric with respect to the line $y = x$.

Finding Equations for Inverse Functions

It is not always easy to find an equation that describes the inverse of a particular function. In many cases, however, the inverse function does have an equation that can be found readily by a straightforward algorithm. The key is the observation that finding f^{-1} from f requires interchanging x and y in each ordered pair (x, y) of f to obtain the ordered pairs in f^{-1}.

Algorithm for Finding an Equation for f^{-1}

1. Write the equation that defines f in the form $y = f(x)$.
2. Interchange y and x to get $x = f(y)$.
3. Solve the equation $x = f(y)$ for y if possible. The result is $y = f^{-1}(x)$.

INVERSE FUNCTIONS AND CRYPTOGRAPHY

This Renaissance crypt-analysis instrument works by rotating the inner disk against the stationary outer disk.

Encoding and decoding secret messages depends on functions and their inverses. Each letter is assigned a number (often, its place in the alphabet) and a coding function is applied to the number. A simple Caesar cipher is given by $f(n) = n + 5 \pmod{26}$, meaning that $n + 5$ is reduced by multiples of 26 when necessary. $S = 19$ becomes $f(19) = 24 = X$. SEND MONEY becomes XJSI RTSJD. Decoding uses the inverse function $f^{-1}(n) = n - 5 \pmod{26}$.

In a slightly more complex function, $F(n) = 3n + 5 \pmod{26}$, the letter S, which corresponds to 19, becomes

$$F(19) = 3 \cdot 19 + 5 \pmod{26}$$
$$= 62 \pmod{26} = 10.$$

Therefore $F(19) = 10$, and since J corresponds to 10, S becomes J. The inverse function to decode JTUQ RXUTB is given by $F^{-1}(n) = 9n + 7 \pmod{26}$.

Even though the coding functions have become extremely complex, involving continual modifications, until very recently *all* cryptology algorithms required the *same* work of the cryptographer and the decrypter. Knowing how to encode (which required the coding function) meant knowing how to decode (which required the inverse function). All this has changed with the invention of trapdoor codes, which have efficient algorithms for both functions and inverses, but for which inverses are effectively impossible to discover, so no one can break the code.

The most impressive are the RST codes (named for their discoverers). These depend on finding large primes whose products cannot easily be factored. A few minutes of computer time can produce 100-digit primes, but factoring the product of two such numbers would typically require millions of years.

EXAMPLE 2 Find a formula for the inverse of $f(x) = 2x - 1$ and verify that $f(f^{-1}(x)) = x$.

Strategy: First write $y = 2x - 1$ and then follow the steps of the algorithm.

Solution

Follow the strategy.

Step 1 $\quad y = 2x - 1$

Step 2 $\quad x = 2y - 1$

Step 3 $\quad y = \dfrac{x + 1}{2}$; therefore, $f^{-1}(x) = \dfrac{x + 1}{2}$.

To verify that $f(f^{-1}(x)) = x$,

$$f(f^{-1}(x)) = f\left(\frac{x + 1}{2}\right) = 2\left(\frac{x + 1}{2}\right) - 1 = (x + 1) - 1 = x. \quad \blacktriangle$$

EXAMPLE 3   Suppose g is the function $g(x) = -\sqrt{x}$. **(a)** Find the domain and range of g. **(b)** Find a formula for the inverse function. **(c)** Draw graphs of $y = g(x)$ and $y = g^{-1}(x)$.

Solution

(a) By the domain convention, g is defined whenever $x \geq 0$, so the domain is the interval $[0, \infty)$. We observe that when $x \geq 0$, we have $\sqrt{x} \geq 0$, so $-\sqrt{x} \leq 0$. Therefore, the range consists of the nonpositive real numbers $(-\infty, 0]$.

(b) Use the algorithm to find $g^{-1}(x)$ as follows.

Step 1 $y = -\sqrt{x}$.

Step 2 $x = -\sqrt{y}$

Step 3 $y = x^2$, therefore $g^{-1}(x) = x^2$. We must remember that the domain of g^{-1} is the same as the range of g, namely $(-\infty, 0]$. Since the limitation on x is not apparent in the formula $g^{-1}(x) = x^2$, we write

$$g^{-1}(x) = x^2, x \leq 0.$$

(c) In graphing

$$y = -\sqrt{x} \quad \text{and} \quad y = x^2, x \leq 0,$$

we are more familiar with the latter. The graph of $y = x^2, x \leq 0$, is the left half of the parabola $y = x^2$ (see Figure 2.43). The graph of $y = -\sqrt{x}$ is the reflection of the graph of $y = x^2$, $x \leq 0$, about the line $y = x$. Each point we identify on the graph of one function also gives us a point on the graph of its inverse, as shown in Figure 2.43. ▲

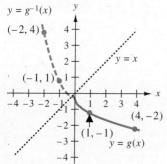

FIGURE 2.43

Existence of Inverse Functions

Not every function has an inverse. For the function $y = x^2$, if we interchange x and y to get $x = y^2$ and then solve for y, we have $y = \pm\sqrt{x}$. For each $x > 0$ there are two corresponding values of y, so we do not have a function. This means that the function $f(x) = x^2$ does not have an inverse.

To determine whether or not a function f has an inverse, we look back at ordered pairs (x, y) of f, where $y = f(x)$. We know that for every x in the domain D of f, there is exactly one value of y. Now suppose we interchange x and y. The set of ordered pairs (y, x) will be a function only if for each y there is exactly one x. Therefore, for $y = f(x)$ to have an inverse each x must correspond to exactly one y (so f is a function) and every y to exactly one x. We call such a function a **one–one function.**

Existence of an Inverse Function—Part I

A function has an inverse if and only if the function is one–one.

How can we tell when a function is one–one? The best way is to draw a graph. Section 2.2 introduced the vertical line test to determine whether a graph represents a function. If we combine this test with the horizontal line test described below, we can determine whether or not a graph is that of a one–one function.

Horizontal Line Test

If every horizontal line intersects the graph of a function in at most one point, then that function is one–one. Therefore, it has an inverse.

Figure 2.44 shows graphs of three functions. The graphs in panels **(a)** and **(b)** represent one–one functions while that in panel **(c)** does not. In panel **(c)** horizontal lines like L_1 intersect the graph at one point, but lines such as L_2 intersect the graph at more than one point.

| **EXAMPLE 4** | Determine which functions have inverses:

(a) $f(x) = 2x$ **(b)** $g(x) = \frac{1}{x}$ **(c)** $h(x) = x^2 - 2x.$

Strategy: In each case sketch a graph and then see if every horizontal line intersects the graph in at most one point.

Solution

(a) The graph of $y = 2x$ is a line as shown in Figure 2.45(a). Every horizontal line intersects the graph at exactly one point, so f is a one–one function and it has an inverse.

(b) As seen in Section 2.2, the graph of $y = \frac{1}{x}$ is that shown in Figure 2.45(b). Every horizontal line except $y = 0$ (the x-axis) intersects the graph at one point and the line $y = 0$ does not intersect at any point. Thus g is a one–one function and it has an inverse.

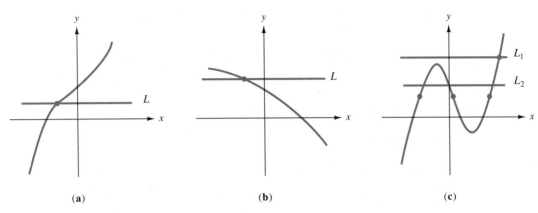

(a)   (b)   (c)

FIGURE 2.44

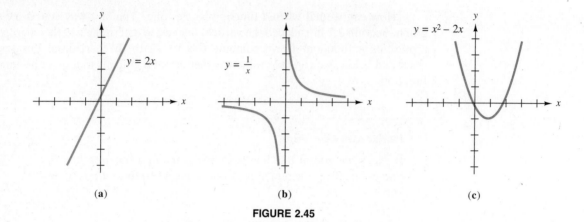

FIGURE 2.45

(c)   The graph of $y = x^2 - 2x$ is a parabola, as shown in Figure 2.45(c). Clearly there are horizontal lines that intersect the graph in more than one point, so h does not have an inverse.   ▲

A useful criterion for determining whether a function has an inverse comes from a property that graphs make readily observable.

Definition: Increasing Functions, Decreasing Functions

Suppose b and c are any numbers in the domain of a function f where $b < c$. The function f is an increasing function if $f(b) < f(c)$, and it is a decreasing function if $f(b) > f(c)$.

A graph shows immediately whether a function is increasing or decreasing. Moving from left to right, the graph of an increasing function rises (increases) while the graph of a decreasing function drops (see Figure 2.46).

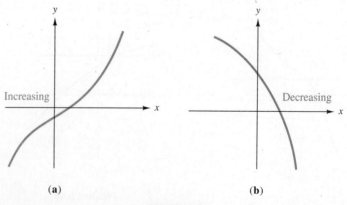

FIGURE 2.46

By the horizontal line test, every increasing function or decreasing function is one–one. The following test will be useful when dealing with important functions that have inverses, such as the exponential and logarithmic functions in Chapter 4.

Existence of an Inverse—Part II

A function f has an inverse if f is either an increasing function or a decreasing function.

EXAMPLE 5   Determine whether the given function is increasing, decreasing, or neither.

(a) $f(x) = x^3$ (b) $g(x) = -x^2$ (c) $h(x) = -x^2$, for $x \geq 0$

Strategy: In each case draw a graph and determine whether the function is increasing, decreasing, or neither.

Solution

Follow the strategy.

(a) The graph of $y = x^3$ is shown in Figure 2.47a. Clearly f is an increasing function.

(b) The graph of $y = -x^2$ is a parabola as shown in Figure 2.47b. The graph shows that g is neither increasing nor decreasing.

(c) The graph of $y = -x^2$, $x \geq 0$, is the portion shown in Figure 2.47c. The graph indicates that h is a decreasing function. ▲

In some situations, particularly in applications, we are accustomed to using letters other than x and y to describe functions. Usually in such cases we want to keep the original labels when finding formulas for inverse functions. Rather than interchange variables, we simply solve for the variable we want, as illustrated in the following example.

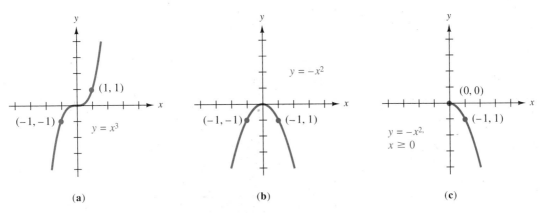

(a)   **(b)**   **(c)**

FIGURE 2.47

INVERSE FUNCTIONS

The fact that the inverse of a function can be obtained by interchanging coordinates allows us to use **parametric mode,** a remarkable way to visualize inverse functions. Parametric equations are used extensively in calculus and will be discussed more fully later in this course, but we need no general theory to use them for inverse functions

In parametric mode the calculator is set to accept function pairs for x and y in terms of T. Instructions in "Using a Graphing Calculator" (p. xx) explain how to put the calculator in parametric mode to graph $f(x) = \sqrt{x}$ in parametric form. This also gives the function obtained by interchanging x- and y-coordinates, which we now recognize as the inverse of f. Follow the instructions:

1.   Enter the function $f(x) = \sqrt{x}$ as $x = T, y = \sqrt{T}$.
2.   Enter the inverse function by interchanging coordinates, setting $x = \sqrt{T}, y = T$.
3.   Enter the line $y = x$, setting $x = T, y = T$. Now GRAPH.

As you Trace, the cursor moves along one of the curves. The up and down arrows switch the cursor from one curve to another for the same t-value so that we can see the points on each curve that correspond to a given t value. Experiment with the arrow keys; for any t value in the range, the point on the curve $y = f(x)$ and the point on the curve $y = f^{-1}(x)$ are reflections in the line $y = x$.

Exercises

Exercises 1–6   **(a)** For the function f, find an equation for the inverse function, f^{-1}, noting any restrictions on the domain. **(b)** Pick an appropriate window and graph both the functions f and f^{-1}, using parametric equations {so that $(X_1, Y_1) = (T, f(T))$ and $(X_2, Y_2) = (f(T), T)$}. **(c)** If the graphs intersect, use the Trace function to find the coordinates of the intersection points.

1. $f(x) = 2x - 3$
2. $f(x) = 2 - x$
3. $f(x) = \frac{-x + 1}{3}$
4. $f(x) = \sqrt{1 - x}$
5. $f(x) = -\sqrt{x + 2}$
6. $f(x) = x^2 - 1$ for $x \geq 0$

Exercises 7–9   **(a)** Graph $(T, f(T))$ using the range $(-3, 3)$ for each variable, and find an interval where the function f is increasing and an interval where f is decreasing. (Answers are not unique).

(b) Graph f^{-1} by using $(f(T), T)$ and explain why f^{-1} is not a function. (*Hint:* Use the vertical line test.)

(c) Limit the T range to an interval where f is increasing and graph both f and f^{-1}. Verify that f^{-1} is now a function.

(d) Repeat part **(c)** for an interval where f is decreasing.

7. $f(x) = x^2 - 1$
8. $f(x) = x^3 - 2x$
9. $f(x) = 2x^2 - x^3$

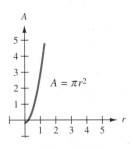

FIGURE 2.48

Area of a circle as a function of the radius

| EXAMPLE 6 | The area A of a circle is a function f of its radius r, $f(r) = \pi r^2$, or $A = \pi r^2$, where $r > 0$. Find an equation for the inverse function.

Solution

The graph of $A = \pi r^2$, shown in Figure 2.48, indicates that f is an increasing function, so it has an inverse. To find a formula for the inverse, it would certainly be confusing to switch the variables A and r. Therefore, simply solve the equation $A = \pi r^2$ for r and get $r = \sqrt{\frac{A}{\pi}}$. Therefore, the inverse function is given by $f^{-1}(A) = \sqrt{\frac{A}{\pi}}$, or by $r = \sqrt{\frac{A}{\pi}}$, where $A > 0$. ▲

Often, in applications like Example 6, one can omit the formalism of introducing f and f^{-1}. It is sufficient to say that the area A and the radius r are related and that the equation $A = \pi r^2$ defines A as a function of r, while $r = \sqrt{\frac{A}{\pi}}$ defines r as a function of A. The two functions are inverses of each other.

EXERCISES 2.7

Check Your Understanding

Exercises 1–5 True or False. Give reasons for your conclusion. For these exercises, assume that f is a function that has an inverse.

1. If $f(x) = -\sqrt{x}$, then the domain of f^{-1} is the set $\{x \mid x \geq 0\}$.

2. If $(-2, -3)$ is a point on the graph of f, then $(2, 3)$ must be a point on the graph of f^{-1}.

3. If the graph of f has an x-intercept point, then the graph of f^{-1} must also have an x-intercept point.

4. If the graph of f has a y-intercept point, then the graph of f^{-1} must have an x-intercept point.

5. The graph of any function that has an inverse cannot cross the x-axis at more than one point.

Exercises 6–10 Complete the sentence by selecting from the list below *all choices* that make the statement truc.
(a) 0   (b) 2   (c) -2 (d) $\frac{1}{x}$
(e) x (f) $\frac{1}{4}$ (g) $(2, 5)$ (h) $(-5, 2)$
(i) $(2, -\frac{1}{5})$ (j) Quad I   (k) Quad II
(l) Quad III   (m) Quad IV

6. If $f(-2) = 4$, then $f^{-1}(4) =$ _____.

7. If $f(x) = x$, then $f^{-1}(x) =$ _____.

8. If the graph of f contains a point in Quadrant II, then the graph of f^{-1} must contain a point in _____.

9. If $f(2) = -5$, then a point on the graph of f^{-1} is _____.

10. If $f(x) = 3x + 4$, then $f^{-1}(4)$ equals _____.

Explore and Discover

1. Write a paragraph that explains some of the differences between what we learn from the vertical line test (Section 2.2) and the horizontal line test (Section 2.7).

2. If a function f has an inverse, then we can get the graph of f^{-1} by taking the reflection of the graph of f through the line $y = x$. What happens if we reflect the graph of f^{-1} through the line $y = x$? Explain how these observations about graphs are related to the inverse function identities.

Develop Mastery

Exercises 1–4 Function f is given as a set of ordered pairs. (a) Interchange the two entries in each ordered pair and get a new set S of ordered pairs. (b) Is S a function?

1. $f = \{(0, -1), (1, 3), (2, 5)\}$

2. $f = \{(-1, 1), (0, 3), (1, 1)\}$

3. $f = \{(-3, 4), (-1, 2), (1, 1), (3, 2)\}$

4. $f = \{(0, 0), (\frac{\pi}{2}, 1), (\frac{-3\pi}{2}, -1)\}$

Exercises 5–8 Use the definition of inverse function to determine whether or not functions f and g are inverses of each other, that is, determine whether $f(g(x)) = x$ and $g(f(x)) = x$.

5. $f(x) = -1 - 2x$, $g(x) = -\frac{x+1}{2}$

6. $f(x) = \frac{x+1}{2x}$, $g(x) = \frac{1}{1-2x}$

7. $f(x) = 2 + \frac{1}{x}$, $g(x) = \frac{1}{2 - x}$

8. $f(x) = 4 - \frac{1}{x}$, $g(x) = \frac{1}{4 - x}$

Exercises 9–14 Function f has an inverse.

(a) Draw a graph of $y = f(x)$.

(b) From the graph in part **(a)**, draw a graph of $y = f^{-1}(x)$.

9. $f(x) = x + 2$ **10.** $f(x) = 2x - 4$

11. $f(x) = 4 - 2x$ **12.** $f(x) = -x$

13. $f(x) = x^2 + 1$, $x \geq 0$

14. $f(x) = 1 - x^2$, $x \leq 0$

Exercises 15–24 Function f has an inverse. Apply the algorithm in this section to find an equation that describes f^{-1}.

15. $f(x) = 2x + 5$ **16.** $f(x) = 2 - 5x$

17. $f(x) = \frac{1 + x}{x}$ **18.** $f(x) = \frac{2x}{3 - x}$

19. $f(x) = \frac{2 - x}{x}$ **20.** $f(x) = 1 - \frac{3}{x}$

21. $f(x) = x$ **22.** $f(x) = -\sqrt{-x}$

23. $f(x) = x^2 - 2x + 1$, $x \geq 1$

24. $f(x) = x^2 - 2x - 3$, $x \leq 1$

Exercises 25–30 **(a)** Draw a graph of $y = f(x)$. **(b)** Use the horizontal line test to determine whether the function is one–one. **(c)** Does f have an inverse?

25. $f(x) = 2x + 3$ **26.** $f(x) = 1 - x^2$

27. $f(x) = 4 - x^2$ **28.** $f(x) = 3 - x$

29. $f(x) = \sqrt{x}$ **30.** $f(x) = x^3$

Exercises 31–36 **(a)** Draw a graph of the function and determine whether it is increasing, decreasing, or neither. **(b)** Does the function have an inverse?

31. $f(x) = 3 - 2x$ **32.** $g(x) = 2 + 3x$

33. $f(x) = -x$ **34.** $f(x) = x^2 - 2x + 1$

35. $g(x) = \sqrt{x}$ **36.** $f(x) = -\sqrt{-x}$

37. Verify that the two points A and B are symmetric with respect to the line $y = x$. (*Hint:* You need to show that the line $y = x$ is the perpendicular bisector of $\overline{AB}$.)

(a) $A(-2, 3)$, $B(3, -2)$

(b) $A(4, 7)$, $B(7, 4)$

(c) $A(-3, -5)$, $B(-5, -3)$

38. Find an equation for line L such that $A(-4, 2)$ and $B(2, 6)$ are symmetric with respect to L. (*Hint:* L must be the perpendicular bisector of the segment $\overline{AB}$.)

39. Find an equation for line L such that $A(2, -4)$ and $B(4, -2)$ are symmetric with respect to L. (*Hint:* See Exercise 38.)

40. If function f has an inverse and if $f(2) = -3$ and $f(-1) = 4$, find $f^{-1}(-3)$ and $f^{-1}(4)$.

41. Given that $f(x) = x^3 + 4x - 3$ has an inverse:

(a) What is $f^{-1}(-3)$?

(b) Find $f(1)$ and $f(-1)$. What is $f^{-1}(2)$? $f^{-1}(-8)$?

42. If $f(x) = 2x + 1$ and $g(x) = 4x + c$, then for what value of c will $f(g(x))$ be equal to $g(f(x))$?

43. **(a)** The function $f(x) = \frac{-3x}{2x + 3}$ has an inverse. Show that $f^{-1}(x) = f(x)$.

(b) If c is a constant and $f(x) = \frac{cx}{x - 2}$, then find the value of c such that $f(x)$ will have an inverse equal to itself, that is, find c such that $f(f(x)) = x$.

44. If $f(x) = \frac{2x + 3}{3x - 2}$, then show that $f(f(x)) = x$ for every real number x (except $\frac{2}{3}$).

45. If $f(x) = \frac{ax + b}{cx - a}$, then show that $f(f(x)) = x$ for every real number x (except $\frac{a}{c}$).

46. The graph of function f consists of the line segment joining the points $A(-3, -1)$ and $B(6, 2)$.

(a) Draw the graph of f and explain why f has an inverse.

(b) What are $f^{-1}(-1)$ and $f^{-1}(2)$? Draw a graph of f^{-1} and state its domain and range.

47. For the function f defined in Exercise 46, draw a graph of each of the following. On each graph label the intercept points. (*Hint:* Use translations.)

(a) $y = f(x - 1)$ **(b)** $y = f^{-1}(x - 1)$

(c) $y = f(x) + 2$ **(d)** $y = f^{-1}(x) + 2$

48. The graph of the function f is the union of the two line segments $\overline{AB}$ and $\overline{BC}$, with the points $A(-3, 2,)$, $B(-2, -2)$, and $C(4, -5)$.

(a) Sketch the graph of f and explain why f has an inverse. What is $f^{-1}(2)$? $f^{-1}(-2)$? $f^{-1}(-5)$?

(b) Draw a graph of $y = f^{-1}(x)$.

49. The volume of a sphere of radius r is given by the formula $V = \frac{4}{3}\pi r^3$, defining V as a function f of r.

(a) Solve for r in terms of V to get $r = f^{-1}(V)$.

(b) Use your formula to complete the following table with r values rounded to two decimal places.

V	3.47	4.83	5.72
r	—	—	—

50. A ball is dropped from the top of a building that is 144 feet tall. The position of the ball at any time t seconds after it is dropped is given by the formula $s = 16t^2$, where s is the distance in feet from the top of the building. This determines s as a function of t.

(a) What is the domain of this function?

(b) Solve for t in terms of s and then find the time (to one decimal place) that the ball takes to reach distances of 20 feet, 40 feet, and 80 feet from the top of the building.

51. A rectangle $DEFG$ is inscribed in an isosceles triangle ABC as shown in the diagram, where $|\overline{AC}| = |\overline{BC}| = 3$ and $|\overline{AB}| = 2$. Let $|\overline{DE}| = x$.

(a) Find a formula that gives the area K of the rectangle as a function f of x.

(b) Give the domain and range of f.

(c) Is f a one–one function?

(d) What value or values of x will give a rectangle of area 0.5?

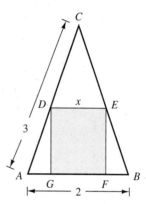

52. The function to convert from degrees Fahrenheit (°F) to degrees Celsius (°C) is given by $C = \frac{5}{9}(F - 32)$. Find a formula for the inverse function.

53. Suppose a cone has a fixed height of 9 inches and variable radius r. Its volume V is a function of r given by $V = 3\pi r^2$. Find an equation that describes the inverse function.

54. Given functions $f(x) = 2x - 1$ and $g(x) = 3 - 2x$.

(a) Find equations for $f^{-1}(x)$ and $g^{-1}(x)$.

(b) Find an equation that describes the function $f^{-1} \circ g^{-1}$.

SECTION 2.8 **Functions and Mathematical Models**

....

At one time [Conway] would be making constant appeals to give him a year, and he would immediately respond with the date of Easter, or to give him a date, so that he could tell you the day of the week or the age of the moon.

         Richard K. Guy

In this section our discussion will be limited to a few different types of problems that involve familiar functions. Applications that require other kinds of functions (such as exponential, logarithmic, or trigonometric functions) will be discussed in later chapters.

    First we consider a widely used mathematical model for motion due to gravitational attraction. Theoretically our model applies to objects under the sole influence of gravity, which really implies that the object is in a vacuum, and not affected by air resistance. Although we do not live in a vacuum, for many practical applications this model closely approximates what actually occurs when an object falls. Unless we make an explicit exception, we will assume that all falling-body problems are unaffected by air resistance.

    This kind of analysis of motion dates back to the time of Isaac Newton and before. We really need only two types of functions for motion due to gravity, one function of time to give the location of the object at time t (the height, usually measured from the earth's surface), and one to give the velocity as a function of t.

Begin with some terminology. *Speed* indicates how fast an object is moving, while *velocity* includes both speed and the direction of motion. Except for this distinction, we use the words *speed* and *velocity* interchangeably. The problems in this section will suppose an object moving vertically either upward or downward, so its motion is one-dimensional. *Positive speed* means the body is moving upward, while *negative speed* means the body is moving downward (toward the surface of the earth).

Formulas for Objects Moving under the Influence of Gravity

When an object is launched, thrown, or dropped vertically at an initial speed and is then subject only to gravity, we speak of a *freely falling body*. The motion of any falling body is determined by its initial velocity and initial height. The same formulas for velocity and height apply to any such body. These formulas are stated in terms of feet and seconds.

Height and Speed Formulas for Falling Bodies

The height and velocity of a falling body with initial height s_0 (feet) and initial velocity v_0 (feet per second) after t seconds are given by:

$$s(t) = s_0 + v_0 t - 16t^2 \qquad \textbf{(1)}$$

$$v(t) = v_0 - 32t \qquad \textbf{(2)}$$

Strategy: (a) First get a formula for s as a function of t by substituting 320 for s_0 and 64 for v_0 in Equation 1. Draw a graph of the quadratic function and find its maximum value. **(c)** To find when the ball hits the ground, set $s = 0$ and solve the equation $320 + 64t - 16t^2 = 0$.

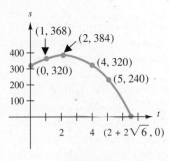

$s(t) = 320 + 64t - 16t^2$

FIGURE 2.49

EXAMPLE 1   A ball is thrown vertically upward from the top of a 320-foot high building at a speed of 64 feet per second.

(a)   How far above the ground is the ball at its highest point?

(b)   What is the total distance traveled by the ball in the first 5 seconds?

(c)   When does the ball hit the ground?

(d)   What is the velocity of the ball when t is 1? When t is 4?

Solution

Follow the strategy.

$$s(t) = 320 + 64t - 16t^2.$$

(a)   The graph (Figure 2.49) is part of a parabola that opens downward and has its highest point (vertex) where

$$t = \frac{-b}{2a} = \frac{-64}{2(-16)} = 2, \; s(2) = 320 + 64(2) - 16(2^2) = 384.$$

Note that this partial parabola is *not* the path of the ball (which goes straight up and down), but we can use it to easily read off the value of s for a given time t. For instance, at the end of 1 second, the height of the ball is 368 feet above the ground; in 2 seconds the ball is 384 feet above the ground, its maximum height. At the end of 4 seconds, $s = 320$, and so on.

Alternate Solution   A physical consideration provides a different approach to finding the time when the ball reaches its highest point. At the highest point, the velocity must be zero since at that instant the ball is going neither up nor down. For this problem, $v = 64 - 32t$, so we want to find the value of t for which v is 0. Solve the equation $64 - 32t = 0$, from which t is 2, as we found above.

(b)   To find the total distance traveled during the first 5 seconds, note that the ball travels upward a distance of $384 - 320 = 64$ feet during the first 2 seconds and then downward a distance of $384 - 240 = 144$ feet during the next 3 seconds. (Look at the graph.) Therefore, the total distance traveled during the first 5 seconds is $64 + 144$, or 208 feet.

(c)   When the ball hits the ground, the height is 0. Setting $s(t)$ equal to 0 and solving for t gives the time when the ball reaches ground level. Solving $320 + 64t - 16t^2 = 0$ yields two values, one positive $(2 + 2\sqrt{6})$ and one negative $(2 - 2\sqrt{6})$. Since only a positive time value has physical significance in this problem, the ball must hit the ground when t is $2 + 2\sqrt{6}$, or about 6.9 seconds after being thrown.

(d)   Replacing v_0 by 64 and substituting 1 for t in formula (2) gives

$$v_1 = 64 - 32 \cdot 1 = 32.$$

Hence when t is 1, the ball is moving upward at 32 feet per second. When t is 4,
$$v_4 = 64 - 32 \cdot 4 = 64 - 128 = -64.$$

The negative sign indicates that the ball is moving downward, so at the end of 4 seconds the ball is falling at a speed of 64 feet per second.   ▲

In the next example we look at a slightly more involved problem.

EXAMPLE 2   A stone is dropped from the top of a building and falls past an office window below. Watchers carefully time the stone and determine that it takes 0.20 seconds to pass from the top to the bottom of the window, which measures 10 feet high. From what distance above the top of the window was the stone dropped? (That is, how far is it from the roof to the top of the window?)

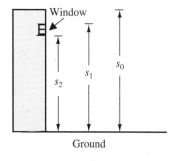

Window

s_2 s_1 s_0

Ground

FIGURE 2.50

Solution

The diagram in Figure 2.50 identifies the distances s_0, s_1, and s_2. Given that $s_1 - s_2 = 10$ (feet), let t_1 be the time it takes for the stone to reach the top of the window and t_2 be the time to reach the bottom of the window. The problem states that $t_2 - t_1 = 0.20$, and we wish to find $s_0 - s_1$.

Equation 1 applies, where $v_0 = 0$, so

$$s = s_0 - 16t^2$$

$$s_1 = s_0 - 16t_1^2$$

$$s_2 = s_0 - 16t_2^2 = s_0 - 16(t_1 + 0.20)^2.$$

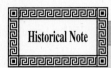

MATHEMATICAL MODELS AND GRAVITY

Historical Note

Galileo's experiments with falling objects led to a mathematical model of the force of gravity.

When we write an equation or function to describe a real-world situation, we almost always need to simplify. Einstein said this well: "Everything should be made as simple as possible, but not simpler." The test of a mathematical model is its capacity to accurately describe and predict real events.

Galileo measured falling bodies and decided that the distance fallen is proportional to the square of the time [in modern terms, $f(t) = 16t^2$]. His timing instrument was his pulse! We may wonder what his results might have been if his pulse had been less steady.

How good is his simple model? For heavy bodies near the earth it works beautifully. For objects like feathers or paper airplanes, the model is too simple.

Another example occurs in Newton's account of his discovery of the inverse square law of the force of gravity. Newton, born in 1642, the year of Galileo's death, took refuge at age 24 on an isolated farm to avoid the plague, which was then ravaging London. He devoted himself to study and within a year he had his model for the gravitational attraction between two bodies, $F = g(\frac{mM}{r^2})$. To test it, he "compared the force requisite to keep the moon in her orb with the force of gravity at the surface of the earth, and found the answer fits 'pretty nearly.'" Newton's model was good enough to analyze the motion of the planets.

Subtracting, and using the fact that $s_1 - s_2 = 10$, gives

$$s_1 - s_2 = -16t_1^2 + 16(t_1 + 0.20)^2$$

$$10 = 6.4t_1 + 0.64$$

$$t_1 = \frac{9.36}{6.4} = 1.4625$$

Substituting this value of t_1 into $s_1 = s_0 - 16t_1^2$, we get

$$s_0 - s_1 = 16t_1^2 \approx 34.22.$$

Considering the precision of timing the fall past the window (two significant digits), the distance from the top of the window to the top of the building is about 34 feet. To avoid rounding error, carry out all intermediate calculations with full calculator accuracy and then round off the final result to be consistent with the accuracy of the data. ▲

Revenue Functions

We now look at a problem from the field of economics and business. The **revenue** R generated by selling x units of a product at p dollars per unit is given by the simple formula, $R = px$. The price per unit, p, is determined by a **demand function,** which is usually based on some sort of market analysis or, preferably,

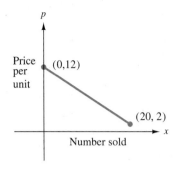

FIGURE 2.51

experience. Generally the number of units sold increases when the price goes down, and analysts often assume a linear demand function. We illustrate some of these concepts in the next example.

EXAMPLE 3   The demand function for a certain product is given by

$$p = 12 - \tfrac{1}{2}x \quad \text{for} \quad 0 \le x \le 20,$$

where x is the number of units sold. As Figure 2.51 shows, the price decreases as more units are sold. **(a)** Find a formula for the revenue R as a function of x. **(b)** How many units should be sold to maximize revenue? **(c)** What is the maximum revenue and what is the corresponding price per unit?

Solution

(a) $R(x) = px = (12 - \tfrac{1}{2}x)x = 12x - \tfrac{1}{2}x^2.$

(b)   The revenue function is a quadratic function whose graph is a parabola that opens downward. To find the maximum value, locate the vertex of the parabola, which occurs when $x = \dfrac{-b}{2a} = \dfrac{-(12)}{2(-\tfrac{1}{2})} = 12$. Therefore the maximum revenue will be produced when 12 units are sold.

(c)   The maximum revenue, which corresponds to $x = 12$, occurs when the unit price is $p(12) = 12 - \tfrac{1}{2}(12) = 6$ dollars per unit. The revenue is given by

$$R(12) = 12(12) - \tfrac{1}{2}(12)^2 = 144 - 72 = 72 \text{ dollars} \quad \blacktriangle$$

In the next example we look at a common type of problem in calculus.

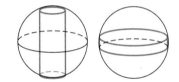

(a) Tall, skinny cylinder   **(b)** Wide, flat cylinder

EXAMPLE 4   What are the dimensions of the cylinder with the greatest volume that can be contained in a sphere of diameter 8?

Solution

First, get a feeling for the problem by trying to visualize various cylinders in the sphere, as in Figure 2.52. A tall cylinder is too skinny to have a large volume; at the other extreme, a wide flat cylinder also has a small volume. From one extreme to the other the cylinder volume first increases and then decreases, so the one with maximum volume must be somewhere in between.

Set up the problem mathematically by expressing the volume V of the cylinder as a function of its radius r. The formula for the volume of a cylinder with radius r and height h (see inside front cover) is $V = \pi r^2 h$.

It may be easier to see in cross section, as in diagram **(d)**. A right triangle has a hypotenuse of 8 (the diameter of the sphere) and legs of h and $2r$. By the Pythagorean theorem,

$$h^2 + (2r)^2 = 8^2 \quad \text{or} \quad h = 2\sqrt{16 - r^2}.$$

(c) Cylinder with height h and radius r

(d) Cross section

FIGURE 2.52

Substituting into the formula for the volume of the sphere,

$$V = \pi r^2 h = 2\pi r^2 \sqrt{16 - r^2}$$

Now the problem requires determining the value of r that gives the greatest volume. This is not a quadratic function, and without calculus there is no simple way to obtain the exact value of r. Calculating a few values, however, can give a pretty good experimental approximation. Tabulate volumes for some r values:

r	1	2	3	3.5	3.2	3.3	3.25
V	24.3	87.1	149.6	149.0	154.4	154.7	154.8

We increase r until V begins to get smaller ($r = 3.5$) and then zero in to find the largest possible value of V. The maximum appears to be about 154.8 with a radius of 3.25. The corresponding height is

$$h = 2\sqrt{16 - (3.25)^2} \approx 4.66$$

In calculus you will learn how to find an exact value for r. For this problem $r = \sqrt{\frac{32}{3}}$ (≈ 3.266), and the maximum volume is given by $V = 256\pi \frac{\sqrt{3}}{9}$ (≈ 154.8), which agrees closely with the experimental value. ▲

EXERCISES 2.8

Check Your Understanding

Exercises 1–10 True or False. Give reasons for your conclusion.

1. A ball dropped from a height of 256 feet takes 4 seconds to hit the ground.

2. It takes twice as long for a ball to fall to the ground from a height of 64 feet than from a height of 32 feet.

3. If a ball is dropped from a height of 256 feet and at the same instant a second ball is thrown upward from ground level at a speed of 128 feet per second, the two balls will meet at a point 192 feet above the ground.

4. In Exercise 3, the two balls will meet in 2 seconds.

5. A ball rolls down a long inclined plane. It takes longer to roll down the first 10 feet than it does to roll down the next 10 feet.

6. It takes the same amount of time to travel 240 miles at 55 mph as it takes to travel the first 120 miles at 50 mph and the final 120 miles at 60 mph.

7. If a square and an equilateral triangle are inscribed in the same circle, then the square has greater area than the triangle.

8. For any rectangle with a perimeter of 16, the length of one side must be at least 4.

9. No triangle can have sides of lengths 3, 4, and 8.

10. If a sphere has diameter d, then its volume V is given by $\frac{\pi d^3}{12}$.

Explore and Discover

1. As an application that involves lattice points, it appears that free throws may determine the basketball championship in the Pan-Freedom Conference. When Fred Wolner steps up to the line for his fifth try in the game, the broadcast announcer observes that he has hit 3 of 4 tries from the line in the game so far and that his season percentage has increased from 68% to 70%. If m is the number of foul shots Fred has made before the game and a is the total number of attempts, then we know that $0.675 \le \frac{m}{a} < 0.685$. Assuming that the announcer is relying on accurate statistics, is it possible to determine the number of free throws Fred has attempted this season prior to the championship game? If so, how many free throws has Fred attempted and how many has he made? If not, explain why not.

Develop Mastery

Exercises 1–23 Apply the formulas for motion due to gravitational attraction.

1. A stone is dropped form the top of a cliff that is 160 feet tall. How long will the stone take to hit the ground?

2. A stone is dropped from the top of a building and hits the ground 3.5 seconds later. How tall is the building?

3. A helicopter is ascending vertically at a speed of 25 feet per second. At a height of 480 feet, the pilot drops a box.
   (a) How long will it take for the box to reach the ground?
   (b) At what speed does the box hit the ground?

4. A helicopter is climbing vertically at a speed of 24 feet per second when it drops a pump near a leaking boat. The pump reaches the water 4 seconds after being dropped.
   (a) How high is the helicopter when the pump is dropped?
   (b) How high is the helicopter when the pump reaches the water?

5. A baseball is thrown vertically upward. When it leaves the player's fingers it is 6 feet off the ground and traveling at a speed of 48 feet per second.
   (a) How high will it go?
   (b) How many seconds after the ball is thrown will it hit the ground?

6. A rock is dropped from the top of a cliff 360 feet directly above a lake.
   (a) State a formula that gives the height s as a function of t.
   (b) What is the domain of this function?
   (c) How far above the lake is the rock 2 seconds after being dropped?
   (d) How far does the rock fall during the third second?

7. A rock is blasted vertically upward from the ground at a speed of 128 feet per second (about 80 mph).
   (a) Find a formula that relates s and t.
   (b) How far from the ground is the rock 2 seconds after the blast?
   (c) How high will the rock go?

8. A vertical cliff 160 feet tall stands at the edge of a lake. A car is pushed over the edge. How many seconds will it take to hear the sound of the splash at the top of the cliff? Assume that sound travels at a speed of 1080 feet per second.

9. A rock is dropped into a deep well. It takes 4.5 seconds before the sound of the splash is heard. Assume that sound travels at a speed of 1080 feet per second. Determine s_0, the distance from the top of the well to the water level. If you measure the height s above water level, then the formula for motion due to gravity applies.
   (a) Show that the rock takes $t_1 = \dfrac{\sqrt{s_0}}{4}$ seconds to reach the water.
   (b) Show that the sound of the splash takes $t_2 = \dfrac{s_0}{1080}$ seconds to be heard.
   (c) Since the total time that elapses before hearing the splash is 4.5 seconds, you have the equation
   $$\frac{s_0}{1080} + \frac{\sqrt{s_0}}{4} = 4.5.$$
   Clear the fractions and simplify to get
   $$s_0 + 270\sqrt{s_0} - 4860 = 0,$$
   which is a quadratic equation in $\sqrt{s_0}$. Use the quadratic formula to solve for $\sqrt{s_0}$ and then find s_0.

10. A ball is released from rest at point A, the top of an inclined plane 30 feet long (see the diagram). If $S(t)$ denotes the number of feet the ball rolls down the incline in t seconds after its release, then $S(t) = 8\sqrt{2}\,t^2$.
    (a) How long does it take for the ball to reach the end of the plane?
    (b) How far does the ball roll during the first 1.5 seconds?
    (c) How long does it take for the ball to roll down the final 12 feet of the plane?

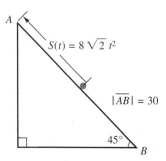

11. A stone is dropped form the top of New York's Empire State Building, which is 1476 feet tall.
    (a) How long does it take for the stone to reach the ground?
    (b) What is the speed of the stone when its hits the ground?

12. If a kangaroo jumps 8 feet vertically, how long is it in the air during the jump?

13. With what minimum vertical speed must a salmon leave the water to jump to the top of a waterfall that is 2.4 feet high?

14. A rock is thrown upward at an initial speed of 16 feet per second from the edge of a cliff 160 feet above a lake. One second later a second rock is dropped from the edge of the cliff. Which rock will hit the water first? By how many seconds?

15. A stone is dropped from the roof of a tall building. One second later a second stone is dropped from the same roof. How many feet apart are the stones two seconds after the second stone begins to fall?

16. A diver in Acapulco leaps horizontally from a point 112 feet above the sea.
    (a) How long does it take for the diver to reach the water?
    (b) At what speed does the diver enter the water?

17. A ball player catches a ball 5 seconds after throwing it vertically upward.
    (a) At what initial speed was the ball thrown?
    (b) What was the speed of the ball when it was caught?

18. A stone is thrown vertically upward with a speed of 32 feet per second from the edge of a cliff that is 240 feet high.
    (a) How many seconds later will it reach the bottom of the cliff?
    (b) What is its speed when it hits the ground?
    (c) What is its speed when it is 120 feet above the bottom of the cliff?
    (d) What is the total distance traveled by the stone?

19. Robin, a skydiver, leaves the plane at an altitude of 1000 feet above the ground and accidentally drops her binoculars. If she descends at a constant speed of 20 feet per second, how much time elapses between the arrival of the binoculars on the ground and the time when Robin lands?

20. Frank is ballooning at an altitude of 480 feet when he turns on the burner and accidentally knocks his lunch out of the balloon. If he immediately starts to ascend at a constant speed of 4.8 feet per second, how high will he be when his lunch hits the ground?

21. A stone is dropped from the top of a building 240 feet high. It is observed to take 0.20 seconds to go past an office floor-to-ceiling window that is 12 feet high. How far is it from the bottom of the window down to the street? (*Hint:* See Example 2.)

22. A toy rocket is fired upward from ground level near an office building. Its initial velocity is 80 feet per second. An observer in one of the offices determines that the rocket takes 0.32 seconds to pass by the office window, which is 16 feet tall. How far is it from the ground to the bottom of the window?

23. The acceleration of gravity on the moon is about one-sixth of what it is on earth. The formula for a freely falling object on the moon is given by $s = s_0 + v_0 t - \frac{8}{3} t^2$. If an object is thrown upward on the moon, how much higher will it go than it would have on the earth, assuming the same initial velocity of 64 feet per second?

24. The manager of a store estimates that the demand function for calculators (see Example 4) is given by

    $$p = 36 - \frac{1}{3}x \qquad 0 \le x \le 96,$$

    where x is the number of calculators sold and p is the price of each calculator. The revenue R is given by $R = px$.
    (a) Express R as a function of x.
    (b) How many calculators should be sold to get the maximum revenue?

25. Answer the questions in Exercise 24 if the demand function is given by

    $$p = 36 - (0.2)x \qquad 0 \le x \le 160.$$

26. A car rental agency rents 400 cars a day at a rate of $40 for each car. For every dollar increase in the rental rate, it rents 8 fewer cars per day.
    (a) What is the agency's income if the rental rate is $40? $42? $45?
    (b) What rental rate will give the greatest income? What is this maximum income?

27. A car rental agency rents 200 cars a day at a rate of $30 for each car. For every dollar increase in the rental rate, it rents 4 fewer cars per day.
    (a) What is the agency's income if the rental rate is $30? $35? $40?
    (b) What rental rate will give the greatest income? What is the maximum income?

28. A computer is purchased for $2000. After 5 years its salvage value (for tax purposes) is estimated to be $400. Linear depreciation implies that the tax value V of the computer is a linear function of t, the number of years after purchase.
    (a) Find a formula for the linear depreciation function.
    (b) In how many years after purchase will the tax value of the computer be zero?

29. Repeat Exercise 28 if the original cost of the computer is $3000 and its tax value after 8 years is $500.

30. An indoor gymnastics arena is to be built with a rectangular region and semicircular regions on each end (see the diagram). Around the outside is a running track whose inside length is to measure 220 yards (one-eighth of a mile).
   (a) What dimensions for the rectangle will maximize the area of the rectangular region?
   (b) For the dimensions in part **(a)**, what is the area of the entire region enclosed by the track?

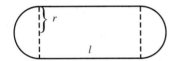

31. A rancher has 240 feet of fencing to enclose two adjacent rectangular pens (see the diagram). What dimensions will give a maximum total enclosed area?

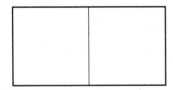

32. In Exercise 31 suppose that the rancher wants to make three adjacent pens (see the diagram) What dimensions will give a maximum total enclosed area?

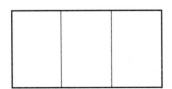

33. A pan is full of water when it springs a leak at the bottom. The volume V of water (in cubic inches) that remains in the pan t seconds after the leak occurs is given by

$$V = 1000 - 30t + 0.1t^2$$

   (a) How much water is in the pan when the leak starts?
   (b) In how many seconds will the pan be empty?
   (c) What is the domain of the function?
   (d) How many seconds will it take for half of the water to leak out of the pan? How long for the final half?

34. *Looking Ahead to Calculus*   A right circular cylinder is inscribed in a right circular cone that has a height of 24 inches and a radius of 8 inches (see the diagram). Let x denote the radius of the cylinder and h denote its height.
   (a) Express h as a function of x.
   (b) Express the volume V of the cylinder as a function of x.
   (c) Compute V when x is 1, 3, 5, 6, and 7.
   (d) From your data, make a reasonable guess of the value of x that will give the cylinder with the largest volume.

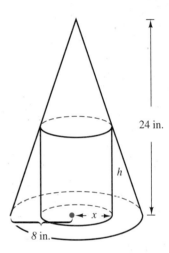

35. A water tank in the shape of an inverted circular cone is initially full of water (see the diagram for dimensions). A control valve at the bottom of the tank allows water to drain from the tank. At any depth d, the water remaining in the tank is the shape of a cone with radius r.
   (a) Express r as a function of d and then express the volume V of water remaining as a function of d.

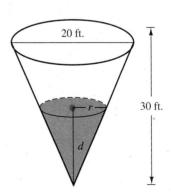

(b) If the depth of the water t minutes after starting to drain the tank is given by $d = 30 - 5\sqrt{t}$, then express V as a function of t.

(c) What is the volume of water that remains at the end of 16 minutes?

(d) How long will it take to empty the tank?

36. *Looking Ahead to Calculus*   A right triangle has a fixed hypotenuse of length 12, but legs whose lengths can vary. The triangle is rotated about a vertical leg to generate a cone of radius x and height h, where x and h are the lengths of the legs of the triangle (see the diagram).

(a) Express h as a function of x.

(b) Express the volume V of the cone as a function of x.

(c) Evaluate the volume when x is 1, 5, 8, 10, and 11.

(d) From your data, make a reasonable guess about the dimensions of the triangle that will give a cone with the maximum possible volume.

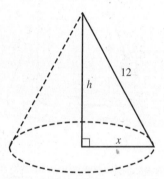

37. *Looking Ahead to Calculus*   A freshwater pipeline is to be constructed from the shore to an island located as shown in the diagram. The cost of running the pipeline along the shore is $8,000 per mile, but construction offshore costs $12,000 per mile.

(a) Express the construction cost C as a function of x.

(b) What is the cost when x is 3, 5, 6, 8, 10, and 15?

(c) From your data, make a reasonable guess of the value of x that will minimize the construction cost. What is the minimum cost?

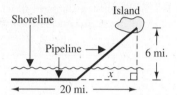

38. *Looking Ahead to Calculus*   A ladder of length L is placed so that it rests on the top of a 4 foot wall and leans against a building that is 8 feet from the wall. The ladder touches the ground x feet from the wall (see the diagram).

(a) Show that L can be written as a function of x as follows:

$$L = (x + 8)\sqrt{1 + \frac{16}{x^2}}.$$

(b) Evaluate L when x is 2, 3, 4, 5, 6, and 7.

(c) From your data, make a reasonable estimate of the value of x that would require the shortest ladder.

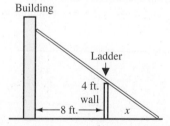

CHAPTER 2 REVIEW

Test Your Understanding

Determine the truth value (T or F). Give reasons for your conclusion.

1. A line with slope 2 is perpendicular to any line that has a slope of -2.

2. The solution set for $|x - 1| + 1 = 0$ is the empty set.

3. The solution set for $|x - 1| + 1 \geq 0$ is the empty set.

4. The graph of $2x + y + 1 = 0$ does not pass through the first quadrant.

5. There is no function with a domain of two numbers and a range of three numbers.

6. There is no function with a domain of three numbers and a range of two numbers.

7. A line with negative slope must pass through the third quadrant.

8. A line with positive slope must pass through the third quadrant.

9. The graph of any parabola that opens upward must contain some points in the second quadrant.

10. The graph of every quadratic function must contain points in at least two of the four quadrants.

11. The graph of $y = x^2 + x + 1$ is entirely above the x-axis.

12. The graph of $y = x^2 - 3x$ does not pass through the origin.

13. If function f has an inverse, then f is a one–one function.

14. Every increasing function has an inverse.

15. The function $f(x) = x$ is one–one.

16. If $f(x) = \sqrt{x}$ and $g(x) = x^2$, then $f(g(x)) = x$ for every x in R.

17. The graph of the quadratic function $f(x) = x^2 - x + 2$ does not cross the x-axis.

18. The graph of $y = \sqrt{x^2 + 1}$ has no y-intercept point.

19. If a function f has an inverse, then every horizontal line must intersect the graph of $y = f(x)$ in exactly one point.

20. Suppose f has an inverse. If $(-2, 3)$ is on the graph of $y = f(x)$, then $(-3, 2)$ must be on the graph of $y = f^{-1}(x)$.

21. Points $(-2, 4)$ and $(4, -2)$ are symmetric with respect to the line $y = x$.

22. The graph of $y = |x| + 2$ has no x-intercept point.

23. The graph of $y = |x| + 1$ has no y-intercept point.

24. The two lines $y = 2x$ and $y = -2x$ are perpendicular to each other.

25. There is no point that is on the graphs of both $y = 2x$ and $y = 2x - 1$.

26. If f is any even function, then f cannot be one–one.

27. Every odd function has an inverse.

28. The function $f(x) = -|x|$ is an even function.

29. If f is an even function, then for every number k the function g given by $g(x) = f(x) + k$ must be even.

30. If f is an odd function, then $g(x) = f(x) + k$ is an odd function for every number k.

31. The graph of $y = |x| - 1$ can be obtained by translating the graph of $y = |x|$ horizontally 1 unit to the right.

32. The function $f(x) = -x^2$ has no maximum value.

33. The function $f(x) = |2x + 3|$ is a linear function.

34. The function $f(x) = |x^2 - 2x - 3|$ is a quadratic function.

35. The equation $x^2 - 4|x| + 3 = 0$ has exactly two roots.

36. The equation $|2x + 3| = 1$ has only one root.

37. The graph of every parabola that passes through the origin must contain points in exactly three quadrants.

38. If the graph of an even function contains points in the third quadrant, then it must also contain points in the fourth quadrant.

39. If the graph of an odd function contains points in the second quadrant, then it must also contain points in the fourth quadrant.

Exercises 40–43 Assume that the function f has an inverse.

40. If the graph of f has an x-intercept point, then the graph of f^{-1} must have a y-intercept point.

41. If $(-2, 0)$ is an x-intercept point for the graph of f, then $(0, 2)$ is not a y-intercept point for the graph of f^{-1}.

42. If $f^{-1}(-3) = 4$, then $f(3)$ must be equal to -4.

43. The graph of f cannot have more than one x-intercept point.

Mastery Exercises

Exercises 1–2 Determine whether or not the set of ordered pairs represents a function. If not, explain why. Otherwise, state the domain and range.

1. $\{(-1, 2), (0, 4), (1, 6), (2, 8)\}$

2. $\{(3, -1), (4, 2), (5, -3), (3, 2)\}$

Exercises 3–8 State the domain.

3. $f(x) = 2 - 3x^2$ 4. $f(x) = \sqrt{x^2 + 4}$

5. $g(x) = \sqrt{2 - x}$ 6. $g(x) = \sqrt{3 - |x|}$

7. $h(x) = \frac{x}{x^2 - 4}$ 8. $h(x) = \frac{\sqrt{x}}{x - 2}$

9. Find an equation for the line that passes through $(-1, 3)$ and $(2, 5)$.

10. Find an equation for the line that passes through the point $(2, 4)$ and is
    (a) parallel to the line $2x - 3y + 4 = 0$
    (b) perpendicular to the line $x + 2y - 3 = 0$.

11. Point P is $(-1, 2)$ and line L is given by $2x - 3y + 8 = 0$. If P is on L, then find an equation for the line that passes through P and is perpendicular to L. If P is not on L, then find an equation for the line that passes through P and is parallel to L.

12. Find an equation for the line that is the perpendicular bisector of the line segment joining $(-1, 4)$ and $(3, -2)$.

Exercises 13–18 Sketch a graph. In each case label the x- and y-intercept points.

13. $2x - y = 4$

14. $3x + 2y = 6$

15. $y = x^2 - 4x + 3$

16. $y = x^2 - 2x + 1$

17. $y = |x - 1| + 1$

18. $y = 1 - |x + 1|$

Exercises 19–26 Find the solution set for the open sentence.

19. $2x - 3 < 6 - x$

20. $|x| - 4 = 0$

21. $|x - 1| - 1 > 0$

22. $x^2 - 3x - 4 = 0$

23. $x^2 - 3x - 4 \leq 0$

24. $\sqrt{x - 1} - 2 = 0$

25. $|x| - x = 4$

26. $x(x^2 - 4) < 0$

Exercises 27–32 Functions f and g are

$$f(x) = x + 1 \quad \text{and} \quad g(x) = 2x - x^2.$$

Evaluate.

27. $(f + g)(2)$

28. $(\frac{f}{g})(-1)$

29. $(f \circ g)(-2)$

30. $(g \circ f)(3)$

31. $(f \circ g)(2)$

32. $(f - g)(2)$

Exercises 33–36 Solve the equation, where $f(x) = 2 - 3x$ and $g(x) = x^2 - x$.

33. $(f - g)(x) - 2 = 0$

34. $(f \circ g)(x) - 3x = 0$

35. $(g \circ f)(x) - 2 = 0$

36. $(\frac{f}{g})(x) = \frac{5}{2}$

Exercises 37–40 Determine whether the function is (a) Increasing, decreasing, or neither (b) one–one.

37. $f(x) = x^2 - x$

38. $f(x) = 3 - 2x$

39. $f(x) = \sqrt{x}$

40. $f(x) = |x - 1| + 1$

Exercises 41–44 Find a formula for the inverse of f. Give the domain and range of f^{-1}.

41. $f(x) = 2x - 4$

42. $f(x) = 3 - x$

43. $f(x) = \sqrt{x - 1}$

44. $f(x) = 1 + \frac{1}{x}$

45. Function f is described by the equation

$$f(x) = \begin{cases} \sqrt{x} & \text{for } x \geq 0 \text{ and} \\ -|x| & \text{for } x < 0. \end{cases}$$

   (a) Sketch a graph of $y = f(x)$.
   (b) Use the horizontal line test to determine whether or not f is a one–one function.

46. Function f is described by the equation

$$f(x) = x^2 - 4x$$

and the domain $\{x \mid x \leq 2\}$. (a) Sketch a graph of $y = f(x)$. (b) Is f an increasing function, decreasing function, or neither? (c) Does f have an inverse?

Exercises 47–50 (a) Sketch a graph of $y = f(x)$. (b) Determine the maximum and minimum values of $f(x)$.

47. $f(x) = x^2 - 2x + 2$

48. $f(x) = x^2 - 2x - 1, \ 0 \leq x \leq 3$

49. $f(x) = 1 + \sqrt{x}$

50. $f(x) = -x^2 - 2x, \ -3 \leq x \leq 0$

51. If $f(x) = \frac{3x}{x - 3}$ show that $f^{-1}(x) = f(x)$.

52. A rectangle is inscribed in a circle of radius 4. If x denotes the length of one side of the rectangle, express the area A and the perimeter P as functions of x. State the domain of each function.

53. A ball is thrown upward from a point 160 feet above ground level at an initial speed of 48 feet per second.
   (a) Give a formula for the distance s of the ball from ground level as a function of time (in seconds) after the ball is thrown.
   (b) How many seconds will the ball take to hit the ground?
   (c) What is the highest distance that the ball will reach?

54. The sale price of a graphing calculator after a 25 percent discount is $60. What was the price before the discount?

55. After 12 noon, when will the hour and minute hands of a clock first point in opposite directions. Round off your answer to the nearest second.

56. From 1970 to 1980 the population of Hazelton increased by 8 percent; from 1980 to 1990 it increased by 15 percent. What is the percentage increase in population over the 20-year period, 1970 to 1990?

57. If c is a constant and $f(x) = \frac{x}{2x + c}$, find the value of c such that $f(f(x)) = x$. That is, find c such that $f^{-1}(x) = f(x)$.

58. If points $A(0, 0)$, $B(2, 4)$, and $C(6, 0)$ are vertices of a triangle, find the number k such that the horizontal line $y = k$ divides the triangle into two regions of equal area.

59. If points $A(0, 0)$, $B(2, 0)$, and $C(0, 4)$ are vertices of a triangle, find the number m such that the line $y = mx$ divides the triangle into two regions of equal area.

60. The lengths of the sides of a right triangle are given by x, $x + 2$, and $x + 4$. Find the value of x.

61. What is the smallest integer k such that the graph of $y = x^2 + kx + 5$ lies entirely above the x-axis?

62. A rock is blasted vertically upward from ground level with a velocity of 144 feet per second. **(a)** How high does the rock go before it starts to fall back down? **(b)** Is it going upward or downward when $t = 5$? **(c)** What is its velocity when it is 200 feet above the ground on the way up?

63. The volume (in cubic inches) of water remaining in a leaking pail after t seconds is given by

$$V = 1200 - 40t + 0.2t^2.$$

(a) How much water was in the pail at time $t = 0$?
(b) What is the volume of water in the pail when $t = 4$? 10? 20?
(c) How long does it take for all the water to leak out of the pail?

64. A stone dropped from the edge of a cliff takes 4.5 seconds to hit the ground. How high is the cliff?

65. How long will it take for a brick to reach the ground if it is dropped from a height of 180 feet?

66. Megan rides a bicycle up a hill at a speed of 12 feet per second and then comes back down the same hill at a speed of 24 feet per second. What is her average speed for the entire trip up and back down?

67. When traveling a distance of 150 miles, how much less time does it take at a speed of 60 mph compared to the same trip at a speed of 50 mph?

68. A car traveling at 90 kilometers per hour is 150 meters behind a truck traveling at 60 kilometers per hour.

(a) How soon will the car reach the truck?
(b) If the car and truck, continue at the same speed and the truck is x meters ahead of the car, let $T(x)$ be the time it takes for the car to reach the truck. Find a formula to express $T(x)$ as a function of x.

CHAPTER

3

POLYNOMIAL AND RATIONAL FUNCTIONS

In Chapter 2 we looked at the behavior of linear and quadratic functions, the simplest members of the family of polynomials. In Chapter 3 we broaden our scope to introduce the rest of the clan.

Frequently work with polynomials requires finding solutions to polynomial equations or inequalities such as

$$x^3 - 3x^2 + 0.5x - 1 = 0 \qquad \text{or} \qquad 3x^2 - 5x + 4 \geq 0.$$

Polynomials crop up in a diverse range of problems such as maximizing profits or efficiency in a production facility, solving a differential equation for electronic circuit analysis, or finding eigenvalues to avoid resonances in matrix analysis of rocket motors. The problem of finding roots of polynomial equations has taken on an entirely different complexion with modern technology, but technology can be applied meaningfully only when we have understanding.

While we assume no special equipment, our approach to this material has been influenced by available technology. As new technology becomes more widespread, students are more likely to encounter problems that lack neat, carefully tailored answers. Our goal is to develop techniques that can be used whether working with pencil and paper or with the most sophisticated graphing utilities on the most powerful computers.

Section 3.1 begins with basic definitions and graphical concepts. Section 3.2 develops fundamental evaluation tools, including algorithms based on synthetic division, to locate zeros of polynomial functions. Sections 3.2 and 3.3 contain central ideas about the nature of polynomial equations and their roots, including some of the classical theorems. The final section of the chapter builds on the earlier material to define and discuss rational functions, or quotients of polynomials.

Polynomial Functions

I knew formulas for the quadratic and the cubic, and they said there was a subject called Galois theory, which was a general theory giving conditions under which any equation could be solved. That there could be such a thing was beyond my wildest comprehensions!
Paul Cohen

In earlier courses you learned that expressions such as

$$x^2 + 2x - 1, \qquad x^3 + 3x, \qquad -x^5 + 3x - 8.$$

are called polynomials. The following are not polynomials:

$$\frac{1 - x}{x}, \qquad 2x^{-2} + 3x, \qquad |x| - 4, \qquad 4^x + 5.$$

To make clear the kinds of creatures the class of polynomial functions includes, we begin with a definition.

Definition: Polynomial Function

A **polynomial function** of degree n is a function that can be written in the form

$$p(x) = a_n x^n + a_{n-1} x^{n-1} + \cdots + a_1 x + a_0 \qquad (1)$$

where n is a nonnegative integer, $a_n \neq 0$, and $a_n, a_{n-1}, \ldots, a_1, a_0$ are numbers called coefficients. This course assumes that all coefficients are real numbers. The **leading term** is $a_n x^n$, the **leading coefficient** is a_n, and a_0 is the **constant term**. Equation 1 is the **standard form** for a polynomial function.

When I was thirteen, . . . I needed an emergency operation for appendicitis. I read two books in hospital. One was Jerome's Three Men in a Boat, *and the other was Lancelot Hogben's* Mathematics for the Million. *Some of it I couldn't understand, but much of it I did. I remember coming across the idea of dividing one polynomial by another. I knew how to multiply them together, but I had never divided them before. So every time my father came to visit me in hospital he brought some more polynomials that he'd multiplied out.*

Robin Wilson

It should be obvious from the definition that the domain of every polynomial function is the set of all real numbers. We already know about polynomial functions of degree 2 or less.

Degree 0: $f(x) = k$, $k \neq 0$ (constant function; the graph is a horizontal line).

Degree 1: $f(x) = ax + b$ (linear function; the graph is a line).

Degree 2: $f(x) = ax^2 + bx + c$ (quadratic function; the graph is a parabola).

For technical reasons, the zero polynomial function, $f(x) = 0$, is not assigned a degree.

Combining Polynomial Functions

It is appropriate to ask how the usual operations on functions apply to polynomial functions. What about sums, differences, products, quotients, or composition? All of these except quotients are also polynomials. The quotient of two polynomial functions is never a polynomial function unless the denominator is a constant function.

Roots, Zeros, Factors, and Intercepts

Let p be a polynomial function and suppose that a is any real number for which $p(a) = 0$. Then the following are equivalent statements:

a is a **root** of the equation $p(x) = 0$

a is a **zero** of the polynomial function p

$(x - a)$ is a **factor** of the polynomial $p(x)$

$(a, 0)$ is an x-**intercept point** of the graph of p

EXAMPLE 1   If $P(x) = x^3 - 4x^2 + x + 6 = (x - 2) \times (x^2 - 2x - 3)$, find the solution set for **(a)** the equation $P(x) = 0$ and **(b)** the inequality $P(x) > 0$.

Solution

The most difficult work is already done since the polynomial is partially factored. Completing the factorization,

$$P(x) = (x - 2)(x + 1)(x - 3).$$

(a) $P(x)$ is 0 only when one of its factors is 0, so the solution set is $\{2, -1, 3\}$.

(b) The values of x that satisfy the equation $P(x) = 0$ give cut points at -1, 2, and 3, and the function has the same sign (see Section 1.5) on intervals between consecutive cut points on the number line. Checking a value within each interval reveals the sign of the function on that interval. For instance, using the factored form,

$$P(-2) = (-4)(-1)(-5) = -20; P(x) \text{ is negative on } (-\infty, -1).$$

$$P(1) = (-1)(2)(-2) = 4; P(x) \text{ is positive on } (-1, 2).$$

$$P(2.5) = (0.5)(3.5)(-0.5) = -0.875, P(x) \text{ is negative on } (2, 3).$$

$$P(4) = (2)(5)(1) = 10, \text{ so } P(x) \text{ is positive on } (3, \infty).$$

This gives the solution set for the inequality $P(x) > 0$ as the union of two intervals, $(-1, 2) \cup (3, \infty)$. ▲

EXAMPLE 2   For the polynomial function $f(x) = 2x - x^3$, find the factors and the zeros, and then sketch the graph.

Solution

The polynomial may be readily factored:

$$f(x) = x(2 - x^2) = -x(x - \sqrt{2})(x + \sqrt{2}).$$

From the factored form, 0, $\sqrt{2}$, and $-\sqrt{2}$ are the zeros, and they tell where the graph crosses the x-axis. The y-intercept point is $(0, 0)$, and it is easy to see that $f(1) = 1$ and $f(-1) = -1$, giving points $(1, 1)$ and $(-1, -1)$. Observe that $f(-x) = -f(x)$ for every x, so the graph is symmetric with respect to the origin. Draw the graph in Figure 3.1. ▲

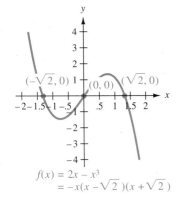

$f(x) = 2x - x^3$
$= -x(x - \sqrt{2})(x + \sqrt{2})$

FIGURE 3.1

Cubic Polynomial Functions and Graphs

The general shapes of the graph of the cubic in Examples 1 and 2 suggest some observations about the roots of a cubic equation. We have seen that a quadratic polynomial can have two, one, or no real zeros because a parabola can meet the x-axis at two points, one point, or not at all. In contrast, the graph of a cubic polynomial must cross the x-axis at least once, so a cubic polynomial function must have *at least one* real zero. If the leading coefficient is positive, the graph climbs steeply toward the right; with a negative leading coefficient, the graph drops steeply toward the right, as in Figure 3.1.

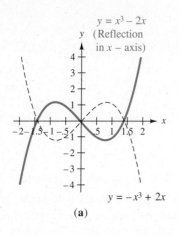

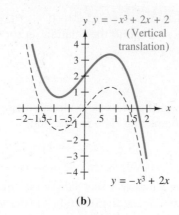

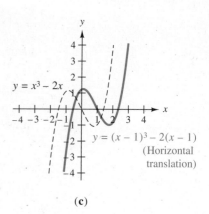

(a)   (b)   (c)

FIGURE 3.2

Reflection and translation of the graph of $y = -x^3 + 2x$

EXAMPLE 3 $F(x) = x^3 - 2x$, $G(x) = -x^3 + 2x + 2$, $H(x) = (x - 1)^3 - 2(x - 1)$. Show that the graph of each function is related to the graph of the function $f(x) = -x^3 + 2x$ in Example 2, and then sketch the graph of each function.

Strategy: Look for reflections or translations of $F(x) = 2x - x^3$.

Solution

Clearly $F(x) = -f(x)$, so the graph of F is the reflection of the graph of f in the x-axis (tipped upside down).

$G(x) = f(x) + 2$, so that translating the graph of f upward 2 units will give the graph of G.

$H(x) = F(x - 1)$, so the graph of H is the graph of F translated 1 unit to the right.

The graphs of these functions appear, paired with reference graphs, in Figure 3.2. ▲

A vertical translation of a polynomial can drastically change the nature of the zeros. As a very simple case, consider function G in Example 3. The graph of G is a vertical translation of the graph of $f(x) = -x(x - \sqrt{2})(x + \sqrt{2})$. Although we know the zeros of f precisely, the function $G(x) = f(x) + 2$ cannot be factored, even in terms of square roots. Figure 3.2 shows that there is only one x-intercept, and hence only one real zero rather than three. We will discuss ways to find decimal approximations for the zeros of such functions in Section 3.2.

EXAMPLE 4   Verify that one solution for the polynomial equation $x^3 - 2x + 4 = 0$ is -2. Then find the remaining solutions.

Strategy: Replacing x by -2 gives 0, so -2 is one solution from which $x + 2$ must be a factor of the left side. To get the other factor, use long division.

Solution

Follow the strategy and divide $x^3 - 2x + 4$ by $x + 2$. Long division gives the other factor, $x^2 - 2x + 2$. Hence the given equation can be written

$$(x + 2)(x^2 - 2x + 2) = 0.$$

For Graphers 3.1

POLYNOMIAL FUNCTIONS

Exercises

1. Draw a graph of $f(x) = x^3 - 4x^2 + x + 6$ and find the solution set for
   (a) $f(x) = 0$
   (b) $f(x) > 0$. See Example 1. (*Calculator Hint:* Use the Familiar Window; the important information for this exercise is where the graph crosses the x-axis.)

Exercises 2–3 On the same set of axes draw the graphs of functions f and g. Describe how the graphs are related.

2. $f(x) = x^3 - 4x$, $g(x) = 4x - x^3$
3. $f(x) = x^3 - 2x$, $g(x) = x^3 - 3x^2 + x + 1$

Exercises 4–5 Draw graphs of both functions, first in the Familiar Window, then in a $[-10, 10] \times [-500, 500]$ window. Discuss the end behavior of the functions.

4. $f(x) = \dfrac{-x^5}{5} + x^3 + 1$; $g(x) = \dfrac{-x^5}{5}$

5. $f(x) = \dfrac{2}{5}x^4 - 2x^3 + x + 1$; $g(x) = \dfrac{2}{5}x^4$

Exercises 6–9 Use your calculator to help solve Develop Mastery Exercises 43–46.

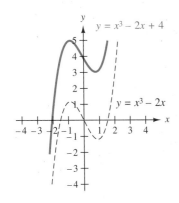

FIGURE 3.3

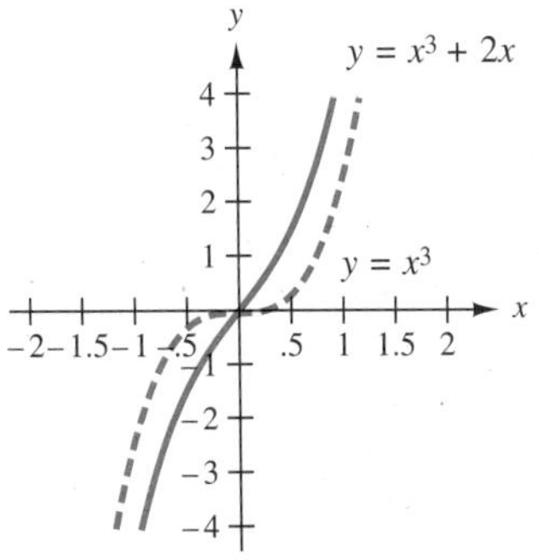

FIGURE 3.4

Graphs of cubics without turning points

Using the zero product principle, find the other two roots by solving the quadratic equation $x^2 - 2x + 2 = 0$. From the quadratic formula, $x = 1 \pm i$.

Therefore the given equation has three roots: -2, $1 + i$, and $1 - i$. If the domain of the variable is restricted to be the set of real numbers, then the solution set is $\{-2\}$; if the domain is the set of complex numbers, then the solution set is $\{-2, 1 + i, 1 - i\}$. ▲

In Example 4 let $g(x) = x^3 - 2x + 4$. The graph of g is a vertical translation of the graph of $F(x) = x^3 - 2x$ (Figure 3.2a) 4 units upward. The graph shown in Figure 3.3 shows clearly why the function g has only one real zero. The humps, or tuning points, in the graph do not reach the x-axis, so the graph crosses the x-axis only once.

Not all graphs of cubic polynomials have turning points. The graph of the simplest cubic, $y = x^3$ should be familiar to every algebra student. It levels out to run tangent to the x-axis at the origin; the function is always increasing and so there are no turning points. The graph of the cubic function $f(x) = x^3 + 2x$ does not even level out. See Figure 3.4.

End Behavior of Polynomial Functions

All of the graphs of polynomial functions in this section rise or fall very steeply without bound toward either right or left. This is characteristic of the graph of any polynomial function of degree greater than one. What happens as x becomes large and positive or large and negative (indicated by the notation $x \to \infty$ or $x \to -\infty$)? This **end behavior** depends solely on the degree of the polynomial and the sign of the leading coefficient.

The four kinds of end behavior are summed up in the box and illustrated by the graphs in Figure 3.5. Figure 3.5a shows typical graphs of polynomial functions of odd degree; when the degree is odd, the graph must cross the x-axis *at least once*. Figure 3.5b shows graphs of two polynomial functions of even

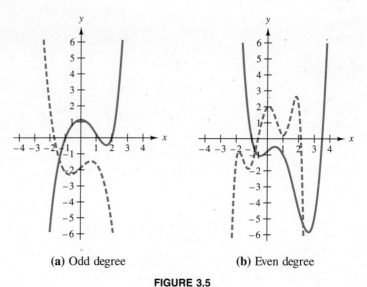

(a) Odd degree   (b) Even degree

FIGURE 3.5

Typical end behavior

degree. While both of these graphs cross the x-axis, vertical translations could give graphs that would not cross the x-axis at all.

End Behavior

If f has odd degree and $a_n > 0$, the graph goes from $-\infty$ to ∞.
$\quad\quad\quad\quad\quad\quad\quad\quad\quad\quad\quad a_n < 0$, the graph goes from ∞ to $-\infty$.

If f has even degree and $a_n > 0$, the graph starts from ∞ and returns.
$\quad\quad\quad\quad\quad\quad\quad\quad\quad\quad\quad\quad a_n < 0$, the graph starts from $-\infty$ and returns.

EXERCISES 3.1

Check Your Understanding

Exercises 1–4   True or False. Give reasons for your conclusion.

1. The function $p(x) = x^4 - 1$ has the same number of real zeros as imaginary zeros.

2. The function $f(x) = x(x^2 - 1) + 1$ has no real zeros.

3. If the graph of $f(x) = 1 - x^3$ is translated one unit to the right, the resulting graph is that of $g(x) = -x^3 + 3x^2 - 3x$.

4. If f and g are any two polynomial functions, both of degree 3, then $f + g$ must also be a polynomial function of degree 3.

Exercises 5–10   Complete the sentence by selecting from the list below *all choices* that make the statement true.

(a) 1   (b) (1, 0)   (c) 2
(d) $(-1, 0)$ (e) 3   (f) $(0, 2)$
(g) Quadrant I   (h) Quadrant II
(i) Quadrant III   (j) Quadrant IV

5. The function $f(x) = x^3 + x(1 - x^2)$ has degree _____ .

6. The graph of $f(x) = x^3 - 2x^2 + x$ has an x-intercept point at _____ .

7. An x-intercept point for the graph of $f(x) = x^3 - 2x^2 - x + 2$ is _____ .

8. If k is any positive number, then the graph of $f(x) = -kx^3$ contains points in _____ .

9. If k is any positive number, then the graph of $f(x) = 1 - kx^3$ contains no points in _____ .

10. The number of y-intercept points for the graph of any polynomial function is _____ .

Explore and Discover

Exercises 1–4 Write out the indicated translations as polynomial functions in standard form. Graph function G.

1. $f(x) = x^3 + 3x^2 + 2x - 1$
$F(x) = f(x - 1); G(x) = f(x - 1) + 1$

2. $f(x) = x^3 - 3x^2 + x - 1$
$F(x) = f(x + 1); G(x) = f(x + 1) + 2$

3. $f(x) = x^3 - 6x^2 + 4x + 12$
$F(x) = f(x + 2); G(x) = f(x + 2) - 4$

4. $f(x) = x^3 - x^2 + \frac{1}{3}x + \frac{26}{27}$
$F(x) = f(x + \frac{1}{3}); G(x) = f(x + \frac{1}{3}) - 1$

5. **(a)** On the basis of Exercises 1 through 4, if $f(x) = x^3 + bx^2 + cx + d$, for what h will the function $F(x) = f(x - h)$ have the form $F(x) = x^3 + Cx + D$; that is for what h will $f(x - h)$ have no x^2 term?
(b) Let $G(x) = F(x) - D = x^3 + Cx$. What are the roots of $G(x) = 0$? Graph $y = G(x)$.

Develop Mastery

Exercises 1–6 Determine whether or not f is a polynomial function. If it is, give its degree.

1. $f(x) = 2 - 3x$

2. $f(x) = 4 - 3x - 2x^4$

3. $f(x) = x^2 + \sqrt{x^2} - 3$

4. $f(x) = x(x + 1)(x + 2)$

5. $f(x) = \frac{2x}{(x + 1)}$

6. $f(x) = \sqrt{x^2 + 9}$

Exercises 7–14 Use the polynomial functions f, g, and h, where

$f(x) = 3x + 2 \qquad g(x) = 5 - x \qquad h(x) = 2x^2 - x.$

(a) Determine an equation that describes the function obtained by combining f, g, and h.

(b) If it is a polynomial function, give the degree, the leading coefficient, and the constant term.

7. $f + g$ **8.** $f - h$ **9.** fg **10.** gh

11. $h \circ f$ **12.** $f \circ h$ **13.** $\frac{f}{g}$ **14.** $\frac{h}{f}$

Exercises 15–20 A polynomial $p(x)$ is given in factored form.

(a) Express $p(x)$ in standard form and give the leading coefficient and the constant term.

(b) Give the coordinates of the x- and y-intercept points for the graph of $y = p(x)$.

15. $p(x) = x(x - 1)(x + 2)$

16. $p(x) = x^2(x - 2)(x - 1)$

17. $p(x) = (x - 1)(x + 1)(2x - 1)$

18. $p(x) = 2(x - 1)(x - 2)(2 - x)$

19. $p(x) = 3x(x - 1)(x + 1)(x + 2)$

20. $p(x) = -x(x^2 - 1)(x + 3)$

Exercises 21–32 **(a)** Express the polynomial in factored form, where the factors are linear or quadratic expressions. Determine the zeros if the domain (replacement set) is **(b)** the set of real numbers or **(c)** the set of complex numbers.

21. $f(x) = x^2 - 1$ **22.** $g(x) = x^2 - 3x - 4$

23. $p(x) = x^3 - 8$ **24.** $H(x) = x^3 + 1$

25. $g(x) = x^3 - 3x^2 + 2x$

26. $g(x) = 2x^3 + x^2 + 2x + 1$

27. $f(x) = x^4 + 3x^2 - 4$

28. $G(x) = x^3 - 3x^2 - x + 3$

29. $f(x) = 2x^2(x + 3) - x^2$

30. $p(x) = x^2(x^2 + 1) - 5x^2$

31. $P(x) = 3x^4 - 2x^3 - 3x + 2$

32. $F(x) = 4x^4 - x^3 - 4x + 1$

Exercises 33–36 Find the solution set for $f(x) < 0$. See Example 1.

33. $f(x) = (1 - x)(x^2 - x - 6)$

34. $f(x) = (x + 2)(-x^2 + 4x - 3)$

35. $f(x) = x^3 + 3x^2 - x - 3$

36. $f(x) = x^3 - 2x^2 - 3x + 6$

Exercises 37–42 **(a)** Factor $p(x)$. **(b)** Find the zeros of p. **(c)** Sketch a graph.

37. $p(x) = x^3 - 1$ **38.** $p(x) = x^3 - 4x$

39. $p(x) = 4x - x^3$ **40.** $p(x) = x^3 - 3x^2 + 2x$

41. $p(x) = x^4 - 5x^2 + 4$

42. $p(x) = x^4 - 10x^2 + 16$

Exercises 43–46   Draw graphs of the three functions on the same set of axes. Note that the given functions are related, so consider translation and reflection.

43. **(a)** $y = x^3$ **(b)** $y = -x^3$
     (c) $y = -x^3 + 1$

44. **(a)** $y = x^3 - x$ **(b)** $y = x - x^3$
     (c) $y = (x - 1)^3 - (x - 1)$

45. **(a)** $y = x^3 - 4x$ **(b)** $y = x^3 - 4x - 1$
     (c) $y = x^3 - 4x + 2$

46. **(a)** $y = x^4 - 4x^2$ **(b)** $y = x^4 - 4x^2 + 4$
     (c) $y = -x^4 + 4x^2$

Exercises 47–52   Determine the end behavior of the graph of the function when $x \to \infty$ and when $x \to -\infty$.

47. $f(x) = 2x - 3x^2$ **48.** $g(x) = x^4 - 3x^2 + 4$

49. $h(x) = 1 + 3.4x - 5.2x^3 - 2x^5$

50. $f(x) = -\frac{2}{5}(2x - x^3)$

51. $g(x) = (3 - 2x)(4 - x^3)$

52. $h(x) = (1 - 2x)(3 - 4x^2)$

Exercises 53–57   If f and g are given polynomial functions where f has degree m and g has degree n, with $m \geq n > 0$, what is the greatest possible degree of the combined function?

53. $f + g$ **54.** $f - g$ **55.** fg

56. $f \circ g$ **57.** $g \circ f$

Exercises 58–62   A graph of a polynomial function is given, where the vertical scale is not necessarily the same as the horizontal scale. From the following list of polynomials, select the one that most nearly corresponds to the given graph.

(a) $f(x) = x^2(x - 1)(x - 3)$
(b) $f(x) = x^2 + 3x$
(c) $f(x) = x^2(x - 2)^2$
(d) $f(x) = x(x - 1)^2(x + 2)^2$
(e) $f(x) = 4x - x^3$
(f) $f(x) = x(x - 1)(3 - x)$
(g) $f(x) = x(1 - x)(3 - x)$
(h) $f(x) = x^4 - 5x^2 + 4$

Exercises 63–64   Determine whether the function f has an inverse. Explain. (*Hint:* Consider end behavior.)

63. $f(x) = x^4 - 2x^3 + 3$ **64.** $f(x) = x^6 - x + 1$

65. Can a polynomial of even degree have an inverse? Give reasons.

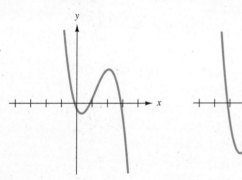

58.

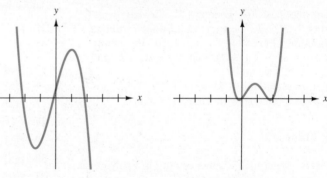

59.

60.

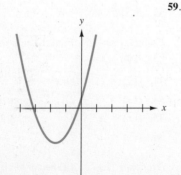

61.

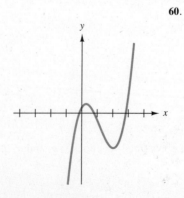

62.

Locating Zeros

The man who breaks out into a new era of thought is usually himself still a prisoner of the old. Even Isaac Newton, who invented the calculus as a mathematical vehicle for his epoch-making discoveries in physics and astronomy, preferred to express himself in archaic geometrical terms.
Freeman Dyson

I had a good teacher for freshman algebra. I think he was simultaneously the football coach. Then I took sophomore geometry. It was apparently thought that students couldn't learn geometry in one year so they had a second course in the junior year. The teacher in this second course didn't understand the subject and I did. I made a lot of trouble for her.

Saunders MacLane

In Section 3.1, when we began to study polynomial functions, we observed that quotients of polynomials are not generally polynomials. Nonetheless, division provides an effective tool for evaluating polynomial functions. In this section we develop a shortcut method called *synthetic division*. Synthetic division provides many kinds of information about polynomial functions, including factors, bounds for zeros, and locations of zeros.

Locator Theorem

Graphs of all polynomial functions share some common properties. The graphs are continuous and smooth, without corners, breaks, or jumps, and the end behavior is as described in Section 3.1.

The idea of continuity (the absence of breaks or jumps) is studied and justified in calculus and subsequent courses, but the following theorem agrees with intuition. It says, in effect, that a polynomial function cannot change from positive to negative without going through 0. The locator theorem is a special case of a theorem from analysis called the Intermediate Value Theorem.

Locator (Sign-Change) Theorem

Suppose p is a polynomial function and a and b are numbers such that $p(a)$ and $p(b)$ have opposite signs. The function p has at least one zero between a and b, or equivalently, the graph of $y = p(x)$ crosses the x-axis between $(a, 0)$ and $(b, 0)$.

EXAMPLE 1 Suppose $f(x) = -2x + 7$ and $g(x) = 3x^2 + 2x - 4$.

(a) Use the locator theorem to show that f has a zero in the interval $(3, 4)$ and g has a zero between 0.5 and 1.

(b) Sketch the graphs of f and g and find all zeros in exact form.

Solution

(a) Evaluating, $f(3) = 1$ (positive) and $f(4) = -1$ (negative). Since f changes sign in the interval $(3, 4)$, there must be a zero in the interval. For g,

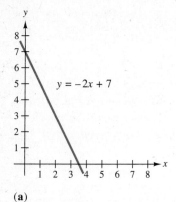

(a)

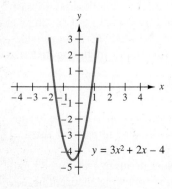

(b)

FIGURE 3.6

$g(0.5) = -\frac{9}{4}$ (negative), and $g(1) = 1$ (positive), so the locator theorem guarantees a zero between 0.5 and 1.

(b) Find the exact values of the zeros by solving the equations

$$-2x + 7 = 0 \quad \text{and} \quad 3x^2 + 2x - 4 = 0.$$

The solution to the first equation is $\frac{7}{2}$, which is in the interval $(3, 4)$, as the theorem asserts. From the quadratic formula, the zeros of the second equation are $\frac{-1 \pm \sqrt{13}}{3}$. The zero we located between 0.5 and 1 is $\frac{-1 + \sqrt{13}}{3}$, about 0.87. Graphs are shown in Figure 3.6. ▲

Without something like the quadratic formula for higher degree polynomials (see the Historical Note "Is There a Cubic Formula?" on p. 163), we are often forced to settle for approximations to zeros. The locator theorem is a powerful tool. With it we can locate a zero to any degree of precision compatible with our evaluation skills. We illustrate the idea in the next example.

EXAMPLE 2   Use the locator theorem to verify that the polynomial function

$$p(x) = 2x^3 - 2x^2 - 3x + 1$$

has a zero c between 0 and 1, then approximate c to two decimal places.

Solution

To show that there is a zero in $(0, 1)$, simply evaluate $p(0)$ and $p(1)$: $p(0) = 1$, and $p(1) = -2$. The sign change, by the locator theorem, indicates that there is a zero between 0 and 1.

To locate c in this interval more closely, simply check values of $p(x)$ on smaller subintervals to see where sign changes occur. Graphs can be very helpful in guiding guesses. Figure 3.7 zooms in on c, showing enlarged portions of the graph near the intercept point. This shows that the zero is nearer 0.29 than 0.30. The desired approximation for c is 0.29. ▲

Function values	Sign change: zero is between
$p(0) = 1.000$ $p(1) = -2.000$	0.00 and 1.00
$p(0.2) = 0.336$ $p(0.3) = -0.026$	0.20 and 0.30
$p(0.29) = 0.011$ $p(0.30) = -0.026$	0.29 and 0.30

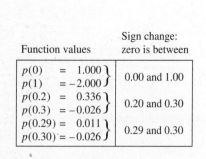
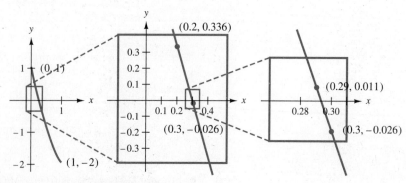

FIGURE 3.7

Zooming in on a zero of $p(x) = 2x^3 - 2x^2 - 3x + 1$

Historical Note

IS THERE A CUBIC FORMULA?

Although Cardan is known for developing the first cubic formula, credit actually belongs to Tartaglia, pictured here.

The Babylonians could solve some quadratics nearly four thousand years ago, as could the ancient Greeks and Egyptians, although they thought only positive roots had meaning. In essence, the quadratic formula has been around for at least a thousand years.

From at least 1200 A.D. people have searched for a comparable formula for cubics. The story of who first succeeded, and when, gets muddled by conflicting claims. At least part of the credit belongs to Scipione del Ferro (ca. 1510). By about 1540, Tartaglia had learned enough to win a public contest, solving 30 cubics in 30 days. Somehow, Cardan got the method from

Tartaglia and published it in 1545, much to Tartaglia's dismay. The solution is often called Cardan's even though he did credit Tartaglia.

The methods of this chapter are much easier to apply, but the formula from Cardan's book still works. Given a cubic of the form

$$x^3 + ax + b = 0,$$

first calculate

$$A = \left(\frac{a}{c}\right)^3 + \left(\frac{b}{2}\right)^2.$$

Cardan's solution is given by

$$x = \sqrt[3]{\sqrt{A} - \frac{b}{2}} - \sqrt[3]{\sqrt{A} + \frac{b}{2}}.$$

The reason for the name of the locator theorem is obvious. Finding an interval (a, b) in which a polynomial function changes sign locates a zero within the interval. By considering smaller and smaller intervals, as in Example 2, we can locate the zero with any desired degree of accuracy. The only limitation is function evaluation.

Calculator Evaluation and Informal Interpolation

Even with a calculator evaluation can be tedious, but there are techniques to make the process tolerable. Among the many possible approaches, two can be implemented on a wide variety of calculators.

A basic difference in calculators is in the number of memory registers available. If a calculator has a MEM , M+ , or Min key, then it has one primary memory register. If it has a STO or → key and alphabetic keys, those indicate multiple addressable memories. We outline separate procedures for the two kinds of calculators. To allow you to compare displays, we illustrate with an evaluation similar to those from Example 2. You should work with your calculator to make sure you can get the same (or comparable) display and the same result.

Calculator Evaluation Algorithms

For the polynomial function $f(x) = 2x^4 - 5x^2 + 3x - 6$, evaluate $f(1.5)$.

Single Memory Calculators

1. Store 1.5 in memory: 1.5 [M in]   [1.5]
2. Enter the leading coefficient: 2   [2]
3. Now for each coefficient (including 0), follow the same steps: [×], [RCL], add or subtract next coefficient:

[×]	[RCL]	[+]	0	[=]	[3]
[×]	[RCL]	[−]	5	[=]	[−0.5]
[×]	[RCL]	[+]	3	[=]	[2.25]
[×]	[RCL]	[−]	6	[=]	[−2.265]

Multiple Memory Calculators

1. Store 1.5 in a register, say register A: 1.5 and then [STO] (or [→]) A.   [1.5]
2. Type in the polynomial, using A in place of x, indicating powers in the way appropriate for your calculator. Your display should look something like:

$$2A\hat{\ }4 - 5A^2 + 3A - 6$$

Now press [EXE] or [ENTER]   [−2.265]

To see how the algorithm for single-memory calculators works, write $f(x)$ in **nested form:** $f(x) = (((2x + 0)x - 5)x + 3)x - 6$. At each step, the algorithm evaluates the expression within a set of parentheses.

If your calculator has a REPLAY feature (usually associated with arrow keys on the keyboard), then you can evaluate a given polynomial for several input numbers without going through all of the steps outlined in the algorithm. Key in the following display:

$$2(1.5)^{\hat{\ }}4 - 5(1.5)^2 + 3(1.5) - 6.$$

After evaluating $f(1.5)(= -2.265)$ by pressing [EXE] or [ENTER] or [=], then press a replay key (most often a left or up arrow), and move the cursor to change each 1.5 to the next input number. Insert extra digits if needed.

EXAMPLE 3   The polynomial $f(x) = 2x^4 - 5x^2 + 3x - 6$ has a zero c between 1.6 and 1.7. Use the locator theorem and repeated evaluations to find c, accurate to four decimal places.

Strategy: Find smaller and smaller intervals in which the function changes signs.

Solution

Follow the strategy. The entries in the following table are calculator evaluations. Each time the sign changes, look at the values of f at each endpoint to make the next guess. This guessing process has an impressive name, **informal linear interpolation.**

$f(x)$ Negative		$f(x)$ Positive		Interval
$f(1.6)$	−0.8928	$f(1.7)$	1.3542	(1.6, 1.7)
$f(1.64)$	−0.0601	$f(1.65)$	0.1615	(1.64, 1.65)
$f(1.642)$	−0.0162	$f(1.643)$	0.0058	(1.642, 1.643)
$f(1.6427)$	−0.0008	$f(1.6428)$	0.0014	(1.6427, 1.6428)

By the locator theorem, c belongs to each of the intervals in the rightmost column of the table. Since $f(1.6427)$ is nearer zero than $f(1.6428)$, it is apparent that c is nearer 1.6427 than 1.6428; to four-decimal place accuracy, c is 1.6427. ▲

Clearly, with patience and a good calculator we can locate zeros of polynomial functions with as much accuracy as needed. A programmable calculator can simplify the work, and a graphing calculator can get considerable accuracy to begin with, but the most significant limitations are time, patience, and the calculator.

In some cases, we can get exact values for zeros of polynomial functions, but we need to do some factoring, as in the next example.

EXAMPLE 4   Verify that -1 is a zero of the polynomial function from Example 2,

$$p(x) = 2x^3 - 2x^2 - 3x + 1,$$

and find the other two zeros in exact form.

Strategy: Show that $p(-1) = 0$. Factor $p(x)$, knowing $(x + 1)$ is a factor, by dividing $p(x)$ by $x + 1$, then use the zero product principal.

Solution

Substituting -1 for x, $p(-1) = 0$. Dividing $p(x)$ by $(x + 1)$ gives the factorization

$$p(x) = (x + 1)(2x^2 - 4x + 1).$$

Hence, the remaining zeros of p are the roots of $2x^2 - 4x + 1 = 0$. By the quadratic formula, the zeros are $\frac{2 \pm \sqrt{2}}{2}$ (in exact form). The smaller of these zeros is about 0.29289, from which we can see that the locator theorem in Example 2 gives us a very close approximation. ▲

Example 4 illustrates the fact that if we can find one zero of a cubic polynomial function in exact form, then we can find all of the zeros. Unfortunately, in most cases where we need the zeros of a given polynomial function, there is no dependable procedure for finding one zero in exact form. With polynomial functions of higher degree, even knowing one zero may not be enough. For some polynomial functions, zeros can be expressed in exact form using radicals and the ordinary operations of algebra.

The Division Algorithm and Synthetic Division

Just as we can divide one integer by another, to get an integer part and a remainder r, we can divide one polynomial by another. The case we will use the most is the situation where we divide a polynomial by a divisor of the form $x - c$, where c is a given number. As with any division, this gives a polynomial part $q(x)$ and a remainder r, but when the divisor has the form $x - c$, the remainder is a constant. The division is expressed as an identity:

$$\frac{p(x)}{x - c} = q(x) + \frac{r}{x - c}, \quad \text{or} \quad p(x) = (x - c)q(x) + r.$$

We state the division algorithm in more precise terms.

Historical Note

THERE IS NO "QUINTIC FORMULA"

Very shortly after discovery of the general solution of the cubic equation (see "Is There a Cubic Formula?" in Section 3.2), Ferrari (Italy, ca. 1545) derived a method for quartics (polynomials of degree 4). Nearly three hundred years passed before much more was done, then, within two years, two brilliant young men completely resolved the question.

For $n = 2$, 3, or 4, solutions for equations of degree n involve nth roots. Why not for degree 5? In 1820 Niels Henrik Abel of Norway was 18 when he thought he had the desired formula. Before it could be checked by others, however, he found his error and proved that there could be no general solution for quintic equations.

In Paris in 1829 another 18-year-old, Evariste Galois, took the final step. In papers written during 1829 and 1830, Galois found the conditions that determine just which polynomial equations of degree 5 or higher can be solved in terms of their coefficients.

Abel died of tuberculosis in 1829 at age 26. In 1831, at the age of 20, Galois was killed in a duel he himself recognized as stupid. During their brief careers, they laid the foundations for modern group theory, which has applications as diverse as solutions for Rubik's cube and the standard model of elementary particle physics at the beginning of the universe.

Division Algorithm

If $p(x)$ is a polynomial of degree greater than 0, then dividing by $(x - c)$ yields a unique polynomial $q(x)$ called the polynomial part and a unique number r called the *remainder* to produce the identity:

$$p(x) = (x - c)q(x) + r \qquad \textbf{(1)}$$

Long division can be used to divide $p(x)$ by $x - c$, but the process may be done more efficiently by an algorithm called **synthetic division.** Without launching a detailed justification of the synthetic division algorithm, we will look at the duplication involved in long division and suggest a way to eliminate most of it. In the next example we divide a polynomial by a linear factor by long division.

EXAMPLE 5   If $p(x) = 2x^3 - x^2 + 3$, divide $p(x)$ by $x - 2$ and give the polynomial part $q(x)$ and the remainder r. Write the result in the form of Equation 1.

Solution

The familiar process of long division produces the following.

$$\begin{array}{r}
\boxed{2}x^2 + \boxed{3}x + \boxed{6} \\
x - 2\,\overline{)\,\boxed{2}x^3 - x^2 + 0 \cdot x + 3} \\
\underline{\boxed{2}x^3 - 4x^2} \\
\boxed{3}x^2 + 0 \cdot x + 3 \\
\underline{\boxed{3}x^2 - 6x} \\
\boxed{6}x + 3 \\
\underline{\boxed{6}x - 12} \\
15 \text{ remainder}
\end{array}$$

Thus $q(x) = 2x^2 + 3x + 6$ and $r = 15$. In the form of Equation 1,

$$p(x) = (x - 2)(2x^2 + 3x + 6) + 15. \quad \blacktriangle$$

A close look at the steps in the solution to Example 5 reveals lots of duplication. The essential information is the -2 (from $x - 2$) and the coefficients of $p(x)$.

A stripped-down version of the long division appears below:

$$\begin{array}{r}
-2 \quad \boxed{2} \qquad -1 \qquad 0 \qquad 3 \\
\searrow -4 \\
\boxed{3} \qquad 0 \qquad 3 \\
\searrow -6 \\
\boxed{6} \qquad 3 \\
\searrow -12 \\
15
\end{array}$$

At each step, multiply the boxed number by -2 and subtract the product (shown by the arrow) from the number above to get the next boxed number.

Rather than subtracting (changing signs and adding) it is easier to change the sign of -2 so that we need only multiply by 2 and add. This eliminates unnecessary repetition and compresses the notation, as shown:

Change sign

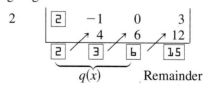

$$2 \quad \left|\begin{array}{cccc} \boxed{2} & -1 & 0 & 3 \\ & \nearrow 4 & \nearrow 6 & \nearrow 12 \\ \boxed{2} & \boxed{3} & \boxed{6} & \boxed{15} \end{array}\right.$$

$$\underbrace{}_{q(x)} \qquad \text{Remainder}$$

Bring down the leading coefficient of $p(x)$, multiply by 2 and add each product to the next coefficient, following the arrows. From the bottom line read the coefficients of $q(x)$ where the degree is one less than the degree of $p(x)$, and the remainder.

This process is called *synthetic division*. We will use it repeatedly throughout the rest of this chapter.

Synthetic Division Algorithm

To divide a polynomial $p(x)$ of degree n by $x - c$:

1. On the top line, at the left, write c (change the sign from $-c$).
2. Write all coefficients of $p(x)$ in order of decreasing powers of x (including any zero coefficients) and bring down the leading coefficient to the bottom line.
3. Multiply each entry on the bottom line by c and add the product to the next coefficient to get the new entry on the bottom line.
4. The first n entries on the bottom line are the coefficients of $q(x)$, whose degree is one less than the degree of $p(x)$.
5. The last entry on the bottom line is the remainder r.

EXAMPLE 6 Let

$$p(x) = 2x^4 - 5x^2 + 3x - 6.$$

Find the polynomial part $q(x)$ and remainder r when $p(x)$ is divided by **(a)** $x - 2$ **(b)** $x + 1$ **(c)** $x + 2$.

Solution

For each division operation, write out the coefficients of $p(x)$, including 0 for the x^3 term. To divide by $x - c$, write c at the left and proceed as follows.

(a)

$$
\begin{array}{r|rrrrr}
2 & 2 & 0 & -5 & 3 & -6 \\
  &   & 4 & 8 & 6 & 18 \\
\hline
  & 2 & 4 & 3 & 9 & \boxed{12}
\end{array}
$$

$$q(x) = 2x^3 + 4x^2 + 3x + 9, \; r = 12$$

(b)

$$
\begin{array}{r|rrrrr}
-1 & 2 & 0 & -5 & 3 & -6 \\
   &   & -2 & 2 & 3 & -6 \\
\hline
   & 2 & -2 & -3 & 6 & \boxed{-12}
\end{array}
$$

$$q(x) = 2x^3 - 2x^2 - 3x + 6, \; r = -12$$

(c)

$$
\begin{array}{r|rrrrr}
-2 & 2 & 0 & -5 & 3 & -6 \\
   &   & -4 & 8 & -6 & 6 \\
\hline
   & 2 & -4 & 3 & -3 & \boxed{0}
\end{array}
$$

$$q(x) = 2x^3 - 4x^2 + 3x - 3, \; r = 0 \quad \blacktriangle$$

Factor and Remainder Theorems

In Example 6c, dividing $p(x)$ by $x + 2$ gives a polynomial part of $2x^3 - 4x^2 + 3x - 3$ and $r = 0$. In the form of Equation 1,

$$2x^4 - 5x^2 + 3x - 6 = (x + 2)(2x^3 - 4x^2 + 3x - 3)$$

In other words division has identified factors of $p(x)$. The form of the equation in the division algorithm is critical here:

$$p(x) = (x - c)q(x) + r.$$

It should be clear that whenever we divide $p(x)$ by a linear factor $x - c$, if the remainder is 0, then $(x - c)$ is a factor of $p(x)$. Conversely, if $(x - c)$ is a factor of $p(x)$, then $p(x) = (x - c)q(x)$, so r must be 0.

We can also read another extremely useful relation from the division algorithm. Equation 1 is an identity, so we can replace x by any number from the domain of p and obtain a true statement. In particular, if we substitute the number c for x, we obtain

$$p(c) = (c - c)q(c) + r = 0 \cdot q(c) + r = 0 + r = r.$$

The remainder is always equal to the value of the function p at the number c.

These observations are summed up in two important theorems called the remainder theorem and the factor theorem. For each theorem, $p(x)$ is a polynomial, c is any number, and $q(x)$ and r denote the polynomial part and the remainder in the division algorithm.

Remainder and Factor Theorems

When $p(x)$ is divided by $x - c$, the remainder is $p(c)$.
When $p(x)$ is divided by $x - c$, then $x - c$ is a factor of $p(x)$ if and only if $p(c) = 0$.

EXAMPLE 7 Let $p(x) = x^4 - 3x^3 + 3x - 1$. Use the remainder theorem to evaluate **(a)** $p(-2)$ and **(b)** $p(1 + \sqrt{2})$.

Solution

Synthetic division is frequently easier than direct substitution.

(a) Divide by $x + 2$; $p(-2)$ is the remainder.

$$
\begin{array}{r|rrrrr}
-2 & 1 & -3 & 0 & 3 & -1 \\
   &   & -2 & 10 & -20 & 34 \\
\hline
   & 1 & -5 & 10 & -17 & \boxed{33 = p(-2)}
\end{array}
$$

As a check, we can verify by direct substitution that $p(-2)$ is 33.

(b) Direct substitution works fairly well for simple numbers like -2, but for something more complicated, such as $1 + \sqrt{2}$, it is not nearly so appealing. Most of us would rather not evaluate an expression such as $(1 + \sqrt{2})^4$. Synthetic division is easier.

$$
\begin{array}{r|rrrrr}
1 + \sqrt{2} & 1 & -3 & 0 & 3 & -1 \\
   &   & 1 + \sqrt{2} & -\sqrt{2} & -2 - \sqrt{2} & -1 \\
\hline
   & 1 & -2 + \sqrt{2} & -\sqrt{2} & 1 - \sqrt{2} & \boxed{-2 = p(1 + \sqrt{2})}
\end{array}
$$

This shows that $p(1 + \sqrt{2})$ is -2. ▲

For Graphers 3.2

APPROPRIATE WINDOWS

Perhaps the most critical effect on the usefulness of the graph of a polynomial function is the view, the calculator window. Depending on the information needed, a particular problem may require a large x- or y-range (to show end behavior or display all the zeros or the turning points), or it may need a tiny window to zoom in on zeros or intersection points. Information about values of the function for different x values can be a guide. Still, it is often necessary to experiment, to try several different windows. The window choices in the following example are not unique, and they were selected by experimenting.

EXAMPLE   For $p(x) = 2x^3 - 2x^2 - 3x + 1$ (from Examples 2 and 4 of Section 3.2), choose windows that show approximately the views in Figure 3.7, and Trace to approximate the zero to four decimal places.

Solution

Window, Scale	Zero
$[-2, 2.5] \times [-2, 1]$, 1	0.3
$[0, 0.4] \times [-0.3, 0.3]$, 0.1	0.29
$[0.28, 0.31] \times [-0.03, 0.02]$, 0.01	0.293
$[0.290, 0.295] \times [-0.002, 0.002]$, 0.001	0.2929

▲

Exercises

1. Beginning with the Familiar Window, zoom in as needed to approximate the accuracy of the zero in the example above (that is, until the y value for the nearest Trace pixel is less than 10^{-5}).

2. Use your graphing calculator to duplicate the solution to Example 3 in Section 3.2.

3. Calculators cannot distinguish between rational and irrational numbers, but they carry more precision internally than they display. As we learned in Example 7 of Section 3.2 for $p(x) = x^4 - 3x^3 + 3x - 1$, $p(1 + \sqrt{2}) = -2$.
   (a) Using six-decimal-place accuracy, $1 + \sqrt{2} = 2.414214$. Evaluate $(2.414214)^2 - 3(2.414214)^3 + 3(2.414214) - 1$.   How closely does this approximate -2?
   (b) Store $1 + \sqrt{2}$ (with full calculator accuracy) in memory register X ($1 + \sqrt{2} \boxed{\rightarrow} X \boxed{\text{EXE}}$). Type on your home screen $X^\wedge 4 - 3X^\wedge 3 + 3X - 1$ and $\boxed{\text{EXE}}$. Finally, add 2 to the displayed result ($\boxed{\text{ANS}} + 2 \boxed{\text{EXE}}$).

   (c) Explain how you know that the calculator result in (b) is not an integer. Why does the calculator display an integer for $p(1 + \sqrt{2})$? Is $p(1 + \sqrt{2})$ exactly equal to -2 or not? Explain.

4. Experiment to find a window that shows the turning points for the graph of $f(x) = x^3 - 3x^2 - 9x + 1$ (see DM Exercise 64). Trace to approximate the coordinates of the turning points to one decimal place. Explain why your calculator approximation is not as accurate as solving the quadratic equation $3ax^2 + 2bx + c = 0$.

5. Repeat the preceding exercise for $f(x) = x^3 - 3x^2 - 6x + 1$ (see DM Exercise 67).

6. Experiment with various windows for the function $f(x) = x^3 + 6x$ (see DM Exercise 68). Explain why it is difficult to conclude on the basis of your calculator graphs whether or not the function has any turning points.

The remainder theorem also gives an alternative way to find a remainder without performing a lengthy division.

| **EXAMPLE 8** | Let $p(x) = 4x^{15} + 5x^7 + 3x^4 + 2$. Find the remainder when $p(x)$ is divided by $x + 1$.

Solution

Strategy: Evaluate $p(-1)$. By the remainder theorem, r is $p(-1)$.

Follow the strategy.

$$p(-1) = 4(-1)^{15} + 5(-1)^7 + 3(-1)^4 + 2 = -4 - 5 + 3 + 2 = -4.$$

Hence $p(-1) = -4$, so r is -4. ▲

| **EXAMPLE 9** | Let $p(x) = x^3 - x^2 - 3x - 1$. **(a)** Use the factor theorem to show that $x + 1$ is a factor of $p(x)$. **(b)** Find all roots of the equation $p(x) = 0$.

Solution

By direct evaluation, it is easy to see that $p(-1) = 0$, so $x + 1$ is a factor of $p(x)$. This does not give us the other factor, though. Synthetic division also tells us that $p(-1) = 0$, and it gives us the other factor.

$$
\begin{array}{r|rrrr}
-1 & 1 & -1 & -3 & -1 \\
   &   & -1 & 2 & 1 \\
\hline
   & 1 & -2 & -1 & \boxed{0 = p(-1)}
\end{array}
$$

Since $x + 1$ is one factor of $p(x)$ and, from the bottom row, the other factor is $x^2 - 2x - 1$. We have

$$p(x) = (x + 1)(x^2 - 2x - 1).$$

(b) Now use the zero product principle to solve the equation $p(x) = 0$:

$$x + 1 = 0 \qquad \text{or} \qquad x^2 - 2x - 1 = 0.$$

By the quadratic formula the roots of the second equation are $1 \pm \sqrt{2}$. The roots of the equation are: -1, $1 + \sqrt{2}$, and $1 - \sqrt{2}$. ▲

EXERCISES 3.2

Check Your Understanding

Exercises 1–6 True or False. Give reasons for your conclusion.

1. The function $p(x) = 4x^3 - x$ has three real zeros.

2. The positive zero of $f(x) = x^3 - 3x$ is less than 1.73.

3. If k is any positive number, then $p(x) = x^3 - kx$ has exactly one real zero.

4. If p and q are polynomial functions and $p(x) = (x - c)q(x)$, then c is a zero of p.

5. A polynomial function of degree 5 must have at least one real zero.

6. Every polynomial function of degree 4 must have at least two real zeros.

Exercises 7–10 Complete the sentence by selecting from the list below *all choices* that make the statement true.

    (a) 0   **(b)** 1   **(c)** 2   **(d)** positive
    (e) negative   **(f)** in $(1, 2)$ **(g)** in $(0, 0.5)$
    (h) in $(1.5, 2)$ **(i)** in $(0, 1)$

7. If $f(x) = 3x^3 + x^2 - 1$, then at least one zero of f is _____.

8. When $2x^3 + 3x^2 - 3x$ is divided by $x - 1$, the remainder is _____.

9. If $\quad x^3 + 2x^2 + 1 = (x + 1)(x^2 - x - 1) + r$, then r is _____.

10. If $p(x) = x^3 - kx$ has three distinct real zeros, then k cannot be _____.

Explore and Discover

1. (a) Factor the polynomials $x^2 - 1$, $x^3 - 1$, and $x^4 - 1$.
    (b) Use synthetic division to show that $x - 1$ is a factor of $x^5 - 1$ and find the other factor. Do the same for $x^6 - 1$.
    (c) Explain why $x - 1$ must be a factor of $x^n - 1$ for any positive integer n. Find the other factor.
    (d) Show that $x + 1$ is a factor of $x^3 + 1$ and of $x^5 + 1$. Of what other polynomials of the form $x^n + 1$ is $x + 1$ a factor?

2. Find a graph of some function f in one of the figures in Section 2.2 and find an interval (a, b) such that the numbers $f(a)$ and $f(b)$ have opposite signs, but for which f has *no* zero between a and b. Discuss how the graph of your function f differs from the graph of a polynomial function, so the locator theorem does not apply.

3. (a) Show that 0.5 is a zero of $p(x) = 6x^3 + x^2 - 4x + 1$, but that both $p(0)$ and $p(1)$ are positive.
    (b) From **(a)** it is true that p has a zero (namely 0.5) between 0 and 1 even though there is no sign change on the interval. Does this contradict the locator theorem? Explain.

4. *Calculator Limitations* Write out four or five terms of each sequence of equations. Use the quadratic formula with your calculator to find numerical approximations for the roots of each equation. Continue until your calculator gives an answer you know to be wrong.
    (a) $x^2 - ax + 1 = 0$, where $a = 100$; 1,000; 10,000; etc.
    (b) $x^2 - 4x + b = 0$, where $b = 3.99$; 3.999; 3.9999; 3.99999; etc.

5. If class members have different calculators, compare the results obtained in the previous exercise for calculators that display 8, 10, 12 digits. Write a paragraph to discuss the limitations you observed and explain differences in the failure points for different calculators.

Develop Mastery

Exercises 1–6 Use the locator theorem to determine which half of the interval contains a zero of the function.

1. $p(x) = x^3 - 3x + 1$; $[-2, -1]$
2. $f(x) = 2x^3 + 3x^2 - x - 2$; $[0, 1]$
3. $g(x) = x^3 - 5x^2 + 5x + 3$; $[-1, 0]$
4. $p(x) = x^3 - 5x^2 + 7x - 2$; $[2.5, 3]$
5. $p(x) = x^3 - 5x^2 + 7x - 2$; $[0, 0.5]$
6. $g(x) = -2x^3 - 3x^2 + x + 2$; $[0.7, 0.8]$

Exercises 7–12 Locate each of the zeros of the function p between successive integers.

7. $p(x) = x^3 - 3x^2 - x + 2$
8. $p(x) = x^3 - 3x^2 - 3$
9. $p(x) = x^3 - 2x^2 - x + 3$
10. $p(x) = x^3 + 2x^2 - 3x - 2$
11. $p(x) = x^4 - 3x^3 - x^2 + 2$
12. $p(x) = x^4 - 3x^3 - 4x - 5$

Exercises 13–14 There is a zero c of the function in the given interval. Use the locator theorem to find c to the nearest hundredth.

13. $p(x) = x^3 - 2x - 6$; $[2, 3]$
14. $p(x) = x^3 - 2x^2 + 3x + 5$; $[-1, 0]$

Exercises 15–18 **(a)** Sketch the graph of both functions on the same system of coordinates and let c be the x-coordinate of the single point where the graphs intersect. **(b)** Approximate c to the nearest hundredth.

15. $y = x^3 - 3x$ **16.** $y = x - x^3$
    $y = -3$ $y = 1$

17. $y = x^3$ **18.** $y = 1 - x^3$
    $y = x + 1$ $y = x^2 - 2$

Exercises 19–28 Use synthetic division to find the polynomial part $q(x)$ and remainder r when $p(x)$ is divided by the given divisor. Write the result in the form $p(x) = (x - c)q(x) + r$, and find $p(c)$.

19. $p(x) = 2x^3 + 3x^2 - x - 2$; $x - 1$
20. $p(x) = 2x^3 + 3x^2 - x - 2$; $x + 2$

21. $p(x) = 3x^4 + x^3 - 2x^2 + x - 1; \quad x + 1$

22. $p(x) = x^3 - 3x^2 - x + 2; \quad x - 4$

23. $p(x) = 2x^3 - 3x^2 + 9x - 4; \quad x - \frac{1}{2}$

24. $p(x) = 2x^4 - 5x^3 - 5x^2 + 3x + 2; \quad x + \frac{1}{2}$

25. $p(x) = x^5 - 4x + 2; \quad x - 1$

26. $p(x) = 3x^4 + 2x^3 + x - 1; \quad x + 2$

27. $p(x) = 4x^3 + 3x - 3; \quad x - \frac{1}{2}$

28. $p(x) = 3x^3 + 7x^2 - 3; \quad x - \frac{2}{3}$

Exercises 29–32 Find the remainder when the polynomial is divided by $x - c$.

29. $4x^{12} - 3x^8 + 5x^2 - 2x + 3; \quad c = -1$

30. $x^{10} - 64x^4 + 3; \quad c = 2$

31. $x^{10} - 1024; \quad c = 2$

32. $3x^{50} + 5x^{35} + x^{15} - 5; \quad c = 1$

Exercises 33–36 Use the factor theorem to determine whether the linear expression is a factor of the polynomial. If it is, find the other factor.

33. $x^{10} - 8x^6 + 16x^5; \quad x + 2$

34. $x^6 + 2x^4 + 6x^3 - 2x - 6; \quad x + 3$

35. $x^4 - 25x^2 - 60x - 36; \quad x - 2$

36. $x^4 - 25x^2 - 60x - 36; \quad x + 3$

Exercises 37–42 Find the value of k for which the linear expression is a factor of the polynomial.

37. $2x^3 + 4x^2 + kx - 3; \quad x + 2$

38. $x^4 + kx^2 + kx + 2; \quad x - 2$

39. $kx^3 + 3x^2 - 4kx - 7; \quad x - 3$

40. $x^3 - k^2x + (k + 1); \quad x - k$

41. $2x^{17} + 5x^{13} + kx^7 - 8x; \quad x + 1$

42. $25x^{40} + 32x^{23} - 5kx^5 + 13; \quad x - 1$

Exercises 43–50 Use synthetic division to show that $x - c$ is a factor of the polynomial and then express the polynomial as a product of linear factors.

43. $3x^3 + x^2 - 3x - 1; \quad c = 1$

44. $x^3 - x^2 - 10x - 8; \quad c = -2$

45. $3x^3 + 4x^2 - 5x - 2; \quad c = 1$

46. $2x^3 - 3x^2 - 8x + 12; \quad c = 1.5$

47. $3x^3 + x^2 - 27x - 9; \quad c = -\frac{1}{3}$

48. $4x^3 - 11x^2 - 6x + 9; \quad c = \frac{3}{4}$

49. $x^3 - 5x^2 + 3x + 9; \quad c = 3$

50. $x^3 - 2x^2 - 5x + 6; \quad c = -2$

Exercises 51–56 Find the value of k such that dividing $p(x)$ by the linear expression gives the listed remainder.

51. $p(x) = 2x^3 + 4x^2 + kx - 3; \quad x + 2; \quad r = 0$

52. $p(x) = 2x^3 + 4x^2 + kx + 3; \quad x + 2; \quad r = 3$

53. $p(x) = x^3 + kx^2 - kx + 8; \quad x - 2; \quad r = 1$

54. $p(x) = x^3 + kx^2 - kx + 8; \quad x - 2; \quad r = 0$

55. $p(x) = 27x^4 - 81x^3 + kx; \quad x - 3; \quad r = 0$

56. $p(x) = x^3 - kx^2 + kx + 4; \quad x - 1; \quad r = k$

Exercises 57–58 **(a)** Use the locator theorem to locate the roots between successive integers. **(b)** Find all roots in exact form.

57. $x^4 - 4x^2 + 1 = 0$ **58.** $x^4 - 2x^2 - 1 = 0$

59. An isosceles triangle has the dimensions shown in the diagram. If the area is equal to 10 square units, find the length of the altitude h (to the nearest tenth).

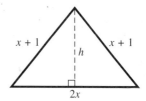

60. A storage tank consists of a right circular cylinder mounted on top of a hemisphere, as shown in the diagram. If the height of the cylindrical portion is 12 feet and the tank is to have a capacity of 1250π cubic feet, find the radius r of the cylinder to 3 significant digits.

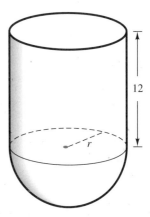

61. What are the dimensions of a rectangle of area 7 square inches that has a diagonal 1 inch longer than the length of one of its sides? Give the result rounded off to 3 significant digits.

62. A storage tank has the shape of a cube. If one of the dimensions is increased by 2 and another by 3, while the third is decreased by 4, then the resulting rectangular tank will have a volume of 600 cubic units. What is the length of an edge of the original cube to 3 significant digits?

63. A rectangular storage container is 3 by 4 by 5 feet.
   (a) What is its capacity (volume)?
   (b) If we increase each of the dimensions by x feet in order to get a container with a capacity five times as large as the original, how large must x be, rounded off to 3 significant digits?

Looking Ahead to Calculus—Turning Points   In general, graphs of polynomial functions have humps, whose high and low points are called *turning points,* as in the diagram. Techniques for finding turning points are studied in calculus. For a cubic polynomial function, say $f(x) = ax^3 + bx^2 + cx + d$, the x-coordinates of the turning points, if any, are the real roots of the quadratic equation

$$3ax^2 + 2bx + c = 0.$$

Note how this equation is related to the formula for f. If the quadratic equation has two real roots, the graph of f will have two turning points; otherwise the graph is simply increasing or decreasing.

Exercises 64–69   **(a)** Find the coordinates, if any, of all turning points. If there are none, determine whether the function is increasing or decreasing. **(b)** Sketch a graph.

64. $f(x) = x^3 - 3x^2 - 9x + 1$

65. $f(x) = x^3 - 6x^2 + 9x$

66. $f(x) = x^3 - 3x^2$

67. $f(x) = x^3 - 3x^2 - 6x + 1$

68. $f(x) = x^3 + 6x$

69. $f(x) = -x^3 + 3x^2 - 6x$

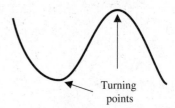

Turning points

Exercises 70–73   The function f is either increasing or decreasing (determine which), so it has an inverse. Evaluate (rounded off to 2 significant digits) **(a)** $f^{-1}(3)$ and **(b)** $f^{-1}(-2)$. (*Hint:* Write $y = f(x)$, interchange x and y, replace x by 3 for **(a)**, and solve for y to 1 decimal place.)

70. $f(x) = 2x^3 + 3x - 4$

71. $f(x) = x^3 - 3x^2 + 4x + 5$

72. $f(x) = 2 - x + x^2 - 2x^3$

73. $f(x) = 4 - 3x - 2x^3$

SECTION 3.3   **More about Zeros**

Why do we try to prove things anyway? I think because we want to understand them. We also want a sense of certainty. Mathematics is a very deep field. Its results are stacked very high, and they depend on each other a lot. You build a tower of blocks but if one block is a bit wobbly, you can't build the tower very high before it will fall over. So I think mathematicians are concerned about rigor, which gives us certainty. But I also think proofs are so that we can understand. I guess I like explanations better than step-by-step rigorous demonstrations.

William P. Thurston

When the graph of a polynomial function just touches the x-axis, as the graph of

$$y = x^2 - 2x + 1 = (x - 1)^2$$

does, it has a **repeated zero.** If $f(x) = (x - c)^k q(x)$ and $q(c) \neq 0$, then c is a zero of **multiplicity k.**

Strategy: From the factor theorem, if c is a zero of function p then $x - c$ is a factor of $p(x)$.

EXAMPLE 1 Find a polynomial function **(a)** of degree 3 with leading coefficient 1 that has -1, 1, and 2 as zeros **(b)** of degree 4 with leading coefficient 2 that has -1, -1, 1, and $\frac{1}{2}$ as zeros.

Solution

(a) Following the strategy, $p(x)$ must have factors $x + 1$, $x - 1$, and $x - 2$. The product of these factors will be of degree 3 and have leading coefficient 1. We can write $p(x)$ as a product of factors and in expanded form:

$$p(x) = (x + 1)(x - 1)(x - 2) = x^3 - 2x^2 - x + 2$$

(b) Listing -1 as a zero twice indicates that -1 is a zero of multiplicity 2. With a repeated zero, $q(x)$ must have a repeated factor. Thus $q(x)$ has factors $x + 1$, $x + 1$, $x - 1$, and $x - \frac{1}{2}$. To get the desired leading coefficient, multiply by 2. The polynomial function is

$$q(x) = 2(x + 1)(x + 1)(x - 1)(x - \tfrac{1}{2}) = (x + 1)^2(x - 1)(2x - 1)$$
$$= 2x^4 + x^3 - 3x^2 - x + 1. \quad \blacktriangle$$

Number of Zeros of Polynomial Functions

How many zeros does a polynomial function of degree n have? The graph of every quadratic function is a parabola, so every quadratic equation has exactly two roots. These can by repeated, and they need not be real numbers. The nature of the zeros is apparent in the graph of a function. In the following example we consider a cubic function F whose graph has three x-intercept points that indicate three real zeros, and another cubic function G with one real zero and two imaginary zeros.

Strategy: Since $F(x)$ can be factored, its zeros are easy to find. $G(x) = F(x) + 4$, so the graph of G is a vertical translation of the graph of F. Use the graph of G as a guide to find zeros.

EXAMPLE 2 If $F(x) = x^3 - 2x$ and $G(x) = x^3 - 2x + 4$, sketch the graphs of F and G on the same system of coordinates and find the zeros of these functions.

Solution

Follow the strategy.

$$F(x) = x(x^2 - 2) \quad \text{or} \quad F(x) = x(x - \sqrt{2})(x + \sqrt{2}).$$

Hence the zeros of F are 0 and $\pm\sqrt{2}$. Plotting a few more points gives the graph shown in Figure 3.8.

To get the graph of G, translate the graph of F 4 units up. Since the point $(-2, -4)$ is on the graph of F, the point $(-2, 0)$ is on the graph of G. (See Figure 3.8). That means that -2 is a zero of G, and hence $x + 2$ is a factor of $G(x)$. Synthetic division gives the other factor.

$$
\begin{array}{r|rrrr}
-2 & 1 & 0 & -2 & 4 \\
   &   & -2 & 4 & -4 \\
\hline
   & 1 & -2 & 2 & 0 = G(-2)
\end{array}
$$

Thus $G(x) = (x + 2)(x^2 - 2x + 2)$, and the other two zeros of G are found by solving $x^2 - 2x + 2 = 0$, giving $x = 1 \pm i$. The graph of G crosses the x-axis just once. The zeros of G are 1, $1 + i$, and $1 - i$; one real zero and two complex conjugate zeros. $\quad \blacktriangle$

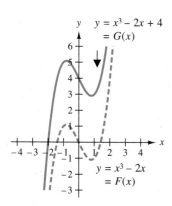

$y = x^3 - 2x + 4$
$= G(x)$

$y = x^3 - 2x$
$= F(x)$

FIGURE 3.8

CARL FRIEDRICH GAUSS (1777–1855)

Mathematician, astronomer, and physicist Carl Friedrich Gauss

Called the "prince of mathematicians," Gauss is clearly among the greatest mathematicians of all time. He contributed to all areas of mathematics, as well as to astronomy and physics, and we are still building directly on foundations he laid.

Most of us could construct an equilateral triangle or a square with a compass and ruler. The Greeks also constructed a pentagon. Angle bisection allows us to double the number of sides, so it is theoretically possible to construct regular polygons of n sides if n is a power of 2 or $n = 2^k \cdot 3$ or $n = 2^k \cdot 5$, where k is any nonnegative integer. Gauss made the first significant progress in 2000 years when he discovered how to construct a regular polygon

of 17 sides when he was almost 17 himself. His construction was published before he turned 19.

Gauss was the first to use i for $\sqrt{-1}$ and thoroughly understood the importance of complex numbers in the solution of equations. Although he left college before receiving his doctorate, he submitted his dissertation and attained the degree by the age of 21. His thesis established the fundamental theorem of algebra. This theorem so fascinated him that he gave three different proofs during his lifetime.

Returning to constructions, he proved in 1826 that an n-gon is constructible for an odd prime n only when n has the form $2^{2^k} + 1$ (for instance, 3, 5, and 17).

Fundamental Theorem of Algebra

The general situation is summed up in the **fundamental theorem of algebra** and some of its consequences, called *corollaries*. These are stated in terms of the complex-number system and proofs necessarily involve complex numbers, as well. The fundamental theorem was first proved by one of the greatest mathematicians of all times. See the Historical Note, "Carl Friedrich Gauss."

Fundamental Theorem of Algebra

Suppose p is a polynomial function of degree n, $n \geq 1$. There is at least one number c where $p(c) = 0$; that is, p has at least one zero (which may be an imaginary number.)

Corollary 1: In the complex number system, p has exactly n zeros (counting multiplicities).

Corollary 2: If the coefficients of $p(x)$ are real numbers, then the graph of p can cross (or touch) the x-axis in at most n points.

*The problem that infected me
with such virulence . . .
concerned solving cubic
equations and the answer
had been known since
Cardano published it in
1545. What I did not know
was how to derive it. The
sages who had designed the
mathematics curricula . . .
had stopped at solving
quadratic equations
Questions by curious
students about cubic and
higher-order equations were
deflected with answers such
as "This is too advanced for
you" or "You will learn this
when you study higher
mathematics," thereby
creating a forbidden-fruit
aura about the subject.*

Mark Kac

The fundamental theorem of algebra is what mathematicians call an **existence theorem.** For any given polynomial function of positive degree, the theorem states that zeros exist, but it provides no help for finding any particular zero. For linear and quadratic functions we can find the zeros exactly; for higher-degree polynomial functions, the situation becomes more difficult.

For most of the problems that arise in applications we can only approximate zeros. Virtually all numerical techniques to do this are rooted in the locator theorem, our most fundamental tool. Mathematicians have found a number of theorems, however, that can help in the search for certain kinds of zeros.

Gauss' proof of the fundamental theorem applies to polynomial functions with both imaginary and real coefficients. We emphasize, however, that in this chapter, we discuss only polynomial functions with real number coefficients.

Nature of Zeros of Polynomial Functions

The next theorem generalizes what we already know about quadratic polynomials. In certain situations zeros of quadratic functions come in pairs. For example,

if $f(x) = x^2 - 4x + 1$, then the zeros of f are $2 + \sqrt{3}$ and $2 - \sqrt{3}$;

if $g(x) = x^2 - 2x + 2$, then the zeros of g are $-1 + i$ and $-1 - i$.

The numbers $a + bi$ and $a - bi$ are called **complex conjugates.** Certain kinds of zeros must occur in pairs in higher-degree polynomials, as well.

Conjugate Zeros Theorem

Let p be any polynomial function with *real number coefficients.*

If the imaginary number $a + bi$ is a zero of p, then $a - bi$ is also a zero. Here b is not zero.

If, in addition, p has *integer coefficients* and $a + \sqrt{b}$ is a zero of p, then $a - \sqrt{b}$ is also a zero. Here b is not a perfect square.

The conjugate zeros theorem is illustrated in the next example.

EXAMPLE 3 Given that $p(i) = 0$, find all the zeros of
$$p(x) = 2x^4 - 2x^3 + x^2 - 2x - 1.$$

Solution

Strategy: Since the coefficients of p are real numbers, the conjugate zeros theorem applies; if i is a zero, then $-i$ must also be a zero.

As the strategy suggests, both i and $-i$ are zeros. Thus $p(x)$ has $(x - i) \times (x + i) = x^2 + 1$ as a factor. To find the other factor of $p(x)$, use synthetic division twice, once with i and once with $-i$, or use long division to divide $p(x)$ by $x^2 + 1$. Either way,

$$p(x) = (x^2 + 1)(2x^2 - 2x - 1).$$

The remaining two zeros of p are the roots of $2x^2 - 2x - 1 = 0$, which the quadratic formula gives as $\frac{1 \pm \sqrt{3}}{2}$. Therefore, the polynomial p has two pairs of conjugate zeros: $\frac{1}{2} + \frac{1}{2}\sqrt{3}$ and $\frac{1}{2} - \frac{1}{2}\sqrt{3}$, i and $-i$. ▲

Clearing Fractions and Rational Zeros

The second part of the conjugate zeros theorem is stated for polynomials with integer coefficients. The theorem requires only that coefficients be rational numbers. It is often convenient to work with integers, and the next theorem does depend on having on integer coefficients.

Multiplying an equation by a nonzero constant to clear fractions does not change the roots of the equation. For example, multiplying both sides of the equation

$$x^3 + \frac{7}{2}x^2 + \frac{7}{3}x - \frac{2}{3} = 0,$$

by 6, we get an equation with integer coefficients having the same roots,

$$6x^3 + 21x^2 + 14x - 4 = 0.$$

If all coefficients are integers, then the following theorem provides a complete list of all the rational numbers that can possibly be zeros.

Rational Zeros Theorem

Let p be any polynomial function with *integer coefficients*. The only rational numbers that can possibly be zeros of p are the numbers of the form $\frac{r}{s}$, where r is a divisor of the constant term, and s is a divisor of the leading coefficient.

   If none of these numbers is a zero, then p has no rational zeros.

The rational zeros theorem is useful and important because it lists all the possibilities for rational zeros. The theorem does not indicate whether a given polynomial function has any rational zeros at all; many do not. Used with care, the theorem can effectively guide the search for zeros. For an outline of the proof, see Explore and Discover Exercises 1 to 3.

Strategy: (b) To get integer coefficients, multiply through by 20 and then apply the rational zeros theorem. Zeros of $20R$ are the same as the zeros of R.

EXAMPLE 4   Use the rational zeros theorem to list all possible rational zeros of P and R.

(a) $P(x) = x^3 - 4x^2 + x - 6$

(b) $R(x) = \frac{1}{5}x^4 - \frac{3}{5}x^3 - \frac{13}{20}x^2 + \frac{9}{4}x - \frac{9}{10}$.

Solution

(a) For P, begin by listing all possible numerators (factors of -6) and denominators (factors of 1):

Possible numerators:	$\pm$ 1, 2, 3, 6
Possible denominators:	$\pm$ 1

The only possibilities for rational zeros of P are the integers $-6, -3, -2,$ $-1, 1, 2, 3,$ and 6.

(b) For R, follow the strategy and find possible rational zeros of S where

$$S(x) = 20R(x) = 4x^4 - 12x^3 - 13x^2 + 45x - 18.$$

Possible numerators (factors of -18): $\pm$ 1, 2, 3, 6, 9, 18
Possible denominators (factors of 4): $\pm$ 1, 2, 4

The rational zeros theorem tells us that S, and hence R, has 24 possible rational zeros:

$$\pm[1, 2, 3, 6, 9, 18, \tfrac{1}{2}, \tfrac{3}{2}, \tfrac{9}{2}, \tfrac{1}{4}, \tfrac{3}{4}, \tfrac{9}{4}] \quad \blacktriangle$$

EXAMPLE 5 Find all rational roots.

(a) $2x^3 + 3x^2 - 1 = 0$ **(b)** $2x^3 - 3x^2 + x - 1 = 0$

Strategy: List possible roots for each equation and then use synthetic division to test the possibilities.

Solution

Both equations have the same leading coefficient and constant term, so the possible rational roots are the same, namely ± 1 and $\pm\tfrac{1}{2}$. When testing for zeros, list the coefficients only once and write only the bottom row of synthetic division for each divisor.

(a) Let $P(x) = 2x^3 + 3x^2 - 1$.

Coefficients of $P(x)$

Possible rational roots	2	3	0	-1	
1	2	5	5	$4 = P(1)$	1 is not a zero.
$\dfrac{1}{2}$	2	4	2	$0 = P\left(\dfrac{1}{2}\right)$	$\dfrac{1}{2}$ is a zero.

For any zero or root there is a factor. *Factor immediately* and then work with the reduced polynomial, whose coefficients are indicated in the bottom row above. In this case,

$$P(x) = (x - \tfrac{1}{2})(2x^2 + 4x + 2)$$
$$= (2x - 1)(x^2 + 2x + 1) = (2x - 1)(x + 1)^2.$$

By the zero product principle, -1 is a zero of multiplicity 2 The zeros of P are $\tfrac{1}{2}, -1, -1,$ and these are the roots of the given equation.

(b) Let $Q(x) = 2x^3 - 3x^2 + x - 1$.

Coeficients of $Q(x)$

Possible rational roots	2	-3	1	-1	
1	2	-1	0	$-1 = Q(1)$	1 is not a zero.
$\dfrac{1}{2}$	2	-2	0	$-1 = Q\left(\dfrac{1}{2}\right)$	$\dfrac{1}{2}$ is not a zero.

We could try -1 and $-\tfrac{1}{2}$, but any negative value of x will make $Q(x)$ negative, so Q cannot have any negative zeros. The given equation has no rational zeros. $\blacktriangle$

For the next example, return to the polynomial function S from Example 4b, which has 24 possible rational zeros. The use of a rough sketch helps guide the choices of which possible rational zeros to try.

| EXAMPLE 6 |

Find all zeros of the function

$$S(x) = 4x^4 - 12x^3 - 13x^2 + 45x - 18.$$

Solution

From Example 4b, the possible rational zeros are $\pm[1, 2, 3, 6, 9, 18, \frac{1}{2}, \frac{3}{2}, \frac{9}{2}, \frac{1}{4}, \frac{3}{4}, \frac{9}{4}]$. Try synthetic division with some of these, beginning with integer values. At the same time record points on a graph, starting with the observation that $S(0) = -18$. See Figure 3.9.

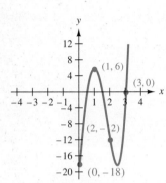

FIGURE 3.9

Graph of $y = 4x^4 - 12x^3 - 13x^2 + 45x - 18$

	4	−12	−13	45	−18	
1	4	−8	−21	24	6 = S(1)	There is a zero in (0, 1).
2	4	−4	−21	3	−12 = S(2)	There is a zero in (1, 2).
3	4	0	−13	6	0 = S(0)	3 is a zero.

S has a zero (not necessarily rational) between 0 and 1, and another between 1 and 2. Also, 3 is a zero. Factor $S(x)$ using the coefficients in the last line of the synthetic division.

$$S(x) = (x - 3)(4x^3 - 13x + 6)$$

The zeros of S in the intervals $(0, 1)$ and $(1, 2)$ must be zeros of the reduced polynomial function, $s(x) = 4x^3 - 13x + 6$. Furthermore, the reduced function s has fewer possible rational zeros to check: $\pm[1, 2, 3, 6, \frac{1}{2}, \frac{3}{2}, \frac{1}{4}, \frac{3}{4}]$. Working with the coefficients of s, check the rational possibilities in $(0, 1)$:

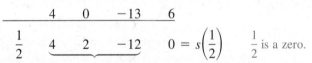

With this factor of $s(x)$, factor $S(x)$ further.

$$S(x) = (x - 3)(x - \tfrac{1}{2})(4x^2 + 2x - 12)$$

$$= (x - 3)(2x - 1)(2x^2 + x - 6)$$

$$= (x - 3)(2x - 1)(2x - 3)(x + 2).$$

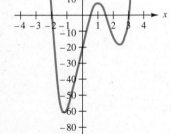

FIGURE 3.10

Another view of the graph in Figure 3.9

The zeros of S are 3, -2, $\frac{1}{2}$, and $\frac{3}{2}$. The graph in Figure 3.9 looks as if it might belong to a cubic function, but -2 is also a zero. A more complete graph is shown in Figure 3.10. ▲

Upper and Lower Bounds

Synthetic division can reveal still more information about the zeros of a polynomial function. Knowledge of **bounds** can reduce work significantly. Better still, the bounds theorem requires no extra work; simply watch for certain sign patterns in the bottom row of each synthetic division.

First some terminology is necessary, though. For a polynomial function p, u is an **upper bound** and l is a **lower bound** for the zeros of p, if every real zero of p lies between u and l.

<table>
<tr><td>**For Graphers**
3.3</td></tr>
</table>

CALCULATORS AND THE NATURE OF ZEROS

Since calculators cannot distinguish between rational and irrational numbers, it may be necessary to use other information to determine the nature of zeros of some polynomial functions.

EXAMPLE The polynomial function $f(x) = 3x^3 - 4x^2 - 5x + 2$ has a zero c in the interval $(0, 1)$. **(a)** Using successively smaller windows, approximate c to 3 decimal places. **(b)** Determine whether or not c is a rational number.

Solution

(a) In the Familiar Window Trace to find that the y-coordinate changes sign between $X = 0.3$ $(Y = 0.221)$ and $X = 0.4$ $(Y = -0.448)$, so $0.3 < c < 0.4$. Zoom in by drawing smaller and smaller boxes to squeeze c into smaller and smaller intervals:

$$0.3 < c < 0.4$$
$$0.332 < c < 0.339$$
$$0.333 < c < 0.3337$$
$$0.33331 < c < 0.333334$$

Your boxes will undoubtedly give slightly different intervals. It is clear that to four decimal places, $c = 0.3333$.

(b) On the basis of the results in part **(a)**, it may seem reasonable to guess that $c = \frac{1}{3}$, but calculators can only approximate $p(\frac{1}{3})$. Synthetic division, however, verifies that $p(\frac{1}{3}) = 0$, so c is a rational number (Check!) ▲

Exercises

1. Examples 7 and 8 of this section showed that the polynomial function $p(x) = x^4 - x^3 - 2x^2 + 5x + 12$ has no rational zeros, and that all real zeros (if any) lie in $(-2, 2)$. Determine whether or not p has any real zeros. (*Hint:* Does the graph cross the x-axis in $(-2, 2)$?)

2. Explain how to use your graphing calculator to determine whether $-\sqrt{3}$ is a zero of $f(x) = x^3 - 2x - \sqrt{3}$. (See Check Your Understanding Exercise 3.)

3. The volume function for the open box in Develop Mastery Exercise 80 can be written in factored form as $V(x) = x(9 - 2x)(12 - 2x)$. **(a)** Choose a window to graph $y = V(x)$ that will show the domain of the volume function. (*Hint:* Can you enter V in factored form?) **(b)** What is an appropriate y range to show the intersections of the line $y = 81$ with the graph of $y = V(x)$? **(c)** Find the desired corner size requested in Develop Mastery Exercise 80.

4. What is the maximum possible volume for the box described in Develop Mastery Exercise 80?

> **Bounds Theorem**
>
> Let p be any polynomial function with real coefficients and a positive leading coefficient. For a given trial zero c, look at the bottom line of synthetic division and consider two cases:
>
> > If $c > 0$ and the last line contains no negative numbers, then c is an upper bound for the zeros of p.
> >
> > If $c < 0$ and the numbers in the last line alternate in sign, then c is a lower bound for the zeros of p.
>
> A zero in the last line can be considered as either sign.

EXAMPLE 7   If $p(x) = x^4 - x^3 - 2x^2 + 5x + 12$, show that all real zeros of p lie between -2 and 2.

Strategy: Complete synthetic division with -2 and 2 and apply the bounds theorem.

Solution

$$
\begin{array}{r|rrrrr}
-2 & 1 & -1 & -2 & 5 & 12 \\
   &   & -2 & 6 & -8 & 6 \\
\hline
   & 1 & -3 & 4 & -3 & 18 \\
\end{array}
\quad \text{Signs alternate}
$$

Since the entries in the last alternate in sign, -2 is a lower bound.

$$
\begin{array}{r|rrrrr}
2 & 1 & -1 & -2 & 5 & 12 \\
  &   & 2 & 2 & 0 & 10 \\
\hline
  & 1 & 1 & 0 & 5 & 22 \\
\end{array}
\quad \text{No negatives}
$$

The last line contains no negative entries, so 2 is an upper bound. ▲

EXAMPLE 8   Find all rational zeros, if any, for $p(x) = x^4 - x^3 - 2x^2 + 5x + 12$.

Solution

Since the leading coefficient of p is 1, the only possible rational zeros of p are the integer factors of 12: $\pm[1, 2, 3, 4, 5,$ and $12]$. Example 7 shows, however, that all real zeros of p must lie in the interval $(-2, 2)$, and neither -2 nor 2 is a zero of p. The only remaining possible rational zeros in $(-2, 2)$ are 1 and -1. Either by direct evaluation or by synthetic division, show that $p(-1) = 7$ and $p(1) = 15$. It follows that p has no rational zeros. If the graph of $y = p(x)$ meets the x-axis at all, it must do so at irrational numbers between -2 and 2. ▲

EXERCISES 3.3

Check Your Understanding

Exercises 1–3   True or False. Give reasons for your conclusion.

1. If 2 is an upper bound for the real zeros of a polynomial function, then 3 is also an upper bound.

2. The equation $2x^3 - 5x^2 + 4x - 1 = 0$ has no rational roots.

3. Since $\sqrt{3}$ is a zero of $f(x) = x^3 - 2x - \sqrt{3}$, then $-\sqrt{3}$ must also be a zero.

Exercises 4–10   Complete the sentence by selecting from the list below *all choices* that make the statement true.
(a) an integer   (b) a rational number
(c) an irrational number   (d) positive
(e) negative   (f) between -1 and 0
(g) between 2 and 3   (h) an imaginary number.

4. The largest root of $x^3 + 3x^2 - 2 = 0$ is _____ .

5. The only real zero of $f(x) = (2x + 1)(x^2 + 1)$ is _____ .

6. Each zero of $g(x) = x^4 + 2x^2 + 1$ is _____ .

7. The only real root of the equation $x^3 + 2x + 1 = 0$ is _____ .

8. The largest real root of $2x^3 - 5x^2 + 2x - 5 = 0$ is _____ .

9. At least one of the real roots of $x^3 + x + 1 = 0$ is _____ .

10. Every zero of $g(x) = (x + 1)(x + 2)(2x + 1)$ is _____ .

Explore and Discover

Exercises 1–3   *Proof of the Rational Zeros Theorem*

1. Let $p(x) = 12x^3 + 4x^2 - 5x - 2$. Suppose $\frac{r}{s}$ is a rational root of the equation $p(x) = 0$, where $\frac{r}{s}$ is in lowest terms. Substitute $\frac{r}{s}$ for x in the equation $p(x) = 0$ and then clear fractions by multiplying both sides of the equation by s^3.

2. (a) Explain why r must be a divisor of $2s^3$ in the result of Exercise 1. (*Hint:* Collect all terms that involve r on one side of the equation and then factor out an r.) Could r have a factor in common with s^3? Why can we conclude that r must be a divisor of 2?
   (b) Explain why s must be a divisor of $12r^3$ and hence a divisor of 12. (*Hint:* Collect all terms that involve an s on one side of the equation and then factor out an s.)

3. Follow the line of reasoning from Exercises 1 and 2 to explain why, if $\frac{r}{s}$ in reduced form is a rational zero of a polynomial function p with integer coefficients, then r must be a divisor of the constant term of $p(x)$, and s must be a divisor of the leading coefficient.

Develop Mastery

Exercises 1–8   Apply the rational zeros theorem to list all possible rational zeros of f. If the theorem does not apply, explain why.

1. $f(x) = 6x^3 + 3x^2 - 2x - 1$

2. $f(x) = 6x^3 - 2x^2 - 9x + 3$

3. $f(x) = 2x^4 - 2x^3 - 6x^2 + x + 2$

4. $f(x) = 6x^3 - x^2 - 13x + 8$

5. $f(x) = 3x^3 - 1.5x^2 + x - 0.5$

6. $f(x) = x^3 - 2x^2 + \sqrt{2}x - 2$

7. $f(x) = 2x^4 - 3x^3 - 8x^2 - 5x - 3$

8. $f(x) = x^4 - x^2 - 4x + 4$

Exercises 9–12   Apply the bounds theorem to determine whether you can conclude that the given value c is an upper or lower bound for the zeros of the function.

9. $f(x) = 2x^4 - x^2 + 5x + 3$; $c = 1$, $c = -1$, $c = -2$

10. $f(x) = x^3 - 3x^2 + 4x - 1$; $c = -1$, $c = 2$, $c = 3$

11. $f(x) = x^4 + 2x^3 + 15x^2 - 17x + 5$; $c = 2$, $c = -1$, $c = -2$

12. $f(x) = x^5 - 3x^2 + 25$; $c = 1$, $c = 1.5$, $c = -1$

In Exercises 13 to 36, assume that the domain (replacement set) of the variable is the set of complex numbers.

Exercises 13–24   Find all zeros of f.

13. $f(x) = x^3 - 4x^2 + 2x - 8$

14. $f(x) = 4x^3 - 4x^2 - 19x + 10$

15. $f(x) = x^3 - 2.5x^2 - 7x - 1.5$

16. $f(x) = 3x^3 - 1.5x^2 + x - 0.5$

17. $f(x) = 3x^3 + 11x^2 + 12x + 4$

18. $f(x) = x^3 - \frac{5}{3}x^2 - \frac{11}{3}x - 1$

19. $f(x) = x^3 - 3.5x^2 + 0.5x + 5$

20. $f(x) = 5x^3 + x^2 - 15x - 3$

21. $f(x) = 6x^4 - 13x^3 + 2x^2 - 4x + 15$

22. $f(x) = 2x^4 + 3x^3 + 2x^2 - 1$

23. $f(x) = 4x^4 - 4x^3 - 7x^2 + 4x + 3$

24. $f(x) = 4x^4 + 8x^3 + 9x^2 + 5x + 1$

Exercises 25–36   Find all roots.

25. $6x^3 - 2x^2 - 9x + 3 = 0$

26. $6x^3 - x^2 - 13x + 8 = 0$

27. $x^4 - x^3 - 3x^2 + x + 2 = 0$

28. $x^4 - x^3 - 8x + 8 = 0$

29. $x^3 - 3x + 2 = 0$

30. $18x^3 + 27x^2 + 13x + 2 = 0$

31. $x^3 + 2 = -\frac{(14x^2 + 17x)}{3}$

32. $x^4 + 4x^3 - 5x^2 = 36x + 36$

33. $(1.5x - 2.5)x^2 = 7x + 2$

34. $12(x^4 - 1) + 7x(x^2 + 1) = 0$

35. $x^4 - 2x^3 - 3x^2 + 4x + 4 = 0$

36. $6x^4 + 13x^3 - 13x - 6 = 0$

Exercises 37–44   Find a polynomial function of lowest degree with integer coefficients, a leading coefficient of 1, and the given numbers as zeros. Give the result in standard (expanded) form. Use the conjugate root theorem, if needed.

37. $0, 1, -2$

38. $-1, -1, 2$

39. $-3, 0, 0, 1$

40. $1, \sqrt{2}$

41. $-2, -1 + \sqrt{3}$

42. $\sqrt{2}, 1 - i$

43. $0, 1, 1 + \sqrt{3}$

44. $\sqrt{3}, 2i$

Exercises 45–48   The given number is a zero of f. Find the remaining zeros. (*Hint:* Use the conjugate zeros theorem.)

45. $f(x) = x^3 - 4x^2 + 3x + 2;\quad 1 - \sqrt{2}$

46. $f(x) = x^3 - 2x^2 - 9x - 2;\quad 2 + \sqrt{5}$

47. $f(x) = 2x^3 - 9x^2 + 2x + 1;\quad 2 - \sqrt{5}$

48. $f(x) = 2x^3 - 3x^2 - 4x - 1;\quad 1 + \sqrt{2}$

Exercises 49–56   Write $p(x)$ in factored form with linear factors.

49. $p(x) = 2x^3 + 7x^2 - 5x - 4$

50. $p(x) = 3x^3 - 4x^2 - 5x + 2$

51. $p(x) = 16x^3 - 20x^2 - 4x + 5$

52. $p(x) = 4x^4 - 37x^2 + 9$

53. $p(x) = 4x^4 + 16x^3 + 11x^2 - 4x - 3$

54. $p(x) = 4x^4 + 24x^3 + 35x^2 - 6x - 9$

55. $p(x) = 3x^4 + 5x^3 - x^2 - 5x - 2$

56. $p(x) = 8x^4 + 34x^3 + 43x^2 + 11x - 6$

Exercises 57–58   Find the solution set.

57. **(a)** $3x^2 - 12x = (x - 1)(x^2 - 4x)$

   (b) $\dfrac{3x^2 - 12x}{x^2 - 4x} = x - 1$

58. **(a)** $3x^3 - 12x = (x + 2)(x^3 - 4x)$

   (b) $\dfrac{3x^3 - 12x}{x + 2} = x^3 - 4x$

Exercises 59–60   Find the smallest integer that is greater than all of the roots of the equation.

59. $2x^3 - 3x^2 - 2x + 3 = 0$

60. $x^3 - 3x^2 - 2x + 4 = 0$

Exercises 61–62   Find the greatest integer that is less than all of the real roots of the equation.

61. $x^4 - 2x^2 - 3 = 0$

62. $x^3 - 3x^2 - 2x + 8 = 0$

Exercises 63–64   Sketch a graph of f.

63. $f(x) = 2x^4 + x^3 - 6x^2 + x + 2$

64. $f(x) = 2x^4 - 3x^3 - 7x^2 + 3x + 5$

Exercises 65–68   Find the solution set for **(a)** $f(x) = 0$, **(b)** $f(x - 1) = 0$, **(c)** $f(x) \le 0$. (*Hint:* For part **(c)**, first factor and get cut points.)

65. $f(x) = 2x^3 - 3x^2 - 3x + 2$

66. $f(x) = x^4 - 2x^3 - 3x^2 + 4x + 4$

67. $f(x) = x^3 - 3x + 2$

68. $f(x) = 4x^3 - 4x^2 - 19x + 10$

Exercises 69–72   The function f is an increasing function and hence has an inverse.

69. $f(x) = x^3 + 3x + 2$; find $f^{-1}(16), f^{-1}(-12)$

70. $f(x) = 8x^3 + 4x^2 + 2x - 3$; find $f^{-1}(-9)$, $f^{-1}(-3)$

71. $f(x) = x^5 + 4x + 36$; find $f^{-1}(31), f^{-1}(-4)$

72. $f(x) = x^3 - x^2 + 3x - 4$; find $f^{-1}(6), f^{-1}(-9)$

Exercises 73–74   **(a)** Find all integer values of k such that the equation will have at least one rational root. **(b)** For what value(s) of k does the equation have one rational and two irrational roots?

73. $x^3 - kx + 2 = 0$

74. $x^3 + kx - 3 = 0$

Exercises 75–76   Use the rational zeros theorem to show that the given number c is not rational. (*Hint:* Use the conjugate zeros theorem to construct a polynomial function p with integer coefficients and c as zero, then show that p has no rational zeros.)

75. $c = -1 + \sqrt{2}$

76. $c = 2 + \sqrt{5}$

77. A rectangle with an area of 48 square feet has a diagonal that is 2 feet longer than one of the sides. What are the dimensions of the rectangle?

78. A block of cheese has the shape of a rectangular solid with dimensions x by x by $3x$. (It has a square cross section and is three times as long as it is wide.) When a 2-inch slice is cut parallel to the square ends, the volume of the remaining piece is 160 cubic inches. **(a)** What are the dimensions of the original block of cheese? **(b)** What is the volume of the 2-inch slice?

79. A block of wood has the shape of a cube. A slice 2 inches thick is cut parallel to one of the faces. What is the length of each edge of the cube if the volume of the remaining piece is 75 cubic inches?

80. A box with an open top is constructed from a rectangular piece of tin that measures 9 inches by 12 inches by cutting out from each corner a square of side x, and then folding up the sides as shown in the diagram.

(a) If V denotes the volume of the box, find a formula for V as a function of x. What is the domain of the function?

(b) What size corners should be cut out so that the box will have a capacity of 81 cubic inches? (*Hint:* There are two answers, both between 1 and 2.)

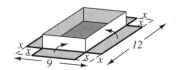

Rational Functions

What is mathematics about? I think it's really summed up in what I frequently tell my classes. That is that proofs really aren't there to convince you that something is true—they're there to show you why it is true. That's what is's all about—it's to try to figure out how it's all tied together.

> Freeman Dyson

In this section we consider **rational functions,** which are quotients of polynomial functions. Describing the properties of rational functions will involve what we already know about polynomials.

Definition: Rational Function

Suppose p and q are polynomial functions, where q is not the zero function. Then the function f, where

$$f(x) = \frac{p(x)}{q(x)},$$

is called a rational function, sometimes written $f = \frac{p}{q}$. The domain of f consists of all real numbers for which $q(x)$ is nonzero.

If $f = \frac{p}{q}$, the denominator q cannot equal 0, but we are interested in the behavior of f at x values near zeros of q. The fact that the denominator can approach zero is responsible for some of the characteristics of rational functions. In analyzing rational functions it is useful to think in terms of reciprocals. We will first introduce some notation.

Arrow Notation

$x \to a^+$ means that x approaches a from above; that is, x takes on values near a, but greater than a (such as $a + 0.01$, $a + 0.001$, . . .).

$x \to a^-$ means that x approaches a from below; that is, x takes on values near a, but less than a (such as $a - 0.01$, $a - 0.001$, . . .).

Similarly, $x \to \infty$ and $x \to -\infty$ mean that x assumes larger and larger positive or negative values, respectively. The same notation is used to indicate functional behavior.

The only idea of real mathematics that I had came from Men of Mathematics. *In it, I got my first glimpse of a mathematician per se. I cannot overemphasize the importance of such books about mathematics in the intellectual life of a student like myself completely out of contact with research-mathematicians.*

Julia Robinson

Reciprocals and Graphing

To begin, consider one of the simplest reciprocal functions, $f(x) = \frac{1}{x}$. The function f is not defined at 0, but what happens to f when x is *near* 0? Consider a table of values:

x	$f(x)$	x	$f(x)$
1	1	-1	-1
0.1	10	-0.1	-10
0.01	100	-0.01	-100
0.001	1000	-0.001	-1000

Clearly, as $x \to 0^+$, $f(x) \to \infty$, and, as $x \to 0^-$, $f(x) \to -\infty$. What happens as $x \to \infty$ and as $x \to -\infty$?

x	$f(x)$	x	$f(x)$
10	0.1	-10	-0.1
100	0.01	-100	-0.01
1000	0.001	-1000	-0.001

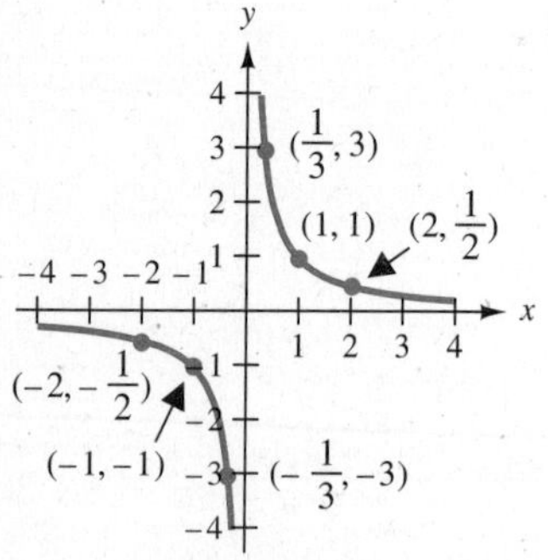

As $x \to \infty$, $f(x) \to 0^+$, and as $x \to -\infty$, $f(x) \to 0^-$. Including this information on a graph, together with the points from $f(1) = 1$ and $f(-1) = -1$, we get Figure 3.11.

The analysis of the graph of $y = \frac{1}{x}$ applies broadly to graphs of reciprocals. For a function f, $\frac{1}{f}$ denotes the reciprocal function. In the following we summarize some key observations about relations between f and $\frac{1}{f}$ that are helpful in drawing the graph of $\frac{1}{f}$ from the graph of f.

FIGURE 3.11

Graph of $y = \frac{1}{x}$

Relations between f and $\frac{1}{f}$

1. At values of x where $f(x) = \pm 1$, we have $\frac{1}{f(x)} = \pm 1$.

   The graphs of f and $\frac{1}{f}$ meet where $f(x) = \pm 1$.

2. At values of x where $f(x) = 0$, $\frac{1}{f(x)}$ is undefined.

   As $f(x) \to 0^+$, then $\frac{1}{f(x)} \to \infty$, and as $f(x) \to 0^-$, then $\frac{1}{f(x)} \to -\infty$.

3. As $f(x) \to \infty$, then $\frac{1}{f(x)} \to 0^+$, and as $f(x) \to -\infty$, then $\frac{1}{f(x)} \to 0^-$.

The following Graphing Tips illustrate how these relations between f and $\frac{1}{f}$ apply to graphing.

Graphing Tips

Use the graph of the function $f(x) = x^2 - 2x$ to graph the reciprocal function, $\frac{1}{f}$.

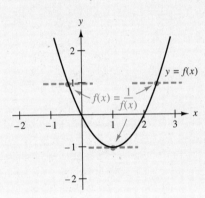

Step 1. Sketch the graph of $y = f(x)$ and find where $f(x) = \pm 1$ (where the graph of $f(x)$ meets the lines $y = 1$ or $y = -1$)

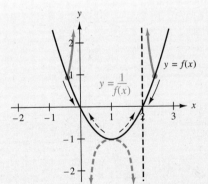

Step 2. Find where $f(x) = 0$ (where $\frac{1}{f(x)}$ is undefined.) As $f(x) \to 0^+$, $\frac{1}{f(x)} \to \infty$ (solid arrows); as $f(x) \to 0^-$, $\frac{1}{f(x)} \to -\infty$ (dashed arrows).

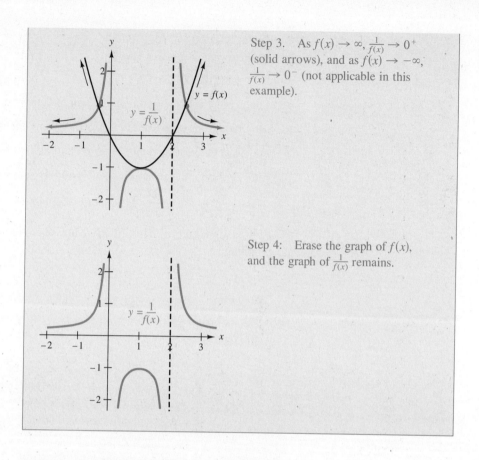

Step 3. As $f(x) \to \infty$, $\frac{1}{f(x)} \to 0^+$ (solid arrows), and as $f(x) \to -\infty$, $\frac{1}{f(x)} \to 0^-$ (not applicable in this example).

Step 4: Erase the graph of $f(x)$, and the graph of $\frac{1}{f(x)}$ remains.

Symmetry, Asymptotes, Translations, and Reflections

The graph of $y = \frac{1}{x}$ (Figure 3.11) is clearly symmetric about the origin. This is hardly surprising because the function is an odd function. Similarly, the graph of $y = \frac{1}{x^2 - 2x}$ in the Graphing Tips box above has the same symmetry (about the line $x = 1$) as the parabola $y = x^2 - 2x$. It is always wise to look first for **symmetry** when drawing any graph, especially for odd and even functions.

The graphs of $y = \frac{1}{x}$ and $y = \frac{1}{x^2 - 2x}$ also have **asymptotes.** Without attempting a more precise definition, a line is an asymptote for a curve if the curve gets arbitrarily closer to the line as we move out along the line. The y-axis is a

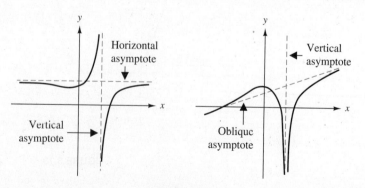

FIGURE 3.12

vertical asymptote for both graphs above, as is the vertical line $x = 2$ for the graph of $y = \frac{1}{x^2 - 2x}$. The x-axis is a **horizontal asymptote** for both graphs. Asymptotes for rational functions can be vertical, horizontal, or oblique lines, as illustrated in Figure 3.12.

From a core graph, we can use translations and reflections to get other graphs, as illustrated in the next example.

EXAMPLE 1 Use the graph of $f(x) = \frac{1}{x}$ to graph

$$\textbf{(a)}\ y = \frac{1}{x - 1} \qquad \textbf{(b)}\ y = \frac{2}{2 - x} \qquad \textbf{(c)}\ y = \frac{1 + x}{x}$$

Strategy: Try to relate each function to $f(x) = \frac{1}{x}$. In **(a)** $f(x - 1)$ gives a horizontal translation. In **(b)** factor out -2 to get $-2 \cdot f(x - 2)$. In **(c)** $y = \frac{1}{x} + 1$, for a vertical translation.

Solution

(a) Since $f(x - 1) = \frac{1}{x - 1}$, graph $y = \frac{1}{x - 1}$ by translating the graph of f one unit to the right. As a useful check, observe that $y = \frac{1}{x - 1}$ has a vertical asymptote where the denominator is 0, at $x = 1$. The result of the translation is shown in Figure 3.13a.

(b) If we factor out -1 from the denominator, then $\frac{2}{2 - x} = \frac{-2}{x - 2}$, so $\frac{2}{2 - x} = -2f(x - 2)$. Translate the graph of f two units to the right, reflect it through the x-axis and stretch it vertically by a factor of 2. Plotting a few points gives the graph shown in Figure 3.13b.

(c) To relate $\frac{1 + x}{x}$ to $f(x)$, rewrite $\frac{1 + x}{x}$ as

$$\frac{1 + x}{x} = \frac{1}{x} + \frac{x}{x} = \frac{1}{x} + 1 = f(x) + 1.$$

Translate the graph of f one unit up, as shown in Figure 3.13c. ▲

Graphing Other Rational Functions

When there is not a core graph to work from, there are several steps for graphing rational functions.

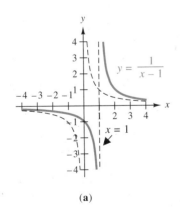

(a)

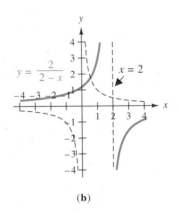

(b)

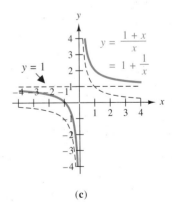

(c)

FIGURE 3.13

Translation and reflection of $y = \frac{1}{x}$

Algorithm for Graphing Rational Functions

Given a rational function $f(x) = \frac{p(x)}{q(x)}$, where $\frac{p(x)}{q(x)}$ is reduced (p and q have no common zeros).

Step 1   Symmetry and Intercepts

(a)   Check for symmetry: Does $f(-x) = \pm f(x)$?

(b)   Evaluate $f(0)$, if it exists, to find the y-intercept point.

(c)   Find x-intercept points [where $p(x) = 0$]. Plot them.

Step 2   Vertical Asymptotes and Sign Analysis

(d)   Find vertical asymptotes [where $q(x) = 0$]. Sketch each asymptote as a broken vertical line.

(e)   Find whether $f(x)$ is positive or negative on each interval between consecutive cut points (the zeros of p and q).

(f)   Determine whether $f(x) \to \infty$ or $f(x) \to -\infty$ to the right and left of each vertical asymptote.

Step 3   Other Asymptotes

What happens as $x \to \infty$ or as $x \to -\infty$ depends on the degrees of p and q. Suppose $f(x) = \dfrac{ax^m + \cdots}{bx^n + \cdots}$.

> If $m < n$:   Horizontal asymptote is the x-axis ($y = 0$).
>
> $m = n$:   Horizontal asymptote is the line $y = \frac{a}{b}$.
>
> $m = n + 1$:   Slant (oblique) asymptote. Use division to find an equation for the asymptote. See Example 5. Sketch in any nonvertical asymptotes.

Plot additional points, if needed, and complete the graph.

EXAMPLE 2   Find the intercepts, cut points, and asymptotes, and sketch the graph for the rational function

$$f(x) = \frac{x + 1}{4x(x - 1)}.$$

Solution

Symmetry, Intercepts

(a) $f(-x) \neq f(x)$ and $f(-x) \neq -f(x)$, so f is neither even nor odd.

(b) $f(0)$ is not defined, so there is no y-intercept point.

(c)   The numerator has one zero, $x = -1$, so $(-1, 0)$ is the only x-intercept point.

Vertical Asymptotes, Sign Analysis

(d)   The zeros of the denominator are 0 and 1. Vertical asymptotes are at $x = 0$ (the y-axis) and $x = 1$. Figure 3.14a shows the intercept point and vertical asymptotes.

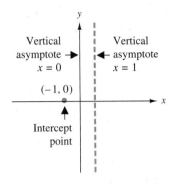

(a) Vertical asymptotes and intercept points

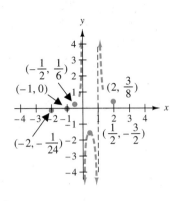

(b) Sign analysis

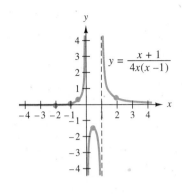

(c) Graph of $y = \dfrac{x + 1}{4x(x - 1)}$

FIGURE 3.14

(e) Cut points are -1, 0, and 1. Evaluate f at a point in each interval:

$$f(-2) = -\frac{1}{24}; f\left(-\frac{1}{2}\right) = \frac{1}{6}; f\left(\frac{1}{2}\right) = -\frac{3}{2}; f(2) = \frac{3}{8}.$$

This gives four points on the graph and shows that $f(x)$ is negative on the intervals $(-\infty, -1)$ and on $(0, 1)$ and positive elsewhere in its domain. Thus $f(x) \to \infty$ as $x \to 0^-$ and as $x \to 1^+$, and $f(x) \to -\infty$ as $x \to 0^+$ and as $x \to 1^-$.

(f) Plotting four points and entering the behavior near the vertical asymptotes give the part of the graph in Figure 3.14b.

Other Asymptotes
The numerator has degree 1, and the denominator has degree 2, so $m < n;$ the x-axis is a horizontal asymptote. The graph is shown in Figure 3.14c. ▲

> **EXAMPLE 3**   Graph the rational function
>
> $$f(x) = \frac{x^2 - 4}{x^2 + 2}.$$

Solution

Symmetry, Intercepts

(a) $f(-x) = f(x)$, so f is an even function; the graph is symmetric about the y-axis. **(b)** $f(0) = -2$, so $(0, -2)$ is the y-intercept point. **(c)** The zeros of the numerator are ± 2, so the x-intercept points are $(-2, 0)$ and $(2, 0)$. Plot the intercept points.

Vertical Asymptotes, Sign Analysis.

(d) The denominator has no real zeros, so there are no vertical asymptotes. **(e)** Cut points are -2 and 2, giving three intervals to check signs. Evaluating f

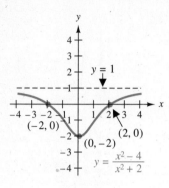

FIGURE 3.15

at a point in each interval, $f(-3) = f(3) = \frac{5}{11}$, and we already know that $f(0)$ is negative. Add these points to the graph.

Other Asymptotes

The degrees of numerator and denominator are both 2, so $m = n$. Since the leading coefficients are also equal ($a = b = 1$), the line $y = 1$ is a horizontal asymptote. This gives the graph shown in Figure 3.15.   ▲

EXAMPLE 4   Graph the rational function

$$g(x) = \frac{x^2}{1 + x - 2x^2}.$$

Solution

Symmetry , Intercepts

(a) There is no obvious symmetry. **(b)** Factor the denominator.

$$g(x) = \frac{x^2}{(1 + 2x)(1 - x)}.$$

(c) The only zero of the numerator is 0; the origin is the only intercept point.

Vertical Asymptotes, Sign Analysis

(d) The zeros of the denominator give vertical asymptotes $x = -\frac{1}{2}$ and $x = 1$; sketch them with broken lines. **(e)** Cut points are $-\frac{1}{2}$, 0, and 1. Check the sign of g at a point in each of the four resulting intervals: g is negative on the intervals $(-\infty, -\frac{1}{2})$ and $(1, \infty)$, and positive between the vertical asymptotes (except at the origin). **(f)** Plot the four points and sketch in the graph near the vertical asymptotes.

Other Asymptotes

Since $m = n = 2$, the graph has a horizontal asymptote, $y = \frac{a}{b}$. The asymptote is the line $y = -\frac{1}{2}$. Sketch in the horizontal asymptote with the point $(-1, -\frac{1}{2})$ where the graph crosses the asymptote. The graph is shown in Figure. 3.16.   ▲

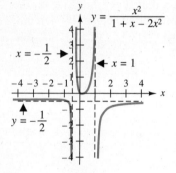

FIGURE 3.16

Slant (Oblique) Asymptotes

According to the algorithm for graphing rational functions, there is a slant asymptote when the degree of the numerator exceeds the degree of the denominator by 1. Divide $q(x)$ into $p(x)$ to get a linear polynomial part of the form $ax + b$ and a remainder $r(x)$. The degree of $r(x)$ is less than n, so rewrite the rational function in the form,

$$f(x) = \frac{p(x)}{q(x)} = ax + b + \frac{r(x)}{q(x)}.$$

Because the degree of r is less than the degree of q as $x \to \pm\infty$, $\frac{r(x)}{q(x)} \to 0$. Consequently, the graph of $y = \frac{p(x)}{q(x)}$ approaches the line $y = ax + b$, which means that $y = ax + b$ is an asymptote for the graph of the rational function.

Slant (Oblique) Asymptotes

If $f(x) = \frac{p(x)}{q(x)}$, where the degree of p is 1 greater than the degree of q, then use long division to write $f(x)$ in the form

$$f(x) = \frac{p(x)}{q(x)} = ax + b + \frac{r(x)}{q(x)},$$

where the degree of r is less than the degree of q. The line $y = ax + b$ is a slant asymptote to the graph of f.

EXAMPLE 5   Graph the rational function

$$h(x) = \frac{x^2 + 2x}{2x + 2}.$$

Solution

Symmetry, Intercepts

(a)   There is no obvious symmetry.

(b)   and **(c)**   Factor the numerator and denominator:

$$h(x) = \frac{x(x + 2)}{2(x + 1)}.$$

The graph contains the origin $(0, 0)$, and $(-2, 0)$ is also an x-intercept point.

Vertical Asymptotes, Sign Analysis

(d)   The only zero of the denominator is -1, so $x = -1$ is a vertical asymptote.

(e)   Cut points are 0, -1, and -2, giving four intervals for sign analysis. To find the sign of $h(x)$ on each interval, evaluate and plot four points and sketch in the portion of the graph near the vertical asymptote, as shown in Figure 3.17a.

Other Asymptotes

The numerator has degree 2 and the denominator has degree 1, so there is an oblique asymptote. Dividing $q(x)$ into $p(x)$ using long division, we get

$$h(x) = \frac{1}{2}x + \frac{1}{2} - \frac{1}{2(x + 1)}.$$

The slant asymptote is the line $y = \frac{1}{2}x + \frac{1}{2}$. As with horizontal asymptotes, we must consider the possibility of the graph of $y = h(x)$ intersecting the asymptote. Such an intersection would come from a solution to the equation $h(x) = \frac{1}{2}x + \frac{1}{2}$, which clearly has no solution. Sketch in the asymptote and complete the graph, as shown in Figure 3.17b.

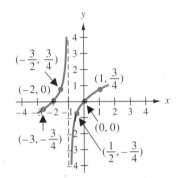

(a) Intercept points, vertical asymptote, and sign analysis

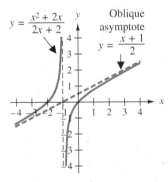

(b) Oblique asymptote and graph of $y = \dfrac{x^2 + 2x}{2x + 2}$

FIGURE 3.17

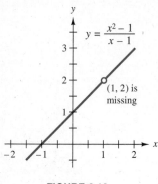

FIGURE 3.18

Rational Functions Not Reduced

A rational function $f(x) = \frac{p(x)}{q(x)}$ is not in reduced form if there are common factors in the numerator and denominator. To handle common zeros, remember that if $p(x)$ and $q(x)$ have the same zero, say $x = c$, then since $\frac{0}{0}$ is not defined, c is not in the domain of the function. In such a case the graph has a single point removed. Consider the function

$$f(x) = \frac{x^2 - 1}{x - 1}.$$

Factor the numerator.

$$f(x) = \frac{(x - 1)(x + 1)}{x - 1}.$$

This is identical to the function $g(x) = x + 1$ *except* when x is 1. When x is 1, $g(1) = 2$, but $f(1)$ is not defined. Therefore, the graph of $y = f(x)$ is the same as the graph of $y = x + 1$ with the point $(1, 2)$ removed (see Figure 3.18).

Looking Ahead to Calculus

One of the kinds of problems for which calculus is most useful is finding local maximum or minimum values of functions, or, in terms of graphs, finding turning points. The following example illustrates one noncalculus approach that can be used for certain types of functions.

Strategy: Use the techniques of this section to draw a graph. At a turning point, a horizontal line will just meet the graph at a single local point so we can look at intersections of the horizontal line $y = k$ with the graph of f.

EXAMPLE 6 Sketch a graph of $f(x) = \frac{x^2 + 1}{x}$ and find the coordinates of the turning points.

Solution

First rewrite the equation for f.

$$f(x) = x + \frac{1}{x}$$

We see that the y-axis (the line $x = 0$) is a vertical asymptote and the line $y = x$ is an oblique asymptote. Since $f(-x) = -f(x)$, the graph is symmetric about the origin, and plotting a few points gives the graph shown in Figure 3.19 with turning points A and B.

Follow the strategy. Find the horizontal line $y = k$ that has a single intersection with the graph of $y = f(x)$. Setting $\frac{x^2 + 1}{x} = k$ and multiplying through by x,

$$x^2 + 1 = kx, \quad \text{or} \quad x^2 - kx + 1 = 0.$$

There is exactly one solution to a quadratic when the discriminant is zero (see Section 1.5).

$$b^2 - 4ac = (-k)^2 - 4 \cdot 1 \cdot 1 = k^2 - 4$$

Thus, find k for which $k^2 - 4 = 0$; $k = \pm 2$. Therefore, line $y = 2$ intersects the graph of $y = f(x)$ at exactly one point, point A whose y-coordinate is 2. Solving for the corresponding x-coordinate gives $x = 1$. Hence point A is $(1, 2)$. By symmetry, B has coordinates $(-1, -2)$. ▲

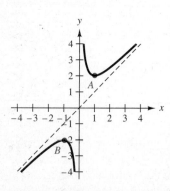

FIGURE 3.19

Turning points of $y = \frac{x^2 + 1}{x}$

For Graphers 3.4

RATIONAL FUNCTIONS

Exercises

1. Use your calculator to draw graphs of
   (a) $y = \frac{1}{x}$ (b) $y = \frac{1}{x-1}$
   (c) $y = \frac{1}{1-x}$ (d) $\frac{x+1}{x}$.
   How are the graphs of parts (b), (c), and (d) related to the core graph in part (a)?

2. Use your calculator to draw a graph of the function
$$f(x) = \frac{x^2}{1 + x - 2x^2}$$
   in Example 4. Compare this with the graphs shown in Figure 3.16.

3. (a) Use your calculator to graph the function
$$f(x) = \frac{x^2 + 2x}{2x + 2}$$
   in Example 5, using a window close to the Familiar Window. Compare this with Figure 3.7.
   (b) Zoom out two or three times. How does the graph of the given function compare with the graph of the oblique asymptote, $y = \frac{x+1}{2}$?

4. Repeat Exercise 3 with the function
$$f(x) = \frac{x^2 - 3}{x - 1}$$
   (see Develop Mastery Exercise 43).

5. (a) Draw a graph of the function
$$f(x) = \frac{x^2 - 1}{x - 1}$$
   in the Familiar Window. Compare this with Figure 3.18. Find the coordinates of the missing pixel.
   (b) Now change the x-range by 0.1 (make it either larger or smaller) and regraph. Trace. Is the graph now a line, as it appears, or is there still a hole? Explain why there is no missing pixel in the graph. Zoom in to magnify the graph near the point $(1, 2)$. Does the missing pixel reappear?

6. Use your calculator to locate the turning points in Example 6.

EXERCISES 3.4

Check Your Understanding

Exercises 1–5 True or False. Give reasons for your conclusion.

1. If the graph of $y = \frac{1}{x}$ is translated two units left, then the resulting graph will be that of $y = \frac{1}{x-2}$.

2. If the graph of $y = \frac{1}{x+2}$ is translated down one unit, then the resulting graph will be that of $y = \frac{-x-1}{x+2}$.

3. If the graph of $y = \frac{1}{x+2}$ is translated up one unit, then the resulting graph will be that of $y = \frac{x+1}{x+2}$.

4. The line $y = \frac{x}{2}$ is an asymptote to the graph of $y = \frac{x+1}{2x+1}$.

5. The horizontal line $y = -2$ is an asymptote to the graph of $y = \frac{1 - 2x^2}{5 + 2x + x^2}$.

Exercises 6–10 Complete the sentence by selecting from the list below *all choices* that make the statement true.

(a) 0   (b) 1   (c) 2   (d) $(2, \infty)$ (e) $(-\infty, -2)$
(f) $(-2, -1)$ (g) $(-\infty, 2)$ (h) $(-1, 2)$

6. The number of vertical asymptotes for the graph of $y = \frac{x}{x^2 - x - 2}$ is _____.

7. The number of vertical asymptotes for the graph of $y = \frac{x-2}{x^2 - x - 2}$ is _____.

8. The number of vertical asymptotes for the graph of $y = \frac{x-2}{x^2 - x + 2}$ is _____.

9. The function $f(x) = \frac{x+1}{x^2 - 4}$ is positive on the interval _____.

10. The function $f(x) = \frac{x+1}{x^2 - 4}$ is negative on the interval _____.

Explore and Discover

Exercises 1–3   Looking Ahead to Calculus   Determine the area of the shaded region under the graph of $y = x^2$ as shown in the diagram.

1. Subdivide the interval $[0, 1]$ on the x-axis into n equal subintervals. Find the area of each of the rectangles shown. For instance, the first rectangle has size $\frac{1}{n}$ by $(\frac{1}{n})^2$, the second is $\frac{1}{n}$ by $(\frac{2}{n})^2$, and so on.

2. Show that the sum S_n of the n rectangles is given by

$$S_n = \left(\frac{1}{n}\right)^3 (1^2 + 2^2 + \cdots + n^2).$$

3. In Chapter 8 we will show that the sum $1^2 + 2^2 + \cdots + n^2$ is equal to $\frac{n(n+1)(2n+1)}{6}$. Use this to get a simpler expression for S_n in Exercise 2. As the number n of subintervals becomes larger and larger, it is reasonable to assume that S_n approaches the area of the shaded region. What number does S_n approach as $n \to \infty$?

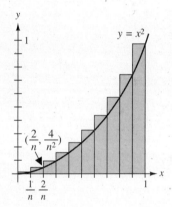

Develop Mastery

1. The line $x = 1$ is a vertical asymptote for the function

$$f(x) = \frac{x^3}{x^2 - 2x + 1}.$$

(a) To see what happens to the graph of f as $x \to 1$, evaluate f at $x = 0.8, 0.9, 0.99$, etc. For what values of x is $f(x)$ larger than 100? Larger than 1000?
(b) Repeat part (a) as $x \to 1^+$.

2. The line $y = 1$ is a horizontal asymptote for the function

$$f(x) = \frac{x^2 + 2x}{x^2 + 1}.$$

To see how closely the graph of f approaches the line $y = 1$, evaluate f at $\pm 5, \pm 10$, etc. For what values of x is the vertical distance between the graph of f and $y = 1$ less than 0.01? Less than 0.0001?

3. Repeat Exercise 2 for the function

$$f(x) = \frac{x^2 + 2x}{2x + 2}$$

and its oblique asymptote $y = \frac{x+1}{2}$.

Exercises 4–13   **(a)** Draw a graph of $y = f(x)$, and then **(b)** use your graph to help you draw a graph of the reciprocal function, $y = \frac{1}{f(x)}$. See the Graphing Tips feature.

4. $f(x) = x - 1$ 5. $f(x) = 2x + 4$
6. $f(x) = \frac{x^2 + 2}{2}$ 7. $f(x) = x^2 + 1$
8. $f(x) = x^2 - 4$ 9. $f(x) = 4 - x^2$
10. $f(x) = x^2 + x - 2$ 11. $f(x) = x^2 - 2x - 3$
12. $f(x) = (x - 2)^2$ 13. $f(x) = (x + 1)^2$

Exercises 14–19   Use translations, reflection, or stretching of the core graph of $y = \frac{1}{x}$ to sketch a graph. See Example 1.

14. $y = \frac{1}{x + 2}$ 15. $y = \frac{1}{1 - x}$ 16. $y = \frac{2}{x - 3}$

17. $y = \frac{2}{3 - x}$ 18. $y = \frac{2x + 1}{x}$ 19. $y = \frac{x - 1}{x}$

Exercises 20–34   Follow the steps of the algorithm for graphing rational functions in this section to sketch a graph of f.

20. $f(x) = \frac{1}{x - 1}$ 21. $f(x) = \frac{2}{x + 2}$

22. $f(x) = \frac{x}{x - 1}$ 23. $f(x) = \frac{2x - 3}{x + 2}$

24. $f(x) = \frac{2x^2}{(x - 1)^2}$ 25. $f(x) = \frac{x^2}{x^2 - 4}$

26. $f(x) = \frac{x + 2}{x^2 - 3x - 4}$ 27. $f(x) = \frac{x}{x^2 - 2x + 1}$

28. $f(x) = \frac{2}{(x + 2)^2}$ 29. $f(x) = \frac{2}{x^2 + 1}$

30. $f(x) = \frac{2x}{x^2 + 1}$ 31. $f(x) = \frac{x^2 + 2}{x^2 + 1}$

32. $f(x) = \frac{4}{x^2 - 3x - 4}$ 33. $f(x) = \frac{x - 2}{x^3 - 3x^2 - 4x}$

34. $f(x) = \frac{2x - 4}{x^3 - 3x^2 - 4x}$

Exercises 35–38 Sketch a graph of f. (*Hint:* First express the function in reduced form; keep in mind the domain.)

35. $f(x) = \frac{x}{x^2 + 2x}$

36. $f(x) = \frac{x^3}{x^2 - 2x}$

37. $f(x) = \frac{x^2 - 2x + 1}{x^2 + 2x - 3}$

38. $f(x) = \frac{x^2 + 2x - 3}{x^2 + x - 2}$

Exercises 39–42 Find an equation for the horizontal asymptote and find the coordinates of the points (if any) where the graph of $y = f(x)$ intersects the horizontal asymptote.

39. $f(x) = \frac{x^2 - 6}{x^2 - 2x}$

40. $f(x) = \frac{2x^2 - 2}{x^2 - 3x + 2}$

41. $f(x) = \frac{x^2 - x}{x^2 + x + 2}$

42. $f(x) = \frac{x^2 - x}{x^2 - x - 2}$

Exercises 43–46 The graph of f has an oblique asymptote. Find an equation for the asymptote and find the coordinates of the points (if any) where the graph of $y = f(x)$ intersects the asymptote. Graph the function.

43. $f(x) = \frac{x^2 - 3}{x - 1}$

44. $f(x) = \frac{x^2 + x - 2}{x + 1}$

45. $f(x) = \frac{2x^2 + 3x + 1}{x}$

46. $f(x) = \frac{x^2 + 3x - 2}{x + 1}$

Exercises 47–54 Match the graph with the appropriate function from the following list.

(a) $f(x) = \frac{x + 1}{x - 1}$

(b) $f(x) = \frac{1}{x - 1}$

(c) $f(x) = \frac{x + 1}{(x - 1)^2}$

(d) $f(x) = \frac{x^2}{x^2 + 1}$

(e) $f(x) = \frac{1}{1 - x}$

(f) $f(x) = \frac{x^2}{x^2 - x - 2}$

(g) $f(x) = \frac{x}{x^2 - x - 2}$

(h) $f(x) = \frac{x^3}{x^2 - x - 2}$

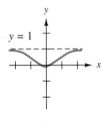

47.

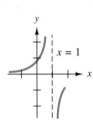

48.

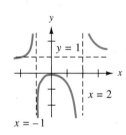

49.

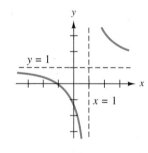

50.

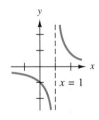

51.

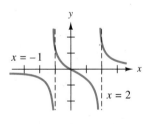

52.

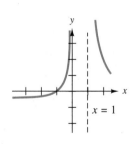

53.

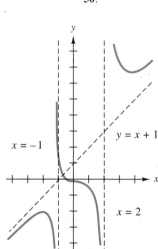

54.

55. This exercise is intended primarily to give you a chance to practice your algebra skills.

$$f(x) = \frac{\left(x + \frac{1}{x}\right)^4 - \left(x^4 + \frac{1}{x^4}\right) - 2}{\left(x + \frac{1}{x}\right)^2 + \left(x^2 + \frac{1}{x^2}\right)}.$$

Simplify and then draw a graph. (*Hint:* Verify that $(x^4 + \frac{1}{x^4}) + 2 = x^4 + 2 + \frac{1}{x^4} = (x^2 + \frac{1}{x^2})^2$.)

Exercises 56–58 Looking Ahead to Calculus Draw a graph of the function and find the coordinates of the turning points on the graph (*Hint:* See Example 6.)

56. $f(x) = \frac{x^2 + x + 1}{x}$ **57.** $f(x) = \frac{x^2 - x + 4}{x}$

58. $f(x) = \frac{4x^2 + x + 1}{x}$

Exercises 59–61 Looking Ahead to Calculus Find the minimum value of the function. Follow the hint given in Exercise 59.

59. $f(x) = x^2 + \frac{1}{x^2} + 1$. [*Hint:* Write $f(x)$ to include a perfect square, as follows: $f(x) = (x^2 - 2 + \frac{1}{x^2}) + 3$ or $f(x) = (x - \frac{1}{x})^2 + 3$, then find the x value that gives a minimum value for f.]

60. $f(x) = x^2 + \frac{4}{x^2} + 2$ **61.** $f(x) = 4x^2 + \frac{1}{x^2} + 1$

Exercises 62–63 The cost C of producing x units of a certain product is given. The average cost per unit is given by $A = \frac{C}{x}$. **(a)** Sketch a graph of A as a function of x. Remember that $x > 0$. (Why?) **(b)** Use your graph to estimate the number of units that will give the smallest average cost per unit. Although your graph will show a value of A for every positive x, remember that you are interested only in values of x that are integers. (Why?)

62. $C = 0.4x^2 + 15x + 10$

63. $C = 0.5x^2 + 10x + 12$

CHAPTER 3 REVIEW

Test Your Understanding

Determine the truth (T or F). Give reasons for your conclusion.

1. The leading coefficient of $f(x) = 4x - x^3$ is 4.

2. The constant term of $f(x) = x^3 + 4x$ is 4.

3. A factored form for $f(x) = x^3 - x$ is $f(x) = x(x + 1)(x - 1)$.

4. $F(x) = x^{-2} + x^{-1} + 1$ is a polynomial function of degree -2.

5. The equation $x^3 + x + 1 = 0$ has no positive roots.

6. The equation $x^3 + x - 1 = 0$ has no negative roots.

7. The equation $x^3 + x^2 - 1 = 0$ has no positive roots.

8. Every polynomial function of degree 3 has at least one real zero.

9. Every polynomial function of degree 4 has at least one real zero.

10. The graph of $y = x^3 + x^2 + 1$ is the same as that of $y = x^3 + x^2$ translated upward by 1 unit.

11. The graph of $y = (x + 1)^3 + (x + 1)$ crosses the y-axis at the point $(-1, 0)$.

12. The equation $x^3 + 2x^2 - 1 = 0$ has no rational roots.

13. The equation $x^4 + 3x^3 - x + 1 = 0$ has no rational roots.

14. The function $f(x) = x(x - \sqrt{3})(x + \sqrt{3})$ is a polynomial function with integer coefficients.

15. The function $f(x) = \sqrt{x^3 + x - 1}$ is a polynomial function of degree 3.

16. Every polynomial function of degree 5 has at least one real zero.

17. The graph of every polynomial function of degree 3 crosses the x-axis at least once.

18. The graph of $y = x^3 + x^2 - 2x - 1$ crosses the x-axis at exactly two points.

19. The point $(1, 3)$ is on the graph of $y = x^4 + x^2 - 2x + 3$.

20. An x-intercept point on the graph of $y = x^4 + x^2 - 2x$ is $(1, 0)$.

21. The graph of $y = x^3 + x + 1$ crosses the x-axis at a point between $(-1, 0)$ and $(0, 0)$.

22. The graph of $y = x^4 + x^2 + 1$ crosses the x-axis at four points.

23. The equation $x^4 + 2x^3 - 3x - 1 = 0$ has an irrational root between 1 and 2.

24. All real roots of $x^4 + 3x^3 - 3x - 1 = 0$ are irrational.

25. The graphs of $f(x) = x^3 + 5x - 4$ and $g(x) = (x^2 + 1)(x^3 + 5x - 4)$ cross the x-axis at precisely the same points.

26. Given that $\sqrt{3}$ is a root of $x^3 + \sqrt{3}x^2 - 6x = 0$, then $-\sqrt{3}$ is also a root.

27. The graph of $y = x^4 + 1$ does not cross the y-axis.

28. The graph of every polynomial function crosses the y-axis at exactly one point.

29. $f(x) = \frac{x-1}{x^2+1}$ is a rational function.

30. $f(x) = x^{-2} - x$ is a rational function.

31. An irrational root of $x^4 - 2x^2 - 3 = 0$ is $\sqrt{3}$.

32. A factor of $3x^4 - 2x^3 + x - 4$ is $x + 1$.

33. When $x^{15} - 2x^{10} + x^8 - 3x^2 + 1$ is divided by $x + 1$, the remainder is -4.

34. A factor of $x^{12} - 2x^8 + x^5 - 4x - 2$ is $x + 1$.

35. If $f(x) = x^3 + 2$ and $g(x) = x^2 - 1$, then $f \circ g$ is a polynomial function of degree 5.

36. The function $F(x) = x^3 - 2x^2 + x - 1$ has an irrational zero between -1 and -2.

37. The graph of every rational function has at least one vertical asymptote.

38. Every polynomial function is also a rational function.

39. The graph of $y = \frac{3x^2 + 1}{x^2 + 1}$ has no horizontal asymptotes.

40. The graph of $y = \frac{x^2 - 4x}{x^2 - 1}$ crosses the x-axis at exactly two points.

41. If c is a root of the polynomial equation $f(x) = 0$, then $c + 1$ is a root of $f(x - 1) = 0$.

42. If c is a root of the polynomial equation $f(x) = 0$, then $c - 3$ is a root of $f(x + 3) = 0$.

43. If $f(x) = (x + 3)(x + 1)(x - 2)$, then $f(x)$ is negative for every x in the interval $(-1, 2)$.

44. The graph of $y = x^4 - x^3 + 2x^2 + 1$ has no points in the third quadrant.

45. The graph of $y = x^3 + 2x + 1$ has no points in the fourth quadrant.

46. Every horizontal line must intersect the graph of any polynomial function of degree 3 in at least one point.

47. Every vertical line will intersect the graph of any polynomial function of degree 4 in exactly one point.

48. The graph of every rational function must have a horizontal asymptote.

49. The graph of every polynomial function of degree 4 must have a y-intercept point.

50. Every vertical line will intersect the graph of any polynomial function.

51. If f is a polynomial function and both $f(1)$ and $f(2)$ are positive, then f cannot have a zero between 1 and 2.

Mastery Review

1. For $f(x) = 2x^3 - 3x^2 + x - 4$, evaluate $f(1.5)$ and $f(2)$.

2. For $f(x) = 2x^3 - 3x^2 + x - 4$ (see Exercise 1), locate a zero between successive integers.

3. Find the quotient and remainder when $3x^3 - 4x^2 - x + 1$ is divided by $x + 1$.

4. For $f(x) = x^4 - 3x^2 + 2x - 5$, find $q(x)$ and r such that $f(x) = (x - 3)q(x) + r$.

5. Determine the remainder when $3x^{16} + 2x^{10} - 5x^3 + 3x^2 - 1$ is divided by $x + 1$.

6. Sketch a graph of $y = (x - 1)(x^2 - 4)$. Label on your graph the x- and y-intercept points.

7. Sketch a graph of $y = (x + 2)(x - 1)^2$. Label the x- and y-intercept points on your graph.

8. (a) List the *possible* rational roots given by the rational zeros theorem for $2x^3 - 3x^2 - 5x + 3 = 0$.
   (b) Which, if any, are roots of the given equation?

9. Find all zeros of $f(x) = x^3 - 5x^2 + 4x$.

10. Find all rational zeros of $f(x) = 2x^3 - 3x^2 - 12x - 5$.

11. Find all rational zeros of $f(x) = 2x^3 + 9x^2 + 7x - 6$.

12. Locate each of the irrational roots of $x^4 + 2x^3 - 4x^2 - 6x + 3 = 0$ between two consecutive integers.

13. Locate each of the irrational roots of $x^3 - 5x + 3 = 0$ between (a) two consecutive integers and (b) two consecutive tenths. (c) Determine the largest root rounded off to two decimal places.

14. (a) Locate each of the zeros of $f(x) = 3x^3 - 2x^2 - x + 1$ between two consecutive integers.
    (b) Determine the largest zero rounded off to one decimal place.

15. (a) Find all roots of $x^4 - 3x^2 = 0$ in exact form.
    (b) Sketch a graph of $y = x^4 - 3x^2$.

16. Find a polynomial function of lowest degree with leading coefficient 1 that has -1, 1, and 3 as zeros. Give your answer in expanded form.

17. Find a polynomial function of degree 4 that has each of -2 and 2 as double zeros. Give your answer in expanded form.

18. Find a polynomial function of lowest degree that has integer coefficients, a leading coefficient of 2, and $\frac{1}{2}$ and $\sqrt{3}$ as zeros. Give your answer in expanded form.

19. Sketch the graph of $y = x^3 - 3x^2 - x + 3$. Label the x- and y-intercept points on your graph.

20. (a) Find all roots of $x^3 + x^2 - 6x - 6 = 0$ in exact form.
    (b) Draw a graph of $y = x^3 + x^2 - 6x - 6$ and label the intercept points.

21. Draw a graph of each function.
    (a) $y = x^3 - 4x$ (b) $y = x^3 - 4x - 1$
    (c) $y = (x - 1)^3 - 4(x - 1)$

22. Find the zeros in exact form for the functions f and g.
    (a) $f(x) = x^3 + x^2 - 5x - 5$
    (b) $g(x) = (x - 1)^3 + (x - 1)^2 - 5(x - 1) - 5$

Exercises 23–25   For the graph of the function,

(a) give the x- and y-intercept points

(b) determine the equations of any vertical or horizontal asymptotes

(c) sketch the graph.

23. $f(x) = \frac{x + 3}{2 - x}$

24. $f(x) = \frac{x^2 - 9}{x^2 - x - 2}$

25. $f(x) = \frac{x^2 - 2x + 1}{x^2 - 4x}$

Exercises 26–30   Find the solution set. (*Hint:* Draw a graph or use cut points.)

26. $x^3 - 4x^2 + x + 6 < 0$

27. $x^3 - 3x^2 + x - 3 \geq 0$

28. $x^4 + 4x^3 + 2x^2 - 4x - 3 > 0$

29. $x^2 + \frac{4}{x - 3} \geq 0$ 30. $x^2 - \frac{3x}{x - 2} \geq 0$

Exercises 31–32   Given that f has an inverse, find the indicated values of f^{-1}.

31. $f(x) = x^3 + x + 8$
    (a) $f^{-1}(18)$ (b) $f^{-1}(-2)$

32. $f(x) = 2x^3 - 4x^2 + 3x - 5$
    (a) $f^{-1}(22)$ (b) $f^{-1}(-14)$

Exercises 33–34   Find the solution set for
(a) $f(x) = 0$ (b) $f(x - 1) = 0$
(c) $f(x + 2) = 0$.

33. $f(x) = 2x^3 - 5x^2 - 4x + 3$

34. $f(x) = (2x - 3)(12 - x - x^2)$

Exercises 35–36   Find the solution set for
(a) $f(x) \geq 0$ (b) $f(x - 1) \geq 0$.

35. $f(x) = 2x^3 + 5x^2 - 4x - 3$

36. $f(x) = (x + 3)(x^2 - 16)$

4

EXPONENTIAL AND LOGARITHMIC FUNCTIONS

In Chapter 3 we discussed polynomial functions. This chapter looks at two closely related families of functions, exponential and logarithmic functions. Section 4.1 reviews properties of exponents and uses those properties to introduce exponential functions. Exponential functions are one–one functions, so they have inverses. Sections 4.2 and 4.3 explore these inverses, called logarithmic functions. The last two sections of the chapter show how to evaluate and apply both exponential and logarithmic functions.

Exponents and Exponential Functions

What I really am is a mathematician. Rather than being remembered as the first woman this or that, I would prefer to be remembered, as a mathematician should, simply for the theorems I have proved and the problems I have solved.
Julia Robinson

Elementary algebra courses define expressions of the form b^x for integer exponents (and a few rational-number exponents). We need to expand this to allow more kinds of numbers as exponents. This requires extending definitions to **nth roots** and then to **rational exponents.** The extension to irrational exponents is properly left to calculus, but we can at least get a feeling for what a calculator does when we evaluate an expression such as $3^{\sqrt{2}}$ or 2^{π}. In the following definitions, n and m denote positive integers.

We had a thing at high school called the algebra team, which consisted of five kids, and we would travel to different schools as a team and have competitions. A teacher, who was running the contest, would take out an envelope, and on the envelope it says, "forty-five seconds." She . . . writes the problem on the blackboard, and says, "Go!" One thing was for sure: It was practically impossible to do the problem in any conventional, straightforward way . . . so you had to think, "Is there a way to see it?"

Richard P. Feynman

Definition: Exponents, Roots, and Radicals

Integer Exponents $\quad b^n = b \cdot b \cdot \ldots \cdot b$ (product of n factors); $b^0 = 1$, if $b \neq 0$; $b^{-n} = \frac{1}{b^n}$, if $b \neq 0$.

Principal nth Root $\quad b^{1/n}$, also denoted by $\sqrt[n]{b}$, is the real-number root of $x^n = b$ if there is only one root; if there are two, then $b^{1/n}$ is the positive root. When n is 2, $b^{1/2}$ in radical form is written as $\sqrt{b}$, not as $\sqrt[2]{b}$.

Rational Exponents, $\quad$ If $\frac{m}{n}$ is in lowest terms, then $b^{m/n} = (b^m)^{1/n} = \sqrt[n]{b^m}$. The expression $\sqrt[n]{b^m}$ is called **radical form.**

The following example shows how to simplify expressions with rational number exponents.

EXAMPLE 1   Simplify **(a)** $(-8)^{1/3}$ **(b)** $(-8)^{-1/3}$
(c) $(-8)^{2/3}$ **(d)** $\sqrt[3]{-64}$ **(e)** $(-4)^{3/2}$

Solution

(a) Let $x = (-8)^{1/3}$. Then $x^3 = -8$. The polynomial equation $x^3 + 8 = 0$ has precisely one real-number solution, -2. Hence $(-8)^{1/3} = -2$.

(b) $(-8)^{-1/3}$ is defined to be the reciprocal of $(-8)^{1/3}$, so from part **(a)**

$$(-8)^{-1/3} = \frac{1}{(-8)^{1/3}} = \frac{1}{(-2)} = -\frac{1}{2}.$$

(c) Apply the definition for rational exponents,

$$(-8)^{2/3} = [(-8)^2]^{1/3} = 64^{1/3}.$$

The real number with a cube of 64 is 4. Alternatively, if $x = (-8)^{2/3}$, then $x^3 = (-8)^2 = 64$. The only real-number solution of $x^3 - 64 = 0$ is 4. Therefore, $(-8)^{2/3} = 4$.

(d) The radical $\sqrt[3]{-64}$ is defined to be $(-64)^{1/3}$, which is a root of the polynomial equation $x^3 = -64$. The only real root of $x^3 + 64 = 0$ is -4. Hence, $\sqrt[3]{-64} = -4$.

(e) $(-4)^{3/2} = \sqrt{(-4)^3} = \sqrt{-64}$. As we saw in Section 1.3, $\sqrt{-64}$ is the imaginary number $8i$.   ▲

Irrational Exponents

Certain theoretical considerations require care in defining a number like $2^{\sqrt{2}}$, but properties of the real number system guarantee its existence. We use calculators to evaluate exponential expressions. Since

$$\sqrt{2} \approx 1.41421356\ldots,$$

we would expect the numbers $2^{1.4}$, $2^{1.41}$, $2^{1.414}$, . . . (where all of the exponents are rational) to approach $2^{\sqrt{2}}$. The calculator makes the conclusion reasonable:

$$2^{1.4} = 2^{7/5} \approx 2.639 \qquad 2^{1.41} \approx 2.6574 \qquad 2^{1.414} \approx 2.66475$$

$$2^{\sqrt{2}} \approx 2.6651441.$$

Check to see that you know how to get the same results on your calculator, using either the $\boxed{y^x}$ or $\boxed{\wedge}$. If the base b is negative, a calculator will not give a value for b^t if t is irrational (and perhaps for some rational values of t, also); try $(-5)^\pi$ and $(-5)^{5/3}$.

EXAMPLE 2   Get an approximation rounded off to four decimal places: **(a)** $4^{2/3}$ **(b)** $(-4)^{5/3}$ **(c)** $4^{\sqrt{2}}$

Solution

In each case, for calculator evaluation, use $\boxed{y^x}$ or $\boxed{\wedge}$.

(a) $4^{2/3} \approx 2.5198$

(b) Many calculators give error messages when ordered to evaluate $(-4)^{5/3}$ directly. Remember that cube roots of negative numbers are defined, so that if $b > 0$, then $\sqrt[3]{-b} = -\sqrt[3]{b}$. $(-4)^{5/3} = \sqrt[3]{(-4)^5} = -\sqrt[3]{(4^5)} = -(4^{5/3})$. Therefore, evaluate $4^{5/3}$ by calculator and then get -10.0794 as the desired approximation $(-4)^{5/3}$.

(c)   For $4^{\sqrt{2}}$, the desired approximation is 7.1030.   ▲

Use your own calculator to check our evaluations.

Properties of Exponents

In the expression b^x we call b the **base** and x the **exponent.** If b is a positive number, then b^x is a real number for every value of x. If, however, b is negative, then b^x is a real number for some values of x, but it is imaginary for other values of x. For instance, $(-4)^{5/3}$ is a real number (see Example 2**b**), but $(-4)^{3/2}$ is imaginary (see Example 1**c**). Our primary interest in this chapter is the exponential function, which requires a positive base. Therefore, the following properties of exponents assume positive numbers as bases.

Properties of Exponents

If b and c are positive numbers and x and y are any real numbers, then

E1. $b^x b^y = b^{x+y}$ **E2.** $\dfrac{b^x}{b^y} = b^{x-y}$ **E3.** $(b^x)^y = b^{xy}$

E4. $(bc)^x = b^x c^x$ **E5.** $\left(\dfrac{b}{c}\right)^x = \dfrac{b^x}{c^x}$.

EXAMPLE 3   Use a calculator to approximate (to four decimal places) $\dfrac{5^\pi}{5^{\sqrt{2}}}$ and $5^{\pi - \sqrt{2}}$. How does your result compare with E2?

Solution

Using $\boxed{y^x}$ or $\boxed{\wedge}$ and dividing, we get 16.1208 as the four-decimal-place approximation for both $\dfrac{5^\pi}{5^{\sqrt{2}}}$ and $5^{\pi - \sqrt{2}}$. According to E2, the two numbers are equal, and so we have at least a calculator check on equality.   ▲

EXAMPLE 4   Simplify. Express the result without negative exponents.

Strategy: (a) Use E4 first, followed by E3, and simplify.
(b) First replace x^{-2} by $\frac{1}{x^2}$ and $4x^{-1}$ by $\frac{4}{x}$, then simplify.

(a) $(x^{-2}y^3)^{-2}$ (b) $\dfrac{x^{-2} - 4x^{-1} - 5}{5x - 1}$

Solution

(a) $(x^{-2}y^3)^{-2} = (x^{-2})^{-2}(y^3)^{-2} = x^4 y^{-6} = x^4\left(\dfrac{1}{y^6}\right) = \dfrac{x^4}{y^6}$.

(b) $\dfrac{x^{-2} - 4x^{-1} - 5}{5x - 1} = \dfrac{\dfrac{1}{x^2} - \dfrac{4}{x} - 5}{5x - 1} = \dfrac{\dfrac{1 - 4x - 5x^2}{x^2}}{5x - 1} = \dfrac{(1 - 5x)(1 + x)}{x^2(5x - 1)}$

$$= -\frac{x + 1}{x^2}. \quad \blacktriangle$$

EXAMPLE 5   Rationalize the denominator of $\frac{x-1}{\sqrt{x}+1}$.

Strategy: Multiply numerator and denominator by $\sqrt{x} - 1$ and simplify to get rid of the radical in the denominator.

Solution

Follow the strategy.

$$\frac{x - 1}{\sqrt{x} + 1} = \frac{(x - 1)(\sqrt{x} - 1)}{(\sqrt{x} + 1)(\sqrt{x} - 1)} = \frac{(x - 1)(\sqrt{x} - 1)}{x - 1} = \sqrt{x} - 1. \quad \blacktriangle$$

EXAMPLE 6   Solve the equation $2x^{-2} + 7x^{-1} - 4 = 0$.

Strategy: First get rid of the negative exponents by multiplying both sides by x^2, then solve the resulting quadratic equation.

Solution

Follow the strategy.

$$x^2(2x^{-2} + 7x^{-1} - 4) = x^2 \cdot 0 \qquad 2 + 7x - 4x^2 = 0$$

Factoring $(2 - x)(1 + 4x) = 0$. By the zero product principle, the solutions are 2 and $-\frac{1}{4}$. $\quad \blacktriangle$

EXAMPLE 7   Solve the equation $3^{2x-1} - \frac{27}{\sqrt[3]{9}} = 0$.

Strategy: First express $\frac{27}{\sqrt[3]{9}}$ as a power of 3, then use properties of exponents.

Solution

Follow the strategy.

$$\frac{27}{\sqrt[3]{9}} = \frac{3^3}{\sqrt[3]{3^2}} = \frac{3^3}{3^{2/3}} = 3^{3-(2/3)} = 3^{7/3}$$

Therefore, the given equation is equivalent to

$$3^{2x+1} = 3^{7/3}.$$

In this form it is intuitively clear that the two exponents must be equal: $2x + 1 = \frac{7}{3}$. Thus the solution is $\frac{2}{3}$.

     If we had been unable to express $\frac{27}{\sqrt[3]{9}}$ as a simple power of 3, then the solution of this problem would have had to await the techniques of Section 4.4. $\quad \blacktriangle$

EXAMPLE 8   Prove that $1 + \sqrt[3]{2}$ is an irrational number.

Strategy: First let $x = 1 + \sqrt[3]{2}$ so that $x - 1 = \sqrt[3]{2}$. Cube both sides and get a polynomial equation with integer coefficients that has $1 + \sqrt[3]{2}$ as a root. Use the rational zeros theorem from Section 3.3 to show that the resulting equation has no rational roots.

Solution

Follow the strategy.

$$(x - 1)^3 = (\sqrt[3]{2})^3$$

Expand and simplify to get

$$x^3 - 3x^2 + 3x - 3 = 0.$$

We now know that $1 + \sqrt[3]{2}$ is a root of this cubic equation. The rational zeros theorem given in Section 3.3 implies that the only possible rational roots are $\pm 1, \pm 3$. It is easy to verify that none of these is a root. Therefore, $1 + \sqrt[3]{2}$ must be irrational. ▲

The next example illustrates how two very different expressions can represent the same number.

| EXAMPLE 9 | If $b = 1 + \sqrt{5}$ and $c = \sqrt{5 + \sqrt{21 + 4\sqrt{5}}}$,

then determine whether b is less than, greater than, or equal to c.

Strategy: First, try calculator evaluations. If they are equal, then try to show that $b = c$ by first showing that $b^2 = c^2$.

Solution

Follow the strategy.

$$1 + \sqrt{5} \approx 3.236067977 \qquad \text{and} \qquad \sqrt{5 + \sqrt{21 + 4\sqrt{5}}} \approx 3.236067977.$$

Since the decimal approximations are equal, we have good reason to suspect that b and c may be equal, but we cannot know for certain that they are. (Why?) To show that $b = c$, try to compare b^2 and c^2, using the property: If two *positive* numbers have equal squares, then the numbers are equal.

$$b^2 = (1 + \sqrt{5})^2 = 1 + 2\sqrt{5} + 5 = 6 + 2\sqrt{5} \qquad \text{and}$$
$$c^2 = 5 + \sqrt{21 + 4\sqrt{5}}.$$

It is still not obvious that $b^2 = c^2$, so try squaring again, or it may seem simpler to square $c^2 - 5$, and then compare $(b^2 - 5)^2$ and $(c^2 - 5)^2$.

$$(b^2 - 5)^2 = (1 + 2\sqrt{5})^2 = 1 + 4\sqrt{5} + 4 \cdot 5 = 21 + 4\sqrt{5}.$$
$$(c^2 - 5)^2 = (\sqrt{21 + 4\sqrt{5}})^2 = 21 + 4\sqrt{5}.$$

Finally, we get $(b^2 - 5)^2 = (c^2 - 5)^2$, and both $b^2 - 5$ and $c^2 - 5$ are positive, so $b^2 - 5 = c^2 - 5$, from which $b^2 = c^2$. Since both b and c are positive, $b = c$. ▲

Exponential Functions

There is exactly one value of the expression 5^x for any given real number x, so the equation $f(x) = 5^x$ defines a function whose domain is R. The following sequence gives a feeling about the behavior of $f(x)$ as x increases:

$$\ldots, 5^{-2} = \tfrac{1}{25}, 5^{-1} = \tfrac{1}{5}, 5^0 = 1, 5^1 = 5, 5^2 = 25, 5^3 = 125, \ldots$$

We see that $f(x)$ is very small when x is negative, that the function is increasing (for example, $5^0 < 5^{1/2} < 5^1$), and that the values grow very rapidly as x gets large and positive. This sort of behavior is typical of functions called **exponential functions**.

> **Definition: Exponential Function**
>
> An exponential function is any function that can be expressed in the form
>
> $$f(x) = b^x,$$
>
> where b is a fixed positive number other than 1.

Because we want the domain of f to be the set of all real numbers, the base must be positive (see Explore and Discover Exercise 2). Notice that b cannot equal 1 because 1^x is equal to 1 for every real number x, so $f(x) = 1^x$ is equivalent to the linear function $f(x) = 1$. The function $F(x) = x^2$ is not an exponential function because it has a variable base, but $G(x) = 2^{2x}$ is an exponential function because $2^{2x} = (2^2)^x = 4^x$, so $G(x) = 4^x$.

Graphs of Exponential Functions with Base Greater than 1 The graph of every exponential function has one of essentially two different shapes, depending on whether the base is greater than 1 or less than 1. First, look at two examples where b is greater than 1.

EXAMPLE 10 Draw the graphs of the functions $f(x) = 2^x$ and $g(x) = 3^x$ on the same set of coordinates.

Solution
The following table lists several values of $f(x)$ and $g(x)$

x	-3	-2	-1	0	1	2	3
$f(x)$	0.125	0.25	0.50	1	2	4	8
$g(x)$	0.037	0.11	0.33	1	3	9	27

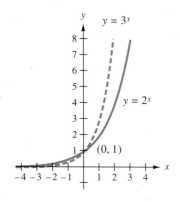

FIGURE 4.1

Exponential functions with bases greater than 1

After plotting the points from the table and drawing smooth curves through the plotted points, we get the graphs shown in Figure 4.1. ▲

The exponential curves in Figure 4.1, with bases 2 and 3 respectively, are very similar. They are typical of the graphs of functions of the form $y = b^x$ where the base b is greater than 1. If the base b is a number near 1, then the curve is relatively flat; as b increases, the curve $y = b^x$ rises more and more steeply with increasing values of x.

Exponential Functions with Base Less than 1 When the base b is a number less than 1, then the values of b^x are reciprocals of another exponential function with base greater than 1, as the following example shows.

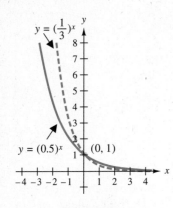

FIGURE 4.2

Exponential functions with bases less than 1

| EXAMPLE 11 | Draw graphs of $f(x) = (0.5)^x$ and $g(x) = (\frac{1}{3})^x$ on the same set of coordinates.

Solution

First note that $f(x) = (0.5)^x = (\frac{1}{2})^x = \frac{1}{2^x}$ and $g(x) = \frac{1}{3^x}$. Make a table of values by taking reciprocals of the entries in the table from Example 10. Plotting points and drawing smooth curves gives the graphs shown in Figure 4.2. ▲

Properties of Exponential Functions   The graphs in Figures 4.1 and 4.2 suggest some general properties of exponential functions.

Properties of Exponential Functions

Suppose f is an exponential function, $f(x) = b^x$, where b is positive and not 1.

Domain: All real numbers   Range: $(0, \infty)$

x-intercept points: None y-intercept point: $(0, 1)$

Asymptotes: The x-axis is a horizontal asymptote.

If $b > 1$, then f is an increasing function; if $0 < b < 1$, then f is a decreasing function.

The function f is one–one and therefore it has an inverse.

The Euler Number e and the Natural Exponential Function

An important number between 2 and 3, denoted by e, serves as the base of an important exponential function. The number e, sometimes called the Euler number, can be defined in various ways (see the Historical Note, "π and e," Part I). For example, the discussion of compound interest in Section 4.5 will show that the expression $(1 + x)^{1/x}$ arises in a natural way, and as x approaches 0, the value of $(1 + x)^{1/x}$ approaches a number near 2.718; see Develop Mastery Exercise 47. In calculus courses it is shown that the limit of $(1 + x)^{1/x}$, as x approaches 0, is the number e:

$$\lim_{x \to 0} (1 + x)^{1/x} = e.$$

Rounded off to 25 decimal places,

$$e \approx 2.71828 \ 18284 \ 59045 \ 23536 \ 02875.$$

Your calculator has a key that can be used to directly evaluate e^x. It may be located above the $\boxed{\ln}$, and hence is activated by pressing $\boxed{\text{2nd}}$ or $\boxed{\text{INV}}$ or $\boxed{\text{SHIFT}}$. To see what your calculator gives for e, evaluate e^1 (enter 1 and $\boxed{e^x}$, or type $\boxed{e^x}$ 1 $\boxed{\text{EXE}}$). Your display should show part of the approximation given above.

For reasons that will become clearer when we look at applications, the function $f(x) = e^x$ is called the **natural exponential function.**

Historical Note

π AND e, PART I

Leonhard Euler

Leonhard Euler (Switzerland, 1707–1783) first used the letter e for the base of natural logarithms; e is often called *Euler's number*. Euler proved in 1737 that e is irrational, 24 years before π was shown to be irrational. Euler discovered a relationship between π and e that some thought to have mystical significance:

$$e^{\pi i} + 1 = 0, \text{ where } i = \sqrt{-1}.$$

The numbers π and e share another property. Any number that is a root of a polynomial equation with integer coefficients is called an **algebraic number.** The set of algebraic numbers includes all of the rational numbers and some of the irrational numbers. For example, $\sqrt{2} + \sqrt{6}$ is an irrational number and it is also algebraic since it is a root of $x^4 - 16x^2 + 16 = 0$. Real numbers that are not algebraic are called **transcendental numbers.** It was long suspected that π and e might be transcendental, but not until 1873 did Hermite (France) prove the transcendence of e. Nine years later, Lindemann (Germany) extended Hermite's result to include π (as well as many numbers involving trigonometric and logarithmic functions).

Definition: Natural Exponential Function

When the base of an exponential function f is the number e, then $f(x) = e^x$ is called the *natural exponential function.*

EXAMPLE 12   Get calculator values for the natural exponential function $f(x) = e^x$ and sketch a graph of $y = f(x)$. Compare the graph with the graphs of $y = 2^x$ and $y = 3^x$ from Figure 4.1.

Solution

Make a table as in Example 10.

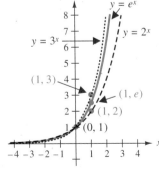

FIGURE 4.3

Natural exponential function, $y = e^x$

x	-3	-2	-1	0	1	2	3
$f(x)$	0.05	0.14	0.37	1.0	2.7	7.4	20

Note that e is between 2 and 3 (nearer 3) and that the values of e^x are all between corresponding values of 2^x and 3^x (nearer 3^x). Plot points and connect them with a smooth curve to get a curve very similar to the ones in Example 10. Figure 4.3 shows all three graphs. ▲

Using the graph of the natural exponential function (Figure 4.3) as a *core graph*, the graphing techniques from Chapter 2 allow us to graph many functions that are related to exponential functions. For convenience, we recall some information on translations and reflections with examples using exponential functions to illustrate.

Translations and Reflections of Core Graphs

Given a core graph $y = f(x)$ and a positive number c:

$y = f(x) \pm c$: Translate vertically c units up $(+)$ or down $(-)$.   Example: $y = e^x + 1$.

$y = f(x \pm c)$: Translate horizontally c units left $(+)$ or right $(-)$.   Example: $y = e^{x-2}$.

$y = -f(x)$: Reflect through the x-axis.   Example $y = -e^x$.

$y = f(-x)$: Reflect through the y-axis.   Example: $y = e^{-x}$.

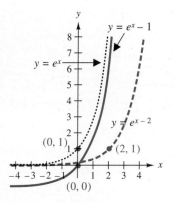

FIGURE 4.4

Translations of $y = e^x$

EXAMPLE 13   Simplify the equations that describe functions f and g, then draw graphs of f and g.

$$f(x) = \frac{e^{2x} - e^x}{e^x} \qquad g(x) = \frac{e^x}{e^2}$$

Solution

$$f(x) = \frac{e^{2x}}{e^x} - \frac{e^x}{e^x} = e^x - 1, \text{ so } f(x) = e^x - 1.$$

$$g(x) = e^x \cdot e^{-2} = e^{x-2}, \text{ so } g(x) = e^{x-2}.$$

Therefore the graph of $y = f(x)$ is a vertical translation of the core graph, $y = e^x$, one unit down. The graph of $y = g(x)$ is a horizontal translation of the core graph two units right. Both graphs are shown in Figure 4.4. ▲

EXAMPLE 14   Find the solution set for **(a)** $xe^x - 3e^x = 0$ **(b)** $xe^x - 3e^x > 0$.

Solution

(a)   In factored form the given equation is $e^x(x - 3) = 0$. By the zero product principle, either $e^x = 0$ or $x - 3 = 0$. Since e^x is positive for all real numbers [the range is $(0, \infty)$], there is no value of x for which $e^x = 0$. From $x - 3 = 0$, the solution set is $\{3\}$.

(b)   The given inequality is equivalent to $e^x(x - 3) > 0$. Since e^x is positive for all real numbers, the product is positive whenever the other factor is positive. We want $x - 3 > 0$, or $x > 3$. The solution set is $\{x \mid x > 3.\}$ ▲

EXERCISES 4.1

Check Your Understanding

Exercises 1–5 · True or False. Give reasons for your conclusion.

1. For every real number x, $\sqrt[3]{\sqrt{64x^6}} = 2x$.
2. For every real number x, $(x - 2)^0 = 1$.
3. For every negative number x, $\sqrt{(-x)^2} = -x$.
4. The solution set for $2^{-x} + 1 = 0$ is the empty set.
5. Every exponential function is either an increasing or a decreasing function.

Exercises 6–10 Complete the sentence by selecting from the list below *all choices* that make the statement true.

(a) a positive integer   (b) a negative integer
(c) an even integer   (d) an odd integer
(e) positive for every x (f) an increasing function
(g) negative for every x (h) a decreasing function

6. $(5^{\sqrt{2}})^{\sqrt{2}}$ is _____.
7. $(-1)^{215} + (-3)^{72}$ is _____.
8. $(\sqrt{2})^6 + (\sqrt[3]{-3})^{27}$ is _____.
9. The function $g(x) = 1 + 3^{-x}$ is _____.
10. The function $f(x) = -2^x$ is _____.

Explore and Discover

1. Explain why we require $\frac{m}{n}$ to be in lowest terms in the definition of rational exponents. Consider the expressions $(-1)^{1/3}$ and $(-1)^{2/6}$ and other examples to illustrate.

2. Explain why the base b for an exponential function $f(x) = b^x$ must be positive. In your explanation, you might take a number like -2 for b and evaluate $(-2)^x$ where x assumes various values, such as integers or rational numbers like $\frac{1}{2}$, $\frac{1}{3}$, ... , or irrational numbers like $\sqrt{2}$, π, ...

Exercises 3–6 Looking Ahead to Calculus Let $F(x) = e^x$, $C(x) = e^x + e^{-x}$, and $S(x) = e^x - e^{-x}$.

3. (a) Show that
$$\frac{F(x + h) - F(x)}{h} = \frac{e^x(e^h - 1)}{h}.$$

(b) Evaluate $\frac{e^h - 1}{h}$ for different values of h near 0. From your computations, guess the value of the limit of $\frac{e^h - 1}{h}$ as h approaches 0.

4. Is S even or odd or neither? What about C?
5. Evaluate and simplify $[C(x)]^2 - [S(x)]^2$.
6. Show that the product function $C \cdot S$, where $(CS)(x) = C(x) \cdot S(x)$ is equal to $S(2x)$.

Develop Mastery

Exercises 1–8 Simplify. Give answer in exact form.

1. $\frac{3^{-1} + 2^{-2}}{6^{-1}}$
2. $(2^{-3} + 4^{-1})^{-3}$
3. $\left(\frac{3^{-1} \cdot 2^2}{6^{-1}}\right)^{-1}$
4. $(\sqrt{8} - \sqrt{2})^{-4}$
5. $\frac{7^{5/2} - 63^{3/2}}{\sqrt{7}}$
6. $\left(\frac{\sqrt[3]{4}\sqrt[4]{2}}{\sqrt[6]{8}}\right)$
7. $(\sqrt{5} + \sqrt{11})^0$
8. $\frac{\sqrt{105}(\sqrt{35})^{-1}}{3}$

Exercises 9–16 Give a calculator approximation, rounding off to four significant digits.

9. $(-3)^{5/3}$
10. $(\sqrt{5} - 1)^{\pi}$
11. $(1 + \pi)^{-2/5}$
12. $(\sqrt{2} + \sqrt{5})^{-1/2}$
13. $5^{\sqrt{5}}$
14. $(-1.47)^{2/3}$
15. $3^{5/3} - 9^{1/3}$
16. $(1 - \sqrt{3})^{2/5}$

Exercises 17–18 Rationalize the denominator and simplify.

17. (a) $\frac{8}{\sqrt{5} + 1}$ (b) $\frac{x - 4}{\sqrt{x} - 2}$
18. (a) $\frac{6}{\sqrt{3} + 1}$ (b) $\frac{x^2 - 9x}{\sqrt{x} + 3}$

Exercises 19–24 Simplify.

19. $\sqrt{1 - (1 + x)(1 - x)}$
20. $\frac{x^2(x^{-2} - 2x^{-1} + 1)}{x - 1}$
21. $x^{5/2}x^{-3/2}$
22. $4^{2-3x}8^{x-2}$
23. $\frac{27^{x-1}}{9^{1-3x}}$
24. $\left(\sqrt{x} + \frac{1}{\sqrt{x}}\right)^2 - \frac{1}{x}$

Exercises 25–30 Find the solution set.

25. $x^{-2} - 3x^{-1} + 2 = 0$
26. $x^{-2} - 2x^{-1} + 1 = 0$
27. $2x^{-2} - 5x^{-1} = 0$
28. $4^{x-1} - 4\sqrt{2} = 0$

29. $(x^2 - 1)^0 = 1$ **30.** $(x^2 - 2x - 3)^0 = 1$

Exercises 31–34 Is the function an exponential function? Give reasons.

31. $f(x) = \pi^x$

32. $g(x) = (\sqrt{3} - 1)^x$

33. $f(x) = (1 - \sqrt{2})^x$

34. $g(x) = \dfrac{e^{2x}}{e^x}$

Exercises 35–36 Give results rounded off to two decimal places.

35. $F(x) = xe^x$; find **(a)** $F(-1)$ **(b)** $F(\sqrt{2})$

36. $F(x) = e^x + e^{-x}$; find **(a)** $F(-1)$ **(b)** $F(\sqrt{5})$

Exercises 37–40 Determine which of the two numbers is greater.

37. $3^{\sqrt{3}}$ or $(\sqrt{3})^3$

38. e^3 or 3^e

39. $5^{\sqrt{5}}$ or $(\sqrt{5})^5$

40. π^e or e^π

Exercises 41–46 **(a)** Draw a graph and use it to determine the range of the function. Note that -3^x means $-(3^x)$, not $(-3)^x$. **(b)** Is the function increasing, decreasing, or neither?

41. $f(x) = -3^x$

42. $g(x) = -3^{-x}$

43. $f(x) = e^{x+1}$

44. $g(x) = e^x + 1$

45. $f(x) = 1 - e^x$

46. $f(x) = (\sqrt{2} - 1)^x$

47. If $f(x) = (1 + x)^{1/x}$, evaluate $f(x)$ when $x = \pm 0.1$, ± 0.05, ± 0.01, ± 0.001, etc.

48. Simplify **(a)** $(1 + x)^{-1} + (1 + x^{-1})^{-1}$
(b) $(1 + x^2)^{-1} + (1 + x^{-2})^{-1}$

Exercises 49–56 Find the solution set.

49. $\sqrt{\sqrt{\sqrt{4\sqrt{2}x}}} = 2$

50. $x^2 \cdot 2^x - 4 \cdot 2^x = 0$

51. $2^x = 6 - 8 \cdot 2^{-x}$

52. $2^{2x-1} 4^{2x+5} = 8^{2x+3}$

53. $\sqrt{1 + x^2 - 2\sqrt{1 - x^2}} = x$

54. $(2^x)^2 - 2(2^x) - 8 = 0$

55. **(a)** $4x^{-1} = 1$ **(b)** $4x^{-1} \le 1$
(c) $(4x)^{-1} \le 1$ **(d)** $4x^{-1} = x$

56. $x + \sqrt{x^2 + 1} - 10 = \dfrac{1}{x + \sqrt{x^2 + 1}}$
(*Hint*: First rationalize the denominator.)

Exercises 57–60 Simplify the equation describing f and then draw a graph. Use translations where appropriate.

57. $f(x) = e^2 e^x$

58. $f(x) = 1 + \dfrac{2^x}{8}$

59. $f(x) = (e^x + e^{-x})^2 - (e^{2x} + e^{-2x})$

60. $f(x) = (3^x + 3^{-x})^2 - (9^x + 9^{-x})$

Exercises 61–64 Is b equal to c, less than c, or greater than c? Calculator evaluation is not sufficient to establish equality. (*Hint:* See Example 9.)

61. $b = \dfrac{\sqrt{3}+1}{2}$ $c = \dfrac{1}{\sqrt{3} - 1}$

62. $b = \sqrt{3} + \sqrt{5}$ $c = \sqrt{8 + 2\sqrt{15}}$

63. $b = 1 + \sqrt{3}$, $c = \dfrac{110{,}771}{40{,}545}$

64. $b = 1 + \sqrt{3}$ $c = \sqrt{3 + \sqrt{13 + 4\sqrt{3}}}$

Exercises 65–66 Use the rational zeros theorem to prove that the given number is irrational.

65. $1 + \sqrt{5}$

66. $\sqrt[3]{3} - 1$

Exercises 67–68 Find the solution set.

67. $x^2 e^{-x} - 5e^{-x} > 0$

68. $2^x \ge 6 - 8 \cdot 2^x$

69. What is the smallest integer that is greater than $(1 + \sqrt{2})^4$? than $(\sqrt{2} + \sqrt{3})^5$?

70. If $f(x) = (x^x)^x$ and $g(x) = x^{(x^x)}$, which number is larger
(a) $f(2)$ or $g(2)$?   **(b)** $f(3)$ or $g(3)$?
(c) $f(0.5)$ or $g(0.5)$?

71. If $f(x) = 1 + 2^x$, then evaluate $\dfrac{1}{f(x)} + \dfrac{1}{f(-x)}$ and simplify your answer.

72. Rationalize the denominator and simplify: $\dfrac{2\sqrt{10}}{\sqrt{2} + \sqrt{5} + \sqrt{7}}$.

73. If $f(x) = 3^x$, show that **(a)** $f(u + v) = f(u) \cdot f(v)$
(b) $f(2x) = [f(x)]^2$ **(c)** $f(3x) = [f(x)]^3$.

74. The volume V of a sphere of radius r is given by $V = \dfrac{4\pi r^3}{3}$.
(a) Solve for r and get an equation that gives r as a function of V.
(b) Use the results in part **(a)** to find the radius of a sphere whose volume is 148.4 cubic centimeters. Give the result rounded off to four significant digits.

75. A spherical balloon is being inflated in such a manner that its radius r is given by $r = 1 + 2\sqrt{t}$, where t represents the time in seconds after inflation begins and r is measured in centimeters. The balloon will burst if the radius exceeds 15 centimeters.
(a) Find an equation that describes the volume of the balloon as a function of t and state the domain of this function.
(b) What is the volume at the end of 4 seconds? At the end of 1 minute?

76. Suppose an inverted circular cone with a height of 20 centimeters and a base of radius 10 centimeters is partially filled with water. Let r represent the radius of the water surface and h the height, as shown in the diagram.

(a) Find an equation that describes the volume V of water as a function of r.

(b) From the result in part (a) find an equation that describes r as a function of V, then find r when the volume of water is 1200 cubic centimeters.

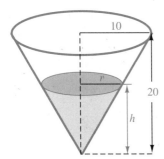

77. A container in the form of a right circular cone with its vertex at the bottom has a height of 16 cm. There is a control valve at the vertex through which the container can be emptied. When the height of the water in the container is h cm ($0 \le h \le 16$) and the valve is opened, it will take T seconds to empty the container, where T is given by

$$T = 0.04[16^{5/2} - (16 - h)^{5/2}].$$

How long will it take to empty the container, when h is equal to (a) 12 cm   (b) 6 cm   (c) 3 cm?

Exercises 78–79   A demand function p that determines the unit price (in dollars) of a certain product is given, where x is the number of units sold.

(a) Calculate p when 1200 units are sold.

(b) Find the corresponding revenue R (where $R = x \cdot p$) when 2000 units are sold.

78. $p = 400 - 0.4(2^{0.003x})$

79. $p = 300\left(1 - \dfrac{5}{5 + 2^{-0.003x}}\right)$

80. It is predicted that the population P of Brouwer's Ferry is given by $P = 2000(2^{0.03t})$, where t is the number of years after 1990. What does this model predict for the population at the end of

(a) The year 1996?   (b) The year 2000?

(c) The year 2020?

Exercises 81–85   Huge Numbers and Estimation   It is often difficult to get a good feeling for the size of numbers that appear in the daily news. For instance, the size of the federal debt ($4 trillion) is so huge that we have little basis for comparison, but working with more familiar numbers may help.

81. (a) How many days are there in a million seconds? A billion seconds?

(b) How many years are there in a billion seconds? Four trillion seconds?

82. At the end of 1992 the federal debt reached $4.1 trillion and was increasing at the rate of $13,000 per second. Assume that the debt continues to increase at this rate.

(a) What will the debt be at the end of 1996?

(b) During what year will the debt reach $7 trillion?

83. If you can stack 250 dollar bills per inch, how many miles high would a stack of seven trillion (7×10^{12}) dollars be? (*Hint:* The distance from the earth to the moon is approximately 240,000 miles.)

84. Assuming that dollar bills are made from paper and that paper comes from wood, estimate the number of trees required to produce seven trillion (7×10^{12}) dollar bills. Assume that one pound of wood yields one pound of paper and that a pound of paper makes about 400 bills, that an average tree is a cylinder 50 feet high and 2 feet in diameter and that wood weighs 50 pounds per cubic foot.

85. The largest known prime (discovered in March 1992) is the number given by $P = 2^{756,839} - 1$. If P were written out in ordinary base ten notation, how many digits would it contain? Estimate the number of pages it would take to print out P. (Assume as many characters on a page as on a typical page of this book.)

SECTION 4.2   **Logarithmic Functions**

A piece of advice: do examples. Do a million examples. I think there are shameful cases of people making (I'll even say) silly and reckless conjectures just because they didn't take the trouble to look at the first few examples. A well-chosen example can teach you so much.

Irving Kaplansky

In the preceding section we observed that every exponential function has an inverse. The inverse of an exponential function is called a **logarithmic function**. In this section and the next we study properties of such functions.

In Section 2.7 we developed a useful algorithm to find an equation for inverse functions. Basically, we write $y = g(x)$ and interchange the x and y values. If we can solve the resulting equation for y, the result gives the inverse of the function g. Unfortunately, this algorithm depends on solving an equation for y, which is not always an easy task.

The Inverse of an Exponential Function

Consider the exponential function $f(x) = 3^x$. Since f is one–one, we know that it has an inverse. Applying the algorithm, we write $y = 3^x$, interchange variables, $x = 3^y$, and we stop; we have no way to solve for y. To describe the value of y verbally:

$$y \text{ is the power to which 3 must be raised to get } x. \qquad \textbf{(1)}$$

Such a rule describes a function, but it is not easy to apply. Without something more, we have no way to find the power of 3 that gives 2, for example, even though the graph of $y = 3^x$ indicates that there is exactly one such number.

We introduce a new name and notation for the function described in (1):

$$y = \log_3 x$$

That is, $\log_3$ (read "log base 3") is the name of a function, the inverse of the exponential function $f(x) = 3^x$. We usually write $\log_3 x$ without parentheses around x unless they are needed for clarity.

> If $f(x) = 3^x$, then $f^{-1}(x) = \log_3 x$, where $\log_3 x$ is the power to which 3 must be raised to get x.

| EXAMPLE 1 | Evaluate **(a)** $\log_3 1$, **(b)** $\log_3 \sqrt{3}$, and **(c)** $\log_3 9$. |

Solution

(a) Recall that $\log_3 1$ is the power to which we must raise 3 to get 1. Since $3^0 = 1$, $\log_3 1$ is 0. We write $\log_3 1 = 0$.

(b) In the same way $\log_3 \sqrt{3}$ is the power of 3 that gives $\sqrt{3}$. Since $\sqrt{3} = 3^{1/2}$, then $\log_3 \sqrt{3} = \frac{1}{2}$.

(c) Similarly, since $3^2 = 9$, $\log_3 9 = 2$. ▲

We used our knowledge of some of the powers of 3 to find the values in Example 3, but we need a calculator to evaluate numbers such as $\log_3 2$. In Section 4.4, we will learn how to find that $\log_3 2 \approx 0.6309297536$. Check this by using your calculator to evaluate $3^{0.6309297536}$.

Graph, Domain, and Range of $\log_3 x$

In Section 2.7 we discussed several key ideas about graph, domain, and range of an inverse function. Since the number pairs that define a function are interchanged in defining the inverse, the graph of f^{-1} is the reflection of the graph of f through the line $y = x$; the domain and range are also interchanged accordingly. We graphed $y = 3^x$ in the preceding section (Figure 4.1). We can use that

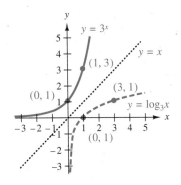

FIGURE 4.5

The graph of $y = \log_3 x$ is reflection of the graph of $y = 3^x$ in the line $y = x$.

graph to draw the graph of $y = \log_3 x$ (see Figure 4.5), and we can easily read the domain and range of both functions from the graphs. Every point pair (u, v) from $y = 3^x$ gives a corresponding point pair (v, u) for the inverse function, $y = \log_3 x$.

Logarithmic Functions

There is nothing special about the base 3 in the discussion above. The exponential function $f(x) = 3^x$ has an inverse function, namely the logarithmic function for base 3, denoted by $\log_3$. Just as there is an exponential function for every positive base b other than 1, there is a corresponding logarithmic function for every such base.

Definition: Logarithmic Functions

Suppose b is any positive number other than 1. The exponential function $f(x) = b^x$ has an inverse function called the **logarithmic function**, $f^{-1}(x) = \log_b x$, where $\log_b x$ is the power to which b must be raised to get x, that is, $b^{\log_b x} = x$.

Since each logarithmic function is the inverse of an exponential function, knowledge of exponential functions and their graphs implies much about the domains and ranges of logarithmic functions. Since $b^0 = 1$ and $b^1 = b$, the definition gives two values that are common to all logarithmic functions, as well as a very helpful equivalence.

Domain and Range: Special Values and Equivalence

The domain of $\log_b$ is $\{x \mid x > 0\}$. The range is $\log_b$ is R.

$$\log_b 1 = 0 \quad \text{and} \quad \log_b b = 1. \tag{2}$$

$$y = \log_b x \text{ is equivalent to } b^y = x. \tag{3}$$

Strategy: Use equivalence (3) and knowledge of powers.

| EXAMPLE 2 | Evaluate **(a)** $\log_5 25$, **(b)** $\log_{10} 0.01$, **(c)** $\log_{0.5} 2\sqrt{2}$.

Solution

(a) If $y = \log_5 25$, then by (3), $5^y = 25 = 5^2$, so y is 2. Thus $\log_2 25 = 2$.

(b) Let $y = \log_{10} 0.01$. By (3), $10^y = 0.01 = 10^{-2}$. Hence y is -2, or $\log_{10} 0.01 = -2$.

(c) Let $y = \log_{0.5} 2\sqrt{2}$. By (3), $(0.5)^y = 2\sqrt{2}$. Since $2\sqrt{2} = 2^{3/2}$ and $0.5 = \frac{1}{2} = 2^{-1}$,

$$(2^{-1})^y = 2^{3/2} \quad \text{or} \quad 2^{-y} = 2^{3/2}$$

so y is $-\frac{3}{2}$. Thus, $\log_{0.5} 2\sqrt{2} = -\frac{3}{2}$. ▲

Inverse Function Identities

In Section 2.7 we showed that, if a function f has an inverse, then

$$f(f^{-1}(x)) = x \text{ for every } x \text{ in the domain of } f^{-1}, \text{ and}$$

$$f^{-1}(f(x)) = x \text{ for every } x \text{ in the domain of } f.$$

For the exponential function $f(x) = b^x$ and its inverse $f^{-1}(x) = \log_b x$, this gives the following inverse function identities.

Inverse Function Identities

$$b^{\log_b x} = x \text{ for every } x > 0 \qquad\qquad (4)$$

$$\log_b b^x = x \text{ for every real number } x \qquad\qquad (5)$$

EXAMPLE 3   Evaluate (a) $7^{\log_7 5}$ (b) $\log_3(\log_5 5)$

Solution

(a)   From Equation 4, where b is 7 and x is 5, $7^{(\log_7 5)} = 5$.

(b)   From Equation 2, $\log_5 5 = 1$. Therefore, $\log_3(\log_5 5) = \log_3 1$. Also by Equation 2, $\log_3 1 = 0$, so $\log_3(\log_5 5) = 0$. ▲

EXAMPLE 4   Simplify. Give the values of x for which the result is valid.

(a) $3^{\log_3(x-2)}$ (b) $\log_5 5^{\sqrt{x}}$

Solution

(a)   From Equation 4,

$$3^{\log_3(x-2)} = x - 2 \text{ for } x - 2 > 0.$$

Thus, $3^{\log_3(x-2)}$ is identically equal to $x - 2$ when x is greater than 2, but it is undefined if x is less than or equal to 2.

(b)   From Equation 5,

$$\log_5 5^{\sqrt{x}} = \sqrt{x} \text{ for every } x \geq 0. ▲$$

EXAMPLE 5   Solve the equation $\log_3(x^2 - 3x + 5) = 2$.

Strategy: Use Equation 3 to write the given equation in exponential form, then solve the resulting quadratic equation.

Solution

Follow the strategy.

$$x^2 - 3x + 5 = 3^2, \qquad x^2 - 3x - 4 = 0 \qquad (x - 4)(x + 1) = 0$$

The solutions are -1 and 4. Exercise 29 asks you to verify that 4 and -1 are solutions of the equation $\log_3(x^2 - 3x + 5) = 2$. ▲

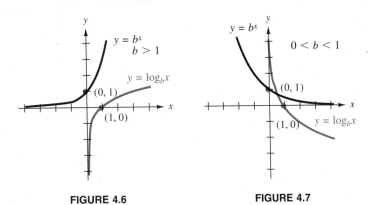

FIGURE 4.6 **FIGURE 4.7**

Graphs of Logarithmic Functions

For any given base b, the graph of $y = \log_b x$ is the reflection about the line $y = x$ of the graph of $y = b^x$. It is helpful to become very familiar with the shapes of the graphs of the exponential and logarithmic functions. For $b > 1$, the general shapes of $y = b^x$ and $y = \log_b x$ are shown in Figure 4.6. For $0 < b < 1$, the graphs of $y = b^x$ and $y = \log_b x$ look like those shown in Figure 4.7.

| EXAMPLE 6 | Draw a graph of (a) $y = \log_2 x$ and (b) $y = \log_{0.5} x$. |

Solution

(a) The graph of $y = \log_2 x$ is a reflection about the line $y = x$ of the graph of $y = 2^x$. See Figure 4.8a.

(b) Reflect the graph of $y = (0.5)^x$ about the line $y = x$ to get the graph of $y = \log_{0.5} x$. See Figure 4.8b. ▲

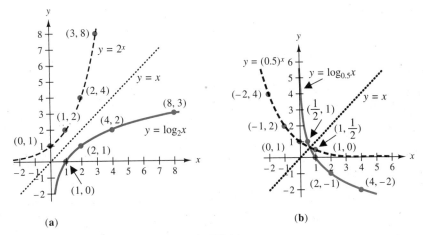

(a) (b)

FIGURE 4.8

For Graphers 4.2

Exercises

Exercises 1–4   **(a)** Use parametric equations (see For Graphers 2.7) to draw graphs of both f and f^{-1}. Explain how you know that the inverse of f is a function. **(b)** Find the domain of f^{-1} and determine whether f is increasing, decreasing, or neither. **(c)** Use your graph to evaluate (to two-place accuracy) $f^{-1}(3)$ and $f^{-1}(4.8)$.

1. $f(x) = 2^x$ **2.** $f(x) = 2^{-x}$

3. $f(x) = 2^{2x}$ **4.** $f(x) = 1 + e^x$

Exercises 5–8   Draw a graph of f. (*Calculator Hint:* Since $y = \log_3 x$ is the inverse of $y = 3^x$, use parametric equations to draw the graph of the inverse of $y = 3^x$.)

5. $f(x) = \log_3 x$ **6.** $f(x) = \log_3 (x - 1)$

7. $f(x) = -\log_3 x$ **8.** $f(x) = 1 + \log_3 x$

9. **(a)** Let $f(x) = \log_{10} x$ and $g(x) = 10^x$. According to the inverse function identities, $g(f(x)) = x$ and $f(g(x)) = x$. Graph $y = g(f(x))$ and $y = f(g(x))$ in the Familiar Window. (Use the $\boxed{\text{2nd}}$ $\boxed{\text{10}^x}$ and $\boxed{\text{LOG}}$ keys.)

(b) Explain why the graphs of $y = g(f(x))$ and of $y = f(g(x))$ are not the same. (*Hint:* Consider domains.)

Exercises 9–10   Use graphs to help solve Develop Mastery Exercises 74 and 75.

Strategy: If $f(x) = \log_2 x$, then $\log_2 x - 1 = f(x) - 1$ and $\log_2 (x - 1) = f(x - 1)$.

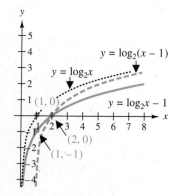

FIGURE 4.9

Translations of $y = \log_2 x$

Strategy: For each part, find where the argument is positive; that is, for f, find the solution set for $x^2 - 2x - 3 > 0$. For g, solve $5^x > 0$.

EXAMPLE 7   Use translations to draw a graph of **(a)** $y = \log_2 x - 1$ and **(b)** $y = \log_2(x - 1)$.

Solution

(a) Following the strategy, translate the graph of $y = \log_2 x$ shown in Figure 4.8a one unit down to get the graph of $y = \log_2 x - 1$.

(b) The graph of $y = \log_2(x - 1)$ is a horizontal translation of the graph of $y = \log_2 x$ one unit to the right. See Figure 4.9.   ▲

EXAMPLE 8   Find the solution set for the inequality $\log_2 x - 1 < 0$.

Solution

Let $y = \log_2 x - 1$. Find all values of x for which y is negative. From the graph in Figure 4.9, when x is between 0 and 2, y is negative. Therefore, the solution set is $\{x \mid 0 < x < 2\}$, or in interval notation, $(0, 2)$.   ▲

EXAMPLE 9   Determine the domain of f and g.

(a) $f(x) = \log_3 (x^2 - 2x - 3)$ and **(b)** $g(x) = \log_3 5^x$

Solution

It is important to understand that any logarithmic function can be evaluated only at positive numbers. Follow the strategy.

$$x^2 - 2x - 3 > 0 \qquad (x + 1)(x - 3) > 0.$$

(a) The solution set is $\{x \mid x < -1 \text{ or } x > 3\}$. Consequently, the domain of f is $\{x \mid x < -1 \text{ or } x > 3\}$, or in interval notation, $(-\infty, -1) \cup (3, \infty)$.

(b) Since 5^x is positive for every real number x, $\log_3 5^x$ is defined for any real number x; the domain of g is R. ▲

EXERCISES 4.2

Check Your Understanding

Exercises 1–4 True or False. Give reasons for your conclusion.

1. $\log_3 7 < \log_2 7$ (*Hint:* Think exponents.)
2. $\log_5 \pi < \log_2 \pi$ (*Hint:* See Exercise 1.)
3. If $f(x) = \log_2 x$, then $f^{-1}(x) = 2^x$.
4. The domain of $g(x) = \log_2 x^2$ is the set of all real numbers.
5. The domain of $g(x) = \log_2(x^2 + 1)$ is the set of all real numbers.

Exercises 6–10 Complete the sentence by selecting from the list below *all choices* that make the statement true.

(a) a positive number (b) a negative number
(c) between 1 and 2 (d) between 2 and 3
(e) equal to 2 (f) equal to x
(g) equal to $-x$ (h) equal to 3^{-x}

6. $\log_2 \sqrt{16}$ is _____ .
7. For every x between 0 and 1, $\log_2 x$ is _____ .
8. For every negative number x, $\log_2(2^{-x})$ is _____ .
9. For every positive number x, $\log_3(3^{-x})$ is _____ .
10. If x is between 4 and 8, then $\log_2 x$ is _____ .

Explore and Discover

1. The diagram shows graphs of $y = 2^x$ and $y = 5^x$ with their inverse functions $y = \log_2 x$ and $y = \log_5 x$.
   (a) On the same set of axes, add graphs of the functions $f(x) = 3^x$, $g(x) = 6^x$, $f^{-1}(x) = \log_3 x$, and $g^{-1}(x) = \log_6 x$.
   (b) Which of the exponential functions on your graph grows fastest (which graph climbs most steeply to the right) in QI?
   (c) Which of your logarithmic functions grows fastest in QI?

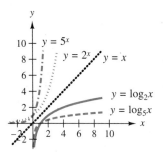

2. On the basis of your observation of graphs in Exercise 1, if $1 < b < c$, which is larger, b^5 or c^5? Which of $\log_b 17$ and $\log_c 17$ is larger? How do $\log_b k$ and $\log_c k$ compare when k is any number greater than 1?

Develop Mastery

Exercises 1–2 Write the equation in equivalent logarithmic form with appropriate base.

1. **(a)** $5^3 = 125$ **(b)** $4^{-2} = \frac{1}{16}$ **(c)** $3^{x-1} = 5$
2. **(a)** $(0.5)^2 = 0.25$ **(b)** $7^{-1} = \frac{1}{7}$
   (c) $5^{x+3} = 7$

Exercises 3–6 Express the equation in exponential form and then solve for y.

3. **(a)** $y = \log_4 16$ **(b)** $y = \log_4(\frac{1}{16})$
4. **(a)** $y = \log_8 512$ **(b)** $y = \log_8(\frac{1}{64})$
5. **(a)** $y = \log_{\sqrt{3}}(\frac{1}{3})$ **(b)** $y = \log_{\sqrt{3}}(9\sqrt{3})$
6. **(a)** $y = \log_{\sqrt{5}}\sqrt{5}$ **(b)** $y = \log_{\sqrt{5}}(\frac{1}{25})$

Exercises 7–14 Evaluate. Express the result in exact form.

7. (a) $\log_3 1$ (b) $\log_e \sqrt[3]{e}$

8. (a) $\log_5 5$ (b) $\log_4 16$

9. (a) $e^{\log_5 \sqrt{5}}$ (b) $7^{\log_3 1}$

10. (a) $5^{\log_5 \sqrt{3}}$ (b) $3^{\log_{10} 10}$

11. (a) $4^{\log_2 4}$ (b) $7^{\log_7 17}$

12. (a) $2^{\log_4 2}$ (b) $5^{\log_5 24}$

13. $[\log_2(\sqrt{2} \log_3 9)]^2$

14. $\log_3(\sqrt{3} \log_2 8)$

Exercises 15–18 Simplify and state the values of x for which the result is valid.

15. (a) $\log_5 5^x$ (b) $5^{\log_5(x+1)}$

16. (a) $\log_3 3^{x-2}$ (b) $3^{\log_3(x-2)}$

17. (a) $\log_3(\sqrt{3})^{4x}$ (b) $5^{\log_5(5x)}$

18. (a) $\log_4 2^{2x}$ (b) $\log_5(\sqrt{5})^{2x}$

Exercises 19–28 Solve.

19. $\log_7(2x - 3) = 1$

20. $\log_5(4 - 3x) = 2$

21. $\log_2(x^2 - 2x - 1) = 1$

22. $\log_3(x^2 - 4x) = 2$

23. $\log_5 5^{3x-4} = 1$

24. $\log_3 3^{x^2} = 9$

25. $3^{\log_3(x^2-1)} = 4$

26. $5^{\log_5(x^2-2x-2)} = 1$

(*Hint:* Treat the equations in Exercises 27 and 28 as quadratic equations in expressions that involve logarithms.)

27. $(\log_3 x)^2 = 3 + 2 \log_3 x$

28. $(\log_2 x)^2 = 8 + 2 \log_2 x$

29. Verify that 4 and -1 are solutions of the equation $\log_3(x^2 - 3x + 5) = 2$. (See Example 5.)

Exercises 30–31 Find b in terms of c.

30. $b = \log_4 49$, $c = \log_8 7$

31. $b = \log_8 289$, $c = \log_2 17$

Exercises 32–33 Determine b.

32. (a) $\log_b \pi = 1$ (b) $\log_b 0.49 = 2$

33. (a) $\log_b 2 = 2$ (b) $\log_b 7 = -\frac{1}{2}$

Exercises 34–35 The given number is between which two consecutive integers? (*Hint:* Think in terms of exponents.)

34. (a) $\log_3 31$ (b) $\log_6 0.16$

35. (a) $\log_2(1 + \sqrt{35})$ (b) $\log_3 47$

Exercises 36–39 Which of the pair of numbers is larger?

36. $\log_3 4$, $\log_5 120$

37. $\log_2 6$, $\log_3 6$

38. $\log_5 36$, $\log_6 32$

39. $\log_2 0.4$, $\log_2 0.2$

Exercises 40–43 Find the smallest *even* integer that is greater than the number.

40. $\log_2 16$ 41. $\log_3 17$ 42. $\log_3 9$ 43. $\log_5 120$

Exercises 44–47 Determine how many integers lie between the number pair.

44. $\log_2 8$, $\log_2 64$

45. $\log_3 7$, $\log_3 250$

46. $\log_3 2$, $\log_3 96$

47. $\log_2 3$, $\log_3 47$

Exercises 48–51 Graph the function, using appropriate translations or reflections of core graphs.

48. (a) $y = \log_3 x$ (b) $y = \log_3(x - 1)$

49. (a) $y = \log_4 x$ (b) $y = \log_4(x - 2)$

50. (a) $y = 2 + \log_2 x$ (b) $y = \log_2(-x)$

51. (a) $y = \log_4(x + 1)$ (b) $y = \log_4(-x)$

Exercises 52–55 (a) Determine the domain, (b) simplify the equation, and (c) graph the function.

52. $y = \log_3 3^{2x}$

53. $y = x \log_3 3^{-x}$

54. $y = 3^{\log_3 x}$

55. $y = 2^{\log_2(2-x)}$

Exercises 56–61 Determine the domain.

56. $f(x) = \log_3(x - 4)$

57. $f(x) = \log_{10}(x^2 - 1)$

58. $f(x) = \log_3 3^x$

59. $f(x) = \log_5(5^x - 1)$

60. $f(x) = \log_3(-x)$

61. $f(x) = \log_3(x^2 - 2x)$

Exercises 61–65 (a) Graph the function and label the intercept points. (b) Find the solution set for $f(x) < 0$.

62. $f(x) = \log_3 x$

63. $f(x) = \log_3(x + 1)$

64. $f(x) = \log_4(x - 2)$

65. $f(x) = \log_2 x - 2$

Exercises 66–69 Use the graph of $y = \log_2 x$ to help match the function with one of the graphs a, b, c, or d. Think in terms of translations and reflections.

66. $f(x) = 1 + \log_2 x$

67. $f(x) = -\log_2 x$

68. $f(x) = \log_2(x - 1)$

69. $f(x) = -\log_2(-x)$

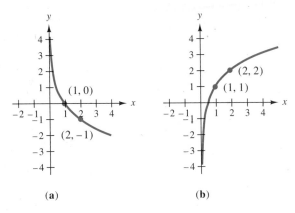

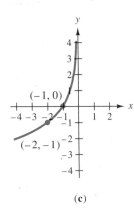

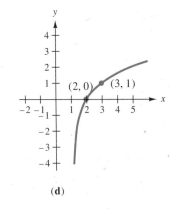

(a)   (b)   (c)   (d)

Exercises 70–73 Function f has an inverse. Find an equation that describes f^{-1}. (*Hint:* Use the algorithm for inverse functions in Section 2.7.)

70. $f(x) = \log_3(x - 1)$ **71.** $f(x) = \log_3 x + 1$

72. $f(x) = \frac{3^{x+1}}{9}$ **73.** $f(x) = \log_3 x + \log_3 3$

Exercises 74–76 Function f has an inverse. **(a)** Find the domain and range of f. **(b)** Find an equation that describes f^{-1}. **(c)** Find the domain and range of f^{-1}.

74. $f(x) = \frac{1}{1 + 3^x}$ **75.** $f(x) = \frac{3^x}{1 + 3^x}$

76. $f(x) = \frac{3^{-x}}{1 + 3^{-x}}$

| SECTION 4.3 | **Properties of Logarithmic Functions** |

If one remembers . . . the useful concepts . . . [as well as] the countless misconceptions and errors that rigorous mathematical development avoids without touching, then mathematics begins to resemble not as much a nerve as the thread that Ariadne used to guide her lover Thesus out of the Labrynith in which he slew the dreaded Minotaur.
    Hans C. von Baeyer

As defined in the preceding section, logarithms are exponents, so we would expect logarithms to have properties analogous to those of exponents. The list of some of the most important properties of both logarithms and exponents emphasizes the parallels between them.

Properties of Logarithms and Exponents

	Logarithms		*Exponents*
L1.	$\log_b(uv) = \log_b u + \log_b v$	E1.	$b^u b^v = b^{u+v}$
L2.	$\log_b\left(\dfrac{u}{v}\right) = \log_b u - \log_b v$	E2.	$\dfrac{b^u}{b^v} = b^{u-v}$
L3.	$\log_b(u^p) = p(\log_b u)$	E3.	$(b^u)^p = b^{up}$
L4.	$\log_b 1 = 0$ and $\log_b b = 1$	E4.	$b^0 = 1$ and $b^1 = b$

I think it was during that semester in Berkeley, when I was not quite fifteen, that I really switched into being serious about mathematics. As soon as I saw what geometry was about, it was immediately clear to me how the whole thing worked—I mean absolutely clear. I could visualize the figures rather well, and I didn't have any problem with understanding what proofs were supposed to be.

Andrew M. Gleason

Since logarithmic functions are only defined for positive numbers, we must keep in mind that properties L1 through L3 are valid only when both u and v are positive numbers.

We outline a proof of logarithm property L1; proofs for properties L2 and L3 are similar and are left as exercises (see Exercises 53 and 54). In words, property L1 states that the logarithm of a product is the sum of the logarithms.

$$\log_b u = s \quad \text{and} \quad \log_b v = t.$$

In terms of exponents

$$u = b^s \quad \text{and} \quad v = b^t.$$

Since the equation in property L1 involves uv, multiply the two exponential equations and apply exponent property E1 to get

$$uv = b^s b^t = b^{s+t}$$

Returning to logarithmic form,

$$\log_b(uv) = s + t.$$

Replacing s and t by $\log_b u$ and $\log_b v$,

$$\log_b(uv) = \log_b u + \log_b v.$$

The first three logarithm properties involve logarithms of products, quotients, and powers. We do not give similar formulas for sums and differences because there are no simple ways to express $\log_b(u + v)$ and $\log_b(u - v)$ in terms of $\log_b u$ and $\log_b v$. Similarly, for exponents, we have for instance, $b^2 \cdot b^3 = b^5$, but there is no simple expression for $b^2 + b^3$.

EXAMPLE 1   Use properties L1 through L4 to evaluate

(a) $\log_3 81$ (b) $\log_{10} 0.001$ (c) $\log_3\left(\frac{1}{\sqrt{3}}\right)$.

Strategy: Rewrite each argument as a power of the base: $81 = 3^4$, $0.001 = 10^{-3}$, $\frac{1}{\sqrt{3}} = 3^{-1/2}$, then use logarithm properties as appropriate.

Solution

We indicate under the equals sign the property that gives the equality. Follow the strategy.

(a) $\log_3 81 = \log_3 3^4 \underset{L3}{=} 4(\log_3 3) \underset{L4}{=} 4(1) = 4$, hence $\log_3 81 = 4$.

(b) $\log_{10} 0.001 = \log_{10} 10^{-3} \underset{L3}{=} (-3)\log_{10} 10 \underset{L4}{=} (-3)(1) = -3$, hence $\log_{10} 0.001 = -3$.

(c) $\log_3\left(\frac{1}{\sqrt{3}}\right) \underset{L2}{=} \log_3 1 - \log_3 \sqrt{3} \underset{L4}{=} 0 - \log_3 3^{1/2} \underset{L3}{=} -\left(\frac{1}{2}\right)\log_3 3 \underset{L4}{=} -\frac{1}{2}$, hence $\log_3\left(\frac{1}{\sqrt{3}}\right) = -\frac{1}{2}$ ▲

EXAMPLE 2   Simplify.

(a) $\log_5 10 - \log_5 2$ (b) $\log_7 3 + 4(\log_7 2)$

Solution

(a) $\log_5 10 - \log_5 2 \underset{L_2}{=} \log_5\left(\frac{10}{2}\right) = \log_5 5 \underset{L_4}{=} 1$

(b) $\log_7 3 + 4(\log_7 2) \underset{L_3}{=} \log_7 3 + \log_7 2^4 = \log_7 3 + \log_7 16$

$\underset{L_1}{=} \log_7(3 \cdot 16) = \log_7 48$ ▲

It is important to learn to use logarithm properties L1 through L3 going from right to left, as well as left to right. For instance, in Example 2b we used property L3 to write

$$4(\log_7 2) \underset{L_3}{=} \log_7 2^4,$$

and then we used property L1 to combine logarithms and get

$$\log_7 3 + \log_7 16 \underset{L_1}{=} \log_7(3 \cdot 16) = \log_7 48.$$

We call $\log_7 48$ a simplified form of $\log_7 3 + 4(\log_7 2)$. In a similar manner, using L1 and L3 gives

$$\log_7 48 = \log_7(3 \cdot 2^4) \underset{L_1}{=} \log_7 3 + \log_7 2^4 \underset{L_3}{=} \log_7 3 + 4(\log_7 2).$$

Thus, $\log_7 48$ can be written as a sum of logarithms, $\log_7 3 + 4(\log_7 2)$.

EXAMPLE 3　Simplify.

$$\log_b x + 4 \log_b(x - 1) - \log_b 5.$$

Solution

$\log_b x + 4 \log_b(x - 1) - \log_b 5 \underset{L_3}{=} \log_b x + \log_b(x - 1)^4 - \log_b 5$

$\underset{L_1}{=} \log_b[x(x - 1)^4] - \log_b 5$

$\underset{L_2}{=} \log_b \dfrac{x(x - 1)^4}{5}$

Hence, $\log_b x + 4 \log_b(x - 1) - \log_b 5 = \log_b \frac{x(x-1)^4}{5}$ ▲

EXAMPLE 4　In the next section we will show that four-place decimal approximations to $\log_5 3$ and $\log_5 6$ are:

$$\log_5 3 \approx 0.6826 \qquad \log_5 6 \approx 1.1133.$$

Use these values along with logarithm properties L1 through L4 to get three-decimal place approximations for　(a) $\log_5 2$ and (b) $\log_5 18$.

Strategy: Write each of 2 and 18 as a product, quotient, power, etc. in terms of the numbers 3 and 6, whose logarithms we have: $2 = \frac{6}{3}$, $18 = 3 \cdot 6$, then use the properties of logarithms.

Solution

Follow the strategy.

(a) $\log_5 2 = \log_5\left(\frac{6}{3}\right) = \log_5 6 - \log_5 3$

$\approx 1.1133 - 0.6826$

$= 0.4307.$

Therefore, $\log_5 2 \approx 0.431$ to three decimal places.

(b) $\log_5 18 = \log_5(3 \cdot 6) = \log_5 3 + \log_5 6$

$$\approx 0.6826 + 1.1133$$

$$= 1.7959.$$

Hence, $\log_5 18 \approx 1.796.$ ▲

EXAMPLE 5   Solve (a) $\log_4 x - \log_4(x - 1) = \frac{1}{2}$

(b) $\log_4 x - \log_4(x + 1) = \frac{1}{2}$.

Strategy: Combine the terms on the left by using property L2 to get a single logarithm equal to a constant, then express the result in exponential form. Since property L2 applies only to positive numbers, check all results in the original equation.

Solution

(a) Follow the strategy,

$$\log_4 x - \log_4(x - 1) \underset{L_2}{=} \log_4\left(\frac{x}{x - 1}\right)$$

so the given equation can be written as

$$\log_4\left(\frac{x}{x - 1}\right) = \frac{1}{2}, \qquad \frac{x}{x - 1} = 4^{1/2}, \qquad \text{or} \qquad \frac{x}{x - 1} = 2.$$

Solving for x, we find that $x = 2$. Since $\log_4(2)$ and $\log_4(2 - 1)$ are both defined, we know that 2 belongs to the replacement set for the original equation and therefore 2 is the desired solution.

(b) As in part (a), the given equation can be written as

$$\log_4\left(\frac{x}{x + 1}\right) = \frac{1}{2}, \qquad \frac{x}{x + 1} = 4^{1/2}, \qquad \text{or} \qquad \frac{x}{x + 1} = 2.$$

In this case, when we solve for x we find $x = -2$. However, if we replace x with -2, the left side involves $\log_4(-2)$ and $\log_4(-2 + 1)$, neither of which is defined. Since -2 is not in the replacement set for the original equation, it cannot be the solution. The given equation has no solution.

▲

Example 5 illustrates an important point. Properties L1, L2, and L3 are valid for only positive values of all arguments; logarithmic functions are defined for only positive arguments. We could check the domains at each step, but it is good enough to check the final result in the original equation.

EXAMPLE 6   Solve the equation

$$2 \log_9 x + 2 \log_9 (x + 2) = 1.$$

Solution

Divide through by 2 and write the left side in simpler form:

$$\log_9 x + \log_9(x + 2) = \tfrac{1}{2}, \qquad \log_9[x(x + 2)] = \tfrac{1}{2}.$$

In exponential form,

$$x(x + 2) = 9^{1/2}, \qquad x^2 + 2x = 3, \qquad \text{or} \qquad x^2 + 2x - 3 = 0.$$

Solutions to the quadratic equation are 1 and -3. Since the domain of the original equation is the set of positive numbers, 1 is a solution, but -3 is not. ▲

| **EXAMPLE 7** | Find the solution set for

(a) $\log_2(8^x + 8^x) = x - 1$ **(b)** $\log_2(8^x + 8^x) = 3x + 1$
(c) $\log_2(8^x + 8^x) = 3x.$

Strategy There is no formula to simplify the logarithm of a sum, rewrite $8^x + 8^x$ as a power of 2 (the base) and then simplify.

Solution

To simplify all three equations, begin with the expression $8^x + 8^x$

$$8^x + 8^x = 2 \cdot 8^x = 2 \cdot (2^3)^x = 2 \cdot 2^{3x} = 2^{3x+1}$$

from which $\log_2(8^x + 8^x) = \log_2(2^{3x+1}) = 3x + 1$. Since $8^x + 8^x$ is positive for every x in R, $\log_2(8^x + 8^x) = 3x + 1$ for every real number. In each case, replace $\log_2(8^x + 8^x)$ by $3x + 1$ and solve the resulting equation.

(a) $3x + 1 = x - 1$, so $x = 1$; the solution set is $\{1\}$.

(b) $3x + 1 = 3x + 1$, which is an identity, so the solution set is R.

(c) $3x + 1 = 3x$, or $0 \cdot x = 1$. The solution set is the empty set. ▲

| **EXAMPLE 8** | If $f(x) = \log_3(x^2 - 5x + 6)$ and $g(x) = \log_3(x - 2) + \log_3(x - 3)$, then find the domain of each function. Are functions f and g equal? Explain.

Strategy: The domain of the $\log_3$ function is the set of positive real numbers. For f this requires $x^2 - 5x + 6 > 0$, and for g, both $x - 2 > 0$ *and* $x - 3 > 0$.

Solution

Follow the strategy. To find the domain of function f, solve the inequality

$$x^2 - 5x + 6 > 0, \quad \text{or} \quad (x - 2)(x - 3) > 0.$$

The solution set is $\{x \mid x < 2 \text{ or } x > 3\}$, so the domain of f is $(-\infty, 2) \cup (3, \infty)$.

For the function g, the strategy emphasizes that both $x > 2$ *and* $x > 3$. The solution set is $\{x \mid x > 3\}$, so the domain of g is $(3, \infty)$.

Finally, since functions f and g have different domains, they cannot be equal. However, $f(x) = g(x)$ for all $x > 3$. ▲

EXERCISES 4.3

Check Your Understanding

Exercises 1–5   True or False. Give reasons for your conclusion.

1. $\log_5(\sqrt{2} + \sqrt{3}) = \frac{1}{2}(\log_5 2 + \log_5 3)$.

2. There is no number x for which $\log_2(2x) = 2 \log_2 x$.

3. The graph of $y = \log_4(4x)$ is the same as the graph of $y = 1 + \log_4 x$.

4. The graph of $y = \log_2(4x)$ can be drawn by translating the graph of $y = \log_2 x$ up 2 units.

5. For every real number x, $\log_2(2x) = 1 + \log_2 x$.

Exercises 6–10   Complete the sentence by selecting from the list below *all choices* that make the statement true.

(a) positive   **(b)** negative   **(c)** equal to 2
(d) less than 2   **(e)** greater than 2
(f) $3 \log_3 x$ **(g)** $1 + \log_3 x$ **(h)** x
(i) $\log_2 8 - \log_2 5$ **(j)** equal to $\log_2(1.6)$

(k) equal to $\frac{\log_2 8}{\log_2 5}$ **(l)** equal to $3 - \log_2 5$

6. $\log_2(\sqrt{3} + \sqrt{5})$ is _____.

7. $\log_2(\frac{8}{5})$ is _____ .

8. For every positive x, $\log_3(3x) =$ _____ .

9. If $f(x) = 3^x$ and $g(x) = \log_3 x$, then $f(g(2))$ is _____ .

10. The graph of $y = \log_3(3x)$ is the same as the graph of $y =$ _____ .

Explore and Discover

1. Explain briefly why the sentence $\log_2(2x) = 1 + \log_2 x$ is neither true nor false. (*Hint:* You may want to look at Section 1.4.)

2. Write a paragraph that compares the truth values of the sentence in Exercise 1 and each of the following two sentences:
   (a) For every positive number x, $\log_2(2x) = 1 + \log_2 x$.
   (b) $\log_2(2x) = 1 + \log_2 x$ is an identity.

Develop Mastery

Exercises 1–4   (a) Express the equation in exponential form. (b) Use the properties of logarithms to find a simpler expression for k.

1. $k = \log_3(3\sqrt{3})$ 2. $k = \log_5(5\sqrt[3]{25})$
3. $k = \log_e(e^2\sqrt{e})$ 4. $k = \log_e(\frac{\sqrt{e}}{e^3})$

Exercises 5–10   Simplify. See Example 3.

5. $\log_3 6 - \log_3 2$ 6. $\log_7 2 + 3\log_7 3$
7. $2\log_3 2 + \frac{1}{2}\log_3 4$ 8. $3\log_5 2 - \frac{1}{4}\log_5 16$
9. $\log_{10} 50 - 2\log_{10} 5$ 10. $\frac{2}{3}\log_2 27 - 3\log_2 4$

Exercises 11–16   Use properties of logarithms to write the expression as a sum or difference.

11. $\log_3(2x^3)$ 12. $\log_4(\frac{16}{x^4})$
13. $\log_5(x\sqrt{x^2 + 4})$ 14. $\log_5(25x\sqrt{x^2 + 1})$
15. $\log_2(\frac{8x^2}{\sqrt{x^2 + 1}})$ 16. $\log_3[9x(x + 1)]$

Exercises 17–20   Simplify.

17. $2\log_3 x - \log_3(x + 2)$
18. $\log_5 3 + \log_5 x - \log_5 \sqrt{x}$
19. $\frac{1}{2}\log_3 x^2 - 2\log_3 x + \log_3 4$
20. $\frac{3}{2}\log_5 x^2 + \log_5 3 - 2\log_5 \sqrt{x}$

Exercises 21–24   If $\log_3 4 \approx 1.2619$ and $\log_3 5 \approx 1.4650$, find an approximation rounded off to three decimal places. (See Example 4).

21. (a) $\log_3 2$ (b) $\log_3 10$
22. (a) $\log_3 20$ (b) $\log_3 0.8$
23. (a) $\log_3(\frac{4}{\sqrt{5}})$ (b) $\log_3(5\sqrt{2})$
24. (a) $\log_3(20\sqrt{5})$ (b) $\log_3(\frac{16}{5})$

Exercises 25–28   If $\log_{10} 2 = u$ and $\log_{10} 3 = v$, express the logarithm in terms of u and v.

25. (a) $\log_{10} 5$,   (b) $\log_{10}(\frac{1}{5})$
26. (a) $\log_{10} 30$,   (b) $\log_{10} 1.5$
27. (a) $\log_{10} \sqrt[3]{18}$,   (b) $\log_{10} \sqrt{24}$
28. (a) $\log_{10} \frac{16}{27}$,   (b) $\log_{10} 80$

Exercises 29–32   If $\log_b 5 = u$ and $\log_b 45 = v$, express the logarithm in terms of u and v.

29. (a) $\log_b 9$,   (b) $\log_b 3$
30. (a) $\log_b 15$,   (b) $\log_b 1.8$
31. (a) $\log_b 25$,   (b) $\log_b 135$
32. (a) $\log_b \frac{1}{3}$,   (b) $\log_b \sqrt{1.8}$

Exercises 33–42   Solve. Check to see that your solutions are in the domain of the original equation. See Examples 5 and 6.

33. $\log_3(x + 1) - \log_3 x = 1$
34. $2\log_2 x - \log_2 32 = 1$
35. $\log_4(2x + 3) - \log_4 x = 2$
36. $\log_3(2x + 3) - \log_3 x = \log_3 5$
37. $\log_2 x + \log_2(x + 2) = 3$
38. $\log_4(3x - 2) - \log_4(2x) = \log_4 3$
39. $\log_3(x + 8) + \log_3 x = 2$
40. $\log_5(4x) - \log_5(2x - 1) = 0$
41. $2\log_2 x - \log_2(x + 1) = 1$
42. $\log_3 x - \log_3(x + 1) = -1$

Exercises 43–48   Determine the domain of the function.

43. $f(x) = \log_3(x - 3) + 5$
44. $f(x) = \log_5(x^2 - 2x)$
45. $g(x) = \log_7(4x - x^2)$
46. $g(x) = \log_4(x + 3) + \log_4(2 - x)$
47. $f(x) = 2(\log_{10} x) + \log_{10}(x + 3)$
48. $f(x) = \log_{10} x^2 + \log_{10}(x + 3)$

49. Verify that 1 is a solution and that -3 is not a solution of

$$2 \log_9 x + 2 \log_9(x + 2) = 1.$$

See Example 6.

50. Are there any numbers x for which the expression

$$\log_3(x - 1) + \log_3(1 - x)$$

is defined? Give reasons for your answer.

51. For what values of x is $\log_5(x^2 - 3x - 4)$ equal to $\log_5(x - 4) + \log_5(x + 1)$?

52. (a) For what values of x is $\log_3 x^2$ equal to $2 \log_3 x$?
(b) For what values of x is $\log_3 x^2$ equal to $2 \log_3(-x)$?
(c) For what values of x is $\log_3 x^2$ equal to $2 \log_3 |x|$?

53. Prove the validity of logarithm property L2.

54. Prove the validity of logarithm property L3.

55. If $a = 8$ and $b = 16$, show that $\log_2(ab)$ is not equal to $(\log_2 a)(\log_2 b)$.

56. If $a = 16$ and $b = 8$, show that $\log_2(\frac{a}{b})$ is not equal to $\frac{\log_2 a}{\log_2 b}$.

57. If $c = 4$ and $n = 3$, show that $\log_2(c^n)$ is not equal to $(\log_2 c)^n$.

Exercises 58–60 Find the solution set. See Example 7.

58. (a) $\log_2(2^x + 2^x) = x + 1$
(b) $\log_3(3^x + 3^x) = 1$

59. (a) $\log_3(3^x + 3^x) = x$
(b) $\log_3(3^x + 3^x + 3^x) = x + 1$

60. (a) $\log_4(4^x + 4^x) = 2x$
(b) $\log_2(4^x + 4^x) = x$

61. Show that $\log_3(\sqrt{3} + \sqrt{2}) = -\log_3(\sqrt{3} - \sqrt{2})$.

62. Show that $\log_5(\sqrt{6} + \sqrt{5}) = -\log_5(\sqrt{6} - \sqrt{5})$.

63. Show that for any positive number k,
$$\log_b(\sqrt{k + 1} + \sqrt{k}) = -\log_b(\sqrt{k + 1} - \sqrt{k}).$$

Exercises 64–65 Given that the function f has an inverse, find an equation that describes f^{-1}. What is the domain of f? (*Hint:* Use the algorithm in Section 2.7.)

64. $f(x) = \log_2(\sqrt{x^2 + 1} + x)$
65. $f(x) = \log_3(\sqrt{x^2 + 1} - x)$

SECTION 4.4 | Calculator Evaluation

Galileo's observation that all bodies accelerate equally in the Earth's gravity is counterintuitive precisely because it is usually wrong. Everybody knows that a lump of coal falls faster than a feather. Galileo's genius was in spotting that the differences which occur in reality are an incidental complication caused by air resistance, and are irrelevant to the properties of gravity as such.
P. W. C. Davies

Because logarithms are exponents, evaluation in exact form is possible only in special cases. We can, for example, evaluate $\log_3(9\sqrt{3})$ in exact form because $9\sqrt{3}$ is a power of the base 3:

$$9\sqrt{3} = 3^{5/2}, \text{ so } \log_3 9\sqrt{3} = \frac{5}{2}.$$

More generally, we need assistance to approximate logarithms. This section covers the use of calculators to evaluate logarithmic and exponential functions to any base. All scientific calculators are programmed to evaluate the natural exponential function, $f(x) = e^x$, and its inverse, the natural logarithm function $f^{-1}(x) = \log_e x$. As we will see, these functions are sufficient to handle calculator evaluation for exponential and logarithmic functions with any base.

Natural and Common Logarithms

Before calculators, evaluation of logarithms depended on extensive tables produced over lifetimes of laborious hand computations (see the Historical Note, "Invention of Logarithms"). Because the table makers used the decimal system, tables were calculated for base 10 logarithms; these are called **common logarithms.** Historically, common logarithms were so pervasive that most textbooks and calculators reserve a shorthand symbol, log x, for $\log_{10} x$.

I was in the ninth grade of Powell Junior High School in Washington, D.C. I was doing very poorly in my first course in algebra. To be precise, I was flunking. Later on, after recovering from my poor start in algebra, I began to get top marks. I was good in math and science in high school.

George B. Dantzig

We include common logarithms here only for historical reasons. We really need only one logarithmic function key on our calculators. For numerical applications and theoretical work, the most important function is the **natural logarithm,** which uses the Euler number e ($\approx 2.7182818\ldots$) as a base. The natural exponential function, $f(x) = e^x$, and the natural logarithm function, $f^{-1}(x) = \log_e x$, arise so often in mathematical models of all kinds of natural growth that we use $\ln x$ as a shorthand symbol for $\log_e x$.

> **Notation: Natural and Common Logarithms**
>
> The natural logarithmic function, $\log_e$, is denoted by *ln*.
>
> The common logarithmic function, $\log_{10}$, is denoted by *log*.

All scientific calculators have a key labeled $\boxed{\texttt{ln}}$ for natural logarithms; most also have one labeled $\boxed{\texttt{log}}$ for common logarithms. To evaluate a number like ln 4.3, simply enter 4.3 and press $\boxed{\texttt{ln}}$, or, if the calculator has $\boxed{\texttt{EXE}}$, press $\boxed{\texttt{ln}}$ 4.3 (display: ln 4.3) and $\boxed{\texttt{EXE}}$. The calculator returns 1.458615023.

EXAMPLE 1   Give an approximation rounded off to four decimal places of **(a)** ln 2, **(b)** log 0.253, **(c)** ln $(2 - \sqrt{5})$.

Solution

(a) Enter 2 and press $\boxed{\texttt{ln}}$ (or $\boxed{\texttt{ln}}$ 2 $\boxed{\texttt{EXE}}$) to get ln 2 $\approx$ 0.6931.

(b) Enter 0.253 and press $\boxed{\texttt{log}}$ (or $\boxed{\texttt{log}}$ 0.253 $\boxed{\texttt{EXE}}$) to get log 0.253 ≈ -0.5969.

(c) First evaluate $2 - \sqrt{5}$. With that result displayed, press $\boxed{\texttt{ln}}$. The calculator indicates an error because $2 - \sqrt{5}$ is negative and logarithmic functions are defined only for positive numbers. That is, $2 - \sqrt{5}$ is not in the domain of the ln function. The calculator is programmed to accept only numbers in the function's domain. (Some more sophisticated calculators that perform complex number operations may accept negative numbers for the ln function and return complex number pairs.) ▲

Change of Base and Evaluating Logarithms In Other Bases

The calculator has no key labeled $\log_3$ so to evaluate $\log_3 4$, change $y = \log_3 4$ to exponential form.

$$y = \log_3 4, \qquad 3^y = 4.$$

Historical Note

INVENTION OF LOGARITHMS

mi.	Sinus		Logarithmi	Differentia
30	3826834		9605468	8813731
31	3829521		9598448	8805506
32	3832208		9591454	8797285
33	3834895		9584416	8789069
34	3837581		9577424	8780859
35	3840267		9570417	8772653
36	3842953		9563456	8764452
37	3845638		6556451	8756256
38	3848323		9549472	8748065
39	3851008		9542493	8719878
40	3853692		9535550	8731696
41	3856376		9528567	8713518
42	3859060		9521610	8715345
43	3861743		9514619	8707177
44	3864426		9507713	8699013
45	3867109		9500703	8690854
46	3869791		9493839	8682700
47	3872473		9486911	8674551
48	3875155		9479988	8666405
49	3877837		9473071	8658264
50	3880518		9466160	8650128
51	3883199		9459154	8641996
52	3885880		9452354	8633870
53	3888560		9445460	8625749
54	3891240		9438571	8617632
55	3893919		9431688	8609520
56	3896598		9424810	8601412
57	3899277		9417938	8593103
58	3901955		9411071	8585210
59	3904633		9404210	8577116
60	3907311		9397354	8569026

Part of a page from Napier's *Logarithmic Tables.*

As the need for more accuracy in trigonometric computations grew (see the Historical Note, Trigonometric Tables in Section 5.3), so did the need for better ways to do the arithmetic. Logarithms have been called "the most universally useful mathematical discovery of the seventeenth century." They significantly reduced the time required to perform computations and may have been as important for the exploration of the globe as any improvement in marine technology in two hundred years.

One basic idea motivated the development of logarithms: to multiply powers of the same base, simply add exponents. For example, to multiply 16 by 64, use tables to identify equivalent numbers 2^4 and 2^6, from which

$$16 \cdot 64 = 2^4 \cdot 2^6 = 2^{4+6} = 2^{10}$$
$$= 1024.$$

To be useful, of course, tables must identify the exponents of all the numbers we might need to multiply.

John Napier (1550–1617) spent twenty years compiling tables of exponents (called *logarithms* or *ratio numbers*). He started with a large number for accuracy ($N = 10,000,000$) and calculated a hundred terms in a geometric sequence, successively subtracting $\frac{1}{10,000,000}$ of each number from the one before, and rounding each to 14 digits.

This produced one table of exponents. If he had simply continued with this sequence, it would have required years of calculation just to get from 10 million to 5 million, producing an unusable table with nearly 7 million entries. Napier's genius lay in his construction of other tables to allow interpolation between numbers. Rather than millions of entries, his second table had only 50 entries, and the third had fewer than 1500. A user would locate a pair of exponents from the first two tables and then use the third table to compute the logarithm.

After his logarithms of numbers, Napier produced a table to give seven-place logarithms of sines of angles for every minute from 0° to 90°. Kepler credited Napier's tables for making possible the incredible calculations required to analyze the motion of the planets about the sun.

Now apply the natural logarithm function to both sides of the last equation and solve for y.

$$\ln 3^y = \ln 4, \qquad y \ln 3 = \ln 4, \qquad \text{so}$$

$$y = \frac{\ln 4}{\ln 3}, \qquad \text{or} \qquad \log_3 4 = \frac{\ln 4}{\ln 3}.$$

Evaluate the final form by calculator to get $\log_3 4 \approx 1.2619$.

The same procedure can be used to establish a formula for evaluating any logarithmic function.

Change-of-Base Formula

For any positive real numbers c and b where b is not 1, $\log_b c = \frac{\ln c}{\ln b}$.

The change-of-base formula allows us to evaluate logarithmic functions for any base, including base 10, so that $\boxed{\log}$ is not really necessary.

EXAMPLE 2   Find an approximation rounded off to four decimal places.

(a) $\log_5 0.43$ (b) $\log_8(1 + \sqrt{3})$ (c) $\log 79.442$

Solution
Use the change-of-base formula.

(a) $\log_5 0.43 = \dfrac{\ln 0.43}{\ln 5} \approx -0.5244.$

(b) $\log_8(1 + \sqrt{3}) = \dfrac{\ln(1 + \sqrt{3})}{\ln 8} \approx 0.4833.$

For the numerator, evaluate $1 + \sqrt{3}$ and then press $\boxed{\ln}$.

(c)   With no base shown, $\log 79.442$ refers to the common logarithm (base 10). Use $\boxed{\log}$ directly if the calculator has such a key, or use the change-of-base formula.

$$\log 79.442 = \frac{\ln 79.442}{\ln 10} \approx 1.9001.$$

Check each of the above computations using your calculator.   ▲

Inverse Function Identities
If f is the natural exponential function, $f(x) = e^x$, then $f^{-1}(x) = \ln x$. Since $f(f^{-1}(x)) = x$ for all x in the domain of f^{-1} and $f^{-1}(f(x)) = x$ for all x in the domain of f, we have two identities.

Inverse Function Identities

$$e^{\ln x} = x \qquad \text{for all } positive \text{ numbers } x. \tag{1}$$

$$\ln e^x = x \qquad \text{for } all \text{ real numbers } x. \tag{2}$$

Some calculators do not have $\boxed{e^x}$, but do have $\boxed{\text{INV}}$ to activate inverse functions. In such cases, evaluate e^x by entering the number and then pressing $\boxed{\text{INV}}$ $\boxed{\text{ln}}$.

EXAMPLE 3 Use inverse function identities to simplify. Express the result in exact form and then give a five-decimal-place approximation.

$$\textbf{(a)}\ e^{\ln\sqrt{3}} \qquad \textbf{(b)}\ e^{-2\ln 7} \qquad \textbf{(c)}\ \ln e^{-\sqrt{5}}$$

Strategy: Rewrite each part as needed to use inverse function identities.

Solution

(a) By identity 1, $e^{\ln\sqrt{3}} = \sqrt{3} \approx 1.73205$. The exact form is $\sqrt{3}$ and 1.73205 is the desired approximation.

(b) For the exact form, first use logarithm property L3 to rewrite $-2\ln 7$ as $\ln 7^{-2}$, or $\ln(\frac{1}{49})$, then use identity 1.

$$e^{-2\ln 7} = e^{\ln(\frac{1}{49})} = \frac{1}{49} \approx 0.02041$$

Thus $e^{-2\ln 7}$ is exactly equal to $\frac{1}{49}$ and 0.02041 is the five-decimal-place approximation.

(c) Identity 2 gives $\ln e^{-\sqrt{5}} = -\sqrt{5} \approx -2.23607$. An exact form for $\ln e^{-\sqrt{5}}$ is $-\sqrt{5}$ and -2.23607 is the desired approximation. ▲

Solving Equations that Involve Logarithm or Exponential Functions

The following examples illustrate techniques for solving equations when the variable appears in a logarithmic or exponential expression.

EXAMPLE 4 Solve. Express the result in exact form and then give a three-decimal-place approximation.

$$\textbf{(a)}\ \ln(2x - 3) + \ln 5 = 2 \qquad \textbf{(b)}\ 2\ln x + 2\ln(x + 2) = 1$$

Strategy: Use the properties of logarithms to write the left side in simplified form, then express the equation in exponential form.

Solution

(a) Simplifying gives $\ln 5(2x - 3) = 2$. In exponential form,

$$e^2 = 5(2x - 3) \qquad e^2 = 10x - 15 \qquad \text{or} \qquad x = (e^2 + 15)/10.$$

An approximation by calculator is $x \approx 2.239$.

(b) First divide both sides by 2 and simplify to get $\ln x(x + 2) = \frac{1}{2}$. In exponential form,

$$x(x + 2) = e^{1/2} \qquad \text{or} \qquad x^2 + 2x - \sqrt{e} = 0.$$

Apply the quadratic formula.

$$x = \frac{-2 \pm \sqrt{4 + 4\sqrt{e}}}{2} = \frac{-2 \pm 2\sqrt{1 + \sqrt{e}}}{2} = -1 \pm \sqrt{1 + \sqrt{e}}.$$

The domain of the original equation requires that both $x > 0$ and $x + 2 > 0$, so the domain is $\{x \mid x > 0\}$. Since $-1 - \sqrt{1 + \sqrt{e}}$ is not in the domain, it cannot be a solution; $-1 + \sqrt{1 + \sqrt{e}}$ is positive and is a solution in exact form. The only solution is $\sqrt{1 + \sqrt{e}} - 1$, and 0.627 is the decimal approximation. ▲

Using Inverse Function Identities to Solve Equations

In Section 4.1 we solved the equation $3^{2x-1} = 3^{7/3}$ by using our intuitive under-standing of exponents. To justify equating exponents, we now know that expo-nential and logarithmic functions are one–one; if two numbers are equal, their logarithms are equal, or in mathematical notation, if $u = v$, then $\log_b u = \log_b v$. Applying the logarithm function to both sides, if $3^{2x-1} = 3^{7/3}$, then $\log_3(3^{2x-1}) = \log_3(3^{7/3})$, from which $2x - 1 = \frac{7}{3}$, and so $x = \frac{5}{3}$.

| **EXAMPLE 5** | Solve. Express your solution in exact form and give a four-decimal-place approximation.

$$\textbf{(a) } e^{2x-1} = 4 \qquad \textbf{(b) } 5^x = 3 \cdot 4^{1-x}$$

Strategy: Apply the natural logarithm function to both sides and simplify, using properties of logarithms.

Solution

(a)   From the strategy,

$$\ln e^{2x-1} = \ln 4 \qquad \text{or} \qquad 2x - 1 = \ln 4.$$

Therefore $x = \frac{1 + \ln 4}{2} \approx 1.1931$, so $\frac{1 + \ln 4}{2}$ is the exact solution and 1.1931 is the desired approximation.

(b)   In a similar fashion, $\ln 5^x = \ln(3 \cdot 4^{1-x})$. By logarithm property L3, $\ln 5^x = x \ln 5$, and by properties L1 and L3, $\ln(3 \cdot 4^{1-x}) = \ln 3 + (1 - x)\ln 4$. Therefore, the given equation is equivalent to

$$x \ln 5 = \ln 3 + (1 - x) \ln 4.$$

We now have a linear equation in x. Solve it as follows:

$$x \ln 5 = \ln 3 + \ln 4 - x \ln 4$$

$$x (\ln 5 + \ln 4) = \ln 3 + \ln 4$$

$$x = \frac{\ln 3 + \ln 4}{\ln 5 + \ln 4} = \frac{\ln 12}{\ln 20} \approx 0.8295.$$

Therefore, the exact solution is $\frac{\ln 12}{\ln 20}$ and 0.8295 is the approximation.   ▲

Notice that $\frac{\ln 12}{\ln 20}$ cannot be simplified further in the exact form solution of Example 5. In particular, $\frac{\ln 12}{\ln 20}$ is not equal to $\ln \frac{12}{20}$, since $\frac{\ln 12}{\ln 20} \approx 0.8295$ and $\ln \frac{12}{20} \approx -0.5108$.

| **EXAMPLE 6** | Solve the equation $e^x + e^{-x} = 4$.

Strategy: Note that the strategy of Example 5 is not helpful, since $\ln(e^x + e^{-x})$ does not simplify. Multiply through by e^x to get a quadratic equation in e^x. Use the quadratic formula to solve for e^x, and then take logarithms to solve for x.

Solution

Follow the strategy and multiply both sides by e^x.

$$e^{2x} + e^x e^{-x} = 4e^x \qquad \text{or} \qquad (e^x)^2 - 4e^x + 1 = 0.$$

Use the quadratic formula to get two roots for e^x,

$$e^x = 2 + \sqrt{3} \quad \text{and} \quad e^x = 2 - \sqrt{3}.$$

Apply the ln function to both sides of each and use identity 2 to get

$$\ln e^x = \ln(2 + \sqrt{3}) \quad \text{or} \quad x = \ln(2 + \sqrt{3}) \approx 1.317$$

$$\ln e^x = \ln(2 - \sqrt{3}) \quad \text{or} \quad x = \ln(2 - \sqrt{3}) \approx -1.317.$$

The exact solutions are $\ln(2 + \sqrt{3})$ and $\ln(2 - \sqrt{3})$. Decimal approximations are 1.317 and -1.317, respectively. ▲

Applications

Exponential and logarithmic functions are used to model many natural phenomena. The following section is devoted entirely to such applications. Here we discuss just one example.

The Sounds We Hear   Logarithmic functions are used in modeling the sounds we hear. Loudness of sound is a sensation in the brain. We cannot measure it directly, but there is a related physically measurable quantity: the *intensity* of the sound wave. Sound waves travel through the air, and these wave vibrations force the eardrums to vibrate, producing a sound sensation. The intensity I of a sound wave is measured in watts per square meter $\left(\frac{w}{m^2}\right)$.

The intensity of a barely audible sound wave, about $10^{-12} \frac{w}{m^2}$, corresponds to pressure vibrations less than a billionth of the atmospheric pressure at sea level. The human ear is very sensitive. A sound wave of intensity of $1 \frac{w}{m^2}$ would damage the eardrum.

The human ear does not respond to sound intensity in a linear fashion. If the intensity doubles, we do not hear the sound as twice as loud. The sound level β is logarithmically related to the intensity I.

$$\beta(I) = 10 \log\left(\frac{I}{I_0}\right) = 10\,(\log I - \log I_0) \tag{3}$$

where I is the measured intensity and I_0 is the intensity of sound we can just barely hear, $10^{-12} \frac{w}{m^2}$. The sound level β is measured in decibels (dB), a unit named for Alexander Graham Bell.

For a sound just at the hearing threshold, I is I_0, so

$$\beta(I) = 10 \log\left(\frac{I_0}{I_0}\right) = 10 \log 1 = 10 \cdot 0 = 0.$$

Thus 0 dB measures the threshold hearing level. At an intensity of $10\,I_0$, $\beta(10\,I_0) = 10 \log 10 = 10$. Similarly, if I is $100\,I_0$, then the sound level is given by $\beta(100\,I_0) = 10 \log 100 = 10 \cdot 2 = 20$. Multiplying the intensity by a factor of 10 only doubles the loudness of the sound we hear.

EXAMPLE 7   Four trumpets are playing at the same time, each at an average loudness of 75 dB. What is the resulting sound level?

Solution

If $\beta(I_1)$ denotes the loudness level of one trumpet, then Equation 3 can give the corresponding intensity I_1.

$$\beta(I_1) = 10 \log\left(\frac{I_1}{I_0}\right) = 10 \log I_1 - 10 \log I_0.$$

| For Graphers 4.4 | DOMAIN AND GRAPHING MORE LOGARITHMIC FUNCTIONS |

Exercises

1. On the same set of axes in the Familiar Window (or another Equal Scale window), draw graphs of $f(x) = e^x$ and $g(x) = \ln x$, then add the graph of $y = x$. Do the graphs of f and g appear to be symmetric about the line $y = x$?

Exercises 2–4 Find the domain of f. (*Calculator Hint:* Use the change-of-base formula to rewrite $f(x)$ in terms of the ln function, then draw a graph.)

2. $f(x) = \log_3 x$

3. $f(x) = \log_3 x + \log_3(x - 2)$

4. $f(x) = \log_2 x - \log_2(4 - x)$

Exercises 5–6 Use graphs to determine whether or not functions f and g might be identical. Why do we say *might be* rather than *are*?

5. $f(x) = \ln x + \ln(x - 2)$, $g(x) = \ln[x(x - 2)]$

6. $g(x) = \ln x^2$, $g(x) = 2 \ln x$.

Exercises 7–10 Use graphs to find the solution set (to two-place accuracy).

7. $\ln x + \ln(x - 2) = \ln[x(x - 2)]$ (*Hint:* Graph each side on the same screen and look for points of intersection.)

8. $e^x + e^{-x} = 4$

9. (a) $\ln x + e^x = 0$ (b) $\ln x < e^x$

10. $5^x = 3 \cdot 4^{1-x}$ (*Hint:* See Example 5b.)

Exercises 11–13 Use graphs to find the solution set (to two-place accuracy). (*Calculator Hint:* For Exercise 11, draw graphs of $y = 2^x$ and $y = x^2$ on the same screen and look for points of intersection. You may need a different window for each exercise.)

11. $2^x = x^2$ 12. $2^x = x^3$ 13. $2^x = x^4$

Since $I_0 = 10^{-12}$, $\log I_0 = -12$. Since $\beta(I_1) = 75$, we have

$$75 = 10 \log I_1 + 120 \qquad \log I_1 = -4.5 \qquad \text{and} \qquad I_1 = 10^{-4.5}.$$

The intensity of sound for one trumpet is $10^{-4.5}$ so four trumpets have a sound intensity of $4 \cdot I_1$, or $4 \cdot 10^{-4.5}$. Thus

$$\beta(4 \cdot I_1) = 10 \log \left[\frac{4 I_1}{I_0} \right] = 10 \log \left[4 \left(\frac{I_1}{I_0} \right) \right]$$

$$= 10 \log 4 + 10 \log \left(\frac{I_1}{I_0} \right) = 10 \log 4 + 75 \approx 81.02$$

Therefore, the loudness of the four trumpets is about 81 dB. A fourfold increase in sound wave intensity increases the loudness level by less than 10 percent. This is why a solo instrument can be heard in a symphony concert even when the full orchestra is playing at the same time. ▲

| EXERCISES 4.4 |

Check Your Understanding

Exercises 1–5 True or False. Give reasons for your conclusion.

1. $\ln 4 < \log 4$

2. $\ln(\sqrt{2} + \sqrt{5}) = \frac{1}{2}(\ln 2 + \ln 5)$

3. For all positive numbers c and d, $\ln(c + d) = \ln c + \ln d$.

4. The graph of $y = \log x$ is above the graph of $y = \ln x$ for all $x > 1$.

5. The graph of $y = \ln x$ has no x-intercept point.

Exercises 6–10 Complete the sentence by selecting from the list below *all choices* that make the statement true.

(a) less than 1   **(b)** greater than 1
(c) greater than 0   **(d)** less than 0
(e) between 1 and 2   **(f)** greater than 2

6. If $0 < x < 1$, then $\ln x$ is —————— .

7. If $x > 1$, then $\log x$ is —————— .

8. If x is any nonzero number, $\ln \frac{x^2}{x^2 + 1}$ is —————— .

9. The domain of $\log(-x^2 + 3x - 2)$ consists of all numbers —————— .

10. The domain of $\ln(x - 1)$ consists of all numbers —————— .

Explore and Discover

1. (a) For what x does the graph of $y = \ln x$ reach a height of 50?
   (b) For what x does the graph of $y = e^x$ reach a height of 50?
   (c) If you were to draw a graph of $y = \ln x$ with 1 cm as the unit on your axes, how far out would you have to go on the x-axis before reaching the point where y is 50? Compare your answer with the distance from the Earth to the sun, 93 million miles, or about 1.5×10^{13} cm.

2. (a) Verify that for each of the following values of x, the number $\frac{5x + 3}{x + 1}$ is between 3 and 5: $x = 1$ $x = 0.01$ $x = 4$ $x = 17$.
   (b) Is it true that whenever $x > 0$, $\frac{5x + 3}{x + 1} < 5$? Is $\frac{5x + 3}{x + 1} > 3$? Explain. (*Hint:* If $x > 0$, why does multiplication or division by $x + 1$ leave an inequality unchanged?)
   (c) Write a paragraph to explain how we can know that for any positive number x,

$$1 < \ln\left(\frac{5x + 3}{x + 1}\right) < 2.$$

In your explanation, you may want to use the fact that $1 < \ln 3$ and $\ln 5 < 2$. Consider, as well, the nature of the graph of $y = \ln x$.

Develop Mastery

Exercises 1–8 Evaluate. Give the result rounded off to four decimal places. If your calculator indicates an error, explain why.

1. (a) $\ln 5$ **(b)** $\log 15.6$

2. (a) $\ln \sqrt{3}$ **(b)** $\log(1 + \sqrt{3})$

3. (a) $\frac{\ln 3}{\ln 5}$ **(b)** $\ln\left(\frac{3}{5}\right)$ **(c)** $\frac{\ln 3 + \ln 4}{\ln 5}$

4. (a) $\ln\sqrt{0.5}$ **(b)** $\sqrt{\ln 0.5}$ **(c)** $(0.5)\ln 0.5$

5. (a) $\ln \sqrt{2}$ **(b)** $\sqrt{\ln 2}$ **(c)** $2(\ln \sqrt{2})$

6. (a) $\log_3 7$ **(b)** $\log_8 0.8$ **(c)** $\log_4(3 - \sqrt{10})$

7. (a) $\log_5(\ln 7)$ **(b)** $\log_3(\ln 0.3)$ **(c)** $\log_8 2^{\sqrt{3}}$

8. (a) $\log_2(\ln 4)$ **(b)** $\log_5(\ln 0.4)$ **(c)** $\log_3 3^{\sqrt{3}}$

Exercises 9–12 Simplify. Express your result in exact form and give a two-decimal-place approximation.

9. (a) $e^{\ln \sqrt{5}}$ **(b)** $e^{-\ln \sqrt{5}}$

10. (a) $e^{-\ln \sqrt{6}}$ **(b)** $e^{-2(\ln 13)}$

11. (a) $\ln e^{\sqrt{3}}$ **(b)** $\ln \sqrt[6]{e}$

12. (a) $\ln e^{-\sqrt{7}}$ **(b)** $\ln \sqrt[7]{e}$

Exercises 13–18 Enter $=$, $<$, or $>$ in the blank to get a true statement.

13. $\log_2 3$ ————— $\log_3 2$ **14.** $\log_5 15$ ————— $\log_2 5$

15. $\log_5 25$ ————— $\log_3 9$ **16.** $\log_2 12$ ————— $\log_{12} 60$

17. $\log_{0.5} 5$ ————— $\log_3 0.04$

18. $\log_5 0.3$ ————— $\log_3 0.5$

Exercises 19–36 Solve. Express the result in exact form and give a three-decimal-place approximation.

19. $3 \ln x - 1 = 0$

20. $2 \ln x - 1 = 0$

21. $\ln(3x - 2) + \ln 5 = 1$

22. $\ln(3 - 2x) - \ln 3 = 1$

23. $\log(3x - 1) - \log x = -1$

24. $\log(2x - 5) - \log x = -1$

25. $2 \log x - 2 \log(x - 1) = 1$

26. $2 \ln x - \ln(2x + 1) = 1$

27. $3^x = 4$ **28.** $5^x = 8$

29. $e^{-x} = 0.56$ **30.** $e^{-x} = 1.43$

31. $3^x - \ln 4 = 0$ **32.** $4^{-x} - \ln 5 = 0$

33. $e^x = 3 \cdot 4^x$ **34.** $5^{-x} = 6 \cdot 7^x$

35. $e^{-x} + 1 = \ln 8$ **36.** $e^x - 1 = \ln 3$

Exercises 37–42 For the graph of the equation, find the x- and y-intercept points. Round off to two decimal places as needed.

37. $y = \ln(x + 1) - 1$ **38.** $y = 2 \ln(x + 1) - 3$

39. $y = 2 \cdot 4^x - 5$ **40.** $y = 3 \cdot 5^{-x} - 4$

41. $y = \ln(x + 2) - \ln(x + 1) - 1$

42. $y = 3 \cdot 2^x - 5^{-x}$

Exercises 43–46 **(a)** Use appropriate translations of a core graph to sketch the graph of $y = f(x)$. Label the x-intercept points. **(b)** Use the graph to help find the solution set for $f(x) \geq 0$.

43. $f(x) = \ln(x - 1) - 1$ 44. $f(x) = \ln(x + 2)$
45. $f(x) = e^x - 2$ 46. $f(x) = e^{-x} - 2$

Exercises 47–49 First express the equation in quadratic form and then solve for x. See Example 6.

47. $e^x - 2e^{-x} - 1 = 0$ 48. $3^{2x} - 3^x - 2 = 0$
49. $5^x + 10 \cdot 5^{-x} = 7$

Exercises 50–55 Solve. Express the result in exact form and give a three-decimal-place approximation. (*Hint:* Consider quadratic equations.)

50. $(\ln x)^2 - 2\ln x - 3 = 0$ 51. $(\ln x)^2 = \ln x$
52. $e^{2x} + 2e^x - 3 = 0$ 53. $e^{2x} = e^x + 2$
54. $e^{2x} + 4e^x + 4 = 0$ 55. $4^x - 2^{x+1} - 3 = 0$

Exercises 56–68 Find the solution set.

56. (a) $e^{-x} = -3$ (b) $\ln(-x) = -3$
57. $2\log x = \log 2x$
58. $\ln(x^2 - 2) - \ln x = 0$
59. $\ln(e^x + 1) = \ln(e^{-x} + 1) + x$
60. $x^{\log x} = \frac{x^4}{1000}$ (*Hint:* Take the log of each side.)
61. $(4x)^{\log 4} = (3x)^{\log 3}$ (*Hint:* Take the log of each side.)
62. $x^{\ln x} = x^2 e^3$ (*Hint:* Take the ln of each side.)
63. (a) $x^{\log 3} = 3$ (b) $x^{\ln x} = e^4$
64. $\log(x^2 + 3) - 2\log x = 1$
65. $(\log_5 x)(\log_x 7) = \log_5 7$ (*Hint:* Use the change-of-base formula.)
66. $(\log_2 x)(\log_x 5) = \log_2 5$ (See Exercise 65.)
67. $\frac{1}{\log_2 x} + \frac{1}{\log_3 x} = \frac{1}{\log_6 x}$ (See Exercise 65.)
68. How many times more intense is a 70 dB sound than (a) a 60 dB sound? (b) a 40 dB sound?

69. The loudness level near a lawn mower is 90 dB. What is the corresponding intensity in $\frac{w}{m^2}$?

70. The average loudness level of one trombone is about 70 dB.
    (a) What is the loudness level when 76 trombones are playing at the same time?
    (b) What is the percentage increase in the loudness level from one trombone to 76 trombones?

71. What is the loudness level of 110 cornets playing simultaneously if the average loudness level of each is 75 dB? What is the percentage increase in loudness level over that of one cornet?

Exercises 72–73 Looking Ahead to Calculus In calculus we define a function, called the *hyperbolic sine*, by $\sinh x = \frac{1}{2}(e^x - e^{-x})$. The graph of the hyperbolic sine is shown in the diagram. The graph shows that the sinh function is one–one and hence has an inverse.

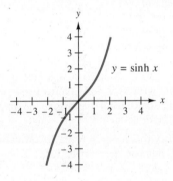

72. If $f(x) = \sinh x$, find an equation that describes f^{-1}. (*Hint:* Use the algorithm in Section 2.7.)

73. The function $g(x) = \ln(\sqrt{x^2 + 1} + x)$ has an inverse. Use the algorithm in Section 2.7 to find an equation that describes g^{-1}. Compare with Exercise 72.

SECTION 4.5   Models for Growth, Decay, and Change

I find that I may have emphasized the need to escape from the devils of mathematics to embark on the pleasures of the real world. But it works both ways, and sometimes the devils of the real world drive one into the pleasures of studying mathematics.
                Cathleen S. Morawetz

Exponential and logarithmic functions are used to model many real-world processes, some of which we mentioned in earlier sections. In this section we look at additional applications.

I developed a proficiency [in junior high school] in simple algebra that lasted for a long time and has been very useful. My mother gave me her college algebra book. I learned from it how to solve word problems, although I remember distinctly that I never really understood them. I could do only the problems that followed the pattern of the examples in the book. My view is that if you have a firm grasp of technique, you can then concentrate on theory without having to think about the technical details.

Ralph P. Boas, Jr.

Exponential Growth

When scientists measure population size, they see regular changes. Whether they study fish, bacteria, or mammals, they observe that the rate of change is proportional to the number of organisms present; with more bacteria in a culture, colonies grow faster (as long as there is adequate food). A similar kind of growth occurs in a financial setting with compound interest. The amount of interest depends on the amount of money invested, and a larger investment grows faster.

We learn in calculus that exponential functions can model any kind of growth for which the rate of change is proportional to the amount present. Hence this kind of growth is called **exponential growth.**

To express exponential growth mathematically, suppose $A(t)$ denotes the amount of substance or the number of organisms present at time t. Then $A(t)$ is given by

$$A(t) = Ce^{kt},$$

where C and k are constants. When t is 0, the formula gives $A(0) = Ce^{k \cdot 0}$, or $A(0) = C$. Hence, for any exponential growth, C is the amount present at the time measurement begins, when t is 0; we replace C by A_0.

Exponential Growth Formula

Suppose the rate of change of some substance or quantity is proportional to the amount present, then the amount or number $A(t)$ at time t is given by

$$A(t) = A_0e^{kt} \tag{1}$$

where A_0 is the initial amount (the amount present when t is 0), and k is a positive constant determined by the particular substance.

In many problems the constant k is determined experimentally. For instance, a scientist may find that the number of bacteria in a culture doubles every 72 minutes. This information is enough to determine the value of k, as shown in the following example.

Strategy: Use Equation 1 with $A_0 = 500$ and $A(1.2) = 1000$, since 72 minutes is 1.2 hours. Find k.

EXAMPLE 1   A sample culture medium contains approximately 500 bacteria when first measured, and 72 minutes later the number has doubled to 1000. **(a)** Determine a formula for the number $A(t)$ at any time t hours after the initial measurement. **(b)** What is the number of bacteria at the end of 3 hours? **(c)** How long does it take for the number to increase tenfold to 5000?

Solution

(a)   Follow the strategy. When t is 1.2, Equation 1 becomes

$$1000 = 500e^{k(1.2)}.$$

Divide by 500, take the natural logarithm of both sides, and solve for k.

$$2 = e^{1.2k}, \qquad \ln 2 = \ln e^{1.2k} = 1.2k, \qquad k = \frac{\ln 2}{1.2} \approx 0.578.$$

Replacing k by 0.578 and A_0 by 500 gives the desired equation.

$$A(t) = 500e^{0.578t} \tag{2}$$

(b)   When t is 3, $A(3) = 500e^{0.578(3)} = 500e^{1.734} \approx 2832$, so at the end of 3 hours there are approximately 2800 bacteria in the culture.

(c)   To find t when $A(t)$ is 5000, substitute 5000 for $A(t)$ in Equation 2 and solve for t.

$$5000 = 500e^{0.578t} \qquad 10 = e^{0.578t}$$

$$\ln 10 = \ln e^{0.578t} = 0.578t$$

$$t = \frac{\ln 10}{0.578} \approx 3.98$$

It takes about 4 hours for the number of bacteria to increase tenfold.   ▲

Compound and Continuous Interest

If money is invested in an account that pays interest at a rate r compounded n times a year, the growth is not described by Equation 1. We need another formula. When the annual interest rate is given as a percentage, we express r as a decimal; for a rate of 6 percent we write $r = 0.06$.

Compound Interest Formula

Suppose A_0 dollars are invested in an account that pays interest at rate r compounded n times a year. The number of dollars $A(t)$ in the account t years later is given by

$$A(t) = A_0\left(1 + \frac{r}{n}\right)^{nt}. \tag{3}$$

Compound interest is paid only at the end of each compounding period. If interest is compounded quarterly, then the interest is credited at the end of each three-month period. To apply Equation 3 for other values of t, we should replace the exponent nt by the greatest integer $[nt]$.

As the number of times a year that interest is compounded increases, we approach what is called **continuous compounding.** To see what happens to $A(t)$ as n becomes large ($n \to \infty$), replace $\frac{r}{n}$ by x and rewrite the exponent nt as $\left(\frac{n}{r}\right)(rt)$, or $\left(\frac{1}{x}\right)(rt)$, so Equation 3 becomes

$$A(t) = A_0[(1 + x)^{1/x}]^{rt}. \tag{4}$$

Now, as $n \to \infty$, $\frac{r}{n} \to 0$, so $x \to 0$. We are interested in what happens to the expression $(1 + x)^{1/x}$ as $x \to 0$. This is precisely the problem we considered in introducing the number e in Section 4.1: $(1 + x)^{1/x} \to e$ as $x \to 0$. Thus, when interest is compounded continuously at rate r for t years, compound interest becomes exponential growth; Equation 4 becomes $A(t) = A_0e^{rt}$.

Continuous Interest Formula

Suppose A_0 dollars are invested in an account that pays interest at rate r compounded continuously. Then the number of dollars $A(t)$ in the account t years later is given by

$$A(t) = A_0e^{rt}. \qquad \text{(5)}$$

EXAMPLE 2   Suppose \$2400 is invested in an account on which interest is compounded twice a year at the rate of 8 percent.

(a) How much is in the account at the end of ten years?

(b) How long does it take to double the initial investment?

(c) Answer the same questions if the money is compounded continuously.

Strategy: For **(a)** and **(b)**, replace A_0 by 2400, r by 0.08, and n by 2 in Equation 3, then use the resulting equation. For **(c)**, replace A_0 by 2400 and r by 0.08 in Equation 5, then use the resulting equation.

Solution

Follow the strategy.

$$A(t) = 2400(1 + 0.04)^{2t} = 2400(1.04)^{2t}.$$

(a) In ten years, t is 10, so

$$A(10) = 2400(1.04)^{20} \approx 5258.70$$

At the end of ten years the account will be worth \$5258.70.

(b) Solve the following for t:

$$4800 = 2400\,(1.04)^{2t}, \qquad 2 = (1.04)^{2t},$$

$$\ln 2 = \ln(1.04)^{2t} = 2t \ln 1.04, \qquad \text{or} \qquad t = \frac{\ln 2}{2 \ln 1.04} \approx 8.8.$$

The \$2400 investment doubles in about 8 years and 10 months, but the account will not be credited with the last interest until the end of the year.

(c) Using Equation 5 instead of Equation 3,

$$A(t) = 2400e^{0.08t}.$$

In ten years, $A(10) = 2400e^{0.8} \approx 5341.30$, so continuous interest returns nearly \$83 more on a \$2400 investment than semiannual compounding over that time. To see how long it takes to double the investment, solve for t:

$$4800 = 2400e^{0.08t} \qquad t = \frac{\ln 2}{0.08} \approx 8.66.$$

The investment doubles in 8 years and 8 months. ▲

Exponential Decay

Certain materials, such as radioactive substances, decrease with time, rather than growing, with the rate of decrease proportional to the amount. Such negative growth is described by exponential functions, very much like exponential growth except for a negative sign in the exponent.

Exponential Decay Formula

Suppose the rate of decrease of some substance is proportional to the amount present. The amount $A(t)$ at time t is given by

$$A(t) = A_0 e^{-kt} \qquad\qquad \textbf{(6)}$$

where A_0 is the initial amount (the amount present when t is 0), and k is a positive constant determined by the particular substance.

EXAMPLE 3   Strontium-90 has a half-life of 29 years. Beginning with a 10 mg sample, **(a)** determine an equation for the amount $A(t)$ after t years and **(b)** find how long it takes for the sample to decay to 1 mg.

Strategy: First, replace A_0 by 10 in Equation 6, then in the resulting equation use $A(29) = 5$ and solve for k. Using this value of k in Equation 6 gives the decay equation for strontium-90.

Solution

(a) Follow the strategy. $A(t) = 10e^{-kt}$, and in 29 years, half the sample will remain, so $A(29) = 5$. Substitute 29 for t and 5 for A, so

$$5 = 10e^{-29k} \quad \text{or} \quad e^{-29k} = \frac{1}{2}, \text{ so } -29k = \ln\left(\frac{1}{2}\right).$$

$$k = \frac{\ln\left(\frac{1}{2}\right)}{-29} = \frac{-\ln 2}{-29} \approx 0.0239.$$

Therefore, the decay equation for strontium-90 is $A(t) = 10e^{-0.0239t}$.

(b) To find when $A(t)$ is 1, replace $A(t)$ by 1 and solve the resulting equation for t.

$$1 = 10e^{-0.0239t}, \quad \ln\left(\frac{1}{10}\right) = \ln e^{-0.0239t} = -0.0239t,$$

$$t = \frac{\ln\left(\frac{1}{10}\right)}{-0.0239} \approx 96.$$

It takes 96 years for 90 percent of the original amount of strontium-90 to decay. ▲

Carbon Dating

Radioactive decay is used to date some fossils. The method involves the element carbon. Carbon-12 is a stable isotope, while carbon-14 is a radioactive isotope with a half-life of approximately 5700 years. Fortunately for us, the concentration of C^{14} in the air we breath and the food we eat is extremely small (about 10^{-6} percent). Although C^{14} disintegrates as time passes, the amount of C^{14} in the atmosphere remains in equilibrium because it is constantly being formed by cosmic rays. All living things regularly take in carbon, and the proportion of C^{14}

EXPONENTIAL FUNCTIONS, DATING, AND FRAUD DETECTION

Bust of Piltdown Man

The discovery of radiocarbon dating in 1949 by Willard F. Libby opened new ways to learn about the past. The half-life of carbon-14 allows dependable dating of organic material within a range of 10,000 or 20,000 years.

Potassium allows dating on a much longer scale, albeit less precisely. Each of our bodies contains about a pound of potassium, including a miniscule fraction of radioactive potassium-40, which is changing (into argon gas) at a rate of about 500 atoms per second. Potassium-argon dating established the age of the fossil hominid Lucy at over 3 million years.

In 1908 bits of bone that comprised part of a human skull were found in a gravel pit in Piltdown, Sussex, England. Four years later part of an apelike jawbone showed up in the same location. Thus was born Piltdown Man, one of the strangest puzzles in human paleontology.

Joining a human cranium with an apelike jaw raised problems for students of human evolution and fueled a vigorous controversy that raged for years. Not until 1953 did fluorine dating (based on the fact that bones and teeth absorb fluorine from soil and groundwater at a constant rate) finally show that the cranium and jawbone did not belong together. The newly discovered radiocarbon dating showed that the skull dated from near Chaucer's time (about 600 years earlier—hardly prehistoric), and the jaw was even younger. It had belonged to an orangutan from the East Indies.

The whole Piltdown affair was perhaps the greatest hoax in the history of science. Professionals and amateurs alike (including Sir Arthur Conan Doyle, creator of Sherlock Holmes) became embroiled in the disputes. The identity of the perpetrators remains unresolved, but progress in the methods of science, including mathematical dating analyses, helped to uncover the fraud.

in living organisms reflects the proportion in the atmosphere. When an organism dies, however, the C^{14} is not replenished and the decay process decreases the ratio of C^{14} to C^{12}. By measuring this ratio in organic material, it is possible to determine the number of years since the time of death. The technique is known as *carbon dating* (see the Historical Note, "Exponential Functions, Dating, and Fraud Detection").

EXAMPLE 4   A tree felled by the eruption that created Crater Lake in Oregon was found to contain 44 percent of its original amount of carbon-14. Use 5700 years as the half-life of carbon-14 and determine the age of Crater Lake.

Strategy: Crater Lake was formed when the tree died, so find how long the tree has been dead. Use Equation 6 and when t is 5700, $A(t)$ is $\frac{A_0}{2}$. Solve for k. Substitute this value in Equation 6 to get the decay equation for carbon-14. Now replace $A(t)$ by $0.44A_0$ and solve the resulting equation for t.

Solution

Follow the strategy.

$$A(t) = A_0 e^{-kt}$$

$$\frac{1}{2}A_0 = A_0 e^{-5700k} \qquad \text{or} \qquad \frac{1}{2} = e^{-5700k}$$

Take natural logarithms and use the fact that $\ln\left(\frac{1}{2}\right) = -\ln 2$:

$$-\ln 2 = \ln e^{-5700k} \qquad \text{or} \qquad -\ln 2 = -5700k \qquad \text{or } k = \frac{\ln 2}{5700} \approx 0.0001216.$$

Therefore, the decay equation for carbon-14 is

$$A(t) = A_0 e^{-0.0001216t} \tag{7}$$

Since 44 percent of the original amount of carbon-14 still remained when the tree was discovered, find the value of t for which $A(t)$ is $(0.44)A_0$. Substitute $(0.44)A_0$ for $A(t)$ in Equation 7:

$$(0.44)A_0 = A_0 e^{-0.0001216t} \qquad \text{or} \qquad 0.44 = e^{-0.0001216t}$$

$$\ln 0.44 = \ln e^{-0.0001216t} \qquad \text{or} \qquad \ln 0.44 = -0.0001216t$$

$$t = -\frac{\ln 0.44}{0.0001216} \approx 6751.$$

Crater Lake was formed approximately 7000 years ago. ▲

The next example presents another illustration of exponential decay.

EXAMPLE 5   Standard atmospheric pressure at sea level is 1035 g/cm². Experimentation shows that up to about 80 km ($\approx$ 50 mi), the pressure decreases exponentially. The atmospheric pressure (in g/cm²) at an altitude of h kilometers is given by

$$P(h) = 1035e^{-0.12h} \tag{8}$$

Find **(a)** the atmospheric pressure at 40 km, and **(b)** the altitude where the atmospheric pressure drops to 20 percent of that at sea level.

Solution

(a)   From equation 8, $P(40) = 1035e^{(-0.12)(40)} \approx 8.5$. Hence the atmospheric pressure at 40 km ($\approx$ 25 mi) is only 8.5 g/cm², less than 1 percent of the pressure at sea level.

(b)   Find the value of h for which $P(h)$ is 20 percent of the pressure at sea level. Replace $P(h)$ in equation 8 by $(0.2)(1035)$ and solve for h, dividing by 1035 and then taking logarithms.

$$(0.2)(1035) = 1035e^{-0.12h} \qquad \text{or} \qquad e^{-0.12h} = 0.2 \qquad \text{or}$$

$$-0.12h = \ln 0.2 \qquad \text{or} \qquad h = \frac{\ln 0.2}{-0.12} \approx 13.4.$$

Since $h \approx 13.4$, at an altitude of 13.4 km (≈ 8.3 mi, not quite 44,000 ft), the atmospheric pressure drops to 20 percent of the atmospheric pressure at sea level. ▲

In the previous section we saw an example of an application of logarithms to measure sound levels. The next two examples also illustrate models that apply logarithms.

Measuring Earthquakes

An earthquake produces seismic waves whose amplitude is measured on a seismograph. Charles Richter, an American geologist, recognized the great variation in amplitudes of earthquakes and proposed a logarithmic scale to measure their severity. The magnitude $M(A)$ of an earthquake with amplitude A is a number on the Richter scale given by

$$M(A) = \log\left(\frac{A}{A_0}\right), \tag{9}$$

where A_0 is a standard amplitude.

EXAMPLE 6 How many times larger was the amplitude of the Alaskan earthquake on March 28, 1964, which measured 8.6 on the Richter scale, than the amplitude of a relatively minor aftershock that measured 4.3?

Strategy: Use Equation 9. Let A_1 and A_2 be the two amplitudes, and replace $M(A_1)$, $M(A_2)$, by 8.6 and 4.3, respectively. Find A_1 and A_2 in terms of A_0.

Solution

Follow the strategy.

$$8.6 = \log\left(\frac{A_1}{A_0}\right) \quad \text{and} \quad 4.3 = \log\left(\frac{A_2}{A_0}\right).$$

Write each equation in exponential form and solve for A_1 and A_2.

$$A_1 = A_0\, 10^{8.6} \quad \text{and} \quad A_2 = A_0\, 10^{4.3}.$$

Solve the second equation for A_0 and substitute into the first equation,

$$A_0 = A_2\, 10^{-4.3}, \text{ so } A_1 = (A_2\, 10^{-4.3})10^{8.6} = 10^{4.3}A_2 \approx 19{,}953A_2.$$

The amplitude A_1 of the 8.3 magnitude earthquake was nearly 20,000 times larger than the amplitude of the 4.3 aftershock, which explains the enormous amount of damage done by the original earthquake. ▲

Acidity Measurement

Chemists determine the acidity of a solution by measuring the hydrogen ion concentration (denoted by $[H^+]$, in moles per liter). Such concentrations are very small numbers. To deal with numbers in a more familiar range, the quantity denoted by pH essentially puts hydrogen ion concentration on a logarithmic scale.

| For Graphers 4.5 | **PLAYBACK AND ITERATION** |

Graphing calculators have several features that facilitate root-finding. In particular, they can be set to easily handle the iteration procedure described in Explore and Discover Exercise 1 to find roots for equations of the form $f(x) = x$.

EXAMPLE   Use iteration to find the negative root of the equation $e^x - 2 = x$.

Solution   Begin by graphing $Y = e^\wedge X - 2 - X$ in the Familiar Window. Trace along the curve to find a negative root near -1.9; return to the home screen and enter -1.9 as x_0: $\boxed{-}$ 1.9 $\boxed{\text{EXE}}$. This enters an initial guess, which can be recalled as the $\boxed{\text{ANS}}$, so we essentially write $e^x - 2$ in terms of $\boxed{\text{ANS}}$: $\boxed{e^x}$ $\boxed{\text{ANS}}$ $\boxed{-}$ 2 (subtract key, not change-sign) and $\boxed{\text{EXE}}$. The display reads -1.850431381. Now each time we press $\boxed{\text{EXE}}$ (or $\boxed{\text{ENTER}}$), the calculator repeats the last operation, giving -1.842830648. As we iterate, the display soon becomes constant, displaying -1.84140566, which, to calculator accuracy, is the desired solution. ▲

Exercises

Exercises 1–2   Draw graphs to find an initial guess. Then write the equation in the form $x = f(x)$ and iterate $f(\text{ANS})$ to find the root of the equation.

1. $x + \log(0.2x) = 1$

2. $e^{x-2} + x - 2 = 0$

3. In Develop Mastery Exercise 4, the formula for the world population n years after 1968 at an annual rate of increase of 1.5 percent, is given by $P(n) = 3.5(1.015)^n$.

(a) Evaluate $P(24)$ to show that the given formula predicts a world population of only about 5 billion people, rather than the 5.5 billion given in Develop Mastery Exercise 3. (*Hint:* $P(24) = 3.5(1.015)^\wedge 24$.)

(b) Replay the last calculation (up-arrow on a TI or left-arrow on a Casio) and change the 1.015 to 1.016, then evaluate. What does the displayed number represent in terms of population?

(c) Repeat part (b), changing the last digit (1.016, 1.017, . . .) until you have a value for $P(24)$ that approximates 5.5 billion. What percentage of population increase is needed to have $P(24) \approx 5.5$?

4. Use the replay feature as described in Exercise 3 to approximate the answer to Develop Mastery Exercise 12, then compare your result with the exact form of the solution to that exercise.

Formula for Determining Acidity of a Solution

For a solution with hydrogen ion concentration of $[H^+]$ moles per liter, the corresponding pH value is given by

$$pH = -\log[H^+]. \tag{10}$$

If the pH number for a solution is less than 7, then the solution is called *acidic;* if the pH is greater than 7, then the solution is called *basic.* Solutions with pH equal to 7 are called *neutral.* For a solution with 10^{-1} moles of hydrogen ions per liter ($[H^+] = 10^{-1}$), the pH is $-\log 10^{-1} = -(-)1 = 1$; such a solution is very strongly acidic (even one-tenth of a mole of hydrogen ions indicates *lots* of freely reacting ions in the solution). At the other end of the scale, if $[H^+] = 10^{-13}$, then pH $= -\log (10^{-13}) = 13$, indicating a strongly basic solution.

EXAMPLE 7   A certain fruit juice has a hydrogen ion concentration of 3.2×10^{-4} moles per liter. Find the pH value for the juice and decide whether it is acidic or basic.

Solution

Given that $[H^+] = 3.2 \times 10^{-4}$, substitute into Equation 10:

$$pH = -\log (3.2 \times 10^{-4}) = -\log (0.00032) \approx 3.5.$$

A pH of less than 7 indicates that the juice would be classified as acidic.   ▲

EXERCISES 4.5

Check Your Understanding

Exercises 1–6 If $1000 is invested in an account that earns interest compounded continuously at an interest rate that doubles the investment in value every 12 years, then select from the choices below the amount that is closest to the total value of the investment after the indicated period of time. As in the text, $A(t)$ denotes the amount of money in the account t years after the investment is made.

(a) $1400   (b) $1500   (c) $2000
(d) $2800   (e) $3000   (f) $4000
(g) $6000   (h) $7000   (i) $8000

1. $A(24) =$ _____.   2. $A(36) =$ _____.

3. $A(6) =$ _____.   4. $A(18) =$ _____.

5. The interest earned during the first 18 years is _____.

6. The interest earned during the years from $t = 12$ to $t = 24$ is _____.

Exercises 7–10 A radioactive substance has a half-life of 30 days. Select from the list below the choice that is closest to the amount of the substance that remains after the indicated period of time. A_0 denotes the number of grams of the substance when t is 0, and $A(t)$ denotes the number of grams t days later.

(a) $0.25A_0$ (b) $0.35A_0$ (c) $0.50A_0$
(d) $0.70A_0$ (e) $0.75A_0$ (f) $0.80A_0$

7. $A(60) =$ _____.   8. $A(15) =$ _____.

9. $A(45) =$ _____.

10. The amount of the substance that decays during the first 60 days is _____.

Explore and Discover

1. To find the root of $e^{-x} = x$, try the following. Enter a number in your calculator, call it x_0, and then evaluate e^{-x_0}; call the result x_1, so $x_1 = e^{-x_0}$. Let $x_2 = e^{-x_1}$, let $x_3 = e^{-x_2}$, and so on. Continue the process until you observe something interesting.

2. Try the procedure outlined in Exercise 1 to solve the equation $e^x - 2 = x$. Compare what happens if you start with $\frac{1}{2}$, -1, or 2. See example in For Graphers.

3. Exercises 1 and 2 use iteration to find the calculator solution to equations of the form $f(x) = x$. Rather than using subscripts, take an initial value, say c, and evaluate $f(c), f(f(c)), f(f(f(c))), \ldots$ continuing until the display, say k, no longer changes. To calculator accuracy evaluate $f(k) = k$.

   (a) Draw a graph of the functions $F(x) = x^2$ and $G(x) = 2^x$. Your graph should show three points of intersection, two in Quadrant I (which you should be able to identify exactly), and one in QII.

(b) Take the square root of both sides of the equation $2^x = x^2$ to get $x = \sqrt{2^x}$ or $x = -\sqrt{2^x}$. Iterate $F_1(x) = \sqrt{2^x}$, starting with some positive initial value. What solution on the graph does your calculator appear to indicate? Iterate $F_2(x) = -\sqrt{2^x}$, starting with a negative initial value. What solution on the graph does your calculator appear to indicate?

(c) Find another way to solve the equation $x^2 = 2^x$ for x, to get another function you can iterate to find the third intersection on your graph. (*Hint:* Take the natural logarithm of both sides.)

4. (a) The equation $x^{10} = 2^x$ also has three solutions, one with x negative, one with x near 1, and one with x near 60. Solve the equation for x in three different ways, much as in Exercise 3, and iterate each of the resulting functions to find the three solutions.

(b) Two of the solutions of the equation in part **(a)** can be shown quite easily as intersections of the graphs of $y = x^{10}$ and $y = 2^x$. To show the third solution, how large a piece of graph paper would you need? Assume a scale of 1 cm for each unit, so that you would need to have paper about 65 cm wide. How long would it need to be? The distance form Earth to the sun is about 1.5×10^{13} cm (93 million miles).

Develop Mastery

1. The number of bacteria in a culture doubles every 1.5 hours. If 4000 are present initially,
(a) How many will there be three hours later?
(b) Four hours later?
(c) How long does it take for the number to increase to 40,000?

2. If the number of bacteria in a sample increases from 1000 to 1500 in two hours, how long does it take for the number of bacteria **(a)** to double? **(b)** to triple?

3. The world population in 1968 was 3.5 billion; in 1992 it was 5.5 billion. Assume exponential growth.
(a) Predict the population in the year 2000.
(b) When will the population reach 7 billion?

4. Assuming an annual population increase of 1.5 percent since 1968 (when the world population was 3.5 billion)
(a) Show that n years after 1968, the population $P(n)$ is $(3.5)(1.015)^n$ billion.
(b) Determine the population for 1992. How does your calculation agree with the information in Exercise 3?

5. In 1960 the population of the United States was 180 million; in 1970 it was 200 million. Assume an exponential rate of growth and predict the population for the year 2000.

Exercises 6–12 Assume interest is compounded continuously and that all interest rates are annual.

6. Suppose $1000 is invested in an account that earns 8 percent interest.
(a) How much interest is in the account 10 years later?
(b) How long does it take the money to double?
(c) To triple?

7. Suppose $1000 invested in a savings account increases over three years to $1200. What rate of interest is being paid?

8. An investment of $800 in a savings certificate that pays 10 percent interest has grown to $2000. How many years ago was the certificate purchased?

9. An investment doubles in 8 years. What is the rate of interest?

10. How long does it take for an investment to double if the rate of interest is
(a) 8 percent? **(b)** 12 percent?
(c) r percent?

11. Suppose you invest $1000 in a savings account at 5 percent interest, and at the end of 6 years you use the accumulated total to purchase a savings certificate that earns 6 percent interest. What is the value of the savings certificate 6 years later?

12. An annuity pays 12 percent interest. What amount of money deposited today will yield $3000 in 8 years?

13. A radioactive isotope, radium-226, has a half-life of 1620 years. A sample contained 10 grams in 1900. How many grams will remain in the year
(a) 2000? **(b)** 3000?

14. Radioactive lead, lead-212, has a half-life of 11 days. How long will it take for 20 pounds of lead-212 to decay to 8 pounds?

15. Another isotope of lead, lead-210, has a half-life of 22 years. How much of a 10-pound sample would remain after 10 years?

16. Radioactive iodine-131 is a component of nuclear fallout.
(a) If 10 mg of iodine-131 decays to 8.4 mg in 2 days, what is the half-life of the isotope?
(b) In how many days does the 10 mg sample decay to 2 mg?

17. After two years, a sample of a radioactive isotope has decayed to 70 percent of the original amount. What is the half-life of the isotope?

18. A 12 mg sample of radioactive polonium decays to 7.26 mg in 100 days.
  (a) What is polonium's half-life?
  (b) How much of the 12 mg sample remains after six months (180 days)?

Exercises 19–22   Use the carbon dating information discussed in this section.

19. A piece of petrified wood contains 40 percent of its original amount of C^{14}. How old is it?

20. If the Dead Sea Scrolls contain about 80 percent of their original C^{14}, how old are they?

21. How old is a fossil skeleton that contains 85 percent as much C^{14} as a living person?

22. If the Piltdown cranium (the Historical Note, "Exponential Functions, Dating, and Fraud Detection") was found to contain 93 percent of the C^{14} found in a modern skeleton, what is the approximate age of the cranium?

23. A 1933 earthquake in Japan registered 8.9 on the Richter scale, the highest reading ever recorded. Compare its amplitude to that of the 1971 earthquake in San Fernando, California, which measured 6.5.

24. The famous San Francisco earthquake of 1906 registered 8.4 on the Richter scale. Compare its amplitude with that of the 1976 earthquake in Guatemala, which measured 7.9.

25. If an earthquake in Ethiopia had an amplitude 100 times larger than an earthquake that measured 5.7 on the Richter scale, what would the Ethiopian earthquake measure?

26. Example 5 contains a formula for the atmospheric pressure $P(h)$ (in g/cm^2) at an altitude of h km. If h is measured in miles and pressure is measured in lb/in^2, then the corresponding equation is $P(h) = 14.7e^{-0.19h}$.
  (a) Find the atmospheric pressure at an altitude of 25 miles.
  (b) At what altitude is the atmospheric pressure one-tenth of that at sea level?

27. Use the equation for atmospheric pressure in Example 5 to find the altitude at which the atmospheric pressure is 100 g/cm^2.

28. A satellite is powered by a radioactive isotope. The power output $P(t)$ (measured in watts) generated in t days is given by $P(t) = 50e^{-t/250}$.
  (a) How much power is available at the end of a year (365 days)?
  (b) What is the half-life of the power supply?

(c) If the equipment aboard the satellite requires 10 watts of power to operate, what is the operational life of the satellite?

29. The hydrogen ion concentration for a sample of human blood is found to be 4.5×10^{-8} moles per liter. Find the pH value of the sample. Is it acidic or basic?

30. Find the pH value for
  (a) vinegar, $[H^+] = 6.3 \times 10^{-4}$
  (b) milk, $[H^+] = 4 \times 10^{-7}$
  (c) water, $[H^+] = 5.0 \times 10^{-8}$
  (d) sulphuric acid, $[H^+] = 1$.

31. Oil is being pumped from a well. If we assume that production is proportional to the amount of oil left in the well, then it can be shown that the number of barrels of oil, $A(t)$, left in the well t years after pumping starts, is given by $A(t) = Ce^{-kt}$, where C and k are constants. When t is 0 it is estimated that the well holds 1 million barrels of oil, and after six years of pumping, 0.5 million barrels remain. It is not profitable to keep pumping when fewer than 50,000 barrels remain in the well. What is the total number of years during which pumping remains profitable?

32. The population of Taunton is growing exponentially at an annual rate of 5 percent.
  (a) Show that after t years the population increases from 13,000 to N (in thousands) given by $N = 13(1.05)^t$.
  (b) In how many years will the population double?
  (c) In how many years will the population triple?

33. *Looking Ahead to Calculus*   A 500 gallon tank of brine starts the day with 150 pounds of salt. Fresh water runs into the tank at the rate of 5 gallons per minute and the well-stirred mixture drains at the same rate. In calculus it can be shown that the number of pounds, $A(t)$, of salt still in the tank t minutes later is given by $A(t) = 150e^{-0.01t}$.
  (a) How many pounds of salt remain in the tank after 30 minutes?
  (b) How many minutes does it take to reduce the amount of salt in the tank to 50 pounds?

34. In Example 3 we developed an equation for the amount $A(t)$ of strontium-90 (half-life 29 years) left after t years, starting with an initial amount A_0: $A(t) = A_0e^{-0.0239t}$. Show that $A(t)$ is also given by $A(t) = A_0(2^{-t/29})$. (*Hint:* In Example 3 $k = \frac{\ln 2}{29}$, so $A(t) = A_0e^{-(t \ln 2)/29}$.)

35. A rumor is spreading about the safety of county drinking water. Suppose P people live in the county and $N(t)$ is the number of people who have not yet heard the rumor after t days. If the rate at which $N(t)$

decreases is proportional to the number of people who have not yet heard the rumor, then $N(t)$ is given by $N(t) = Pe^{-kt}$, where k is a constant to be determined from observed information. In Calaveras County, population 50,000, suppose 2000 people have heard the rumor after the first day (when t is 1).

(a) How many people will have heard the rumor after 10 days?

(b) After how many days will half of the population have heard the rumor?

36. Use the equation in Exercise 35. If 10 percent of a county population of 20,000 have heard the rumor after the first two days, then how many people will have heard the rumor after three additional days?

CHAPTER 4 REVIEW

Test Your Understanding

Determine the truth value (T or F). Give reasons for your conclusion.

1. $\ln x$ is positive for every positive x.

2. $\ln x^2$ is defined for every real number x.

3. $\ln 1 = e$.

4. $\ln e = 1$.

5. $(\ln x)^2 = 2(\ln x)$ for every $x > 0$.

6. If x and y are positive numbers, then $\ln(\frac{x}{y}) = \frac{\ln x}{\ln y}$.

7. $\frac{1}{2}(\ln x^2) = \ln x$ for every positive x.

8. For any real numbers x and y, $3^x + 3^y = 3^{x+y}$.

9. For any real number x, $e^{x+1} = e^x + e$.

10. For every real number x, $4^x = 2^{2x}$.

11. If $f(x) = 3^{x/2}$ and $g(x) = (\sqrt{3})^x$, then $f(x) = g(x)$ for every real number x.

12. For every real number x, e^{-x} is positive.

13. The domain of $\ln(x - 1)$ is $\{x \mid x > 0\}$.

14. The solution set for $e^{x-1} < 1$ is $\{x \mid x < 1\}$.

15. There is only one real number x that satisfies $\ln(x + 2)^2 = \ln(x^2 + 4)$.

16. If x is any number between 0 and 1, then $\ln x$ is negative.

17. The graph of $f(x) = e^x$ crosses the x-axis at $(0, 1)$.

18. $e^{-\ln x} = \frac{1}{x}$ for every positive number x.

19. There is no number x for which $e^{-x} = e^x$.

20. $\log(5 + 2) = \log 5 + \log 2$.

21. $\log 5 + \log 2 = 1$.

22. The solution set for $(\ln x)^2 = \ln x$ is the set $\{1, e\}$.

23. $e^0 = 0$.

24. $\log(\frac{1}{10}) = -1$.

25. For every $x \geq 0$, $2^{-x} \geq 3^{-x}$.

26. The formula $f(x) = (-3)^x$ does not define an exponential function.

27. For every real number x, $2^x \leq 3^x$.

28. $e^{\ln(-5)} = -5$.

29. The graph of $y = 1 + \ln x$ crosses the x-axis at $(\frac{1}{e}, 0)$.

30. The equation $\ln x + \ln(x + 1) = 0$ has no solutions.

31. $\ln x + \ln(x - 1) = \ln[x(x - 1)]$ when $x > 1$.

32. For every real number x, $2^x + 2^x = 2^{x+1}$.

33. If $\log_2 x = 3$, then $x = 8$.

34. (a) $2^0 = 1$ (b) $(-2)^0 = 1$
    (c) $0^{-2} = 0$ (d) $0^0 = 1$

35. There is no real number x for which $\ln x = -1$.

36. The formula $g(x) = (\sqrt{5} - 2)^x$ defines g as an exponential function.

37. The formula $g(x) = (2 - \sqrt{5})^x$ defines g as an exponential function.

38. The graph of $y = \ln(x + 2)$ crosses the x-axis at $(-1, 0)$.

39. $(x^2 - 1)^0 = 1$ for every real number x.

40. $\ln(-x)$ is undefined for any real number x.

41. The equation $e^{-x} + 1 = 0$ has no solution.

42. A root of $e^{-x} - 1 = 0$ is 0.

43. The function $f(x) = 2^{-x}$ is a decreasing function.

44. The graph of the function $f(x) = e^x + 1$ lies above the line $y = 1$.

45. The range of the natural exponential function is R.

46. The graph of every exponential function contains the point $(0, 1)$.

47. If $b > 1$, then $\log_b x$ is an increasing function.

48. (a) $\log_2 4 > \log_4 2$ (b) $(\log_2 4)(\log_4 2) = 1$

49. For every positive x, $\ln(-x) = -\ln x$.

50. For every positive x, $\ln(\frac{1}{x}) = \frac{1}{\ln x}$.

51. $\frac{\ln 5}{\ln 3} = \ln 5 - \ln 3$.

52. $\sqrt[3]{x}$ is a real number only for $x \geq 0$.

53. $\sqrt[4]{x}$ is a real number only for $x \geq 0$.

54. $-(3^x) = (-3)^x$ for every real number x.

55. To draw a graph of $y = e^{x+2}$, translate the graph of $y = e^x$ horizontally 2 units to the left.

56. If $f(x) = \frac{1}{1 + 2^x}$, then f is a decreasing function.

57. For every real number x, $\frac{3^x}{1 + 3^x}$ is a number between 0 and 1.

58. The graph of $y = \frac{3^{-x}}{1 + 3^{-x}}$ is the same as the graph of $y = \frac{1}{1 + 3^x}$.

Exercises 59–64 A graph is shown. Select from the following list the function corresponding to the graph.
(a) $f(x) = \ln x$ (b) $f(x) = \ln(x - 2)$
(c) $f(x) = \ln(x + 2)$ (d) $f(x) = \ln x + 1$
(e) $f(x) = e^{x+1}$ (f) $f(x) = 2^{-x} + 1$
(g) $f(x) = e^{\ln x}$ (h) $f(x) = \ln e^x$
(i) none of the above

Mastery Review

Exercises 1–9 Evaluate and give the result in exact form.

1. $5(5^{-1} + 5^{-2})$ **2.** $(49 \cdot 7^{-1})^{-1}$ **3.** $\log_3 \sqrt{27}$

4. $\ln \sqrt{e}$ **5.** $\ln(\log 10)$ **6.** $e^{-\ln 7}$

7. $10^{-2(\log 7)}$ **8.** $\log_3(\frac{3}{\sqrt{27}})$

9. $\log \sqrt{40} - \log 2$

Exercises 10–15 Give an approximation rounded off to three decimal places.

10. $\log 6$ **11.** $\ln 47$ **12.** $\log(\ln 5)$

13. $\log(e - 1)$ **14.** $e + e^{-1}$ **15.** e^π

16. (a) If $b = \sqrt{2}$ and
$$c = \frac{\sqrt{\sqrt{5} + 2} - \sqrt{\sqrt{5} - 2}}{\sqrt{\sqrt{5} - 1}},$$
use your calculator to get approximations for b and c.
(b) Is $b = c$? Justify your conclusion.

17. If $c = \frac{\sqrt{3}(\sqrt{2} + \sqrt{6})}{3 + \sqrt{3}}$
find a simpler expression for c. (*Hint:* First find c^2.)

Exercises 18–21 Evaluate $f(x)$ at the given values of x. Give the result rounded off to two decimal places.

18. $f(x) = xe^x$; $-1, \sqrt{2}$

19. $f(x) = x \ln(x - 1)$; $3, \sqrt{3}$

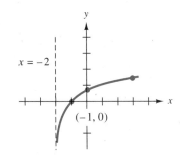

59.

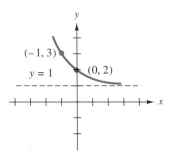

60.

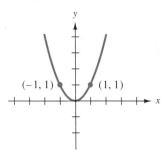

61.

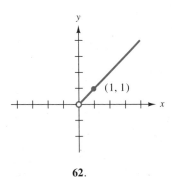

62.

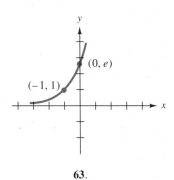

63.

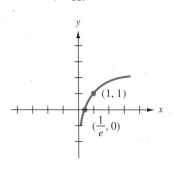

64.

20. $f(x) = \log_3 x; \quad 5, \sqrt{5}$

21. $f(x) = e^x - e^{-x}; \quad -1, \pi$

Exercises 22–30   Solve. Give the result in exact form.

22. $5^{2x+1} = \sqrt{5}$ **23.** $\log(2x + 1) = 1$

24. $\log_5(5^{x-1}) = 2$ **25.** $\log_7(2x - 1) = 1$

26. $9^x = 27^{1-2x}$ **27.** $\ln x + \ln(x + 1) = \ln 2$

28. $1 + \log x = 0$ **29.** $\ln x - \ln(x - 1) = 1$

30. $x + \ln e^x = 2$

Exercises 31–39   Solve. Give the result rounded off to two decimal places.

31. $\ln(2x + 1) = 1$ **32.** $e^x = 10^{1-x}$

33. $5^x = 3(2^x)$ **34.** $3^{x-3} = 4$

35. $3e^x - 4 = 0$ **36.** $\log x + \log(x - 1) = 1$

37. $\ln(x - e) + \ln(x - 1) = 1$

38. $e^x = \ln 2$ **39.** $e^{2x} + e^x - 2 = 0.$

Exercises 40–45   Determine the domain of f.

40. $f(x) = \ln(x - 2)$

41. $f(x) = \ln(x^2 - 2x)$

42. $f(x) = \ln e^{x-1}$

43. $f(x) = \ln(e^x - 1)$

44. $f(x) = \ln[x(x - 1)]$

45. $f(x) = \ln x + \ln(x - 1)$

Exercises 46–51   Draw a graph.

46. $y = \ln(x - 1)$ **47.** $y = 1 + \ln x$

48. $y = e^{-x}$ **49.** $y = 1 + e^{-x}$

50. $y = e^{\ln x}$ **51.** $y = x^2 e^{-\ln x}$

Exercises 52–55   Find the x-intercept point for the graph of f.

52. $f(x) = \ln x + \ln(x - 1)$

53. $f(x) = e^x - 2$

54. $f(x) = e^x - e^{-x} - 1$

55. $f(x) = \ln(2x - 4)$

56. Is there a real number x such that
    (a) $3^{-x} = 1$?   **(b)** $3^{-x} = -1$?
    (c) $e^x + 1 = 0$?   **(d)** $\ln(-e^{-x}) = 1$?
    Give reasons.

57. Is the graph of $y = \ln x + \ln(x - 1)$ the same as the graph of $y = \ln(x^2 - x)$?

58. From a graph of $y = 1 + \ln x$, find the x-intercept point, and the solution set for the inequality $1 + \ln x < 0$.

59. Show that $\frac{1}{\log_2 x} + \frac{1}{\log_3 x} + \frac{1}{\log_4 x} = \log_x 24$ for every positive number x not equal to 1.

60. A sum of $800 is invested in a savings account that earns 5 percent interest compounded continuously.
    (a) How much is in the account at the end of 10 years?
    (b) How long will it take for the account to reach $5000?

61. How much money should be invested in an annuity that earns 10 percent interest compounded continuously to have an investment worth $5000 in 8 years?

62. Radioactive iodine-131 has a half-life of 8 days. What percentage of a sample will remain after 3 days? After 20 days?

63. A fossil tree has 75 percent as much carbon-14 as a living tree. How old is the fossil tree?

64. The population of a city increases at the rate of 8 percent yearly. Assuming exponential growth, in how many years will the population double?

65. Two firecrackers produce a sound of 90 dB. What would be the loudness level of one alone?

66. The following table lists measured intensity values for some commonly heard sound sources. Complete the table by entering the corresponding loudness levels. Recall Equation 3 of Section 4.4, $I_0 = 10^{-12}$. Extended exposure to sounds of loudness levels exceeding 90 dB usually results in permanent ear damage and hearing loss.

Source of Sound	Intensity (w/m²)	Loudness Level (dB)
Whisper	1×10^{-10}	_____
Busy downtown traffic	1×10^{-5}	_____
Siren (at 30 meters)	1×10^{-2}	_____
Indoor rock concert	1	_____
Jet plane (at 30 meters)	100	_____

TRIGONOMETRIC AND CIRCULAR FUNCTIONS

In Chapter 2 we introduced the concept of functions. Chapters 3 and 4 explored important special functions, namely polynomial, exponential, and logarithmic functions. Equally important in both applications and theoretical mathematics are the trigonometric functions we introduce in this chapter.

Trigonometry (meaning "triangle measurement") has a long and remarkable history. Some of its roots and applications go back to antiquity, but it continues to find new applications through the space age and beyond. Trigonometry has provided tools for surveying and navigation for thousands of years. Today it is built into sophisticated devices that, for example, help satellites navigate among the planets or determine how fast the spreading ocean floor is pushing continents apart.

Partly because it has served so many different uses, trigonometry may appear somewhat schizophrenic in its presentation. Triangle and circle measurement commonly use degree measure, while all modern applications of trigonometry that describe periodic phenomena—from tides to orbiting satellites to the wave nature of quantum physics—require functions of real numbers, not degrees. In Section 5.1 we introduce both modes of angle measure because it is important to become familiar with both. In Section 5.2 the trigonometric functions are also defined in terms of both modes.

Angles and Units of Measure

. . . mathematics, just as all other scientific branches, is developed in the process of examining, verifying, and modifying itself.
  Yi Lin

I intended to take either physics or mathematics . . . and intended to become a high school teacher. I found myself very excited by a course called Physical Measurements. We kept measuring things to more and more decimal places by more and more ingenious methods.

Frederick Mosteller

The study of plane geometry considers all geometric figures as sets of points in a plane. An angle, for instance, is the union of two rays with a common endpoint. In trigonometry we talk about angles of a triangle as the union of two line segments that have a common endpoint. More critically, however, the *measure* of an angle involves the notion of rotation. For most purposes, we consider an angle as being generated by rotating a ray in the plane about its endpoint, from an initial position to a final position. The initial position is called the **initial side** and the final position is called the **terminal side** of the angle. The point about which the ray rotates is called the **vertex** of the angle. An angle is the union of two rays together with a rotation.

The measure of an angle is described by the amount of rotation. An angle has **positive measure** if the rotation is counterclockwise, and **negative measure** if the rotation is clockwise. For brevity, we say the angle is positive if its measure is positive. Figure 5.1 illustrates the labeling of angles and rotation. The curved arrow indicates the direction and amount of rotation. Angles A and B are positive while angle C is negative. The rotation in angle B is greater than one revolution.

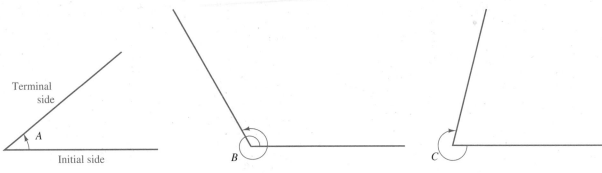

FIGURE 5.1

Units of Angular Measure

Your calculator operates in three modes, degrees, radians, and grads. The three modes are related by their measures of a complete revolution. One revolution is measured by 360 degrees, or 2π radians, or 400 grads. Grads are often used with the metric system because a right angle measures 100 grads. In this book we use only degree and radian measures.

Degree Measure   In geometry angles are most often measured in degrees, minutes, and seconds. An angle of 1 **degree,** written 1°, is $\frac{1}{360}$ of a complete rotation. More precise measurements involve either minutes and seconds or decimal fractions of a degree.

>   One degree is $\frac{1}{360}$ of a revolution.
>   One minute is $\frac{1}{60}$ of a degree.
>   One second is $\frac{1}{60}$ of a minute, or $\frac{1}{3600}$ of a degree.

For instance,

$$30°15' = 30° + \left(\frac{15}{60}\right)° = 30.25°$$

and

$$42°12'45'' = \left(42 + \frac{12}{60} + \frac{45}{3600}\right)° = 42.2125°.$$

Figure 5.2 illustrates several angles and their degree measures. Again for brevity, we write, for example, $A = 90°$ to denote "the measure of angle A is 90°."

EXAMPLE 1   Express 36°16'23" in decimal form and give the result as a decimal approximation rounded off to three decimal places.

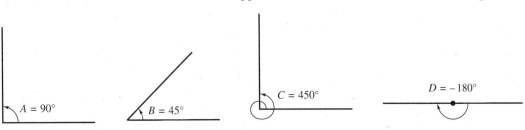

FIGURE 5.2

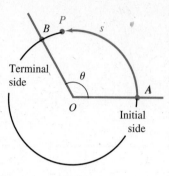

FIGURE 5.3

Directed arc length s is the distance P travels along the circle from A to B.

Solution

$$36°16'23'' = \left(36 + \frac{16}{60} + \frac{23}{3600} \right)° \approx 36.273° \quad \blacktriangle$$

EXAMPLE 2   Express 64.24° in degrees, minutes, and seconds.

Solution

First convert the decimal part, 0.24°, into minutes. Since 1° is 60′,

$$0.24° = (0.24)(60') = 14.4'.$$

Next convert the 0.4′ into seconds.

$$0.4' = (0.4)(60'') = 24''.$$

Therefore, 64.24° is 64°14′24″.   ▲

Radian Measure   The unit of angular measure of particular interest to us is the **radian.** Just as a degree is defined in relation to one complete revolution (measured by 360°), the radian measure of one revolution is **2π radians.**

To introduce the notion of radian measure of an angle θ of any size, let C be a circle of radius r with its center at the vertex of θ. Let A be the point where the initial side of the angle meets C and let B be the point where the terminal side of θ meets C (see Figure 5.3). The measure of θ is determined by the rotation of ray $\overrightarrow{OA}$ to the ray $\overrightarrow{OB}$. Let s be the corresponding distance that a point P travels along the circle from A to B. We call s the **directed arc length** associated with θ.

If the rotation is counterclockwise, then s is positive; if the rotation is clockwise, then s is negative. For a counterclockwise rotation of more than one revolution, the number s is greater than $2\pi r$ (the circumference of the circle). Thus s can be any real number (positive, negative, or zero). The radian measure of θ is defined as the ratio of s to r.

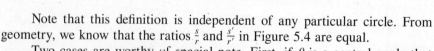

Definition: Radian Measure of an Angle

Suppose θ is any angle and C is a circle of radius r with its center at the vertex of θ. If s is the directed arc length associated with θ, then the radian measure of θ is $\frac{s}{r}$; that is,

$$\theta = \frac{s}{r}.$$

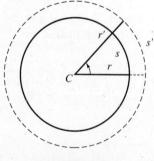

FIGURE 5.4

Note that this definition is independent of any particular circle. From geometry, we know that the ratios $\frac{s}{r}$ and $\frac{s'}{r'}$ in Figure 5.4 are equal.

Two cases are worthy of special note. First, if θ is a central angle that subtends an arc length equal to r, the length of the radius, then the radian measure of θ is equal to $\frac{r}{r}$, or 1. *An angle of 1 radian subtends an arc whose length is equal to the radius.* Second, one complete revolution subtends an arc

For Graphers 5.1

Exercises

1. *Looking Ahead to Calculus*   A sector with a central angle of x radians is cut out of a circular piece of tin of radius 12 inches and a cone is formed from the remaining piece, as described in Develop Mastery Exercise 41. Show that the volume of the cone is given by

$$V = 72\left(2 - \frac{x}{\pi}\right)^2 \sqrt{4\pi x - x^2}.$$

2. Since $0 < x < 2\pi$, evaluate V for several values of x. Use your values to choose an appropriate y range and draw a graph of $y = V$. Find the approximate value of x for which V is a maximum. What is the maximum volume?

3. Using calculus, we can show that the x-value in Exercise 2 giving a maximum volume is a root of the equation

$$3x^2 - 12\pi x + 4\pi^2 = 0.$$

Does your answer in Exercise 2 satisfy the equation?

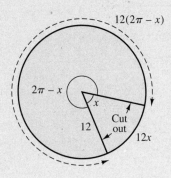

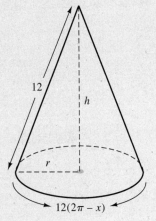

of length $2\pi r$. Thus if θ is one revolution, then the radian measure of θ is $\frac{2\pi r}{r}$, or 2π.

Observe that radian measure involves the ratio of two lengths; thus radian measure is simply a real number. For example, suppose θ is an angle such that in a circle of radius 2 centimeters, the length of the arc subtended by θ is 2.6 centimeters (see Figure 5.5). Then the measure of θ in radians is given by

$$\theta = \frac{s}{r} = \frac{2.6 \text{ centimeters}}{2 \text{ centimeters}} = 1.3.$$

The units of length cancel so $\theta = 1.3$. We can, if desired, emphasize the radian measure by writing $\theta = 1.3$ radians as shorthand for "the radian measure of θ is 1.3." Our normal convention will be that *radians* need not be written. When the measure of an angle is given as a real number with no units specified, it will be understood that the unit of measure is radians.

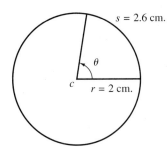

FIGURE 5.5

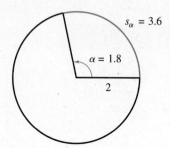

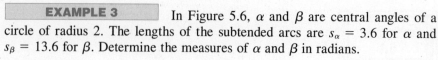

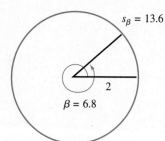

FIGURE 5.6

In Figure 5.6, α and β are central angles of a circle of radius 2. The lengths of the subtended arcs are $s_\alpha = 3.6$ for α and $s_\beta = 13.6$ for β. Determine the measures of α and β in radians.

Solution

$$\alpha = \frac{s_\alpha}{r} = \frac{3.6}{2} = 1.8$$

The measure of α is 1.8 radians.

$$\beta = \frac{s_\beta}{r} = \frac{13.6}{2} = 6.8$$

The measure of β is 6.8 radians. The measure of β is greater than one revolution ($2\pi \approx 6.28$), as the arrow in the figure indicates.   ▲

Degree–Radian Relationships

In many cases we may have the measure of an angle in degrees when we need the radian measure, or vice versa. This requires a technique for conversion. Since one complete rotation is measured by either $360°$ or 2π radians, we have the necessary equivalence. The basic relationship $360° = 2\pi$ radians connects degree and radian measures:

$$180° = \pi \text{ radians.} \tag{1}$$

From Equation 1,

$$1° = \frac{\pi}{180} \text{ radians} \qquad \text{or} \qquad 1° \approx 0.017453 \text{ radians,}$$

$$1 \text{ radian} = \left(\frac{180}{\pi}\right)° \qquad \text{or} \qquad 1 \text{ radian} \approx 57.296°.$$

See Figure 5.7 for equivalent measures of selected angles.

To sum up the procedure for conversion between modes:

To convert radians to degrees, multiply by $\frac{180}{\pi}$; to convert degrees to radians, multiply by $\frac{\pi}{180}$.

Most of us are more familiar with degree measure than with radian measure. Since radian measure is so important in calculus, you should begin to get accustomed to thinking in radians. As a start, you should have some idea of the size of an angle of 1 radian, about $57.296°$. Thus, when you encounter an angle

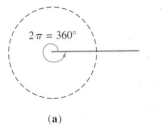

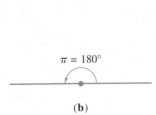

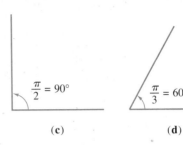

FIGURE 5.7

Degree–radian measure for some familiar angles

of 1 radian, think "about 57°," (or just a little less than 60°). Similarly, an angle of 3 radians is slightly less than π radians, or very nearly a straight angle. Table 5.1 gives some key reference angles that may help you become more familiar with radian measure.

EXAMPLE 4   Draw a diagram that shows the angle and then find the corresponding radian measure. Give the result both in exact form and as a decimal approximation rounded off to two decimal places.

$$\textbf{(a) } \alpha = 210° \qquad \textbf{(b) } \beta = 585° \qquad \textbf{(c) } \gamma = -150°$$

Solution

Diagrams in Figure 5.8 show the angles. To convert from degree measure to radian measure, multiply by $\frac{\pi}{180}$.

(a) $\alpha = 210° = 210(\frac{\pi}{180}) = \frac{7\pi}{6} \approx 3.67$

(b) $\beta = 585° = 585(\frac{\pi}{180}) = \frac{13\pi}{4} \approx 10.21$

(c) $\gamma = -150° = -150(\frac{\pi}{180}) = -\frac{5\pi}{6} \approx -2.62$ ▲

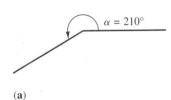

(a)

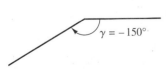

(b)

(c)

FIGURE 5.8

TABLE 5.1   Degree–Radian Equivalence

Degrees	Radians	Radian Approximations
30°	$\frac{\pi}{6}$	0.52
45°	$\frac{\pi}{4}$	0.79
60°	$\frac{\pi}{3}$	1.05
90°	$\frac{\pi}{2}$	1.57
120°	$\frac{2\pi}{3}$	2.09
135°	$\frac{3\pi}{4}$	2.36
180°	π	3.14
270°	$\frac{3\pi}{2}$	4.71

If the radian measure of θ is 2.47, find its degree measure rounded off to one decimal place and then to the nearest minute.

Strategy: To get the degree measure, multiply by $\frac{180}{\pi}$. Convert the decimal part of a degree to minutes by multiplying by 60.

Solution

Follow the strategy.

$$2.47 \text{ radians} = 2.47\left(\frac{180}{\pi}\right)^{\circ} \approx 141.5205754^{\circ}.$$

Rounded off to one decimal place, 2.47 radians $\approx 141.5^{\circ}$; to the nearest minute, 2.47 radians $\approx 141^{\circ}31'$. Hence, θ is approximately $141^{\circ}31'$. ▲

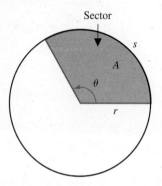

Sector

A

θ

s

r

FIGURE 5.9

Applications of Radian Measure: Arc Length and Area

In a circle a given central angle between 0 and 2π determines a portion of the circle called a **sector,** as indicated by the shaded region shown in Figure 5.9. For the sector shown in the figure with central angle θ, suppose the length of the subtended arc is s and the area of the sector is A. The ratios of θ, s, and A to the respective measures 2π, $2\pi r$, and πr^2 for the entire circle are equal, that is,

$$\frac{\theta}{2\pi} = \frac{s}{2\pi r}, \qquad \frac{\theta}{2\pi} = \frac{A}{\pi r^2}, \qquad \frac{s}{2\pi r} = \frac{A}{\pi r^2}.$$

Solving for s and A,

$$s = r\theta, \qquad A = \frac{1}{2}r^2\,\theta, \qquad A = \frac{1}{2}rs.$$

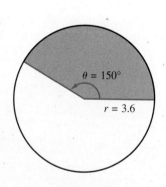

$\theta = 150^{\circ}$

$r = 3.6$

FIGURE 5.10

Arc Length and the Area of a Circular Sector

Suppose θ is a central angle of a circle of radius r. Let s denote the length of the subtended arc and let A denote the area of the sector. If θ is measured in radians, then s and A are given by

$$s = r\theta \qquad\qquad\qquad (2)$$

$$A = \tfrac{1}{2}r^2\,\theta \qquad A = \tfrac{1}{2}rs \qquad (3)$$

The radius of a circle is 3.6 centimeters and the central angle of a circular sector is 150°. Draw a diagram to show the sector and find the arc length and the area of the sector.

Strategy: Equations 2 and 3 require θ to be in radians. First convert 150° to radians and then use Equations 2 and 3.

Solution

The sector is the shaded region in Figure 5.10. Following the strategy,

$$\theta = 150^{\circ} = 150\left(\frac{\pi}{180}\right) = \frac{5\pi}{6}.$$

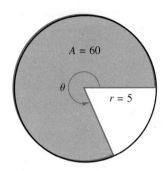

FIGURE 5.11

Substitute 3.6 for r and $\frac{5\pi}{6}$ for θ in Equations 2 and 3

$$s = 3.6\left(\frac{5\pi}{6}\right) = 3\pi \approx 9.42,$$

$$A = \tfrac{1}{2}(3.6)^2\left(\frac{5\pi}{6}\right) = 5.4\pi \approx 16.96.$$

Round off to two significant digits to get an arc length of 9.4 cm and an area of 17 cm². ▲

EXAMPLE 7　　The radius of a circular sector is 5.0 cm and its area is 60 cm². Draw a diagram to show the sector and find the central angle and the arc length.

Solution

The sector is shown in Figure 5.11. In Equations 2 and 3 replace r by 5.0 and A by 60:

$$s = 5\theta \quad \text{and} \quad 60 = \tfrac{1}{2} \cdot 5 \cdot s.$$

From the second equation, $s = 24$, so the arc length is 24 cm. Substitute 24 for s in the first equation to get $\theta = \frac{24}{5}$, or $\theta = 4.8$. Hence the central angle is 4.8 radians, or slightly greater than 270°, as shown in Figure 5.11. ▲

EXAMPLE 8　　Assume that the moon travels around the Earth in a circular path of radius 240,000 miles and that it makes a complete revolution once every 28 days. Find the distance traveled by the moon in 10 days along its path around the Earth.

Strategy: In 10 days the moon goes through a fraction, $\frac{10}{28}$, of one revolution. Draw a diagram to show the circular path of the moon and find the central angle that corresponds to $\frac{10}{28}$ of a revolution.

Solution

Follow the strategy. Draw a diagram to show the length of the arc that corresponds to $\frac{5}{14}$ (about $\frac{1}{3}$) of a revolution (see Figure 5.12). For the radian measure of θ,

$$\theta = \frac{10}{28}(2\pi) = \frac{5\pi}{7} \approx 2.24.$$

Using Equation 2,

$$s = 240,000\left(\frac{5\pi}{7}\right) \approx 540,000 \text{ miles.}$$

The moon travels 540,000 miles in its rotation about the Earth in 10 days. We round off two significant digits to be consistent with the accuracy of the given data. ▲

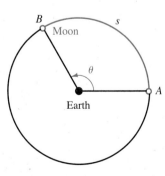

FIGURE 5.12

Linear and Angular Speed

There are two kinds of speeds associated with rotational motion. To introduce the basic ideas, consider an example. Suppose a bicycle wheel is rotating at a constant rate of 40 revolutions per minute (40 rpm). One measure of speed,

MEASUREMENT OF THE CIRCUMFERENCE OF THE EARTH

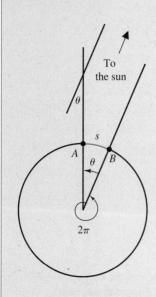

One of the earliest and most dramatic applications of trigonometry was made by Eratosthenes a little before 200 B.C. As his name suggests, Eratosthenes was of Greek descent, but he spent his life in Egypt during the reign of Ptolemy II and later became the head of the greatest scientific library in the ancient world at Alexandria.

Travelers reported that at Syene (the modern city Aswan), the sun cast no shadow at noon on the summer solstice (the longest day of the year). Eratosthenes reasoned, then, that at Syene on that date, the sun's rays were coming directly toward the center of the Earth. Alexandria was supposed to be directly north of Syene. By measuring the angle of the sun's rays at Alexandria at noon on the same day, Eratosthenes realized that he could use geometric relationships to find the circumference of the Earth.

In the diagram, A represents Alexandria and B, Syene. The ratio of the distance from A to B, the arc length s, to the entire circumference C must equal the ratio of angle θ to the entire central angle (a complete revolution). Symbolically,

$$\frac{s}{C} = \frac{\theta}{\text{One revolution}}$$

By the best estimates of the day, the distance from Alexandria to Syene was 5000 stadia, a distance estimated from travel by camel caravans by surveyors trained to count paces of constant length. Eratosthenes measured angle θ at Alexandria to be $\frac{1}{50}$ of a complete revolution, leading to the equation,

$$\frac{5000}{C} = \frac{1}{50},$$

from which he calculated the circumference of the earth to be

$$C = 50 \cdot 5000 = 250{,}000 \text{ stadia.}$$

Comparison with modern measurements is difficult because the measuring unit, the stadium, varied in size, but Eratosthenes' estimate would compare to something near 24,000 miles. Several compensating errors probably contributed to the truly remarkable accuracy of his figure, but the real genius of Eratosthenes lay in his analysis of the problem and his recognition that geometric figures can tell us something about the nature of the world that we can learn in no other way.

angular speed, gives the rate of rotation, frequently denoted by the Greek letter ω. The bicycle wheel's angular speed is 40 rpm by one measure. Since one revolution is equivalent to 2π radians, the angular speed can also be expressed as $40(2\pi)$ or 80π radians per minute, or 4800π radians per hour.

Suppose the diameter of the bicycle wheel is 26.4 inches, so that its radius r is 13.2 inches or 1.1 feet. In 1 minute a point on the circumference turns through an angle θ equal to 80π radians, and the distance s traveled by point on

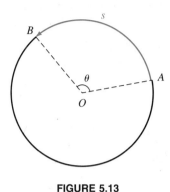

FIGURE 5.13

the circumference in 1 minute is

$$s = r\theta = (1.1)(80\pi) = 88\pi.$$

Hence, the point travels 88π feet in 1 minute. The **linear speed** of a point on the circumference is $88 \frac{\text{ft}}{\text{min}}$.

Relationship Between Linear and Angular Speeds For a particle moving in a circular path at a uniform rate, the linear and angular speeds are obviously related. Suppose that such a particle P moves from point A to point B along a circle of radius r, as indicated in Figure 5.13. If the central angle AOB is θ, the distance (arc length) from A to B is s, and P moves from A to B in time t, then the linear and angular speeds are

$$v = \frac{s}{t} \quad \text{and} \quad \omega = \frac{\theta}{t}.$$

Since $s = r\theta$ (where θ is measured in radians),

$$v = \frac{s}{t} = \frac{r\theta}{t} = r\left(\frac{\theta}{t}\right) = r\omega$$

Linear and Angular Speed Relationship

For a particle moving in a circular path of radius r at a uniform rate, the linear speed v and angular speed ω are related by the equation

$$v = r\omega. \tag{4}$$

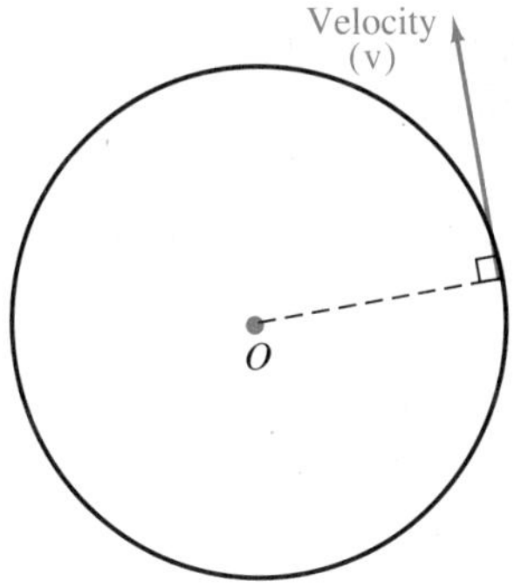

FIGURE 5.14

Linear speed and angular speed are sometimes called linear *velocity* and angular *velocity,* but we reserve the term *velocity* for directed speeds. Velocity is a vector quantity, meaning that it has both a magnitude and a direction (see Section 7.5). In uniform circular motion, the magnitude of the linear velocity vector is the linear speed defined above, in a direction tangent to the circular path of motion, as indicated by the arrow in Figure 5.14.

EXAMPLE 9 The wheel of a grindstone with a radius of 8 inches is rotating at 300 rpm. **(a)** Find the angular speed in radians per second. **(b)** Find the linear speed of a point on the circumference of the wheel in feet per second. **(c)** For a certain job, it is desirable to have the linear speed of the grinding edge of the wheel at 30 ft/sec. What change in angular speed (in revolutions per minute) is required?

Strategy: First convert r and ω to units that are consistent with feet per second.

Solution

Given that r is 8 inches and ω is 300 rpm, follow the strategy and express r and ω in units of feet and seconds.

$$r = 8 \text{ in} \times \left(\frac{1 \text{ ft}}{12 \text{ in}}\right) = \frac{2}{3} \text{ ft}$$

and $\quad \omega = \dfrac{300 \text{ rev}}{\text{min}} \times \left(\dfrac{2\pi \text{ rad}}{\text{rev}}\right) \times \left(\dfrac{1 \text{ min}}{60 \text{ sec}}\right) = 10\pi$ rad/sec

(a) The angular speed is $10\pi \frac{\text{rad}}{\text{sec}}$.

(b) Using Equation 4,

$$v = r\omega = \left(\dfrac{2}{3}\right)(10\pi) = \dfrac{20\pi}{3} \approx 20.9.$$

Hence, the linear speed of a point on the grinding edge of the wheel is 20.9 ft/sec.

(c) For v to be $30 \frac{\text{ft}}{\text{sec}}$, specify $r\omega = 30$, or

$$\omega = \dfrac{30}{r} = \dfrac{30}{\frac{2}{3}} = 45 \text{ rad/sec}.$$

To express ω in revolutions per minute, convert radians per second.

$$\omega = 45 \,\dfrac{\text{rad}}{\text{sec}} \times \left(\dfrac{1 \text{ rev}}{2\pi \text{ rad}}\right) \times \left(\dfrac{60 \text{ sec}}{\text{min}}\right) = \dfrac{1350 \text{ rev}}{\pi \text{ min}} \approx 430 \text{ rpm}$$

For a linear speed of 30 ft/sec, the wheel speed must increase to about 430 rpm, almost half again as fast as the present angular speed. ▲

Does This Answer Make Sense?   Always ask yourself if a solution is reasonable and make an independent check or a simple estimate, if possible. In Example 9, for instance, we found in part **(b)** that when ω is 300 rpm, the speed is near 20 ft/sec. Therefore, in part **(c)** an angular speed of 30 ft/sec should correspond to about $\frac{3}{2}$ of 300 rpm, giving an estimate of about 450 rpm. The result of 430 rpm in part **(c)** is entirely reasonable.

EXERCISES 5.1

Check Your Understanding

Exercises 1–5   True or False. Give reasons for your conclusion.

1. An angle of $\frac{22}{7}$ radians is equal to an angle of 180°.

2. An angle of 180° is greater than an angle of 3.16 radians.

3. The sector of a circle with a central angle of 1 radian and radius r cm has an area of $\frac{1}{2}r^2$ cm².

4. If the central angle θ of a circle measures 1 radian, then the length of the arc subtended by θ is equal to the length of the radius.

5. Assume that the planets travel in circular orbits about the sun. If the planet Venus takes 225 days for one revolution about the sun and the Earth takes 365 days, then the angular speed of Venus is less than the angular speed of the Earth.

Exercises 6–10   Complete the sentence by selecting from the list below *all choices* that make the statement true.

(a) 1 radian   (b) $\frac{\pi}{4}$ radians   (c) 60°
(d) 0.5 radians   (e) 120°   (f) 30π rad/min
(g) $\left(\frac{15}{2\pi}\right)$ rad/min   (h) 0.5π rad/sec

6. An angle of 45° is equal to an angle of _____ .

7. An angle of $\frac{2\pi}{3}$ radians is equal to angle of _____ .

8. An angle of 58° is greater than an angle of _____ .

9. The central angle of a circular sector with an arc length of 58 cm and a radius of 50 cm is greater than _____ .

10. An angular speed of 15 rpm is equal to _____ .

Explore and Discover

Exercises 1–4 For the following exercises, consider a satellite in circular polar orbit (passing over both the North and South Poles) at an altitude of 140 miles above the earth. It completes an orbit every 150 minutes. If classroom circumstances allow, it may be helpful to use some visual aids to set up these exercises. One student can rotate a globe slowly (which way does the globe turn?) while another student indicates the orbit of the satellite in a vertical plane.

1. Since the earth rotates on its axis once every 24 hours, through what angle does the earth rotate while the satellite completes one orbit?

2. Suppose that the satellite passes over Washington D.C. in one orbit. Assuming an average of $15°$ $(= \frac{360°}{24})$ per time zone, about where will it cross the United States on its next orbit after passing over Washington D.C.? If you do not have a globe with time zones indicated, a telephone directory will do.

3. Reread the introduction to Section 1.1 and determine the approximate distance of the satellite from an observer when it first becomes visible over the horizon.

4. Write a brief essay to explain why a satellite in a south–north polar orbit does not appear to a ground observer to be flying due north.

5. Develop Mastery Exercise 53 shows how a paddle wheel might be used to determine the speed of the current of a river. What other methods might be used to determine current speed? Write a paragraph to describe another method that might be used to find current speed as a check on the paddle wheel method.

Develop Mastery

Unless otherwise specified, results given as decimal approximations should be rounded off to the number of significant digits consistent with the given data.

Exercises 1–4 Draw a diagram to show the angle. Include a curved arrow to indicate the amount and direction of rotation from the initial side to the terminal side.

1. (a) $A = 240°$ (b) $B = 720°$ (c) $C = -210°$

2. (a) $A = 540°$ (b) $B = -135°$ (c) $C = 67°30'$

3. (a) $A = \frac{2\pi}{3}$ (b) $B = -\frac{7\pi}{4}$ (c) $C = 1.8$

4. (a) $A = \frac{5\pi}{3}$ (b) $B = -3\pi$ (c) $C = -2.36$

Exercises 5–6 Sketch an angle θ that satisfies the inequality. Include a curved arrow and also illustrate the range of position for the terminal side with dashed rays.

5. (a) $\frac{\pi}{2} < \theta < \pi$ (b) $-\pi < \theta < -\frac{\pi}{2}$
   (c) $1.7 < \theta < 2.5$

6. (a) $\frac{3\pi}{4} < \theta < \pi$ (b) $-\frac{5\pi}{5} < \theta < -\pi$
   (c) $0.79 < \theta < 1.05$

Exercises 7–8 Express the angle as a decimal number of degrees rounded off to three decimal places.

7. (a) $23°38'$ (b) $143°16'23''$ (c) $-95°31'$

8. (a) $57°34'$ (b) $241°15'51''$ (c) $-73°43'$

Exercises 9–10 Find the radian measure of the angle and give the result in both exact form (involving the number π) and decimal form rounded off to two decimal places.

9. (a) $60°$ (b) $330°$ (c) $22°30'$ (d) $105°$

10. (a) $90°$ (b) $450°$ (c) $67°30'$ (d) $-165°$

Exercises 11–12 Express the angle in decimal degree form, rounded off, if necessary, to one decimal place.

11. (a) $\frac{2\pi}{3}$ (b) $\frac{5\pi}{12}$ (c) 4π (d) 3.6

12. (a) $\frac{7\pi}{4}$ (b) $\frac{11\pi}{12}$ (c) -5π (d) 5.4

Exercises 13–14 Complete the tables by entering the equivalent angle measure (in exact form, using π when necessary) in each blank space.

13.

	(a)	(b)	(c)	(d)
Degrees	$45°$	_____	$135°$	_____
Radians	_____	$\frac{\pi}{3}$	_____	$\frac{7\pi}{12}$

14.

	(a)	(b)	(c)	(d)
Degrees	$195°$	_____	$375°$	_____
Radians	_____	$\frac{7\pi}{4}$	_____	$\frac{11\pi}{6}$

Exercises 15–18 Order angles α, β, and γ from smallest to largest (as, for example, $\alpha < \gamma < \beta$).

15. $\alpha = 47°24'$, $\beta = 47.48°$, $\gamma = 0.824$

16. $\alpha = 154°35'$, $\beta = 154.32°$, $\gamma = 2.705$

17. $\alpha = \frac{22}{7}$, $\beta = \frac{355}{113}$, $\gamma = \pi$

18. $\alpha = 120°36'$, $\beta = 120.53°$, $\gamma = \frac{21}{10}$

Exercises 19–22 Two of the three angles A, B, and C of a triangle are given. Find the third angle. Remember that the sum of the three angles of any triangle is equal to $180°$ (or π).

19. $A = 58°, B = 73°$ **20.** $B = 37°41', C = 84°37'$

21. $A = \frac{\pi}{4}, C = \frac{5\pi}{12}$ **22.** $A = \frac{2\pi}{3}, B = \frac{\pi}{15}$

Exercises 23–28   The radius r and the central angle θ of a circular sector are given. Draw a diagram that shows the sector and determine **(a)** the arc length s and **(b)** the area A for the sector.

23. $r = 24, \theta = 30°$ **24.** $r = 32.1, \theta = 96.3°$

25. $r = 164, \theta = 256°$ **26.** $r = 47, \theta = \frac{3\pi}{5}$

27. $r = 36, \theta = 4.3$ **28.** $r = 16.2, \theta = \frac{7\pi}{8}$

Exercises 29–30   Each column contains information about a circular sector. Complete the table.

29.

	(a)	**(b)**	**(c)**	**(d)**
r	2.5	5.7	___	15
θ	0.60	___ (rad)	48°	___ (deg)
s		1.5	7.5	56
A				

30.

	(a)	**(b)**	**(c)**	**(d)**
r	6.3	14.3	___	___
θ	1.2	___ (rad)	65°	___ (deg)
s		31.5	18	56
A				340

31. The radius of a circular sector is 12.5 centimeters and its area is 182 square centimeters. Find the central angle **(a)** in radians and **(b)** in degrees.

32. What is the radius of a circular sector with central angle 37.5° and area 6.80 square feet?

33. Assume that the Earth travels a circular orbit of radius 93 million miles about the sun and that it takes 365 days to complete an orbit. **(a)** Through what angle (in radians) will the radial line from the sun to the Earth sweep in 73 days? **(b)** How far does the Earth travel in its orbit about the sun in 73 days?

34. The diameter of a bicycle wheel is 26 inches. Through what angle does a spoke of the wheel rotate when the bicycle moves forward 24 feet? Give your result in radians to two significant digits.

35. What is the measure in degrees of the smaller angle between the hour and minute hands of a clock **(a)** At 2:30? **(b)** At 2:45?

36. At what times to the nearest tenth of a minute between 1:00 and 2:00 is the smaller angle between the hour and minute hands 15°?

37. The minute hand of a clock is 6 inches long. **(a)** How far does the tip of the hand travel in 15 minutes? **(b)** How far does the tip of the hand travel between 8:00 A.M. and 4:15 P.M. of the same day?

38. **(a)** What is the linear speed (in inches per hour) of the tip of the minute hand in Exercise 37? **(b)** What is the linear speed of a point 1 inch from the tip of the minute hand?

39. What is the angular speed in radians per minute of **(a)** the hour hand of a clock? **(b)** the minute hand?

40. A nautical mile is the length of an arc of a great circle subtended on the surface of the Earth by an angle of one minute (1') at the center of the Earth. Assuming that the Earth is a sphere of radius 3960 miles, a nautical mile is equal to how many ordinary miles (5280 ft)?

41. A circular sector with central angle 90° is cut out of a circular piece of tin of radius 15 inches. The edges of the remaining piece are seamed together to form a cone. Find the radius of the base and the volume of the cone. See the diagram. (The volume of a cone is $V = \frac{\pi r^2 h}{3}$.)

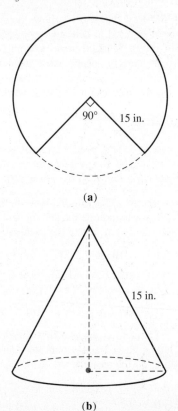

90°   15 in.

(a)

15 in.

(b)

42. Repeat Exercise 41, reducing the central angle of the sector cut out of the piece of tin to 60°.

43. A circular piece of tin of radius 12 inches is cut into three equal sectors, each of which is then formed into a cone. **(a)** What is the height of each cone? **(b)** What is the volume of each cone?

44. In the diagram A is the center of the circle. Find in exact form **(a)** the area of $\triangle ABC$, **(b)** the area of the circular sector, **(c)** the area of the shaded region.

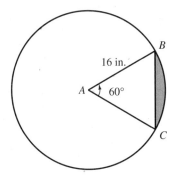

45. In the diagram C is the center and AD is a diameter of the circle with radius 24 cm. $\angle BCD$ measures 60°. Find in exact form the area of **(a)** $\triangle ABC$, **(b)** circular sector BCD, **(c)** the shaded region.

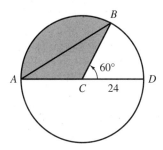

46. In the diagram A is the center of the circle of radius 4.8 cm and line BC is tangent to the circle at C. $\angle BAC$ measures 45°. Find the area of the shaded region in exact form.

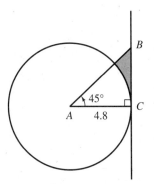

47. A satellite travels in a circular orbit 140 miles above the surface of the Earth. It makes one complete revolution every 150 minutes. **(a)** What is its angular speed in revolutions per hour and in radians per hour? **(b)** What is its linear speed? Assume that the radius of the Earth is 3960 miles.

48. The face of a windmill is 4.0 meters in diameter and a wind is causing it to rotate at 30 rev/min. What is the linear speed of the tip of one of the blades (in meters per minute)?

49. Assume that the moon follows a circular orbit about the Earth with a radius of 239,000 miles and that one revolution takes 27.3 days. Find the linear speed (in miles per hour) of the moon in its orbit about the Earth.

50. Assume that the Earth travels about the sun in a circular orbit with a radius of 93 million miles and that one revolution takes 365 days. Find the linear speed (in miles per hour) of the Earth in its orbit about the sun.

51. Two pulleys, one with a radius of 4 inches and the other with a radius of 12 inches, are connected by a belt (see the diagram). If the smaller pulley is being driven by a motor at 8 rev/min, **(a)** determine the angular speed of the larger pulley (in revolutions per minute). **(b)** What is the linear speed of a point on the belt?

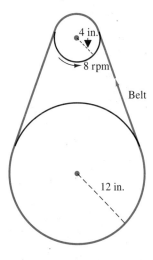

52. The diameter of a bicycle wheel is 26 inches. When the bicycle moves at a speed of 30 mph, determine the angular speed of the wheel in revolutions per minute.

53. To measure the approximate speed of the current of a river, a circular paddle wheel with a radius of 3 feet is lowered into the water just far enough to cause it to rotate. If the wheel rotates at a speed of 12 rev/min, what is the speed of the current in miles per hour?

54. The blade of a rotary lawnmower is 34 cm long and rotates at 31 rad/sec. (a) What is the blade's angular speed in revolutions per minute? (b) What is the linear speed (in kilometers per hour) of the tip of the blade?

55. A record was set in rope turning with 49,299 turns in 5 hours and 33 minutes. (a) What is the average angular speed of the rope in revolutions per minute? (b) Assuming that the rope forms an arc so that its midpoint travels in a circular path of radius 3.5 feet, what is the average linear speed (in feet per minute) of the midpoint of the rope? (c) How far (in miles) did the midpoint travel during the record-setting turning session?

SECTION 5.2   Trigonometric Functions and the Unit Circle

Since Plato, it has not been uncommon to regard mathematics as composed of divine, eternal, perfect, absolute, certain, infallible, immutable, necessary, a priori, exact, and self-evident truths or ideal forms existing in their own world.
          W. G. Holladay

Somehow I obtained some popular books on mathematics, and about a year later I was helping my brother and sisters with their math homework. When Sylvia started college and was taking trigonometry, she would ask me for help. I would read the section and then figure out how to do the problems.

          Paul Cohen

Chapter 3 was devoted to polynomial functions and Chapter 4 to exponential and logarithmic functions. Now we introduce a third major class of functions called the **trigonometric functions.** Evidence of the importance of trigonometric functions appears on scientific calculators, which have keys that allow evaluation of trigonometric functions and their inverses. Similarly, computer programming languages have built-in capabilities to handle the same functions.

Historically, trigonometry was developed to solve problems in navigation, agriculture, and surveying using triangles. The very word *trigonometry* refers to triangle measurement. The use of triangles is still vitally important throughout physics, engineering, and other disciplines, but what one author called the "ingenious and enduring usefulness" of trigonometric functions depends on much broader applications, many of which have no relation at all to triangles. Analysis of wave motion in electronics, engineering, and quantum mechanics requires trigonometric functions as does the study of economic cycles and other cyclical phenomena.

Leonhard Euler is responsible for the modern concept of a function, which he introduced in his book *Introductio in Analysin Infinitorum* (1748). His ideas have continued to gain importance through the centuries, and we define the trigonometric functions in much the same was as Euler did, by the use of the unit circle.

The Unit Circle
The circle with its center at the origin and a radius of 1 is called the **unit circle.** Its equation is

$$x^2 + y^2 = 1.$$

We define trigonometric functions in terms of coordinates of points on the unit circle. The point $A(1, 0)$ is called the **initial point.** Starting at point A, think

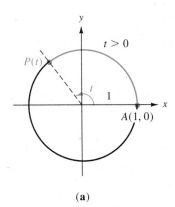

(a)

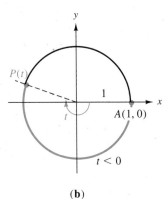

(b)

FIGURE 5.15

of a point moving around the unit circle along an arc of length t. $P(t)$ is called the **terminal position point.** Each real number t determines $P(t)$ uniquely according to the following.

Let t be any given real number.

If $t > 0$, then $P(t)$ is the point reached by moving counterclockwise on the unit circle a distance of t units from $A(1, 0)$.

If $t < 0$, then $P(t)$ is the point reached by moving clockwise along the unit circle a distance of $-t$ units from $A(1, 0)$.

If $t = 0$, then $P(t)$ is point $A(1, 0)$.

Point $P(t)$ can be located in either of two ways. Suppose θ is an angle with its vertex at the origin, the positive x-axis as its initial side and its terminal side passing through the point $P(t)$. For t between 0 and 2π we have a circular sector with central angle θ, where r is 1, and s is t. Using Equation (2) of Section 5.1, $s = r\theta$, and substituting t for s and 1 for r, $t = 1 \cdot \theta$, or $\theta = t$ radians. Therefore, if we draw an angle of t radians, then $P(t)$ is the point on the unit circle on the terminal side of the angle as illustrated in Figure 5.15a.

Extending this idea to describe central angles of any size or direction of rotation, for any real number t there is a corresponding central angle that has a measure of t radians. Figure 5.15b illustrates the case where t is negative and the corresponding central angle is a clockwise rotation.

> The point $P(t)$ on the unit circle is located either by a directed arc of length t from $A(1, 0)$, or as the point on the terminal side of a central angle of t radians.

Since the distance around the unit circle is the circumference of the circle, which is 2π, we can easily identify the coordinates of $P(t)$ for a number of values of t. The distance around a quarter-circle is $\frac{2\pi}{4}$, or $\frac{\pi}{2}$. If we label the points $B(0, 1)$, $C(-1, 0)$, and $D(0, -1)$ where the unit circle meets the coordinate axes, then we know that $P(\frac{\pi}{2})$ is point B, and $P(\frac{-\pi}{2})$ is point D (see Figure 5.16a).

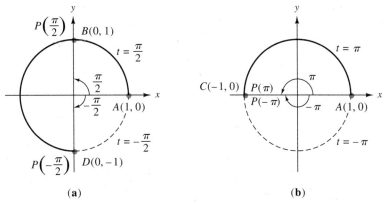

(a)   **(b)**

FIGURE 5.16

Similarly, the arc length along the circle from A to C, in either direction, is π and so both $P(\pi)$ and $P(-\pi)$ are point C as in Figure 5.16b.

When we know that the coordinates of a particular $P(t_1)$ are, say (x_1, y_1), then $P(t_1) = (x_1, y_1)$. Thus, for the points shown in Figure 5.16,

$$P\left(\frac{\pi}{2}\right) = (0, 1) \qquad P\left(-\frac{\pi}{2}\right) = (0, -1) \qquad P(\pi) = P(-\pi) = (-1, 0).$$

It is clear that point $A(1, 0)$ is the terminal position for $t = 0$, that is, $P(0) = (1, 0)$, but notice also $(1, 0) = P(2\pi) = P(-4\pi)$ going around counterclockwise once or clockwise twice. In fact, $P(t) = (1, 0)$ whenever t is an even multiple of π, that is, for every value of t in the set

$$\{0, \pm 2\pi, \pm 4\pi, \dots \}.$$

In addition to the points on the coordinate axes, there are other special points on the unit circle for which we can identify the coordinates of $P(t)$ in exact form. To do this it will be helpful first to recall some information concerning certain right triangles.

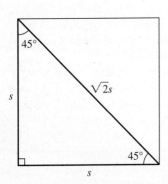

FIGURE 5.17

Special Right Triangles

When one of the angles of a triangle is 90°, the triangle is a right triangle. We will often indicate that the length of a side of a triangle is k by the phrase "the side is (or equals) k." Two special right triangles occur frequently in trigonometry.

The **45°–45° right triangle** is related to a square If the square has side s, then its diagonal (the hypotenuse of two triangles) is $\sqrt{s^2 + s^2}$ or $\sqrt{2}s$ (see Figure 5.17).

The **30°–60° right triangle** is related to an equilateral triangle. The key relationship is that the shorter leg is half the length of the hypotenuse (which is the side of the equilateral triangle). If the hypotenuse is s, the short leg is $\frac{1}{2}s$, and by the Pythagorean theorem, the other leg is $\frac{\sqrt{3}}{2}s$ (see Figure 5.18).

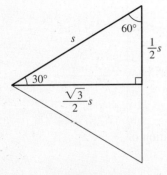

FIGURE 5.18

Special Right Triangles

In a 45°–45° right triangle, if each leg has length a, then the hypotenuse has length $\sqrt{2}a$.

In a 30°–60° right triangle, if the hypotenuse has length c, then the shorter leg is $\frac{c}{2}$ and the longer leg is $\frac{\sqrt{3}}{2}c$.

EXAMPLE 1   Find the coordinates of $P(\frac{\pi}{4})$ and of $P(\frac{-5\pi}{4})$.

Solution

The first step should always be to draw a diagram to locate the given points on the unit circle. Recall that $\frac{\pi}{2}$ is a right angle, so $\frac{\pi}{4}$ is 45°. Thus, $P(\frac{\pi}{4})$ is on the line $y = x$, and $P(\frac{-5\pi}{4})$ is five-eighths of the way around the circle in the clockwise

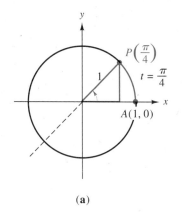

(a)

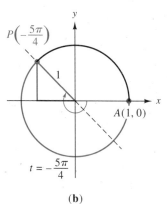

(b)

FIGURE 5.19

Strategy: Consider $\frac{7\pi}{6}$ as $\pi + \frac{\pi}{6}$. To locate $P(\frac{7\pi}{6})$ on the unit circle, move counterclockwise from $A(1, 0)$ an arc of π (one-half rotation) plus $\frac{\pi}{6}$, giving $P(\frac{7\pi}{6})$ in the third quadrant and a 30°–60° right triangle.

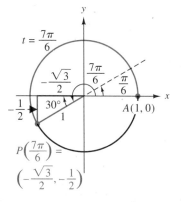

FIGURE 5.20

direction, that is, $P(\frac{-5\pi}{4})$ is in the second quadrant on the line $y = -x$ (see Figure 5.19). If we draw perpendiculars from the two position points to the x-axis, we have 45°–45° triangles, as shown in color in the diagrams. The hypotenuse of each triangle is 1, so the legs have length $\frac{1}{\sqrt{2}}$. Therefore,

$$P\left(\frac{\pi}{4}\right) = \left(\frac{1}{\sqrt{2}}, \frac{1}{\sqrt{2}}\right).$$

In the second quadrant, the x-coordinate is negative, so

$$P\left(\frac{-5\pi}{4}\right) = \left(-\frac{1}{\sqrt{2}}, \frac{1}{\sqrt{2}}\right). \quad \blacktriangle$$

EXAMPLE 2 Draw a diagram and find the coordinates of $P(\frac{7\pi}{6})$.

Solution
Follow the strategy. Point $P(\frac{7\pi}{6})$ is shown in Figure 5.20. As in Example 1, draw a perpendicular to the x-axis and get a right triangle, in this case a 30°–60° triangle with a hypotenuse of length 1. The short leg is $\frac{1}{2}$ and the other leg is $\frac{\sqrt{3}}{2}$. In the third quadrant both coordinates are negative, so

$$P\left(\frac{7\pi}{6}\right) = \left(-\frac{\sqrt{3}}{2}, -\frac{1}{2}\right). \quad \blacktriangle$$

For a number of values of t we can find the coordinates of $P(t)$ in exact form, including all those values for which we can make use of a 45°–45° triangle or a 30°–60° triangle as illustrated in Examples 1 and 2. In general, however, no simple geometric relationship will allow us to determine exact coordinates of $P(t)$. For instance, the central angle for $P(1)$ has a radian measure of 1, or an approximate degree measure of 57.296°, but there is no simple way to relate the legs and hypotenuse of a right triangle with an acute angle of 1 radian. Although we cannot express the coordinates of $P(1)$ in exact decimal form, we use trigonometric functions to give names to the coordinates of $P(1)$. In the next section we will see how we can get approximations to the coordinates.

Terminology
Since we can identify distances around a unit circle with the measure of central angles, we can also use the language of angles to describe certain numbers and distances. If, for a given value of t, point $P(t)$ is in the first quadrant, then we say that t is in the first quadrant, and similarly for the other quadrants. For instance, if t is 2.34, since $\frac{\pi}{2} \approx 1.57$ and $\pi \approx 3.14$, we have $\frac{\pi}{2} < 2.34 < \pi$, so 2.34 is in the second quadrant. When $P(t)$ is located on one of the coordinate axes, we say that t is a **quadrantal number,** meaning that t is not in any quadrant. For example, 0, $\frac{\pi}{2}$, and $\frac{-3\pi}{2}$ are quadrantal numbers.

Because we think of $P(t)$ as the terminal position of a moving point, two numbers are said to be **coterminal** if they have the same terminal position point. That is, numbers t_1 and t_2 are coterminal if $P(t_1) = P(t_2)$. In general, the set of numbers coterminal with any given t_1 is $\{t_1 + k \cdot 2\pi \mid k$ is any integer$\}$.

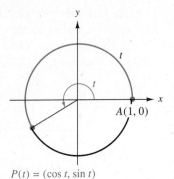

$P(t) = (\cos t, \sin t)$

FIGURE 5.21

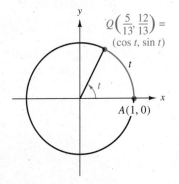

FIGURE 5.22

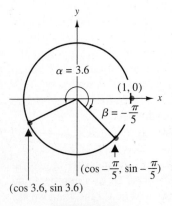

FIGURE 5.23

Strategy: (a) With no units indicated, 3.6 must be radians. Since $3.6 > \pi$ (≈ 3.1), 3.6 radians is about one-half radian ($\approx 30°$) more than π, so $P(3.6)$ is in QIII. **(b)** $\frac{-\pi}{5}$ is less than a rotation of $\frac{\pi}{2}$ in the negative direction, so $P(\frac{-\pi}{5})$ is in QIV.

Trigonometric Functions

We first define the sine and cosine functions and then use them to define the remaining trigonometric functions.

Sine and Cosine Functions   Since every real number t determines a unique point $P(t)$ on the unit circle, both the x- and y-coordinates of $P(t)$ are also uniquely determined, that is, both coordinates are functions of t. These functions, the **cosine** and **sine,** are referred to as **circular,** or **trigonometric functions.**

> **Definition: Cosine and Sine Functions**
>
> Suppose t is any real number and $P(t)$ is the corresponding terminal position point on the unit circle. Then the functions cosine and sine are defined by
>
> cosine (t) is the x-coordinate of $P(t)$.
>
> sine (t) is the y-coordinate of $P(t)$.
>
> Abbreviating cosine (t) by $\cos t$ and sine (t), by $\sin t$, every point on the unit circle has coordinates of the form
>
> $$P(t) = (\cos t, \sin t).$$

A typical point with coordinates $(\cos t, \sin t)$ is shown in Figure 5.21. For some values of t we can find the coordinates exactly, and hence exact values for $\cos t$ and $\sin t$. Conversely, if we have the coordinates of a point on the unit circle, we may know exact values for $\cos t$ and $\sin t$, but still be unable to get an exact value for t. Thus, for example, since $(\frac{5}{13})^2 + (\frac{12}{13})^2 = 1$, point $Q(\frac{5}{13}, \frac{12}{13})$ is a point on the unit circle, as shown in Figure 5.22. It follows that for the arc length t shown in the figure, we have $\cos t = \frac{5}{13}$, and $\sin t = \frac{12}{13}$. We have no way of finding a numerical value for t without the aid of a calculator, however, a problem we consider later in this chapter.

EXAMPLE 3   Determine the sign (positive or negative) of

(a) $\sin 3.6$ **(b)** $\cos(-\frac{\pi}{5})$

Solution

Draw central angles of 3.6 and $-\frac{\pi}{5}$, as shown in Figure 5.23. From the figure, **(a)** $\sin 3.6$ (the y-coordinate) is negative and **(b)** $\cos(\frac{-\pi}{5})$ (the x-coordinate) is positive. ▲

Other Trigonometric Functions   In addition to the cosine and sine, there are four other trigonometric functions, each of which we define in terms of cosine or sine: **tangent, cotangent, secant,** and **cosecant,** abbreviated, respectively, by tan, cot, sec, and csc.

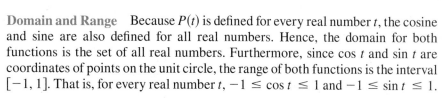

> **Definition: Trigonometric Functions**
>
> Suppose t is any real number, and the corresponding position point $P(t)$ has coordinates (x, y) on the unit circle. The six trigonometric functions of t are
>
> $$\cos t = x \qquad\qquad \sin t = y \qquad\qquad \tan t = \frac{\sin t}{\cos t} = \frac{y}{x}$$
>
> $$\sec t = \frac{1}{\cos t} = \frac{1}{x} \qquad \csc t = \frac{1}{\sin t} = \frac{1}{y} \qquad \cot t = \frac{\cos t}{\sin t} = \frac{x}{y}$$

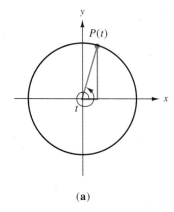

(a)

Domain and Range   Because $P(t)$ is defined for every real number t, the cosine and sine are also defined for all real numbers. Hence, the domain for both functions is the set of all real numbers. Furthermore, since $\cos t$ and $\sin t$ are coordinates of points on the unit circle, the range of both functions is the interval $[-1, 1]$. That is, for every real number t, $-1 \le \cos t \le 1$ and $-1 \le \sin t \le 1$.

The domain of cos is R.

The domain of sin is R.

The range of cos is $\{y \mid -1 \le y \le 1\}$.

The range of sin is $\{y \mid -1 \le y \le 1\}$.

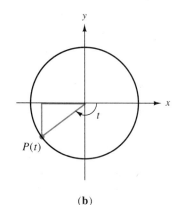

(b)

Each of the other four trigonometric functions involves the reciprocal of one coordinate of $P(t)$. Thus, the tangent, cotangent, secant, and cosecant all have restricted domains. Each is defined for all real numbers except those for which the denominator is 0. For instance, $\tan t = \frac{\sin t}{\cos t}$, so $\tan t$ is not defined when $\cos t$ is zero, such as when t is $\frac{\pi}{2}$ or $\frac{3\pi}{2}$ (or any odd multiple of $\frac{\pi}{2}$). For each quadrantal number, exactly two trigonometric functions are undefined.

Trigonometric Functions and Reference Triangles   We may think of the coordinates of $P(t)$ as functions of either the directed arc length t or an angle of measure t. In many applications it helps to consider the trigonometric functions in terms of angles. One advantage of using angles comes from an association with triangles. For any nonquadrantal number t, an important triangle called the **reference triangle** is obtained by drawing a perpendicular from the point $P(t)$ to the x-axis. Figure 5.24 shows reference triangles for three different terminal position points.

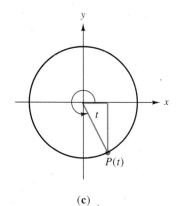

(c)

FIGURE 5.24

In Section 5.3 we discuss evaluation of the trigonometric functions for general angles and numbers. This section concludes by considering trigonometric functions for numbers that are coterminal with integer multiples of $\frac{\pi}{6}$ or $\frac{\pi}{4}$ (30° or 45°). For these values of t, we can evaluate trigonometric functions in exact form. Some multiples of $\frac{\pi}{6}$ and $\frac{\pi}{4}$, such as $3(\frac{\pi}{6})$ and $-4(\frac{\pi}{4})$, are quadrantal; and we have exact coordinates for all quadrantal numbers. Every other multiple of $\frac{\pi}{6}$ or $\frac{\pi}{4}$ has a reference triangle that is either a 45°–45° triangle or a 30°–60° triangle. To illustrate the use of such reference triangles, consider the example.

| EXAMPLE 4 | Evaluate all trigonometric functions of t where t |

is **(a)** $\frac{5\pi}{6}$ **(b)** $-\frac{2\pi}{3}$.

Solution

Always begin with a diagram.

(a)   Since $\frac{5\pi}{6} = \pi - \frac{\pi}{6}$, the reference triangle is the 30°–60° triangle shown in Figure 5.25a. Therefore, the coordinates of the point $P(\frac{5\pi}{6})$ are $(\frac{-\sqrt{3}}{2}, \frac{1}{2})$. From the definitions of trigonometric functions,

$$\cos \frac{5\pi}{6} = x, \text{ so } \cos \frac{5\pi}{6} = -\frac{\sqrt{3}}{2} \qquad \sin \frac{5\pi}{6} = y, \text{ so } \sin \frac{5\pi}{6} = \frac{1}{2}$$

$$\tan \frac{5\pi}{6} = \frac{y}{x}, \text{ so } \tan \frac{5\pi}{6} = -\frac{1}{\sqrt{3}} \qquad \cot \frac{5\pi}{6} = \frac{x}{y}, \text{ so } \cot \frac{5\pi}{6} = -\sqrt{3}$$

$$4 \sec \frac{5\pi}{6} = \frac{1}{x}, \text{ so } \sec \frac{5\pi}{6} = -\frac{2}{\sqrt{3}} \qquad \csc \frac{5\pi}{6} = \frac{1}{y}, \text{ so } \csc \frac{5\pi}{6} = 2$$

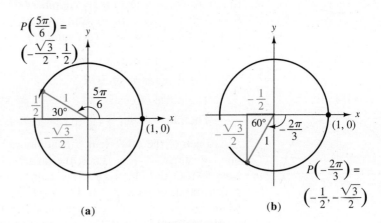

(a)   **(b)**

FIGURE 5.25

(b)   The number $\frac{-2\pi}{3}$ corresponds to a clockwise rotation of $\frac{2\pi}{3}$, or 120°. When we draw a perpendicular to the x-axis, the reference triangle is 30°–60° triangle as shown in Figure 5.25b. Both x and y values for $P(\frac{-2\pi}{3})$ are negative, so $P(-\frac{2\pi}{3})$ is $(\frac{-1}{2}, \frac{-\sqrt{3}}{2})$. From the definitions of the trigonometric functions,

$$\cos \left(-\frac{2\pi}{3}\right) = -\frac{1}{2} \qquad \sin \left(-\frac{2\pi}{3}\right) = -\frac{\sqrt{3}}{2} \qquad \tan \left(-\frac{2\pi}{3}\right) = \sqrt{3}$$

$$\sec \left(-\frac{2\pi}{3}\right) = -2 \qquad \csc \left(-\frac{2\pi}{3}\right) = -\frac{2}{\sqrt{3}} \qquad \cot \left(-\frac{2\pi}{3}\right) = \frac{1}{\sqrt{3}} \quad ▲$$

By using reference triangles and symmetry, we can get the coordinates of all the points shown in Figure 5.26. In the preceding section we stressed the importance of learning to think in radians. You should be able to see in your mind's eye the reference triangle for each nonquadrantal point, but the figure is an excellent reference and we recommend its use.

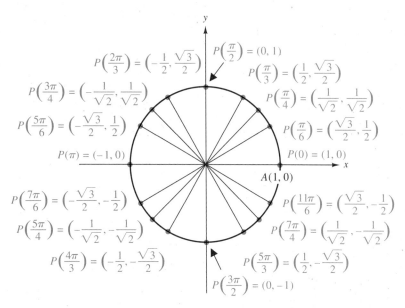

FIGURE 5.26

| EXAMPLE 5 | Evaluate all trigonometric functions of $\frac{11\pi}{4}$. |

Solution

Since $\frac{11\pi}{4}$ is greater than 2π, find a coterminal number. Note that $\frac{11\pi}{4} - 2\pi = \frac{3\pi}{4}$, so $\frac{11\pi}{4}$ is coterminal with $\frac{3\pi}{4}$. From Figure 5.26, read the coordinates $P(\frac{3\pi}{4}) = (\frac{-1}{\sqrt{2}}, \frac{1}{\sqrt{2}})$; $P(\frac{11\pi}{4})$ has the same coordinates. Using the coordinates of $P(\frac{11\pi}{4})$ in the definitions of the trigonometric functions,

$$\cos\frac{11\pi}{4} = -\frac{1}{\sqrt{2}} \qquad \sin\frac{11\pi}{4} = \frac{1}{\sqrt{2}} \qquad \tan\frac{11\pi}{4} = -1$$

$$\sec\frac{11\pi}{4} = -\sqrt{2}, \qquad \csc\frac{11\pi}{4} = \sqrt{2} \qquad \cot\frac{11\pi}{4} = -1. \quad \blacktriangle$$

EXERCISES 5.2

Check Your Understanding

Exercises 1–5 True or False. Give reasons for your conclusion.

1. If both sin t and cos t are negative, then tan t is also negative.

2. There is no number t for which cos t is negative and sec t is positive.

3. There is no number t for which sin $t > 1$.

4. The point $(\frac{-5}{13}, \frac{12}{13})$ is not on the unit circle.

5. If t is any number in the interval $(\frac{-\pi}{2}, 0)$, then cos $t < 0$.

Exercises 6–10 Complete the sentence by selecting from the list below *all choices* that make the statement true.

(a) in Quadrant I   (b) in Quadrant II
(c) in Quadrant III   (d) in Quadrant IV
(e) positive   (f) negative
(g) between 0 and 0.5   (h) between 0.5 and 1
(i) between -1 and -0.5 (j) between -0.5 and 0

6. If sin $t < 0$, then $P(t)$ could be _____ .

7. If cos $t < 0$ and tan $t < 0$, then $P(t)$ is _____ .

8. Point $P(4.5)$ is _____.

9. The number cos 3 is _____.

10. The number tan $\left(\frac{\pi}{6}\right)$ is _____.

Explore and Discover

Exercises 1–5 Pythagorean Triples For each given slope m, the line $y = mx - 1$ intersects the unit circle at the point $(0, -1)$ and at one other point, which we may denote by $P(\theta)$ (see the diagram.)

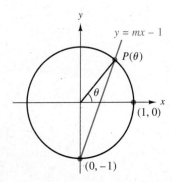

1. For any fixed slope m, express the coordinates of $P(\theta)$ in terms of m.

2. Suppose the slope m is a rational number, say $m = \frac{u}{v}$. Use the result of Exercise 1 to express the coordinates of $P(\theta)$ in terms of u and v, and show that in this case both coordinates of $P(\theta)$ are also rational numbers.

3. Suppose the coordinates of a point $P(t)$ on the unit circle are both rational numbers, say $P(t) = (\frac{a}{c}, \frac{b}{c})$. Find the slope of the line through $P(t)$ and the point $(0, -1)$. Is the slope a rational number?

4. If point $P(t) = (\frac{a}{c}, \frac{b}{c})$ is on the unit circle, where a, b, and c are positive integers, then show that (a, b, c) is a Pythagorean triple; that is, show that $a^2 + b^2 = c^2$.

5. Explain how the results of Exercises 2 through 4 can be used to find formulas that generate all Pythagorean triples.

6. Consider the unit circle and a position point $P(t)$. Write a brief paragraph to explain why, if $P(t)$ is not one of the points where the coordinate axes intersect the unit circle, then there is always another number, say u, such that $\cos u = \cos t$, and another number v such that $\sin v = \sin t$. Where are the position points $P(u)$ and $P(v)$ located relative to $P(t)$?

Develop Mastery

Exercises 1–10 **(a)** Draw a diagram to show the approximate location of $P(t)$ on the unit circle and also show the reference triangle. **(b)** Determine the sign (positive or negative) of $\sin t$, $\cos t$, and $\tan t$.

1. $t = \frac{\pi}{3}$ 2. $t = \frac{3\pi}{4}$ 3. $t = -\frac{\pi}{6}$

4. $t = \frac{9\pi}{4}$ 5. $t = -\frac{7\pi}{6}$ 6. $t = -\frac{2\pi}{3}$

7. $t = -2$ 8. $t = 2.6$ 9. $t = \frac{9}{4}$

10. $t = -\frac{5}{4}$

Exercises 11–16 Locate $P(t)$ on the unit circle for the quadrantal number t. Evaluate all of the trigonometric functions that are defined for t.

11. $t = \frac{5\pi}{2}$ 12. $t = -4\pi$ 13. $t = -3\pi$

14. $t = 7\pi$ 15. $t = -\frac{15\pi}{2}$ 16. $t = \frac{3\pi}{2}$

Exercises 17–24 The reference triangle is one of the special right triangles described in this section. Sketch the reference triangle and evaluate all six trigonometric functions for t.

17. $t = \frac{5\pi}{6}$ 18. $t = \frac{5\pi}{3}$ 19. $t = \frac{7\pi}{4}$

20. $t = -\frac{3\pi}{4}$ 21. $t = -\frac{11\pi}{6}$ 22. $t = \frac{11\pi}{4}$

23. $t = \frac{13\pi}{3}$ 24. $t = -\frac{13\pi}{6}$

Exercises 25–36 Describe the set of all real numbers t satisfying the given condition. Figure 5.26 may be helpful.

25. $\cos t = 1$ 26. $\tan t = 1$ 27. $\sec t = 2$

28. $\sec t = -2$ 29. $\cot t = \sqrt{3}$ 30. $\sin t = 0$

31. $\cot t = -1$ 32. $\csc t = 1$

33. $\sin t = \frac{1}{2}$, $\cos t < 0$

34. $\cos t = \frac{-\sqrt{3}}{2}$, $\sin t > 0$

35. $\tan t = -1$, $\cos t < 0$

36. $\sec t = -2$, $\sin t < 0$

Exercises 37–40 Determine the quadrant or quadrants in which $P(t)$ lies, where both inequalities are satisfied.

37. $\cos t > 0$, $\sin t < 0$ 38. $\tan t > 0$, $\cos t < 0$

39. $\sec t < 0$, $\cos t < 0$ 40. $\csc t < 0$, $\sin t < 0$

Exercises 41–44 Determine the sign (positive or negative). First draw a diagram to show the quadrant in which the terminal position point is located.

41. (a) cos 3   (b) cot 3

42. (a) tan $\left(\frac{8\pi}{5}\right)$ (b) sec $\left(\frac{8\pi}{5}\right)$

43. (a) sec (−2.3)   (b) tan (−2.3)

44. (a) csc (−0.01)   (b) cos (−0.01)

Exercises 45–48 For the terminal position point $P(t)$, find all trigonometric functions of t. First show that $P(t)$ is a point on the unit circle.

45. $P(t) = \left(-\frac{3}{5}, \frac{4}{5}\right)$

46. $P(t) = \left(-\frac{8}{17}, \frac{15}{17}\right)$

47. $P(t) = \left(\frac{7}{25}, -\frac{24}{25}\right)$

48. $P(t) = \left(\frac{1}{4}, \frac{\sqrt{15}}{4}\right)$

Exercises 49–54 If $P(t)$ is a terminal position point on the unit circle, find (a) all possible values of x or y and (b) cos t and sin t.

49. $P(t) = \left(\frac{1}{2}, y\right)$ **50.** $P(t) = \left(x, \frac{1}{3}\right)$

51. $P(t) = (x, -x)$ **52.** $P(t) = (x, x + 1)$

53. $P(t) = (2y, y)$ **54.** $P(t) = \left(\frac{y}{2}, y\right)$

Exercises 55–59 Find all numbers t that satisfy the conditions.

55. sin t = sin $\frac{7\pi}{6}$ and $-\frac{\pi}{2} < t < 0$

56. sin t = cos $\frac{3\pi}{4}$ and $\frac{3\pi}{2} < t < 2\pi$

57. cos t = cos $\frac{5\pi}{6}$ and $\pi < t < 2\pi$

58. cos t = sin $\frac{3\pi}{4}$ and $\pi < t < 2\pi$

59. sin t = sin $\frac{\pi}{2}$ and $-2\pi < t < 0$

Exercises 60–63 Find the smallest positive number t satisfying the conditions.

60. cos t = $-\frac{1}{2}$ and tan $t < 0$

61. cot t = 1 and sin $t < 0$

62. sec t = 2 and sin $t < 0$

63. tan t = 1 and cos $t > 0$

Exercises 64–67 Find cos t and sin t if the terminal position point $P(t)$ on the unit circle satisfies the conditions.

64. The x-coordinate of $P(t)$ is $\frac{3}{5}$ and $P(t)$ is in the fourth quadrant.

65. The y-coordinate of $P(t)$ is $-\frac{3}{4}$ and $P(t)$ is in the third quadrant.

66. The y-coordinate of $P(t)$ is $-\frac{\sqrt{2}}{2}$ and the x-coordinate of $P(t)$ is positive.

67. The x-coordinate of $P(t)$ is $-\frac{3}{5}$ and t is between 0 and π.

Exercises 68–71 For the given values of t, evaluate $(\sin t)^2 + (\cos t)^2$. Based on your answers, make a guess about the value of the expression $(\sin t)^2 + (\cos t)^2$ for any number t.

68. $t = \frac{\pi}{4}$; $t = \frac{5\pi}{6}$ **69.** $t = \frac{\pi}{3}$; $t = -\frac{5\pi}{4}$

70. $t = \frac{\pi}{2}$; $t = \frac{-7\pi}{6}$ **71.** $t = \frac{3\pi}{2}$; $t = \frac{-5\pi}{6}$

Exercises 72–75 For the given value of t, evaluate (a) sin $(2t)$ (b) 2 sin t (c) 2(sin t)(cos t). Based on your answers, make a guess about sin $(2t)$ for any number t.

72. $t = \frac{\pi}{4}$ **73.** $t = \frac{-5\pi}{4}$ **74.** $t = \frac{5\pi}{6}$ **75.** $t = \frac{\pi}{2}$

76. A weight is suspended on a spring and rests in equilibrium position. It is then pulled downward and allowed to oscillate. The formula that gives the displacement y from the equilibrium position t seconds after release is

$$y = 3 \cos (4\pi t), \text{ where } y \text{ is in inches.}$$

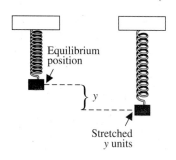

Equilibrium position

y

Stretched y units

Find the displacement for each of the following times.

(a) $t = 0$ **(b)** $t = \frac{1}{8}$ **(c)** $t = \frac{1}{4}$

(d) $t = \frac{3}{8}$ **(e)** $t = \frac{1}{2}$

77. Give a verbal description of the oscillation motion in Exercise 76.

78. Repeat Exercise 76 with a formula that includes a damping effect due to friction: $y = 3e^{-t} \cos (4\pi t)$.

| SECTION 5.3 | **Evaluation of Trigonometric Functions** |

The importance of the limit concept in mathematics lies in the fact that many numbers are defined only as limits. This is why the field of rational numbers, in which such limits may not exist, is too narrow for the needs of mathematics.

Courant and Robbins

The values of the six trigonometric functions at any real number t are determined by the coordinates of the terminal position $P(t)$ on the unit circle. Except for comparatively few values of t, however, we have no direct way to find a simple form for the coordinates of $P(t)$. In Section 5.2 we learned how to evaluate the trigonometric functions for all angles that are coterminal with any multiple of $\frac{\pi}{6}$ or $\frac{\pi}{4}$. Representatives of all such angles appear in Figure 5.26, including quadrantal angles.

In this section we consider the problem of evaluating the trigonometric functions for arbitrary angles. We begin by considering angles in standard position. If we know the coordinates in exact form for a point on the terminal side of such an angle, then we show how to find exact values for all trigonometric functions of the angle. For most angles, however, the calculator is the most convenient way to evaluate the trigonometric functions. This section concludes with a discussion of calculator evaluations.

Angles in Standard Position

Initially I thought I was going to become a chemist because in the little high school that I was going to, it was not clear that any other scientific careers were open. I had read a book . . . which said that chemistry was a great field. It was only after I went to college that I shifted to mathematics.

Saunders MacLane

An angle in **standard position** has its vertex at the origin and the positive x-axis as its initial side (see Figure 5.27). The advantage of having an angle in standard position is that all trigonometric functions of the angle are determined by the coordinates of any point, other than the origin, on the terminal side.

Suppose $Q(a, b)$ is an arbitrary point on the terminal side of angle θ in standard position. The point where the terminal side of θ intersects the unit circle is $P(\theta)$. To see how to get the coordinates of $P(\theta)$ from the coordinates of $Q(a, b)$, draw a perpendicular from Q to the x-axis. We get a triangle OQR that is similar to the reference triangle for $P(\theta)$, triangle OPS (see Figure 5.28). We label the legs of triangle OQR with the coordinates of $Q(a, b)$ to remind us of appropriate signs in the various quadrants. The length of the hypotenuse of triangle OQR is the distance from the origin to Q, the positive number given by $r = \sqrt{a^2 + b^2}$. Since triangles OQR and OPS are similar, corresponding sides

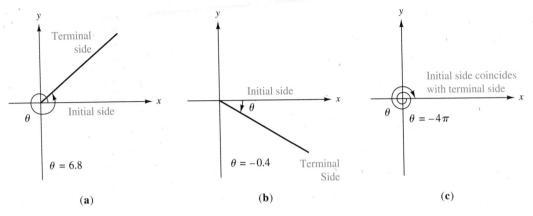

FIGURE 5.27

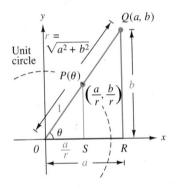

FIGURE 5.28

Triangle OQR has sides a, b, $r = \sqrt{a^2 + b^2}$; triangle OPS has sides $\frac{a}{r}$, $\frac{b}{r}$, 1.

are in proportion. If $P(\theta) = (x, y)$, then we have

$$\frac{b}{r} = \frac{y}{1}, \quad y = \frac{b}{r}$$

$$\frac{a}{r} = \frac{x}{1}, \quad x = \frac{a}{r}$$

Thus, the coordinates of $P(\theta)$ are given by

$$P(\theta) = (x, y) = \left(\frac{a}{r}, \frac{b}{r}\right).$$

Figure 5.28 shows a first-quadrant angle, but the same relations hold for any angle in any quadrant. For instance, see Figure 5.29.

Once we have the coordinates of the terminal position $P(\theta)$ on the unit circle, we immediately have the values for the trigonometric functions at θ. The cosine and sine of θ are the coordinates of $P(\theta)$, the remaining four functions are defined as in Section 5.2.

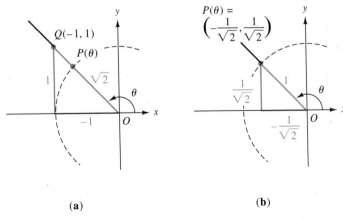

FIGURE 5.29

Trigonometric Functions of an Angle in Standard Position

Suppose θ is an angle in standard position, and $Q(a, b)$ is any point on the terminal side of θ, other than the origin. The distance r from the origin to Q is $\sqrt{a^2 + b^2}$, and the trigonometric functions of θ are given by

$$\cos \theta = \frac{a}{r} \qquad \sin \theta = \frac{b}{r} \qquad \tan \theta = \frac{b}{a}$$

$$\sec \theta = \frac{r}{a} \qquad \csc \theta = \frac{r}{b} \qquad \cot \theta = \frac{a}{b}. \qquad \textbf{(1)}$$

It may help you remember these definitions to think in terms of the x-coordinate and y-coordinate rather than a and b. The cosine is expressed as the x-coordinate over r, etc. It is understood, also, that the tangent and secant are undefined when $a = 0$ (when the terminal side is on the y-axis), and that the cosecant and cotangent are undefined when $b = 0$ (when the terminal side is on the x-axis).

From the diagrams in Figures 5.28 and 5.29, it should be apparent that we could as easily use $\triangle OQR$ for an arbitrary point Q on the terminal side of the angle for determining the trigonometric functions as the reference triangle OPS in the unit circle. Accordingly, we broaden the definition of *reference triangle* for use with any point on the terminal side of an angle in standard position.

Definition: Reference Triangle

Given a nonquadrantal angle θ in standard position and a point Q on the terminal side of θ, draw a perpendicular from Q to the x-axis. If R is the foot of the perpendicular and O is the origin, then the right triangle OQR is called a **reference triangle** for θ.

EXAMPLE 1 Let t be an angle in standard position with $Q(-3, 4)$ on the terminal side. Evaluate all trigonometric functions at t.

Strategy: Draw a diagram with a reference triangle by dropping a perpendicular from Q to the x-axis. Find the distance $r = |\overline{OQ}|$ and use the formulas in Equation 1.

Solution

Follow the strategy. Figure 5.30 shows a reference triangle for t. First, we find r.

$$r = \sqrt{(-3)^2 + (4)^2} = \sqrt{25} = 5.$$

With -3 for a, 4 for b, and 5 for r, use Equation 1 to get

$$\cos t = \frac{a}{r} = -\frac{3}{5} \qquad \sin t = \frac{b}{r} = \frac{4}{5} \qquad \tan t = \frac{b}{a} = -\frac{4}{3}$$

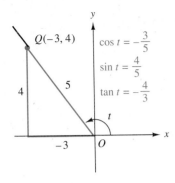

$$\cos t = -\frac{3}{5}$$

$$\sin t = \frac{4}{5}$$

$$\tan t = -\frac{4}{3}$$

FIGURE 5.30

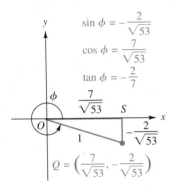

$$\sin \phi = -\frac{2}{\sqrt{53}}$$

$$\cos \phi = \frac{7}{\sqrt{53}}$$

$$\tan \phi = -\frac{2}{7}$$

FIGURE 5.31

Strategy: Begin with a diagram that shows θ and a reference triangle. For a point $Q(a, b)$ on the terminal side of θ, $\tan \theta = \frac{b}{a}$. The fraction $\frac{-7}{24}$ can be written as $\frac{7}{-24}$. Choose Q as $(-24, 7)$. Draw a perpendicular to the x-axis to get a reference triangle.

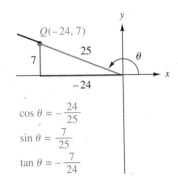

$$\cos \theta = -\frac{24}{25}$$

$$\sin \theta = \frac{7}{25}$$

$$\tan \theta = -\frac{7}{24}$$

FIGURE 5.32

$$\sec t = \frac{r}{a} = -\frac{5}{3} \qquad \csc t = \frac{r}{b} = \frac{5}{4} \qquad \cot t = \frac{a}{b} = -\frac{3}{4} \quad \blacktriangle$$

EXAMPLE 2 Let ϕ be the angle shown in standard position in Figure 5.31 whose terminal side contains the point $Q(\frac{7}{\sqrt{53}}, \frac{-2}{\sqrt{53}})$. Find $\cos \phi$, $\sin \phi$, and $\tan \phi$.

Solution

First, draw a perpendicular from Q to the x-axis to obtain a reference triangle, OQS (see Figure 5.31). Next, determine r.

$$r = \sqrt{\left(\frac{7}{\sqrt{53}}\right)^2 + \left(-\frac{2}{\sqrt{53}}\right)^2} = \sqrt{\left(\frac{49}{53}\right) + \left(\frac{4}{53}\right)} = 1.$$

Since r is 1, point Q is on the unit circle, so

$$\cos \phi = \frac{\dfrac{7}{\sqrt{53}}}{1} = \frac{7}{\sqrt{53}}$$

$$\sin \phi = \frac{-\dfrac{2}{\sqrt{53}}}{1} = -\frac{2}{\sqrt{53}}$$

$$\tan \phi = -\frac{\dfrac{2}{\sqrt{53}}}{\dfrac{7}{\sqrt{53}}} = -\frac{2}{7} \quad \blacktriangle$$

EXAMPLE 3 If $\tan \theta = -\frac{7}{24}$ and θ is in the second quadrant, find the exact values of the other trigonometric functions of θ.

Solution

Follow the strategy. Draw a diagram (Figure 5.32), and then find r.

$$r = \sqrt{(-24)^2 + (7)^2} = \sqrt{625} = 25$$

Therefore r is 25, and equation 1 gives

$$\cos \theta = \frac{a}{r} = -\frac{24}{25} \qquad \sin \theta = \frac{b}{r} = \frac{7}{25} \qquad \tan \theta = \frac{b}{a} = -\frac{7}{24}$$

$$\sec \theta = \frac{r}{a} = -\frac{25}{24} \qquad \csc \theta = \frac{r}{b} = \frac{25}{7} \qquad \cot \theta = \frac{a}{b} = -\frac{24}{7} \quad \blacktriangle$$

Calculator Evaluation of Trigonometric Functions

Before calculators, evaluation of trigonometric functions required tables of some sort. Literally lifetimes of computation were invested in the production of tables of sufficient accuracy for scientific calculations. Now, the touch of a calculator key gives instant access to more accurate information than was ever

TABLE 5.2   Calculator Evaluations

To Evaluate	Mode	Enter	Key(s)	Partial Display
sin 34°	Deg	34	sin	0.55919
tan (−2)	Rad	−2	tan	2.18504
cos ($\frac{7\pi}{5}$)	Rad	7 × π ÷ 5	cos	−0.30902
sec 14.3	Rad	14.3	cos $\frac{1}{x}$	−6.16848
sec 14.3°	Deg	14.3	cos $\frac{1}{x}$	1.03197

available previously. Develop Mastery Exercises 60 and 61 illustrate how calculators can be programmed to evaluate the sine and cosine functions.

Scientific calculators have keys labeled $\boxed{\texttt{sin}}$, $\boxed{\texttt{cos}}$, and $\boxed{\texttt{tan}}$, and they function in distinct modes as well, since angles can be measured in degrees, radians, or grads. (We will not consider grad measure here.) Thus, we may think of two different sets of trigonometric functions, one for angles measured in degrees and one for angles in radians, but we will not stress the distinction.

Problem solving requires that the calculator be in the correct mode. Our convention is that evaluation is to be done with real numbers (radian mode) unless we specifically see the degree symbol. Before going further, make sure you know how to put your calculator in the appropriate mode.

Table 5.2 illustrates calculator keystrokes for evaluating trigonometric functions with a scientific calculator that does not have a key labeled $\boxed{\texttt{EXE}}$ or $\boxed{\texttt{ENTER}}$. For instance, to evaluate sin 34°, with the calculator in degree mode, enter 34, then press $\boxed{\texttt{sin}}$. The calculator immediately displays 0.5591929. It is not necessary to press $\boxed{=}$. If your calculator has $\boxed{\texttt{EXE}}$ or $\boxed{\texttt{ENTER}}$ and the calculator is in degree mode, press $\boxed{\texttt{sin}}$ 34, and "sin 34" appears in the display. When you press $\boxed{\texttt{EXE}}$ or $\boxed{\texttt{ENTER}}$, the decimal approximation of sin 34° is displayed.

Your calculator does not have keys to directly evaluate the cotangent, secant, and cosecant functions, but evaluation is a simple matter, using the reciprocal key. For example, to evaluate sec 14.3, first check to see that the calculator is in radian mode. Since the secant is the reciprocal of the cosine, sec 14.3 = $\frac{1}{\cos 14.3}$. First evaluate cos 14.3 and then press the reciprocal key, $\boxed{\texttt{1/x}}$. If your calculator displays the calculation before evaluating, after you have cos 14.3 (−0.16211443) press $\boxed{\texttt{ANS}}$ $\boxed{\texttt{x}^{-1}}$ or 1 ÷ $\boxed{\texttt{ANS}}$ and then $\boxed{\texttt{EXE}}$ or $\boxed{\texttt{ENTER}}$. The calculator displays −6.1684821.

Use your calculator to verify the evaluations in Table 5.2.

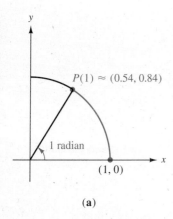

(a)

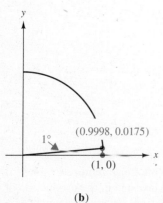

(b)

FIGURE 5.33

EXAMPLE 4   Make a rough sketch that shows central angles of 1 radian and 1° in a unit circle. Evaluate cos 1, sin 1, cos 1°, and sin 1° and explain why sin 1 ≠ sin 1° and cos 1 ≠ cos 1°.

Solution

In the unit circle a central angle of 1 radian subtends an arc of length 1. The coordinates of $P(1)$ are (cos 1, sin 1), and in radian mode the calculator gives cos 1 ≈ 0.54 and sin 1 ≈ 0.84. Thus $P(1)$ ≈ (0.54, 0.84). Figure 5.33a shows $P(1)$ and the central angle of 1 radian (almost 60°).

Whereas 1 radian is nearly $\frac{1}{6}$ of a full revolution, $1°$ is only $\frac{1}{360}$ of a revolution. A central angle of $1°$ is very small, and $P(t)$ is so near $(1, 0)$ that we must exaggerate even to show $1°$ in Figure 5.33b. In degree mode the calculator gives the coordinates of $P(t)$ as $(\cos 1°, \sin 1°) \approx (0.99985, 0.01745)$. ▲

EXAMPLE 5   Draw a rough sketch that shows $P(t)$ on the unit circle, and give a five-decimal-place approximation for all six trigonometric functions of **(a)** $t = 1.85$ and **(b)** $t = -9$.

Strategy: For a rough sketch of $P(1.85)$ and $P(-9)$, remember that half a revolution is measured by π (just over 3), so that 1.85 is a little more than $\frac{\pi}{2}$. Thus $P(1.85)$ is in the second quadrant. Since 9 is slightly less than $3\pi (\approx 9.42)$ and 3π is $2\pi + \pi$, move clockwise from $(1, 0)$ one complete revolution and then slightly less than half a revolution. Hence, $P(-9)$ is in the third quadrant.

Solution

Follow the strategy and draw the diagrams shown in Figure 5.34. Using a calculator in radian mode, evaluate the six trigonometric functions when t is 1.85 and then when t is -9.

$\cos 1.85 \approx -0.27559$ $\sin 1.85 \approx 0.96128$ $\tan 1.85 \approx -3.48806$

$\sec 1.85 \approx -3.62858$ $\csc 1.85 \approx 1.04028$ $\cot 1.85 \approx -0.28669$

$\cos (-9) \approx -0.91113$ $\sin (-9) \approx -0.41212$ $\tan (-9) \approx 0.45232$

$\sec (-9) \approx -1.09754$ $\csc (-9) \approx -2.42649$ $\cot (-9) \approx 2.21085$

▲

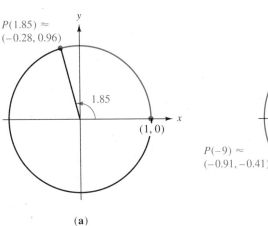
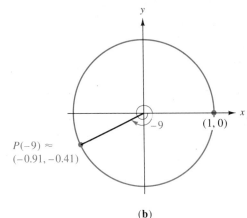

(a)   **(b)**

FIGURE 5.34

As a check on our diagrams,

$$P(1.85) = (\cos 1.85, \sin 1.85) \approx (-0.28, 0.96)$$

$$P(-9) = (\cos -9, \sin -9) \approx (-0.91, -0.41).$$

Right Triangle Trigonometry

Our original definition of trigonometric functions made use of coordinates of points on the unit circle (p. 271). We also saw that the trigonometric functions can be defined using coordinates of *any* point on the terminal side of an angle in standard position (p. 278). In many situations we want trigonometric functions of acute angles in right triangles.

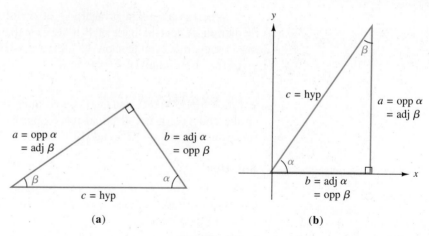

FIGURE 5.35

In working with right triangles we do not want to be dependent on any particular orientation of the triangle. Figure 5.35a shows a right triangle with acute angles α and β, and legs labeled a and b. Since side a is opposite angle α, we denote it by *opp* α, and similarly *opp* β indicates side b, the side opposite angle β. The hypotenuse c is labeled *hyp*. By placing the triangle in a coordinate system with leg b along the positive x-axis and angle α in standard position (see Figure 5.35b), we see that the point with coordinates (b, a) is on the terminal side of angle α at a distance c from the origin. Hence the definitions on p. 278 apply and we can express the trigonometric functions of α in terms of opp α, adj α, and hyp.

Definition: Trigonometric Functions of an Acute Angle

Suppose α is an acute angle of a right triangle. The trigonometric functions of α are

$$\sin \alpha = \frac{\text{opp } \alpha}{\text{hyp}} \qquad \cos \alpha = \frac{\text{adj } \alpha}{\text{hyp}} \qquad \tan \alpha = \frac{\text{opp } \alpha}{\text{adj } \alpha}$$

$$\csc \alpha = \frac{\text{hyp}}{\text{opp } \alpha} \qquad \sec \alpha = \frac{\text{hyp}}{\text{adj } \alpha} \qquad \cot \alpha = \frac{\text{adj } \alpha}{\text{opp } \alpha}$$

In a similar manner, for angle β we have

$$\sin \beta = \frac{\text{opp } \beta}{\text{hyp}} \qquad \cos \beta = \frac{\text{adj } \beta}{\text{hyp}} \qquad \tan \beta = \frac{\text{opp } \beta}{\text{adj } \beta}.$$

In Figure 5.35a, in addition to the right angle, we refer to α, β, a, b, and c, as **parts of the triangle.**

Given information about some parts of a right triangle, we can use trigonometric functions to determine other parts. The process of using given data to

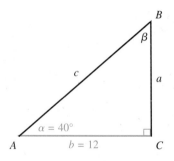

FIGURE 5.36

solve for remaining parts is called **solving the triangle.** In virtually all instances, to solve a triangle we look for trigonometric functions that relate known information to a single unknown, giving us equations that we can solve for the desired quantities. We illustrate with an example that is typical of the applications of right triangles we explore in more depth in Section 7.1.

EXAMPLE 6 In the right triangle in Figure 5.36, b is 12, and α is 40°. Find β, a, and c.

Solution

Since the sum of the acute angles of a right triangle is 90°, $\beta = 90 - \alpha = 90° - 40° = 50°$. To find the lengths of the unknown sides, look for trigonometric functions that involve just one of the unknowns. In this case,

$$\cos 40° = \frac{\text{adj}}{\text{hyp}} = \frac{12}{c} \quad \text{and} \quad \tan 40° = \frac{\text{opp}}{\text{adj}} = \frac{a}{12}.$$

Solving for c and a, respectively,

$$c = \frac{12}{\cos 40°} \approx 15.66 \quad \text{and} \quad a = 12 \tan 40° \approx 10.07$$

Rounding off to two significant digits, c is 16 and a is 10. ▲

EXAMPLE 7 A wheel of radius 2 is rotating in a counterclockwise direction at a uniform angular speed ω of 12 rev/min. Take a coordinate system with the origin at the center of rotation and designate a point P on the circumference of the wheel. **(a)** If P is located at $(2, 0)$ at time $t = 0$, find formulas to give the coordinates of $P(x, y)$ at any time t in seconds. **(b)** Give the coordinates of point P to two decimal places at times $t = 1, 2, 4$, and 5 seconds.

Solution

First, draw a diagram. Since t is in seconds, express the angular speed in units of radians per second.

$$\omega = 12 \frac{\text{rev}}{\text{min}} = \frac{12 \text{ rev}}{\text{min}} \cdot \frac{2\pi \text{ rad}}{1 \text{ rev}} \cdot \frac{1 \text{ min}}{60 \text{ sec}} = \frac{2\pi \text{ rad}}{5 \text{ sec}}$$

Therefore, in t seconds the radial line OP will rotate through an angle θ where θ is $\left(\frac{2\pi}{5}\right)t$.

(a) From the reference triangle OPS in Figure 5.37, $\cos \theta = \frac{x}{2}$ so $x = 2 \cos \theta = 2 \cos \left(\frac{2\pi}{5}\right)t$. Similarly, $y = 2 \sin \left(\frac{2\pi}{5}\right)t$.

(b) If $t = 1$, then $x = 2 \cos \left(\frac{2\pi}{5}\right) \approx 0.618$, $y = 2 \sin \left(\frac{2\pi}{5}\right) \approx 1.902$. Hence at 1 second, point P is at $(0.62, 1.90)$. When $t = 2$, $x = 2 \cos \left(\frac{4\pi}{5}\right) \approx -1.62$, $y = 2 \sin \left(\frac{4\pi}{5}\right) \approx 1.18$, so P is at $(-1.62, 1.18)$. Similarly, when $t = 4$, P is at $(0.62, -1.90)$, and when t is 5, P is at $(2, 0)$, back to the starting point. ▲

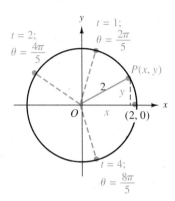

FIGURE 5.37

TRIGONOMETRIC TABLES

Astronomers at the Paris Observatory in the 17th century

The urgent need for accurate trigonometric calculations arose from astronomy and navigation. After all, 1 degree of longitude is $\frac{1}{360}$ of the circumference of the earth. To a navigator out in the middle of the unknown, even a minute ($\frac{1}{60}$ of a degree) covers a big chunk of ocean.

Claudius Ptolemy of Alexandria laid out principles of astronomy and geography in the second century A.D. that remained the supreme authority for well over a thousand years. Some of his views of the world were surprisingly modern; it was his idea to divide the equator into 360 equal parts or degrees. So great was the authority of men like Ptolemy that people were unwilling to challenge what was written even when it was contradicted by direct experience.

By the end of the sixteenth century, explorers were pushing ever farther into the unknown and had to rely increasingly on celestial navigation. Astronomers also needed more accurate trigonometric calculations. At that time, sines and cosines were not functions, they were lengths of chords in a circle. Larger circles had larger sines, so to increase accuracy, users increased the size of the radius.

Napier criticized some of his contemporaries for using a radius of only 1 million, writing "the more learned put 10,000,000, whereby the difference of all sines is better expressed." Prodigious (and tedious) efforts went into calculating trigonometric tables. Rheticus (1514–1576) began to compile 15-place tables, an effort that wasn't completed until 20 years after his death.

Valuable as the tables may have been, their use still involved horrendous problems. Just think of multiplying and dividing three or four 15-digit numbers! There was really no alternative until Napier's invention of logarithms in 1614 (see the Historical Note, "Invention of Logarithms" in Section 4.5).

Relating Trigonometric Functions of Any Angle and Right Triangle Trigonometry   In Section 5.2 we defined trigonometric functions of any angle θ by using coordinates of a point on the unit circle (see Figure 5.38a). At the beginning of this section, we defined trigonometric functions of θ in terms of coordinates of an arbitrary point on the terminal side of θ (Figure 5.38b). In both cases for nonquadrantal angles we used the reference triangle, the right triangle formed by dropping a perpendicular from a point Q on the terminal side to the x-axis. If we label the sides of the reference triangle with the signed-number coordinates of Q, then we can read all trigonometric functions of θ (including signs) from the right triangle definitions for the reference triangle (Figure 5.38c).

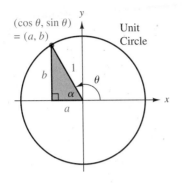

(a) Unit circle definitions

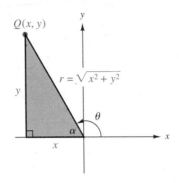

(b) Reference triangle definitions

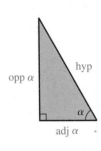

(c) Right triangle definitions

FIGURE 5.38

For any nonquadrantal angle θ with a point Q on the terminal side, if α is the acute angle at the origin in the reference triangle and the legs of the reference triangle are labeled with the signed-number coordinates of Q, then the trigonometric functions of θ are the same as the corresponding right triangle functions for α in the reference triangle.

EXERCISES 5.3

Check Your Understanding

Exercises 1–5 True or False. Give reasons for your conclusion.

1. If point $(3, 4)$ is on the terminal side of θ, then $(-3, -4)$ is on the terminal side of $-\theta$.

2. If point $(-2, 4)$ is on the terminal side of θ, then so is $(-1, 2)$.

3. The smallest integer that is greater than $\tan 5$ is -3.

4. If point $(1, 1)$ is on the terminal side of θ, then θ must be equal to $\frac{\pi}{4}$.

5. The number $\tan (1 + 9\pi)$ is negative.

Exercises 6–10 Complete the sentence by selecting from the list below *all choices* that make the statement true.

(a) Quadrant I
(b) Quadrant II
(c) Quadrant III
(d) Quadrant IV
(e) a positive number
(f) a negative number
(g) less than **1**
(h) greater than 1
(i) less than -30
(j) between -1 and -0.7.

6. If $\theta = 3$, then the terminal side of θ is in _____.

7. If $\theta = -4$, then the terminal side of θ is in _____.

8. If the terminal side of θ is in Quadrant III, then the terminal side of $\theta - \pi$ is in _____.

9. If $\theta = 1.6$, then $\sec \theta$ is _____.

10. If $\frac{3\pi}{4} < \theta < \pi$, then $\cos \theta$ is _____.

Explore and Discover

1. Evaluate $(\sin t)^2 + (\cos t)^2$ when t is **(a)** $\frac{2}{3}$, **(b)** $-\pi$, **(c)** 1.33, **(d)** $\frac{2\pi}{3}$.

2. What do your results in Exercise 1 suggest about the expression $(\cos t)^2 + (\sin t)^2$? Test your guesses for some additional values of t. See the next exercise.

3. Draw a diagram with an arbitrary angle t in standard position showing point $P(t)$ on the unit circle. Use the fact that the coordinates of every point on the unit circle must satisfy the equation of the circle to prove that your guess in Exercise 2 is correct.

4. Use the same values of t as in Exercise 1 and evaluate the expressions **(a)** $\cos t + \sin t$, **(b)** $(\cos t)^3 + (\sin t)^3$. Does it appear that either expression is constant?

5. Compare values of **(a)** $\sqrt{(\tan t)^2 - (\sin t)^2}$ and **(b)** $(\sin t)(\tan t)$ for four different numbers t from the first and fourth quadrants. What do your results suggest? See the next exercise.

6. Compare values of the expressions in Exercises 5a and 5b for four different second- and third-quadrant numbers t. Modify the guess you made for Exercise 5. How should the expression in Exercise 5b be changed so that it is equal to that in Exercise 5a for every real number t where $\tan t$ is defined?

Develop Mastery

Exercises 1–16   Point Q is on the terminal side of angle θ. From a diagram that shows Q and a reference triangle for θ, evaluate the six trigonometric functions of θ in exact form.

1. $Q(-3, 4)$ **2.** $Q(-6, 8)$ **3.** $Q(5, 12)$

4. $Q(-5, -12)$ **5.** $Q(-7, -24)$ **6.** $Q(3.5, -12)$

7. $Q(3, -3)$ **8.** $Q(-4, 2)$ **9.** $Q(-2, -4)$

10. $Q(-1, 2)$ **11.** $Q(2, 3)$ **12.** $Q(4, -1)$

13. $Q(\sqrt{5}, -2)$ **14.** $Q(\sqrt{3}, \sqrt{6})$ **15.** $Q(-1.5, 2)$

16. $Q(2.5, -6)$

Exercises 17–25   An angle ϕ is specified. From a diagram that shows ϕ and a reference triangle, evaluate $\cos \phi$, $\sin \phi$, and $\tan \phi$ in exact form, and also in decimal form rounded off to two places.

17. $\tan \phi = \frac{1}{2}$ and ϕ is in Quadrant III.

18. $\sin \phi = \frac{2}{3}$ and ϕ is in Quadrant II.

19. $\sin \phi = \frac{2}{5}$ and $\cos \phi$ is negative.

20. $\sin \phi = -\frac{2}{5}$ and $\cos \phi$ is negative.

21. $\tan \phi = -\frac{3}{4}$ and $\sin \phi$ is negative.

22. $\cos \phi = \frac{1}{10}$ and $\tan \phi$ is positive.

23. $\sec \phi = 2$ and $\cot \phi$ is negative.

24. $\cot \phi = \frac{2}{3}$ and $\csc \phi = \frac{-\sqrt{13}}{3}$.

25. $\tan \phi = -5$ and $\sec \phi$ is positive.

Exercises 26–37   Give a decimal approximation rounded off to three places.

26. $\sin 2.41$ **27.** $\cos 13.5$ **28.** $\tan (-1.29)$

29. $\cos 13.5°$ **30.** $\csc 37.2°$ **31.** $\cot 97°23'$

32. $\sin 21°37'$ **33.** $\tan 5$ **34.** $\cot \left(\frac{2\pi}{5}\right)$

35. $\sec \left(\frac{-\pi}{7}\right)$ **36.** $\cos \left(\frac{5\pi}{8}\right)$ **37.** $\csc \left(\frac{-8\pi}{11}\right)$

Exercises 38–45   **(a)** Give the coordinates of point $P(t)$ on the unit circle. Round off to two decimal places. Show $P(t)$ in a diagram. **(b)** Evaluate the six trigonometric functions at t (rounded off to two decimal places).

38. $t = -1$ **39.** $t = 8$ **40.** $t = -1.32$

41. $t = \frac{-\pi}{5}$ **42.** $t = \sqrt{\pi}$ **43.** $t = \pi + 1$

44. $t = \sqrt{6}$ **45.** $t = e$

Exercises 46–49   Evaluate and round off to three decimal places. Be certain your calculator is in radian mode. If your calculator gives an error message, explain why. However, you should still be able to find the requested function value. (*Hint:* Consider reference triangles.)

46. (a) $\sin (3 + 16\pi)$ **(b)** $\cos 31$

47. (a) $\cos (2 + 15\pi)$ **(b)** $\tan 36$

48. (a) $\tan (2 - 9\pi)$ **(b)** $\sec 30$

49. (a) $\sin (2 - 35\pi)$ **(b)** $\csc 40$

Exercises 50–51   For each value of θ, evaluate $\cos \theta$ and $\sin \left(\theta + \frac{\pi}{2}\right)$. Based on your results, make a guess about a relationship between the values of $\cos \theta$ and $\sin \left(\theta + \frac{\pi}{2}\right)$ for any angle θ.

50. $\theta = \frac{\pi}{3}$; $\theta = 4.5$; $\theta = -2.6$

51. $\theta = \frac{5\pi}{6}$; $\theta = 4.8$; $\theta = -2.9$

Exercises 52–53   Evaluate expressions $1 + (\tan \theta)^2$ and $(\sec \theta)^2$. Based on your results, make a guess about a relationship between the values of the two given expressions for any angle θ.

52. (a) $\theta = 36°$; $\theta = 158°$; $\theta = -215°$
  (b) $\theta = \frac{3\pi}{5}$; $\theta = 3.8$; $\theta = -6$

53. (a) $\theta = 65°$; $\theta = 210°$; $\theta = -115°$
  (b) $\theta = \frac{5\pi}{8}$; $\theta = 4.8$; $\theta = -7.2$

Exercises 54–55 For each value of θ, evaluate the expressions $\cos(2\theta)$, $2\cos\theta$, $(\cos\theta)^2 - (\sin\theta)^2$ and $2(\cos\theta)^2 - 1$. Based on your answers, which expressions appear to be equal for any angle θ?

54. (a) $\theta = 63°$; $\theta = 258°$; $\theta = -135°$
(b) $\theta = \frac{2\pi}{7}$; $\theta = 4.3$; $\theta = -1.5$

55. (a) $\theta = 73°$; $\theta = 510°$; $\theta = -135°$
(b) $\theta = \frac{5\pi}{8}$; $\theta = 5.3$; $\theta = -1.2$

56. A wheel of radius 3 is rotating counterclockwise at a uniform angular speed of 2 rev/min. Take a coordinate system with the origin at the center of rotation and designate a point Q on the circumference of the wheel. (a) If Q is located at $(3, 0)$ when t is 0, find equations that give the coordinates of $Q(x, y)$ at any time t in seconds. (b) Give the coordinates (to two decimal places) of point Q when t is 10, 20, 25, and 40 seconds.

57. Repeat Exercise 56 with a wheel of radius 4 whose uniform angular speed is 4 rev/min, with point Q located at $(4, 0)$ when t is 0.

58. One end of a spring is anchored to the ceiling and a weight is attached to the other end. When the weight is at rest, it is in equilibrium position, however, if the weight is pulled downward and released, it oscillates. Its displacement d (in millimeters) at any time t seconds after release is given by the equation $d = 40 \cos(1.5\, t)$. What is the displacement (to three significant digits) of the weight when t is (a) 1 second, (b) 2 seconds, (c) 4 seconds?

59. In Exercise 58, if friction is taken into account, we get a damping effect and the formula for the displacement becomes $d = 40\, e^{-t} \cos(1.5\, t)$. Find the displacement when t is (a) 1 second, (b) 2 seconds (c) 4 seconds.

Exercises 60–61 *Looking Ahead to Calculus* In calculus the sine and cosine functions can be expressed as infinite series as follows, where (x is in radians):

$$\sin x = x - \frac{x^3}{6} + \frac{x^5}{120} - \cdots$$

and

$$\cos x = 1 - \frac{x^2}{2} + \frac{x^4}{24} - \cdots .$$

For small values of x, the functions obtained by taking the first few terms of each series can be used for good approximations of the sine and cosine. Thus let $S(x) = x - \frac{x^3}{6}$ and $C(x) = 1 - \frac{x^2}{2} + \frac{x^4}{24}$.

60. Complete the table (rounding off to four decimal places).

x	0.1	0.2	0.3	0.4	0.5	0.6
$\sin x$	—	—	—	—	—	—
$S(x)$	—	—	—	—	—	—

61. Repeat Exercise 60 using $\cos x$ and $C(x)$ in place of $\sin x$ and $S(x)$, respectively.

SECTION 5.4 **Properties and Graphs**

Why does nature require a nontrivial and yet entirely manageable amount of mathematics for the successful description of such a large part of it?
P. W. C. Davies

The trigonometric functions are defined in terms of the coordinates of the point $P(t)$ as it moves around the unit circle. All of the properties of the trigonometric functions ultimately derive from this fact. Since we need to understand trigonometric functions thoroughly, we devote this section to an examination of their properties and graphs, with particular emphasis on what the graphs can tell us about functional behavior.

I was, and have always remained, a problem solver rather than a creator of ideas. I cannot, as Bohr and Feynman did, sit for years with my whole mind concentrating upon one deep question. I am interested in too many things.

Freeman Dyson

We first observe that all the trigonometric functions are **periodic.** We say that a function f has period p if p is the smallest positive number such that $f(x + p) = f(x)$ for every x in the domain of f.

After point $P(t)$ makes a complete circuit around the unit circle, it retraces its path exactly. Thus the coordinates of $P(t + 2\pi)$ are the same as the coordinates of $P(t)$, for any real number t, and hence the value of any trigonometric function at $t + 2\pi$ is equal to its value at t. In particular, if f is either the sine or the cosine function, we shall see from the graph of f that 2π is the smallest positive number p such that $f(t + p) = f(t)$. Therefore the period of f is 2π.

Period of Cosine and Sine

Suppose t is any real number. Then

$$\cos (t + 2\pi) = \cos t$$

$$\sin (t + 2\pi) = \sin t$$

The sine and cosine functions have period 2π.

Graphs

To graph the sine and cosine functions we use the fact that the coordinates of $P(t)$ on the unit circle are $(\cos t, \sin t)$. We consider how the coordinates change as $P(t)$ moves around the unit circle. The periodicity of the sine and cosine functions implies that their entire graphs can be obtained by repeating the portions that correspond to one complete circuit.

We begin with the sine function and see what happens to the y-coordinate of $P(t)$ as t goes from 0 to 2π. It is convenient to refer to the points where the unit circle meets the coordinates axes, labeled A, B, C, and D in Figure 5.39. As t increases from 0 to $\frac{\pi}{2}$, $P(t)$ moves counterclockwise on the unit circle from $A(1, 0)$ to $B(0, 1)$, so the y-coordinate increases from 0 to 1. As $P(t)$ moves from $B(0, 1)$ to $C(-1, 0)$, the y-coordinate decreases back to 0. Thus on the interval $(0, \pi)$ the sine function increases smoothly from 0 to 1, and then decreases back to 0.

To display this information graphically, we plot the length t along the horizontal axis and the value of $\sin t$ vertically. The result is the arch shown in Figure 5.39.

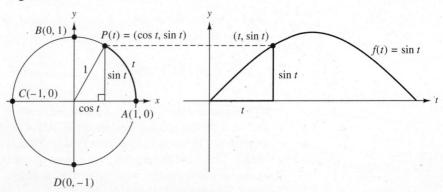

FIGURE 5.39

As $P(t)$ continues on from $C(-1, 0)$ to $D(0, -1)$ and then back around to $A(1, 0)$, the y-coordinate of $P(t)$ goes from 0 to -1 and back to 0, giving the next portion of the graph, as shown in Figure 5.40. The section of the graph of the sine function in Figure 5.40, that corresponds to one complete circuit of $P(t)$, is called a **fundamental cycle** of the sine curve. A fundamental cycle looks like part of a wave. The full graph is often called a **sine wave,** complete with crests and troughs. In Figure 5.40, the quadrants are not as apparent as they are in the unit circle. It is important, however, to recognize the portions of the cycle that correspond to each quadrant, as indicated in the figure.

Having returned to the initial point $A(1, 0)$, point $P(t)$ retraces its path around the unit circle, making the sine function periodic with period 2π. This periodicity means that the entire graph can be drawn simply by repeating the fundamental cycle in both directions.

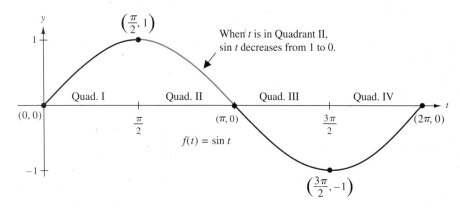

FIGURE 5.40

Fundamental cycle for $y = \sin t$

The graph of the cosine function looks very much like the graph of the sine function. Starting at $A(1, 0)$, the x-coordinate (that is, $\cos t$) begins at 1, decreases to 0 when t is $\frac{\pi}{2}$ and $P(t)$ reaches $B(0, 1)$. It then decreases further to -1 when t is π and $P(t)$ gets to $C(-1, 0)$. It then increases in a similar manner and returns to 1 when t is 2π. A fundamental cycle of the cosine curve is shown in Figure 5.41.

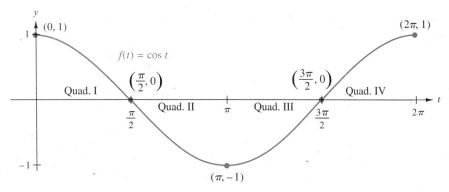

FIGURE 5.41

Fundamental cycle for $y = \cos t$

A larger portion of the graphs of the sine and cosine functions (Figure 5.42), shows that the shapes of the two curves are identical. Both are called **sinusoidal curves;** each is a sine wave.

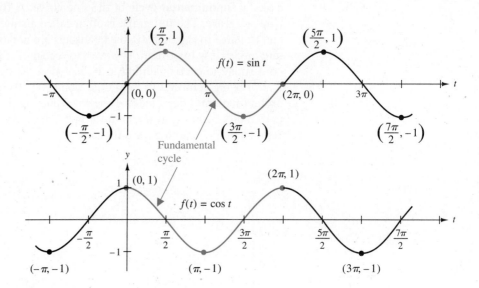

FIGURE 5.42

Graphs of $y = \sin t$ and $y = \cos t$

We may think of the cosine curve as simply a delayed sine curve—it lags behind the sine curve by a distance $\frac{\pi}{2}$ in the sense illustrated in Figure 5.43. The $\frac{\pi}{2}$ delay from the sine curve to the cosine curve can be read from Figure 5.43 at the place where the y values of the two points are equal. In equation form, for every real number t,

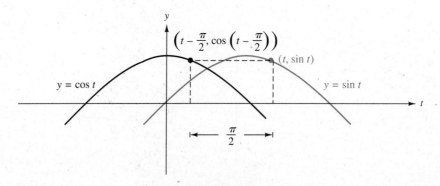

FIGURE 5.43

$\cos\left(t - \frac{\pi}{2}\right) = \sin t$ for every t

Reduction Formulas

The equation $\cos\left(t - \frac{\pi}{2}\right) = \sin t$ is called a **reduction formula.** Reduction formulas play a significant role throughout trigonometry. Other important relations could be read from the graphs in Figure 5.42, but most can be seen more easily from the unit circle.

The key to using a unit circle for reduction formulas is finding congruent reference triangles. As an example, the graphs in Figure 5.42 suggest that the sine curve is symmetric about the origin, while the cosine is symmetric about the y-axis. Using terminology from Chapter 2, it appears that the sine is an odd function and the cosine is an even function, or in equation form, for every real number t,

$$\sin(-t) = -\sin t \qquad \text{and} \qquad \cos(-t) = \cos t.$$

In the following example we justify these claims.

Strategy: Draw a unit circle diagram that shows angles t and $-t$, with reference triangles for each, then compare coordinates of $P(t)$ and $P(-t)$.

> **EXAMPLE 1** Show that for any real number t,
>
> $$\sin(-t) = -\sin t \qquad \text{and} \qquad \cos(-t) = \cos t.$$

Solution

Because on the unit circle $P(t) = (\cos t, \sin t)$ and $P(-t) = (\cos(-t), \sin(-t))$, we want to relate the coordinates of $P(t)$ and $P(-t)$. Begin with an arbitrary $P(t)$ in Figure 5.44. $P(-t)$ is located the same distance around the unit circle in the opposite direction. The reference triangles are clearly congruent, so $P(t)$ and $P(-t)$ have the same x-coordinates and their y-coordinates are equal but have opposite signs. You may find it helpful to draw diagrams that show different $P(t)$, $P(-t)$ pairs. If $P(t)$ has coordinates (a, b), then $P(-t) = (a, -b)$. Expressing the coordinates in terms of cosine and sine,

$$\begin{cases} \cos t = a \\ \sin t = b \end{cases} \qquad \text{and} \qquad \begin{cases} \cos(-t) = a \\ \sin(-t) = -b \end{cases}$$

Therefore $\cos(-t) = \cos t$ and $\sin(-t) = -\sin t$. ▲

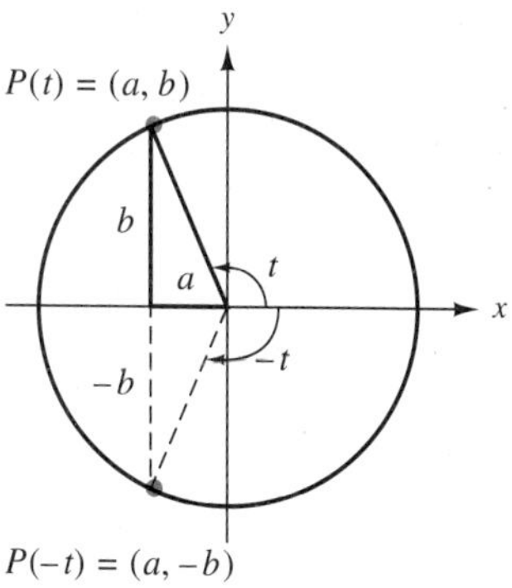

FIGURE 5.44

Since the sine is an odd function and the cosine is even, we can classify the other trigonometric functions similarly.

> **EXAMPLE 2** Find formulas that relate $f(-t)$ and $f(t)$, for the tan, cot, sec, and csc functions.

Solution

From Example 1 and the equations defining the other trigonometric functions in terms of sine and cosine,

$$\tan(-t) = \frac{\sin(-t)}{\cos(-t)} = \frac{-\sin t}{\cos t} = -\tan t$$

$$\cot(-t) = \frac{\cos(-t)}{\sin(-t)} = \frac{\cos t}{-\sin t} = -\cot t$$

$$\sec(-t) = \frac{1}{\cos(-t)} = \frac{1}{\cos t} = \sec t$$

$$\csc(-t) = \frac{1}{\sin(-t)} = \frac{1}{-\sin t} = -\csc t \quad \blacktriangle$$

Example 2 demonstrates that the cosine and secant functions are even and the other four trigonometric functions are odd.

| EXAMPLE 3 | From a unit circle diagram that shows $P(t)$ and $P(t + \pi)$, find reduction formulas for $\cos(t + \pi)$, $\sin(t + \pi)$, and $\tan(t + \pi)$.

Strategy: For any position point $P(t)$, point $(t + \pi)$ is diametrically opposite, so if $P(t)$ has coordinates (a, b) then $P(t + \pi)$ has coordinates $(-a, -b)$.

Solution

Look at Figure 5.45. $P(t)$ and $P(t + \pi)$ are end points of a diameter, so their coordinates have opposite signs. Thus, if $P(t) = (a, b)$, then $P(t + \pi) = (-a, -b)$. Therefore

$$\begin{cases} \cos t = a \\ \sin t = b \end{cases} \quad \text{and} \quad \begin{cases} \cos(t + \pi) = -a \\ \sin(t + \pi) = -b \end{cases}$$

This suggests the reduction formulas

$$\cos(t + \pi) = -\cos t \quad \text{and} \quad \sin(t + \pi) = -\sin t$$

For $\tan(t + \pi)$,

$$\tan(t + \pi) = \frac{\sin(t + \pi)}{\cos(t + \pi)} = \frac{-\sin t}{-\cos t} = \frac{\sin t}{\cos t} = \tan t. \quad \blacktriangle$$

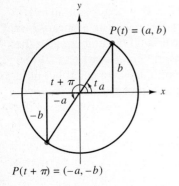

$P(t + \pi) = (-a, -b)$

FIGURE 5.45

Periods of the Trigonometric Functions

The cosine and sine functions have period 2π. The reciprocals of these two functions, the secant and cosecant, must have the same period. While it is also true that, for every real number t in the domain of the tangent, $\tan(t + 2\pi) = \tan t$, 2π is not the *smallest* positive number for which the tangent repeats. It turns out that the period of the tangent function is π. From Example 3, $\tan(t + \pi) = \tan t$ for every t in the domain of the tangent function. From the graph of the tangent function (Figure 5.49), we can see that the period of the tangent function is π.

Since the cotangent function is the reciprocal of the tangent function, it must have the same period as the tangent, so the period of the cotangent is also π. Table 5.3 summarizes these results.

TABLE 5.3 Periods of the Trigonometric Functions

Function	Period	Function	Period
Sine	2π	Cosecant	2π
Cosine	2π	Secant	2π
Tangent	π	Cotangent	π

For Graphers 5.4

GRAPHS OF TRIGONOMETRIC FUNCTIONS

Exercises

1. Draw graphs of $y = \sin x$, $y = \cos x$, and $y = \tan x$. Compare them with the graphs in this section. Both the TI and Casio have automatic Trigonometric Window settings that correspond to an x range of $(-2\pi, 2\pi)$. On the TI, after entering the functions to be graphed on the $\boxed{\text{Y=}}$ screen, press $\boxed{\text{ZOOM}}$ and $\boxed{7}$ for the Trigonometric Window. On the Casio home screen, press $\boxed{\text{Graph}}$ $\boxed{\text{sin}}$ $\boxed{\text{EXE}}$, so that the display reads "Graph $Y = \sin$" *with no X*. If you have "Graph $Y = \sin X$" and press $\boxed{\text{EXE}}$, the sine function will be graphed on the window that is already set in the machine.

2. Since calculators have keys only for sin, cos, and tan, to draw graphs of the other trigonometric functions it is necessary to use reciprocal identities. To graph $y = \sec x$, for example, graph the reciprocal of the cosine function, $y = \frac{1}{\cos x}$. In the Trigonometric Window, graph **(a)** $y = \frac{1}{\cos x}$, **(b)** $y = (\cos x)^{-1}$, **(c)** $y = \cos x^{-1}$, **(d)** $y = \cos^{-1} x$. For parts **(b)** and **(c)**, use $\boxed{\text{x}^{-1}}$. For part **(d)**, use $\boxed{\cos^{-1}}$ (above $\boxed{\cos}$).

Exercises 3–6 Draw graphs of the two functions on the same screen. Explain how the two graphs are related.

3. $f(x) = \sin x$, $g(x) = 2 \sin x$
4. $f(x) = \cos x$, $g(x) = -2 \cos x$
5. $f(x) = \sin x$, $g(x) = \sin (x - \frac{\pi}{2})$
6. $f(x) = \cos (x - \frac{\pi}{2})$, $g(x) = \sin x$

Exercises 7–10 Use a graph to approximate the x-intercept points in the interval $[-2\pi, 2\pi]$.

7. $f(x) = \sin x$
8. $g(x) = \cos x$
9. $f(x) = 0.5 + \sin x$
10. $g(x) = \cos x - \sin x$

Exercises 11–12 Draw graphs of the two functions on the same screen. Use the graphs to approximate the solutions to the equation $f(x) = g(x)$ in the interval $[-2\pi, 2\pi]$.

11. $f(x) = \sin x$, $g(x) = \cos x$
12. $f(x) = \cos x$, $g(x) = \tan x$

Exercises 13–16 Use a graph to help you determine whether the function is even or odd.

13. $f(x) = \sin |x|$
14. $g(x) = |\sin x|$
15. $f(x) = \cos |x|$
16. $g(x) = |\cos x|$

Graphs of the Other Trigonometric Functions

As $P(t)$ moves around the unit circle, we can observe the changes in the coordinates $(\cos t, \sin t)$ we have graphed. Labeling the sides of the reference triangle, $\triangle OPR$ in Figure 5.46a, with the coordinates of $P(t)$, we can visualize the behavior of the graphs of $y = \cos t$ and $y = \sin t$ by mentally following how the sides of the triangles vary. For example, in Figure 5.46b we show $P(t)$ for several values of t from 0 to π. The horizontal legs of the triangles carry the label of the cosine function and show how $\cos t$ decreases from 1 to -1.

Careful use of similar triangles allows us to visualize all the trigonometric functions as signed sides of triangles. Consider the triangles in Figure 5.46c, where the line through T, A, and C is perpendicular to the x-axis at A, and $\overline{OC}$ is perpendicular to $\overline{OT}$. It follows that $\angle OCA = t$ (see Develop Mastery Exercise 6). Therefore the right triangles, $\triangle OTA$ and $\triangle COA$, are both similar to $\triangle OPR$ in Figure 5.46a. Using the similar triangles OTA and OPR and the fact that $|\overline{OA}| = 1$, we have

$$\frac{|\overline{AT}|}{|\overline{OA}|} = \frac{|\overline{RP}|}{|\overline{OR}|} \qquad \text{so} \qquad \frac{|\overline{AT}|}{1} = \frac{\sin t}{\cos t} \qquad \text{or} \qquad |\overline{AT}| = \tan t.$$

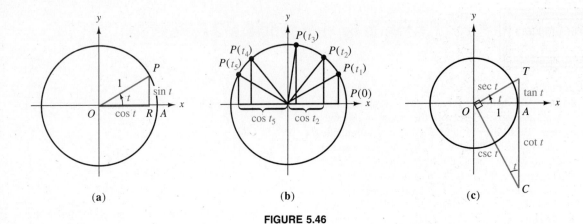

FIGURE 5.46

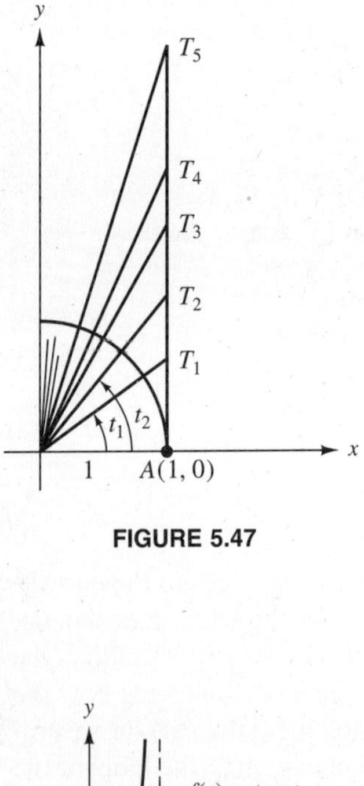

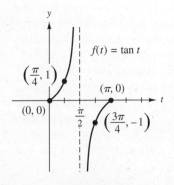

FIGURE 5.47

Similarly (see Develop Mastery Exercise 6), the other sides in Figure 5.46(c) are as labeled.

$$|\overline{AT}| = \tan t \qquad |\overline{OT}| = \sec t \qquad |\overline{AC}| = \cot t \qquad |\overline{OC}| = \csc t$$

By observing how the lengths of these line segments change as t varies, we can get a good idea of the behavior of the graphs of the corresponding functions.

Graph of the Tangent   Consider what happens to $|\overline{AT}|$ in Figure 5.46c as $P(t)$ moves around the circle from $A(1, 0)$ toward $B(0, 1)$. Point T initially coincides with A. As t increases, the length of $|\overline{AT}|$ increases without bound, as suggested in Figure 5.47. It is apparent why the tangent function is not defined at $\frac{\pi}{2}$. For t in the second quadrant, the situation is reversed. We still have $\tan t = \frac{\sin t}{\cos t}$, but, because the cosine is negative, so is the tangent. If we carefully plot some points for various first-quadrant values of t, we obtain the fundamental portion for the graph of $y = \tan t$ shown in Figure 5.48.

In Section 3.4 we observed that graphs of rational functions often involve vertical asymptotes. Since the tangent is a quotient $\frac{\sin t}{\cos t}$ it should not be surprising that the graph has a vertical asymptote at each zero of the denominator. The cosine is zero at every odd multiple of $\frac{\pi}{2}$, so the tangent function has infinitely many vertical asymptotes. The period of the tangent function is π, so the graph of $y = \tan t$ repeats the portion shown in Figure 5.48. (See Figure 5.49a.)

The graph of $y = \cot t$ can be analyzed in much the same way as the graph of $y = \tan t$, by observing how $|\overline{AC}|$ in Figure 5.46c varies. When $t = 0$, $\cot t$ is undefined, but as t increases, the length of the line segment $\overline{AC}$ steadily decreases to 0 when t is $\frac{\pi}{2}$ and continues negatively as t approaches π. (See Figure 5.49b.)

The graphs of $y = \sec t$ and $y = \csc t$ can be obtained by considering the way the lengths of the line segments $\overline{OT}$ and $\overline{OC}$ in Figure 5.46c vary, or by looking at the cosine and sine graphs and considering reciprocals. The graphs of tangent, cotangent, secant, and cosecant are all shown in Figure 5.49, along with their periods and vertical asymptotes.

FIGURE 5.48

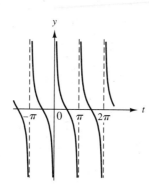

(a) $y = \tan t$
odd; period π

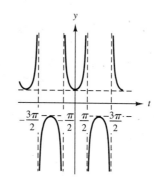

(b) $y = \cot t$
odd; period π

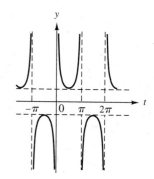

(c) $y = \sec t$
even; period 2π

(d) $y = \csc t$
odd; period 2π

FIGURE 5.49

More Reduction Formulas

In Example 2 we observed that $\cos (t + \pi) = -\cos t$ and $\sin (t + \pi) = -\sin t$. With these reduction formulas, we got $\tan (t + \pi) = \tan t$. The other trigonometric functions have similar formulas.

$$\sec (t + \pi) = \frac{1}{\cos (t + \pi)} = -\frac{1}{\cos t} = -\sec t$$

$$\csc (t + \pi) = \frac{1}{\sin (t + \pi)} = -\frac{1}{\sin t} = -\csc t$$

$$\cot (t + \pi) = \frac{1}{\tan (t + \pi)} = \frac{1}{\tan t} = \cot t$$

We illustrate the derivation of another set of reduction formulas in the next example.

EXAMPLE 4 Let $P(\theta)$ on the unit circle have coordinates (a, b). Find the coordinate of the point $P(\theta + \frac{\pi}{2})$ in terms of a and b, and get reduction formulas for $\cos (\theta + \frac{\pi}{2})$ and $\sin (\theta + \frac{\pi}{2})$ in terms of $\cos \theta$ and $\sin \theta$.

Solution

As in the previous examples, begin with a diagram that shows $P(\theta)$ and a reference triangle for some arbitrary θ. (See Figure 5.50a.)

To locate $P(\theta + \frac{\pi}{2})$, add a right angle to θ, then draw a perpendicular to the x-axis to get the reference triangle shown in color in Figure 5.50b. It is easy to see that the reference triangles are congruent. Hence, the length of the short leg in each diagram is b and the longer leg has length a. The coordinates of $P(\theta + \frac{\pi}{2})$ are $(-b, a)$ since all x-coordinates in the second quadrant are negative. As a reminder, label the horizontal leg in Figure 5.50b as $-b$ even though its length is b.

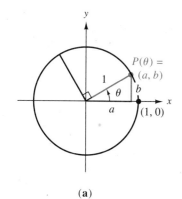

(a)

(b)

FIGURE 5.50

$$(\cos \theta, \sin \theta) = (a, b) \qquad \text{and} \qquad \left(\cos \left(\theta + \frac{\pi}{2}\right), \sin \left(\theta + \frac{\pi}{2}\right)\right) = (-b, a)$$

Equate coordinates:

$$\cos \theta = a \qquad\qquad \sin \theta = b$$

$$\cos \left(\theta + \frac{\pi}{2} \right) = -b \qquad \sin \left(\theta = \frac{\pi}{2} \right) = a.$$

From these equations, we get the desired reduction formulas:

$$\sin \left(\theta + \frac{\pi}{2} \right) = \cos \theta \qquad \text{and} \qquad \cos \left(\theta + \frac{\pi}{2} \right) = -\sin \theta. \quad \blacktriangle$$

Table 5.4 summarizes a number of useful reduction formulas. The table gives formulas for only sine, cosine, and tangent. The others can be derived by taking reciprocals, as illustrated in the following example.

TABLE 5.4   Reduction Formulas

	$-t$	$\frac{\pi}{2} - t$	$\frac{\pi}{2} + t$	$\pi - t$	$\pi + t$	$\frac{3\pi}{2} - t$	$\frac{3\pi}{2} + t$
sin	$-\sin t$	$\cos t$	$\cos t$	$\sin t$	$-\sin t$	$-\cos t$	$-\cos t$
cos	$\cos t$	$\sin t$	$-\sin t$	$-\cos t$	$-\cos t$	$-\sin t$	$\sin t$
tan	$-\tan t$	$\cot t$	$-\cot t$	$-\tan t$	$\tan t$	$\cot t$	$-\cot t$

EXAMPLE 5   Use Table 5.4 to simplify $\csc \left(t - \frac{\pi}{2} \right)$.

Solution

Remember that $\csc \left(t - \frac{\pi}{2} \right) = \dfrac{1}{\sin(t - \frac{\pi}{2})}$. Table 5.4 has $\sin \left(\frac{\pi}{2} - t \right)$, but not $\sin \left(t - \frac{\pi}{2} \right)$, so first use the fact that sine is an odd function to get,

$$\sin \left(t - \frac{\pi}{2} \right) = \sin \left(-\left(\frac{\pi}{2} - t \right) \right) = -\sin \left(\frac{\pi}{2} - t \right)$$

From Table 5.4, $\sin \left(\frac{\pi}{2} - t \right) = \cos t$. Putting all this together,

$$\csc \left(t - \frac{\pi}{2} \right) = \frac{1}{\sin \left(t - \frac{\pi}{2} \right)} = \frac{-1}{\sin \left(\frac{\pi}{2} - t \right)} = \frac{-1}{\cos t}$$

$$= -\sec t.$$

Thus, $\csc \left(t - \frac{\pi}{2} \right) = -\sec t$ is a reduction formula (an identity). $\blacktriangle$

EXERCISES 5.4

Exercises 1–5   True or False. Give reasons for your conclusion.

1. For every real number x, $\cos |x| - \cos x = 0$.

2. For every real number x, $\sin |x| - \sin x \geq 0$.

3. The graph of $y = \cos |x|$ is the same as the graph of $y = \cos x$.

4. The function $f(x) = |\sin x|$ is an even function.

5. The graph of $y = \cos \left(\frac{\pi}{2} - x \right)$ is the same as the graph of $y = \sin x$.

Exercises 6–10 Complete the sentence by selecting from the list below *all choices* that make the statement true.

(a) $y = \cos x$ **(b)** $y = \sin x$ **(c)** $y = \tan x$

(d) $y = \sec x$ **(e)** $y = \cos(\frac{1}{x})$ **(f)** $(0, 0)$

(g) $(\frac{\pi}{2}, -1)$ **(h)** $(0, 1)$ **(i)** $(\frac{\pi}{2}, 0)$

(j) $(\pi, 1)$ **(k)** $(\pi, 0)$

6. The graph of $y = \sin(\pi - x)$ is the same as the graph of _____ .

7. The graph of $y = \dfrac{\cos(\frac{\pi}{2} - x)}{\cos x}$ is the same as the graph of _____ .

8. The graph of $y = \frac{1}{\cos x}$ is the same as the graph of _____ .

9. The graph of $y = \sin(x + \frac{\pi}{2})$ passes through _____ .

10. The graph of $y = \tan(x + \pi)$ passes through _____ .

Explore and Discover

1. From the Pythagorean theorem and triangle *OPR* in Figure 5.46a, we can see that for all nonquadrantal numbers t, $(\cos t)^2 + (\sin t)^2 = 1$. Verify that $(\cos t)^2 + (\sin t)^2 = 1$ for quadrantal numbers, as well. (*Hint:* What are the possible values of $\cos t$ and $\sin t$ for quadrantal numbers t?)

2. From Figure 5.46c, verify each of the following relations for nonquadrantal numbers t.
   (a) $(\tan t)^2 + 1 = (\sec t)^2$
   (b) $(\cot t)^2 + 1 = (\csc t)^2$
   (c) $(\sec t)^2 + (\csc t)^2 = (\tan t + \cot t)^2$

3. Which of the relations in Exercise 2 are valid for quadrantal numbers t?

Develop Mastery

Exercises 1–4 Use a calculator to complete the table. Note that x increases in steps of $\frac{\pi}{20}$. Give entries to two decimal places, then make a large-scale graph to plot the points from your table and sketch the graph of the function on the indicated interval. In each case compare with the graphs in Figures 5.42 and 5.49.

1. Graph $y = \cos x$ on the interval $[0, \frac{\pi}{2}]$.

x	0	$\frac{\pi}{20}$	$\frac{\pi}{10}$	$\frac{3\pi}{20}$	$\frac{\pi}{5}$	$\frac{\pi}{4}$	$\frac{3\pi}{10}$	$\frac{7\pi}{20}$	$\frac{2\pi}{5}$	$\frac{9\pi}{20}$	$\frac{\pi}{2}$
$\cos x$											

2. Graph $y = \sin x$ on the interval $[\frac{\pi}{2}, \pi]$.

x	$\frac{\pi}{2}$	$\frac{11\pi}{20}$	$\frac{3\pi}{5}$	$\frac{13\pi}{20}$	$\frac{7\pi}{10}$	$\frac{3\pi}{4}$	$\frac{4\pi}{5}$	$\frac{17\pi}{20}$	$\frac{9\pi}{10}$	$\frac{19\pi}{20}$	π
$\sin x$											

3. Graph $y = \tan x$ on the interval $[\frac{\pi}{4}, \frac{3\pi}{4}]$.

x	$\frac{\pi}{4}$	$\frac{3\pi}{10}$	$\frac{7\pi}{20}$	$\frac{2\pi}{5}$	$\frac{9\pi}{20}$	$\frac{\pi}{2}$	$\frac{11\pi}{20}$	$\frac{3\pi}{5}$	$\frac{13\pi}{20}$	$\frac{7\pi}{10}$	$\frac{3\pi}{4}$
$\tan x$											

4. Graph $y = \sec x$ on the interval $[0, \frac{\pi}{2}]$.

x	0	$\frac{\pi}{20}$	$\frac{\pi}{10}$	$\frac{3\pi}{20}$	$\frac{\pi}{5}$	$\frac{\pi}{4}$	$\frac{3\pi}{10}$	$\frac{7\pi}{20}$	$\frac{2\pi}{5}$	$\frac{9\pi}{20}$	$\frac{\pi}{2}$
$\sec x$											

5. From the reduction formulas derived in Example 4, find reduction formulas for $f(\theta + \frac{\pi}{2})$ for the remaining four trigonometric functions.

6. Refer to the diagram in Figure 5.46.
   (a) From the fact that $\angle TOA = t$, show that $\angle OCA$ is equal to t.
   (b) Use right triangle trigonometry to show that $|\overline{OT}| = \sec t, |\overline{AC}| = \cot t,$ and $|\overline{OC}| = \csc t$.

Exercises 7–12   Use Table 5.4 to simplify the expression.

7. $\cos (t - \frac{\pi}{2})$ 8. $\tan (t - \pi)$ 9. $\sin (t - \frac{3\pi}{2})$

10. $\sec (\frac{\pi}{2} + t)$ 11. $\cot (t - \frac{\pi}{2})$ 12. $\csc (t - \frac{\pi}{2})$

Exercises 13–18   Given the coordinates of a point $Q(a, b)$ on the terminal side of an angle θ in standard position, draw a diagram to evaluate in exact form the six trigonometric functions of the indicated angle.

13. $Q(-3, 4)$; $\theta + \pi$ 14. $Q(-3, 4)$; $\theta + \frac{\pi}{2}$

15. $Q(12, -5)$; $\theta - \frac{\pi}{2}$ 16. $Q(8, -6)$; $-\theta$

17. $Q(-8, -15)$; $-\theta + \frac{\pi}{2}$ 18. $Q(24, 7)$; $\theta + \frac{3\pi}{2}$

Exercises 19–26   For point $P(t)$ on the unit circle, one of the coordinates is given. From a diagram showing $P(t)$ and $P(\theta)$ for the indicated angle θ, find the coordinates of each. Evaluate the six trigonometric functions of θ.

19. $P(\frac{5}{13}, y)$, $y > 0$; $\theta = t + \pi$

20. $P(\frac{5}{13}, y)$, $y < 0$; $\theta = \pi - t$

21. $P(x, -\frac{3}{5})$, $x > 0$; $\theta = -t$

22. $P(-\frac{8}{17}, y)$, $y < 0$; $\theta = t - \pi$

23. $P(x, \frac{7}{25})$, $x < 0$; $\theta = t + \pi$

24. $P(x, \frac{4}{5})$, $x > 0$; $\theta = \frac{\pi}{2} - t$

25. $P(\frac{24}{25}, y)$, $y < 0$; $\theta = t + \frac{\pi}{2}$

26. $P(\frac{12}{13}, y)$, $y < 0$, $\theta = t + \frac{3\pi}{2}$

Exercises 27–30   A value of t or θ is given. Let $s = \frac{\pi}{2} + t$ and $\alpha = 90° + \theta$. Use a calculator to complete the table to three decimal places. Compare the results with Table 5.4.

27.

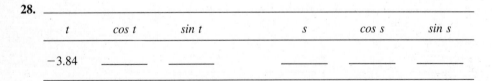

t	$\cos t$	$\sin t$	s	$\cos s$	$\sin s$
1.25					

28.

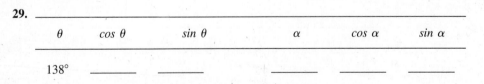

t	$\cos t$	$\sin t$	s	$\cos s$	$\sin s$
−3.84					

29.

θ	$\cos \theta$	$\sin \theta$	α	$\cos \alpha$	$\sin \alpha$
138°					

30.

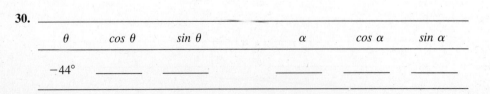

θ	$\cos \theta$	$\sin \theta$	α	$\cos \alpha$	$\sin \alpha$
−44°					

Exercises 31–36 Determine whether the equation is a valid reduction formula.

31. $\cos\left(\frac{5\pi}{2} - t\right) = \cos t$ **32.** $\sin(3\pi + t) = -\sin t$

33. $\cos\left(t - \frac{3\pi}{2}\right) = \sin t$ **34.** $\sec(t - 3\pi) = \sec t$

35. $\csc\left(t + \frac{7\pi}{2}\right) = -\sec t$ **36.** $\tan(5\pi - t) = \cot t$

Exercises 37–40 Sketch a graph of f for x in $[-2\pi, 2\pi]$. (*Hint:* First use an appropriate reduction formula.)

37. $f(x) = \cos\left(\frac{\pi}{2} - x\right)$ **38.** $f(x) = \sin\left(\frac{3\pi}{2} + x\right)$

39. $f(x) = \tan(\pi + x)$ **40.** $f(x) = \sec(\pi - x)$

Exercises 41–44 Sketch a graph of the equation for x in $[-\pi, \pi]$.

41. $y = 2\sin x$ **42.** $y = -2\cos x$

43. $y = -\tan x$ **44.** $y = -\csc x$

Exercises 45–49 Use appropriate reduction formulas (identities) from Table 5.4 to find a simpler equation to describe the function. In each case, give the domain of the function.

45. $f(x) = \dfrac{\sin\left(x - \frac{\pi}{2}\right)}{\cos\ x}$

46. $g(x) = \dfrac{\cos\left(x + \frac{3\pi}{2}\right)}{\sin x}$

47. $f(x) = \frac{\tan(x + \pi)}{\tan x}$

48. $g(x) = \frac{1}{2}\left[\sin x - \cos\left(x + \frac{\pi}{2}\right)\right]$

49. $f(x) = \frac{1}{2}\left[\cos x + \sin\left(\frac{\pi}{2} - x\right)\right]$

Exercises 50–54 Sketch a graph of f for x in $[-\pi, \pi]$. (*Hint:* First use an appropriate reduction formula to get a simpler equation for $f(x)$.)

50. $f(x) = \frac{\cos(-x)}{\cos x}$ **51.** $f(x) = \dfrac{\cos\left(x + \frac{\pi}{2}\right)}{\sin x}$

52. $f(x) = \frac{\sin(x + \pi)}{\cos x}$

53. $f(x) = \frac{1}{2}\left[\sin x + \cos\left(\frac{\pi}{2} - x\right)\right]$

54. $f(x) = \frac{1}{2}\left[\cos x + \sin\left(\frac{\pi}{2} - x\right)\right]$

Exercises 55–62 Use the graphs of the sine, cosine, and tangent functions to help you draw a graph of f for x in $[-2\pi, 2\pi]$. In each case determine whether f is odd, even, or neither. If f is periodic, find its period.

55. $f(x) = |\sin x|$ **56.** $f(x) = \sin |x|$

57. $f(x) = \cos |x|$ **58.** $f(x) = |\cos x|$

59. $f(x) = |\tan x|$ **60.** $f(x) = \tan |x|$

61. $f(x) = \frac{1}{2}(\sin x + |\sin x|)$

62. $f(x) = \frac{1}{2}(\cos x + |\cos x|)$

Exercises 63–66 On the same set of coordinate axes draw graphs of f and g. At how many points do the graphs intersect? Draw as many periods of the sine or cosine function as needed to be certain that you have all points of intersection.

63. $f(x) = \sin x$, $g(x) = \frac{x}{2}$

64. $f(x) = \sin x$, $g(x) = \frac{x}{4}$

65. $f(x) = \sin x$, $g(x) = \frac{x}{8}$

66. $f(x) = \cos x$, $g(x) = x^2$

SECTION 5.5   Inverse Trigonometric Functions

Quite often [mathematicians] do not deliver a frontal attack against a given problem, but rather they shape it, transform it, until it is eventually changed into a problem that they have solved before.
     Rózsa Péter

Given the equation $\sin t = 0.723$, how can we find the solution set, that is, the number or numbers whose sine is 0.723? If we look at the graph of the sine function in Figure 5.51, it is apparent that there are infinitely many numbers whose sine is 0.723. All such numbers are coterminal with one of the numbers x_1 or x_2 in the figure. In most cases, there is little hope of finding an exact

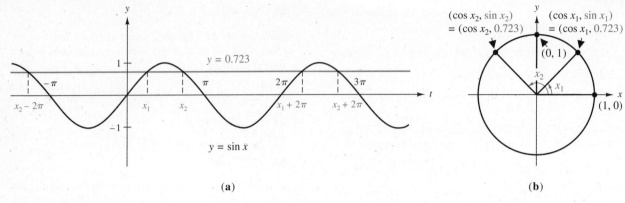

FIGURE 5.51

solution, but calculators are programmed to approximate one solution. In this instance, if we enter 0.723 and press $\boxed{\texttt{sin}^{-1}}$, the calculator immediately returns 0.808134999 (in radian mode) or 46.3027247 (in degree mode). The number x_1 in Figure 5.51 is the one the calculator approximates as 0.808134999.

In this section, we want to understand the inverse trigonometric functions, to learn how to use the calculator to evaluate them, and to learn how to find solutions the calculator does not give.

Trigonometric Functions with Restricted Domains

In Section 2.7 we learned that only one–one functions have inverses. In particular, any function that is increasing or decreasing throughout its domain has an inverse. Because all trigonometric functions are periodic, no trigonometric function is one–one. In order to get inverses for trigonometric functions, we restrict their domains to intervals on which they are increasing or decreasing. To clarify notation we name new functions that coincide with the trigonometric functions on restricted domains. The graphs of these functions, with their names and limited domains, are shown in Figure 5.52.

I didn't like the symbols for sine, cosine, tangent, and so on. So I invented other symbols. Now the inverse sine was the same [symbol] but left-to-right reflected . . . NOT sin^{-1}—that was crazy! To me sin^{-1} meant $\frac{1}{sine}$, the reciprocal. So my symbols were better.

Richard Feynman

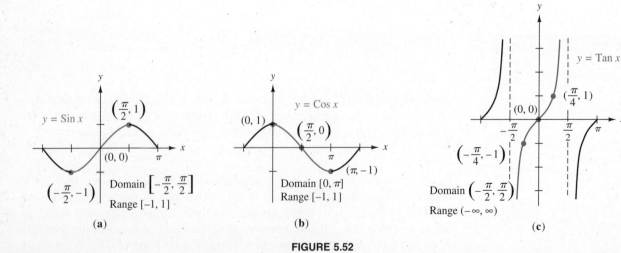

FIGURE 5.52

$$\text{Sin } x = \sin x \text{ on } \left[-\tfrac{\pi}{2}, \tfrac{\pi}{2}\right]$$

$$\text{Cos } x = \cos x \text{ on } [0, \pi]$$

$$\text{Tan } x = \tan x \text{ on } \left(-\tfrac{\pi}{2}, \tfrac{\pi}{2}\right)$$

Observe that the restrictions are chosen so that Sin and Tan are increasing, while Cos is decreasing, but the domains of all three include the numbers between 0 and $\frac{\pi}{2}$. The restricted domains make all three functions one–one, and each has an inverse function. We denote the inverses, respectively, by Sin^{-1}, Cos^{-1}, and Tan^{-1}, read "inverse sine," "inverse cosine," and "inverse tangent." This notation is consistent with the notation we used in Section 2.7. As we cautioned in that section, *the inverse is not the same as the reciprocal:* $\text{Sin}^{-1}x$ is not equal to $\frac{1}{\text{Sin } x}$.

From Section 2.7, recall that we get the inverse by interchanging the coordinates of each point. When we interchange coordinates on a graph, the graph of the inverse function is a reflection of the graph of the function through the line $y = x$.

Since points $\left(-\frac{\pi}{2}, -1\right)$, $(0, 0)$, and $\left(\frac{\pi}{2}, 1\right)$ are on the graph of $y = \text{Sin } x$, $\left(-1, -\frac{\pi}{2}\right)$, $(0, 0)$, and $\left(1, \frac{\pi}{2}\right)$ are points on the graph of $y = \text{Sin}^{-1}x$. (See Figure 5.53a.) Similarly, since $(0, 1)$, $\left(\frac{\pi}{2}, 0\right)$ and $(\pi, -1)$ are on the graph of $y = \text{Cos } x$, $(1, 0)$, $\left(0, \frac{\pi}{2}\right)$ and $(-1, \pi)$ are on the graph of $y = \text{Cos}^{-1}x$. (See Figure 5.53b.)

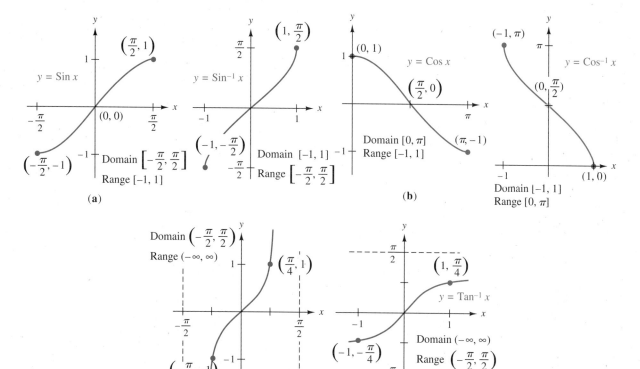

FIGURE 5.53

Finally, since the graph of $y = \text{Tan } x$ contains $(-\frac{\pi}{4}, -1)$, $(0, 0)$, $(\frac{\pi}{4}, 1)$ and is bounded between the vertical asymptotes $x = -\frac{\pi}{2}$ and $x = \frac{\pi}{2}$, the graph of $y = \text{Tan}^{-1}x$ contains the points $(-1, -\frac{\pi}{4})$, $(0, 0)$, and $(1, \frac{\pi}{4})$ and the graph lies between the horizontal asymptotes $y = -\frac{\pi}{2}$ and $y = \frac{\pi}{2}$. (See Figure 5.53c.)

Calculator Evaluation

Just as the calculator simplifies finding extremely accurate values of trigonometric functions, it makes the evaluation of inverses just as simple using $\boxed{\texttt{sin}^{-1}}$, $\boxed{\texttt{cos}^{-1}}$, and $\boxed{\texttt{tan}^{-1}}$. The labels may appear above or below the corresponding $\boxed{\texttt{sin}}$, $\boxed{\texttt{cos}}$, and $\boxed{\texttt{tan}}$ and are often activated by another key labeled $\boxed{\texttt{INV}}$ or $\boxed{\texttt{2nd}}$. On some calculators, the inverse functions are not even labeled and it is understood that $\boxed{\texttt{INV}}$ $\boxed{\texttt{sin}}$ or $\boxed{\texttt{2nd}}$ $\boxed{\texttt{sin}}$, for example, will evaluate the inverse sine.

With algebraic entry calculators, we first enter the entire expression to be evaluated (the function and argument) and then press $\boxed{\texttt{EXE}}$ or $\boxed{\texttt{ENTER}}$ to execute the instructions. For the first example in Table 5.5, the following sequence of keystrokes would give the correct result on a Casio calculator.

$$\boxed{\texttt{SHIFT}}\;\boxed{\texttt{Cos}^{-1}} - 0.5 \;\boxed{\texttt{EXE}}$$

The display should read "Cos^{-1} $- 0.5$" before pressing $\boxed{\texttt{EXE}}$. The resulting display should show "120." Remember that many calculators distinguish between the subtraction key and the change sign key. In this case we want the inverse cosine of the negative number -0.5. The calculator is programmed to know that it is not possible to subtract 0.5 from Cos^{-1}.

Use the examples in Table 5.5 to make certain that you know how to get the information you need from your calculator. Remember that we must always specify the appropriate mode. The last entry is included to emphasize that there is no number whose sine is 1.4. Since the range of the Sin and Cos functions is the interval $[-1, 1]$, the domain of Sin^{-1} and Cos^{-1} is also $[-1, 1]$, and the calculator is programmed to not accept any number outside that interval for those functions.

The inverse trigonometric functions are also sometimes called the **arc-trigonometric functions**. Since both sets of names are common, you should become familiar with both. Arcsin, Arccos, and Arctan are other names for Sin^{-1}, Cos^{-1}, and Tan^{-1}, respectively.

TABLE 5.5   Calculator Evaluations

Evaluate	Mode	Enter	Key	Display	Check
Cos^{-1} -0.5(deg)	Deg	-0.5	cos^{-1}	120.00	cos $120° = -0.5$
Cos^{-1} -0.5(rad)	Rad	-0.5	cos^{-1}	2.09	cos $2.09 \approx -0.5$
Tan^{-1} 3.2(deg)	Deg	3.2	tan^{-1}	72.60	tan $72.6° \approx 3.2$
Tan^{-1} 3.2(rad)	Rad	3.2	tan^{-1}	1.27	tan $1.27 \approx 3.2$
Sin^{-1} 1.4	Either	1.4	sin^{-1}	ERROR	

| EXAMPLE 1 | Evaluate and give results rounded off to three

decimal places. Show the corresponding point on the appropriate graph from Figure 5.53.

(a) $\text{Sin}^{-1}\, 0.324$ (b) $\text{Cos}^{-1} (\sin 3.82)$ (c) $\text{Arctan}\, \pi$

Solution

The calculator approximations (in radian mode) are:

(a) $\text{Sin}^{-1}\, 0.324 \approx 0.330$

(b) $\text{Cos}^{-1} (\sin 3.82) \approx \text{Cos}^{-1}(-0.62755) \approx 2.249$

(c) $\text{Arctan}\, \pi \approx \text{Arctan}\,(3.1416) \approx 1.263$.

In **(b)** and **(c)** intermediate steps allow you to check your computations, but we suggest that you *not* record intermediate calculations. In **(b)**, for instance, enter 3.82 and then use only two keystrokes: $\boxed{\text{sin}}\ \boxed{\text{cos}^{-1}}$. Record the final display. With an algebraic entry calculator, press $\boxed{\text{cos}^{-1}}$, $\boxed{\text{sin}}$, 3.82, $\boxed{\text{ENTER}}$ (or $\boxed{\text{EXE}}$). The points that correspond to these calculations are shown in Figure 5.54. ▲

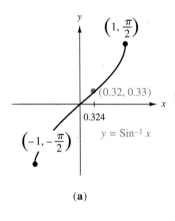

(a)

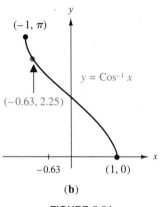

(b)

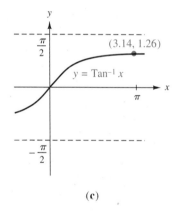

(c)

FIGURE 5.54

Inverse Function Identities

Perhaps the most important characteristic of inverse functions and their inverses is that they "undo each other" in the sense described in Section 2.7.

$$f(f^{-1}(x)) = x \text{ for all } x \text{ in the domain of } f^{-1}$$
$$f^{-1}(f(x)) = x \text{ for all } x \text{ in the domain of } f$$

This is true for the inverse trigonometric functions, as well.

Inverse Trigonometric Function Identities

$\sin(\mathrm{Sin}^{-1} x) = x$ and $\cos(\mathrm{Cos}^{-1} x) = x$ for all x in $[-1, 1]$

$\mathrm{Sin}^{-1}(\sin x) = x$ for all x in $[\frac{-\pi}{2}, \frac{\pi}{2}]$

$\mathrm{Cos}^{-1}(\cos x) = x$ for all x in $[0, \pi]$

$\tan(\mathrm{Tan}^{-1} x) = x$ for all real numbers x

$\mathrm{Tan}^{-1}(\tan x) = x$ for all x in $(\frac{-\pi}{2}, \frac{\pi}{2})$

The same information contained in the above identities can also be stated in the following equivalent form.

$y = \mathrm{Sin}^{-1} x$ means $\sin y = x$ where $-1 \le x \le 1$ and $-\frac{\pi}{2} \le y \le \frac{\pi}{2}$

$y = \mathrm{Cos}^{-1} x$ means $\cos y = x$ where $-1 \le x \le 1$ and $0 \le y \le \pi$

$y = \mathrm{Tan}^{-1} x$ means $\tan y = x$ where x can be any real number and
$$\frac{-\pi}{2} < y < \frac{\pi}{2}$$

The identity $\sin(\mathrm{Sin}^{-1} x) = x$ suggests a way to think about the inverse trigonometric functions that many people find helpful.

$\mathrm{Sin}^{-1} x$ is the number (or angle) whose sine is x.

EXAMPLE 2   Evaluate in exact form.

   (a) $\mathrm{Arcsin}\left(\frac{1}{\sqrt{2}}\right)$ **(b)** $\mathrm{Tan}^{-1}(-\sqrt{3})$ **(c)** $\mathrm{Cos}^{-1}\left(-\frac{1}{2}\right)$

Strategy: Look back at Figure 5.26 on p. 273. Find the numbers θ such that $\sin\theta = \frac{1}{\sqrt{2}}$. Since we know that the inverse sine is a number between $\frac{-\pi}{2}$ and $\frac{\pi}{2}$, we can identify $\mathrm{Arcsin}\left(\frac{1}{\sqrt{2}}\right)$.

Solution

(a) Let $\theta = \mathrm{Arcsin}\left(\frac{1}{\sqrt{2}}\right)$, so θ is the number whose sine is $\frac{1}{\sqrt{2}}$. We know two things about θ:

$$\sin\theta = \frac{1}{\sqrt{2}} \quad \text{and} \quad -\frac{\pi}{2} \le \theta \le \frac{\pi}{2}.$$

There are relatively few angles for which we can evaluate trigonometric functions in exact form. We listed most of them in Figure 5.26 on page 273. Accordingly, look for an angle that has one of the special triangles as a reference triangle. In this case, the first-quadrant angle whose sine is $\frac{1}{\sqrt{2}}$ is $\frac{\pi}{4}$, so $\theta = \frac{\pi}{4}$. Thus, $\mathrm{Arcsin}\left(\frac{1}{\sqrt{2}}\right) = \frac{\pi}{4}$.

(b) Let $t = \mathrm{Tan}^{-1}(-\sqrt{3})$, so t is the angle in $\left(-\frac{\pi}{2}, \frac{\pi}{2}\right)$ whose tangent is $-\sqrt{3}$. Since $\tan t$ is negative in the fourth quadrant,

$$\tan t = -\sqrt{3} \quad \text{and} \quad -\frac{\pi}{2} < t < 0.$$

Either by sketching a $30°$–$60°$ right triangle or checking Figure 5.26, we can identify the fourth quadrant angle whose tangent is $-\sqrt{3}$: $-\frac{\pi}{3}$. Thus $\mathrm{Tan}^{-1}(-\sqrt{3}) = -\frac{\pi}{3}$.

(c) $\mathrm{Cos}^{-1}\left(-\frac{1}{2}\right)$ is an angle in $[0, \pi]$ whose cosine is $-\frac{1}{2}$. The cosine is negative in the second quadrant, so the angle we want is $\frac{2\pi}{3}$. Hence, $\mathrm{Cos}^{-1}\left(-\frac{1}{2}\right) = \frac{2\pi}{3}$. ▲

π AND e, PART II

Because π and e are transcendental, there is no polynomial equation with integer coefficients—not of degree ten or ten million—whose graph has an x-intercept at either number. How are such numbers approximated to thousands of decimal places? Some limiting process is needed, usually an infinite series. Various series differ dramatically in their rates of convergence (the number of terms needed for a good approximation). We list below some series that have

actually been used to calculate digits of π and e.

Most recent computer calculations use series for the inverse tangent function (the source of Gregory's approximation). The 1986 program on the CRAY-2 supercomputer that produced 29 million digits of π used a new iteration algorithm due to the two Borwein brothers of Dalhousie University in Nova Scotia.

Mathematicians Peter (left) and Jonathan Borwein

$$e = 1 + \frac{1}{1} + \frac{1}{1 \cdot 2} + \frac{1}{1 \cdot 2 \cdot 3} + \cdots$$

$$\frac{\pi^2}{6} = 1 + \frac{1}{4} + \frac{1}{9} + \frac{1}{16} + \cdots$$

Euler (The series for e is very fast but for π is quite slow.)

$$\frac{\pi}{4} = 1 - \frac{1}{3} + \frac{1}{5} - \frac{1}{7} + \cdots$$

Gregory, 1688 (very slow)

$$\frac{\pi}{2} = \frac{2 \cdot 4 \cdot 4 \cdot 6 \cdot 6 \cdot 8 \cdot 8 \cdot \cdots}{1 \cdot 3 \cdot 3 \cdot 5 \cdot 5 \cdot 7 \cdot 7 \cdot \cdots}$$

Wallis, 1650

The calculator can seldom give exact form, but it is an excellent means of checking answers. It is always wise to obtain a calculator check when possible. For example, to check the number in Example 2(**b**), enter $-\sqrt{3}$ and evaluate $\mathrm{Tan}^{-1}(-\sqrt{3}) \approx -1.047$, which is a 3-decimal place approximation of $\frac{-\pi}{3}$.

EXAMPLE 3   Evaluate in exact form (**a**) $\sin(\mathrm{Arcsin}\ \frac{2}{3})$ and (**b**) $\mathrm{Cos}^{-1}(\cos\frac{5\pi}{4})$.

Strategy: Since $\mathrm{Cos}^{-1}(\cos x) = x$ only when $x \in [0, \pi]$ and $\frac{5\pi}{4}$ is not in that interval, first evaluate $\cos(\frac{5\pi}{4})$ and then find $\mathrm{Cos}^{-1}(\frac{-1}{\sqrt{2}})$ Check by calculator.

Solution

(**a**) Since $\frac{2}{3}$ is a number in the interval $[-1, 1]$, we may apply $\sin(\mathrm{Sin}^{-1}x) = x$ directly and obtain $\sin(\mathrm{Arcsin}\ \frac{2}{3}) = \frac{2}{3}$.

(**b**) The identity $\mathrm{Cos}^{-1}(\cos x) = x$ applies only when x is in $[0, \pi]$, and $\frac{5\pi}{4}$ is not in that interval. To evaluate (**b**) in exact form then, first evaluate $\cos\frac{5\pi}{4}$.

$$\mathrm{Cos}^{-1}\left(\cos\frac{5\pi}{4}\right) = \mathrm{Cos}^{-1}\left(\frac{-1}{\sqrt{2}}\right) = \frac{3\pi}{4}.$$

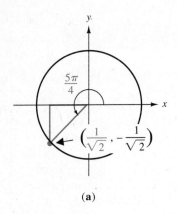

(a)

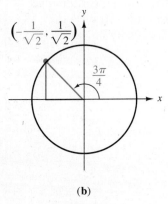

(b)

FIGURE 5.55

Strategy: (a) First let $\theta = \text{Sin}^{-1} \frac{-2}{3}$, so $\sin \theta = -\frac{2}{3}$ and $-\frac{\pi}{2} \le \theta \le \frac{\pi}{2}$. Draw a diagram that shows θ in QIV and a reference triangle with $y = -2$ and $r = 3$. Use the Pythagorean theorem to find x and then use the triangle to evaluate $\tan \theta$.

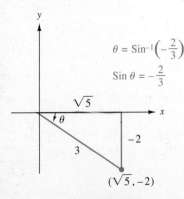

FIGURE 5.56

Hence $\text{Cos}^{-1} (\cos \frac{5\pi}{4}) = \frac{3\pi}{4}$. Notice that $\text{Cos}^{-1} (\cos \frac{5\pi}{4})$ is not equal to $\frac{5\pi}{4}$. (See Figure 5.55.) As a check, evaluate $\text{Cos}^{-1} (\cos \frac{5\pi}{4})$ by calculator. ▲

In evaluating an inverse trigonometric function, it is essential to understand the information given by the calculator. The result is in the range of the function. If we enter a positive number, all inverse trigonometric functions return first-quadrant numbers (or angles). For a negative number, Cos^{-1} returns a second-quadrant number (or angle), but Sin^{-1} and Tan^{-1} both give negative numbers (or angles) from the fourth quadrant.

<table>
<tr><td>EXAMPLE 4</td></tr>
</table>

Evaluate in exact form **(a)** $\tan (\text{Sin}^{-1} -\frac{2}{3})$ and **(b)** $\cos (\pi + \text{Tan}^{-1} 2)$.

Solution

(a) Follow the strategy. The diagram in Figure 5.56 shows that the x value for the reference triangle is $\sqrt{3^2 - (-2)^2}$ or $\sqrt{5}$. From the reference triangle, $\tan \theta = \frac{-2}{\sqrt{5}}$. Therefore, $\tan (\text{Sin}^{-1} -\frac{2}{3}) = \frac{-2}{\sqrt{5}}$.

(b) First let $\alpha = \text{Tan}^{-1} 2$ and then use the reduction formula $\cos (\pi + \alpha) = -\cos \alpha$ from Table 5.4.

$$\cos (\pi + \text{Tan}^{-1} 2) = \cos (\pi + \alpha) = -\cos \alpha$$

Now to evaluate $\cos \alpha$, draw a diagram for which $\tan \alpha = 2$, $-\frac{\pi}{2} < \alpha < \frac{\pi}{2}$. (See Figure 5.57.) From the reference triangle $\cos \alpha = \frac{1}{\sqrt{5}}$. Therefore

$$\cos (\pi + \text{Tan}^{-1} 2) = \frac{-1}{\sqrt{5}}.$$

Use your calculator to check the answers for both **(a)** and **(b)**. ▲

<table>
<tr><td>EXAMPLE 5</td></tr>
</table>

Solve the equations **(a)** $\text{Sin}^{-1} x = 0.84$ and **(b)** $\text{Cos}^{-1} x = 3.5$.

Solution

(a) First check that 0.84 is in the range of Sin^{-1}, that is, in the interval $[-\frac{\pi}{2}, \frac{\pi}{2}]$. Since $0.84 < \frac{\pi}{2}$, then $x = \sin (0.84)$, or $x \approx 0.74$.

(b) Check 3.5 and the range of Cos^{-1}, and find that 3.5 is not in the range. (Why?) Therefore, there can be no number whose inverse cosine is 3.5, so the equation has no solution.
 If you had blindly solved for x by taking the cosine of both sides,

$$\cos (\text{Cos}^{-1} x) = \cos 3.5 \qquad \text{or} \qquad x = \cos 3.5 \approx -0.94.$$

Replace x by $\cos 3.5$ in the original equation to verify that this is not a solution:

$$\text{Cos}^{-1} (\cos 3.5) \approx \text{Cos}^{-1} (-0.94) \approx 2.79 \ne 3.5. \quad ▲$$

**For Graphers
5.5**

INVERSE TRIGONOMETRIC FUNCTIONS

EXAMPLE Compare the graphs of $f(x) = \sin(\text{Cos}^{-1}x)$ and $g(x) = \sqrt{1 - x^2}$. Are the domains of f and g the same? Compare Example 6.

Solution If we simply graph $Y1 = \sin(\cos^{-1}X)$ and $Y2 = \sqrt{(1 - X^2)}$, the graphics screen shows only one curve, a semicircle centered at the origin. To better compare the graphs, try an Equal Scale Window, say $[-2.4, 2.4] \times [-1.6, 1.6]$ and set

$$Y1 = \sin(\cos^{-1}X) \quad \text{and} \quad Y2 = \sqrt{(1 - X^2)} + 0.5.$$

By translating the second graph up by one-half unit, you can see the two graphs at the same time. Tracing along the curves comparing y values, to calculator accuracy, the y-coordinates differ by exactly 0.5. The graphs make it appear that the the domain of both functions is the interval $[-1, 1]$. The domain of g is the set of numbers that satisfy $1 - x^2 \geq 0$, or $-1 \leq x \leq 1$. The sine function is defined for all real numbers, so the domain of f is the same as the domain of Cos^{-1}, $[-1, 1]$. Thus f and g have the same domain, as suggested by the graphs. ▲

Exercises

1. Compare the graphs of $F(x) = \cos(\text{Sin}^{-1}x)$ and $f(x) = \sin(\text{Cos}^{-1}x)$.

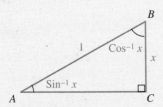

2. In the diagram, express the length of side $\overline{AC}$ in terms of x. Explain why the names for the angles are correct, and then use the length of side $\overline{AC}$ to explain the results of Exercise 1.

3. Compare the graphs of $f(x) = \cos(\text{Tan}^{-1}x)$ and $g(x) = \dfrac{1}{\sqrt{1 + x^2}}$. Are the functions identical?

4. Compare the graphs of $F(x) = \sin(\text{Tan}^{-1}x)$ and $G(x) = \dfrac{x}{\sqrt{1 + x^2}}$. Are the functions identical?

5. (a) Use the graphs of $f(x) = \text{Sin}^{-1}x$ and $g(x) = \text{Cos}^{-1}x$ to determine whether each function is even, odd, or neither.

(b) Knowing that sine is an odd function and cosine is even, predict which of the following functions should be even, odd, and neither.

$$\text{Cos}^{-1}(\cos x), \qquad \text{Cos}^{-1}(\sin x)$$

$$\text{Sin}^{-1}(\cos x), \qquad \text{Sin}^{-1}(\sin x)$$

(c) Graph each of the functions in part **(b)** and check your predictions. Write a brief paragraph to explain why your predictions were correct or what you did not anticipate.

6. From graphs, determine the solution set for the equations $\text{Cos}^{-1}(\cos x) = x$ and $\text{Sin}^{-1}(\sin x) = x$. Compare your result with the inverse trigonometric function identities.

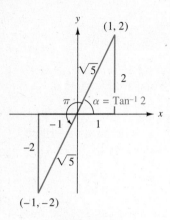

FIGURE 5.57

| EXAMPLE 6 | Show that $\sin(\text{Cos}^{-1} x) = \sqrt{1 - x^2}$ for $-1 \leq x \leq 1$.

Solution

Let $u = \text{Cos}^{-1} x$ so that $\cos u = x$. We want to work with $\sin u$, and we know that $\sin u$ and $\cos u$ are related. Since $(\sin u)^2 + (\cos u)^2 = 1$,

$$(\sin u)^2 = 1 - (\cos u)^2 = 1 - x^2, \text{ so}$$

$$\sin u = \pm\sqrt{1 - x^2} \quad \text{and} \quad \sin(\text{Cos}^{-1} x) = \pm\sqrt{1 - x^2}.$$

In order to determine which of the signs is appropriate, recall the range of the inverse cosine, the interval $[0, \pi]$, so $0 \leq \text{Cos}^{-1} x \leq \pi$. Since the sine function is positive in the first and second quadrants, use the positive sign. Therefore $\sin(\text{Cos}^{-1} x) = \sqrt{1 - x^2}$. ▲

Inverse Functions for Secant, Cosecant, and Cotangent

By suitably restricting the domains of the secant, cosecant, and cotangent, we can define inverse functions. Unfortunately, there is no universal agreement as to which domains are most useful. We are not going to do much with these inverse functions except to recognize that when a need arises, it is almost always possible to translate problems involving Sec^{-1}, Csc^{-1}, or Cot^{-1} into terms of Cos^{-1}, Sin^{-1}, or Tan^{-1}, as in the following example.

| EXAMPLE 7 | Evaluate $\text{Sec}^{-1} 3$, rounded off to three decimal places.

Solution

Let $\theta = \text{Sec}^{-1} 3$. Then $\sec \theta = 3$, and so $\frac{1}{\cos \theta} = 3$, or $\cos \theta = \frac{1}{3}$. If the range of Sec^{-1} agrees with the range of Cos^{-1}, then use a calculator:

$$\theta = \text{Cos}^{-1}\left(\frac{1}{3}\right) \approx 1.231.$$

Therefore, $\text{Sec}^{-1} 3 \approx 1.231$. ▲

EXERCISES 5.5

Exercises 1–5 True or False. Give reasons for your conclusion.

1. There is no number (or angle) θ such that $\theta = \text{Sin}^{-1}\left(\frac{20}{29}\right)$ and $\theta = \text{Cos}^{-1}\left(\frac{21}{29}\right)$.

2. There is no number (or angle) θ such that $\theta = \text{Sin}^{-1}\left(\frac{2}{3}\right)$ and $\theta = \text{Cos}^{-1}\left(\frac{1}{3}\right)$.

3. The function $f(x) = \text{Cos}^{-1} x$ is an increasing function.

4. The point $\left(\frac{\pi}{2}, 1\right)$ is on the graph of $y = \text{Sin}^{-1} x$.

5. The range of $f(x) = \text{Cos}^{-1} x$ contains four integers.

Exercises 6–10 Complete the sentence by selecting from the list below *all choices* that make the statement true.

(a) -2	(b) -1	(c) 0	(d) 1
(e) 2	(f) 3	(g) 4	(h) I
(i) II	(j) III	(k) IV	

6. The largest integer in the range of $f(x) = \text{Cos}^{-1} x$ is _____ .

7. The smallest positive integer not in the range of $f(x) = \mathrm{Sin}^{-1} x$ is _____ .

8. If $\mathrm{Tan}^{-1} x = -\frac{\pi}{4}$, then x equals _____ .

9. The graph of $y = \mathrm{Cos}^{-1} x$ contains points in Quadrant _____ .

10. The graph of $y = \mathrm{Tan}^{-1} x$ contains points in Quadrant _____ .

Explore and Discover

Exercises 1–4 One of the main applications of trigonometry involves finding angles that satisfy particular equations or conditions. We will consider such problems in some detail in parts of Chapters 6 and 7. Because the trigonometric functions are periodic, most such equations have more than one solution, and calculators give at most one solution. The key to finding solutions in such situations is understanding the graphs of the trigonometric functions and how they relate to the inverse trigonometric functions. In each of the following, verify that the statement in part **(a)** is true (to calculator accuracy), and find *two* solutions to the equation in part **(b)**.

1. (a) $\sin 37.4° = \sin 142.6°$
   (b) $\sin x = 0.6074$, $0 \le x \le 360°$

2. (a) $\cos 138° = \cos 222°$
   (b) $\cos x = -0.7431$, $0 \le x \le 360°$

3. (a) $\tan 57.1° = \tan 237.1°$
   (b) $\tan x = 1.5458$, $0 \le x \le 360°$

4. (a) $\sec 51.4° = \sec 308.6°$
   (b) $\sec x = 1.352$, $0 \le x \le 360°$

Exercises 5–8 For Exercises 1 through 4, describe how the two angles in part **(a)** are related. Discuss how the graph of the pertinent trigonometric function explains the equality in part **(a)**. What reduction formula could be used for the equality? Do the same graphs and reduction formulas apply to find the solutions requested in part **(b)**? How? Make up similar exercises using radian measurement rather than degree measurement.

Develop Mastery

Exercises 1–12 Evaluate in exact form in radians, using π as needed.

1. $\mathrm{Cos}^{-1} \left(\frac{\sqrt{3}}{2} \right)$ **2.** $\mathrm{Cos}^{-1} \left(-\frac{\sqrt{3}}{2} \right)$

3. $\mathrm{Sin}^{-1} \left(\frac{\sqrt{3}}{2} \right)$ **4.** $\mathrm{Sin}^{-1} \left(-\frac{1}{2} \right)$ **5.** $\mathrm{Tan}^{-1} 1$

6. $\mathrm{Arctan}\ 0$ **7.** $\mathrm{Arcsin} \left(-\frac{1}{\sqrt{2}} \right)$

8. $\mathrm{Sin}^{-1} \left(\frac{1}{2} \right) + \mathrm{Cos}^{-1} \left(\frac{\sqrt{3}}{2} \right)$

9. $\mathrm{Tan}^{-1} 1 - \mathrm{Tan}^{-1}(-1)$

10. $\mathrm{Sin}^{-1} \left(-\frac{1}{2} \right) - \mathrm{Cos}^{-1} \left(-\frac{1}{2} \right)$

11. $\mathrm{Arccos}\ 1 - \mathrm{Arcsin}\ 1$

12. $2\ \mathrm{Arcsin} \left(\frac{1}{2} \right) + \mathrm{Arccos} \left(-\frac{1}{2} \right)$

Exercises 13–24 Evaluate by calculator and give results in radians rounded off to three decimal places. If the display indicates an error, explain why.

13. $\mathrm{Cos}^{-1}(0.399)$ **14.** $\mathrm{Sin}^{-1} 0.25$

15. $\mathrm{Tan}^{-1} \left(-\frac{\pi}{3} \right)$ **16.** $\mathrm{Arctan}\left(-\sqrt{3} \right)$

17. $\mathrm{Arcsin}\ (\sin 5.43)$ **18.** $\mathrm{Arccos}\ (\cos -2)$

19. $\mathrm{Tan}^{-1} \left(\sin \sqrt{3} \right)$ **20.** $\sin\ (\mathrm{Sin}^{-1} 1.3)$

21. $\sin\ (\mathrm{Arcsin}\ 1.01)$ **22.** $\mathrm{Cos}^{-1} \left(-\frac{\sqrt{3}}{2} \right)$

23. $\sin \left(\mathrm{Sin}^{-1} \frac{1}{2} - \mathrm{Tan}^{-1} \frac{1}{\sqrt{2}} \right)$

24. $\sec \left(\mathrm{Cos}^{-1} -\frac{1}{3} \right)$

Exercises 25–36 Evaluate in exact form. In some cases reduction formulas may be helpful; see Table 5.4 in Section 5.4. In case an expression is undefined, explain why.

25. $\sin\ (\mathrm{Sin}^{-1} 0.3)$ **26.** $\mathrm{Sin}^{-1} \left(\sin \frac{3\pi}{2} \right)$

27. $\sec \left(2\ \mathrm{Sin}^{-1} \frac{1}{2} \right)$ **28.** $\csc \left(\mathrm{Cos}^{-1} \frac{1}{\sqrt{2}} \right)$

29. $\cot\ (2\ \mathrm{Tan}^{-1}\ 1)$

30. $\cos \left(\mathrm{Sin}^{-1} \frac{1}{2} + \mathrm{Cos}^{-1} \frac{1}{2} \right)$

31. $\sin \left(\frac{\pi}{2} - \mathrm{Cos}^{-1} \frac{2}{3} \right)$ **32.** $\tan \left(\frac{\pi}{2} + \mathrm{Sin}^{-1} \frac{\sqrt{3}}{2} \right)$

33. $\cos \left(\pi - \mathrm{Sin}^{-1} \frac{2}{7} \right)$ **34.** $\sec\ (\pi + \mathrm{Cos}^{-1} 0.75)$

35. $\cot \left(\frac{\pi}{2} - \mathrm{Arctan} \frac{1}{3} \right)$ **36.** $\tan \left(\mathrm{Cos}^{-1} \frac{1}{\sqrt{10}} - \frac{\pi}{2} \right)$

Exercises 37–42 Give an approximation rounded off to three decimal places. See Example 7.

37. $\mathrm{Cot}^{-1} \left(\frac{1}{10} \right)$ **38.** $\mathrm{Sec}^{-1} 1.532$

39. $\sin\ (\mathrm{Tan}^{-1} 1 + \mathrm{Sec}^{-1} 1)$ **40.** $\tan\ (-2\ \mathrm{Csc}^{-1} 3)$

41. $\mathrm{Sec}^{-1} \left(1 + \sqrt{17} \right)$ **42.** $\cot\ (\mathrm{Csc}^{-1} 2)$

Exercises 43–48   Determine the values of x (if there are any) that will satisfy the equation. Give results rounded off to two decimal places. It may be helpful to refer to the graphs of the inverse functions. See Example 5.

43. $\text{Sin}^{-1}x = -0.36$ **44.** $\text{Cos}^{-1}x = 2.4$

45. $\text{Tan}^{-1}x = 1.9$ **46.** $\text{Tan}^{-1}x = -1.2$

47. $\text{Sin}^{-1}x = 2.1$ **48.** $\text{Cos}^{-1}x = 0.64$

Exercises 49–51   Sketch the graph of f. (*Hint:* Use translations or reflections of core inverse function graphs where appropriate.)

49. (a) $f(x) = -\text{Cos}^{-1}x$ (b) $f(x) = \text{Cos}^{-1}(x + 1)$
(c) $f(x) = \text{Cos}^{-1}x - \frac{\pi}{2}$

50. (a) $f(x) = -\text{Sin}^{-1}x$ (b) $f(x) = \text{Sin}^{-1}(-x)$
(c) $f(x) = \frac{\pi}{2} + \text{Sin}^{-1}x$

51. (a) $f(x) = \text{Sin}^{-1}(\sin x)$ (b) $f(x) = \sin(\text{Sin}^{-1}x)$
(c) $f(x) = \tan(\text{Tan}^{-1}x)$

Exercises 52–53   (a) On the same set of coordinates, draw graphs of f and g. (b) At how many points do the two graphs intersect? (c) Use the graphs and your calculator to approximate (to one decimal place) solutions to the equation $f(x) = g(x)$.

52. $f(x) = \sin x$ $g(x) = \text{Sin}^{-1}x$

53. $f(x) = \cos x$ $g(x) = \text{Cos}^{-1}x$

54. Solve the equation $\text{Sin}^{-1}x = \text{Cos}^{-1}x$. (*Hint:* Take the sine of both sides and use Example 6.)

Exercises 55–57   Draw a graph of f. Use the graph of f to help sketch a graph of g.

55. (a) $f(x) = \text{Sin}^{-1}x$ (b) $g(x) = |\text{Sin}^{-1}x|$

56. (a) $f(x) = \text{Cos}^{-1}x$ (b) $g(x) = \text{Cos}^{-1}|x|$

57. (a) $f(x) = \text{Tan}^{-1}x$ (b) $g(x) = \text{Tan}^{-1}|x|$

Exercises 58–62   Find an equation that does not involve inverse trigonometric functions to describe the function f. See Example 6. In each case, check your work by evaluating your result at several values of x. Use reduction formulas where appropriate.

58. $f(x) = \cos(\text{Sin}^{-1}x)$ **59.** $f(x) = \sin(\text{Tan}^{-1}x)$

60. $f(x) = \cot(\text{Tan}^{-1}x)$ **61.** $f(x) = \sin\left(\frac{\pi}{2} - \text{Tan}^{-1}x\right)$

62. $f(x) = \tan\left(\text{Cos}^{-1}\frac{x}{2}\right)$

63. Show that $\text{Sin}^{-1}x$ and $\text{Tan}^{-1}x$ are both odd functions.

64. Show that $\text{Cos}^{-1}(-x) = \pi - \text{Cos}^{-1}x$ for $-1 \le x \le 1$. Is $\text{Cos}^{-1}x$ an even function? An odd function?

65. Show that $\text{Sin}^{-1}x + \text{Cos}^{-1}x = \frac{\pi}{2}$ for $-1 \le x \le 1$. (*Hint:* Show first that $\sin\left(\frac{\pi}{2} - \text{Cos}^{-1}x\right) = x$.)

66. Show that $\text{Tan}^{-1}x + \text{Tan}^{-1}\frac{1}{x} = \frac{\pi}{2}$ for $x > 0$.

Exercises 67–70   *Looking Ahead to Calculus*

67. In calculus it can be shown that the area A under the curve $y = \frac{1}{1 + x^2}$ between $x = a$ and $x = b$ (the area of the shaded region in the diagram) is given by

$$A = \text{Tan}^{-1}b - \text{Tan}^{-1}a.$$

Draw a diagram that shows the shaded region that corresponds to the given values of a and b. Give an approximation of A rounded off to two decimal places.

   (a) $a = 0, b = 1$ (b) $a = 1, b = 2$

   (c) $a = -1, b = 2$

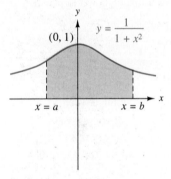

68. In the previous exercise what value does the area A approach as $a \to -\infty$ and $b \to \infty$? Your result might appropriately be called the total area of the region under the curve and above the x-axis. The definition and computation of such areas is a topic studied in calculus.

69. In calculus you will earn that the area A under the curve $y = \frac{1}{\sqrt{1 - x^2}}$ between $x = a$ and $x = b$ (the area of the shaded region in the diagram) is given by

$$A = \text{Sin}^{-1}b - \text{Sin}^{-1}a.$$

Give an approximation of A rounded off to two decimal places. Draw a diagram that shows the shaded region for the given values of a and b.

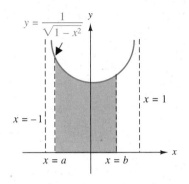

$$y = \frac{1}{\sqrt{1 - x^2}}$$

(a) $a = 0$, $b = 0.5$ (b) $a = -0.5$, $b = 0.5$

(c) $a = -0.9$, $b = 0.9$

70. In Exercise 69 what value does the area A approach as $a \to -1$ and $b \to 1$ (where, of course, $-1 < a$ and $b < 1$)?

CHAPTER 5 REVIEW

Test Your Understanding

Determine the truth value (T or F). Give reasons for your conclusion.

1. There is no number x such that (a) $\sin x = 2$, (b) $\cos x = -\frac{3}{4}$ (c) $\tan x = \frac{\pi}{2}$, (d) $\sec x = \frac{1}{2}$.

2. (a) $\sin 1 = \frac{\pi}{2}$, (b) $\cos (-1) = \pi$, (c) $\tan (\frac{\pi}{2}) = 0$

3. If θ is an angle in the fourth quadrant, then $\cos \theta$ is negative.

4. The numbers $\frac{3\pi}{4}$ and $-\frac{5\pi}{4}$ are coterminal.

5. There is no number x such that (a) $\mathrm{Sin}^{-1} x = \frac{\pi}{4}$, (b) $\mathrm{Sin}^{-1} x = \frac{3\pi}{4}$, (c) $\mathrm{Cos}^{-1} x = \frac{5\pi}{4}$, (d) $\mathrm{Cos}^{-1} x = -\frac{\pi}{3}$.

6. The number $\sec 3$ is negative.

7. The point $(\frac{\pi}{2}, 1)$ is on the unit circle.

8. The point $(-\frac{5}{13}, -\frac{12}{13})$ is on the unit circle.

9. If $\frac{\pi}{4} < t < \frac{\pi}{2}$, then $\frac{1}{\sqrt{2}} < \sin t < 1$.

10. If $\frac{3\pi}{4} < t < \pi$, then $-1 < \cos t < -\frac{1}{\sqrt{2}}$.

11. If $\sin x > 0$ and $\cos x < 0$, then $\tan x < 0$.

12. If $\cos \theta = \frac{3}{5}$, then $\sin (\theta + \frac{\pi}{2}) = \frac{3}{5}$.

13. The numbers $\sin 2°$ and $\sin 2$ are the same.

14. If $\theta = 450°$, then the radian measure of θ is $\frac{5\pi}{2}$.

15. If in a circular sector the length of arc is less than the radius, then the central angle is less than 1 radian.

16. There is no number x for which $\sin x \geq 1$.

17. There is no number x for which $\mathrm{Tan}^{-1} x \geq \frac{\pi}{2}$.

18. If θ is an angle in the second quadrant, then $\tan \theta$ is negative.

19. (a) $\mathrm{Sin}^{-1} (\frac{\pi}{2}) = 1$, (b) $\mathrm{Cos}^{-1} \pi = -1$

20. (a) $\mathrm{Cos}^{-1} (\cos 4) = 4$, (b) $\mathrm{Sin}^{-1} (\sin -\pi) = -\pi$

21. (a) $\mathrm{Tan}^{-1} (\frac{\pi}{2})$ is undefined.
(b) $\cos (\mathrm{Cos}^{-1} -1)$ is undefined.

22. (a) $\sec \pi$ is undefined. (b) $\mathrm{Sin}^{-1} (\frac{\pi}{2})$ is undefined.

23. $\mathrm{Tan}^{-1} 5$ is greater than $\frac{\pi}{2}$.

24. $\tan (\mathrm{Tan}^{-1} x) = x$ for every real number x.

25. $\sin x > \cos x$ for every x in the second quadrant.

26. If $f(x) = \mathrm{Sin}^{-1} x$, then f is an increasing function.

27. If $f(x) = \mathrm{Cos}^{-1} x$, then f is a decreasing function.

28. If angle θ is in the second quadrant and $\sin \theta > \frac{1}{2}$, then $\frac{5\pi}{6} < \theta < \pi$.

29. The function $f(x) = \cos x$ is an even function.

30. The function $f(x) = \sin x$ is neither even or odd.

31. The function $f(x) = \mathrm{Sin}^{-1} x$ is one–one.

32. The function $f(x) = \tan x$ is one–one.

33. Point $(1, \frac{\pi}{2})$ is on the graph of $y = \sin x$.

34. Point $(\pi, -1)$ is on the graph of $y = \cos x$.

35. Point $(0, \frac{\pi}{2})$ is on the graph of $y = \mathrm{Cos}^{-1} x$.

36. The function $f(x) = \mathrm{Cos}^{-1} x$ is an even function.

37. The graph of $y = \mathrm{Sin}^{-1} x$ contains points in all four quadrants.

38. The range of $f(x) = \mathrm{Sin}^{-1} x$ contains only one negative integer.

39. The graph of $y = \mathrm{Cos}^{-1} x$ contains exactly one point for which both coordinates are integers.

40. If $f(x) = \mathrm{Cos}^{-1} x$, then the maximum value of $f(x)$ is π.

Mastery Review

Exercises 1–3   Refer to a circular sector with radius r, central angle θ, arc length s, and area A. Give results to two significant digits.

1. If $r = 24$ cm and $\theta = 30°$, find s and A.

2. If $r = 12$ cm and $s = 20$ cm, find θ and A.

3. If $s = 13$ cm and $A = 64$ cm², find r and θ.

4. What is the degree measure of the smaller angle between the hour and minute hands of a clock at time 2:20?

Exercises 5–10   Point $P(t)$ on the unit circle corresponds to the number t as described in Section 5.2. **(a)** From a diagram showing $P(t)$, give the coordinates of $P(t)$. **(b)** Give the values of the six trigonometric functions at t. In Exercises 5 through 7, give results in exact form, and in Exercises 8 through 10, give results rounded off to two decimal places.

5. $t = \frac{3\pi}{4}$ **6.** $t = \frac{-2\pi}{3}$ **7.** $t = \frac{17\pi}{6}$

8. $t = 4.21$ **9.** $t = -\frac{\pi}{5}$ **10.** $t = 8.3$

11. Determine all real numbers t for which $\cos t = -1$.

12. Determine all real numbers t for which $\sin t = -1$.

13. **(a)** Draw a diagram that shows all points $P(t)$ on the circle where $0 \le t \le 2\pi$ and $\cos t = \frac{1}{4}$. **(b)** What are the coordinates of $P(t)$?

Exercises 14–17   Simplify by using an appropriate reduction formula.

14. $\cos\left(\frac{\pi}{2} - t\right)$ **15.** $\sin\left(t + \frac{3\pi}{2}\right)$

16. $\tan\left(t + \frac{5\pi}{2}\right)$ **17.** $\sec(\pi - t)$

18. Evaluate in exact form **(a)** $\sin\left(\frac{\pi}{2}\right)$, **(b)** $\tan\left(\frac{5\pi}{3}\right)$, **(c)** $\cos\left(-\frac{7\pi}{6}\right)$, **(d)** $\sin\left(\pi - \frac{5\pi}{4}\right)$, **(e)** $\sec\left(\pi + \frac{\pi}{3}\right)$.

19. Determine θ.
(a) $\sin\theta = \frac{-\sqrt{2}}{2}$ and $\pi < \theta < \frac{3\pi}{2}$
(b) $\tan\theta = -\sqrt{3}$ and $\frac{\pi}{2} < \theta < \pi$
(c) $\sec\theta = -1$ and $0 < \theta < 2\pi$.

20. If $\cos t = -0.75$ and $\tan t$ is negative, evaluate **(a)** $\sin t$, **(b)** $\tan t$, **(c)** $\cos\left(t - \frac{\pi}{2}\right)$, **(d)** $\tan(t + \pi)$.

21. Evaluate and give results rounded off to three decimal places **(a)** $\sin 43°$, **(b)** $\tan 152°$, **(c)** $\cos 57°16'$.

22. Evaluate and give results rounded off to three decimal places **(a)** $\sin 1.43$, **(b)** $\tan\left(\frac{5\pi}{8}\right)$, **(c)** $\sec 1.46 + \cos 1.46$.

23. If point $(-3, 4)$ is on the terminal side of the angle θ in standard position, evaluate in exact form **(a)** $\sin\left(\theta + \frac{\pi}{2}\right)$, **(b)** $\cos(\theta + \pi)$.

24. Suppose $P(t)$ is point $\left(\frac{-3}{5}, \frac{4}{5}\right)$. **(a)** Show that $P(t)$ is on the unit circle. **(b)** What are the coordinates of $P\left(t + \frac{\pi}{2}\right)$?

25. Suppose $P(t)$ is the point $\left(\frac{5}{13}, \frac{-12}{13}\right)$. **(a)** Show that $P(t)$ is on the unit circle. **(b)** What are the coordinates of $P(t + \pi)$? **(c)** Evaluate $\sin(t + \pi)$ and $\tan(t + \pi)$.

26. Which of the following points are on the unit circle?
(a) $(1, -1)$, **(b)** $\left(\frac{1}{2}, \frac{1}{2}\right)$, **(c)** $\left(\frac{1}{\sqrt{2}}, \frac{1}{\sqrt{2}}\right)$, **(d)** $\left(\frac{\sqrt{3}}{2}, \frac{-1}{2}\right)$

Exercises 27–30   Point Q is on the terminal side of angle θ in standard position. Assume that $0 \le \theta \le 2\pi$. From a diagram that shows a reference triangle for θ, find $\sin\theta$, $\cos\theta$, and $\tan\theta$ in exact form. Find angle θ in radians rounded off to two decimal places.

27. $Q(3, 4)$ **28.** $Q(-3, 5)$

29. $Q(-4, -3)$ **30.** $Q(\sqrt{2}, \sqrt{7})$

Exercises 31–38   Evaluate in exact form.

31. **(a)** $\operatorname{Sin}^{-1}\left(\frac{\sqrt{2}}{2}\right)$ **(b)** $\operatorname{Cos}^{-1}\left(\frac{-\sqrt{3}}{2}\right)$

32. **(a)** $\operatorname{Tan}^{-1}(-\sqrt{3})$ **(b)** $\tan\left(\operatorname{Sin}^{-1}\frac{-2}{5}\right)$

33. **(a)** $\cos\left(\operatorname{Tan}^{-1} -2\right)$ **(b)** $\sin\left(\operatorname{Sin}^{-1}\frac{\pi}{4}\right)$

34. **(a)** $\operatorname{Cos}^{-1}\left(\cos\frac{-\pi}{6}\right)$ **(b)** $\sin\left(\pi + \operatorname{Cos}^{-1} 0.5\right)$

35. **(a)** $\operatorname{Tan}^{-1}\left(\tan\frac{5\pi}{6}\right)$ **(b)** $\sec\left(\pi - \operatorname{Tan}^{-1} -2\right)$

36. **(a)** $\cos\left(\pi - \operatorname{Cos}^{-1}\frac{4}{7}\right)$ **(b)** $\sin\left(\frac{\pi}{2} + \operatorname{Cos}^{-1}\frac{3}{7}\right)$

37. **(a)** $\tan\left(\pi - \operatorname{Tan}^{-1}\frac{5}{7}\right)$ **(b)** $\cos\left(\frac{3\pi}{2} - \operatorname{Cos}^{-1}\frac{-5}{13}\right)$

38. **(a)** $\cos\left(\pi + \operatorname{Tan}^{-1}\frac{3}{4}\right)$ **(b)** $\sin\left(\pi - \operatorname{Cos}^{-1}\frac{2}{7}\right)$

Exercises 39–40   Evaluate and round off to two decimal places.

39. (a) $\text{Sin}^{-1} 0.47$ **(b)** $\text{Cos}^{-1} -0.25$

40. (a) $\sin (\text{Tan}^{-1} -2.5)$ **(b)** $\sec (\text{Cos}^{-1} 0.48)$

41. For what value(s) of x is $\text{Sin}^{-1} x = \frac{\pi}{3}$?

42. For what value(s) of x is $\text{Cos}^{-1} x = \frac{3\pi}{4}$?

43. For what value(s) of x is $\text{Tan}^{-1} x = \frac{2\pi}{3}$?

Exercises 44–49   Draw a graph of the function for $-\pi \le x \le \pi$.

44. $f(x) = \sin x$ **45.** $f(x) = \cos x$

46. $f(x) = \tan x$ **47.** $f(x) = 1 + \cos x$

48. $f(x) = 1 - \sin x$ **49.** $f(x) = \tan \left(x - \frac{\pi}{2}\right)$

Exercises 50–53   Draw a graph of the function and find the domain and range of f.

50. $f(x) = \sin (\text{Sin}^{-1} x)$ **51.** $f(x) = \cos (\text{Cos}^{-1} x)$

52. $f(x) = \text{Sin}^{-1} x + \frac{\pi}{2}$ **53.** $f(x) = \text{Cos}^{-1} x - \frac{\pi}{2}$

54. Draw a graph of $y = \text{Sin}^{-1} x$. **(a)** Show all points on the graph where $y \ge \frac{\pi}{6}$. **(b)** Find the solution set for the inequality $\text{Sin}^{-1} x \ge \frac{\pi}{6}$.

55. Draw a graph of $y = \text{Cos}^{-1} x$. **(a)** Show all points on the graph where $y \ge \frac{2\pi}{3}$. **(b)** Find the solution set for the inequality $\text{Cos}^{-1} x \ge \frac{2\pi}{3}$.

56. Draw a graph of $y = \text{Tan}^{-1} x$. **(a)** Show all points on the graph where $y \ge \frac{\pi}{4}$. **(b)** Find the solution set for the inequality $\text{Tan}^{-1} x \ge \frac{\pi}{4}$.

6

TRIGONOMETRIC IDENTITIES, EQUATIONS, AND GRAPHS

One of the important features of problem solving involves the replacement of a mathematical expression by another expression that is *identically equivalent* to it. This is particularly true in the study of calculus, where solutions to many problems can be made relatively easy by appropriate substitutions.

In this chapter our first task is to establish familiarity with identities that involve trigonometric functions. Several basic identities are introduced in the first three sections, then the remaining sections use these identities whenever appropriate to solve equations and to draw graphs of general trigonometric functions.

Basic Identities

This is why mathematics is effective: the world exhibits regularities which can be described, independently of the world, by forms which can be studied and then reapplied.
Saunders MacLane

[W]hen I started teaching trigonometric identities, an ingenious student told me of his foolproof way of getting a perfect grade almost every time. If you're told to prove that some expression A is equal to a different-looking B, you put A at the top left corner of the page, B at the bottom right, and using correct but trivial substitutions, keep changing them, working from both ends to the middle. When they meet, stop.
Paul Halmos

Many times in earlier chapters we were able to solve equations that involved polynomial, exponential, or logarithmic functions by using equivalence operation 3 from Section 1.5:

> Replace any expression in an equation by an expression *identically* equal to it.

For example, to solve the equation $x^2 + 3x - 4 = 0$, we may replace $x^2 + 3x - 4$ by $(x + 4)(x - 1)$ since $x^2 + 3x - 4 = (x + 4)(x - 1)$ is an **identity.** Thus the original problem is equivalent to solving the equation $(x + 4)(x - 1) = 0$. The zero-product principle yields solutions -4 and 1.

Similarly, we can replace $\frac{x^2 - 3x}{x}$ by $x - 3$ if we keep in mind that the substitution is valid for every x except 0. We also call the equation $\frac{x^2 - 3}{x} = x - 3$ an identity. As another example, we listed composition identities in Section 4.4 such as $e^{\ln x} = x$, for $x > 0$.

Definition: Identity

Suppose S is the (nonempty) set of real numbers for which both functions f and g are defined. If $f(x)$ equals $g(x)$ for every x in S, then we say that $f(x)$ and $g(x)$ are identically equal, and we call the equation $f(x) = g(x)$ an identity.

| EXAMPLE 1 | Is the equation an identity? |

(a) $x^2 - 4 = 3x$ **(b)** $\sqrt{x^2} = x$ **(c)** $\sqrt{x^2} = |x|$
(d) $e^{\ln(x-1)} = x - 1$

Solution

(a) Both sides are defined for every real number x, but equality holds only when x is -1 or 4. Thus $x^2 - 4 = 3x$ is not an identity.

(b) Both sides are defined for every real number x, but equality holds only when x is positive or zero. Hence $\sqrt{x^2} = x$ is not an identity.

(c) Equality holds for every real number, and so $\sqrt{x^2} = |x|$ is an identity.

(d) The set of numbers S for which both sides are defined is $\{x \mid x > 1\}$. Equality holds for all x in S, so the given equation is an identity. When we replace $e^{\ln(x-1)}$ by $x - 1$, we must remember that such a replacement is valid only when x is greater than 1. ▲

The word *identity* is commonly associated with trigonometry even though the concept occurs throughout mathematics, and the proof of a trigonometric identity often involves the use of algebraic identities. We have already seen several trigonometric identities in Chapter 5 (including the reduction formulas). It is not possible to remember, or even list, all the identities that are useful in problem solving. Instead we concentrate on some key identities from which we can easily obtain others. In this section, and in the two that follow, we list basic identities and illustrate how they can be used to derive or prove others. It is important that you learn these not simply by memorization but by working many problems until you become quite comfortable with the key identities and the various forms in which they occur.

Proving Identities

We illustrate two techniques that can be used in showing that an equation is an identity. Example 2 starts with a known identity to which we apply appropriate operations and derive another desired identity. In Examples 3 and 4 we work only on one side of the equation.

Before illustrating these techniques, we call attention to an important point of logic. Performing the same operation on both sides of a given equation and arriving at an obvious identity does not prove that the original equation is an identity. For instance, if we try to "prove" that $1 + x^2 = 4x - 2$ is an identity we could operate on both sides of the equation, as follows:

$$1 + x^2 = 4x - 2$$

$$x^2 = 4x - 3 \qquad \text{Subtract 1 from both sides}$$

$$0 \cdot x^2 = 0(4x - 3) \qquad \text{Multiply both sides by 0}$$

$$0 \cdot x^2 = 0 \cdot 4x - 0$$

$$0 \cdot x^2 = 0 \cdot 4x$$

Since the last equation is obviously true for all x, can we conclude that the original equation is also an identity? Clearly not, since that equation is satisfied only when $x = 1$ or $x = 3$. All we have accomplished in this "proof" is to show that

"If $1 + x^2 = 4x - 2$ for every x, then $0 = 0$."

which is indeed true, but hardly an enlightening statement. (See the discussion of truth values for conditional statements in Section 1.4.)

To begin our work with identities we list several that we encountered in Chapter 5. Some identities listed here are definitions given in Section 5.2 or 5.3. We use labels such as (I-1) and (I-2) to identify identities for easy reference.

Basic Identities

$$\cot x = \frac{1}{\tan x} \qquad \sec x = \frac{1}{\cos x} \qquad \csc x = \frac{1}{\sin x} \qquad \textbf{(I-1)}$$

$$\tan x = \frac{\sin x}{\cos x} \qquad \cot x = \frac{\cos x}{\sin x} \qquad \textbf{(I-2)}$$

$$\sin(-x) = -\sin x \quad \cos(-x) = \cos x \quad \tan(-x) = -\tan x \qquad \textbf{(I-3)}$$

$$\sin^2 x + \cos^2 x = 1 \quad \text{(Pythagorean identity)} \qquad \textbf{(I-4)}$$

$$1 + \tan^2 x = \sec^2 x \qquad 1 + \cot^2 x = \csc^2 x \qquad \textbf{(I-5)}$$

Note that we write $\sin^2 x$ and $\cos^2 x$ in place of $(\sin x)^2$ and $(\cos x)^2$, respectively. This common notation is used throughout the rest of the book.

EXAMPLE 2 In Chapter 5 we proved the Pythagorean identity (I-4) using the fact that any point on the unit circle has coordinates of the form $(\cos x, \sin x)$. Use (I-4) to show that the equation in (I-5), $1 + \tan^2 x = \sec^2 x$, is an identity.

Solution

We begin with an established identity (I-4), and divide both sides by $\cos^2 x$.

$$\sin^2 x + \cos^2 x = 1$$

$$\frac{\sin^2 x}{\cos^2 x} + \frac{\cos^2 x}{\cos^2 x} = \frac{1}{\cos^2 x}$$

$$\left(\frac{\sin x}{\cos x}\right)^2 + 1 = \left(\frac{1}{\cos x}\right)^2$$

Using (I-1) and (I-2), we have the desired identity

$$\tan^2 x + 1 = \sec^2 x. \quad \blacktriangle$$

Strategy: Multiplication of numerator and denominator of the left-hand side by $1 - \cos x$ gives $1 - \cos^2 x$ in the denominator, which can be replaced by $\sin^2 x$.

> **EXAMPLE 3**   Prove that $\frac{\sin x}{1 + \cos x} = \frac{1 - \cos x}{\sin x}$ is an identity by working with the left-hand side only.

Solution

In general, fractions with a single term in the denominator are simpler. Follow the strategy.

$$\frac{\sin x}{1 + \cos x} \overset{?}{=} \frac{1 - \cos x}{\sin x}$$

$$\frac{\sin x\,(1 - \cos x)}{(1 + \cos x)(1 - \cos x)} \quad \text{Multiply numerator and denominator by } (1 - \cos x)$$

$$\frac{\sin x\,(1 - \cos x)}{1 - \cos^2 x} \quad \text{Algebra}$$

$$\frac{\sin x\,(1 - \cos x)}{\sin^2 x} \quad \text{Pythagorean identity (I-4)}$$

$$\frac{1 - \cos x}{\sin x} \quad \text{Simplify}$$

By the transitivity property of equality, the left-hand side does equal the right, that is, $\frac{\sin x}{1 + \cos x} = \frac{1 - \cos x}{\sin x}$ is an identity. ▲

> **EXAMPLE 4**   Prove that $\frac{\cos x - 1}{\cos x + 1} = \frac{1 - \sec x}{1 + \sec x}$ is an identity.

Solution

Strategy: One obvious place to begin is expressing the right-hand side in terms of $\cos x$, then combine fractions and simplify.

Work on the right-hand side; first replace $\sec x$ by $\frac{1}{\cos x}$.

$$\frac{\cos x - 1}{\cos x + 1} \overset{?}{=} \frac{1 - \sec x}{1 + \sec x}$$

$$\dfrac{1 - \dfrac{1}{\cos x}}{1 + \dfrac{1}{\cos x}} \quad \text{By (I-1)}$$

$$\dfrac{\dfrac{\cos x - 1}{\cos x}}{\dfrac{\cos x + 1}{\cos x}} \quad \text{Get common denominators}$$

$$\frac{\cos x - 1}{\cos x + 1} \quad \text{Simplify}$$

By the transitive and reflexive properties of equality, the given equation is an identity. ▲

In many situations we are interested in simplifying a mathematical expression. We make no attempt to define a simplest form, but in most cases it will be

For Graphers
6.1

GRAPHS AND IDENTITIES

Graphs can help determine whether or not a given equation $f(x) = g(x)$ is an identity. If graphs $f(g)$ and $g(x)$ are different, then the equation cannot be an identity. If the graphs appear to be the same, we have reason to believe that $f(x) = g(x)$ is an identity, and we can attempt to prove it. Occasionally, however, calculator graphs can fail to show important differences. See Exercise 11.

Exercises

Exercises 1–6 For the equation $f(x) = g(x)$, graph $f(x)$ and $g(x)$ to help decide if the equation is an identity. If it is, give a proof; if not, use the graph to find a counterexample.

1. $\sin^4 x - \cos^4 x = \sin^2 x - \cos^2 x$

2. $\cos^2 x - \sin^2 x = 1 - 2\sin^2 x$

3. $\sin x \tan x = 1 - \cos x$

4. $\dfrac{\sin x}{1 - \cos x} = \dfrac{1 + \cos x}{\sin x}$

5. $\dfrac{\sin x}{\cos x - \sin x} = \dfrac{\tan x}{1 - \tan x}$

6. $\sqrt{1 - \cos^2 x} = \sin x$

Exercises 7–10 Find a simpler formula for $f(x)$ and check your answer by drawing graphs.

7. $f(x) = \dfrac{\cos^2 x - 1}{\sin(-x)}$

8. $f(x) = \dfrac{\tan(-x)}{\sin(-x)}$

9. $f(x) = \sin^3 x \cos x + \cos^3 x \sin x$

10. $f(x) = \dfrac{\cos x (\sin x + \tan x)}{1 + \cos x}$

11. (a) Draw separate graphs of $f(x) = 3 + \sin x$ and $g(x) = \sin x + \sqrt{x + 9 - 2\sqrt{x + 8}} + \sqrt{x + 24 - 8\sqrt{x + 8}}$ in the Trigonometric Window. Are the functions identical?

    (b) Is $f(x) = g(x)$ an identity? Explain. (*Hint:* To better understand the graph of $y = g(x)$, draw a graph of
    $$y = \sqrt{x + 9 - 2\sqrt{x + 8}} + \sqrt{x + 24 - 8\sqrt{x + 8}}$$
    in a $[-10, 10] \times [-10, 10]$ window.

---

clear when one form is simpler than another. The next example shows how to use identities to simplify expressions that involve trigonometric functions.

EXAMPLE 5　　Simplify the equation giving the rule for the function f.

$$f(x) = \frac{\tan(-x)}{\sin(-x)} + \sec x.$$

Solution

Follow the strategy.

Strategy: Begin by replacing $\tan(-x)$ by $-\tan x$ and $\sin(-x)$ by $-\sin x$, then replace $\tan x$ by $\frac{\sin x}{\cos x}$ and simplify.

$$f(x) = \frac{\tan(-x)}{\sin(-x)} + \sec x$$

$$= \frac{-\tan x}{-\sin x} + \sec x \qquad \text{By (I-3)}$$

$$= \frac{1}{\cos x} + \sec x \qquad \text{Use (I-2) and simplify}$$

$$= \sec x + \sec x \qquad \text{By (I-1)}$$

$$= 2 \sec x$$

Therefore, the function f is also given by $f(x) = 2 \sec x$. Keep in mind also that we must exclude values of x for which the original formula for $f(x)$ is not defined, namely $0, \pm\frac{\pi}{2}, \pm\pi, \ldots$ since $\tan(-x)$ is undefined at $\pm\frac{\pi}{2}, \pm\frac{3\pi}{2}, \ldots$, and $\sin(-x)$ is zero when x is $0, \pm\pi, \pm2\pi,$. ▲

Examples 2, 3, and 4 asked us to prove that a given equation is an identity. In many instances we may have to determine whether or not a given equation is an identity. If we can find a *single value* of x for which both sides are defined and for which the equality does not hold, then the equation is not an identity. Such an x is called a counterexample. If, however, we cannot find such an x, then we may suspect that the equation is an identity and proceed to try to prove it, as illustrated in the next two examples.

| EXAMPLE 6 | Is $(\sin x + \cos x)^2 = \frac{\csc x \sec x + 2}{\csc x \sec x}$ an identity? |

Solution

First try a few values of x. Since either $\csc x$ or $\sec x$ is undefined when x is any integral multiple of $\frac{\pi}{2}$, avoid such numbers. When x is $\frac{\pi}{4}$ both sides are equal to 2. When x is 1, calculator evaluation gives 1.909297427 for both sides. At this point we suspect that the given equation is an identity and attempt to prove it. We work separately on each side of the equation.

$$(\sin x + \cos x)^2 \overset{?}{=} \frac{\csc x \sec x + 2}{\csc x \sec x}$$

$$\sin^2 x + 2\sin x \cos x + \cos^2 x \quad \Big| \quad \frac{\csc x \sec x}{\csc x \sec x} + \frac{2}{\csc x \sec x}$$

$$(\sin^2 x + \cos^2 x) + 2\sin x \cos x \quad \Big| \quad 1 + \frac{2}{\left(\dfrac{1}{\sin x}\right)\left(\dfrac{1}{\cos x}\right)}$$

$$1 + 2\sin x \cos x \quad \Big| \quad 1 + 2\sin x \cos x$$

Each side is identically equal to $1 + 2\sin x \cos x$, so the two sides are identically equal to each other. The given equation is an identity. ▲

| EXAMPLE 7 | Is the equation $\sqrt{\tan^2 x - \sin^2 x} = \sin x \tan x$ an identity? |

Strategy: Try some values of *x*, keeping in mind that the left-hand side must always be nonnegative. The signs of the right-hand factors can change, but their product must stay nonnegative, so try *x* values with one negative factor.

Solution

First try a few values of *x* to see if the given equation is satisfied. List the results in a table.

Try	$\sqrt{\tan^2 x - \sin^2 x}$	$\sin x \tan x$
$x = 0$	$\sqrt{0^2 - 0^2} = 0$	$0 \cdot 0 = 0$
$x = \dfrac{\pi}{4}$	$\sqrt{1 - \dfrac{1}{2}} = \dfrac{1}{\sqrt{2}}$	$\dfrac{1}{\sqrt{2}} \cdot 1 = \dfrac{1}{\sqrt{2}}$
$x = -\dfrac{\pi}{3}$	$\sqrt{(-\sqrt{3})^2 - \left(-\dfrac{\sqrt{3}}{2}\right)^2} = \dfrac{3}{2}$	$\left(-\dfrac{\sqrt{3}}{2}\right) \cdot (-\sqrt{3}) = \dfrac{3}{2}$
$x = 1$	1.310513412	1.310513412

At this point the equation may seem to be an identity, however, on closer inspection we note that the left side is never negative, while the right side is negative whenever sin *x* and tan *x* have opposite signs. This happens when *x* is in the second or third quadrant. For instance, try $\frac{2\pi}{3}$ for *x*; the left side is equal to $\frac{3}{2}$, while the right side is $-\frac{3}{2}$. Therefore, the given equation is not an identity. There is a related equation that is an identity, however: $\sqrt{\tan^2 x - \sin^2 x} = |\sin x \tan x|$. ▲

> **EXAMPLE 8** (a) Verify that $\ln (\cos x \tan x) = \ln (\sin x)$ is an identity. **(b)** Determine the set of values of *x* for which the equation is valid.

Solution

(a) Using (I2), replace tan *x* by $\frac{\sin x}{\cos x}$ and get

$$\ln (\cos x \tan x) = \ln \left(\cos x \, \frac{\sin x}{\cos x} \right) = \ln (\sin x).$$

(b) Logarithm functions are defined only for positive numbers. Determine the values of *x* for which cos *x* tan *x* and sin *x* are both positive. Recall that sin *x* is positive for all numbers *x* in the first or second quadrant. Both factors of cos *x* tan *x* are positive in the first quadrant, and both are negative in the second quadrant, so the product is positive in both quadrants, but tan *x*, and hence the product, is undefined at $x = \frac{\pi}{2}$. Therefore the given equation is valid only for values of *x* in the first two quadrants. ▲

EXERCISES 6.1

Check Your Understanding

Exercises 1–5   True or False. Give reasons for your conclusion.

1. $\sin x = \cos x \tan x$ is an identity.

2. $\sin (2x) = 2 \sin x$ is an identity.

3. $\tan (\pi + x) = \tan \pi + \tan x$ is an identity.

4. If $f(x) = 1 + x^2$ and $g(x) = \tan x$, then $f(g(x)) = \sec^2 x$.

5. The graphs of $y = \cos x \tan x$ and $y = \sin x$ are identical.

Exercises 6–10   Complete the sentence by selecting from the list below *all choices* that yield identities.

(a) 0   (b) 1   (c) $\sin x$ (d) $\cos x$
(e) $\tan x$ (f) $\cot x$ (g) $\sec x$ (h) $\csc x$

6. $\dfrac{1 - \cos^2 x}{\sin x} = \underline{\qquad}$.

7. $\dfrac{\cos x}{\sec x} + \dfrac{\sin x}{\csc x} = \underline{\qquad}$.

8. $\dfrac{\csc x}{\tan x + \cot x} = \underline{\qquad}$.

9. $\dfrac{\cos x \sec x}{\tan x} = \underline{\qquad}$.

10. $\ln (\sin^2 x + \cos^2 x) = \underline{\qquad}$.

Explore and Discover

1. The equation in Example 7, $\sqrt{\tan^2 x - \sin^2 x} = \sin x \tan x$, has the form $\sqrt{[f(x)]^2 - [g(x)]^2} = f(x)g(x)$. Thus there are functions $f(x)$ and $g(x)$ such that this form is valid for at least some values of x. If $g(x) = x$, then find a function f such that the equation is valid for some values of x. For what values of x is the equation not valid?

Develop Mastery

Exercises 1–2   Determine whether or not the equation is an identity. Give the values of x for which equality holds.

1. (a) $x^3 - x^2 = x^2(x - 1)$
   (b) $|x + 2| = |x| + 2$
   (c) $e^{2 \ln x} = x^2$

2. (a) $x^3 - x^2 - 2x = (x^2 - 2x)(x + 1)$
   (b) $\sqrt{x^2 + 1} = x + 1$
   (c) $\dfrac{x^3 - 1}{x - 1} = x^2 + x + 1$

3. Start with identity (I-4) and show that $1 + \cot^2 x = \csc^2 x$ is an identity.

4. From identity (I-4), show that $\dfrac{\sin^2 x}{1 - \cos x} = 1 + \cos x$ is an identity.

5. From identity (I-2), prove that $\cos x \tan x = \sin x$ is an identity.

6. From identity (I-4), show that $\sin^4 x - \cos^4 x = \sin^2 x - \cos^2 x$ is an identity. (*Hint:* Multiply both sides of (I-4) by an appropriate quantity.)

7. From identity (I-4), by adding an appropriate quantity to both sides, show that $(\sin x + \cos x)^2 = 1 + 2 \sin x \cos x$ is an identity.

8. From the identity $1 + \tan^2 x = \sec^2 x$, show that $\tan^2 x = (\sec x - 1)(\sec x + 1)$ is an identity.

Exercises 9–16   Prove that the equation is an identity. Work only with the left-hand side.

9. $\dfrac{\tan x}{\sin x} = \sec x$

10. $\dfrac{\sin x \csc x}{\cot x} = \tan x$

11. $\dfrac{\cot x}{\sec x} + \sin x = \csc x$

12. $\dfrac{\sin (-x)}{\cos (-x)} = -\tan x$

13. $\tan x \csc x = \sec x$

14. $\sin x \cos x (\tan x + \cot x) = 1$

15. $(1 - \cos x)(\csc x + \cot x) = \sin x$

16. $(1 - \sin x)(\sec x + \tan x) = \cos x$

Exercises 17–24   Show that the equation is an identity. Work only with the right-hand side.

17. $\csc x = \dfrac{\cot x}{\cos x}$

18. $\cot x = \dfrac{\cos x \sec x}{\tan x}$

19. $\tan x + \sec x = \dfrac{1 - \sin (-x)}{\cos (-x)}$

20. $\cos x = \dfrac{\csc (-x)}{\cot (-x) + \tan (-x)}$

21. $\sec x \csc x = \tan x + \cot x$

22. $\csc x = \cos x (\tan x + \cot x)$

23. $1 + \sin^2 x = \cos^2 x (\sec^4 x - \tan^4 x)$

24. $1 + \sin x = \dfrac{\tan x + \sec x}{\sin x \cot x \sec^2 x}$

Exercises 25–40   Show that the equation is an identity.

25. $\cos^2 x - \sin^2 x = 1 - 2 \sin^2 x$

26. $\cos^2 x - \sin^2 x = 2 \cos^2 x - 1$

27. $\dfrac{\sin x}{1 - \cos x} = \dfrac{1 + \cos x}{\sin x}$

28. $\dfrac{\cos x}{\sec x} + \dfrac{\sin x}{\csc x} = 1$

29. $\sec x + \cot x = \dfrac{\cos x + \tan x}{\sin x}$

30. $\dfrac{\sin x}{1 - \cos^2 x} = \csc x$

31. $\dfrac{\csc x}{\tan x + \csc x} = \cos x$

32. $\dfrac{\csc x}{\sin x} + \dfrac{\sec x}{\cos x} = \sec^2 x \csc^2 x$

33. $\dfrac{\sin x + \tan x}{1 + \sec x} = \sin x$

34. $\sec x - \dfrac{\cos x}{1 + \sin x} = \tan x$

35. $\ln (\tan x) = \ln (\sin x) - \ln (\cos x)$

36. $\ln (\sec x) = -\ln (\cos x)$

37. $\sqrt{\sec^2 x - 1} = |\tan x|$

38. $\sqrt{\cot^2 x - \cos^2 x} = |\cot x \cos x|$

39. $\dfrac{\sin^2 \alpha \sin^2 \beta}{\tan^2 \alpha \tan^2 \beta} = \dfrac{\sin^2 \alpha - \sin^2 \beta}{\tan^2 \alpha - \tan^2 \beta}$

40. $\dfrac{\cos^2 \alpha \cos^2 \beta}{\cot^2 \alpha \cot^2 \beta} = \dfrac{\cos^2 \alpha - \cos^2 \beta}{\cot^2 \alpha - \cot^2 \beta}$

Exercises 41–50   Find a simpler equation to describe the function.

41. $f(x) = \dfrac{\cos^2 x - 1}{\sin (-x)}$

42. $f(x) = \sin^4 x + \sin^2 x \cos^2 x$

43. $f(x) = \dfrac{\tan (-x)}{\sin (-x)}$

44. $f(x) = \dfrac{1}{\tan x + \cot x}$

45. $f(x) = \sin^3 x \cos x + \cos^3 x \sin x$

46. $f(x) = \dfrac{\sec x}{\tan x + \cot x}$

47. $f(x) = \dfrac{\sin x + \tan x}{1 + \sec x}$

48. $f(x) = \sqrt{1 - \sin^2 x}$

49. $f(x) = \sin x \left(\dfrac{\cos x}{\sin x} + \dfrac{\sin x}{\cos x} \right)$

50. $f(x) = \sin (-x) + \cot (-x) \cos (-x)$

Exercises 51–64   Determine whether or not the equation is an identity. Give either a proof or a counter-example.

51. $\cos x \tan x = \sin x$

52. $\dfrac{\sin^2 x}{\cos x} = \sec x - \cos x$

53. $\sin x \tan x = 1 - \cos x$

54. $\sin x + \cos x = (\cos x)(1 + \tan x)$

55. $(\sin x - \cos x)^2 = \sin^2 x - \cos^2 x$

56. $\sqrt{1 - \cos^2 x} = \sin x$

57. $\sin^4 x - \cos^4 x = 2 \sin^2 x - 1$

58. $\sqrt{1 + \tan^2 x} = \sec x$

59. $\dfrac{1 + \sin (-x)}{\cos (-x)} = \sec x - \tan x$

60. $\dfrac{\sin x}{\cos x - \sin x} = \dfrac{\tan x}{1 - \tan x}$

61. $(1 - \tan x)^2 = \sec^2 x - 2 \tan x$

62. $\sqrt{\sin^2 x + \cos^2 x} = |\sin x| + |\cos x|$

63. $\sqrt{1 + 2 \cos x + \cos^2 x} = 1 + \cos x$

64. $\sqrt{2 - 2 \cos x - \sin^2 x} = 1 - \cos x$

Exercises 65–67   For functions f and g, find an equation to describe the composite function $f \circ g$. Simplify when possible.

65. $f(x) = \sqrt{1 - x^2}$, $g(x) = \cos x$

66. $f(x) = \dfrac{|x|}{(x^2 - 1)^{1/2}}$, $g(x) = \sec x$

67. $f(x) = \dfrac{\sqrt{1 - x^2}}{|x|}$, $g(x) = \sin x$

68. (a) Draw a graph of $f(x) = \sin x$.
   (b) Draw a graph of $g(x) = \cos x \tan x$.
   (c) Are the two graphs identical? Explain.

69. (a) Draw a graph of $f(x) = \cos x$.
   (b) Draw graph of $g(x) = \sin x \cot x$.
   (c) Are the two graphs identical? Explain.

Exercises 70–71   Determine whether the statement is true or false. Give reasons.

70. If the graphs of functions f and g are identical, then $f(x) = g(x)$ is an identity.

71. If $f(x) = g(x)$ is an identity, then the graphs of functions f and g are identical.

Exercises 72–77   **(a)** Show that the equation is an identity. **(b)** Determine the set of values of x in the interval $[0, 2\pi]$ for which the equation is valid.

72. $\ln \tan x = \ln \sin x - \ln \cos x$

73. $\ln |\tan x| = \ln |\sin x| - \ln |\cos x|$

74. $\ln \tan (-x) = \ln \sin (-x) - \ln \cos (-x)$

75. $\ln (1 + \tan^2 x) = -2 \ln (\cos x)$

76. $\ln (1 + \tan^2 x) = -\ln (\cos^2 x)$

77. $\ln (x^2 \sin x) = 2 \ln x + \ln \sin x$

78. Evaluate the sum
$S = \ln (\tan \frac{\pi}{180}) + \ln (\tan \frac{2\pi}{180}) +$
$\ln (\tan \frac{3\pi}{180}) + \cdots + \ln (\tan \frac{89\pi}{180})$.
(*Hint:* Use the reduction formula $\tan (\frac{\pi}{2} - \theta) = \cot \theta = \frac{1}{\tan \theta}$. Thus $\tan \frac{89\pi}{180} = \frac{1}{\tan (\pi/180)}$.)

SECTION 6.2	**Sum, Difference, and Double-Angle Identities**

[Mathematics] is as incapable of being restricted within assigned boundaries . . . as the consciousness of life, which . . . is forever ready to burst forth into new forms of . . . existence.
  J. J. Sylvester

One important property of numbers is that multiplication is distributive over addition, which means that $a(b + c) = ab + ac$ for all numbers a, b, and c. Our first concern in this section is whether or not functions distribute over addition, that is, is $f(x + y) = f(x) + f(y)$ an identity? Such functions are given a name.

I've worked in so many areas. . . . Basically, I'm not interested in doing research and I never have been. I'm interested in understanding, *which is quite a different thing.*
  David Blackwell

> **Definition: Additive Functions**
>
> A function f is said to be an **additive function** if, and only if,
>
> $$f(x + y) = f(x) + f(y)$$
>
> is an identity; that is, equality holds for all numbers x and y for which both sides are defined.

Most functions we have already considered in this course are not additive. For instance, the natural logarithm function, $f(x) = \ln x$, is not additive because $\ln (x + y)$ is not equal to $\ln x + \ln y$ for all positive numbers x and y. The function $g(x) = x^2$ is not additive since $(x + y)^2$ is not identically equal to $x^2 + y^2$. The function $h(x) = \sqrt{x}$ is not additive either, because $\sqrt{x + y}$ is not equal to $\sqrt{x} + \sqrt{y}$ for all nonnegative x and y.

It should come as no surprise that trigonometric functions are not additive. For instance, to see that the sine function is not additive consider $\sin (\frac{\pi}{2} + \frac{\pi}{2})$ and $\sin \frac{\pi}{2} + \sin \frac{\pi}{2}$.

$$\sin \left(\frac{\pi}{2} + \frac{\pi}{2} \right) = \sin \pi = 0 \quad \text{but} \quad \sin \frac{\pi}{2} + \sin \frac{\pi}{2} = 1 + 1 = 2.$$

Thus, $\sin\left(\frac{\pi}{2} + \frac{\pi}{2}\right) \neq \sin\frac{\pi}{2} + \sin\frac{\pi}{2}$, so the sine function is not additive. We may wonder if, indeed, there are any additive functions. For some possibilities see the Explore and Discover Exercises 1 and 2.

Although trigonometric functions are not additive, some important identities allow us to express functions of sums and differences in relatively simple terms. Collectively, these identities are called the **sum and difference formulas.**

Sum and Difference Identities

$$\sin(\alpha + \beta) = \sin\alpha\cos\beta + \cos\alpha\sin\beta \qquad \textbf{(I-6)}$$

$$\sin(\alpha - \beta) = \sin\alpha\cos\beta - \cos\alpha\sin\beta \qquad \textbf{(I-7)}$$

$$\cos(\alpha + \beta) = \cos\alpha\cos\beta - \sin\alpha\sin\beta \qquad \textbf{(I-8)}$$

$$\cos(\alpha - \beta) = \cos\alpha\cos\beta + \sin\alpha\sin\beta \qquad \textbf{(I-9)}$$

$$\tan(\alpha + \beta) = \frac{\tan\alpha + \tan\beta}{1 - \tan\alpha\tan\beta} \qquad \textbf{(I-10)}$$

$$\tan(\alpha - \beta) = \frac{\tan\alpha - \tan\beta}{1 + \tan\alpha\tan\beta} \qquad \textbf{(I-11)}$$

Proofs of the Sum and Difference Identities

It is convenient first to give a proof of (I-9) and then proceed to use (I-9) to prove (I-6) and (I-10). Proofs of the other identities are left for the reader. See Develop Mastery Exercise 1.

To prove (I-9), we wish to relate $\cos(\alpha - \beta)$ to functions of α and β. It will be helpful to have a diagram that shows each of the angles α, β, and $\alpha - \beta$. We lose no generality in supposing that α, β, and $\alpha - \beta$ are positive. Placing α and β in standard position on a unit circle, $P(\alpha) = (\cos\alpha, \sin\alpha)$ and $P(\beta) = (\cos\beta, \sin\beta)$, as shown in Figure 6.1a. Let us denote $P(\alpha)$ by A and $P(\beta)$ by B. In triangle AOB, angle AOB is $\alpha - \beta$. Angle $\alpha - \beta$ appears in standard position in Figure 6.1b, where C is the point $(\cos(\alpha - \beta), \sin(\alpha - \beta))$.

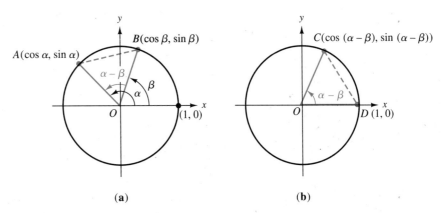

(a)   (b)

FIGURE 6.1

In Figure 6.1, triangles *AOB* and *COD* are congruent. In fact, we may visualize simply rotating triangle *AOB* clockwise until *B* coincides with *D*. In particular, the segments $\overline{AB}$ and $\overline{CD}$ have the same length. We may use the distance formula to calculate the length of each in terms of the coordinates of their endpoints. We leave details as a worthwhile exercise for the reader (using identity (I-4) as needed) to get the following:

$$|\overline{AB}|^2 = (\cos \alpha - \cos \beta)^2 + (\sin \alpha - \sin \beta)^2$$
$$= 2 - 2(\cos \alpha \cos \beta + \sin \alpha \sin \beta).$$

$$|\overline{CD}|^2 = [\cos (\alpha - \beta) - 1]^2 + [\sin (\alpha - \beta)]^2$$
$$= 2 - 2 \cos (\alpha - \beta)$$

Since $|\overline{AB}| = |\overline{CD}|$, we get $2 - 2(\cos \alpha \cos \beta + \sin \alpha \sin \beta) = 2 - 2 \cos (\alpha - \beta)$. After simplifying, we have identity (I-9).

To prove identity (I-6), use (I-9) and these reduction formulas:

$$\cos \left(\frac{\pi}{2} - t \right) = \sin t$$

$$\sin \left(\frac{\pi}{2} - t \right) = \cos t$$

In the first reduction formula, replace *t* with $(\alpha + \beta)$. Reading from right to left,

$$\sin (\alpha + \beta) = \cos \left[\frac{\pi}{2} - (\alpha + \beta) \right] = \cos \left[\left(\frac{\pi}{2} - \alpha \right) - \beta \right]$$

$$= \cos \left(\frac{\pi}{2} - \alpha \right) \cos \beta + \sin \left(\frac{\pi}{2} - \alpha \right) \sin \beta \qquad \text{By (I-9)}$$

$$= \sin \alpha \cos \beta + \cos \alpha \sin \beta \qquad \text{By reduction formulas}$$

Therefore $\sin (\alpha + \beta) = \sin \alpha \cos \beta + \cos \alpha \sin \beta$ is an identity. In a similar manner, (I-8) follows from (I-9); see Develop Mastery Exercise 1.

Now we proceed to (I-10). As a first step, use (I-2), $\tan \theta = \frac{\sin \theta}{\cos \theta}$, where θ is replaced by $(\alpha + \beta)$.

$$\tan (\alpha + \beta) = \frac{\sin (\alpha + \beta)}{\cos (\alpha + \beta)} = \frac{\sin \alpha \cos \beta + \cos \alpha \sin \beta}{\cos \alpha \cos \beta - \sin \alpha \sin \beta} \qquad \text{By (I-6) and (I-9)}$$

Divide each term in the numerator and denominator by $\cos \alpha \cos \beta$ and simplify:

$$\tan (\alpha + \beta) = \frac{\dfrac{\sin \alpha}{\cos \alpha} + \dfrac{\sin \beta}{\cos \beta}}{1 - \dfrac{\sin \alpha}{\cos \alpha} \cdot \dfrac{\sin \beta}{\cos \beta}} = \frac{\tan \alpha + \tan \beta}{1 - \tan \alpha \tan \beta}$$

```
┌─────────────┐
│ For Graphers│          MORE GRAPHS AND IDENTITIES
│     6.2     │
└─────────────┘
```

Exercises

Exercises 1–6 Use graphs to help decide if the equation is an identity.

1. $2 \sin \left(x + \frac{\pi}{6}\right) = \sqrt{3} \sin x + \cos x$

2. $\cos \left(x - \frac{\pi}{3}\right) = \sin \left(x - \frac{5\pi}{6}\right)$

3. $\cos 2x \tan 2x = 2 \sin x \cos x$

4. $(\sin x + \cos x)^2 = 1 + \sin 2x$

5. $\sin 2x = 2 \sin x$

6. $\sin (\text{Sin}^{-1} x - \text{Cos}^{-1} x) = 2x^2 - 1$

Exercises 7–9 Use graphs to help solve the equation. See Develop Mastery Exercises 60–62.

7. $\text{Sin}^{-1}(2x - 1) = \text{Sin}^{-1} x + \text{Cos}^{-1} x$

8. $\text{Sin}^{-1}(4x - 1) = \text{Sin}^{-1} x + \text{Cos}^{-1} x$

9. $\text{Sin}^{-1}(-x) = \text{Sin}^{-1} x - \text{Cos}^{-1} x$

10. Draw a graph of $f(x) = \sin (\text{Sin}^{-1} x + \text{Cos}^{-1} x)$. From your graph, guess a simpler formula for $f(x)$.

EXAMPLE 1 Prove that $\tan \left(x + \frac{\pi}{4}\right) = \frac{\cos x + \sin x}{\cos x - \sin x}$ is an identity.

Solution

Strategy: Begin by using (I-10) and then replace $\tan x$ by $\frac{\sin x}{\cos x}$ and simplify.

Starting with the left-hand side,

$$\tan \left(x + \frac{\pi}{4}\right) = \frac{\tan x + \tan \left(\frac{\pi}{4}\right)}{1 - \tan x \tan \left(\frac{\pi}{4}\right)} = \frac{\tan x + 1}{1 - \tan x} \qquad \text{By (I-10) and } \tan \frac{\pi}{4} = 1$$

$$= \frac{\frac{\sin x}{\cos x} + 1}{1 - \frac{\sin x}{\cos x}} = \frac{\sin x + \cos x}{\cos x - \sin x} \qquad \text{By (I-2) and algebra}$$

Therefore, the given equation is an identity. ▲

EXAMPLE 2 Evaluate $\sin \frac{\pi}{12}$ in exact form. Use a calculator to get a check.

Solution

Strategy: First express $\frac{\pi}{12}$ as a sum or difference of angles for which we know exact values. $\frac{\pi}{12} = 15° = 45° - 30° = \frac{\pi}{4} - \frac{\pi}{6}$.

Follow the strategy and use (I-7).

$$\sin \frac{\pi}{12} = \sin \left(\frac{\pi}{4} - \frac{\pi}{6}\right) = \sin \frac{\pi}{4} \cos \frac{\pi}{6} - \cos \frac{\pi}{4} \sin \frac{\pi}{6}$$

$$= \frac{1}{\sqrt{2}} \cdot \frac{\sqrt{3}}{2} - \frac{1}{\sqrt{2}} \cdot \frac{1}{2} = \frac{\sqrt{3} - 1}{2\sqrt{2}} = \frac{\sqrt{6} - \sqrt{2}}{4}.$$

Therefore, in exact form, $\sin \frac{\pi}{12} = \frac{\sqrt{6} - \sqrt{2}}{4}$. With the calculator in radian mode

$$\sin \frac{\pi}{12} \approx 0.2588190451 \qquad \text{and} \qquad \frac{\sqrt{6} - \sqrt{2}}{4} \approx 0.2588190451. \quad ▲$$

EXAMPLE 3   Suppose α and β satisfy

$$\sin \alpha = \frac{4}{5} \text{ and } \frac{\pi}{2} < \alpha < \frac{3\pi}{2}, \cos \beta = \frac{5}{13} \text{ and } -\pi < \beta < 0.$$

Evaluate in exact form.

(a) $\tan (\alpha - \beta)$ **(b)** $\sec (\alpha + \beta)$ **(c)** $\sin 2\alpha$.

Solution

Strategy: Using the given information, first draw diagrams showing reference triangles for α and β, from which we can get the trigonometric function values of α and β, then use **(a)** (I-11), **(b)** (I-8), **(c)** (I-6).

Follow the strategy and draw diagrams shown in Figure 6.2.

(a) $\tan (\alpha - \beta) = \dfrac{\tan \alpha - \tan \beta}{1 + \tan \alpha \tan \beta}$ By (I-11)

$$= \frac{\left(\dfrac{-4}{3}\right) - \left(\dfrac{-12}{5}\right)}{1 + \left(\dfrac{-4}{3}\right)\left(\dfrac{-12}{5}\right)} = \frac{16}{63} \qquad \begin{array}{l}\text{From Figure 6.2} \\ \text{and arithmetic}\end{array}$$

(b) By (I-1), $\sec (\alpha + \beta)$ is the reciprocal of $\cos (\alpha + \beta)$, so evaluate $\cos (\alpha + \beta)$ and then take the reciprocal

$$\cos (\alpha + \beta) = \cos \alpha \cos \beta - \sin \alpha \sin \beta \qquad \text{By (I-8)}$$

$$= \left(-\frac{3}{5}\right)\left(\frac{5}{13}\right) - \left(\frac{4}{5}\right)\left(-\frac{12}{13}\right) = \frac{33}{65} \qquad \text{From Figure 6.2}$$

Therefore $\sec (\alpha + \beta) = \frac{65}{33}$.

(c) First write 2α as $(\alpha + \alpha)$ and then use (I-6).

$$\sin 2\alpha = \sin (\alpha + \alpha) = \sin \alpha \cos \alpha + \cos \alpha \sin \alpha \qquad \text{By (I-6)}$$

$$= 2 \sin \alpha \cos \alpha = 2\left(\frac{4}{5}\right)\left(-\frac{3}{5}\right) = -\frac{24}{25}.$$

Hence $\sin 2\alpha = -\dfrac{24}{25}$. ▲

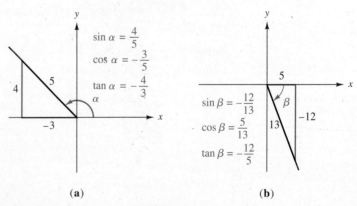

(a)   (b)

FIGURE 6.2

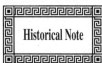

IDENTITIES IN APPLICATION

James Gregory

Trigonometric identities are important because they can sometimes make feasible tasks that otherwise might be difficult or impossible. Consider the strange case of Zacharias Dase, born in Germany in 1824. Dase apparently had very limited abilities in many areas, but he was one of the most remarkable mental calculators who ever lived. He once calculated the product of a pair of hundred-digit numbers *in his head* in nearly nine hours of intense concentration. He enters our story because he was another calculator of the number π.

Not long after the invention of calculus, James Gregory, a Scottish mathematician, found a way to express the function Arctan x as the sum of an infinite series.

Arctan x

$$= x - \frac{x^3}{3} + \frac{x^5}{5} - \frac{x^7}{7} + \cdots$$

Since $\tan \frac{\pi}{4} = 1$, we may substitute 1 for x in Gregory's series to obtain

$$\frac{\pi}{4} = \text{Arctan } 1$$

$$= 1 - \frac{1}{3} + \frac{1}{5} - \frac{1}{7} + \cdots$$

While this series could theoretically be used to approximate π, it has little practical value because it would require 10,000 terms to get four-place accuracy and a million terms for six places. Getting a good approximation with Gregory's series would exceed even Dase's capabilities. Clever use of trigonometric identities, however, put an approximation within reach.

If we let $\alpha = \text{Arctan } \frac{1}{2}$, $\beta = \text{Arctan } \frac{1}{5}$, and $\gamma = \text{Arctan } \frac{1}{8}$, then $\tan \alpha = \frac{1}{2}$, $\tan \beta = \frac{1}{5}$, and $\tan \gamma = \frac{1}{8}$. By using identity (I-10), we can show that $\alpha + \beta + \gamma = \frac{\pi}{4}$. (See the Explore and Discover exercises for this section.) This gives the identity $\pi = 4 \left(\text{Arctan } \frac{1}{2} + \text{Arctan } \frac{1}{5} + \text{Arctan } \frac{1}{8} \right)$. Substituting the values $\frac{1}{2}$, $\frac{1}{5}$, and $\frac{1}{8}$ into Gregory's series yields a manageable sum. In a still prodigious calculating feat, Dase added up hundreds of terms to obtain 200 digits of the expansion of π.

The solution to Example 4c suggests an identity for the sine of twice an angle. We can get $\sin 2\theta$ simply by replacing both α and β by θ in identity (I-6). Similar replacements in (I-8) and (I-10) give **double-angle identities.**

Double-Angle Identities

$$\sin 2\theta = 2 \sin \theta \cos \theta \qquad \textbf{(I-12)}$$

$$\cos 2\theta = \cos^2 \theta - \sin^2 \theta \qquad \textbf{(I-13)}$$

$$\tan 2\theta = \frac{2 \tan \theta}{1 - \tan^2 \theta} \qquad \textbf{(I-14)}$$

The double-angle identities are three more key identities with which you should become very familiar. In addition, two other forms of (I-3) are worth remembering. We may replace $\cos^2 \theta$ by $1 - \sin^2 \theta$, or replace $\sin^2 \theta$ by $1 - \cos^2 \theta$ to get the alternate forms.

Alternate Forms of (I-13)

$$\cos 2\theta = 1 - 2 \sin^2 \theta \qquad \text{or} \qquad \cos 2\theta = 2 \cos^2 \theta - 1$$

EXAMPLE 4   Suppose θ is a number (or angle) between 0 and π where $\tan \theta = -\frac{5}{12}$. Evaluate in exact form **(a)** $\cos 2\theta$, **(b)** $\tan 2\theta$, **(c)** $\sec 2\theta$.

Solution

Begin by drawing a diagram to show θ and a reference triangle (see Figure 6.3).

(a) $\qquad \cos 2\theta = \cos^2 \theta - \sin^2 \theta \qquad$ By (I-13)

$$= \left(-\frac{12}{13}\right)^2 - \left(\frac{5}{13}\right)^2 = \frac{119}{169} \qquad \text{From Figure 6.3}$$

(b) Using (I-14) and Figure 6.3,

$$\tan 2\theta = \frac{2 \tan \theta}{1 - \tan^2 \theta} = \frac{2\left(-\dfrac{5}{12}\right)}{1 - \left(-\dfrac{5}{12}\right)^2} = -\frac{120}{119}$$

(c) Since $\sec 2\theta = \dfrac{1}{\cos 2\theta}$, and $\cos 2\theta = \dfrac{119}{169}$,

$$\sec 2\theta = \frac{169}{119}.$$

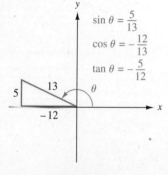

$$\sin \theta = \frac{5}{13}$$
$$\cos \theta = -\frac{12}{13}$$
$$\tan \theta = -\frac{5}{12}$$

FIGURE 6.3

EXERCISES 6.2

Check Your Understanding

Exercises 1–5   True or False. Give reasons for your conclusion.

1. $\sin(1 + \sqrt{3}) = \sin 1 + \sin \sqrt{3}$
2. There is no number x for which $\sin 2x = 2\sin x$.
3. If $0 < x < \frac{\pi}{2}$ and $\sin x = \frac{\sqrt{3}}{2}$, then $\sin 2x = \frac{\sqrt{3}}{2}$.
4. If $0 < x < \pi$ and $\cos x = \frac{\sqrt{3}}{2}$, then $\cos 2x = \frac{\sqrt{3}}{2}$.
5. $\tan(x + \frac{3}{4}) = \frac{1 + \tan x}{1 - \tan x}$ is an identity.

Exercises 6–10   Complete the sentence by selecting from the list *all choices* that make the statement either true or an identity.

(a) 0   (b) $\frac{1}{2}$ (c) 1   (d) $2\sin x$

(e) $2\sin x \cos x$ (f) $\frac{\sqrt{3}\sin x + \cos x}{2}$

(g) $-\frac{\sqrt{3}\sin x + \cos x}{2}$ (h) $-\sin\left(\frac{5\pi}{6} - x\right)$

(i) $\sin x - \frac{1}{2}$ (j) $\cos x - \frac{1}{2}$

6. $\sin\left(x + \frac{\pi}{6}\right) = $ _____.
7. $\sin\left(x - \frac{5\pi}{6}\right) = $ _____.
8. $\cos\left(x - \frac{\pi}{3}\right) = $ _____.
9. $\sin\left(\frac{5\pi}{6} - \frac{\pi}{3}\right) = $ _____.
10. $(\cos 2x)(\tan 2x) = $ _____.

Explore and Discover

1. Try various simple functions such as $f(x) = x + 1$, $f(x) = 2x - 1$, $f(x) = x^2 + 1$, $f(x) - 2x$, $f(x) = -3x$, and so on, to see if any are additive functions.
2. Based on your findings in Exercise 1, with other examples as needed, make a guess about some types of functions that are additive. Briefly explain why you think that the kinds of functions you have identified are additive and why certain other classes of functions are not additive.
3. Let $x + \frac{1}{x} = 2\cos\theta$, where $0 < \theta < \frac{\pi}{2}$.

   (a) Show that $x^2 + \frac{1}{x^2} = 2\cos 2\theta$. (*Hint:* Square both sides of the equation.)

   (b) Show that $x^3 + \frac{1}{x^3} = 2\cos 3\theta$. (*Hint:* Cube both sides of the equation and use the identity in Develop Mastery exercise 50b.)

(c) Show that $x^4 + \frac{1}{x^4} = 2\cos 4\theta$. (*Hint:* Square both sides of the equation in part a.)

(d) Guess formulas for $x^5 + \frac{1}{x^5}$ and $x^6 + \frac{1}{x^6}$.

4. If $x + \frac{1}{x} = 2\cos 15°$, use Exercise 3 to evaluate

   (a) $x^2 + \frac{1}{x^2}$, (b) $x^4 + \frac{1}{x^4}$, (c) $x^8 + \frac{1}{x^8}$.

5. If $x + \frac{1}{x} = 2\cos 15°$, find (a) $x^8 + x^{-8}$, (b) $x^{16} + x^{-16}$, (c) $x^{32} + x^{-32}$. Guess a general formula. (*Hint:* Use the preceding exercise.)

6. Let $f(x) = \text{Sin}^{-1}x + \text{Cos}^{-1}x$.

   (a) What is the domain of f?

   (b) Evaluate $f(x)$ for several values, including $\frac{1}{2}, \frac{\sqrt{2}}{2}, \frac{\sqrt{3}}{2}, \frac{3}{5}, \frac{4}{5}$.

   (c) Based on your data in part (b) guess a simple equation for $f(x)$.

   (d) Show that your equation for part (c) is an identity.

Develop Mastery

1. Replace β by $-\beta$ in each of (I-6), (I-9), and (I-10), and then use (I-3) to get identities (I-7), (I-8), and (I-11).

Exercises 2–4   Use identities given in this section to verify the reduction formulas.

2. (a) $\sin\left(\theta + \frac{\pi}{2}\right) = \cos\theta$

   (b) $\cos(\theta + \pi) = -\cos\theta$

3. (a) $\cos\left(\theta - \frac{3\pi}{2}\right) = -\sin\theta$

   (b) $\tan(\pi - \theta) = -\tan\theta$

4. (a) $\sin(\theta - \pi) = -\sin\theta$

   (b) $\sec\left(\frac{3\pi}{2} + \theta\right) = \csc\theta$

Exercises 5–8   Evalute in exact form and then check by using a calculator to obtain a decimal approximation for your result and for the given expression.

5. $\cos\frac{5\pi}{12}$; use (a) $\frac{5\pi}{12} = \frac{\pi}{6} + \frac{\pi}{4}$ and (b) $\frac{5\pi}{12} = \frac{2\pi}{3} - \frac{\pi}{4}$

6. $\tan\frac{13\pi}{12}$; use (a) $\frac{13\pi}{12} = \frac{5\pi}{6} + \frac{\pi}{4}$ and

   (b) $\frac{13\pi}{12} = \frac{5\pi}{4} - \frac{\pi}{6}$

7. $\sin(-15°)$; use (a) $-15° = 30° - 45°$ and
  (b) $-15° = 45° - 60°$

8. $\sec 255°$; use (a) $255° = 135° + 120°$ and
  (b) $255° = 315° - 60°$

Exercises 9–12 Evaluate in exact form. First express the given angle as a sum or difference of angles whose trigonometric functions you can evaluate in exact form.

9. (a) $\sin 105°$ (b) $\tan 105°$
10. (a) $\cos 285°$ (b) $\sec 285°$
11. (a) $\sin \frac{17\pi}{12}$ (b) $\csc \frac{17\pi}{12}$
12. (a) $\cot \frac{\pi}{12}$ (b) $\csc \frac{\pi}{12}$

Exercises 13–21 For angles α and β, where

$$\sin \alpha = -\frac{3}{5}, 0 < \alpha < \frac{3\pi}{2}$$

$$\cos \beta = -\frac{5}{13}, \frac{\pi}{2} < \beta < \pi,$$

draw diagrams to show α and β in standard position with reference triangles, then evaluate in exact form. See Example 3.

13. $\sin(\alpha + \beta)$
14. $\cos(\alpha - \beta)$
15. $\tan(\beta - \alpha)$
16. $\sin 2\alpha$
17. $\cos 2\beta$
18. $\cot 2\alpha$
19. $\sin(\frac{\pi}{2} - 2\alpha)$
20. $\cos(\frac{3\pi}{2} + 2\alpha)$
21. $\tan(\frac{\pi}{4} - 2\alpha)$

Exercises 22–30 For angle θ that satisfies

$$\sin \theta = -\frac{3}{4}, \quad -\frac{\pi}{2} < \theta < \frac{\pi}{2},$$

draw a diagram to show θ in standard position with a reference triangle, then evaluate in exact form.

22. $\sin 2\theta$
23. $\sec 2\theta$
24. $\tan(\frac{\pi}{3} + \theta)$
25. $\tan(\frac{2\pi}{3} - \theta)$
26. $\sin(\frac{5\pi}{4} + \theta)$
27. $\cos(\frac{5\pi}{6} + \theta)$
28. $\csc(\frac{\pi}{2} - 2\theta)$
29. $\sin(\frac{3\pi}{2} - 2\theta)$
30. $\cot(\frac{\pi}{4} + \theta)$

Exercises 31–33 Use the identities from this section to simplify the expression, then evaluate in exact form.

31. (a) $\sin 20° \cos 40° + \cos 20° \sin 40°$
  (b) $\cos \frac{\pi}{10} \cos \frac{2\pi}{5} - \sin \frac{\pi}{10} \sin \frac{2\pi}{5}$

32. (a) $\cos^2 15° - \sin^2 15°$ (b) $\sin \frac{5\pi}{12} \cos \frac{5\pi}{12}$

33. (a) $\sin 80° \cos 50° - \cos 80° \sin 50°$
  (b) $\frac{1}{2} \sec 15° \csc 15°$

Exercises 34–43 Prove that the equation is an identity.

34. $\tan(x - \frac{\pi}{4}) = \frac{\sin x - \cos x}{\sin x + \cos x}$
35. $\sin(\frac{\pi}{6} - x) = \frac{1}{2}(\cos x - \sqrt{3} \sin x)$
36. $\frac{\cos 2x}{\cos x + \sin x} = \cos x - \sin x$
37. $(\sin x + \cos x)^2 = 1 + \sin 2x$
38. $(\sin x - \cos x)^2 + \sin 2x = 1$
39. $\tan(\frac{5\pi}{4} - x) = \frac{1 - \tan x}{1 + \tan x}$
40. $\sin(x - \frac{\pi}{6}) = \cos(x - \frac{2\pi}{3})$
41. $\frac{\sin 2x}{\cos 2x} = \frac{2 \tan x}{1 - \tan^2 x}$ 42. $\frac{\sin 2x}{\tan 2x} = 2 \cos^2 x - 1$
43. $\cos(x + \frac{\pi}{3}) = \frac{1}{2}(\cos x - \sqrt{3} \sin x)$

Exercises 44–46 Use identities (I10) and (I11). Give answers in exact form.

44. If $\tan \alpha = 2$ and $\tan(\alpha - \beta) = 3$, find $\tan \beta$.
45. If $\tan x = \frac{3}{4}$ and $x + y = \frac{\pi}{4}$, find $\tan y$.
46. If $\sin x = \frac{3}{5}$, x is in the first quadrant, and $x + y = \frac{3\pi}{4}$, find $\tan y$.

Exercises 47–48 Use the sum and difference formulas to simplify the expression.

47. (a) $\sin(x + \frac{\pi}{4}) + \sin(x - \frac{\pi}{4})$
  (b) $\cos(x + \frac{\pi}{4}) + \cos(x - \frac{\pi}{4})$
48. (a) $\sin(x - \frac{\pi}{3}) + \sin(x + \frac{\pi}{3})$
  (b) $\cos(x - \frac{\pi}{3}) + \cos(x + \frac{\pi}{3})$
49. (a) Prove that $\sin 3\theta = 3 \sin \theta \cos^2 \theta - \sin^3 \theta$ is an identity. (*Hint:* $\sin 3\theta = \sin(\theta + 2\theta)$; use (I-6).
  (b) Prove that $\sin 3\theta = 3 \sin \theta - 4 \sin^3 \theta$ is an identity.
50. (a) Prove that $\cos 3\theta = \cos^3 \theta - 3 \sin^2 \theta \cos \theta$ is an identity. (*Hint:* $\cos 3\theta = \cos(\theta + 2\theta)$; use (I-8).)
  (b) Prove that $\cos 3\theta = 4 \cos^3 \theta - 3 \cos \theta$ is an identity.

Exercises 51–54 Evaluate in exact form. Check your results by calculator.

51. $\mathrm{Sin}^{-1}(\frac{5}{13}) + \mathrm{Tan}^{-1}(\frac{12}{5})$ [*Hint:* Let $\alpha = \mathrm{Sin}^{-1}(\frac{5}{13})$ and $\beta = \mathrm{Tan}^{-1}(\frac{12}{5})$ and evaluate $\sin(\alpha + \beta)$.]

52. $\text{Cos}^{-1}\left(\frac{3}{5}\right) + \text{Tan}^{-1}\left(\frac{3}{4}\right)$ (*Hint:* See Exercise 51.)

53. $\text{Tan}^{-1}\left(\frac{1}{3}\right) + \text{Tan}^{-1}\left(\frac{1}{2}\right)$ (*Hint:* Let $\alpha = \text{Tan}^{-1}\left(\frac{1}{3}\right)$ and $\beta = \text{Tan}^{-1}\left(\frac{1}{2}\right)$ and evaluate $\tan(\alpha + \beta)$.)

54. $\text{Tan}^{-1}\left(\frac{1}{7}\right) - \text{Tan}^{-1}\left(\frac{4}{3}\right)$ (*Hint:* See Exercise 53.)

Exercises 55–58 Solve for x. (Hint: For 55–57, take the tangent of both sides.)

55. $\text{Tan}^{-1}x = \text{Tan}^{-1}\left(\frac{1}{4}\right) + \text{Tan}^{-1}\left(\frac{1}{2}\right)$

56. $\text{Tan}^{-1}(2x + 1) = \text{Tan}^{-1}1 - \text{Tan}^{-1}\left(\frac{1}{2}\right)$

57. $\text{Tan}^{-1}(3x - 4) = \text{Tan}^{-1}4 + \text{Tan}^{-1}2$

58. $\text{Sin}^{-1}x = \text{Tan}^{-1}\left(\frac{3}{4}\right) + \text{Cos}^{-1}\left(\frac{3}{5}\right)$

59. (a) Show that $\sin(\text{Sin}^{-1}x + \text{Cos}^{-1}x) = 1$ for every x in $[-1, 1]$.
    (b) Show that $\sin(\text{Sin}^{-1}x - \text{Cos}^{-1}x) = 2x^2 - 1$ for every x in $[-1, 1]$.

Exercises 60–63 Solve the equation. (Hint: Use the identities in Exercise 59.)

60. $\text{Sin}^{-1}(2x - 1) = \text{Sin}^{-1}x + \text{Cos}^{-1}x$

61. $\text{Sin}^{-1}(4x - 1) = \text{Sin}^{-1}x + \text{Cos}^{-1}x$

62. $\text{Sin}^{-1}(-x) = \text{Sin}^{-1}x - \text{Cos}^{-1}x$

63. $\text{Sin}^{-1}(3x - 2) = \text{Sin}^{-1}x - \text{Cos}^{-1}x$

64. *Looking Ahead to Calculus*
    (a) Show that $2\,\text{Tan}^{-1}x = \text{Tan}^{-1}\dfrac{2x}{1 - x^2}$ for $0 \le x < 1$. (*Hint:* Use (I-14).)
    (b) Show that $4\,\text{Tan}^{-1}\left(\frac{1}{5}\right) = \text{Tan}^{-1}\left(\frac{120}{119}\right)$. (*Hint:* Use part (a).)
    (c) Show that $\frac{\pi}{4} = 4\,\text{Tan}^{-1}\left(\frac{1}{5}\right) - \text{Tan}^{-1}\left(\frac{1}{239}\right)$. [*Hint:* Show that the tangent of the right side is equal to 1. Techniques in calculus allow us to evaluate each of the expressions $\text{Tan}^{-1}\left(\frac{1}{5}\right)$ and $\text{Tan}^{-1}\left(\frac{1}{239}\right)$, so the formula in part (c) can be used to evaluate π. In 1706 John Machin used this formula to calculate 100 decimal places of π.]

65. Show that $\text{Tan}^{-1}\left(\frac{1}{2}\right) + \text{Tan}^{-1}\left(\frac{1}{5}\right) + \text{Tan}^{-1}\left(\frac{1}{8}\right) = \frac{\pi}{4}$. [*Hint:* Show that $\text{Tan}^{-1}\left(\frac{1}{5}\right) + \text{Tan}^{-1}\left(\frac{1}{8}\right) = \frac{\pi}{4} - \text{Tan}^{-1}\left(\frac{1}{2}\right)$ using (I-10) and (I-11).]

66. Show that the equation is an identity. Determine the set of values of x in the interval $[0, 2\pi]$ for which the equation is valid.
    (a) $\ln(\sin 2x) = \ln 2 + \ln(\sin x \cos x)$
    (b) $\ln(\sin 2x) = \ln 2 + \ln(\sin x) + \ln(\cos x)$

| SECTION 6.3 | **Half-Angle Formulas; Product–Sum and Factor Identities** |

The idea that buried among the chaotic data of experience are hidden principles of an exact mathematical nature is far from obvious.
          P. W. C. Davies

In this section we derive additional key identities.

Half-Angle Formulas

As noted in the preceding section, identity (I-13) can be expressed in alternate forms:

$$\cos 2\alpha = 1 - 2\sin^2\alpha, \qquad \cos 2\alpha = 2\cos^2\alpha - 1.$$

Replacing 2α by θ, and α by $\frac{\theta}{2}$, these equations become

$$\cos\theta = 1 - 2\sin^2\frac{\theta}{2}, \qquad \cos\theta = 2\cos^2\frac{\theta}{2} - 1.$$

Solving the first of these equations for $\sin\frac{\theta}{2}$ and the second equation for $\cos\frac{\theta}{2}$ gives half-angle identities.

> **Half-Angle Identities**
>
> $$\sin \frac{\theta}{2} = \pm \sqrt{\frac{1 - \cos \theta}{2}} \qquad \textbf{(I1-5)}$$
>
> $$\cos \frac{\theta}{2} = \pm \sqrt{\frac{1 + \cos \theta}{2}} \qquad \textbf{(I-16)}$$

The plus–minus sign does not mean that there are two different values, but rather that we must select the sign that is consistent with the desired function in the quadrant in which $\frac{\theta}{2}$ is located. For instance, if $\pi < \theta < \frac{3\pi}{2}$, then $\frac{\pi}{2} < \frac{\theta}{2} < \frac{3\pi}{4}$, so $\frac{\theta}{2}$ is in the second quadrant. In this case, $\sin\left(\frac{\theta}{2}\right)$ is positive and $\cos\left(\frac{\theta}{2}\right)$ is negative. Keep in mind that the quadrant in which θ lies does not uniquely determine the quadrant of $\frac{\theta}{2}$. In the case above, if we take θ to be the third-quadrant angle $\frac{4\pi}{3}$, then $\frac{\theta}{2}$ is the second quadrant angle $\frac{2\pi}{3}$. However, if we take θ to be the coterminal angle $-\frac{2\pi}{3}$, then $\frac{\theta}{2}$ is the fourth-quadrant angle $-\frac{\pi}{3}$, for which the cosine is positive and the sine is negative.

To get an identity for $\tan \frac{\theta}{2}$ let us first rewrite identities (I-12) and an alternative form of (I-13) by replacing 2θ by θ and θ by $\frac{\theta}{2}$.

$$\sin \theta = 2 \sin \frac{\theta}{2} \cos \frac{\theta}{2}$$

$$1 + \cos \theta = 2 \cos^2 \frac{\theta}{2}$$

Now divide the first equation by the second equation and simplify:

$$\frac{\sin \theta}{1 + \cos \theta} = \frac{2 \sin \frac{\theta}{2} \cos \frac{\theta}{2}}{2 \cos^2 \frac{\theta}{2}} = \frac{\sin \frac{\theta}{2}}{\cos \frac{\theta}{2}} = \tan \frac{\theta}{2}.$$

This gives an identity for $\tan \frac{\theta}{2}$:

$$\tan \frac{\theta}{2} = \frac{\sin \theta}{1 + \cos \theta}.$$

In Example 3 of Section 6.1 we proved that $\frac{\sin \theta}{1 + \cos \theta}$ is identically equal to $\frac{1 - \cos \theta}{\sin \theta}$, so we have two forms for $\tan \frac{\theta}{2}$.

> **Another Half-Angle Identity**
>
> $$\tan \frac{\theta}{2} = \frac{\sin \theta}{1 + \cos \theta} \qquad \text{or} \qquad \tan \frac{\theta}{2} = \frac{1 - \cos \theta}{\sin \theta} \qquad \textbf{(I-17)}$$

The two forms in (I-17) do not require the plus–minus option in identities (I-15) and (I-16). The signs of $\tan \frac{\theta}{2}$ and $\sin \theta$ agree; whenever one is positive so is the other, and when one is negative so is the other.

| **EXAMPLE 1** | Evaluate in exact form. As a partial check, compare calculator evaluation with your result.

(a) $\sin \frac{\pi}{8}$ **(b)** $\cos \frac{5\pi}{8}$ **(c)** $\tan -\frac{7\pi}{12}$

Solution

In each part first express the problem in a form that allows use of one of the half-angle formulas, from which we can get the result in exact form.

(a) Use (I-15) and first take care of the $\pm$ sign. Since $\frac{\pi}{8}$ (or 22.5°) is in the first quadrant, the sine is positive and we use the plus sign. Also, use the fact that $\frac{\pi}{8} = (\frac{1}{2})(\frac{\pi}{4})$.

$$\sin \frac{\pi}{8} = \sin \left(\frac{1}{2} \cdot \frac{\pi}{4} \right) = \sqrt{\frac{1 - \cos \frac{\pi}{4}}{2}} = \sqrt{\frac{1 - \frac{\sqrt{2}}{2}}{2}}$$

$$= \sqrt{\frac{2 - \sqrt{2}}{4}} = \frac{\sqrt{2 - \sqrt{2}}}{2}$$

In exact form $\sin \frac{\pi}{8} = \frac{\sqrt{2 - \sqrt{2}}}{2}$. With the calculator in radian mode, $\sin \left(\frac{\pi}{8} \right) \approx 0.382683432$. The calculator gives the same approximation for $\frac{\sqrt{2 - \sqrt{2}}}{2}$.

(b) Since $\left(\frac{5\pi}{8} \right)$ (or 112.5°) is in the second quadrant, where the cosine is negative, use the minus sign in (I-16).

$$\cos \frac{5\pi}{8} = \cos \left(\frac{1}{2} \cdot \frac{5\pi}{4} \right) = -\sqrt{\frac{1 + \cos \left(\frac{5\pi}{4} \right)}{2}} = -\sqrt{\frac{1 - \frac{\sqrt{2}}{2}}{2}}$$

$$= -\sqrt{\frac{2 - \sqrt{2}}{4}} = -\frac{\sqrt{2 - \sqrt{2}}}{2}$$

Hence, $\cos \frac{5\pi}{8} = \frac{-\sqrt{2 - \sqrt{2}}}{2}$. Calculator evaluation yields $\cos \frac{5\pi}{8} \approx -0.382683432$, the negative of the value in **(a)**.

(c) First use (I-3) to get $\tan \frac{-7\pi}{12} = -\tan \frac{7\pi}{12}$ and then apply (I17).

$$\tan \left(-\frac{7\pi}{12} \right) = -\tan \left(\frac{7\pi}{12} \right) = -\tan \left(\frac{1}{2} \cdot \frac{7\pi}{6} \right) = -\frac{1 - \cos \frac{7\pi}{6}}{\sin \frac{7\pi}{6}}$$

$$= -\frac{1 - \left(-\sqrt{\frac{3}{2}} \right)}{-\frac{1}{2}} = 2 + \sqrt{3}.$$

Calculator evaluation for both $\tan -\frac{7\pi}{12}$ and $2 + \sqrt{3}$ is 3.732050808. ▲

As we noted in Chapter 5, we can get exact-form answers only for special angles. In Example 1 the angles $\frac{\pi}{8}$, $\frac{5\pi}{8}$, and $-\frac{7\pi}{12}$ were carefully selected. The important point is that practice is necessary to understand and remember the half-angle formulas.

EXAMPLE 2 Angle θ is defined by $\sin \theta = -\frac{4}{5}$ and $-\pi < \theta < -\frac{\pi}{2}$. Evaluate in exact form and use a calculator to get a decimal approximation: **(a)** $\sin \frac{\theta}{2}$ **(b)** $\cos \frac{\theta}{2}$ **(c)** $\cot \frac{\theta}{2}$.

Solution

Strategy: First draw a diagram with a reference triangle for θ from which the functions of θ can be read, then use appropriate identities.

Since $-\pi < \theta < -\frac{\pi}{2}$, dividing by 2 gives $-\frac{\pi}{2} < \frac{\theta}{2} < -\frac{\pi}{4}$. Thus $\frac{\theta}{2}$ is a fourth-quadrant angle. In the fourth quadrant, $\cos \left(\frac{\theta}{2}\right) > 0$ and $\sin \left(\frac{\theta}{2}\right) < 0$.

(a) Follow the strategy, using (I15) with a negative sign and $\cos \theta = -\frac{3}{5}$ from Figure 6.4,

$$\sin \frac{\theta}{2} = -\sqrt{\frac{1 - \cos \theta}{2}} = -\sqrt{\frac{1 - (-\frac{3}{5})}{2}} = -\sqrt{\frac{8}{10}} = -\frac{2}{\sqrt{5}}.$$

Hence, in exact form, $\sin \frac{\theta}{2} = -\frac{2}{\sqrt{5}}$.

To get a calculator check, first identify θ. From the diagram in Figure 6.4, $\theta = -\pi + \text{Tan}^{-1}(\frac{4}{3}) \approx -2.2142974$. Therefore, $\sin \frac{\theta}{2} \approx \sin -\frac{2.2142974}{2} \approx -0.8944272$. Also, $-\frac{2}{\sqrt{5}} \approx -0.8944272$.

(b) Using (I16) with a positive sign,

$$\cos \frac{\theta}{2} = \sqrt{\frac{1 + \cos \theta}{2}} = \sqrt{\frac{1 + (-\frac{3}{5})}{2}} = \sqrt{\frac{2}{10}} = \sqrt{\frac{1}{5}} = \frac{1}{\sqrt{5}}.$$

Thus, in exact form, $\cos \frac{\theta}{2} = \frac{1}{\sqrt{5}}$. Checking by calculator, $\cos \frac{\theta}{2} \approx 0.4472136$ and $\frac{1}{\sqrt{5}} \approx 0.4472136$.

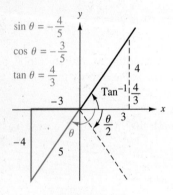

$\sin \theta = -\frac{4}{5}$

$\cos \theta = -\frac{3}{5}$

$\tan \theta = \frac{4}{3}$

FIGURE 6.4

(c) By identity (I-1), $\cot \frac{\theta}{2} = \frac{1}{\tan \frac{\theta}{2}}$, so we could use identity (I-17) and first find $\tan \frac{\theta}{2}$. Since we already have exact form for $\sin \frac{\theta}{2}$ and $\cos \frac{\theta}{2}$, use (I-2) as follows.

$$\cot \frac{\theta}{2} = \frac{\cos \frac{\theta}{2}}{\sin \frac{\theta}{2}} = \frac{\frac{1}{\sqrt{5}}}{-\frac{2}{\sqrt{5}}} = -\frac{1}{2}.$$

Therefore, $\cot \frac{\theta}{2} = -\frac{1}{2}$. ▲

In the first three examples, we were able to get results in exact form. In many cases this is inconvenient or impossible, as may be seen in the next example.

EXAMPLE 3 For angle θ where $\sin \frac{\theta}{2} = 0.64$ and $0 < \theta < \pi$, find a decimal approximation for **(a)** θ, **(b)** $\sin 3\theta$, **(c)** $\tan \frac{\theta}{5}$.

Strategy: For decimal approximations, first get a calculator value for θ. Locate the quadrant for $\frac{\theta}{2}$, evaluate $\frac{\theta}{2}$ with $\boxed{\text{Sin}^{-1}}$, and multiply by 2 to get θ. Store θ in memory and recall it as needed.

Solution

(a) Follow the strategy. Since $0 < \theta < \pi$, also $0 < \frac{\theta}{2} < \frac{\pi}{2}$, so $\frac{\theta}{2}$ is in the first quadrant. Therefore $\frac{\theta}{2} = \text{Sin}^{-1}(0.64)$ and $\theta = 2 \text{Sin}^{-1}(0.64) \approx 1.3889965$.

For Graphers 6.3

EXERCISES

Exercises 1–8   Use graphs to help decide if the equation is an identity by graphing each side separately. If it is, give a proof; if not, use your graphs to find a counterexample.

1. $\tan \frac{x}{2} = \frac{1 - \cos x}{\sin x}$

2. $\sin 2x \cos x = \frac{1}{2}(\sin 3x + \sin x)$

3. $(\cos \frac{x}{2})^2 - (\sin \frac{x}{2})^2 = \cos x$

4. $2(\sin \frac{x}{2})^2 = \sin x \tan \frac{x}{2}$

5. $\sqrt{\frac{1 - \cos x}{2}} = \sin \frac{x}{2}$

6. $\frac{\sin x + \sin 3x}{\cos x + \cos 3x} = \tan 2x$

7. $\frac{\sin 3x - \sin 5x}{\cos 3x + \cos 5x} = \tan x$

8. $\frac{\sin 5x - \sin 3x}{\cos 5x - \cos 3x} = -\cot 2x$

Exercises 9–10   Find a simpler formula for $f(x)$ and check your answer by drawing graphs.

9. $f(x) = \frac{\sin 5x - \sin 3x}{\cos 5x + \cos 3x}$

10. $f(x) = \frac{\sin x + \sin 4x}{\cos x + \cos 4x}$

(b)   Similarly, $\sin 3\theta = \sin (3 \cdot 2 \, \text{Sin}^{-1} 0.64)$, so $\sin 3\theta \approx -0.8549202$.

(c)   Finally, $\tan \frac{\theta}{5} = \tan (\frac{1}{5} \cdot 2 \, \text{Sin}^{-1} 0.64)$, so $\tan \frac{\theta}{5} \approx 0.2851732$.   ▲

We conclude our collection of key identities with two groups of formulas that are useful in a number of special situations. They do not occur as often as (I-1) through (I-17) and they are not easy to remember. However, they are easy to derive from the sum and difference identities (I-6) through (I-9). You should become acquainted with them and their use.

Product-to-Sum Identities

$$\sin \alpha \cos \beta = \tfrac{1}{2} [\sin (\alpha + \beta) + \sin (\alpha - \beta)] \qquad \textbf{(I-18)}$$

$$\cos \alpha \cos \beta = \tfrac{1}{2} [\cos (\alpha + \beta) + \cos (\alpha - \beta)] \qquad \textbf{(I-19)}$$

$$\sin \alpha \sin \beta = \tfrac{1}{2} [\cos (\alpha - \beta) - \cos (\alpha + \beta)] \qquad \textbf{(I-20)}$$

To prove (I-18), we add the equations in (I-6) and (I-7):

$$\sin (\alpha + \beta) = \sin \alpha \cos \beta + \cos \alpha \sin \beta$$

$$\underline{\sin (\alpha - \beta) = \sin \alpha \cos \beta - \cos \alpha \sin \beta}$$

$$\sin (\alpha + \beta) + \sin (\alpha - \beta) = 2 \cdot \sin \alpha \cos \beta$$

Identity (I-18) follows if we divide by 2 and read from right to left. Identities (I-19) and (I-20) can be proved similarly. See Develop Mastery Exercise 60.

> **EXAMPLE 4**   Use (I-19) to express the product of $\cos \theta$ and $\cos 3\theta$ as a sum.

Solution

In (I-19) replace α by θ and β by 3θ.

$$\cos \theta \cdot \cos 3\theta = \frac{1}{2}[\cos (\theta + 3\theta) + \cos (\theta - 3\theta)] \qquad \text{By (I-19)}$$

$$= \frac{1}{2}[\cos 4\theta + \cos (-2\theta)]$$

$$= \frac{1}{2}[\cos 4\theta + \cos 2\theta] \qquad \text{By (I-3)}$$

Hence $\cos \theta \cos 3\theta = \frac{1}{2}(\cos 4\theta + \cos 2\theta)$ is an identity. ▲

Identities (I-18) through (I-20) convert products to sums. Another closely related set of identities converts sums to products. These sum-to-product identities are also known as **factoring identities.**

Sum-to-Product (Factoring) Identities

$$\sin x + \sin y = 2 \sin \left(\frac{x + y}{2}\right) \cos \left(\frac{x - y}{2}\right) \qquad \textbf{(I-21)}$$

$$\sin x - \sin y = 2 \cos \left(\frac{x + y}{2}\right) \sin \left(\frac{x - y}{2}\right) \qquad \textbf{(I-22)}$$

$$\cos x + \cos y = 2 \cos \left(\frac{x + y}{2}\right) \cos \left(\frac{x - y}{2}\right) \qquad \textbf{(I-23)}$$

$$\cos x - \cos y = -2 \sin \left(\frac{x + y}{2}\right) \sin \left(\frac{x - y}{2}\right) \qquad \textbf{(I-24)}$$

Identity (I-21) follows from (I-18) by simple substitutions. First write (I-18) and multiply through by 2:

$$2 \sin \alpha \cos \beta = \sin (\alpha + \beta) + \sin (\alpha - \beta)$$

Now let $\alpha + \beta = x$ and $\alpha - \beta = y$. Then

$$\alpha = \frac{x + y}{2} \qquad \text{and} \qquad \beta = \frac{x - y}{2}.$$

Substituting these values for α and β and reading from right to left gives identity (I-21). Identities (I-22), (I-23), and (I-24) can be proved similarly (see Exercise 67).

> **EXAMPLE 5**   Simplify the expression
>
> $$\frac{\sin 2A - \sin 4A}{\cos 2A + \cos 4A}.$$

Strategy: Find applicable identities to rewrite both numerator and denominator as products, then look for simplifications.

Solution

Apply (I-22) to the numerator and (I-23) to the denominator, and then simplify.

$$\frac{\sin 2A - \sin 4A}{\cos 2A + \cos 4A} = \frac{2 \cos \left(\frac{2A + 4A}{2}\right) \cdot \sin \left(\frac{2A - 4A}{2}\right)}{2 \cos \left(\frac{2A + 4A}{2}\right) \cdot \cos \left(\frac{2A - 4A}{2}\right)}$$

$$= \frac{\cos 3A \cdot \sin (-A)}{\cos 3A \cdot \cos (-A)}$$

$$= \frac{\sin (-A)}{\cos (-A)} = \tan (-A) = -\tan A.$$

Thus $\frac{\sin 2A - \sin 4A}{\cos 2A + \cos 2A} = -\tan A$ is an identity. ▲

Looking Ahead to Calculus Half-angle identities provide the basis for a substitution used in integration in calculus. Quotients that involve sines and cosines can be very difficult to integrate. The substitution illustrated in the next example can change such a quotient into a more manageable rational function in variable u. In Example 6 we show how to deal with $\sin x$. For the substitution for $\cos x$, see Develop Mastery Exercise 77.

| EXAMPLE 6 | Let $u = \tan \left(\frac{x}{2}\right)$, where $0 < x < \pi$ (so $0 < \frac{x}{2} < \frac{\pi}{2}$). **(a)** Express $\sin x$ in terms of u. **(b)** Express $\frac{\sin x}{1 - \sin x}$ in terms of u.

Solution

Follow the strategy. See Figure 6.5.

Strategy: (a) First use the given information to draw a right triangle with angle $\frac{x}{2}$ whose tangent is $\frac{u}{1}$, then find $\sin \frac{x}{2}$ and $\cos \frac{x}{2}$ in terms of u and use identity (I-12).

(a) Express $\sin x$ in terms of $\frac{x}{2}$ by using the double-angle identity (I-12) with θ replaced by $\frac{x}{2}$.

$$\sin x = 2 \sin \frac{x}{2} \cos \frac{x}{2}.$$

From the right triangle,

$$\sin \frac{x}{2} = \frac{u}{\sqrt{1 + u^2}} \quad \text{and} \quad \cos \frac{x}{2} = \frac{1}{\sqrt{1 + u^2}},$$

so

$$\sin x = 2 \frac{u}{\sqrt{1 + u^2}} \frac{1}{\sqrt{1 + u^2}} = \frac{2u}{1 + u^2}.$$

(b) Replace $\sin x$ by $\frac{2u}{1 + u^2}$.

$$\frac{\sin x}{1 - \sin x} = \frac{\frac{2u}{1 + u^2}}{1 - \frac{2u}{1 + u^2}} = \frac{2u}{1 + u^2 - 2u} = \frac{2u}{(u - 1)^2}. \quad ▲$$

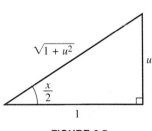

FIGURE 6.5

EXERCISES 6.3

Check Your Understanding

Exercises 1–5   True or False. Give reasons for your conclusion.

1. If θ is an angle in the first quadrant, then $\frac{\theta}{2}$ must also be in the first quadrant.

2. If $\sin x = \dfrac{1}{2}$, then $\sin \dfrac{x}{2} = \dfrac{1}{4}$.

3. The equation $\cos^2 \frac{x}{2} = \frac{1 + \cos x}{2}$ is an identity.

4. $\sqrt{\dfrac{1 - \cos \frac{\pi}{3}}{2}} = \sin \frac{\pi}{6}$.

5. $\tan^2 \frac{x}{2} = \frac{1 - \cos x}{1 + \cos x}$ is an identity.

Exercises 6–10   Complete the sentence by selecting from the list below *all choices* that make the statement true.

(a) $\cos x$ (b) $\sin x$ (c) $\tan x$
(d) positive   (e) negative
(f) between $\frac{1}{\sqrt{2}}$ and 1   (g) between 0 and $\frac{1}{\sqrt{2}}$
(h) between -1 and 0   (i) greater than $\sqrt{3}$

6. For every real number x, $2 \cos^2 \frac{x}{2} - 1 = $ _____ .

7. For every real number x, $2 \sin \frac{x}{2} \cos \frac{x}{2} = $ _____ .

8. If $\frac{\pi}{2} < \theta < \pi$, then $\sin \frac{\theta}{2}$ is _____ .

9. If $\frac{\pi}{2} < \theta < \pi$, then $\cos \frac{\theta}{2}$ is _____ .

10. If $\frac{3\pi}{2} < \theta < 2\pi$, then $\tan \frac{\theta}{3}$ is _____ .

Explore and Discover

1. Show that $\cos \frac{\pi}{4} = \frac{1}{2}\sqrt{2}$, $\cos \frac{\pi}{8} = \frac{1}{2}\sqrt{2 + \sqrt{2}}$, and $\cos \frac{\pi}{16} = \frac{1}{2}\sqrt{2 + \sqrt{2 + \sqrt{2}}}$. Guess a formula for the general case of $\cos \left(\frac{\pi}{2^n}\right)$. What happens when n becomes large?

2. Show that $\cos \frac{\pi}{6} = \frac{1}{2}\sqrt{3}$, $\cos \frac{\pi}{12} = \frac{1}{2}\sqrt{2 + \sqrt{3}}$, and $\cos \frac{\pi}{24} = \frac{1}{2}\sqrt{2 + \sqrt{2 + \sqrt{3}}}$. Guess a general pattern.

3. Follow a procedure similar to that in Exercise 1, but replace cos by sin.

Develop Mastery

In all exercises, express numerical results in exact form unless otherwise specified.

Exercises 1–6   Use half-angle formulas to evaluate the expressions, then make a calculator check.

1. (a) $\sin \left(\frac{\pi}{12}\right)$, (b) $\cos \left(\frac{11\pi}{8}\right)$
2. (a) $\cos \left(\frac{5\pi}{12}\right)$, (b) $\tan \left(\frac{7\pi}{12}\right)$
3. (a) $\sin \left(-\frac{3\pi}{8}\right)$, (b) $\cos \left(-\frac{3\pi}{8}\right)$
4. (a) $\cos \left(-\frac{7\pi}{12}\right)$, (b) $\tan \left(-\frac{13\pi}{12}\right)$
5. (a) $\sec \left(\frac{7\pi}{12}\right)$, (b) $\cot \left(-\frac{5\pi}{12}\right)$
6. (a) $\csc \left(-\frac{7\pi}{12}\right)$, (b) $\cot \left(\frac{17\pi}{8}\right)$

Exercises 7–12   An angle θ is specified. Draw a diagram that shows the angle θ, determine the quadrant that contains $\frac{\theta}{2}$, and find (a) $\sin \left(\frac{\theta}{2}\right)$, (b) $\cos \left(\frac{\theta}{2}\right)$, (c) $\tan \left(\frac{\theta}{2}\right)$.

7. $\cos \theta = -\frac{12}{13}$ and $0 < \theta < \pi$.
8. $\sin \theta = -\frac{3}{4}$ and $\pi < \theta < \frac{3\pi}{2}$.
9. $\cos \theta = -\frac{3}{5}$ and $2\pi < \theta < 3\pi$.
10. $\sin \theta = -\frac{5}{13}$ and $-\frac{5\pi}{2} < \theta < -2\pi$.
11. $\tan \theta = \frac{3}{4}$ and $\frac{\pi}{2} < \theta < 2\pi$.
12. $\sec \theta = -2$ and $\pi < \theta < 2\pi$.

Exercises 13–16   Conditions on x are given. In each case complete the following table by entering a plus sign if the given function is positive, a minus sign if it is negative, and a plus–minus sign if it might be either positive or negative.

$\sin x$	$\cos x$	$\sin \frac{x}{2}$
_____	_____	_____

$\cos \frac{x}{2}$	$\sin 2x$	$\cos 2x$
_____	_____	_____

13. (a) $\pi < x < \frac{3\pi}{2}$. (b) x is in the third quadrant. (*Hint:* At first glance it might appear that conditions (a) and (b) are identical; they are not.)

14. (a) $\frac{3\pi}{2} < x < 2\pi$. (b) x is in the fourth quadrant. (*Hint:* See Exercise 13.)

15. (a) $\frac{3\pi}{4} < x < \pi$. (b) $\pi < x < \frac{5\pi}{4}$.

16. (a) $\pi < x < 2\pi$ and $\tan x > 0$. (b) Both $\cos x$ and $\tan x$ are negative.

17. Let θ be a third-quadrant angle. Determine the signs of $\sin\frac{\theta}{2}$, $\cos\frac{\theta}{2}$, and $\tan\frac{\theta}{2}$ if **(a)** $\pi < \theta < \frac{3\pi}{2}$, **(b)** $-\pi < \theta < -\frac{\pi}{2}$.

18. Is there an angle θ in the third quadrant such that
(a) $\sin\frac{\theta}{2}$ is positive and $\cos\frac{\theta}{2}$ is negative? Explain.
(b) $\sin\frac{\theta}{2}$ is negative and $\cos\frac{\theta}{2}$ is positive? Explain.

Exercises 19–22 Evaluate in two ways as indicated. Although the two answers may look different, evaluate each by calculator to see if approximations are equal.

19. Evaluate $\sin\frac{\pi}{12}$ by using **(a)** (I-15) with $\frac{\pi}{12} = \frac{1}{2}(\frac{\pi}{6})$, **(b)** (I-7) with $\frac{\pi}{12} = \frac{\pi}{3} - \frac{\pi}{4}$.

20. Evaluate $\cos\frac{13\pi}{12}$ by using **(a)** (I-16) with $\frac{13\pi}{12} = \frac{1}{2}(\frac{13\pi}{6})$, **(b)** (I-8) with $\frac{13\pi}{12} = \frac{3\pi}{4} + \frac{\pi}{3}$.

21. Evaluate $\tan -\frac{7\pi}{12}$ by using **(a)** (I-17) with $-\frac{7\pi}{12} = -\frac{1}{2}(\frac{7\pi}{6})$, **(b)** (I-11) with $-\frac{7\pi}{12} = \frac{\pi}{6} - \frac{3\pi}{4}$.

22. Evaluate $\sec\frac{7\pi}{12}$ by using (I-1) and **(a)** (I-16) with $\frac{7\pi}{12} = \frac{1}{2}(\frac{7\pi}{6})$, **(b)** (I-8) with $\frac{7\pi}{12} = \frac{\pi}{4} + \frac{\pi}{3}$.

Exercises 23–34 Prove that the equation is an identity.

23. $\sin x = 2\sin\frac{x}{2}\cos\frac{x}{2}$

24. $(\sin\frac{x}{2} + \cos\frac{x}{2})^2 = 1 + \sin x$

25. $\tan\frac{x}{2} = \csc x - \cot x$

26. $\cos x = \cos^2\frac{x}{2} - \sin^2\frac{x}{2}$

27. $2\sin^2\frac{x}{2} = \frac{\sec x - 1}{\sec x}$

28. $\cot\frac{x}{2} = \frac{\sin x \sec x}{\sec x - 1}$

29. $\sec^2\frac{x}{2} = \frac{2\tan x}{\sin x + \tan x}$

30. $2\sin^2\frac{x}{2} = \sin x \tan\frac{x}{2}$

31. $\sqrt{\frac{1 - \cos x}{2}} = |\sin\frac{x}{2}|$

32. $\sqrt{\frac{1 + \cos x}{2}} = |\cos\frac{x}{2}|$

33. $\frac{\sin x + \sin 3x}{\cos x + \cos 3x} = \tan 2x$

34. $\frac{\sin 5x - \sin 3x}{\cos 5x + \cos 3x} = \tan x$

Exercises 35–44 Determine whether or not the equation is an identity. If it is, give a proof; if it is not, give at least one value of x for which equality does not hold.

35. $\sin\frac{x}{2} = \frac{\sin x}{2}$

36. $\tan\frac{x}{2} = \frac{\sec x - 1}{\sin x \sec x}$

37. $\cos x (\sec x - 1) = 2\sin^2\frac{x}{2}$

38. $\sin^2\frac{x}{2} = 1 - \cos^2\frac{x}{2}$

39. $2\csc x = \sec\frac{x}{2}\csc\frac{x}{2}$

40. $2\cos^2\frac{x}{2} = 1 + \cos x$

41. $\sqrt{\frac{1 - \cos x}{2}} = \sin\frac{x}{2}$

42. $\sqrt{\frac{1 + \cos x}{2}} = \cos\frac{x}{2}$

43. $\frac{\cos 2x - \cos 4x}{2\sin 3x} = \sin x$

44. $\sin(x + \frac{\pi}{6}) - \sin(x - \frac{\pi}{6}) = \cos x$

Exercises 45–48 Use the given information to find θ (in radians) and to get a three-place decimal approximation.

45. $\sin\theta = 0.36$ and $0 < \theta < \frac{\pi}{2}$. Find **(a)** θ, **(b)** $\sin\frac{\theta}{2}$, **(c)** $\cos 3\theta$.

46. $\cos\theta = -0.65$ and $0 < \theta < \pi$. Find **(a)** θ, **(b)** $\tan\frac{\theta}{2}$, **(c)** $\csc\frac{\theta}{2}$.

47. $\tan\theta = -1.64$ and $\pi < \theta < 2\pi$. Find **(a)** θ, **(b)** $\tan\frac{\theta}{2}$, **(c)** $\sin\frac{\theta}{4}$.

48. $\sec\theta = 1.77$ and $-\frac{\pi}{2} < \theta < 0$. Find **(a)** θ, **(b)** $\cos\frac{\theta}{2}$, **(c)** $\tan 2\theta$.

Exercises 49–51 Use the given information to evaluate in exact form.

49. 2θ is between $\frac{3\pi}{2}$ and 2π, and $\cos 2\theta = \frac{4}{5}$. Find **(a)** $\tan 2\theta$, **(b)** $\sin\theta$, **(c)** $\cos\theta$, **(d)** $\tan\theta$.

50. 2θ is between $-\frac{\pi}{2}$ and 0, and $\cos 2\theta = \frac{5}{13}$. Find **(a)** $\sin 2\theta$, **(b)** $\sin\theta$, **(c)** $\cos\theta$, **(d)** $\tan\theta$.

51. θ is between $\frac{3\pi}{2}$ and 2π, and $\sin\theta = -\frac{3}{5}$. Find **(a)** $\sin\frac{3\theta}{2}$, **(b)** $\tan\frac{3\theta}{2}$. (*Hint:* $\frac{3\theta}{2} = \theta + \frac{\theta}{2}$.)

Exercises 52–57 Evaluate in exact form. The indicated identity may be helpful. Check by calculator evaluation.

52. $\sin\frac{5\pi}{12} + \sin\frac{\pi}{2}$; (I-21)

53. $\cos\frac{5\pi}{12} + \cos\frac{\pi}{12}$; (I-23)

54. $\sin\frac{\pi}{12} \cdot \cos\frac{\pi}{12}$; (I-18)

55. $\sin\frac{5\pi}{12} \cdot \cos\frac{\pi}{12}$; (I-18)

56. $\sin\frac{5\pi}{12} \cdot \cos\frac{\pi}{4}$; (I-18)

57. $\cos\frac{5\pi}{12} \cdot \cos\frac{7\pi}{12}$; (I-19)

58. We can derive the half-angle tangent formula for $0 < \theta < \frac{\pi}{2}$ from the diagram with a semicircle of radius 1 and center at D and a central angle of θ.
  (a) Show that $\angle ABC = \frac{\theta}{2}$, $|\overline{AC}| = \sin \theta$, $|\overline{DC}| = \cos \theta$.
  (b) Show that $\tan \frac{\theta}{2} = \frac{\sin \theta}{1 + \cos \theta}$.

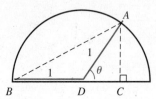

59. If $\sin x + \cos x = u$, then show that **(a)** $\sin 2x = u^2 - 1$. (*Hint:* Square both sides.) **(b)** $\sin^3 x + \cos^3 x = \frac{1}{2}(3u - u^3)$. (*Hint:* Cube both sides of the equation.)

60. A proof of identity (I-18) using (I-6) and (I-7) was given in this section. In a similar manner prove identities (I-19) and (I-20).

Exercises 61–66 Use identities (I-18) through (I-20) to express the product as a sum.

61. $\sin 3x \cos 2x$

62. $\cos x \cos 3x$

63. $\sin 2x \sin 3x$

64. $\cos 2x \sin 3x$

65. $\cos \frac{x}{2} \cos \frac{3x}{2}$

66. $\sin \frac{5x}{2} \sin \frac{x}{2}$

67. A proof of identity (I-21) was given in this section. In a similar manner prove that (I-23) follows from (I-19).

Exercises 68–71 Use identities (I-21) through (I-24) to write the sum or difference as a product.

68. $\sin 2x + \sin 4x$

69. $\cos x + \cos 3x$

70. $\sin 3x - \sin x$

71. $\cos 5x - \cos x$

Exercises 72–75 Simplify. (*Hint:* Use (I-21) through (I-24) to write the numerator and denominator as products.)

72. $\frac{\sin x + \sin 3x}{\cos x + \cos 3x}$

73. $\frac{\sin 4x + \sin x}{\cos 4x + \cos x}$

74. $\frac{\cos x + \cos 3x}{\sin x - \sin 3x}$

75. $\frac{\sin x - \sin 3x}{\cos 3x - \cos x}$

76. Simplify.
  (a) $\cos 20° \cos 40° \cos 80°$. (*Hint:* Use identity (I-19).)
  (b) $\sin 10° \sin 50° \sin 70°$. (*Hint:* Use **(a)**.)

77. *Looking Ahead to Calculus* Using the substitution $u = \tan \frac{x}{2}$, **(a)** express $\cos x$ and $\tan x$ in terms of u, **(b)** express $\frac{1 - \cos x}{\tan x}$ in terms of u. (*Hint:* See Example 6.)

| **SECTION 6.4** | **Solving Trigonometric Equations** |

[The] characterization of mathematics as a study of the order and relation of . . . abstract patterns, forms, and structures . . . provides mathematics with root and substance, yet allows for the full range of the intuitive, creative, and aesthetic impulse for which mathematics is so justly renowned.
  W. G. Holladay

In Section 1.5 we discussed the notion of a domain D for an equation that involves a variable as the nonempty set of real numbers that can be substituted for the variable to yield a numerical statement that is either true or false. The solution set for the equation consists of all numbers in D that yield true statements.

In the preceding three sections of this chapter we considered equations for which the solution set is the entire domain D. Such equations are called *identities*. Equations for which the solution set is not all of D are called **conditional equations.** In this section we are interested in conditional equations that involve trigonometric functions. Techniques for solving such equations can best be explained by considering a variety of examples.

Linear Trigonometric Equations

These include equations that can be expressed in the form $a \cdot f(x) + b = 0$, where a and b are given numbers, a is not zero, and f is one of the six trigonometric functions. The method for solving such equations is straightforward, as the next three examples illustrate.

| **EXAMPLE 1** | Find the solution set for the equation $2 \sin x - 1 = 0$. |

Solution

Since the domain is not specified, we assume (by default) that it is the set of real numbers. The given equation can be written as $\sin x = \frac{1}{2}$. In Figure 6.6 we show two solutions labeled x_1 and x_2, with reference triangles. Each reference triangle is a $30°-60°$ right triangle. From the diagram it is easy to see that $x_1 = \frac{\pi}{6}$ and $x_2 = \frac{5\pi}{6}$. The sine function is periodic with period 2π, so the solution set is

$$\left\{ x \mid x = \frac{\pi}{6} + k \cdot 2\pi \quad \text{or} \quad x = \frac{5\pi}{6} + k \cdot 2\pi \right\},$$

where k is any integer (positive, negative, or zero). ▲

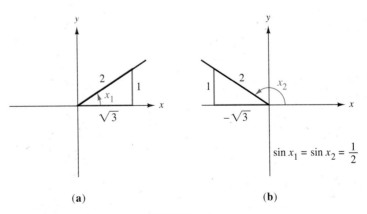

(a)　　　　(b)

FIGURE 6.6

> **For Graphers 6.4**

Since calculators work only with decimal approximations to numbers, they cannot generally provide exact solutions to trigonometric equations. With the help of the Zoom feature, however, we can usually get excellent approximations.

EXAMPLE   Find the solution set for $\tan x + \sqrt{3} = 0$ in the interval $[0, 2\pi]$.

Solution   Select the graphing window and the function (or functions) to graph. You may choose to look at the function $f(x) = \tan x + \sqrt{3}$ and find where it crosses the x-axis, or you can graph two functions, $Y1 = \tan x$, and $Y2 = -\sqrt{3}$, and find out where they intersect.

For the viewing rectangle, the calculator can automatically set a Trig Window (ZOOM 7 (Trig) on the TI, or Graph tan (no x) EXE on the Casio). (What are the dimensions of the Trig Window on your calculator? Recall that $\frac{\pi}{2} \approx 1.57$ and $2\pi \approx 6.28$.) You can, of course, set any window you choose. Since the solution must fall in the interval $[0, 2\pi]$, an x-range of $[0, 6.28]$ would suffice, or to get nice pixel coordinates, choose an x-range that is conveniently divisible by 95 (for TI) or 94 (for Casio), say $[-0.5, 9.0]$ or $[-0.4, 9.0]$ for example.

WARNING: Watch for false asymptotes. Remember that your calculator is programmed to try to connect pixels in adjacent columns. If function values differ by more than the screen height for adjacent columns, the screen may show a vertical line that looks like an asymptote, but is not part of the graph.

Trace along the curve to find that the x coordinates of the desired points are near 1.047 and 4.189. In exact form the solutions are $\frac{\pi}{3}$ (≈ 1.0472) and $\frac{4\pi}{3}$ (≈ 4.1888).

Exercises

Exercises 1–10   Use graphs to approximate the solution. For Exercises 1 through 5, use the domain $[0, 2\pi]$; for the remaining exercises, the domain is $[-\pi, \pi]$.

1. $2 \sin x = \sqrt{2}$
2. $2 \sin x = -\sqrt{3}$
3. $\cos (x - \frac{\pi}{3}) = 1$
4. $2 \cos (x - 1) = 1$
5. $2 \sin^2 x - \sin x = 0$
6. $\sec x = -2$
7. $\cot x - \sqrt{3} = 0$
8. $\cos^2 x - 5 \cos x + 2 = 0$
9. $\cos x \cot x = -\cot x$
10. $\sec^2 x - 4 \sec x - 5 = 0$

Exercises 11–14   Find the solution set. No domain is specified.

11. $2 \, \mathrm{Sin}^{-1}(\sin x) = \pi$
12. $\cos (\mathrm{Sin}^{-1} x) = \frac{\pi}{4}$
13. $3 \sin^2 x - 1 = 0$
14. $2 - \cos^2 x - 2 \sin x = 0$

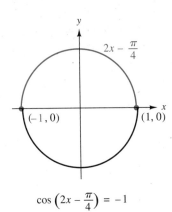

$\cos\left(2x - \frac{\pi}{4}\right) = -1$

FIGURE 6.7

| EXAMPLE 2 | Solve $\cos\left(2x - \frac{\pi}{4}\right) + 1 = 0$, where $0 < x < 2\pi$.

Solution

The given equation is equivalent to $\cos\left(2x - \frac{\pi}{4}\right) = -1$. The cosine is -1 when the terminal point for $2x - \frac{\pi}{4}$ is at $(-1, 0)$ as shown in Figure 6.7. Hence $2x - \frac{\pi}{4}$ must be an odd multiple of π,

$$2x - \frac{\pi}{4} = (2k - 1) \cdot \pi.$$

Solving for x,

$$x = \frac{\pi}{8} + \frac{(2k - 1)}{2}\pi.$$

The problem requires solutions that satisfy $0 < x < 2\pi$. Trying values of k shows that $k = 1$ or $k = 2$ give solutions. Thus, $\frac{5\pi}{8}$ (when k is 1) and $\frac{13\pi}{8}$ (when k is 2) are the desired solutions. ▲

| EXAMPLE 3 | Solve the equation $2 \tan x = 3$, where $-\pi < x < \pi$. Give the results rounded off to two decimal places.

Solution

The equation can be written as $\tan x = \frac{3}{2}$. The tangent is positive in Quadrants I and III. Draw a diagram that shows two possible solutions and their reference triangles (see Figure 6.8). The curved arrows for x_1 and x_2 are helpful reminders that the solutions must be in the interval $(-\pi, \pi)$. From the diagram, $x_1 = \text{Tan}^{-1}\frac{3}{2}$ and $x_2 = -\pi + x_1 = -\pi + \text{Tan}^{-1}\frac{3}{2}$. These expressions are exact-form answers. Use a calculator to get decimal approximations of 0.98 for x_1 and -2.16 for x_2. ▲

Quadratic Trigonometric Equations

Now we consider equations that can be written as $a[f(x)]^2 + bf(x) + c = 0$, where a, b, c, are given numbers, a is not zero, and f is one of the six trigonometric functions.

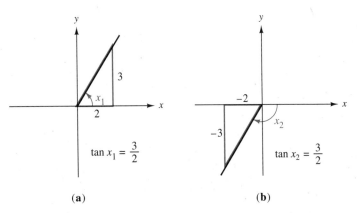

(a)   (b)

FIGURE 6.8

Strategy: The equation is quadratic in sin x. Factor and then use the zero-product principle.

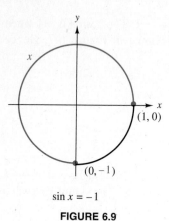

$\sin x = -1$

FIGURE 6.9

EXAMPLE 4 Find the solution set for the equation

$$2 \sin^2 x - 3 \sin x - 5 = 0.$$

Solution

Follow the strategy. From

$$(2 \sin x - 5)(\sin x + 1) = 0,$$

$$2 \sin x - 5 = 0 \quad \text{or} \quad \sin x + 1 = 0,$$

$$\sin x = \frac{5}{2} \quad \text{or} \quad \sin x = -1.$$

Since $-1 \leq \sin x \leq 1$ for every x, there is no number x for which $\sin x = \frac{5}{2}$, and so we get no solutions. For $\sin x = -1$, x can be any number whose terminal point on the unit circle is $(0, -1)$, as in Figure 6.9. Thus x can be any number coterminal with $\frac{3\pi}{2}$. The solution set is $\{x \mid x = \frac{3\pi}{2} + k \cdot 2\pi,$ where k is any integer$\}$. ▲

EXAMPLE 5 Solve the equation $\cos^2 x - 2 \cos x - 2 = 0$, where $-\pi \leq x \leq \pi$. Give the results rounded to two decimal places.

Solution

Strategy: The equation is quadratic in cos x. The left side does not factor, so use the quadratic formula.

Follow the strategy.

$$\cos x = \frac{2 \pm \sqrt{4 + 8}}{2} = \frac{2 \pm 2\sqrt{3}}{2} = \frac{2(1 \pm \sqrt{3})}{2} = 1 \pm \sqrt{3}$$

For $\cos x = 1 + \sqrt{3}$ there is no solution since $1 + \sqrt{3} \approx 2.732$, and $-1 \leq \cos x \leq 1$ for every x. For $\cos x = 1 - \sqrt{3} \approx -0.732$ we do get solutions as shown in Figure 6.10. Again we are careful to draw curved arrows, remembering that $-\pi \leq x \leq \pi$. From the diagrams it is easy to see that

$$x_1 = \text{Cos}^{-1}(1 - \sqrt{3}) \approx 2.39 \quad \text{and} \quad x_2 = -x_1 = -2.39.$$

Thus, the desired solutions are 2.39 and -2.39. ▲

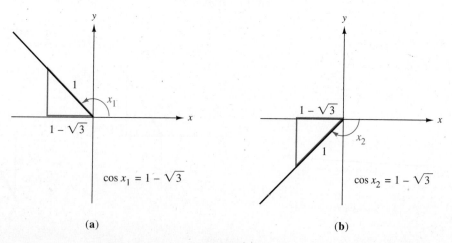

(a)   (b)

FIGURE 6.10

The following example shows the need to check solutions.

EXAMPLE 6   Suppose the domain is $[0, 2\pi]$. Find the solution set for the equation $\sin x \cdot \tan x - \tan x = 0$.

Solution

Strategy: The left side has $\tan x$ as a factor. Factor, and then use the zero-product principle.

Follow the strategy.

$$(\sin x - 1) \cdot \tan x = 0.$$

Therefore, $\tan x = 0$ or $\sin x = 1$. From $\tan x = 0$, $x = 0, \pi, 2\pi$, and from $\sin x = 1$, we get $x = \frac{\pi}{2}$. It would appear that we have four solutions. However, when we check $x = \frac{\pi}{2}$ in the original equation, we recognize that $\tan\frac{\pi}{2}$ is not defined. Hence $x = \frac{\pi}{2}$ is not a solution. Checking the other three numbers we find that they are solutions. The solution set is $\{0, \pi, 2\pi\}$. ▲

EXERCISES 6.4

Check Your Understanding

Exercises 1–5   True or False. Give reasons for your conclusion.

1. The equation $\sin x + 1 = 0$ has two solutions in the interval $[0, 2\pi]$.

2. The solution set for $2 \sin x - \pi = 0$ is the empty set.

3. The solution set for $\sin^2 x + \cos^2 x = 1$ is the empty set.

4. A solution for the equation $\sin x + \cos x = 0$ is $\frac{3\pi}{4}$.

5. The solution set for the equation $\tan^2 x + 1 = 0$ is the empty set.

Exercises 6–10   Complete the sentence by selecting from the list below *all choices* that make the statement true.

(a) 0 **(b)** $\frac{\pi}{6}$ **(c)** $\frac{\pi}{3}$ **(d)** π **(e)** $\frac{\pi}{2}$
(f) $\frac{2\pi}{3}$ **(g)** $-\frac{\pi}{2}$ **(h)** $-\frac{\pi}{3}$ **(i)** $-\frac{4\pi}{3}$
(j) $-\pi$ **(k)** 2π

6. A solution to the equation $2 \cos x + 1 = 0$ is _____.

7. A solution to the equation $\cos^2 x - 1 = 0$ is _____.

8. A number in the solution set for $\cos x (1 - \sin x) = 0$ is _____.

9. A number in the solution set for $\tan x (1 - 2 \cos x) = 0$ is _____.

10. A number not in the solution set for $\sin x \cos x (4 \cos^2 x - 1) = 0$ is _____.

Explore and Discover

1. Solving an equation of the form $\cos x = x$ requires a completely different approach than anything we have done in this section. An interesting approach uses iteration. (See the Explore and Discover Exercises in Section 4.6.)

   (a) First draw graphs of $y = \cos x$ and $y = x$ on the same set of axes to get a picture of where the two graphs intersect, that is, where $\cos x = x$. If c is the x value of the point of intersection, use your graphs to estimate c.

   (b) Using your estimate for c, with your calculator in radian mode, press $\boxed{\text{COS}}$ repeatedly, so that the display shows c, then $\cos c$, then $\cos (\cos c)$, ... Continue until you see something interesting happening in the display of your calculator. Interpret what you see in terms of the equation $\cos x = x$. If you have a graphing calculator, enter your estimate and then press $\boxed{\text{COS}}$ $\boxed{\text{Ans}}$ and $\boxed{\text{ENT}}$. Then press $\boxed{\text{ENT}}$ and repeat.

2. Another technique for solving the equation $\cos x = x$ is to let $f(x) = \cos x - x$ and then use

the locator theorem from Chapter 3, squeezing in to locate the solution to $f(x) = 0$. Use this technique to approximate the solution to two decimal places. Compare the result with Exercise 1.

3. *Looking Ahead to Calculus* In calculus it can be shown that starting with any number between 2 and 4 and iterating the function $f(x) = x - \tan x$ will give a solution to $\sin x = 0$. Carry out the iteration and see what solution you get. Try iteration with other starting values, say 6.

Develop Mastery

Unless otherwise specified, give all results in exact form. Diagrams will help in locating solutions in the domain.

Exercises 1–16 Solve the equation. The domain is the interval $[0, 2\pi]$.

1. $2 \cos x - 1 = 0$ **2.** $2 \sin x - \sqrt{2} = 0$

3. $\sec x + 2 = 0$ **4.** $3 \tan x + \sqrt{3} = 0$

5. $2 \cos\left(x - \frac{\pi}{3}\right) - 1 = 0$

6. $\tan\left(2x - \frac{\pi}{4}\right) + 1 = 0$

7. $\tan\left(x + \frac{\pi}{3}\right) - \sqrt{3} = 0$

8. $\sec\left(x + \frac{\pi}{2}\right) + 2 = 0$

9. $2 \sin^2 x + \sin x = 0$ **10.** $2 \cos^2 x - \cos x = 0$

11. $2 \sin^2 x - 1 = 0$

12. $4 \cos^2 x + 4 \cos x + 1 = 0$

13. $4 \sin^2 x - 4 \sin x + 1 = 0$

14. $2 \cos^2 x - 5 \cos x + 2 = 0$

15. $\sin^2 x - 2 \sin x + 1 = 0$

16. $\cos^2 x - \sin^2 x + 2 \cos x = -1$

Exercises 17–28 Solve the equation where the domain is the interval $[-\pi, \pi]$.

17. $2 \sin x - \sqrt{3} = 0$ **18.** $\sqrt{3} \sec x + 2 = 0$

19. $\tan\left(x - \frac{\pi}{6}\right) - 1 = 0$

20. $2 \cos\left(x + \frac{2\pi}{3}\right) - 1 = 0$

21. $4 \sin^2 x - 3 = 0$ **22.** $\cos^2 x + 2 \cos x + 1 = 0$

23. $3 \tan^2 x - 1 = 0$

24. $\sec^2 x - 4 \sec x + 4 = 0$

25. $2 \csc^2 x - 5 \csc x + 2 = 0$

26. $\sqrt{3} \tan^2 x + 2 \tan x - \sqrt{3} = 0$

27. $\sin x \tan x + \tan x = 0$

28. $\cos x \cot x + \cot x = 0$

Exercises 29–38 No domain is specified. Find the solution set.

29. $2 \cos x - \sqrt{2} = 0$ **30.** $2 \sin x + \sqrt{3} = 0$

31. $\tan^2 x - 3 = 0$ **32.** $\sec^2 x - 4 = 0$

33. $4 \sin^2 x + 4 \sin x + 1 = 0$

34. $2 \cos^2 x + 5 \cos x + 2 = 0$

35. $\sin^2 x - \sin x = 0$ **36.** $2 \cos^2 x + \cos x = 0$

37. $2 \operatorname{Sin}^{-1}(\sin x) - \pi = 0$

38. $\operatorname{Cos}^{-1}(\sin x) - \pi = 0$

Exercises 39–46 The domain is the interval $[0, 2\pi]$. Solve the equation and express the results as decimal approximations rounded off to two decimal places.

39. $3 \sin x - 2 = 0$ **40.** $5 \cos^2 x + 3 = 0$

41. $\sin^2 x - 2 \sin x = 2$ **42.** $2 \cos^2 x - 4 \cos x = 1$

43. $\tan^2 x - 2 \tan x = 1$ **44.** $\cot^2 x - 2 \cot x = 4$

45. $9 \sin^2 x - 6 \sin x + 1 = 0$

46. $9 \cos^2 x + 12 \cos x + 4 = 0$

47. If $\cos x = 2 \sin x$, find the value of $\sin x \cos x$.

48. If $\sin x = 3 \cos x$, find the value of $\sin x \cos x$.

49. Find the smallest number in the interval $(50, \infty)$ that satisfies the equation $\sin x - 1 = 0$.

50. Find the smallest number in the interval $[10\pi, 40\pi]$ that satisfies the equation $2 \cos x + 1 = 0$.

51. Find the largest number in the interval $[10\pi, 50\pi]$ that satisfies the equation $\tan x + 1 = 0$.

52. Find the largest number in the interval $(-\infty, -40)$ that satisfies the equation $3 \sin x - 1 = 0$.

Exercises 53–58. Find the *number of solutions* of the equation in the interval **(a)** $[0, 6\pi]$, **(b)** $[-4\pi, 8\pi]$, **(c)** $[-6, 16]$.

53. $\cos x + 1 = 0$ **54.** $2 \sin x + 1 = 0$

55. $\tan x - 1 = 0$ **56.** $4 \sin^2 x - 1 = 0$

57. $4 \operatorname{Sin}^{-1}(\sin x) - \pi = 0$

58. $3 \operatorname{Cos}^{-1}(\cos x) + 2\pi = 0$

Exercises 59–63 **(a)** What is the largest value that $f(x)$ can have? **(b)** What value(s) of x in the interval $[0, 2\pi]$ will yield this maximum value? Remember that for every x, $-1 \le \sin x \le 1$ and $-1 \le \cos x \le 1$.

59. $f(x) = 2 \sin x$ **60.** $f(x) = 1 + \cos x$

61. $f(x) = 1 + 2 \sin x$ **62.** $f(x) = 3 - \cos x$

63. $f(x) = 4 - 2 \cos x$

64. A one-quart milk carton has a square bottom and top measuring 2.75 by 2.75 inches. The carton is 7.5 inches tall. Suppose the carton is half-full of milk. When it sits upright on a table, the top surface of the milk is a square. However, when the carton is tipped along one of its bottom edges so that the bottom of the carton makes an angle θ with the table, the surface becomes a rectangle (see the diagram). Assume that if the carton is tipped far enough for the milk to reach the top, the milk will spill out.

(a) Find an equation that gives the area A of the rectangle as a function of θ and that is valid up to the time the milk spills.

(b) What is the domain of the function?

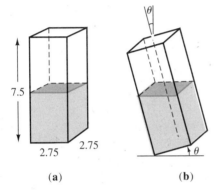

(a)   (b)

65. A cylindrical can with a circular cross section of diameter 8 centimeters is 12 centimeters tall. The can is two-fifths full of water. When the can stands upright, the water surface is circular, but when it is inclined, the surface is elliptical. Suppose the axis of the can makes an angle of θ with the vertical, as shown in the diagram.

(a) Find an equation that gives the elliptical surface area A of the water as a function of θ. The area of an elliptical region is given by the formula $A = \pi ab$, where a and b are indicated in the diagram.

(b) What is the domain of the function in **(a)**, that is, for what values of θ will the surface of the water be elliptical?

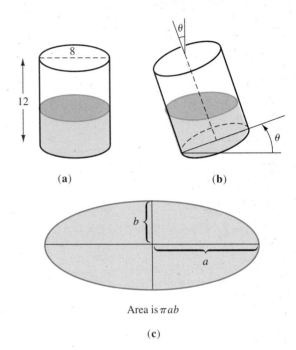

(a)   (b)

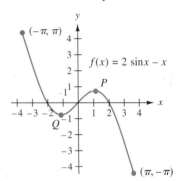

Area is πab

(c)

66. *Looking Ahead to Calculus*   The diagram shows the graph of $f(x) = 2 \sin x - x$ for $-\pi \le x \le \pi$. Is $f(x)$ an even or odd function, or neither? In calculus it is shown that the turning points (the locally highest and lowest points) are given by the solution to the equation $2 \cos x - 1 = 0$. Copy the graph; find and label the coordinates of the turning points, P and Q. Round off to two decimal places.

$(-\pi, \pi)$

$f(x) = 2 \sin x - x$

P

Q

$(\pi, -\pi)$

SECTION 6.5   **Using Identities in Solving Equations**

. . . *the rich and abstract proofs and theorems of mathematics can ultimately be traced back to thoughts and arguments that were once voiced in language* . . . .

F. David Peat

In the preceding section we concentrated on trigonometric equations that can be solved by applying simple methods of algebra to linear and quadratic equations. In this section we are interested in using the identities studied in the first part of this chapter to express an equation in a form to which familiar techniques can be applied. We may need to recognize certain combinations of trigonometric expressions that should remind us of identities studied in previous sections. We illustrate with a variety of examples.

EXAMPLE 1 Solve the equation $\sin^2 x + 2 \sin x + \cos^2 x = 0$, where $0 \le x \le 2\pi$.

Solution

Strategy: Look for identities that can simplify the equation. For example, $\sin^2 x + \cos^2 x$ by (I-4) can be replaced by the number 1.

Follow the strategy. The equation is equivalent to $1 + 2 \sin x = 0$, or $\sin x = -\frac{1}{2}$, whose solutions in the interval $[0, 2\pi]$ are $\frac{7\pi}{6}$ and $\frac{11\pi}{6}$. ▲

EXAMPLE 2 Find the solution set for the equation

$$4 \sin x \cos x - \sqrt{3} = 0 \qquad \text{where} \qquad -\pi \le x \le \pi.$$

Solution

Strategy: First simplify the equation. The expression $\sin x \cos x$ brings to mind (I-12): $2 \sin x \cos x = \sin 2x$.

Following the strategy, the given equation is equivalent to

$$2(2 \sin x \cos x) - \sqrt{3} = 0 \qquad \text{or} \qquad 2 \sin 2x - \sqrt{3} = 0.$$

Thus $\sin 2x = \frac{\sqrt{3}}{2}$. Now draw diagrams to show possible values for the angle $2x$ (see Figure 6.11). From panel a,

$$2x = \frac{\pi}{3} + k \cdot 2\pi \qquad \text{or} \qquad x = \frac{\pi}{6} + k \cdot \pi$$

Now pick values for k that give solutions in the interval $[-\pi, \pi]$. When k is -1, x is $-\frac{5\pi}{6}$, and when k is 0, x is $\frac{\pi}{6}$.

In a similar manner, from panel b in Figure 6.11, $2x = \frac{2\pi}{3} + k \cdot 2\pi$, or $x = \frac{\pi}{3} + k \cdot \pi$. When k is -1, x is $-\frac{2\pi}{3}$ and when k is 0, x is $\frac{\pi}{3}$. ▲

We went to his office, and he showed me a generating function. It was the most marvelous thing I had ever seen in mathematics. It used mathematics that up to that time, in my heart of hearts, I had thought was something that mathematicians just did to create homework problems for innocent students in high school and college.

Frederick Mosteller

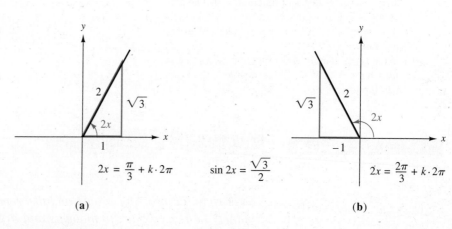

(a) $2x = \frac{\pi}{3} + k \cdot 2\pi$ $\sin 2x = \frac{\sqrt{3}}{2}$

(b) $2x = \frac{2\pi}{3} + k \cdot 2\pi$

FIGURE 6.11

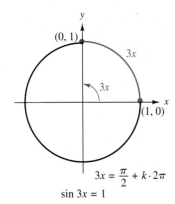

$$\sin 3x = 1$$

FIGURE 6.12

EXAMPLE 3 Solve the equation

$$\sin 2x \cos x + \cos 2x \sin x = 1, \text{ where } 0 \le x \le 2\pi.$$

Solution

The expression on the left-hand side reminds us of the sum formula (I6), $\sin \alpha \cos \beta + \cos \alpha \sin \beta = \sin(\alpha + \beta)$. If we let $\alpha = 2x$ and $\beta = x$, then we may write the left-hand side as

$$\sin 2x \cos x + \cos 2x \sin x = \sin(2x + x) = \sin 3x.$$

The given equation becomes $\sin 3x = 1$. Draw a diagram like Figure 6.12 to see that $3x$ must be coterminal with $\frac{\pi}{2}$, so $3x = \frac{\pi}{2} + k \cdot 2\pi$, or $x = \frac{\pi}{6} + \frac{2k\pi}{3}$. Limiting solutions to those in the interval $[0, 2\pi]$, take $k = 0, 1,$ or 2, giving the solutions $\frac{\pi}{6}, \frac{5\pi}{6}$, and $\frac{3\pi}{2}$. ▲

Equations of the Form $a \sin x + b \cos x = c$

Equations of this form for given numbers a, b, and c occur frequently. We assume $a \ne 0$ and $b \ne 0$, and we discuss two different approaches for solutions, depending on whether $c = 0$ or $c \ne 0$.

Case 1: $c = 0$ In this case we may always convert the equation $a \sin x + b \cos x = 0$ into an equation that involves $\tan x$:

$$a \sin x = -b \cos x,$$

$$\frac{\sin x}{\cos x} = -\frac{b}{a}, \quad \text{or} \quad \tan x = -\frac{b}{a}.$$

The linear equation $\tan x = -\frac{b}{a}$ is of the type discussed in the preceding section.

Case 2: $c \ne 0$ When $c \ne 0$, we need a very different approach, which involves expressing the equation $a \sin x + b \cos x = c$ in the form $\sin(x + \alpha) = k$, reducing the problem to a type we discussed in the preceding section.

To take this approach, we may assume that the coefficient of $\sin x$ is positive (if not, we multiply both sides of the equation by -1). Plotting the point (a, b) gives a diagram similar to one of those in Figure 6.13, depending on whether b is positive or negative. For either angle α in the diagrams,

$$\cos \alpha = \frac{a}{\sqrt{a^2 + b^2}} \quad \text{and} \quad \sin \alpha = \frac{b}{\sqrt{a^2 + b^2}} \tag{1}$$

Since α is between $-\frac{\pi}{2}$ and $\frac{\pi}{2}$, angle α is given by $\alpha = \text{Sin}^{-1}\left(\frac{b}{\sqrt{a^2 + b^2}}\right)$.

Now to solve the equation $a \sin x + b \cos x = c$, we first divide through by $\sqrt{a^2 + b^2}$.

$$\frac{a}{\sqrt{a^2 + b^2}} \sin x + \frac{b}{\sqrt{a^2 + b^2}} \cos x = \frac{c}{\sqrt{a^2 + b^2}} \tag{2}$$

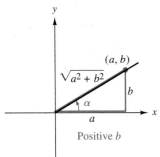

$$\cos \alpha = a/\sqrt{a^2 + b^2}$$
$$\sin \alpha = b/\sqrt{a^2 + b^2}$$

(a)

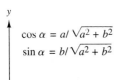

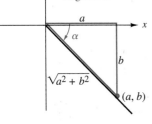

(b)

FIGURE 6.13

Using the formulas in Equation 1, Equation 2 becomes

$$\cos \alpha \sin x + \sin \alpha \cos x = \frac{c}{\sqrt{a^2 + b^2}}.$$

By identity (I-6),

$$\sin(x + \alpha) = \frac{c}{\sqrt{a^2 + b^2}},$$

an equation of the type discussed in the previous section. The technique discussed here can readily be stated as an algorithm.

Algorithm for Solving $a \sin x + b \cos x = c$, $c \neq 0$

Suppose a, b, and c are given, nonzero numbers.

1. Write the equation so that the coefficient of $\sin x$ is positive. (Multiply through by -1 if necessary.)

2. Plot the point (a, b) and let α be the angle in standard position that contains the point (a, b) on the terminal side (as in Figure 6.13), then $\alpha = \text{Sin}^{-1}\left(\frac{b}{\sqrt{a^2 + b^2}}\right)$.

3. Divide the original equation by $\sqrt{a^2 + b^2}$ and get

$$\frac{a}{\sqrt{a^2 + b^2}} \sin x + \frac{b}{\sqrt{a^2 + b^2}} \cos x = \frac{c}{\sqrt{a^2 + b^2}},$$

which is equivalent to

$$\sin(x + \alpha) = \frac{c}{\sqrt{a^2 + b^2}}.$$

4. Now solve by the methods discussed in Section 6.4.

In the next two examples we illustrate techniques for solving equations of the form $a \sin x + b \cos x = c$. In Example 4 c is zero, and in Example 5 we use the algorithm when c is not zero.

EXAMPLE 4   Solve the equation $\sin x - \sqrt{3} \cos x = 0$.

Solution

Strategy: First write the given equation as $\sin x = \sqrt{3} \cos x$, and then divide by $\cos x$.

Follow the strategy.

$$\sin x = \sqrt{3} \cos x, \qquad \frac{\sin x}{\cos x} = \sqrt{3} \qquad \text{or} \qquad \tan x = \sqrt{3}.$$

Now proceed to solve the equation $\tan x = \sqrt{3}$ by drawing diagrams (see Figure 6.14). In both cases, the reference triangle is a $30°$–$60°$ right triangle. From the diagrams, x_1 is $\frac{\pi}{3}$ and x_2 is $\frac{4\pi}{3}$. Since the tangent function is periodic with period π and $\frac{4\pi}{3}$ is $\pi + \frac{\pi}{3}$, all solutions are given by $x = \frac{\pi}{3} + k \cdot \pi$, where k is any integer. ▲

MEETING OLD FRIENDS IN STRANGE PLACES

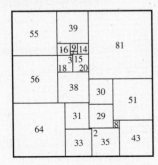

The first example of a square that is a sum of un-equal integer-sided squares, a problem solved with un-expected tools

One source of constant delight in mathematics is discovering completely unexpected relationships, learning a mathematical tool for one purpose and then suddenly finding it to be precisely what is needed to do something entirely different. The algorithm in this section uses identities to translate the problem into a form we have previously solved. Many such unexpected relations either come from or involve trigonometric identities.

In Chapter 8 we discuss briefly the Fibonacci sequence which begins, 1, 1, 2, 3, 5, 8, . . . , where each new term is obtained by adding the two preceding terms.

While we can continue the Fibonacci sequence,
$F_7 = 5 + 8 = 13$;
$F_8 = 8 + 13 = 21$, and so on, to get a term such as $F_{16}(= 987)$, we have no direct way to compute some term far out in the sequence,

say F_{50}. Bernoulli provided a formula in 1728 that appears to involve no integers at all, but that nonetheless always yields integers:

$$F_n = \frac{1}{\sqrt{5}}\left[\left(\frac{1 + \sqrt{5}}{2}\right)^n - \left(\frac{1 - \sqrt{5}}{2}\right)^n\right]$$

Bernoulli's formula lends itself well to calculator evaluation (see the Explore and Discover exercises), but an even more elegant formula involves trigonometric identities. If we allow complex numbers and natural logarithms, F_n is given by

$$F_n = i^{n-1}\frac{\sin(nz)}{\sin z},$$

where z is the special complex number

$$z = \frac{\pi}{2} + i \ln\left(\frac{1 + \sqrt{5}}{2}\right).$$

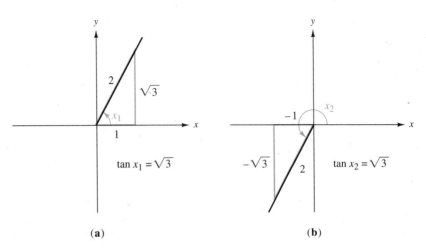

(a)

(b)

FIGURE 6.14

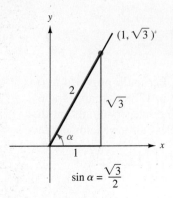

FIGURE 6.15

EXAMPLE 5 Solve the equation $\sin x + \sqrt{3} \cos x = 1$, where $0 \le x \le 2\pi$.

Solution

Follow the steps outlined in the algorithm.

Step 1. The coefficient of $\sin x$ is positive, since a is 1.

Step 2. Plot the point $(1, \sqrt{3})$ and show the angle α with its reference triangle (see Figure 6.15), and

$$\sin \alpha = \frac{\sqrt{3}}{2} \qquad \text{so} \qquad \alpha = \frac{\pi}{3}.$$

Step 3. Divide both sides of the equation by $\sqrt{1^2 + \sqrt{3}^2}$ (which equals 2) and get $\frac{1}{2} \sin x + \frac{\sqrt{3}}{2} \cos x = \frac{1}{2}$, which is equivalent to $\sin(x + \frac{\pi}{3}) = \frac{1}{2}$.

Step 4. To solve the equation $\sin(x + \frac{\pi}{3}) = \frac{1}{2}$, draw diagrams to show the two possibilities for angles whose sine is $\frac{1}{2}$; see Figure 6.16. In the first quadrant,

$$x + \frac{\pi}{3} = \frac{\pi}{6} + k \cdot 2\pi \qquad \text{or} \qquad x = -\frac{\pi}{6} + k \cdot 2\pi.$$

Find solutions in the interval $[0, 2\pi]$. The only value of x in $[0, 2\pi]$ is when k is 1, which gives $-\frac{\pi}{6} + 2\pi$, or $\frac{11\pi}{6}$, as a solution.

In the second quadrant,

$$x + \frac{\pi}{3} = \frac{5\pi}{6} + k \cdot 2\pi, \qquad \text{or} \qquad x = \frac{\pi}{2} + k \cdot 2\pi.$$

The only value of x in $[0, 2\pi]$ is when k is 0, giving $\frac{\pi}{2}$ as a solution. Therefore, the desired solutions are $\frac{11\pi}{6}$ and $\frac{\pi}{2}$. ▲

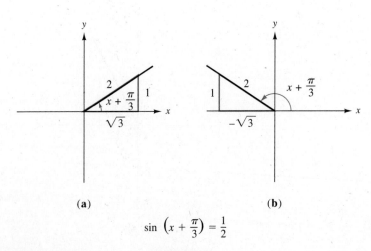

(a)   **(b)**

$$\sin\left(x + \frac{\pi}{3}\right) = \frac{1}{2}$$

FIGURE 6.16

Maximum and Minimum Values of a Function

One of the problems studied in calculus is finding maximum and minimum values of functions. For functions of the type $f(x) = a \sin x + b \cos x$, we can find the maximum and minimum values using a technique similar to that described in the algorithm.

EXAMPLE 6 Find the maximum and minimum values of the function $f(x) = 2 \sin x + 3 \cos x$.

Solution

Strategy: First, express $2 \sin x + 3 \cos x$ in the form $\sin(x + \alpha)$ by factoring out $\sqrt{2^2 + 3^2}$, or $\sqrt{13}$, and then continue with the steps in the algorithm.

Follow the strategy.

$$f(x) = \sqrt{13}\left(\frac{2}{\sqrt{13}}\sin x + \frac{3}{\sqrt{13}}\cos x\right) = \sqrt{13}\,(\sin x \cos \alpha + \cos x \sin \alpha),$$

where α is the angle identified in the algorithm where $\cos \alpha = \frac{2}{\sqrt{13}}$ and $\sin \alpha = \frac{3}{\sqrt{13}}$. We are not particularly concerned here with finding α explicitly, but we do have

$$f(x) = \sqrt{13}\,(\sin x \cos \alpha + \cos x \sin \alpha) = \sqrt{13} \sin(x + \alpha).$$

Since the sine function varies between -1 and 1, the maximum value that $\sin(x + \alpha)$ can assume is 1. Thus the maximum value of $f(x)$ must be $\sqrt{13}$ and the minimum value is $-\sqrt{13}$. The graphs of $y = 2 \sin x$, $y = 3 \cos x$, and $f(x) = 2 \sin x + 3 \cos x$ are shown together in Figure 6.17. ▲

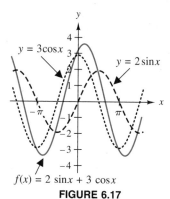

$f(x) = 2 \sin x + 3 \cos x$

FIGURE 6.17

EXERCISES 6.5

Check Your Understanding

Exercises 1–5 True or False. Give reasons for your conclusion.

1. The solution set for $\sin x \cos x = 1$ is the empty set.

2. The number $\frac{5\pi}{4}$ is not in the solution set for $\sqrt{2}\,(\sin x + \cos x) + 2 = 0$.

3. There is only one number in $[0, 2\pi]$ that satisfies $\cos x + 1 = 0$.

4. The solution set for $\sec^2 x - 2 = 0$ is the same as that for $\tan^2 x - 1 = 0$.

5. The solution set for $2 \sin x \cos x = \sin 2x$ is the empty set.

Exercises 6–10 Fill the blank from the list below with *all choices* that have the same solution set.

(a) $2 \cos x - 1 = 0$ (b) $1 + \sin^2 x = 0$
(c) $\cos^2 x = 1 - \sin^2 x$ (d) $\sin x - 2 = 0$
(e) $2 \sin x \cos x = \sin 2x$ (f) $2 \sin(x + \frac{\pi}{2}) = 1$
(g) $2 \tan x = 1$ (h) $\cos x \tan x = \sin x$

6. $\sin^2 x + \cos^2 x = 1$; _____ .

7. $(\sin x - 2)(2 \cos x - 1) = 0$; _____ .

8. $\sin^2 x + \cos^2 x = 2 \cos x$; _____ .

9. $\sin x \cos x = 1$; _____ .

10. $2 \sin x - \cos x = 0$; _____ .

Explore and Discover

Exercises 1–3   Let $\alpha = \frac{1+\sqrt{5}}{2}$ and $\beta = \frac{1-\sqrt{5}}{2}$. Store the values for both α and β in your calculator. Bernoulli's formula for the nth Fibonacci number (see the Historical Note, "Meeting Old Friends in Strange Places") can be written in terms of α and β as $F_n = \frac{\alpha^n - \beta^n}{\sqrt{5}}$.

1. Complete the following table. If your calculator has only one memory, first store $\frac{1+\sqrt{5}}{2}$ and proceed to calculate α^n, then store $\frac{1-\sqrt{5}}{2}$ and calculate β^n.

n	2	5	10
α^n			
β^n			
$\dfrac{\alpha^n - \beta^n}{\sqrt{5}}$			
F_n	1	5	55

n	15	20
α^n		
β^n		
$\dfrac{\alpha^n - \beta^n}{\sqrt{5}}$		
F_n	610	6765

2. By looking at the values β^{10}, β^{15}, and β^{20}, guess the limit approached by β^n as n gets larger and larger.

3. Explain why F_n can be calculated efficiently for large values of n by simply rounding off the number $\frac{\alpha^n}{\sqrt{5}}$ to the nearest integer.

Develop Mastery

Give all results in exact form unless otherwise specified. Use diagrams to help you in your solutions.

Exercises 1–24   The domain is the interval $[0, 2\pi]$. Solve by using identities as needed.

1. $\cos x \cdot \tan x + \sin x = 1$
2. $\sin x \cdot \tan x - \cos x = 0$
3. $\cos (x + \frac{\pi}{2}) - \sin x = 1$
4. $\sin (x + \frac{\pi}{2}) + \cos x = 1$
5. $\cos^2 x + \cos x = 1 - \sin^2 x$
6. $\sin^2 x + 2 \sin x = 2 - \cos^2 x$
7. $\sin^2 x - \cos^2 x - \sin x = -1$
8. $\sin^2 x + \sin x - \cos^2 x = 0$
9. $\sin x - \sqrt{3} \cos x = 0$ 10. $\sin x + \cos x = 0$
11. $\sin 2x - \cos x = 0$ 12. $\sin 2x + \sin x = 0$
13. $2 \sin x + \tan x = 0$ 14. $\sin x - 2 \tan x = 0$
15. $\sin^2 x - \cos^2 x = 0$ 16. $\cos^2 x - \sin^2 x = 1$
17. $(\sin x - \cos x)^2 = 1$
18. $(1 - \tan x) \tan (x + \frac{\pi}{4}) = 2$
19. $2 \sin x \cos x + 1 = 0$ 20. $\sin^2 (\frac{x}{2}) + \cos x = 0$
21. $\cos^2 (\frac{x}{2}) - \cos x = 1$ 22. $\tan (\frac{x}{2}) - \csc x = 1$
23. $\sin 2x \cos x - \cos 2x \sin x = 1$
24. $2 (\cos 2x \cos x + \sin 2x \sin x) + 1 = 0$

Exercises 25–30   The domain is the interval $[0, 2\pi]$. Solve using the algorithm given in this section.

25. $\sin x - \cos x = 1$
26. $\sqrt{3} \sin x + \cos x = 2$
27. $\sin x + \sqrt{3} \cos x = 2$
28. $-\sqrt{3} \sin x + \cos x = -2$
29. $-\sqrt{2} \sin x + \sqrt{2} \cos x = 1$
30. $2 \sin x - 2 \cos x = \sqrt{2}$

Exercises 31–36   The domain is the interval $[-\pi, \pi]$. Find the solution set.

31. $\cos x + \sin x \cot x = 1$
32. $\sin^2 x + \sin x = 1 - \cos^2 x$
33. $\cos x - \sqrt{3} \sin x = 0$ 34. $\sin^2 x + \cos 2x = 1$
35. $\sin 2x + \cos x = 0$ 36. $\sin x + \cos x = 1$

Exercises 37–42   The domain is the interval $[0, 2\pi]$. Solve and give results as decimal approximations rounded off to two decimal places.

37. $\cos x - 2 \sin x = 0$
38. $3 \sin x - 4 \cos x = 0$
39. $\sin^2 x + 4 \sin x = 2 - \cos^2 x$
40. $4 \cos x \tan x - \sin x = 1$
41. $4 \sin x \cot x - \cos x = 2$
42. $\cos 2x + 2 \cos x = 0$

Exercises 43–46   Solve the equation if the domain is $[0, 2\pi]$. Sum-to-product identities from Section 6.3 may be useful.

43. $\sin 3x + \sin x = 0$ 44. $\cos 3x - \cos x = 0$
45. $\sin 3x = \sin x$ 46. $\sin 4x - \sin 2x = \sin x$

Exercises 47–50 **(a)** Express in the form $f(x) = A \sin(x + \alpha)$. **(b)** Find the largest value that $f(x)$ can assume and **(c)** find all values of x in $[0, 2\pi]$ that yield this maximum value of $f(x)$. See Example 6.

47. $f(x) = \sin x + \sqrt{3} \cos x$

48. $f(x) = \sin x - \cos x$

49. $f(x) = 2 \sin x + 2 \cos x$

50. $f(x) = \sqrt{3} \sin x - \cos x$

Exercises 51–62 Find the solution set where the domain is $[0, 2\pi]$.

51. $\sqrt{3} \sin x = \sqrt{2 - \cos^2 x}$

52. $\tan x + \sec x = 1$

53. $\tan x + \sec x = \sqrt{3}$

54. $\tan^2 x + \sec^2 x - 3 = 0$

55. $\sin x = \sin \left(\frac{x}{2}\right)$ (*Hint:* Use identity (I12).)

56. $\cos x = \cos \left(\frac{x}{2}\right)$ (*Hint:* Use (I13).)

57. $\sin 2x + 2 \cos x = 0$

58. $\tan 2x = \tan x$ (*Hint:* Use (I14).)

59. $4 (\sin x \cos^3 x - \cos x \sin^2 x) = 1$

60. $2 (\sin x \cos^3 x + \cos x \sin^3 x) = 1$

61. $2 \cos^2 \left(\frac{x}{2}\right) - 1 = \cos x$

62. $\cos^2 x = 1 - \sin^2 \left(\frac{x}{2}\right)$

Exercises 63–70 Solve where the domain is $[0, 2]$.

63. $\sin \pi x + \cos \pi x = 0$

64. $\sin \pi x + \cos \pi x = 1$

65. $2 \sin \pi x - \tan \pi x = 0$

66. $\sin 2\pi x - \sin \pi x = 0$

67. $\sin^2 \pi x - \cos^2 \pi x + \sin \pi x = 0$

68. $3 \cos \pi x \tan \pi x - \sin \pi x = 1$

69. $\cos 2\pi x + \cos \pi x = 0$

70. $e^{\ln (\cos \pi x)} - \sin \pi x = 0$

Exercises 71–76 Find the solution set.

71. $(\sin x + \cos x)^2 = 1 + \sin 2x$

72. $\cos^2 x = \sin^2 x + \cos 2x$

73. $\sqrt{2} \sin \left(x + \frac{\pi}{4}\right) = \sin x + \cos x$

74. $\cos^2 x (1 + \tan^2 x) = 1$

75. $\ln \tan x = \ln \sin x - \ln \cos x$

76. $\ln \tan (-x) = \ln (-\sin x) - \ln \cos x$

Exercises 77–82 Let S denote the solution set where D is the domain. Find **(a)** the smallest integer that is greater than all of the numbers in S, and **(b)** the largest integer that is less than all of the numbers in S.

77. $2 \sin x - 1 = 0; D = [0, 2\pi]$

78. $4 \sin x - 1 = 0; D = [0, 2\pi]$

79. $\sin 2x - 1 = 0; D = [-2\pi, 2\pi]$

80. $2 \sin 2x - 1 = 0; D = [-\pi, 2\pi]$

81. $\sin^2 x = 1 - \cos^2 x; D = [-\pi, 4\pi]$

82. $\sin x = 2 \sin \left(\frac{x}{2}\right) \cos \left(\frac{x}{2}\right); D = [-\pi, 2\pi]$

Exercises 83–86 Find the solution set.

83. $e^{\cos x} = 1$ **84.** $\ln (\sin x) = 0$

85. $\ln (\sin 2x) = 0$ **86.** $e^{\ln (\sin x)} - \cos x = 0$

87. Solve the equation $\sqrt{2} (\sin x + \cos x) = \tan x + \cot x$, where $0 \le x \le 2\pi$. [*Hint:* Show that the equation can be written in the form $(\sin 2x) \cdot \sin \left(x + \frac{\pi}{4}\right) = 1$. Since both $\sin 2x$ and $\sin \left(x + \frac{\pi}{4}\right)$ are numbers in the interval $[-1, 1]$ for every x, how can the product of such numbers equal 1? Answer, and complete the solution.]

88. Find the smallest positive root (approximated to three decimal places) of the equation $\sec x - \tan x = 0.5$. (*Hint:* Factor the left-hand side of the identity $\sec^2 x - \tan^2 x = 1$, and then solve for the expression $\sec x + \tan x$. Use your result along with the given equation to find $\sec x$.)

SECTION 6.6

Generalized Sine and Cosine Functions; Simple Harmonic Motion

Mathematical models of biological and social phenomena have traditionally relied on the paradigm of classical physics in the development of their mathematical formalisms. The potency of this paradigm lies in the ability of classical physics to relate cause and effect . . . through a sequence of formal implications and thereby to make predictions.

         B. J. West

I think the earliest I remember my father telling me something mathematical was when I was beginning to study Euclidian geometry at school. At that time he also told me about Cartesian geometry. I must have been 12 or 13.

Cathleen Morawetz

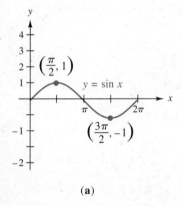

(a)

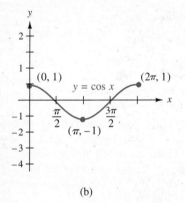

(b)

FIGURE 6.18

In Section 5.4 we discussed graphs of the trigonometric functions. We concentrated most of our attention on the sine and cosine functions since these occur most frequently in applications. In applied work we usually encounter the problem of graphing more general functions, such as $y = 4 \sin\left(x - \frac{\pi}{6}\right)$ or $y = -2 \cos(2x + 3)$. These are examples from a general class of functions that can be expressed in one of the following forms, where A, B, and C are given real numbers called **parameters.**

$$y = A \sin(Bx + C)$$
$$y = A \cos(Bx + C)$$

We make the obvious assumption that A and B are nonzero. First we consider several examples to determine the role played by each of the parameters A, B, and C.

Our approach will use the properties of the basic sine and cosine graphs from Section 5.4. Since $\sin\left(x + \frac{\pi}{2}\right) = \cos x$ is an identity, we recall that the graph of $y = \cos x$ is simply a horizontal translation of the graph of $y = \sin x$ by $\frac{\pi}{2}$ units to the left (see Figure 5.40 in Section 5.4). Therefore, in order to make the discussion easier to follow, we focus our attention on the properties of $y = A \sin(Bx + C)$, from which corresponding properties for $y = A \cos(Bx + C)$ follow.

Before continuing with our task, we remind the reader that it is essential to know the graphs of $y = \sin x$ and $y = \cos x$ on the interval $[0, 2\pi]$. For convenient reference we reproduce them here. The graphs in Figure 6.18 are called *fundamental cycles* of the sine and cosine curves; they are the building blocks from which the entire graphs of $y = \sin x$ and $y = \cos x$ can be drawn. The graph of $y = A \sin(Bx + C)$ also has a fundamental cycle. Sketching a graph is simple as soon as we identify a fundamental cycle. The numbers A, B, and C affect the size, length, or location of the fundamental cycle.

Amplitude (Parameter *A*)

Multiplication of a function by a nonzero constant stretches or compresses the graph vertically. Since the fundamental cycles in Figure 6.18 oscillate between -1 and 1, multiplying by A determines the amplitude of oscillation, as illustrated in the next example.

EXAMPLE 1 Sketch a graph of each function.

(a) $y = 3 \sin x$ **(b)** $y = \frac{1}{2} \sin x$ **(c)** $y = -2 \sin x$

Solution

(a) For each real number x, the y value for the function $y = 3 \sin x$ is three times the y-value of the function $y = \sin x$. To get the graph of $y = 3 \sin x$

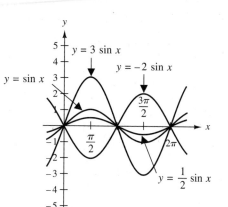

FIGURE 6.19

simply stretch the graph of $y = \sin x$ vertically away from the x-axis by a factor of three. See Figure 6.19, which shows the graph on the interval $[0, 2\pi]$. The complete graph is a repetition of this cycle horizontally in both directions.

(b) The equation $y = \frac{1}{2} \sin x$ presents a similar situation except that each y value is only one-half the y value of $y = \sin x$. Draw the graph by compressing the graph of $y = \sin x$ vertically toward the x-axis by a factor of one-half (see Figure 6.19).

(c) For $y = -2 \sin x$ note that the graph is the same as that of $y = 2 \sin x$ tipped upside down (reflected about the x-axis), as shown in Figure 6.19. ▲

The graphs in Example 1 suggest a generalization:

> For any positive number A, the graph of $y = A \sin x$ can be obtained from the graph of $y = \sin x$ simply by stretching or compressing vertically by a factor of A. The graph of $y = -A \sin x$ is the same as that of $y = A \sin x$ tipped upside down (reflected about the x-axis).

The number $|A|$ is the greatest distance that the graph of $y = A \sin x$ reaches from the axis about which is oscillates. We call $|A|$ the **amplitude** of the function $y = A \sin x$.

Period and Phase Shift (Parameters *B* and *C*)

As noted in Section 5.4, the function $y = \sin x$ is periodic with period 2π, which means that the complete graph is an endless repetition of the portion on the interval $[0, 2\pi]$. We refer to $[0, 2\pi]$ as the **fundamental interval** and the position of the graph on this interval as the **fundamental cycle** of the graph of $y = \sin x$.

The graphs of all general sine and cosine functions are called **sinusoidal** (meaning sine-like). Such graphs show a fundamental cycle when $Bx + C$ varies from 0 to 2π. It is convenient for our discussion to assume that B is positive. If not, we can always obtain an equivalent equation by applying identity (I3).

$$\sin(-Bx + C) = \sin[-(Bx - C)] = -\sin(Bx - C)$$

$$\cos(-Bx + C) = \cos[-(Bx - C)] = \cos(Bx - C)$$

For the graph of $y = \sin(Bx + C)$, where $B > 0$, we have a complete fundamental cycle of the sine curve when $0 \le Bx + C \le 2\pi$. Subtracting C and dividing by the positive number B,

$$-\frac{C}{B} \le x \le \frac{2\pi - C}{B}.$$

Hence, for $y = A\sin(Bx + C)$, the fundamental interval FI, and its length p are given by

$$FI = \left[-\frac{C}{B}, \frac{2\pi - C}{B}\right] \quad \text{and} \quad p = \frac{2\pi}{B}.$$

The graph repeats itself every $\frac{2\pi}{B}$ units and the length of a fundamental interval is the period of the function.

> The graph of $y = A\sin(Bx + C)$ is periodic with period $\dfrac{2\pi}{B}$.

The parameter C shifts a fundamental cycle horizontally. When $C = 0$, and $B > 0$ the graph of $y = \sin Bx$ has the usual fundamental cycle on the interval $[0, \frac{2\pi}{B}]$ (see Figure 6.20a). Figure 6.20 also shows fundamental cycles for the graph of $y = \sin(Bx + C)$ where $C > 0$ and $C < 0$. The fundamental cycle contains all the essential information about the graph.

The fundamental cycles shown in Figure 6.20b and 6.20c are identical with that of $y = \sin Bx$, except they are shifted horizontally $\frac{|C|}{B}$ units. The shift is to the left if $C > 0$, and to the right if $C < 0$. The amount of the shift, $\frac{|C|}{B}$, is called the **phase shift** for the function $y = \sin(Bx + C)$.

The algorithm for graphing general sine functions summarizes the above discussion.

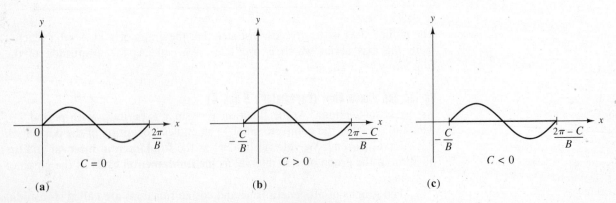

(a) $C = 0$ (b) $C > 0$ (c) $C < 0$

FIGURE 6.20

Algorithm for Graphing $y = A \sin(Bx + C)$

1. Express the equation in the form $y = A \sin(Bx + C)$ where B is positive.

2. Determine the fundamental interval (FI) by solving the inequalities $0 \leq Bx + C \leq 2\pi$ for x.

3. The graph crosses the x-axis at both endpoints of the fundamental interval and also at the midpoint. Plot these points.

4. If $A > 0$, the highest point (where $y = A$) occurs when x is one-quarter across the fundamental interval; the lowest point (where $y = -A$) occurs when x is three-quarters across. Locate these points. If $A < 0$, the graph is the same as that for $A > 0$, but tipped upside down.

5. After locating the key points identified in Steps 3 and 4, draw a fundamental cycle of a sine curve.

6. The entire graph is a repetition of the fundamental cycle. The function $y = A \sin(Bx + C)$ has period $\frac{2\pi}{B}$, amplitude $|A|$, and phase shift $\frac{|C|}{B}$.

Graphing $y = A \cos(Bx + C)$

To graph the cosine function, $y = A \cos(Bx + C)$ perform the steps in the algorithm, except replace Steps 3 and 4:

3a. The graph crosses the x-axis at the quarter and three-quarter points of the fundamental interval.

4a. The graph has its highest and lowest points at the endpoints and midpoint of the fundamental interval.

To find the fundamental interval, we recommend that you do not attempt to memorize its formula, $[-\frac{C}{B}, \frac{2\pi - C}{B}]$. It is more important to understand that the argument of the function $y = \sin(Bx + C)$, the quantity $Bx + C$, varies from 0 to 2π. It is a simple matter to solve the equations $Bx + C = 0$ and $Bx + C = 2\pi$ to identify the endpoints of the interval. We illustrate the procedures outlined above in the following examples.

EXAMPLE 2   Determine the fundamental interval (FI) and the period for **(a)** $y = \sin(2x - \frac{3\pi}{4})$, **(b)** $y = \sqrt{3} \sin(\frac{\pi}{3} - \pi x)$

Solution

Strategy: (a) First determine the FI by solving $0 \leq (2x - \frac{3\pi}{4}) \leq 2\pi$. The period is simply the length of the FI, so subtract the left endpoint from the right endpoint.

(a) Follow the strategy. Solving $0 \leq 2x - \frac{3\pi}{4} \leq 2\pi$ for x gives $\frac{3\pi}{8} \leq x \leq \frac{11\pi}{8}$. Thus the FI is $[\frac{3\pi}{8}, \frac{11\pi}{8}]$ and the period p is the length of the FI: $p = \frac{11\pi}{8} - \frac{3\pi}{8} = \pi$.

(b) First, get a positive coefficient of x:

$$\sin\left(\frac{\pi}{3} - \pi x\right) = -\sin\left(\pi x - \frac{\pi}{3}\right).$$

In this form, the *FI* is determined by $0 \le \pi x - \frac{\pi}{3} \le 2\pi$. Solve for x to get $\frac{1}{3} \le x \le \frac{7}{3}$, from which the *FI* = $[\frac{1}{3}, \frac{7}{3}]$ and the period is given by $\frac{7}{3} - \frac{1}{3}$ or 2.

> **EXAMPLE 3**   Sketch the fundamental cycle and give the amplitude and period for **(a)** $y = \sin 2x$, **(b)** $y = 2 \sin(-\pi x)$.

Solution

Strategy: (b) Replace $\sin(-\pi x)$ by $-\sin \pi x$, giving $y = -\sin \pi x$, then proceed with the steps of the algorithm.

(a) The *FI* is given by $0 \le 2x \le 2\pi$, or $0 \le x \le \pi$. Mark off the interval $[0, \pi]$ on the x-axis and show the midpoint and the quarter points. Step 3 of the algorithm identifies the points $(0, 0)$, $(\frac{\pi}{2}, 0)$, $(\pi, 0)$; Step 4 gives $(\frac{\pi}{4}, 1)$ and $(\frac{3\pi}{4}, -1)$. Plot these points and follow Step 5 to draw the graph shown in Figure 6.21(a). Since $A = 1$, the amplitude is 1. The period is given by $p = \pi - 0 = \pi$.

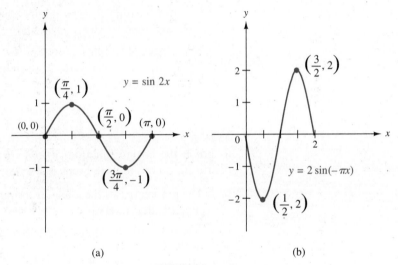

(a)   (b)

FIGURE 6.21

(b) Follow the strategy; $y = -2 \sin(\pi x)$. In this form the *FI* is given by $0 \le \pi x \le 2\pi$, or $0 \le x \le 2$. Now mark off the interval $[0, 2]$ on the x-axis along with the midpoint and quarter points. Locate the key points with Steps 3 and 4: $(0, 0)$, $(1, 0)$, $(2, 0)$, and $(\frac{1}{2}, -2)$, $(\frac{3}{2}, 2)$. Now draw the graph of the fundamental cycle as shown in Figure 6.21(b). Step 6 gives the amplitude, $|-2| = 2$, and the period $p = \frac{2\pi}{\pi} = 2$. ▲

> **EXAMPLE 4**   Follow the steps of the algorithm to sketch the fundamental cycle for $y = 2 \cos(\frac{\pi}{4} - \pi x)$. Give the amplitude, period, and phase shift.

Solution

Strategy: Since cosine is an even function, $\cos(\frac{\pi}{4} - \pi x) = \cos(\pi x - \frac{\pi}{4})$, and so the equation is equivalent to $y = 2 \cos(\pi x - \frac{\pi}{4})$. Now follow the algorithm, using Steps 3a and 4a in place of Steps 3 and 4.

Step 1. Follow the strategy: $y = 2 \cos(\pi x - \frac{\pi}{4})$.

Step 2. For the *FI*: $0 \le \pi x - \frac{\pi}{4} \le 2\pi$, or $\frac{1}{4} \le x \le \frac{9}{4}$. Thus, the *FI* is $[\frac{1}{4}, \frac{9}{4}]$. Mark on the x-axis the endpoints, midpoint, and quarter points of the *FI*.

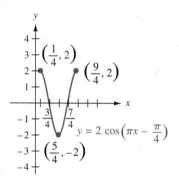

FIGURE 6.22

Step 3a. Plot the x-intercept points $(\frac{3}{4}, 0)$ and $(\frac{7}{4}, 0)$.

Step 4a. Plot the key points $(\frac{1}{4}, 2)$, $(\frac{5}{4}, -2)$, and $(\frac{9}{4}, 2)$.

Step 5. Draw a fundamental cycle for the cosine function as shown in Figure 6.22. The diagram shows a graph of $y = 2 \cos \pi x$ shifted to the right by $\frac{1}{4}$ (the phase shift).

Step 6. The amplitude is 2 and the period is $\frac{2\pi}{\pi}$, or 2. The entire graph is a periodic repetition of that in Figure 6.22. ▲

In some problems it is helpful first to apply one of the reduction formulas to get a simpler equation, as the next example illustrates.

EXAMPLE 5 Sketch a graph of each of **(a)** $y = \sin(\pi - 2x)$, **(b)** $y = -\cos(2x + \frac{\pi}{2})$.

Solution

(a) Applying the reduction formula, $\sin(\pi - \theta) = \sin\theta$, $y = \sin(\pi - 2x) = \sin 2x$. The graph of the given function is the same as the graph of $y = \sin 2x$, for which the fundamental cycle is shown in Example 3a. Draw the fundamental cycle and a periodic repetition, to get the graph shown in Figure 6.23.

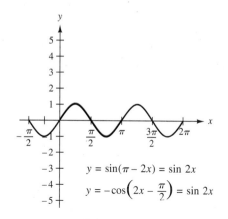

FIGURE 6.23

(b) As a first step, use the reduction formula $\cos(\theta + \frac{\pi}{2}) = -\sin\theta$. Replace θ by $2x$ to get

$$y = -\cos\left(2x + \frac{\pi}{2}\right) = -(-\sin 2x) = \sin 2x.$$

Hence, the graph is the same as that of $y = \sin 2x$, which we already have in Figure 6.23. ▲

EXAMPLE 6 Sketch a graph of $y = \sqrt{3} \sin x + \cos x$.

Solution

The formula does not appear to be that of a sine or cosine function. However, we can apply the technique suggested by the algorithm in the preceding section.

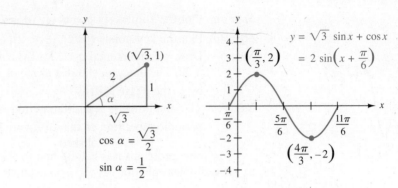

FIGURE 6.24   **FIGURE 6.25**

Factoring out $\sqrt{(\sqrt{3})^2 + 1^2}$, or 2, from the right-hand side,

$$y = 2\left(\frac{\sqrt{3}}{2} \sin x + \frac{1}{2} \cos x\right)$$

Now let α be the angle such that $\cos \alpha = \frac{\sqrt{3}}{2}$ and $\sin \alpha = \frac{1}{2}$. The diagram in Figure 6.24 shows that α is $\frac{\pi}{6}$ (or 30°). Therefore,

$$y = 2(\cos \alpha \sin x + \sin \alpha \cos x)$$

$$= 2\left(\sin x \cos \frac{\pi}{6} + \cos x \sin \frac{\pi}{6}\right)$$

$$= 2 \sin \left(x + \frac{\pi}{6}\right) \qquad \text{By (16)}$$

Now follow the algorithm to draw a graph of $y = 2 \sin \left(x + \frac{\pi}{6}\right)$ as shown in Figure 6.25. ▲

Simple Harmonic Motion

An important class of physical phenomena exhibit oscillating motion. A model for this motion involves a function of the form $f(t) = A \sin (Bt + C)$. Any such motion is said to be **simple harmonic motion** with **amplitude** A and **frequency** f given by the reciprocal of the period:

$$f = \frac{1}{p}.$$

Among such phenomena are all kinds of wave motion—sound waves, light waves (indeed, all electromagnetic waves, from microwave radiation through radio waves, infrared to X-rays).

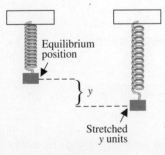

Equilibrium position

$\}$ y

Stretched y units

FIGURE 6.26

  EXAMPLE 7   Suppose a weight is attached to a spring, as shown in Figure 6.26. When the weight is pulled downward 3 inches from its rest (equilibrium) position and then released, it oscillates in simple harmonic motion with a frequency of 2 seconds. Let d denote the distance of the weight from the equilibrium position. **(a)** Write an equation for d as a function of time t (in seconds) after its release. What is the location of the weight when **(b)** t is $\frac{1}{8}$ second, **(c)** t is $\frac{1}{4}$ second?

THE ROSETTA STONE AND FOURIER SERIES

Robert Moog (background) applied Fourier analysis to develop the Moog synthesizer, forerunner of today's synthesizers.

When Napoleon led a military expedition to Egypt in 1798, his forces included the mathematician Joseph Fourier. Napoleon's troops discovered a large slab of polished stone covered with three different kinds of writing, including mysterious hieroglyphics which no one in the world knew how to read. When Fourier returned to France, he brought a rubbing of the writing on the Rosetta Stone.

In Fourier's study an 11-year-old boy became intrigued by the strange pictures on the stone. Young Champollion vowed that he would someday read the ancient Egyptian writing. His fascination led him to become an Egyptologist at the University of Grenoble by age 17. He achieved a translation of the whole hieroglyphic panel in 1822. Fourier was thus indirectly responsible for unlocking the mysteries of Egyptian hieroglyphics.

Fourier is much more directly responsible for the use of trigonometric series to understand and unravel virtually all wave forms. In one of the most imaginative and profoundly important applications of trigonometric identities, Fourier showed how to represent a great variety of functions as sums of sines and cosines. Fourier's remarkable theorem says that, assuming an infinite number of terms, any kind of wave function can be written as a sum of sine and cosine waves.

The unique musical signatures of a violin or a tenor saxophone are no more than complex combinations of sound waves. Fourier analysis can break up any such wave form into a sine–cosine combination in essentially one way. Electronic instruments such as the Moog synthesizer depend on Fourier analysis to combine wave forms to duplicate particular musical sounds or create new combinations and sounds never heard before. With increasing sophistication and computer help, synthesizers can combine thousands of tiny pieces of sine waves as brushstrokes to paint almost any sound picture. Similarly, Fourier analysis makes it possible to take discrete optical or radio signals (which are also wave forms) and filter out atmospheric interference or reconstruct coherent images from data of telescopes located thousands of miles apart—all because of trigonometric identities.

Solution

(a) Since the motion of the weight is simple harmonic motion, assume that the distance $d(t)$ has the form

$$d(t) = A \sin (Bt + C).$$

Further, since the weight oscillates, starting 3 inches from the rest position, it goes from 3 inches to below the rest position to 3 inches above, and

---

> ### For Graphers
> ### 6.6
>
> Graphs of functions of the form $y = f(x) \sin x$ or $y = g(x) \cos x$ have a special form, as illustrated in the diagrams for Explore and Discover Exercises 1 and 2. To see the envelopes pictured in those diagrams, we graph three functions together.
>
> **Exercises**
>
> 1. Draw graphs of the three functions in the same window.
>   (a) $y = x \sin 2\pi x$, $y = x$, $y = -x$
>   (Use the Trigonometric Window.)
>   (b) $y = e^x \cos 2\pi x$, $y = e^x$, $y = -e^x$
>   (Modify your y range appropriately.)
>   (c) $y = e^{-x} \sin 2\pi x$, $y = e^{-x}$, $y = -e^{-x}$
>
> 2. Replace $y = x \sin 2\pi x$ in Exercise 1a by $y = x \sin 10\pi x$ and observe what happens to the graph. Explain how and why this graph differs from the graph in Exercise 1.
>
> 3. (a) Graph the function $y_1 = \sin 18x + \sin 20x$ and then the function $y_2 = 2 \sin 19x \cos x$. Do the graphs appear to be identical? Explain.
>   (b) Now graph the following three functions in the same window.
>
> $$y = \sin 18x + \sin 20x,$$
> $$y = 2 \cos x,$$
> $$y = -2 \cos x.$$
>
>   Write a brief paragraph to explain the graphs in your window.

---

repeats, so the amplitude A equals 3. Recall that $f = 2$. The period of $\sin (Bt + C)$ is given by

$$p = \frac{2\pi}{B} \qquad \text{and} \qquad p = \frac{1}{f} = \frac{1}{2}.$$

Thus,

$$\frac{2\pi}{B} = \frac{1}{2}, \qquad \text{so} \qquad B = 4\pi.$$

Therefore,

$$d(t) = 3 \sin (4\pi t + C), \qquad \text{and} \qquad d(0) = 3.$$

Substituting 0 for t, $3 = 3 \sin (0 + C)$, or $\sin C = 1$. Take $C = \frac{\pi}{2}$ to get an equation for $d(t)$:

$$d(t) = 3 \sin \left(4\pi t + \frac{\pi}{2} \right).$$

A reduction formula can simplify the equation:

$$d(t) = 3 \cos 4\pi t.$$

(b) When t is $\frac{1}{8}$, $d\left(\frac{1}{8}\right) = 3 \cos \frac{\pi}{2} = 0$. Hence at $\frac{1}{8}$ of a second after release, the weight is at the equilibrium position.

(c) When t is $\frac{1}{4}$, $d\left(\frac{1}{4}\right) = 3 \cos \pi = -3$. When t is $\frac{1}{4}$ second, the weight is 3 inches above the equilibrium position. ▲

EXERCISES 6.6

Check Your Understanding

Exercises 1–5   True or False. Give reasons for your conclusion.

1. The graph of $y = \sin(\pi - x)$ is the same as the graph of $y = \sin x$.

2. The graph of $y = -\cos(x + \frac{\pi}{2})$ is the same as the graph of $y = \sin x$.

3. The graph of $y = \cos x \tan x$ is the same as the graph of $y = \sin x$.

4. The function $f(x) = 2 \sin(\pi x - \frac{\pi}{3})$ has period 2.

5. The y-intercept point for the graph of $y = 2 + \cos x$ is $(0, 2)$.

Exercises 6–10   Select from the list below *all choices* whose graphs contain the cycle shown.

(a) $y = \cos x$ **(b)** $y = \sin x$

(c) $y = \sin 2x$ **(d)** $y = -\sin \pi x$

(e) $y = 2 \cos 2x$ **(f)** $y = -2 \cos(x - \frac{\pi}{4})$

(g) $y = \cos(\frac{\pi x}{2})$ **(h)** $y = -2 \cos(x + \frac{\pi}{4})$

(i) $y = 1 + \sin x$

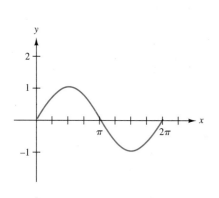

6.

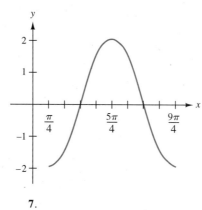

7.

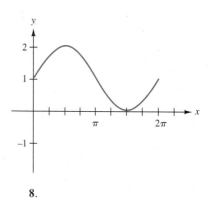

8.

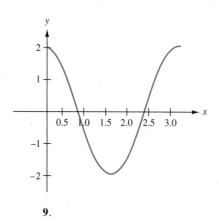

9.

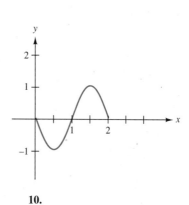

10.

Explore and Discover

Exercises 1–2 Pure musical tones are sound waves that can be described as generalized sine waves. Pitch depends on the frequency of vibration. Two tones near the same frequency add to and interfere with each other so that our ears hear distinct beats. In fact, musicians sometimes use these beats to help tune instruments.

1. The diagrams show the graphs of two functions, $f(x) = x \sin 6\pi x$ (with dotted lines for $y = \pm x$), and $g(x) = e^{-x} \sin 5\pi x$ (with dotted curves for $y = \pm e^{-x}$).

   Explain why the graph of any function of the form $F(x) = k(x) \sin ax$ oscillates between the graphs of $y = k(x)$ and $y = -k(x)$. (*Hint:* For what values of x is the sine factor 0? 1? -1? Where are the corresponding points on the graph?)

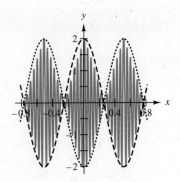

(b) Where on the graph are the beats we hear when two strings are plucked, vibrating at 28 and 30 cycles per second, respectively? Explain how tuning could eliminate the beats.

Develop Mastery

Exercises 1–8 Determine the fundamental interval.

1. $y = \sin 3x$
2. $y = \cos 4x$
3. $y = -\sin\left(\pi x + \frac{3\pi}{4}\right)$
4. $y = -2\cos\left(\pi x - \frac{\pi}{5}\right)$
5. $y = 2\cos(x + 3)$
6. $y = 2\sin(2x - 3)$
7. $y = \sin\left(\frac{\pi}{3} - 2x\right)$
8. $y = \cos\left(\frac{4\pi}{3} - 2x\right)$

Exercises 9–16 (a) Use an appropriate reduction formula to express the equation in simpler form, then (b) use the simpler form to determine the *FI*, amplitude, and period.

9. $y = \sin\left(2x - \frac{\pi}{2}\right)$
10. $y = 2\cos\left(\frac{\pi}{2} - x\right)$
11. $y = -2\cos\left(\frac{3\pi}{2} + x\right)$
12. $y = \sin\left(\frac{3\pi}{2} - 2x\right)$
13. $y = 4\sin(2x + \pi)$
14. $y = 2\sin(x - 3\pi)$
15. $y = \sqrt{3}\cos\left(2x + \frac{3\pi}{2}\right)$
16. $y = \sqrt{5}\sin(2x - \pi)$

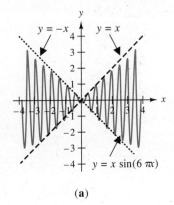

(a)

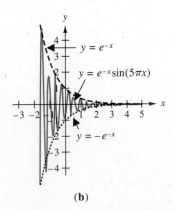

(b)

2. The diagram shows the graph of $f(x) = \sin 56\pi x + \sin 60\pi x$.
   (a) Identify the two dotted curves. (*Hint:* Consider sum-to-product identities.)

Exercises 17–30 Follow the steps outlined in the algorithm of this section to draw a graph of the fundamental cycle. Find the amplitude, period, and phase shift.

17. $y = \sin\left(\frac{\pi x}{2}\right)$
18. $y = \cos \pi x$
19. $y = 2\cos 3x$
20. $y = \sin\frac{x}{2}$
21. $y = -2\cos\frac{x}{2}$
22. $y = -3\cos(-\pi x)$

23. $y = 2 \sin\left(x + \frac{\pi}{3}\right)$ **24.** $y = -2 \cos\left(x + \frac{\pi}{6}\right)$

25. $y = 3 \sin\left(\frac{\pi}{4} - 2x\right)$ **26.** $y = 3 \sin\left(2x + \frac{\pi}{4}\right)$

27. $y = \sqrt{3} \cos\left(\frac{3\pi}{4} - x\right)$ **28.** $y = \sqrt{5} \sin\left(x - \frac{\pi}{3}\right)$

29. $y = 4 \sin\left(\frac{x}{2} - \frac{\pi}{4}\right)$ **30.** $y = 2 \cos\left(\frac{x}{2} + \frac{\pi}{4}\right)$

Exercises 31–36 Sketch a graph. First apply the technique illustrated in Example 6 to get an equivalent equation of the form $y = A \sin(x + \alpha)$, and then use the algorithm with this equivalent form.

31. $y = \sin x + \cos x$

32. $y = \sin x - \cos x$

33. $y = \sin x + \sqrt{3} \cos x$

34. $y = \sqrt{2}(\sin x + \cos x)$

35. $y = 2(\sqrt{3} \sin x - \cos x)$

36. $y = -2(\sin x - \sqrt{3} \cos x)$

Exercises 37–43 The function describes simple harmonic motion. Find the amplitude, period, and frequency of the motion, and give the location when t is zero.

37. $f(t) = 4 \sin 6\pi t$

38. $f(t) = 0.5 \sin\left(\frac{t}{2}\right)$

39. $f(t) = -3 \cos\left(\frac{\pi t}{2}\right)$

40. $E(t) = 3 \sin 80\pi t$

41. $E(t) = 2 \cos \frac{2\pi t}{3} + 0.4 \sin \frac{2\pi t}{3}$

42. $f(t) = 3 \sin 3\pi t + 4 \cos 3\pi t$

43. $V(t) = 2 \cos 120\pi t - 3 \sin 120\pi t$

Exercises 44–47 Sketch a graph.

44. $y = 1 + 2 \sin 2x$ **45.** $y = \sin \pi x - 2$

46. $y = 2 - \cos\left(\frac{\pi x}{2}\right)$ **47.** $y = 3 - \cos 2x$

Exercises 48–63 First use appropriate identities to express the equation in a form studied in this section, then draw a graph.

48. $y = (\sin x + \cos x)^2 - 1$

49. $y = \left(\sin\frac{x}{2} + \cos\frac{x}{2}\right)^2$

50. $y = \left(\sin\frac{x}{2} - \cos\frac{x}{2}\right)^2$

51. $y = 1 + (\sin x + \cos x)^2$

52. $y = 1 + 2 \sin x \cos x$

53. $y = \cos^2 x - \sin^2 x$

54. $y = \cos^2 2x - \sin^2 2x$

55. $y = 2 \sin x \cos x - 1$

56. $y = 2 \sin^2 \frac{x}{2}$

57. $y = 4 \cos^2 \frac{x}{2}$

58. $y = \cos x \tan x$ (*Hint:* First check the domain.)

59. $y = \sin x \cot x$ (*Hint:* First check the domain.)

60. $y = e^{\ln \sin x}$ (*Hint:* Check the domain and then use an appropriate identity from Chapter 4.)

61. $y = e^{\ln \cos x}$ (*Hint:* See Exercise 60.)

62. $y = e^{-\ln \sec x}$ (*Hint:* See Exercise 60.)

63. $y = e^{\ln |\sin x|}$ (*Hint:* See Exercise 60.)

64. Point P moves in simple harmonic motion with an amplitude of 8 inches and a frequency of 3 cycles per second. Write an equation that gives the location of P as a function f of t (in seconds), assuming that P is at $(0, 0)$ when t is 0. The answer is not necessarily unique.

65. A mass suspended from a spring is compressed by 4 cm and released. It oscillates in simple harmonic motion with a frequency of 4 cycles per second. If $d(t)$ denotes its displacement from the rest position, write an equation for $d(t)$ as a function of time t (in seconds) after its release.

66. One of the first astronomical discoveries for measuring distances to other galaxies was a class of stars whose brightness varies regularly. The intensity (brightness) of these Cepheid variables varies according to a function of the form

$$I(t) = A + B \sin \frac{2\pi t}{C},$$

where t is in days, A is the average intensity (magnitude), and the intensity varies by as much as $\pm B$ (magnitudes) every C days.

(**a**) If the average intensity of a particular Cepheid star is 4.0 and the star becomes as much as 10 percent brighter every 10.8 days, write an equation for its intensity as a function of time.

(**b**) What is the intensity when $t = 0$? When $t = 4$ days?

CHAPTER 6 REVIEW

Test Your Understanding

Determine the truth value (T or F) of each of the following statements. Give reasons for your conclusion. It will be helpful to apply an appropriate identity to express the statement in a form that will make it easy to determine the truth values.

1. For every real number x, $-0.5 \le \sin x \cos x \le 0.5$.

2. For every real number x,
   $-2 \le \sqrt{3} \sin x + \cos x \le 2$.

3. For every real number x,
   $0 \le \sin^2 x + \cos 2x \le 1$.

4. For every real number x, $-1 \le \cos^2 2x - \sin^2 2x \le 1$.

5. The graph of $y = \sin^2 x + \cos^2 x$ is a horizontal line.

6. The graph of $y = \cos x - 2\cos^2\left(\frac{x}{2}\right)$ is a horizontal line.

7. The graphs of $y = 1 - 2\sin^2\left(\frac{x}{2}\right)$ and $y = \cos x$ are identical.

8. The graphs of $y = \cos 2x + \sin^2 x$ and $y = \cos^2 x$ are identical.

9. The graphs of $y = \sqrt{1 - \sin^2 x}$ and $y = \cos x$ are identical.

10. The graphs of $y = \cos x \tan x$ and $y = \sin x$ are identical.

11. If $\pi \le x \le \frac{3\pi}{2}$, then $\cos\left(\frac{x}{2}\right) = -\sqrt{\frac{1 - \cos x}{2}}$.

12. If $\frac{\pi}{2} \le x \le \pi$, then $\sin\left(\frac{x}{2}\right) = -\sqrt{\frac{1 - \cos x}{2}}$.

13. For every x in the interval $\left[-\frac{\pi}{2}, 0\right]$, $\cos\left(\frac{x}{2}\right) = -\sqrt{\frac{1 + \cos x}{2}}$.

14. The graphs of $y = \sec x \sin 2x$ and $y = 2\sin x$ are identical.

15. The range of the function $f(x) = \sin x + \cos x$ is the interval $[-1, 1]$.

16. The range of $f(x) = \sqrt{3}\sin x + \cos x$ is the interval $[-2, 2]$.

17. The range of $f(x) = \sqrt{\sin^2 x + \cos^2 x}$ consists of a single number.

18. There is no number x for which $\sin x \cos x$ equals 1.

19. A solution to the equation $\sin 2x - 1 = 0$ is $\frac{\pi}{2}$.

20. A solution to the equation $\cos 2x + 1 = 0$ is $\frac{\pi}{2}$.

21. The equation $1 + \sin^2 x = 0$ has no solution.

22. The equation $\sqrt{1 - \sin^2 x} = \cos x$ is satisfied by every real number x.

23. The function $f(x) = 4\sin(\pi x + 3)$ is periodic with period 2.

24. The function $f(x) = -2\cos(4x + \pi)$ is periodic with period π.

25. The graphs of $y = -2\cos\left(x + \frac{\pi}{2}\right)$ and $y = 2\sin x$ are identical.

26. The amplitude of the graph of $f(x) = -3\sin 2x$ is π.

27. Every point of the form $\left(\frac{(2k + 1)\pi}{2}, 0\right)$, where k is any integer, is an x-intercept point for the graph of $y = \sin 2x$.

28. The graphs of $y = \sin 2x$ and $y = -\sin 2x$ have identical x-intercept points.

29. The graphs of $y = \cos \pi x$ and $y = -3\cos \pi x$ have identical x-intercept points.

30. Every x-intercept for the graph of $y = \sin x$ is also an x-intercept for the graph of $y = \sin 2x$.

31. Every x-intercept point for the graph of $y = \sin 2x$ is also an x-intercept point for the graph of $y = \sin x$.

32. The graph of $y = 2 + \cos x$ has no x-intercept points.

33. The graphs of $y = e^{\ln \sin x}$ and $y = \sin x$ are identical.

34. The graph of $y = e^{\ln \sin x}$ has no x-intercept points.

Mastery Review

Exercises 1–16   Prove that the equation is an identity.

1. $\sin x \cot x = \cos x$

2. $\sec\left(\frac{\pi}{2} - x\right)\tan x = \sec x$

3. $\sec x \sin 2x = 2\sin x$

4. $2\csc^2 x \cos^2\left(\frac{x}{2}\right) = \frac{1}{1 - \cos x}$

5. $\tan\left(x + \frac{\pi}{4}\right) = \frac{\cos x + \sin x}{\cos x - \sin x}$

6. $(\sin x + \cos x)^2 = 1 + \sin 2x$

7. $\cos(x + \pi)\tan(-x) = \sin x$

8. $\sin x \tan\frac{x}{2} = 1 - \cos x$

9. $4\sin^2\frac{x}{2}\cos^2\frac{x}{2} = \sin^2 x$

10. $2\sin\left(x - \frac{\pi}{6}\right) = \sqrt{3}\sin x - \cos x$

11. $\sqrt{2}\cos\left(x - \frac{\pi}{4}\right) = \sin x + \cos x$

12. $\sqrt{1 - \sin^2 x} = |\cos x|$

13. $\cos 2x \tan 2x = 2\sin x \cos x$

14. $(1 + \cos x)(1 - \sec x) = \cos x - \sec x$

15. $\tan\left(\frac{x}{2}\right) + \cot x = \csc x$

16. $\frac{\sin 3x + \sin x}{\cos 3x + \cos x} = \tan 2x$

Exercises 17–20 Determine whether or not the equation is an identity. Give reasons or a proof.

17. $\sqrt{\sec^2 x - \tan^2 x} = 1$ **18.** $\sqrt{1 + \tan^2 x} = \sec x$

19. $\cos 2x + \cos x = \cos 3x$

20. $\cos^4 x - \sin^4 x = \cos 2x$

Exercises 21–24 Find a simpler formula for function f.

21. $f(x) = \sin(-x) \tan x + \sec x$

22. $f(x) = \csc x \tan x$

23. $f(x) = (\sin x + \cos x)^2 - \sin 2x$

24. $f(x) = \cot x \sec x \cos\left(x - \frac{\pi}{2}\right)$

Exercises 25–34 Evaluate in exact form, where angles α, β, and γ satisfy the conditions:

$$\sin \alpha = \tfrac{4}{5} \quad \text{and} \quad \tfrac{\pi}{2} < \alpha < \tfrac{3\pi}{2}$$
$$\tan \beta = -\tfrac{5}{12} \quad \text{and} \quad -\pi < \beta < 0$$
$$\cos \gamma = \tfrac{3}{5} \quad \text{and} \quad 0 < \gamma < \tfrac{\pi}{2}$$

25. $\tan \alpha$

26. $\sin 2\alpha$

27. $\sin\left(\frac{\beta}{2}\right)$

28. $\sin(\alpha - \beta)$

29. $\tan(\beta - \alpha)$

30. $\tan\left(\frac{\gamma}{2}\right)$

31. $\cos^2\left(\frac{\alpha}{2}\right) - \sin^2\left(\frac{\alpha}{2}\right)$

32. $\tan\left(\gamma + \frac{\pi}{4}\right)$

33. $\cos(\gamma + 2\beta)$

34. $\sin^2 \alpha + \cos^2 \beta$

Exercises 35–44 Solve, assuming the domain is the interval $[0, 2\pi]$.

35. $2 \sin^2 x - 1 = 0$ **36.** $\sqrt{3} \sin x + \cos x = 0$

37. $2 \sin^2 x - \sin x - 1 = 0$

38. $\sin x \cos x + \cos^2 x = 0$

39. $\sin x - \cos x = \sqrt{2}$

40. $\sqrt{3} \sin x + \cos x = 2$

41. $4 \cos^2 x - 3 = 0$

42. $2 \cos^2 x - 7 \cos x - 4 = 0$

43. $\cos^2 x - \cos 2x = 1$ **44.** $\sin 2x + \cos x = 0$

Exercises 45–48 Solve, assuming the domain is the interval $[-\pi, \pi]$. Give answers rounded off to two decimal places.

45. $2 \cos x + \sin x = 0$ **46.** $4 \sin x \cos x = \cos x$

47. $2 \sin^2 x - 2 \sin x - 3 = 0$

48. $\sin^2 x - 2 \sin x - 1 = 0$

Exercises 49–56 Draw a graph. Give the period, amplitude, and phase shift.

49. $y = 2 \sin\left(x - \frac{\pi}{4}\right)$ **50.** $y = -2 \cos\left(2x + \frac{\pi}{3}\right)$

51. $y = -2 \sin \pi x$ **52.** $y = 3 \cos\left(\pi x + \frac{\pi}{2}\right)$

53. $y = \sqrt{2}(\sin x - \cos x)$

54. $y = \sqrt{3} \sin x + \cos x$

55. $y = \sin x \cot x$ **56.** $y = \cos^2 x - \sin^2 x$

CHAPTER

7

APPLICATIONS OF TRIGONOMETRIC FUNCTIONS

In Chapter 5 we introduced trigonometric functions defined either on the set of real numbers or on measures of angles (in radians or degrees). In this chapter we apply what we have studied to specific types of problems. Many of these applications involve trigonometric functions of angles measured in degrees.

The first three sections of this chapter focus on solving triangles, using trigonometric functions to relate parts of triangles, which allows us to find distances and angles that may not be directly measurable. These techniques illustrate some traditional applications of trigonometry such as surveying and navigation, but similar techniques are needed for all kinds of problem solving in engineering and physics, as well as throughout mathematics.

Section 7.1 focuses on right triangles. In Sections 7.2 and 7.3 we study more general techniques for dealing with more kinds of triangles. In Section 7.4 we use trigonometric functions to represent complex numbers, which supports work in many areas of physics and electrical engineering. Properties of trigonometric functions provide additional insight into complex roots of polynomial equations. Section 7.5 contains a brief introduction to vectors.

SECTION 7.1 | Solving Right Triangles

I invented a set of right triangle problems. But instead of giving the lengths of two of the sides to find the third, I gave the difference of the two sides. A typical example was: There's a flagpole and there's a rope that comes down from the top. When you hold the rope straight down, it's 3 feet longer than the pole, and when you pull the rope out tight, it's 5 feet from the base of the pole. How high is the pole?
    Richard P. Feynman

In Sections 5.2 and 5.3 we defined trigonometric functions for angles of any size, as long as the angles were in standard position relative to some system of rectangular coordinates. We also defined trigonometric functions for acute angles in a right triangle, and at the end of Section 5.3 we related the various definitions to each other. Applications that use right triangle relations to find unknown distances or angles usually are not set in any particular coordinate system, so in this section we concentrate on right triangle definitions.

Throughout this chapter we will follow a consistent method for labeling any triangle. We will frequently use A, B, and C to label vertices, with the opposite sides labeled with the corresponding lower-case letters, a, b, and c. We will occasionally use a vertex label for an angle, but more often we will use Greek letters α, β, and γ, as in Figure 7.1. When we have a right triangle, we will normally locate the right angle at C, making the hypotenuse c, legs a and b, and the acute angles α and β. We refer to α, β, a, b, and c, as **parts of the triangle** ABC.

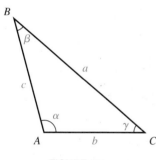

FIGURE 7.1

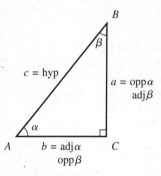

FIGURE 7.2

For convenient reference, we repeat the right triangle definitions of trigonometric functions from Section 5.2. See Figure 7.2.

Definition: Trigonometric Functions of an Acute Angle

Suppose α is an acute angle of a right triangle. The trigonometric functions of α are defined by

$$\sin \alpha = \frac{\text{opp } \alpha}{\text{hyp}} \qquad \cos \alpha = \frac{\text{adj } \alpha}{\text{hyp}} \qquad \tan \alpha = \frac{\text{opp } \alpha}{\text{adj } \alpha}$$

$$\csc \alpha = \frac{\text{hyp}}{\text{opp } \alpha} \qquad \sec \alpha = \frac{\text{hyp}}{\text{adj } \alpha} \qquad \cot \alpha = \frac{\text{adj } \alpha}{\text{opp } \alpha}$$

My trigonometry teacher . . . taught me about adjacent over hypotenuse (all new) and "solving" triangles by logarithms (a crashing bore). He also taught me about identities (capital fun).

Paul Halmos

In a similar manner, the trigonometric functions for the angle β are:

$$\sin \beta = \frac{\text{opp } \beta}{\text{hyp}} \qquad \cos \beta = \frac{\text{adj } \beta}{\text{hyp}} \qquad \tan \beta = \frac{\text{opp } \beta}{\text{adj } \beta}.$$

Solving Right Triangles

Given information about some of the angles or sides of a right triangle, trigonometric functions can be used to determine the other sides and angles. The process of using given data to solve for unknown parts is called **solving the triangle.** In virtually all instances, we look for trigonometric functions that relate known parts of the triangle to the parts we want to find, giving equations that can be solved for the desired quantities. A number of examples illustrate this point.

EXAMPLE 1   A right triangle has a hypotenuse of 4.3 meters and an acute angle of 32°. Find the other acute angle and the lengths of the legs.

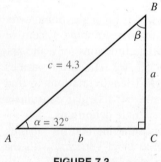

FIGURE 7.3

Solution

Start with a diagram like Figure 7.3 with c as 4.3 and α as 32°. The sum of the acute angles in a right triangle is 90°, so $\beta = 90° - \alpha = 90° - 32° = 58°$. To find a and b, use trigonometric ratios that relate these sides to known parts:

$$\sin \alpha = \frac{\text{opp } \alpha}{\text{hyp}} = \frac{a}{c} \qquad \text{and} \qquad \cos \alpha = \frac{\text{adj } \alpha}{\text{hyp}} = \frac{b}{c}.$$

Solve the first equation for a and the second for b:

$$a = c \sin \alpha = 4.3 \sin 32° \qquad \text{and} \qquad b = c \cos \alpha = 4.3 \cos 32°.$$

Using a calculator, obtain decimal approximations for a and b as $a \approx 2.278652836$, $b \approx 3.646606814$. ▲

Measurements and Accuracy   Recording the lengths of the sides to ten significant digits in Exercise 1 requires some explanation. In Example 1, we recorded the full calculator displays as approximations of the lengths of sides a

and b. What does this imply? If the given values of $\alpha = 32°$ and $c = 4.3$ come from measurements, as is often the case in applications, then we can only assume that c was measured to the nearest tenth of a meter (to within 10 centimeters). Rounding off the decimal display for a to, say 2.27865, would imply knowing the length of side a to a fraction of a millimeter, an assumption that is surely unjustified.

In most of the work in this chapter we will assume that given values represent measurements, (and hence approximations, unless the text specifically indicates otherwise). As a general rule, we cannot justify any more accuracy for calculated values than for the initial data. We will use the following rule of thumb as a guideline.

> In applied problems that involve measured numbers we are not justified in recording final computed results with any more significant digits than the least precise number given.

Working with triangles often involves both linear and angular measurements. We use the following guidelines for linear–angular measurements:

Length Accuracy of	Angle Accuracy of
2 significant digits	nearest 1°
3 significant digits	nearest 10′ or 0.1°
4 significant digits	nearest 1′ or 0.01°
5 significant digits	nearest 10″ or 0.001°

For the problems considered in this chapter, these guidelines should be adequate, and answers should be rounded off to be consistent with the accuracy of the given data. Notation will reflect this convention. When applying these guidelines, we will use $=$ instead of $\approx$ and write, for instance, $x = 2.54$ cm rather than the more precise $x \approx 2.54$ cm.

EXAMPLE 2 In a right triangle $a = 23.4$ cm and $c = 42.3$ cm. Find b, α, β, and the area of the triangle.

Solution

First draw a diagram to show the given information (see Figure 7.4). The Pythagorean theorem gives

$$b = \sqrt{c^2 - a^2} = \sqrt{(42.3)^2 - (23.4)^2} = 35.2$$

Thus $b = 35.2$ cm. Trigonometric relations that involve the given parts a and c are $\sin \alpha = \dfrac{\text{opp } \alpha}{\text{hyp}} = \dfrac{a}{c}$ and $\cos \beta = \dfrac{\text{adj } \beta}{\text{hyp}} = \dfrac{a}{c}$. Therefore,

$$\alpha = \operatorname{Sin}^{-1}\left(\frac{a}{c}\right) = \operatorname{Sin}^{-1}\left(\frac{23.4}{42.3}\right) = 33.6°$$

$$\beta = \operatorname{Cos}^{-1}\left(\frac{a}{c}\right) = \operatorname{Cos}^{-1}\left(\frac{23.4}{42.3}\right) = 56.4°.$$

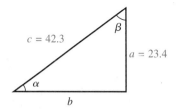

$c = 42.3$

$a = 23.4$

α

b

FIGURE 7.4

Strategy: Express each of the desired quantities in terms of the given a and c, using the right triangle definitions of trigonometric functions. The area of a right triangle equals $\frac{1}{2} ab$.

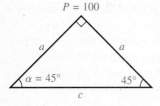

P = 100

FIGURE 7.5

Hence α is 33.6° and β is 56.4°. To find the area K of the triangle, use the formula from geometry. The area is half the base times the height. For the example triangle, $K = \frac{ab}{2} = \frac{(23.4)(35.2)}{2} \approx 411.84$. Rounding off to three significant digits, the area is 412 cm². ▲

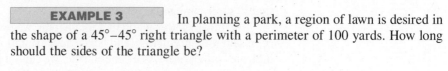

In planning a park, a region of lawn is desired in the shape of a 45°–45° right triangle with a perimeter of 100 yards. How long should the sides of the triangle be?

Solution

Draw a 45°–45° right triangle and label the sides, as in Figure 7.5, with the two legs equal. For the perimeter P, $P = a + a + c = 100$. Apply the Pythagorean theorem to get $c = \sqrt{2}a$. Therefore, the equation for the perimeter becomes $a + a + \sqrt{2}a = 100$, or $(2 + \sqrt{2})a = 100$. Hence,

$$a = \frac{100}{(2 + \sqrt{2})} \approx 29.3 \quad \text{and} \quad c = \sqrt{2}a \approx 41.4$$

The results are rounded off to three significant digits, assuming that all three digits of the given 100-yard perimeter are significant. Thus, the two equal sides should each be 29.3 yards. ▲

For a more general situation, given the perimeter and angle α, we may use $\sin \alpha = \frac{a}{c}$ and $\tan \alpha = \frac{a}{b}$ to express b and c in terms of a and α:

$$b = \frac{a}{\tan \alpha} \quad \text{and} \quad c = \frac{a}{\sin \alpha}.$$

Substituting into the equation for the perimeter,

$$P = a + \frac{a}{\tan \alpha} + \frac{a}{\sin \alpha} = a\left(1 + \frac{1}{\tan \alpha} + \frac{1}{\sin \alpha}\right).$$

This equation may be readily solved for a in terms of the given quantities P and α.

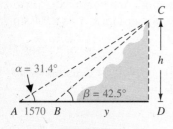

FIGURE 7.6

Strategy: The diagram contains two right triangles, ACD and BCD. Use both triangles to get equations that involve y and h, then eliminate y and solve the resulting equation for h. Do all of the algebra first and then use your calculator for the final evaluation. Round off to three significant digits.

EXAMPLE 4   To find the height of a mountaintop, a surveyor locates two accessible points A and B, as shown in Figure 7.6, and obtains these measurements:

$$|\overline{AB}| = 1570 \text{ feet}, \ \alpha = 31.4°, \ \beta = 42.5°.$$

Find the height h of the mountain.

Solution

Let $|\overline{CD}| = h$ and $|\overline{BD}| = y$. From right triangle ACD, $\tan \alpha = \frac{h}{1570 + y}$, or

$$h = 1570 \tan \alpha + y \tan \alpha. \tag{1}$$

From the right triangle BCD, $\tan \beta = \frac{h}{y}$, or $y = \frac{h}{\tan \beta}$. Substitute into Equation 1 to get

$$h = 1570 \tan \alpha + h \frac{\tan \alpha}{\tan \beta}.$$

Exercises

1. A movie marquee on 35th Street is 1.5 meters tall, with its bottom edge 4 meters above the sidewalk (see the diagram). Tracy, whose eye level is 1.5 meters above the sidewalk, is walking toward the marquee. Her view (measured by angle θ) changes as she gets closer to the marquee, so θ is a function of the distance x in the diagram.
   (a) Show that $\theta = \text{Tan}^{-1}\left(\frac{1.5\,x}{x^2 + 10}\right)$. (*Hint:* Use the right triangle that involves angles α and β, together with (I-11).)

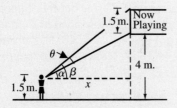

   (b) With the calculator in degree mode (choose an appropriate x-range), draw a graph of the function in part a and find the value of x (to the nearest tenth of a meter) that gives Tracy the best view (the maximum value of θ).

2. Repeat Exercise 1 for a basketball player, Purvis, whose eye level is 2 meters above the sidewalk.

3. If Tracy is standing at the spot that gives her the best view of the movie marquee and Purvis is standing at the spot that gives him his best view, how far behind Tracy is Purvis located? What is the corresponding value of θ for each person?

4. A contractor wishes to build a pipeline from point A to B, where A is located on the shore and B is on an island 2 miles from shore. (See the diagram.)
   (a) If laying pipe costs $3600 per mile on shore (from A to P) and $5000 per mile underwater (from P to B), show that the total cost is given by $C = 3600x + 5000\sqrt{x^2 - 6x + 13}$.
   (b) Determine an appropriate window to draw a graph from which you can find the value of x that gives a minimum cost. What is the minimum cost?

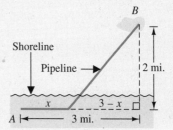

Now solve for h.

$$h - h\frac{\tan \alpha}{\tan \beta} = 1570 \tan \alpha$$

$$h\left(\frac{\tan \beta - \tan \alpha}{\tan \beta}\right) = 1570 \tan \alpha$$

$$h = \frac{1570 \tan \alpha \cdot \tan \beta}{\tan \beta - \tan \alpha} = \frac{1570 \cdot \tan 31.4° \cdot \tan 42.5°}{\tan 42.5° - \tan 31.4°} \approx 2870.4399$$

Rounding off to three significant digits, h is 2870 feet. ▲

It is a good (and efficient) practice to perform first all the necessary algebra, as in Example 4, before doing any calculations. Finding a final formula for h before any evaluation avoids the need to record and use intermediate answers, a practice that often leads to accumulated rounding error.

EXAMPLE 5

Triangle ABC is inscribed in a circle of diameter 7.20 cm, as shown in Figure 7.7, where $\overline{AB}$ is a diameter, O is the center of the circle, and $\alpha = 28.0°$. Find the length of **(a)** chord $\overline{BC}$ and **(b)** circular arc $\overset{\frown}{BC}$.

Solution

Strategy: (a) Since $\overline{AB}$ is a diameter, $\triangle ACB$ is a right triangle. Solve for $\overline{BC}$.
(b) For arc length, $s = r\theta$, so we need the central angle θ (in radians). Use isosceles $\triangle AOC$ to relate θ to α. Round off to three significant digits.

(a) Use the important fact from geometry that any angle inscribed in a half-circle (one that subtends half of the circumference) is a right angle. Since $\overline{AB}$ is a diameter, then $\angle ACB$ is a right angle, so ABC is a right triangle. Then,

$$\sin \alpha = \frac{|\overline{BC}|}{|\overline{AB}|} \qquad \text{so} \qquad |\overline{BC}| = |\overline{AB}|\sin \alpha$$

Therefore, $|\overline{BC}| = 7.2 \sin 28.0° \approx 3.3802 \approx 3.38$.

(b) Let s denote the length of arc $\overset{\frown}{BC}$. From Section 5.1, $s = r\theta$, where θ is measured in radians. First, determine θ using another important fact from geometry, that the measure of any angle inscribed in a circle (such as α) is half the measure of the central angle that subtends the same arc (in this case, θ). This gives $\theta = 2\alpha = 56.0°$. Hence for arc length s,

$$s = r\theta = 3.6\left(56 \cdot \frac{\pi}{180}\right) \approx 3.5186.$$

Rounding off to three significant digits, the length of the chord is 3.38 centimeters and the length of the circular arc is 3.52 centimeters. ▲

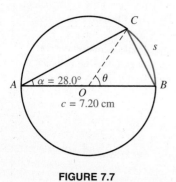

FIGURE 7.7

EXERCISES 7.1

Check Your Understanding

In the following exercises, assume the standard notation for the sides and angles of a right triangle, where $\gamma = 90°$.

Exercises 1–5   True or False. Give reasons for your conclusion.

1. There is no right triangle in which one of the angles is 100°.

2. There is a right triangle with sides $a = 2, b = 3$, and $c = 4$.

3. There is exactly one right triangle with angles $\alpha = 32°$ and $\beta = 58°$.

4. In a right triangle, if $c = 6$ and $\beta = 32°$, then the area $A = 9 \sin 64°$.

5. If in a right triangle the length of the each leg (a and b) is doubled, then the area of the resulting triangle is also doubled.

Exercises 6–10   Complete the sentence by selecting from the list below *all choices* that make the statement true.

(a) between 10 and 12   (b) between 12 and 14
(c) between 14 and 16   (d) less than 10
(e) greater than 30   (f) greater than 35
(g) equal to $8\sqrt{3}$ (h) less than 35°
(i) greater than 50°   (j) between 25° and 35°

Exercises 6–7   In a right triangle; a is 5 and α is 21°.

6. Side c is _____ .

7. The perimeter is _____ .

Exercises 8–10   In a right triangle a is 8 and c is 16.

8. Side b is _____ .

9. Angle α is _____ .

10. Angle β is _____ .

Explore and Discover

1. In a right triangle with legs a and b, $a = m^2 - n^2$, and $b = 2mn$, where m and n are positive integers and $m > n$. Find the length of the hypotenuse c in terms of m and n. Can you know when c will also be an integer? Explain.

2. An equilateral triangle ABC is placed inside a square $ABDE$ with sides of length s. (See the diagram.) The diagonal $\overline{AD}$ of the square intersects $\overline{BC}$ at point M. Find the area of $\triangle ABM$ as a function of s.

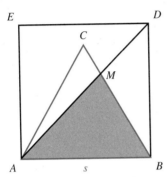

3. Redraw the diagram for Exercise 2 so that $\triangle ABC$ is an isosceles triangle with vertex C as the midpoint of $\overline{ED}$. Find the area of $\triangle ABM$ as a function of s.

Develop Mastery

Use the guidelines stated in this section for rounding off results. In each case before performing computations with your calculator, first write a formula for the desired quantity in terms of the given data. Label angles and sides of a right triangle following the convention used in this section.

Exercises 1–10 Two parts of a right triangle are given. Find the remaining angles or sides.

1. $a = 3.7$, $\alpha = 36°$ 2. $b = 7.3$, $\beta = 42°$
3. $b = 35$, $\alpha = 27°$ 4. $a = 56$, $\beta = 48°$
5. $c = 23.7$, $\beta = 65°20'$
6. $c = 4.36$, $\alpha = 53°40'$
7. $a = 73$, $b = 56$ 8. $a = 0.725$, $b = 0.386$
9. $a = 21.4$, $c = 36.8$ 10. $a = 1648$, $c = 2143$

Exercises 11–16 Information about a right triangle is given. Find its area.

11. $\alpha = 34°$, $b = 0.48$ 12. $\beta = 63°$, $a = 1.4$
13. $c = 1.56$, $\alpha = 52.4°$
14. $c = 0.843$, $\beta = 57.3°$

15. $c = 2.53$, $a = 1.36$ 16. $c = 7.52$, $b = 3.84$

17. A line passes through the two points $(2, 6)$ and $(4, 10)$. Find the acute angle (to the nearest degree) that it makes with the x-axis.

18. A line passes through the points $(-1, 2)$ and $(5, 8)$. Find the acute angle that it makes with the y-axis.

19. Find the perimeter of the right triangle with $a = 1.6$ and $\alpha = 47°$.

20. Find the perimeter of the right triangle with $c = 4.73$ and $\beta = 38.5°$.

21. One angle is $63°15'$ in a right triangle with perimeter 43.71 cm. Find the lengths of the two legs.

22. An angle is $26.3°$ in a right triangle with perimeter 7.45 cm. Find the lengths of the two legs and the hypotenuse.

23. One leg is 3.20 cm in a right triangle with area 5.68 cm². Find the length of the other leg and the angle opposite the given leg.

24. If the hypotenuse of a right triangle is c and its area is K,
    (a) show that $K = \left(\frac{1}{2}\right) c^2 \sin \alpha \cos \alpha$, where one angle is α.
    (b) Use identity (I-12) in Section 6.2 to show that $K = \left(\frac{1}{4}\right) c^2 \sin 2\alpha$.
    (c) For $K = 25$ cm² and $c = 12$ cm, find angle α and the lengths of the two legs.

25. A rope has one end tied to the top of a flagpole. When it hangs straight down it is 2 feet longer than the pole. When the rope is pulled tight with the lower end on the ground, it reaches 8 feet from the base of the pole. How high is the flagpole? (See the epigraph at the beginning of this section.)

Exercises 26–29 Use the diagram where triangle ABC is inscribed in a circle with center O and radius 4.6. $\overline{AB}$ is a diameter and $\beta = 26°$.

26. Find angle θ and the lengths of chord $\overline{AC}$ and arc $\overparen{AC}$.

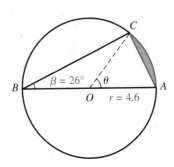

27. Find the area of triangle *ABC*.

28. Find the area of **(a)** triangle *AOC*, **(b)** the circular sector with central angle θ, and **(c)** the shaded segment of the circle.

29. Find the area of **(a)** triangle *BOC*, and **(b)** the circular sector with arc $\overset{\frown}{BC}$.

30. Find the area of an equilateral triangle with a side of length 16 cm.

31. The equal sides of an isosceles triangle are 16.0 cm long and the included angle is 58.0°. Find the perimeter and area of the triangle.

32. The equal sides of an isosceles triangle are 3.48 cm and the equal angles are 52.6°. Find the perimeter and the area of the triangle.

33. A regular polygon (one with *n* equal sides) is inscribed in a circle of radius 24 cm. Find the area of the region inside the polygon if **(a)** $n = 3$ (an equilateral triangle), **(b)** $n = 4$ (a square), **(c)** $n = 6$ (a hexagon), **(d)** $n = 12$ (a dodecagon).

34. Find the height of the flagpole shown in the diagram.

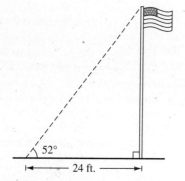

35. Find the height of the flagpole shown in the diagram.

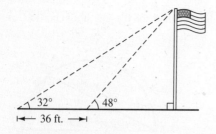

36. (a) Find the height *h* of the mountain peak shown in the diagram in terms of α, β, and *d*.
   (b) A surveyor finds that $\alpha = 43°$, $\beta = 32°$, and $d = 750$ ft. What is the height of the peak?

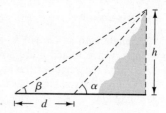

37. Prove identity (I-17) (Section 6.3) for acute angles using the diagram. The hypotenuse of triangle *ABC* is 1 and side *AC* is extended 1 unit to *D*, where $|\overline{AD}| = 1$.
   (a) Show that $\theta = \frac{\alpha}{2}$.
   (b) Show that $\tan\left(\frac{\alpha}{2}\right) = \frac{\sin \alpha}{1 + \cos \alpha}$.

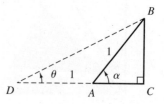

38. A civil engineer wishes to determine the distance across a marshy area between points *A* and *C*. An accessible point *B* is located and $|\overline{AB}|$, $|\overline{BC}|$, and angle θ are measured. (See the diagram.) $|\overline{AB}| = 143$ feet, $|\overline{BC}| = 125$ feet, $\theta = 132.4°$. Find $|\overline{AC}|$.

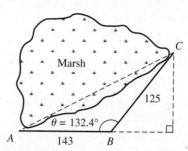

39. In the diagram $\overline{AD}$ and $\overline{BC}$ are parallel. $|\overline{BC}| = 86.0$ feet and $\alpha = 38.0°$. Find $|\overline{AD}|$ and $|\overline{CD}|$.

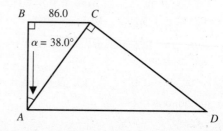

40. In the diagram, $\alpha = 24.0°$, $\beta = 63.0°$, and $|\overline{BC}| = 3.70$. Find $|\overline{CE}|$.

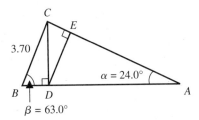

41. A sector with a central angle of $60.0°$ is cut from a circular piece of tin with a radius of 25.0 cm. The edges of the remaining piece are joined together to form a cone. Find the volume of the cone. (See the inside cover for a formula for the volume of a cone).

42. In the diagram $\overline{AB}$ and $\overline{CD}$ are perpendicular diameters of a circle with center at O, point E is on $\overline{AB}$, and $\angle ECO = 30°$. Find the ratio of $|\overline{EO}|$ to $|\overline{AE}|$.

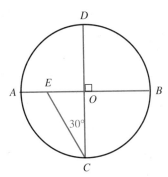

43. In the diagram $ABCD$ is a square, M and N are midpoints of sides $\overline{BC}$ and $\overline{CD}$, respectively, and $\theta = \angle MAN$. Find $\tan \theta$.

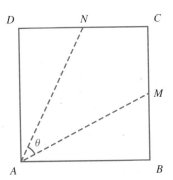

44. In the diagram circles with centers at C and D are tangent to each other at E, and a common tangent line touches the circles at points F and G. The line of

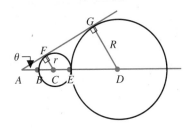

centers meets the common tangent line at A, forming an angle θ.

(a) If $\theta = 30°$ and $|\overline{AB}| = 12$, find the two radii, r and R. (*Hint:* Triangles AFC and AGD are $30°$–$60°$ right triangles.)

(b) If $\theta = 35°$ and $|\overline{AB}| = 16$, find r and R (approximated to two significant digits).

45. Given the circle with equation $x^2 + y^2 - 4y = 0$ and point $P(5, 2)$, draw a diagram to show the circle and the two lines from P that are tangent to the circle. If the points of tangency are A and B, find the angle between the tangent lines, $\angle APB$.

46. Neil Armstrong and Edwin Aldrin made the first landing on the moon on July 20, 1969. Suppose that these men on the surface of the moon at point M measured the angle θ intercepted by the earth to be $\angle QMT = 1.868°$. (See the diagram, where C is the center of the earth and the radius R of the earth is known to be 3963 miles.) Find the distance d from the moon to the earth's surface; that is, find $|\overline{MP}|$.

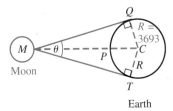

47. In the diagram C is the center of a circle of radius 12 and AE and AD are tangents to the circle. Given that $|\overline{AB}| = 32$, find angle θ (that is, $\angle EAD$).

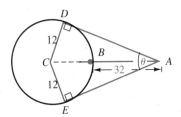

48. Line L is tangent to circle $x^2 + y^2 - 10y = 0$ at point $P(3, 1)$. Find the acute angle that L makes with the x-axis. (*Hint:* Draw a diagram.)

49. For the angle θ, see the diagram. Express as a function of x **(a)** $\sin\theta$, **(b)** $\cos\theta$, and **(c)** θ.

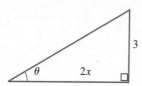

50. A helicopter H and two ships (A and B) are in the same vertical plane, as shown in the diagram. The pilot finds that the angles of depression of A and B are $42°$ and $21°$, respectively. If the altitude h of the helicopter is 3200 feet, find the distance between the two ships.

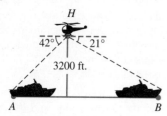

51. In the diagram, $|\overline{AD}| = |\overline{DB}| = 2$, and $\angle BDC = 30°$.
   (a) Show that $|\overline{CD}| = \sqrt{3}$ and that $|\overline{AB}| = 2\sqrt{2 + \sqrt{3}}$.
   (b) Show that $\angle BAD = 15°$.
   (c) Find $\sin 15°$ and $\cos 15°$ in exact form. Check your results by calculator.

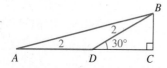

52. Find the area of the region enclosed by the triangle shown in the diagram, where $|\overline{AB}| = 3$, $|\overline{AC}| = 2$, and $\angle BAC = 30°$.

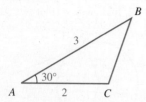

53. A lighthouse is located on the shore of the Atlantic Ocean. The top of the lighthouse (point A in the diagram) is at an elevation of h feet above sea level and a ship S is sailing from Europe toward the lighthouse. Express the distance $d = |\overline{AD}|$ (in miles) at which the ship can first see the light from A (along the tangent line AD) as a function of h. In the diagram E

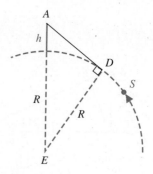

is the center of the earth, and R is the radius of the earth ($=3960$ miles). Since h is small compared to R, show that a good approximation of d is $1.22\sqrt{h}$ miles. See Develop Mastery Exercise 37, Section 1.1.

54. The Nauset Light on Cape Cod rises to 114 feet above the Atlantic Ocean. How far out will a ship be able to see its beacon? Use Exercise 53.

55. To determine the radius of the moon, a person on the earth at point P measures the angle θ subtended by the moon to be $0.513°$. The distance d from the earth to the moon ($|\overline{PM}|$ in the diagram) is about 239,000 miles. Find the radius r of the moon. (*Hint:* Show that $r = \dfrac{d\sin(\theta/2)}{1 - \sin(\theta/2)}$.)

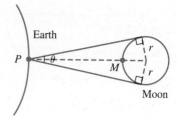

56. When viewed from the top of a 72-foot-tall building, the angle of elevation to the top of a nearby skyscraper is $57°$. When viewed from the bottom of the same building, the angle of elevation is $61°$. (See the diagram.)
   (a) What is the horizontal distance from the bottom of the building to the bottom of the skyscraper?
   (b) What is the height of the skyscraper?

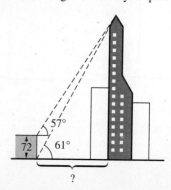

SECTION 7.2 **Law of Sines**

Since that summer . . . when I . . . tasted the fruits of discovery, I have not wanted to do anything except mathematics or, more accurately, mathematics and its applications . . . . I had been stricken by an acute attack of a disease which at irregular intervals afflicts all mathematicians and, for that matter, all scientists: I became obsessed by a problem.

Mark Kac

In Section 7.1 we studied techniques for solving right triangles. However, one frequently encounters triangles in which none of the angles is 90°. Such triangles are usually referred to as **oblique triangles.** Many problems that involve oblique triangles can be solved by the use of right triangles as the preceding section showed. However, we can derive formulas that provide more efficient methods for solving oblique triangles. For instance, in Example 4 of Section 7.1, we saw how we could determine the height of a mountaintop where we used right triangles but required elaborate algebraic manipulations. After introducing the Law of Sines in this section, we shall see a simpler solution to the same problem.

We continue to work with the parts of a triangle, the three angles and the three sides. We use the convention for labeling parts of a triangle introduced in Section 7.1, as shown in Figure 7.8, where a is opposite angle α, b is opposite β, and c is opposite γ.

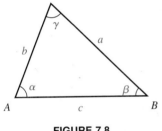

FIGURE 7.8

Solving Triangles

Our primary interest in this section and in the following one, is to develop techniques for solving oblique triangles. As before, to solve a triangle means that we are given sufficient information about its angles and sides to specify a triangle and we determine the remaining angles and sides.

One might first ask what information is sufficient to determine a triangle? In general, we need to know three of the six parts, but this does not mean any three parts. For instance, knowing the three angles does not describe a specific triangle, since many triangles have the same three angles. However, three sides uniquely determine a triangle, and we shall see how to proceed to find the three angles. Of course, this assumes that the given numbers a, b, and c are such that the sum of the two smaller sides is greater than the other side. For instance, sides $a = 2$, $b = 3$, and $c = 6$ would not form a triangle.

We can classify problems of solving triangles into the following four cases based on the given parts.

Case 1 One side and two angles (*SAA* or *ASA*)

Case 2 Two sides and the angle opposite one of them (*SSA*)

Case 3 Two sides and the included angle (*SAS*)

Case 4 Three sides (*SSS*)

In this section we develop the Law of Sines and see how to apply it to solve triangles described in the first two cases. We will introduce the Law of Cosines in the next section to handle problems for the other two cases.

Just because my mathematics has its origin in a real problem doesn't make it less interesting to me—just the other way around. I find it makes the puzzle I am working on all the more exciting.

George Dantzig

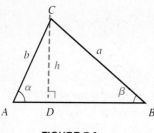

FIGURE 7.9

Law of Sines and Its Application

Here we derive formulas that relate the angles and sides of a triangle. In triangle ABC we draw a perpendicular (altitude $\overline{CD}$) from vertex C to side $\overline{AB}$ as shown in Figure 7.9. Let $h = |\overline{CD}|$. From the two right triangles ADC and BDC, we get:

$$\sin \alpha = \frac{h}{b} \quad \text{and} \quad \sin \beta = \frac{h}{a}$$

$$h = b \sin \alpha \quad \text{and} \quad h = a \sin \beta$$

Since $b \sin \alpha$ and $a \sin \beta$ are both equal to h, we get $a \sin \beta = b \sin \alpha$. Dividing both sides by $\sin \alpha \sin \beta$ gives

$$\frac{a}{\sin \alpha} = \frac{b}{\sin \beta}.$$

In a similar manner,

$$\frac{a}{\sin \alpha} = \frac{c}{\sin \gamma} \quad \text{and} \quad \frac{b}{\sin \beta} = \frac{c}{\sin \gamma}.$$

The three equations derived here make up the **Law of Sines,** which can be written in compact form.

Law of Sines

Suppose α, β, and γ are the three angles of a triangle, and a, b, and c are the sides opposite those angles, respectively. Then we have

$$\frac{a}{\sin \alpha} = \frac{b}{\sin \beta} = \frac{c}{\sin \gamma}$$

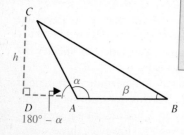

FIGURE 7.10

The triangle in Figure 7.9 is such that the altitude from vertex C is inside the triangle. If the altitude $\overline{CD}$ falls outside triangle ABC, as shown in Figure 7.10, then the derivation of

$$\frac{a}{\sin \alpha} = \frac{b}{\sin \beta}$$

follows from the reduction formula $\sin (180° - \alpha) = \sin \alpha$.

The Law of Sines can be used to solve triangles where the given parts include two angles and a side, or two sides and an angle opposite one of them (Cases 1 and 2). However, the Law of Sines cannot handle problems of the types in Cases 3 and 4. To see this, let us draw circles around the given parts in the Law of Sines equations. For Case 3, suppose a, b, and γ are given (two sides and the included angle).

$$\frac{\textcircled{a}}{\sin \alpha} = \frac{\textcircled{b}}{\sin \beta} = \frac{c}{\sin \textcircled{\gamma}}.$$

Historical Note

One exciting area of trigonometric applications links modern technology with experimental observations made more than three hundred years ago.

The speed of light in a vacuum (186,000 miles per second) is one of the important fundamental physical constants, but light slows down when passing through a material such as water or glass. In consequence, a light ray is bent, or refracted, when it passes from one medium to another, say from water to air. A person standing in water appears to have shortened legs, and a fish in water is not located where our eyes see it.

The amount of bending is related to the speed of light in each medium. The relationship discovered by the Dutch mathematician Willebrord Snellius (or Snell) about 1624, may be expressed as

$$\frac{\sin \theta_1}{v_1} = \frac{\sin \theta_2}{v_2},$$

where the angles are shown in the figure and v_1 and v_2 are the velocities of light in the two materials (air and water in the figure).

When a light ray strikes a surface at a very small angle, the ratio of sines in Snell's law implies that the ray will be completely reflected back into the same medium. This phenomenon, *total internal reflection,* is the basis for the new technology of fiber optics. Light entering one end of a tiny glass fiber is transmitted faithfully to the other end even though the fiber may be bent into curious shapes.

Narrow, flexible "light pipes" allow physicians to examine the interior of a patient's stomach or intestine, or even a beating heart. Knee surgery can now be done with less trauma for the patient by the use of fiber optics in the arthroscope. High fidelity sound can even be transmitted for long distances through optical channels.

Now we have three equations, but it is clear that each equation involves two unknown parts.

In a similar manner, for Case 4, where we are given the three sides, we have

$$\frac{\textcircled{a}}{\sin \alpha} = \frac{\textcircled{b}}{\sin \beta} = \frac{\textcircled{c}}{\sin \gamma}.$$

Each of the three equations has two unknown parts.

The following examples illustrate techniques for solving triangles where the given parts are described by *SAA* and *SSA* (Cases 1 and 2).

EXAMPLE 1   Suppose $\alpha = 43°$, $\beta = 72°$, and $a = 5.4$. Find γ, b, and c.

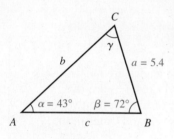

FIGURE 7.11

Solution

First, it is always helpful to draw a diagram of the triangle, and label the given data as shown in Figure 7.11. Angle γ can be determined by using $\alpha + \beta + \gamma = 180°$.

$$\gamma = 180° - (\alpha + \beta) = 180° - (43° + 72°) = 65°$$

To find b, use $\frac{b}{\sin \beta} = \frac{a}{\sin \alpha}$, or $b = \frac{a \sin \beta}{\sin \alpha}$. Similarly, $c = \frac{a \sin \gamma}{\sin \alpha}$.

$$b = \frac{5.4 \sin 72°}{\sin 43°} \quad \text{and} \quad c = \frac{5.4 \sin 65°}{\sin 43°}$$

Evaluate and round off to two significant digits to get 7.5 for b and 7.2 for c. ▲

| **EXAMPLE 2** | In Figure 7.12, h represents the height of a mountain top. A surveyor finds the measurements

$$\theta = 42.5°, \qquad \beta = 31.4°, \qquad c = |\overline{AB}| = 648 \text{ ft.}$$

Find h. (See Example 4 of Section 7.1 for a different solution to a similar problem.)

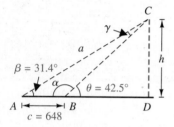

FIGURE 7.12

Strategy: First find the angles of $\triangle ABC$ and then use the Law of Sines to solve for a, which is the hypotenuse of right $\triangle ADC$. Use right-triangle relations to get h.

Solution

Follow the strategy.

$$\alpha = 180° - \theta = 180° - 42.5° = 137.5°$$

$$\gamma = 180° - (\alpha + \beta) = 180° - 168.9° = 11.1°$$

From the Law of Sines, $a = \frac{c \sin \alpha}{\sin \gamma}$. Therefore, from right triangle ADC,

$$h = a \sin \beta = \left(\frac{c \sin \alpha}{\sin \gamma} \right) \sin \beta = \frac{c \sin \alpha \sin \beta}{\sin \gamma}$$

$$h = \frac{648 \sin 137.5° \sin 31.4°}{\sin 11.1°} = 1184.74$$

To three significant digits, h is 1180 feet. ▲

Observe that we did not compute the value of a before calculating h. As noted in Example 4 of Section 7.1, obtaining a complete expression for h before doing any calculations is more efficient and accurate than recording and using any intermediate computations.

Strategy: The area equals half of the base times the height, where the height is the length of the altitude to any side chosen as base. Draw a diagram with the given parts and altitude h. Express the remaining parts of the triangle and h in terms of the given data using the Law of Sines and a right triangle.

| **EXAMPLE 3** | Find the area of the triangle for which $\alpha = 60°$, $\gamma = 48°$, and $c = 25$ cm.

Solution

Follow the strategy. Figure 7.13 shows an altitude from vertex A to side $\overline{BC}$. The formula for the area of a triangle is

$$\text{Area} = \left(\tfrac{1}{2}\right) \cdot (\text{base}) \cdot (\text{height}).$$

Therefore, Area $= \frac{1}{2}ah$, where a is the base. First, find a and h.

$$\beta = 180° - (60° + 48°) = 72°.$$

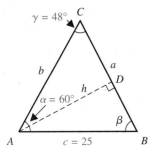

FIGURE 7.13

Using the Law of Sines to find a and right triangle ADB to find h,

$$a = \frac{c \sin \alpha}{\sin \gamma} = \frac{25 \sin 60°}{\sin 48°} \quad \text{and} \quad h = c \sin \beta = 25 \sin 72°.$$

Finally,

$$\text{Area} = \tfrac{1}{2} ah = \frac{1}{2} \left[\frac{25 \sin 60°}{\sin 48°} \right] (25 \sin 72°) \approx 346.3.$$

To be consistent with the given data, round off to two significant digits, and record the area as 350 cm². ▲

The following two examples illustrate techniques for solving triangles described in Case 2, in which the given information consists of two sides and an angle opposite one of them (*SSA*).

Case 2 is called the **ambiguous case** because the given data sometimes determine one triangle, as in Example 4, or sometimes two different triangles, as in Example 5. Also, the given information might describe no triangle, a possibility that may be of mathematical interest but that does not occur in practical situations.

EXAMPLE 4   Suppose $a = 75$, $b = 63$, and $\alpha = 54°$. Find β, γ, and c.

Solution

Strategy: Draw a diagram. Solve for $\sin \beta$ by the Law of Sines and use Sin^{-1} to find β and then $\gamma = 180° - \alpha - \beta$. Remember that there are two angles between 0° and 180° having the same sine. If only one β fits the diagram, we have a unique solution; if there are two, we have two solutions.

First draw a diagram that shows the given data; try drawing angle α first (see Figure 7.14). Using the Law of Sines we may find angle β as follows.

$$\frac{\sin \beta}{b} = \frac{\sin \alpha}{a}$$

$$\sin \beta = \frac{b \sin \alpha}{a} = \frac{63 \sin 54°}{75} \approx 0.67957$$

$$\beta = \text{Sin}^{-1}(0.67957) \approx 42.8°.$$

Again, we recorded the number 0.67957 for purposes of illustration. When it appears in the calculator display, press $\boxed{\text{Sin}^{-1}}$ to get β directly.

Now find angle γ.

$$\gamma = 180° - (54° + 42.8°) = 83.2°$$

Use the Law of Sines again to find c:

$$c = \frac{a \sin \gamma}{\sin \alpha} = \frac{75 \sin 83.2°}{\sin 54°} \approx 92.05.$$

As a final step, round off answers to be consistent with the accuracy of the given data: β is 43°, γ is 83°, and c is 92. ▲

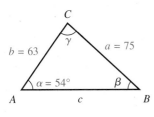

FIGURE 7.14

The solution to Example 4 gave $\sin \beta \approx 0.67957$ and found $\beta \approx 42.8°$. Since $\sin (180° - \beta) = \sin \beta$ is an identity, there are two angles between 0° and 180° for which $\sin \beta = 0.67957$. The other is $180° - 42.8° = 137.2°$. However, this would give a value for γ of $180° - (54° + 137.2°)$ or $-11.2°$, which is not acceptable as an angle of a triangle. The next example shows that the second possibility can indeed give a second solution.

EXAMPLE 5   Suppose $b = 34$, $c = 53$, and $\beta = 32°$. Find γ, α, and a.

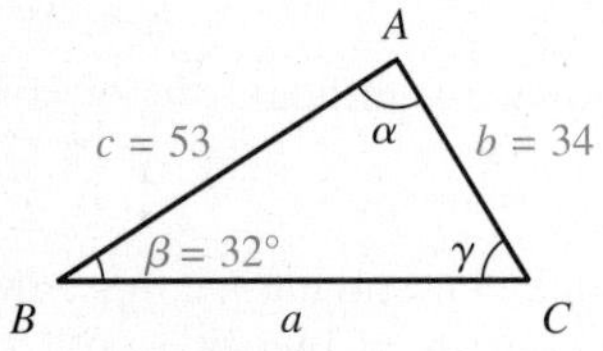

Solution

First, draw a diagram to show a triangle with the given parts (see Figure 7.15). To find γ, apply the Law of Sines:

$$\sin \gamma = \frac{c \sin \beta}{b} = \frac{53 \sin 32°}{34} \approx 0.82605.$$

Hence, $\gamma \approx \text{Sin}^{-1} 0.82605 \approx 55.7°$. For $\gamma = 55.7°$ and $\beta = 32°$, $\alpha = 180° - (\beta + \gamma) \doteq 92.3°$.

To find side a, again apply the Law of Sines:

$$a = \frac{c \sin \alpha}{\sin \gamma} = \frac{53 \sin 92.3°}{\sin 55.7°} \approx 64.1.$$

Round off the results to the accuracy of the given data,

$$\gamma = 56° \qquad \alpha = 92° \qquad a = 64.$$

Since there are two angles, γ and $180° - \gamma$, between $0°$ and $180°$ for which $\sin \gamma = \sin (180° - \gamma) = 0.82605$, consider the possibility of a second solution where

$$\gamma_1 = 180° - \gamma \approx 180° - 55.7° = 124.3°.$$

$$\alpha_1 = 180° - (\beta + \gamma_1) \approx 180° - 156.3° = 23.7°.$$

Since $124.3°$, $23.7°$, and $32°$ are acceptable angles for a triangle, we do indeed have a second solution. Side a_1 is given by

$$a_1 = \frac{c \sin \alpha_1}{\sin \gamma_1} \approx \frac{53 \sin 23.7°}{\sin 124.3°} \approx 25.8.$$

Round off, to get the second solution:

$$\gamma_1 = 124° \qquad \alpha_1 = 24° \qquad a = 26.$$

For a better understanding of the two solutions, look at the geometry of the problem. Rotate side b in Figure 7.16 about vertex A to the position shown. The second triangle ABC_1, does have the same given parts of b, c, and β as the triangle ABC in Figure 7.15. ▲

Summary of the Ambiguous Case   Suppose a, b, and α are given. If α is an acute angle, the number of solutions depends on the length of a as compared with the length of $(b \sin \alpha)$. If $a = b \sin \alpha$, we have one solution, a right triangle, as shown in Figure 7.17. If $a < b \sin \alpha$, there is no solution, as in Figure 7.17b. If $b \sin \alpha < a < b$, there are two solutions, as shown in Figure 7.17c. If $a > b$, we have one solution, as shown in Figure 7.17d. If α is an obtuse angle and $a > b$, then there is only one solution; see Figure 7.17e.

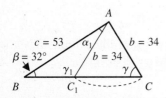

FIGURE 7.15

FIGURE 7.16

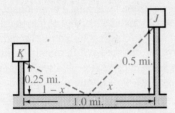

┌─────────────┐
│ **For Graphers** │
│   **7.2**   │
└─────────────┘

Exercises

1. Graph the time function $y = \frac{5}{21} + \frac{14 - 5 \sin x}{70 \cos x}$ from Explore and Discover Exercise 3. Observe that x is to be measured in degrees, so the calculator must be in degree mode. You will need to choose a window to fit the data.

2. From your graph, trace to find the minimum value of y and compare your answer with that given in Explore and Discover Exercise 4.

3. Juan and Karen live in houses J and K just off the same road. Juan's house is set back one-half mile and Karen's is one-quarter mile from the road. (See the diagram.)

   (a) If Juan and Karen want to meet on the road at a point x miles from where Juan's driveway meets the road, show that the total straight-line distance they walk is given by $y = \sqrt{0.25 + x^2} + \sqrt{1.0625 - 2x + x^2}$.

   (b) With an x range of $[0, 0.95]$ on a TI or $[0, 0.94]$ on a Casio and a y range of $[1.2, 1.5]$, draw a graph and determine the value of x for which the total distance is the smallest. What is the minimum distance?

   (c) Compare the minimum distance with the total distance (in feet) walked if Juan and Karen meet where $x = 0.6$ or where $x = 0.75$.

4. Suppose Juan and Karen lived the same distances back from the road, but on opposite sides of the road. Where along the road should they meet to minimize the total distance walked? (*Hint:* What about the path directly from one house to the other?) Compare your answer with the one you obtained in Exercise 3.

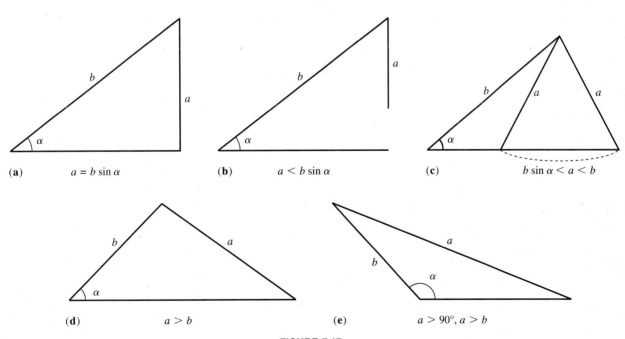

FIGURE 7.17

In any problem, whether it has been identified as ambiguous or not, we strongly suggest that you first draw a diagram to show the given parts. Even a rough sketch will usually clarify the nature of the problem, whether it has two solutions, just one, or none. But keep in mind that two solutions can exist.

EXERCISES 7.2

Assume the labeling of the sides and angles of $\triangle ABC$ is as in the text.

Exercises 1–5 True or False. Given reasons for your conclusion.

Exercises 1–3 $\triangle ABC$ has $\alpha = 53°$, $\beta = 31°$, and $b = 12$.

1. $b < a$ and $a < c$.

2. $a = \frac{12 \sin 31°}{\sin 53°}$ **3.** $c = \frac{12 \sin 84°}{\sin 31°}$

Exercises 4–5 A triangle has $a = 4$, $c = 8$, and $\gamma = 64°$.

4. $\alpha = \text{Sin}^{-1}\left(\frac{\sin 64°}{2}\right)$

5. There is exactly one triangle with the given values for a, c, and γ.

Exercises 6–10 Complete the sentence by selecting from the list below *all choices* that make the statement true.

(a) $24\sqrt{2}$ **(b)** $\frac{12\sqrt{3}}{\sin 20°}$ **(c)** $24 \sin 20°$

(d) $\frac{24}{\sin 20°}$ **(e)** $24 \cot 20°$ **(f)** $\frac{24 \sin 20°}{\sin 60°}$

(g) $24 \csc 20°$ **(h)** $\frac{24 \sin 50°}{\sin 20°}$

6. If $\alpha = 20°$, $\beta = 90°$, and $a = 24$, then $c = $ _____.

7. If $\alpha = 70°$, $\beta = 20°$, and $b = 24$, then $a = $ _____.

8. If $\alpha = 20°$, $\beta = 60°$, and $a = 24$, then $b = $ _____.

9. If $\alpha = 30°$, $\gamma = 20°$, and $c = 24$, then $b = $ _____.

10. If $\alpha = 45°$, $\gamma = 105°$, and $b = 24$, then $a = $ _____.

Explore and Discover

Exercises 1–4 Sound and light both travel at different rates in different materials. For example, sound travels 355 m/sec in air and about 1465 m/sec through water. Thus a sound traveling by paths through two different media will be detected at different times, just as we sometimes hear distinct echoes of a single sound. This fact is used in geological exploration. Suppose a sound is generated by a thumper truck at point P in the diagram, and a detector is located 1000 meters away at Q, where there is a (relatively) homogeneous layer of sandstone 150 meters deep with another denser layer below.

1. Express the distances $|\overline{AB}| (= |\overline{CD}|)$, $|\overline{PB}|$, and $|\overline{BC}|$ as functions of angle θ.

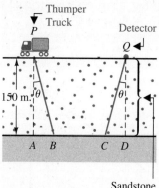

2. If the speed of sound through the upper and lower layers is 1500 and 4200 m/sec, respectively, use the relation distance = rate × time to express the time along each of the following paths in terms of the angle θ.
(a) t_1 along $\overline{PB}$, **(b)** t_2 along $\overline{BC}$, **(c)** total time t_3 along $\overline{PBCQ}$.

3. Show that the total time can be expressed by $t_3 = \frac{5}{21} + \frac{14 - 5 \sin \theta}{70 \cos \theta}$, and evaluate the total time for $\theta = 15°$, $20°$, $25°$, and $30°$.

4. *Looking Ahead to Calculus* From your data in Exercise 3, estimate the angle θ for which sound travels fastest from P to Q. What is the approximate time difference between sound traveling the fastest path and sound through the air from P to Q? Through the upper layer of rock from P to Q? The answer obtained in calculus is $\theta = \text{Sin}^{-1}(\frac{5}{14})$. How close is your estimate?

Develop Mastery

Round off all calculated results to be consistent with the accuracy of the given data. See guidelines stated in Section 7.1.

Exercises 1–16 Three parts of a triangle are given. Find the remaining parts. Begin by drawing a diagram showing a triangle with the given parts labeled.

1. $\alpha = 24.0°$, $\beta = 75.0°$, $a = 15.0$
2. $\beta = 47.0°$, $\gamma = 36.0°$, $a = 253$
3. $\alpha = 43.0°$, $\beta = 116.0°$, $c = 83.0$
4. $\alpha = 48.7°$, $\beta = 74.2°$, $c = 138$
5. $\beta = 31°30'$, $\gamma = 56°15'$, $b = 7.45$
6. $\alpha = 59°45'$, $\beta = 83°15'$, $a = 65.2$
7. $\alpha = 31.9°$, $\beta = 58.1°$, $b = 45.0$
8. $\alpha = 32.7°$, $\gamma = 81.4°$, $b = 4.57$
9. $a = 57$, $b = 68$, $\alpha = 56°$
10. $a = 46$, $b = 64$, $\beta = 116°$
11. $b = 3.4$, $c = 1.7$, $\beta = 124°$
12. $a = 33.0$, $c = 65.0$, $\alpha = 30.5°$
13. $a = 48$, $c = 65$, $\gamma = 56°$
14. $b = 85$, $c = 52$, $\beta = 112°$
15. $a = 16.4$, $b = 23.2$, $\beta = 63°30'$
16. $b = 0.16$, $c = 0.23$, $\beta = 41°$

Exercises 17–22 Find the area of the triangle that has the given measurements.

17. $\alpha = 43.0°$, $\beta = 72.0°$, $a = 24.0$
18. $\beta = 35.0°$, $\gamma = 68.0°$, $a = 43.0$
19. $\alpha = 31.9°$, $\beta = 58.1°$, $c = 53.0$
20. $a = 28.0$, $b = 45.0$, $\beta = 58.1°$
21. $a = 8.6$, $c = 5.3$, $\alpha = 115°$
22. $a = 25$, $b = 45$, $\beta = 36°$
23. To measure the height of clouds, a spotlight is aimed vertically. Two observers at points A and B, 364 feet apart and in line with the spotlight, measure angles α and β as shown in the diagram.

$$\alpha = 72.5° \qquad \beta = 47.8°$$

How far from the ground is the bottom of the cloud level?

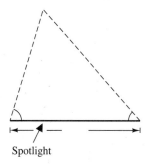

Spotlight

24. An surveyor who wishes to determine the width of a river sees a tree on the opposite bank. She selects two accessible points, A and B, as shown in the diagram and takes the following measurements: $|\overline{AB}| = 64$ feet, $\alpha = 35°$, $\beta = 128°$. Find the width of the river.

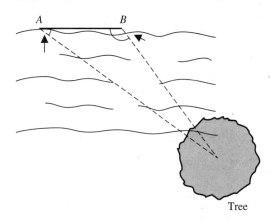

Tree

25. In order to find the height of the Goodyear blimp, observers at A and B, 158 yards apart, measure the following angles: $\alpha = 45.0°$ and $\beta = 60.0°$. (See the diagram.) How high is the blimp?

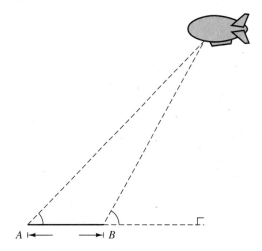

26. A vertical tower AB is located on a hill that is inclined at 14°. (See the diagram.) From point C, 85 feet downhill from the base A of the tower, angle α is measured and found to be 23°. What is the height of the tower?

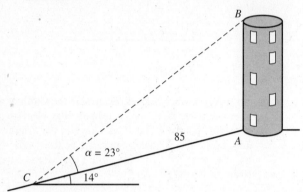

27. Bridget wishes to find the distance from point A to an inaccessible point D. (See the diagram.) Points B and C are located and the following measurements are found: $|\overline{AB}| = 216$ ft, $\alpha = 24.5°$, $\beta = 32.3°$, $\gamma = 124.5°$, $\theta = 73.4°$. Determine the distance from A to D.

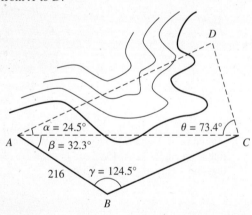

28. Two forest rangers are stationed at points A and B located on a coordinate system with $A(17, 33)$ and $B(82, 16)$. (See the diagram.) They spot a forest fire

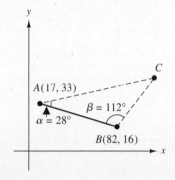

at point C and measure angles $\alpha = 28°$, and $\beta = 112°$. Find the coordinates of point C.

29. Use the following information to find the lengths of $\overline{BC}$ and $\overline{CD}$ in the diagram: $\alpha = 36°$, $|\overline{BD}| = 6.2$, $|\overline{AD}| = 4.8$.

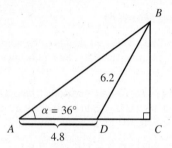

30. Triangle ABC is inscribed in a circle as shown in the diagram. Show that the diameter d of the circle is given by the ratio in the Law of Sines

$$d = \frac{a}{\sin \alpha}$$

(*Hint:* Take point D on the circle so that $\overline{BD}$ passes through the center; $\overline{BD}$ is a diameter. Recall from geometry that angle BDC is equal to angle BAC, which is angle α. Also triangle BCD is a right triangle.)

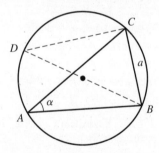

31. In a triangle $a = 1.24$, $b = 1.86$, and $\beta = 2\alpha$. Find angle α in degrees rounded off to one decimal place. (*Hint:* Use the Law of Sines and a double-angle identity.)

32. In $\triangle ABC$, $c = (1.64)b$ and $\gamma = 2\beta$. Find angle β in degrees rounded off to one decimal place.

33. In $\triangle ABC$, D is the midpoint of $\overline{BC}$, $|\overline{AC}| = 16$, and the angles are as shown in the diagram. **(a)** Find the area of $\triangle ABC$. **(b)** Find the area of $\triangle BDE$.

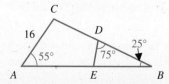

34. In △ABC, angle α is bisected by $\overline{AD}$ as shown in the diagram, where $p = |\overline{CD}|$ and $q = |\overline{BD}|$. Show that $\frac{p}{q} = \frac{|\overline{AC}|}{|\overline{AB}|}$. (*Hint:* Use the Law of Sines for △ACD and for △ABD. Also recall a reduction formula for $\sin(180° - \phi)$.)

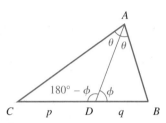

The result of this exercise is often used in advanced Euclidean geometry, where it is usually stated as a theorem: Each angle bisector of a triangle divides the opposite side into segments proportional in length to the adjacent sides.

---

35. The Leaning Tower of Pisa measures 184.5 feet from its base to its top. When a distance of 137.5 feet is measured along the ground from its base in the direction of its lean, the angle of elevation to the top of the tower is found to be 56.72°. At what angle (measured from the vertical) does the tower lean?

Exercises 36–37 The given information refers to the diagram. Find the length x of the segment $\overline{AB}$.

36. $\alpha = 45°$, $\beta = 45°$, $\theta = 60°$, $\phi = 55°$, and $d = 75.2$.

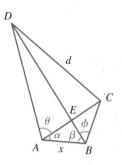

37. $\alpha = 30°$, $\beta = 60°$, $\theta = 70°$, $\phi = 35°$, and $d = 72.6$.

38. Assume that Earth (E) and Venus (V) rotate about the sun (S) in circular orbits of radii 93 million miles and 67 million miles, respectively. Assume that both orbits lie in the same plane. An astronomer measures angle θ between the lines of sight E to S and E to V. (See the diagram.)
(a) If θ is 15°, how far is Venus from the Earth? f There are two possible results.

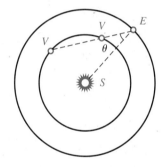

(b) What is the largest possible value of θ? How many solutions are there for this angle?

39. In Exercise 38 replace Venus by the planet Mercury, whose orbital radius is 36 million miles.

| **SECTION 7.3** | **Law of Cosines** |

When people ask [what I do and what kind of mathematician I am], I always try to answer them. I say that there are lots of problems in mathematics that are interesting and have not been solved, and every time you solve one you think up a new one. Mathematics . . . expands rather than contracts.
      Mary Ellen Rudin

In the preceding section we observed that the Law of Sines is not suitable for solving triangles in Cases 3 and 4, where the known information consists of two

FIGURE 7.18

I got a lot of my geometric approach from [my father], and excitement about mathematics too. Sometimes after dinner we would get off on some topic. [For] example, my brother asked how you would find the area of a triangle in terms of its sides, so we all sat down and spent a lot of time deriving Heron's formula.

William Thurston

sides and the included angle or three sides. To handle the *SAS* and *SSS* type problems, we introduce the Law of Cosines.

Consider triangle *ABC* shown in Figure 7.18. Suppose angle γ and sides a and b are given. We wish to find side c. Draw the altitude h from vertex A and then use the two right triangles *ADC* and *ADB* as follows. From *ADC*, we have

$$x = b \cos \gamma \quad \text{and} \quad h = b \sin \gamma. \tag{1}$$

Applying the Pythagorean theorem to triangle *ADB* gives

$$c^2 = h^2 + (a - x)^2 = h^2 + a^2 - 2ax + x^2 \tag{2}$$

Now substitute the expressions for x and h from Equation 1 into Equation 2, and then use identity (I-4):

$$c^2 = (b \sin \gamma)^2 + a^2 - 2a(b \cos \gamma) + (b \cos \gamma)^2$$
$$= a^2 + b^2(\sin^2 \gamma + \cos^2 \gamma) - 2ab \cos \gamma$$
$$= a^2 + b^2 - 2ab \cos \gamma.$$

Therefore, c^2 is given by the formula

$$c^2 = a^2 + b^2 - 2ab \cos \gamma. \tag{3}$$

We derived the formula for c^2 in Equation 3 using the triangle shown in Figure 7.18, where the altitude from vertex A is inside the triangle. If the altitude falls outside the triangle, we still get the same formula; see Exercise 40.

By a process similar to that used to get Equation 3, we can get analogous formulas for a^2 and b^2. The formulas for a^2, b^2, and c^2 are referred to as the **Law of Cosines.**

Law of Cosines

Suppose α, β, and γ are the angles of a triangle, and a, b, and c are the sides opposite, respectively:

$$a^2 = b^2 + c^2 - 2bc \cos \alpha$$
$$b^2 = a^2 + c^2 - 2ac \cos \beta$$
$$c^2 = a^2 + b^2 - 2ab \cos \gamma$$

The following two examples illustrate two methods for solving the same triangle in which two sides and the included angle are given. Example 1 uses the Law of Cosines exclusively, and Example 2 uses both the Law of Cosines and the Law of Sines.

EXAMPLE 1   Suppose $b = 84.0$, $c = 65.0$, and $\alpha = 36.4°$. Find a, β, and γ.

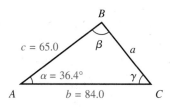

FIGURE 7.19

Solution

First, draw a triangle to show the given data. See Figure 7.19. To find side a, use the first equation in the Law of Cosines:

$$a = \sqrt{b^2 + c^2 - 2bc \cos \alpha} = \sqrt{84^2 + 65^2 - 2(84)(65) \cos 36.4°}$$

$$a \approx 49.91552597.$$

This is the final result given by a calculator to several decimal places. Since subsequent computations will use a, store the full decimal approximation in the calculator. However, when rounded off to be consistent with the given data, $a = 49.9$.

To find angles β and γ, use the second and third equations of the Law of Cosines:

$$\cos \beta = \frac{a^2 + c^2 - b^2}{2ac} = \frac{a^2 + 65^2 - 84^2}{2 \cdot a \cdot 65} = -0.052309956.$$

$$\cos \gamma = \frac{a^2 + b^2 - c^2}{2ab} = \frac{a^2 + 84^2 - 65^2}{2 \cdot a \cdot 84} \approx 0.634710394.$$

The computations used the value of a stored in the calculator. Angles β and γ are

$$\beta \approx \text{Cos}^{-1}(-0.052309956) \approx 92.9985°$$

$$\gamma \approx \text{Cos}^{-1}(0.634710394) \approx 50.6015°.$$

Apply the guidelines for linear-angular measurements stated in Section 7.1 and round off to one decimal place to get 93.0° for β and 50.6° for γ.

Here we recorded numbers to several decimal places only for purposes of illustration. In practice we would not even record the values of $\cos \beta$ and $\cos \gamma$, but when their values appear in the calculator display we would press the $\boxed{\text{Cos}^{-1}}$ key (or equivalent) and then merely record our final rounded-off answers.

Note that after finding β, determining γ would have been easy using $\gamma = 180° - (\alpha + \beta)$. However, it is always wise to have a check on computations. Take the results and see if the sum of the three angles is 180°.

$$\alpha + \beta + \gamma = 36.4° + 93.0° + 50.6° = 180° \quad \blacktriangle$$

In the next example we consider the same problem as in Example 1, but we use the Law of Sines to determine the angles.

EXAMPLE 2 Suppose $b = 84.0$, $c = 65.0$, and $\alpha = 36.4°$. Find a, β, and γ.

Solution

Strategy: For *SAS*, use the Law of Cosines to find a, then find the remaining angles using either the Law of Sines or the Law of Cosines. Always check to see that the angle sum is 180°.

To find a, apply the Law of Cosines as in Example 1 ($a = 49.9$ rounded off, but the full decimal approximation is stored in the calculator).

To find angle β, apply the Law of Sines.

$$\sin \beta = \frac{b \sin \alpha}{a} = \frac{84 \sin 36.4°}{a} \approx 0.998630897.$$

This could lead to the conclusion that

$$\beta \approx \mathrm{Sin}^{-1}(0.998630897) \approx 87.0°.$$

We could then find γ by $\gamma = 180° - (\alpha + \beta) \approx 56.6°$.

Comparing $\beta = 87.0°$, $\gamma = 56.6°$ with the results of Example 1, where $\beta = 93.0°$ and $\gamma = 50.6°$, we see that there is a serious discrepancy. On closer inspection, there are two possible angles β between $0°$ and $180°$ for which $\sin \beta = 0.998630897$. Since $\sin(180° - \beta) = \sin \beta$ is an identity, the desired angle is the supplement of that given by the inverse sine. Hence, $\beta = 180° - 87.0° = 93.0°$, which agrees with the value of β determined in Example 1. ▲

The pitfall we encountered in solving Example 2 suggests a word of caution:

> Exercise care when applying the Law of Sines to determine angles.

Look at the solutions to the same problem in Examples 1 and 2 and notice that the Law of Cosines as in Example 1 gives only one angle β between $0°$ and $180°$ that satisfies the equation $\cos \beta = -0.0523$, and that angle is given by the inverse cosine function. Recall from Section 5.5 that the inverse cosine function is always a number in the interval $[0, 180°]$, while the inverse sine gives values in the interval $[-90°, 90°]$.

In conclusion we generally recommend using the Law of Cosines to solve triangles when there is a choice. Before calculators, lengthy computations were performed using tables of logarithms. However, logarithmic computations are not helpful to add or subtract numbers, and for this reason people avoided using the Law of Cosines whenever possible. Calculators eliminate the need to use logarithms for computations; the calculator can handle all needed computations with ease.

In the next example, we illustrate the method for solving triangles in which the three sides are given.

EXAMPLE 3 Suppose $a = 53$, $b = 86$, and $c \doteq 62$. Find the three angles.

Solution

Strategy: For *SSS*, we must solve an equation in the Law of Cosines for the cosine of an angle. For instance, $\cos \gamma = \frac{a^2 + b^2 - c^2}{2ab}$.

We can solve each of the equations in the Law of Cosines for the cosine of the angle in terms of the three sides. For example,

$$\cos \alpha = \frac{b^2 + c^2 - a^2}{2bc} = \frac{86^2 + 62^2 - 53^2}{2 \cdot 86 \cdot 62}$$

Evaluate by calculator, and with the result in the display, press $\boxed{\mathrm{Cos}^{-1}}$ to get $\alpha = 38°$ (rounded off).

Similarly, using the second and third equations from the Law of Cosines, $\beta = 96°$ and $\gamma = 46°$.

As a check, compute the angle sum:

$$\alpha + \beta + \gamma = 38° + 96° + 46° = 180°. \quad ▲$$

Area of a Triangular Region

In the next example, we illustrate a technique for finding the area of a triangular region. Remember the formula for the area of a triangle:

$$\text{Area} = \left(\frac{1}{2}\right)(\text{base})(\text{altitude}).$$

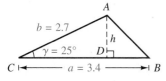

$b = 2.7$

$\gamma = 25°$ D h

$C \longleftarrow a = 3.4 \longrightarrow B$

FIGURE 7.20

EXAMPLE 4   Suppose $a = 3.4$ cm, $b = 2.7$ cm, and $\gamma = 25°$. Find the area K of the region enclosed by triangle ABC.

Solution

As always, first draw a diagram, as shown in Figure 7.20, where the altitude is h and the base is a. From right triangle ACD, $h = b \sin \gamma$. Therefore,

$$K = \tfrac{1}{2}ah = \tfrac{1}{2}a(b \sin \gamma)$$
$$= \tfrac{1}{2}(3.4)(2.7)\sin 25° \approx 1.9398.$$

Rounding off to two significant digits, the area is 1.9 cm². ▲

Ambiguous Case Revisited

In the preceding section we discussed the use of the Law of Sines to solve the so-called ambiguous case where we are given two sides and an angle opposite one of them. The *SSA* case can have a unique solution, two solutions, or no solutions. The Law of Cosines can resolve the possible ambiguity, as we illustrate in the following example.

EXAMPLE 5   Suppose $a = 17, c = 24$, and $\alpha = 40°$. Find the length of side b.

Solution

Strategy: Draw a diagram. The ambiguous case seems to have two solutions. Proceed as in the previous section, or use the Law of Cosines as a quadratic in b and use the quadratic formula to get two solutions automatically.

Start with a diagram to help visualize relationships. See Figure 7.21. The only equation in the Law of Cosines that involves angle α is

$$a^2 = b^2 + c^2 - 2bc \cos \alpha$$

Substitute in the given information to get a quadratic equation in b.

$$17^2 = b^2 + 24^2 - 2 \cdot 24b \cdot \cos 40°$$
$$b^2 - (48 \cos 40°)\, b + (576 - 289) = 0$$
$$b^2 - (48 \cos 40°) \cdot b + 287 = 0$$

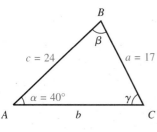

B

β

$c = 24$ $a = 17$

$\alpha = 40°$ γ

A b C

FIGURE 7.21

Apply the quadratic formula:

$$b = \frac{48 \cos 40° \pm \sqrt{(48 \cos 40°)^2 - 4 \cdot 287}}{2}$$

$$\approx \frac{36.770 \pm \sqrt{204.0427}}{2}$$

$$\approx \frac{36.770 \pm 14.284}{2}$$

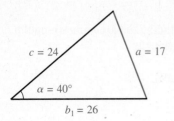

(a)

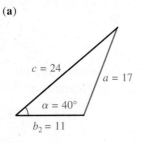

(b)

FIGURE 7.22

There are two solutions,

$$b_1 \approx 25.527 \qquad \text{and} \qquad b_2 \approx 11.243.$$

Rounded off to two significant digits, $b_1 = 26$ and $b_2 = 11$.   ▲

In Example 5, there are two triangles sharing the given data (see Figure 7.22). If we needed complete solutions, it would be a simple matter to find the missing angles in each of the two triangles.

For an *SSA* problem, always begin with a diagram. It may be possible, on the basis of your diagram, to determine the number of solutions. If so, either method may be used. If the number of solutions is not clear from the diagram, then the Law of Cosines will give the information as part of the solution. Applying the quadratic formula, as in Example 5, automatically indicates whether the given information determines no solution, one solution, or two solutions. For instance, if the expression under the radical is negative, we have no solutions; if it is zero, we have one solution (a right triangle); if it is positive, we have two solutions when both roots of the quadratic equation are positive and only one solution when one root is negative.

EXERCISES 7.3

Check Your Understanding

Assume that in $\triangle ABC$ the sides and angles are labeled as in the text.

Exercises 1–5   True or False. Give reasons for your conclusion.

1. There is no triangle with $b = 12$, $c = 10$, and $\gamma = 100°$. (*Hint:* Draw a diagram.)

2. If $a = 2$, $b = 4$, and $c = 4$, then $\cos \alpha = \frac{7}{8}$.

3. If $a = 12$, $b = 35$, and $c = 37$, then $\gamma = 90°$.

4. If $\alpha = 30°$, $b = 12$, and $c = 21$, then the area of $\triangle ABC$ is 126.

5. If $a^2 + b^2 < c^2$, then γ is less than $90°$.

Exercises 6–10   Complete the sentence by selecting from the list below *all choices* that make the statement true.

(a) $5\sqrt{3}$ (b) $2\sqrt{5} - 2\sqrt{3}$ (c) $2\sqrt{5} + 2\sqrt{3}$
(d) less than 4   (e) greater than 5
(f) between 4 and 5   (g) equal to $90°$
(h) less than $90°$ (i) greater than $90°$

6. If $a = 2$, $b = 4$, and $\gamma = 30°$, then $c =$ _____.

7. If $b = 5$, $c = 5$, and $\alpha = 120°$, then $a =$ _____.

8. If $a = 3$, $b = 7$, and $c = 6$, then γ is _____.

9. If $a = \sqrt{3}$, $c = \sqrt{5}$, and $b = 2\sqrt{2}$, then β is _____.

10. If $b = \sqrt{10}$, $a = \sqrt{3}$, and $c = \sqrt{6}$, then β is _____.

Explore and Discover

Exercises 1–4   An integer-sided triangle is one with sides of length a, b, and c, all positive integers. An integer-sided triangle is called a *double-angle triangle* if one of the angles is exactly twice as large as another of the angles. The triple $\{a, b, c\}$ is called a *double-angle triple* if a, b, and c are the sides of a double-angle triangle in which $\beta = 2\alpha$.

1. Show that each of the following is a double-angle triple. (*Hint:* Use the Law of Cosines and recall an identity that relates $\cos 2\alpha$ and $\cos \alpha$.)
   (a) $\{9, 15, 16\}$ (b) $\{9, 12, 7\}$
   (c) $\{9, 21, 40\}$ (d) $\{25, 35, 24\}$
   (e) $\{36, 66, 85\}$ (f) $\{144, 228, 217\}$

2. (a) For each of the triples in Exercise 1, evaluate the quantities $a^2 + ac$ and b^2.
   (b) On the basis of your computations in part (a), guess a general result relating a, b, and c for double-angle triples.

3. Consider the double-angle triples in Exercise 1 and guess a pattern to describe double-angle triples. Check your guess by relating $\cos \alpha$ and $\cos \beta$ for another triple that fits your pattern. (*Hint:* What kind

of number is a? How are a and b related? How do these relations fit with your conjecture in Exercise 2b?)

4. Prove that your guess in Exercise 3 is correct by relating $\cos \alpha$ and $\cos \beta$ for an arbitrary triple that fits your pattern.

Develop Mastery

Round off calculated results to be consistent with the accuracy of the data. See the guidelines stated in Section 7.1. Begin your solution by drawing a diagram.

Exercises 1–20 Three parts of a triangle are given. Find the remaining parts.

1. $a = 35, b = 68, \gamma = 48°$

2. $b = 28, c = 54, \alpha = 75°$

3. $a = 80.5, c = 53.7, \beta = 115.4°$

4. $a = 43.7, c = 58.9, \beta = 125.6°$

5. $a = 4.8, b = 7.3, c = 5.4$

6. $a = 0.43, b = 0.55, c = 0.68$

7. $a = 53.4, b = 42.7, c = 68.4$

8. $a = 75.4, b = 68.5, c = 48.2$

9. $b = 7.45, c = 6.31, \alpha = 53.7°$

10. $a = 5.73, c = 4.58, \beta = 23.6°$

11. $a = 36.4, b = 25.6, \gamma = 34°30'$

12. $b = 73.6, c = 58.1, \alpha = 36°30'$

13. $a = 53, b = 45, c = 28$

14. $a = 36, b = 81, c = 85$

15. $a = 64, b = 57, c = 88$

16. $a = 49, b = 32, c = 58$

17. $a = 45, b = 28, \gamma = 90°$

18. $a = 36, b = 81, \gamma = 90°$.

19. $b = 64, c = 57, \alpha = 90°$

20. $b = 32, c = 49, \alpha = 90°$.

Exercises 21–24 **(a)** Find the altitude from vertex A to side $\overline{BC}$. **(b)** Determine the area of the triangle.

21. $a = 7.3, b = 6.4, \gamma = 43°$

22. $a = 3.5, c = 5.8, \beta = 74°$

23. $a = 5.43, c = 7.52, \beta = 112.4°$

24. $a = 4.58, b = 6.37, \gamma = 125.4°$

Exercises 25–28 Find **(a)** angle α, **(b)** the altitude to side b, **(c)** the area of the triangle.

25. $a = 37.0, b = 62.0, c = 45.0$

26. $a = 4.7, b = 3.5, c = 6.7$

27. $a = 2.45, b = 3.41, c = 4.36$

28. $a = 3.46, b = 5.31, c = 4.27$

29. If $a = 43, b = 65$, and $c = 52$, find the largest angle.

30. If $a = 7.3, b = 6.5$, and $c = 4.2$, find the smallest angle.

31. If $a = 7.2, b = 3.8$, and $\gamma = 68°$, find the perimeter of the triangle.

32. If $b = 7.50$, $c = 6.80$, and $\alpha = 53.0°$, find the perimeter of the triangle.

Exercises 33–34 The coordinates of the vertices of triangle ABC are given. Find **(a)** the perimeter of the triangle rounded off to the nearest whole number, **(b)** the largest angle rounded off to the nearest degree.

33. $A(7, 4), B(-5, 2), C(3, 8)$

34. $A(-5, 3), B(2, -5), C(3, 6)$

Exercises 35–36 The coordinates of the vertices of triangle ABC are given. Find **(a)** the midpoint M of side $\overline{BC}$, **(b)** angles BAM and CAM rounded off to the nearest degree.

35. $A(6, 2), B(-5, 4), C(3, 6)$

36. $A(-3, 4), B(5, -6), C(3, 8)$

Exercises 37–38 Side a, angle γ, and area K of a triangle are given. Find side b. (*Hint:* First find a formula for the area in terms of a, b, and γ.)

37. $a = 36, \gamma = 45°, K = 25$

38. $a = 4.3, \gamma = 36°, K = 3.8$

39. If ABC is a right triangle with $\gamma = 90°$, show that the third equation in the Law of Cosines reduces to $c^2 = a^2 + b^2$, which is consistent with the Pythagorean theorem.

40. In this section the formula for c^2 was derived using the diagram in Figure 7.18, where the altitude from vertex A was inside the triangle. Derive the formula for c^2 when the altitude is outside the triangle, as shown in the diagram. You should get the same formula.

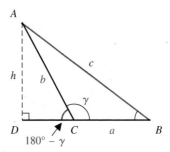

Exercises 41–44   Two sides and an angle opposite one of them are given (*SSA*). Use the quadratic equation approach, as illustrated in Example 5, to solve the problem. If there are two solutions, give both.

41. If $a = 5.4$, $b = 6.8$, and $\alpha = 65°$, find c.

42. If $b = 4.83$, $c = 8.43$, and $\gamma = 124.0°$, find a.

43. If $a = 3.72$, $c = 7.31$, and $\gamma = 48.3°$, find b.

44. If $b = 23$, $c = 35$, and $\beta = 27°$, find a.

45. Given the isosceles triangle shown in the diagram, **(a)** Use the Law of Cosines to show that $r = \dfrac{3}{\sqrt{2 - 2\cos\theta}}$. **(b)** Show that r is also given by $1.5 \csc\left(\frac{\theta}{2}\right)$.

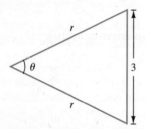

46. A triangle with sides of lengths 40, 60, and 80 has three altitudes. **(a)** What is the length of the shortest altitude? **(b)** Find the area of the triangle. Give results to two significant digits.

47. In a triangle with sides of lengths 12, 16, and 23 **(a)** what is the length of the longest altitude? **(b)** What is the area of the triangle?

48. Katharine walks due east for a distance of 3.0 miles, turns 120° to her left and then walks 4.0 miles in the new direction. How far is she from her starting point?

49. Beginning at 8 A.M. Horacio leaves home and walks due east for 1 hour at the rate of 4 mph, turns 120° to his left, and then walks in the new direction for t hours at the rate of 3 mph. **(a)** Express his distance d from home as a function of t. **(b)** How far is he from home at noon? **(c)** At what time will he be 12 miles from home?

Exercises 50–51   The lengths of the three sides of a triangle, a, b, and c, are related by the equation. Find the angle opposite c.

50. $(a + b + c)(a + b - c) = ab$

51. $(a + b + c)(a + b - c) = (2 + \sqrt{3})ab$

51. The lengths of two sides of a parallelogram are 45 and 63, and one angle is 68°. Find the lengths of the two diagonals.

53. (a) Find the central angle θ of a sector of a circle where the radius is 24.0 and the length of the chord is 18.0 Give the result in radians.
(b) What is the area of the circular sector?

54. Find an equation for the area of a segment of a circle (the shaded region shown in the diagram) in terms of the radius r and central angle θ, where $0 < \theta < \pi$.

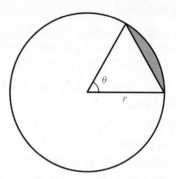

55. Three circles are tangent to each other as shown in the diagram where A, B, and C are the centers and the radii are 3.4, 5.2, and 6.3, respectively. Find the largest angle in triangle ABC.

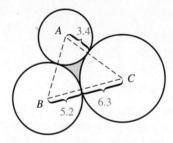

56. Find the area of the shaded region between the circles in the diagram.

57. For the triangle shown in the diagram, M is the midpoint of side $\overline{BC}$, and $|\overline{AB}| = 6$, $|\overline{AC}| = 10$, $|\overline{AM}| = 5$. Find the length of $\overline{BC}$. [*Hint:* Use the Law of Cosines to get $\cos\theta$ in terms of x from $\triangle ABM$ and get $\cos(180° - \theta)$ from $\triangle ACM$.]

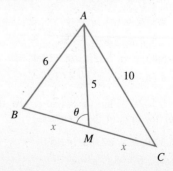

58. Jennifer wishes to find the distance between two points A and D on opposite sides of a lake. See diagram. She locates two accessible points, B and C, and gets the following measurements: $|\overline{AB}| = 426$ ft, $|\overline{BC}| = 537$ ft, $|\overline{CD}| = 562$ ft, $\beta = 106.4°$, $\gamma = 112.5°$. Find the distance from A to D.

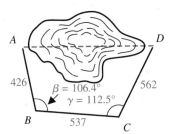

59. Ashley is on the south bank of a river and wishes to determine the distance between points A and B on the north bank. See the diagram. She measures the distance from C to D as 72 meters and the angles as shown in the diagram. Use this information to find the distance from A to B.

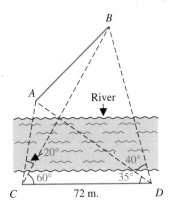

60. In triangle ABC, $a = 4.3$, $b = 5.2$, and $c = 4.1$. If the triangle is inscribed in a circle, find the radius of the circle.

61. In the diagram quadrilateral $OABC$ is inscribed in a quarter circle where $|\overline{AB}| = 4$ and $|\overline{BC}| = 8$. Find the area of the quadrilateral and give your answer in exact form as $a + b\sqrt{2}$ where a and b are whole numbers.

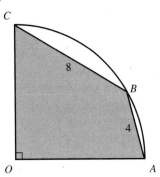

62. A piston is driven by a rotating wheel with a radius of 16.0 cm, as shown in the diagram. The driving arm $\overline{AB}$ is 27.0 cm long and is attached to the piston at B, and pivots at A. Suppose the wheel rotates clockwise at the rate of $12°$ per second. Let t represent the time in seconds and suppose the wheel starts with A located at point E when $t = 0$. If x denotes the displacement of the piston, as shown in the diagram, find x when
(a) $t = 2$ sec, $(\alpha = 24°)$
(b) $t = 10$ sec, $(\alpha = 120°)$
(c) Find an equation that gives x as a function of t.

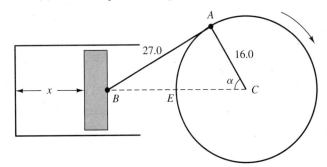

SECTION 7.4	Trigonometry and Complex Numbers

[M]athematics is the science of skillful operations with concepts and rules invented just for this purpose. Most more advanced mathematical concepts, such as complex numbers, algebras, linear operators, Borel sets . . . were so devised that they are apt subjects on which the mathematician can demonstrate his ingenuity and sense of formal beauty.
Eugene P. Wigner

In Section 1.3 we briefly discussed the system of complex numbers as an extension of the system of real numbers. The only direct application of complex numbers that we have made so far in this book is in connection with the zeros of polynomial functions. Trigonometry allows us another way of viewing complex numbers. In this section we discuss the trigonometric or polar form for representing complex numbers and apply it to the task of finding products and quotients. Then we introduce DeMoivre's theorem to find the roots of complex numbers and to explore some geometric relationships.

Recall from Section 1.3 that we may establish a correspondence between the set of complex numbers and the set of points in the plane by letting the complex number $x + yi$ correspond to the point with coordinates (x, y). This identification deals with the **complex plane,** and a point may be labeled either (x, y) or $x + yi$. Real numbers are associated with points on the x-axis, $x = x + 0i \leftrightarrow (x, 0)$, and pure imaginary numbers of the form yi are associated with points on the y-axis, $yi = 0 + yi \leftrightarrow (0, y)$. In the complex plane the x-axis is called the **real axis** and the y-axis is called the **imaginary axis.**

Each point P in the plane may also be identified by a pair of numbers (r, θ), where r is the distance from P to the origin, $|\overline{OP}|$, and θ is the angle from the positive x-axis to the ray $\overline{OP}$. Since θ is in standard position, the coordinates of any point on the terminal side are expressible as $(r \cos \theta, r \sin \theta)$. Thus if P is identified with the complex number $x + yi$, then P has coordinates (x, y) and

$$x = r \cos \theta \quad \text{and} \quad y = r \sin \theta.$$

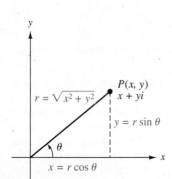

FIGURE 7.23

See Figure 7.23. We may also write the complex number $x + yi$ as

$$x + yi = (r \cos \theta) + i(r \sin \theta) = r(\cos \theta + i \sin \theta).$$

The form $r(\cos \theta + i \sin \theta)$ is called the **trigonometric** or **polar form** of $x + yi$. The nonnegative number r is called the **absolute value** or **modulus,** and θ is the **argument** of the complex number. Any angle that is coterminal with θ is also an argument for the same complex number. Because the coordinates (x, y) are rectangular coordinates, the standard form of a complex number, $x + yi$, is its **rectangular form.** We summarize the relations between rectangular and trigonometric forms of a complex number and rectangular and polar coordinates of a point.

To my astonishment and dismay high school students do not learn complex numbers nowadays, possibly because high school teachers don't know them. The students I met in a recent graduate course never heard of DeMoivre's theorem; even absolute values and complex conjugates made them feel insecure.

Paul Halmos

Trigonometric Form of a Complex Number

Suppose z is the complex number $x + yi$. The rectangular coordinates of z are (x, y) and the polar coordinates of z are (r, θ), where

$$x = r \cos \theta, \quad \text{and} \quad y = r \sin \theta$$

$$r = \sqrt{x^2 + y^2} \quad \text{and} \quad \tan \theta = \frac{y}{x}$$

The trigonometric or polar form of z is given by

$$z = r(\cos \theta + i \sin \theta)$$

The nonnegative number r is the modulus of z, and θ is an argument of z. The complex number zero has a modulus of 0, but is not normally assigned any argument.

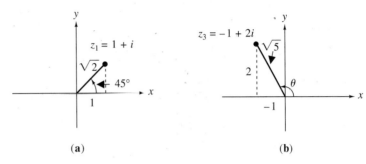

FIGURE 7.24

Solution

The complex numbers are shown in Figure 7.24.

(a) For z, the figure shows that $\theta = 45°$ and $r = \sqrt{1^2 + 1^2} = \sqrt{2}$, so a trigonometric form is $z = \sqrt{2}(\cos 45° + i \sin 45°)$.

(b) For the modulus, $r = \sqrt{(-1)^2 + 2^2} = \sqrt{5}$. From the figure, θ is a second-quadrant angle with $\cos \theta = \frac{-1}{\sqrt{5}}$, so $\theta = \text{Cos}^{-1}\left(\frac{-1}{\sqrt{5}}\right) \approx 116.6°$. Therefore, $w \approx \sqrt{5}(\cos 116.6° + i \sin 116.6°)$. ▲

EXAMPLE 2   Sketch in the complex plane and express in rectangular form.

(a) $z = 2\sqrt{3}(\cos 120° + i \sin 120°)$ **(b)** $w = 2(\cos 3.7 + i \sin 3.7)$

Solution

To sketch a complex number from its polar form, first draw the angle and then locate the point at the distance r along the ray from the origin, as shown in Figure 7.25.

(a) Since $\cos 120° = -\frac{1}{2}$ and $\sin 120° = \frac{\sqrt{3}}{2}$,

$$z = 2\sqrt{3}\left(-\frac{1}{2} + i\frac{\sqrt{3}}{2}\right) = -\sqrt{3} + 3i.$$

(b) In radian mode the calculator returns $\cos 3.7 \approx -0.85$ and $\sin 3.7 \approx -0.53$. Thus an approximate rectangular form for w is $2(-0.85 - 0.53i) \approx -1.7 - 1.1i$. ▲

Trigonometric form gives a very specific representation for a complex number. The modulus r must be nonnegative, and the expression in parentheses must have the precise form $\cos \theta + i \sin \theta$. For example, neither of the complex numbers $-1(\cos 2 - i \sin 2)$ or $1(-\cos 2 + i \sin 2)$ is in trigonometric form.

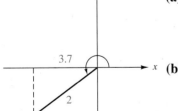

(a)

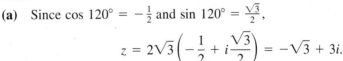

$w = 2(\cos 3.7 + i \sin 3.7)$

(b)

FIGURE 7.25

The next example illustrates how to express such complex numbers in trigono-metric form.

EXAMPLE 3   Express in trigonometric form.

(a) $z = 3(\cos 60° - i \sin 60°)$ **(b)** $w = -3(\sin 38° + i \cos 38°)$

Solution

Strategy: One possibility is to convert each number to rectangular form and plot, then use the diagram to write each in trigonometric form. Reduction formulas should help identify the quadrants and angles.

(a)   First express z in rectangular form.

$$z = 3(\cos 60° - i \sin 60°) = \frac{3}{2} - \frac{3\sqrt{3}}{2}i$$

Now draw a diagram to show z (see Figure 7.26), then find r as follows:

$$r = \sqrt{\left(\frac{3}{2}\right)^2 + \left(-\frac{3\sqrt{3}}{2}\right)^2} = \sqrt{\frac{9}{4} + \frac{27}{4}} = \sqrt{9} = 3.$$

The diagram shows a 30°–60° right triangle, so we may take $\theta = -60°$. Therefore, in trigonometric form,

$$z = 3[\cos (-60°) + i \sin (-60°)].$$

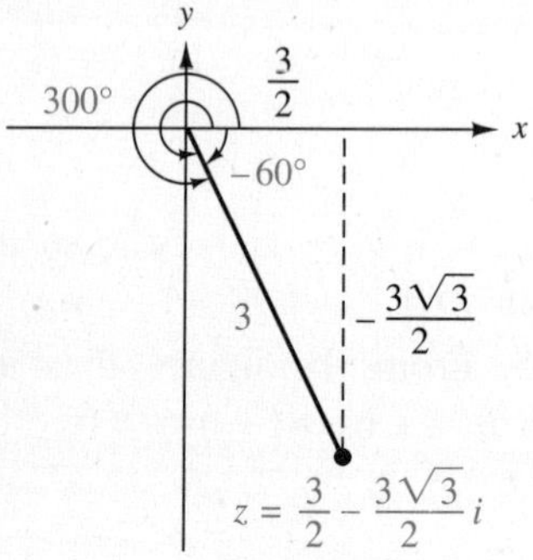

(b) $w = -3(\sin 38° + i \cos 38°) = 3(-\sin 38° - i \cos 38°)$. Find an angle θ such that $\cos \theta = -\sin 38°$ and $\sin \theta = -\cos 38°$. Since both $\cos \theta$ and $\sin \theta$ are negative, θ will be a third-quadrant angle (see Figure 7.27). Use reduction formulas from Section 5.4 to get

$$\cos (270° - t) = -\sin t \qquad \text{and} \qquad \sin (270° - t) = -\cos t$$

Therefore, take $\theta = 270° - 38° = 232°$. In trigonometric form,

$$w = 3(\cos 232° + i \sin 232°). \quad \blacktriangle$$

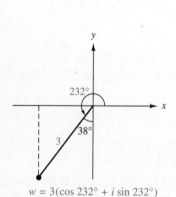

FIGURE 7.26

FIGURE 7.27

Rectangular form is convenient for addition and subtraction of complex numbers, but trigonometric form gives a geometric interpretation of multiplication and division.

Multiplication and Division in Trigonometric Form

Suppose complex numbers z_1 and z_2 are written in trigonometric form:

$$z_1 = r_1(\cos \theta_1 + i \sin \theta_1) \qquad \text{and} \qquad z_2 = r_2(\cos \theta_2 + i \sin \theta_2).$$

To find a trigonometric form for the product $z_1 z_2$, first multiply as complex numbers, and then use the sum identities for $\cos (\theta_1 + \theta_2)$ and $\sin (\theta_1 + \theta_2)$.

$$z_1 z_2 = r_1(\cos \theta_1 + i \sin \theta_1) \cdot r_2(\cos \theta_2 + i \sin \theta_2)$$

$$= r_1 r_2[(\cos \theta_1 \cos \theta_2 - \sin \theta_1 \sin \theta_2) + i(\sin \theta_1 \cos \theta_2 + \cos \theta_1 \sin \theta_2)]$$

$$= r_1 r_2[\cos (\theta_1 + \theta_2) + i \sin (\theta_1 + \theta_2)]$$

The quotient $\frac{z_1}{z_2}$ can be handled in much the same way, and the derivation is left to the exercises (see Exercise 65).

Product and Quotient in Trigonometric Form

Suppose z_1 and z_2 are complex numbers expressed in the form

$$z_1 = r_1(\cos \theta_1 + i \sin \theta_1) \quad \text{and} \quad z_2 = r_2(\cos \theta_2 + i \sin \theta_2).$$

The product of z_1 and z_2 is

$$z_1 z_2 = r_1 r_2 [\cos (\theta_1 + \theta_2) + i \sin (\theta_1 + \theta_2)]. \tag{1}$$

If $z_2 \neq 0$, then the quotient $\frac{z_1}{z_2}$ is

$$\frac{z_1}{z_2} = \left(\frac{r_1}{r_2} \right) [\cos (\theta_1 - \theta_2) + i \sin (\theta_1 - \theta_2)]. \tag{2}$$

The product and quotient of two complex numbers in trigonometric form may be interpreted geometrically.

When multiplying two complex numbers in trigonometric form, the modulus is the product of the moduli, and the argument is the sum of the arguments.

When dividing two complex numbers in trigonometric form, the modulus is the quotient of the moduli, and the argument is the difference of the arguments.

When multiplying add arguments; when dividing subtract arguments.

Strategy: Both product and quotients are easier to compute from trigonometric forms, so begin by expressing all three in trigonometric form and then use Equations 1 and 2.

EXAMPLE 4 Given $z_1 = 1 + i$, $z_2 = 2 - 2\sqrt{3}i$, and $z_3 = -\sqrt{3} - i$. Evaluate in both trigonometric form and rectangular form.

(a) $z_1 z_2$ **(b)** $\frac{z_2}{z_3}$.

Solution

Follow the strategy. Proceeding in a manner similar to the solution in Example 1,

$$z_1 = \sqrt{2}(\cos 45° + i \sin 45°), \qquad z_2 = 4(\cos 300° + i \sin 300°)$$

$$z_3 = 2(\cos 210° + i\ 210°)$$

(a) For $z_1 z_2$, Equation 1 gives

$$z_1 z_2 = \sqrt{2} \cdot 4[\cos (45° + 300°) + i \sin (45° + 300°)]$$

$$= 4\sqrt{2}(\cos 345° + i \sin 345°).$$

To express the product in rectangular form, you can evaluate $\cos 345°$ and $\sin 345°$, but to get exact form it is simpler to multiply directly, as in Section 1.3:

$$z_1 z_2 = (1 + i)(2 - 2\sqrt{3}i) = (2 + 2\sqrt{3}) + (2 - 2\sqrt{3})i$$

Therefore, the product $z_1 z_2$ in trigonometric form is $4\sqrt{2}(\cos 345° + i \sin 345°)$. In rectangular form it is $(2 + 2\sqrt{3}) + (2 - 2\sqrt{3})i$.

(b) Using the trigonometric form of z_2 and z_3 and Equation 2,

$$\frac{z_2}{z_3} = \left(\frac{4}{2}\right)[\cos(300° - 210°) + i \sin(300° - 210°)]$$

$$= 2(\cos 90° + i \sin 90°).$$

Since $\cos 90° = 0$ and $\sin 90° = 1$,

$$\frac{z_2}{z_3} = 2(0 + i \cdot 1) = 2i.$$

The two forms for $\frac{z_2}{z_3}$ are $2(\cos 90° + i \sin 90°)$ and $2i$.   ▲

DeMoivre's Theorem

By repeated application of Equations 1 and 2, we may derive an important theorem for computing powers and roots of complex numbers. Let $z = r(\cos \theta + i \sin \theta)$. By repeated application of Equation 1, it is easy to see that

$$z^2 = r^2(\cos 2\theta + i \sin 2\theta)$$

$$z^3 = r^3(\cos 3\theta + i \sin 3\theta)$$

$$z^4 = r^4(\cos 4\theta + i \sin 4\theta).$$

For negative exponents, Equation 2 gives

$$z^{-1} = \frac{1}{z} = \frac{1(\cos 0° + i \sin 0°)}{r(\cos \theta + i \sin \theta)} = r^{-1}[\cos(-\theta) + i \sin(-\theta)]$$

Similarly,

$$z^{-2} = r^{-2}[\cos(-2\theta) + i \sin(-2\theta)].$$

The pattern exhibited in the above computations holds for every integer n. The result is known as **DeMoivre's theorem.** A formal proof can be made by mathematical induction (see Exercise 34, Section 8.4).

DeMoivre's Theorem

Suppose n is any integer and $z = r(\cos \theta + i \sin \theta)$, then

$$z^n = r^n(\cos n\theta + i \sin n\theta).$$

EXAMPLE 5   Use DeMoivre's theorem to calculate

(a) $(1 + i)^4$ **(b)** $\left(\dfrac{-1 + \sqrt{3}i}{2}\right)^6$.

Solution

(a) If $z = 1 + i$, then, from Example 1, in polar form $z = \sqrt{2}(\cos 45° + i \sin 45°)$. Apply DeMoivre's theorem:

Historical Note

DEMOIVRE'S THEOREM AND EULER'S FUNCTIONS

The theorem credited to Abraham DeMoivre (pictured above) was actually proved by Leonhard Euler.

It soon becomes apparent to anyone who considers the history of mathematics that new discoveries seldom occurred in the order we learn them in school. We observed in the Historical Note in Section 5.3 that sines and cosines did not originate as functions; they were lengths of chords of circles whose value depended on the size of the circles. Likewise, logarithms were not viewed as inverses of exponential functions, but as computational aids for trigonometric calculations.

Credit for the discovery of new theorems or ideas is often given to individuals who may have had little to do with the original discoveries. DeMoivre's theorem was known to, and used by, Abraham DeMoivre (1667–1754), but he never formally proved it. DeMoivre was born in France, but spent most of his life in England. He was closely acquainted with both Newton and Leibnitz. His name is attached to a trigonometric

identity that was certainly not as important to him as his work in probability. A probability frequency distribution usually attributed to Laplace or Gauss was first described by DeMoivre and might more properly be called the DeMoivre distribution.

Leonhard Euler, on the other hand, did state and prove DeMoivre's identity in a paper DeMoivre quoted. Euler is the one who first treated sines and cosines as *functions*. He used the unit circle for his definitions, freeing these functions from dependence on the size of the circle. Furthermore, Euler used DeMoivre's identity to derive relationships among trigonometric, exponential, and logarithmic functions. He derived the equation $e^{ix} = \cos x + i \sin x$; thus he saw that exponentials may be viewed as disguised trigonometry, and vice versa. Mathematicians still marvel at Euler's insight and intuition.

$$(1 + i)^4 = (\sqrt{2})^4 [\cos(4 \cdot 45)° + i \sin(4 \cdot 45)°]$$
$$= 4(\cos 180° + i \sin 180°) = 4(-1 + i \cdot 0) = -4.$$

Hence $(1 + i)^4 = -4$.

(b) A trigonometric form for $\frac{-1 \sqrt{3}i}{2}$ is $1(\cos 120° + i \sin 120°)$. Use DeMoivre's theorem:

$$\left(\frac{-1 + \sqrt{3}i}{2}\right)^6 = 1^6 [\cos(6 \cdot 120°) + i \sin(6 \cdot 120°)]$$

$$= 1(\cos 720° + i \sin 720°)$$

$$= 1(\cos 0° + i \sin 0°) = 1.$$

Therefore, $(\frac{-1 + \sqrt{3}i}{2})^6$ is another name for the number 1. ▲

Finding Roots of Complex Numbers

In Example 5, we found that $1 + i$ is a complex number whose fourth power is -4, that is, $1 + i$ is a fourth root of -4. Similarly, $\frac{-1 + \sqrt{3}i}{2}$ is a sixth root of 1.

We already know that 1 and -1 are sixth roots of 1, because $1^6 = 1$ and $(-1)^6 = 1$. According to the Fundamental Theorem of Algebra in Chapter 3, the polynomial equation $x^6 = 1$ has six roots, so there should be three more in addition to 1, -1, and $\frac{-1 + \sqrt{3}i}{2}$. DeMoivre's theorem can be used to find all of the nth roots of any complex number z. For a given complex number z, we can find all roots of the equation $x^n = z$.

Let the given complex number z be written in trigonometric form as $z = r(\cos \theta + i \sin \theta)$ and suppose that w is a solution to the equation $x^n = z$. The number w also has a trigonometric form, say $w = R(\cos \alpha + i \sin \alpha)$. We wish to determine the modulus R and the argument α so that w satisfies the equation $x^n = z$. Using DeMoivre's theorem, $w^n = R^n(\cos n\alpha + i \sin n\alpha)$. If $w^n = z$, then

$$R^n(\cos n\alpha + i \sin n\alpha) = r(\cos \theta + i \sin \theta) \qquad \textbf{(3)}$$

Two complex numbers in trigonometric form are equal if and only if their moduli are equal and their arguments are coterminal. Thus, from Equation 3 we must have $R^n = r$. To find the modulus R, we are interested only in the nonnegative solution to $R^n = r$, so $R = r^{1/n}$. It follows that all roots of the equation $x^n = z$ have the same modulus, namely the positive real number $r^{1/n}$.

To satisfy Equation 3, the angle $n\alpha$ must be equal to one of the angles that are coterminal with θ. This includes any angle of the form $\theta + k \cdot 360°$, where k can be any integer. We must have $n\alpha = \theta + k \cdot 360°$, so

$$\alpha = \frac{\theta}{n} + k \cdot \frac{360°}{n}.$$

As k ranges through $0, 1, 2, \ldots, n - 1$, we get n distinct arguments. Hence any given nonzero complex number has n distinct complex nth roots.

Roots of a Complex Number

Suppose n is any positive integer, then the nonzero complex number

$$z = r(\cos \theta + i \sin \theta)$$

has exactly n district n^{th} roots, which are given by

$$w_k = \sqrt[n]{r}\left[\cos\left(\frac{\theta}{n} + k \cdot \frac{360°}{n} \right) + i \sin\left(\frac{\theta}{n} + k \cdot \frac{360°}{n} \right) \right] \qquad \textbf{(4)}$$

where $k = 0, 1, 2, \ldots, n - 1$.

Geometrically, the n roots of a complex number all lie on the circle in the complex plane centered at the origin with radius $\sqrt[n]{r}$. Furthermore, they are equally spaced, like the spokes of a wheel, starting with w_0, at arguments differing by $\frac{360°}{n}$. We illustrate this in the next example, in which we find all of the sixth roots of 1.

EXAMPLE 6   Find the sixth roots of 1 and locate them graphically in the complex plane.

Solution

With trigonometric form for 1, $1 = 1(\cos 0° + i \sin 0°)$, use Equation 4 to get the sixth roots of 1:

$$w_k = \sqrt[6]{1}\left[\cos\left(\frac{0°}{6} + k\frac{360°}{6}\right) + i \sin\left(\frac{0°}{6} + k\frac{360°}{6}\right)\right]$$

$$= 1[\cos(k \cdot 60°) + i \sin(k \cdot 60°)]$$

For $k = 0, 1, \ldots, 5$, the arguments are $0°, 60°, 120°, \ldots, 300°$. The six roots of 1 are given by

$$w_0 = 1(\cos 0° + i \sin 0°) \qquad w_1 = 1(\cos 60° + i \sin 60°)$$

$$w_2 = 1(\cos 120° + i \sin 120°), \qquad w_3 = 1(\cos 180° + i \sin 180°)$$

$$w_4 = 1(\cos 240° + i \sin 240°) \qquad w_5 = 1(\cos 300° + i \sin 300°)$$

In rectangular form,

$$w_0 = 1 \qquad w_1 = \frac{1 + \sqrt{3}i}{2} \qquad w_2 = \frac{-1 + \sqrt{3}i}{2}$$

$$w_3 = -1 \qquad w_4 = \frac{-1 - \sqrt{3}i}{2} \qquad w_5 = \frac{1 - \sqrt{3}i}{2}.$$

Hence, there are two real roots and two conjugate complex pairs w_1, w_5 and w_2, w_4. The roots are shown graphically in Figure 7.28. ▲

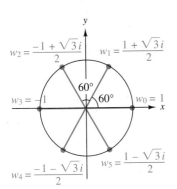

$w_2 = \dfrac{-1 + \sqrt{3}i}{2}$ $w_1 = \dfrac{1 + \sqrt{3}i}{2}$

$w_3 = -1$ $w_0 = 1$

$w_4 = \dfrac{-1 - \sqrt{3}i}{2}$ $w_5 = \dfrac{1 - \sqrt{3}i}{2}$

FIGURE 7.28

EXAMPLE 7   **(a)** Solve the equation $x^4 + 1 = 0$. **(b)** By pairing conjugate roots, factor $x^4 + 1$ as a product of quadratic factors with real coefficients.

Solution

(a) Rewrite the given equation as $x^4 = -1$, and find the fourth roots of -1, which may be expressed in polar form as $-1 = 1(\cos 180° + i \sin 180°)$. Using Equation 4 the roots are w_0, w_1, w_2, and w_3, where

$$w_k = \sqrt[4]{1}\left[\cos\left(\frac{180°}{4} + k\frac{360°}{4}\right) + i \sin\left(\frac{180°}{4} + k\frac{360°}{4}\right)\right]$$

$$= 1[\cos(45° + k \cdot 90°) + i \sin(45° + k \cdot 90°)].$$

Thus,

$$w_0 = \cos 45° + i \sin 45° \qquad w_1 = \cos 135° + i \sin 135°$$

$$w_2 = \cos 225° + i \sin 225° \qquad w_3 = \cos 315° + i \sin 315°.$$

In rectangular form,

$$w_0 = \frac{1 + i}{\sqrt{2}} \qquad w_1 = \frac{-1 + i}{\sqrt{2}} \qquad w_2 = \frac{-1 - i}{\sqrt{2}} \qquad w_3 = \frac{1 - i}{\sqrt{2}}.$$

(b) Clearly w_0 and w_3 are conjugates and w_1 and w_2 are conjugates. By direct multiplication,

$$(x - w_0)(x - w_3) = x^2 - \sqrt{2}x + 1$$
$$(x - w_1)(x - w_2) = x^2 + \sqrt{2}x + 1.$$

For the desired factored form,

$$x^4 + 1 = [(x - w_0)(x - w_3)][(x - w_1)(x - w_2)]$$
$$= (x^2 - \sqrt{2}x + 1)(x^2 + \sqrt{2}x + 1) \quad \blacktriangle$$

EXERCISES 7.4

Check Your Understanding

Exercises 1–5 True or False. Give reasons for your conclusion.

1. A trigonometric form for $1 - i$ is $\sqrt{2}(\cos 45° - i \sin 45°)$.

2. If z is any point in QI of the complex plane, then $-\bar{z}$ is in QII.

3. A cube root of $\frac{1}{2} + \frac{\sqrt{3}}{2}i$ is $\cos 20° + i \sin 20°$.

4. For any angle θ, $(\cos \theta - i \sin \theta)^4 = \cos 4\theta - i \sin 4\theta$.

5. $\left(\frac{1}{\sqrt{2}} - \frac{1}{\sqrt{2}}i\right)^{16}$ is equal to 1.

Exercises 6–10 Complete the sentence by selecting from the list below *all choices* that make the statement true.

(a) 1 (b) -1 (c) $-i$ (d) $\frac{1 + \sqrt{3}i}{2}$
(e) $\frac{1 + \sqrt{3}i}{2}$ (f) $2(\cos 315° + i \sin 315°)$
(g) $2(\cos 120° + i \sin 120°)$
(h) $2(-\cos 60° + i \sin 60°)$

6. $\left(\frac{\sqrt{3}}{2} - \frac{1}{2}i\right)^3 = $ _____.

7. $\left(\frac{\sqrt{3}}{2} - \frac{1}{2}i\right)^6 = $ _____.

8. $\left(-\frac{\sqrt{3}}{2} + \frac{1}{2}i\right)^{10} = $ _____.

9. $-1 + \sqrt{3}i = $ _____.

10. $[\sqrt{2}(\cos 60° + i \sin 60°)]^2 = $ _____.

Explore and Discover

Exercises 1–4 A Gaussian integer is a complex number of the form $a + bi$, where a and b are integers. We will call a Gaussian integer a Pythagorean Gaussian integer (a PGi) if its modulus is also an integer; that is, $a + bi$ is a PGi if and only if $a^2 + b^2$ is a perfect square. There are four Pythagorean Gaussian integers associated with the Pythagorean triple $\{a, b, c\}$. For example, $8 \pm 15i$ and $-8 \pm 15i$ are the four associated with the triple $\{8, 15, 17\}$.

1. (a) Find another Pythagorean triple in the family that contains $\{3, 4, 5\}$, $\{5, 12, 13\}$, and $\{9, 40, 41\}$.
   (b) Find a formula that describes all of the triples of the family in part (a). (*Hint:* $c = b + 1$.)
   (c) Repeat parts (a) and (b) for the family that contains $\{39, 80, 89\}$, $\{45, 108, 117\}$, and $\{51, 140, 149\}$.

2. (a) Take a Pythagorean Gaussian integer z associated with one triple in the family in Exercise 1(a) and another PGi w associated with another triple of the same family. Verify that zw is a PGi.
   (b) Take PGi's z and w associated with triples from the family in Exercise 1(c) and check zw.
   (c) Repeat part (b) if z comes from the first family of triples and w comes from the second family of triples (that is, take one from the family in Exercise 1(a) and one from 1(c)).

3. Suppose that both z and w are PGis. On the basis of your computations in Exercise 2, does it appear that zw will also be a PGi? Either explain why you are convinced that zw is a PGi or find a counterexample to show that zw need not always be a PGi. (*Hint:* Consider z and w in trigonometric form.)

4. Explain why the four PGis associated with a given Pythagorean triple are located on a single circle in the complex plane. Where is the product of two such PGis located? Explain.

Develop Mastery

Exercises 1–8   Sketch in the complex plane and express in trigonometric form using degree measure.

1. (a) -3, (b) $-i$

2. (a) $1 - i$, (b) $1 + \sqrt{3}i$

3. (a) $3 + 5i$, (b) $2 - 3i$

4. (a) $2 + 3i$, (b) $4 - i$

5. (a) $2i + \sqrt{3}$, (b) $i - i^2$

6. (a) $\frac{i-1}{2}$, (b) $i^3 + i^2$

7. (a) $\frac{1}{i}$, (b) $\frac{1}{1+i}$

8. (a) $\frac{1+i}{1-i}$, (b) $\frac{1-\sqrt{3}i}{1+\sqrt{3}i}$

Exercises 9–14   Sketch in the complex plane and express in rectangular form.

9. $2(\cos 45° + i \sin 45°)$

10. $\sqrt{3}(\cos 150° + i \sin 150°)$

11. $4(\cos 450° + i \sin 450°)$

12. $2[\cos(-270°) + i \sin(-270°)]$

13. $1[\cos(-120°) + i \sin(-120°)]$

14. $\sqrt{2}(\cos 480° + i \sin 480°)$

Exercises 15–20   Determine why the number is not in trigonometric form, and then express it in trigonometric form.

15. $2(\cos 45° - i \sin 45°)$

16. $-\sqrt{3}(\cos 150° + i \sin 150°)$

17. $-4(\cos 450° + i \sin 450°)$

18. $2(\cos 36° - i \sin 36°)$

19. $\sin 60° - i \cos 60°$

20. $-(\sin 30° - i \cos 30°)$

Exercises 21–24   Perform the indicated operation and express the result in both trigonometric and rectangular form. (*Hint:* To apply the product and quotient formulas, the numbers must first be in trigonometric form.)

21. $(\cos 17° + i \sin 17°)(\cos 43° + i \sin 43°)$

22. $(\cos 47° - i \sin 47°)(\cos 43° - i \sin 43°)$

23. $\dfrac{\cos 47° + i \sin 47°}{\cos 13° - i \sin 13°}$

24. $\dfrac{8(\cos 150° + i \sin 150°)}{2(\cos 30° + i \sin 30°)}$

Exercises 25–36   Let $z_1 = \sqrt{3} + i$ and $z_2 = \dfrac{-1 + \sqrt{3}i}{2}$. Perform the indicated operation and express the result in both trigonometric and rectangular form. Recall that $\bar{z}$ denotes the complex conjugate of z; that is, if $z = a + bi$, then $\bar{z} = a - bi$.

25. $z_1 z_2$

26. $\bar{z}_1 \bar{z}_2$

27. $\frac{z_1}{z_2}$

28. $\frac{1}{z_2}$

29. $\frac{z_1}{\bar{z}_2}$

30. $z_1 + 2\bar{z}_2$

31. $(z_1)^3$

32. $(z_2)^3$

33. $\left(\frac{z_1}{z_2}\right)^3$

34. $\left(\frac{1}{z_2}\right)^6$

35. $\left(\frac{z_1}{\bar{z}_2}\right)^3$

36. $(z_1 + 2z_2)^4$

Exercises 37–50   Perform the indicated operation and express the result in trigonometric and rectangular form. Give the result in exact form when it is reasonable to do so; otherwise in decimal form with numbers rounded off to two decimal places.

37. $(\cos 30° + i \sin 30°)^4$

38. $[\cos(-45°) + i \sin(-45°)]^4$

39. $(\cos 40° + i \sin 40°)^{-3}$

40. $(\cos 18° + i \sin 18°)^{-5}$

41. $\dfrac{16}{[2(\cos 45° + i \sin 45°)]^4}$

42. $\dfrac{81}{[3(\cos 15° + i \sin 15°)]^4}$

43. $[2(\cos 15° + i \sin 15°)]^4$

44. $[-2(\cos 45° + i \sin 45°)]^4$

45. $(1 - i)^8$ **46.** $[-\sqrt{2} + \sqrt{2}i]^4$

47. $[-\sqrt{2} + \sqrt{2}i]^{-2}$ **48.** $(2 - i)^4$

49. $\dfrac{1}{(1 + \sqrt{3}i)^6}$ **50.** $\dfrac{(1 + 2i)^4}{(1 - 2i)^2}$

Exercises 51–54   Find the cube roots of the complex number and locate all roots graphically on the complex plane.

51. $-i$ **52.** $-1 - i$

53. -1 **54.** $2(\cos 30° + i \sin 30°)$

Exercises 55–60   Solve the equation.

55. $x^5 = 1$ **56.** $x^4 + (\sqrt{3} - i) = 0$

57. $x^4 + i = 0$ **58.** $x^2 = 3 + 4i$

59. $x^2 = 3 - 4i$ **60.** $x^2 = -1 + 2i$

61. Solve the equation $x^4 - 2x^2 + 2 = 0$. (*Hint:* Use the quadratic formula to solve for x^2, then find x.)

62. Solve the equation $x^2 - ix + 2 = 0$. (*Hint:* Use the quadratic formula.)

63. Solve the equation $x^2 - 2ix - 2 = 0$.

64. In Example 6 we solved the equation $x^6 - 1 = 0$ by finding the sixth roots of 1. The equation may also be solved by factoring. As a difference of squares, $x^6 - 1 = (x^3 + 1)(x^3 - 1)$. Each factor may be further factored as a sum or difference of cubes. Find the zeros of the resulting quadratic factors and compare the results with Example 6.

65. Use identities for $\cos(\theta_1 - \theta_2)$ and $\sin(\theta_1 - \theta_2)$ to establish the quotient formula for two complex numbers in trigonometric form.

Exercises 66–68   Given that $x + \frac{1}{x} = 1$, we define E_1, E_2, E_3, . . . by

$$E_1 = x + \frac{1}{x}, \quad E_2 = x^2 + \frac{1}{x^2}, \quad E_3 = x^3 + \frac{1}{x^3}, \ldots$$

Exercises 66 and 67 suggest two different approaches to evaluating E_2, E_3, ...

66. Given that $E_1 = 1$, for E_2, multiply $(x + \frac{1}{x})$ by $(x + \frac{1}{x})$ and use the result to find $x^2 + \frac{1}{x^2}$. For E_3, multiply $(x^2 + \frac{1}{x^2})$ by $(x + \frac{1}{x})$ and use the result to find E_3. Continue in a similar manner to find E_4, E_5, ...

67. Solve the equation $x + \frac{1}{x} = 1$ and show that one of the roots is $\frac{1}{2} + \frac{\sqrt{3}}{2}i$. If $w = \frac{1}{2} + \frac{\sqrt{3}}{2}i$, express w in polar form and use DeMoivre's theorem to find $w^2 + w^{-2}$, $w^3 + w^{-3}$, ...

68. Use the method of Exercise 67 to find **(a)** a general expression for E_n, **(b)** E_{10}, **(c)** E_{24}, **(d)** E_{45}.

SECTION 7.5   *Vectors*

....

I was always interested in practical applications. . . . At Westinghouse, Varga and I related vector lattices to nuclear reactors.
  Garrett Birkhoff

Introduction and Definition

This short introduction foreshadows a very long subject. Vectors are becoming more and more common in applications of mathematics. Entire books are devoted to vector applications; vector analysis forms a significant portion of most calculus books and many introductory physics and engineering texts; courses in linear algebra develop tools to handle vectors and matrices for applications in business and the social and natural sciences as well as the traditional physical sciences. Although our treatment is limited to two-dimensional vectors, the ideas are fundamental to all of vector analysis.

We can describe many of the things we deal with in the real world by a single number; distance, area, mass, volume, time, temperature, etc. These numbers answer questions of magnitude such as how much, how long, how fast, how heavy?

Many questions, however, require more than a single number. Both magnitude and direction may be vital:

"But Officer, I was only doing 20 miles an hour!"   "Yes, but this is a one-way street, and you were going the wrong way."

In birling, two competitors get on a floating log and set the log spinning. The object is to use the spin to make your opponent lose balance and end up in the water. The direction of the spin is at least as important as the strength of the thrust applied.

Quantities that have both magnitude and direction are called **vectors.** We restrict ourselves here to vectors that can be specified by ordered pairs of numbers. The vectors considered in this section can all be represented by directed line segments in the plane.

To begin, we give a definition.

Definition: Vectors

A vector **v** is an ordered pair of real numbers, denoted $\langle a, b \rangle$. The individual numbers a and b are called the **components** of **v.** The **magnitude** of **v,** denoted by $|\mathbf{v}|$, is the number $\sqrt{a^2 + b^2}$, and the **direction** of **v** is the direction in the plane from the origin to point (a, b). Vector notation looks like

$$\mathbf{v} = \langle a, b \rangle \qquad \text{and} \qquad |\mathbf{v}| = \sqrt{a^2 + b^2}.$$

Equality of Vectors

For vectors $\mathbf{u} = \langle a, b \rangle$ and $\mathbf{v} = \langle c, d \rangle$, we say that **u** and **v** are **equal** if and only if $a = c$ and $b = d$. Two vectors are equal if and only if their corresponding components are equal.

Geometric Representations of Vectors

It is customary to represent a vector as a directed line segment, as shown in Figure 7.29, where we may also denote vector **v** by **PQ.** While a vector is technically just a pair of numbers, we will also occasionally use the name vector for a directed line segment that represents the vector, so that we may write $\mathbf{v} = \mathbf{PQ}$. P is the **initial point** (or tail) and Q is the **terminal point** (or tip or head). The length of the directed line segment is the magnitude of the vector, and the arrow indicates the direction. The components of the vector **PQ** are given by

$$\mathbf{PQ} = \langle x_2 - x_1, y_2 - y_1 \rangle, \text{ for the points } P(x_1, y_1) \text{ and } Q(x_2, y_2). \qquad \textbf{(1)}$$

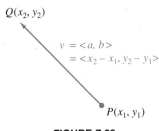

$$Q(x_2, y_2)$$
$$v = <a, b>$$
$$= <x_2 - x_1, y_2 - y_1>$$
$$P(x_1, y_1)$$

FIGURE 7.29

It follows that the vector $\mathbf{v} = \langle a, b \rangle$ can be represented just as well by any other directed line segment **RS** for which the components, the changes in coordinates going from R to S, are a and b, respectively. This means that **v** can be represented by any directed segment that has the same length and direction. If the two directed line segments **RS** and **PQ** represent the same vector, we write $\mathbf{RS} = \mathbf{PQ}$.

In a coordinate system it is often convenient to represent the vector $\mathbf{v} = \langle a, b \rangle$ by a line segment with its initial point at the origin, in which case the terminal point must be the point with coordinates (a, b), as in Figure 7.30 for Example 1. We will call such a representation the **standard representation** or **standard position** for **v.** The **angle between two vectors** is the angle between standard representations of the vectors.

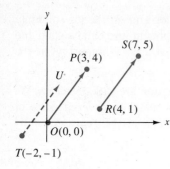

FIGURE 7.30

EXAMPLE 1   Points $O(0, 0)$, $P(3, 4)$, $R(4, 1)$, $S(7, 5)$, and $T(-2, -1)$ are shown in Figure 7.30. Suppose **v** is the vector $\langle 3, 4 \rangle$, so $\mathbf{v} = \mathbf{OP}$. **(a)** Find the components and the magnitude of **v**. **(b)** Show that **RS** represents the same vector **v**. **(c)** Find the point U such that $\mathbf{TU} = \mathbf{v}$.

Solution

(a)   The components of **v** are 3 and 4. Its magnitude is

$$|\mathbf{v}| = \sqrt{3^2 + 4^2} = \sqrt{25} = 5.$$

(b)   From Equation 1, $\mathbf{RS} = \langle 7 - 4, 5 - 1 \rangle = \langle 3, 4 \rangle$, so $\mathbf{RS} = \mathbf{v}$.

(c)   To have $\mathbf{TU} = \mathbf{v}$, the vector **TU** must have components $\langle 3, 4 \rangle$. If **U** has coordinates (u, w), this implies that

$$\mathbf{TU} = \langle u + 2, w + 1 \rangle = \langle 3, 4 \rangle,$$

so by the definition of equality of vectors, $u + 2 = 3$ and $w + 1 = 4$. Thus U has coordinates $(1, 3)$. The directed line segment **TU** is shown in Figure 7.30.   ▲

Algebra of Vectors

The standard operations for vectors include **vector addition** and multiplication of a vector by a number (called **scalar multiplication,** to emphasize that we are not multiplying two vectors). Two other kinds of product can be defined for some vectors, the **dot product** and the **cross product,** but we will not discuss either of them here.

Definition: Vector Addition and Multiplication by a Scalar

Given vectors $\mathbf{v} = \langle a, b \rangle$ and $\mathbf{w} = \langle c, d \rangle$, the sum of **v** and **w** is a vector whose components are the sums of the corresponding components of **v** and **w**.

$$\mathbf{v} + \mathbf{w} = \langle a + c, b + d \rangle.$$

If k is any real number, the scalar product $k\mathbf{v}$ is defined by

$$k\mathbf{v} = \langle ka, kb \rangle.$$

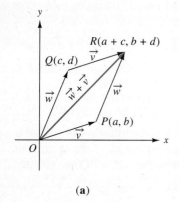

(a)

(b)

FIGURE 7.31

Thus, to add two vectors, add components, and to multiply a vector by a number, multiply both components by the number. The geometric interpretation of vector addition and scalar multiplication is immediate. If $\mathbf{v} = \langle a, b \rangle$ and $\mathbf{w} = \langle c, d \rangle$, then their standard representations are directed line segments **OP** and **OQ** as shown in Figure 7.31. It follows by the definition that their sum $\mathbf{v} + \mathbf{w}$ is represented by the directed line segment **OR**, which is the diagonal of the parallelogram with adjacent edges OP and OQ. In the parallelogram $OPRQ$, the directed line segment **QR** is another representation of **v** and **PR** is another representation of **w**. Thus the vector sum $\mathbf{v} + \mathbf{w}$ is represented by the diagonal of the parallelogram. This is the **parallelogram method** of adding vectors.

> ### Parallelogram Method of Adding Vectors
>
> For a representation of the vector sum **v** + **w**, take any directed line segment **PQ** to represent **v** and a directed line segment **QR** to represent **w** (with the tail of **w** at the tip of **v**). The directed line segment **PR** represents the sum **v** + **w**. It should be obvious that the vector sum satisfies **w** + **v** = **v** + **w** and (**u** + **v**) + **w** = **u** + (**v** + **w**).

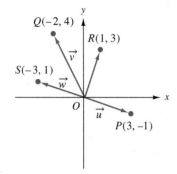

FIGURE 7.32

> **EXAMPLE 2**   Given vectors **u** = $\langle 3, -1 \rangle$, **v** = $\langle -2, 4 \rangle$, and **w** = $\langle -3, 1 \rangle$, find the vector sums **u** + **v** and **u** + **w**. Show the sums as directed line segments in standard position.

Solution

From the definition of vector addition, **u** + **v** = $\langle 3 - 2, -1 + 4 \rangle = \langle 1, 3 \rangle$ and **u** + **w** = $\langle 3 - 3, -1 + 1 \rangle = \langle 0, 0 \rangle$ = **0**. Figure 7.32 shows standard representations for **u, v**, and **w**. The parallelogram method tells us that **OR** represents **u** + **v**, but **u** + **w** is the zero vector, and we cannot show a vector of length zero on the diagram.   ▲

It is often convenient to use polar representation for a point in the plane to express a vector **v** = $\langle a, b \rangle$. The terminal point of **v** in standard position is the point with coordinates (a, b). As Figure 7.33 shows, the coordinates (a, b) can be expressed in terms of the length of the vector, r, and the angle θ from the positive x-axis to the segment that represents **v** in standard position. Then

$$\mathbf{v} = \langle a, b \rangle = \langle r \cos \theta, r \sin \theta \rangle,$$

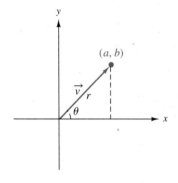

FIGURE 7.33

where $a^2 + b^2 = r^2$ and $\tan \theta = \dfrac{b}{a}$.

> **EXAMPLE 3**   For the vectors **u** = $\langle 3, -1 \rangle$ and **v** = $\langle -2, 4 \rangle$, find the angle between **u** and **v**.

Solution

By the definition of the angle between vectors, find the angle between standard representations, the angle $\theta = \angle QOP$ in Figure 7.34. The Law of Cosines can help if you have the lengths of the three sides of the triangle QOP. The lengths of two of the sides are the lengths of the vectors **u** and **v**, and the distance formula can provide the length of $\overline{QP}$.

$$|\mathbf{u}| = \sqrt{3^2 + (-1)^2} = \sqrt{10} \qquad |\mathbf{v}| = \sqrt{(-2)^2 + 4^2} = \sqrt{20}$$
$$|\overline{QP}| = \sqrt{(3 + 2)^2 + (-1 - 4)^2} = \sqrt{50}.$$

From the Law of Cosines,

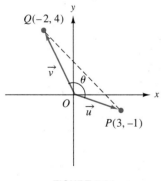

FIGURE 7.34

$$\cos \theta = \frac{10 + 20 - 50}{2\sqrt{10}\sqrt{20}} = \frac{-1}{\sqrt{2}} \quad \text{so} \quad \theta = \frac{3\pi}{4}, \text{ or } 135°.$$

Alternative Solution

Using the polar representations for $\mathbf{v}$ and $\mathbf{u}$ where $\mathbf{v} = \langle r_1 \cos \theta_1, r_1 \sin \theta_1 \rangle$ and $\mathbf{u} = \langle r_2 \cos \theta_2, r_2 \sin \theta_2 \rangle$, the angle θ is given by $\theta = \theta_1 - \theta_2$. See Figure 7.34, and so $\tan \theta_1 = -2$ and $\tan \theta_2 = -\frac{1}{3}$. Using identity (I-11),

$$\tan \theta = \tan(\theta_1 - \theta_2) = \frac{\tan \theta_1 - \tan \theta_2}{1 + \tan \theta_1 \tan \theta_2} = \frac{-2 + \frac{1}{3}}{1 + 2\left(\frac{1}{3}\right)} = \frac{-\frac{5}{3}}{\frac{5}{3}} = -1.$$

As above, $\theta = 135°$.   ▲

If $\mathbf{u} = \langle a, b \rangle$ and $\mathbf{v} = \langle -a, -b \rangle$, then $\mathbf{u} + \mathbf{v} = \langle 0, 0 \rangle = \mathbf{0}$; we say that $\mathbf{v}$ is the negative of $\mathbf{u}$ and write $\mathbf{v} = -\mathbf{u}$. It is clear that multiplying any vector by zero gives the zero vector, and multiplying by the number 1 doesn't change a vector, while multiplying by -1 changes a vector to its negative, that is, reverses its direction. We can also use the negative of a vector to define the operation of subtraction, much as we do for real numbers. We summarize these observations for convenient reference.

Additional Properties of Vectors

$$0 \cdot \mathbf{v} = \mathbf{0} \qquad 1 \cdot \mathbf{v} = \mathbf{v}$$

$-1 \cdot \mathbf{v} = -\mathbf{v}$, where $-\mathbf{v}$ is the vector such that $\mathbf{v} + (-\mathbf{v}) = \mathbf{0}$.

For subtraction, $\mathbf{u} - \mathbf{v} = \mathbf{u} + (-\mathbf{v})$.

A **unit vector** is any vector of length 1. Given any nonzero vector $\mathbf{v}$, the unit vector in the direction of $\mathbf{v}$ is the vector $\mathbf{u} = \frac{1}{|\mathbf{v}|} \mathbf{v}$; that is, multiply $\mathbf{v}$ by the number $\frac{1}{|\mathbf{v}|}$.

EXAMPLE 4   Let $\mathbf{v} = \langle 6, -8 \rangle$ and $\mathbf{w} = \langle -2, -3 \rangle$. **(a)** Find the unit vector $\mathbf{u}$ in the direction of $\mathbf{v}$. **(b)** Find $\mathbf{v} - 2\mathbf{w}$.

Solution

(a)   The length of $\mathbf{v}$ is given by $|\mathbf{v}| = \sqrt{6^2 + (-8)^2} = 10$, so to find $\mathbf{u}$, multiply $\mathbf{v}$ by $\frac{1}{10}$: $\mathbf{u} = \langle \frac{6}{10}, -\frac{8}{10} \rangle = \langle 0.6, -0.8 \rangle$.

(b) $\mathbf{v} - 2\mathbf{w} = \langle 6, -8 \rangle - 2 \langle -2, -3 \rangle = \langle 6, -8 \rangle + \langle 4, 6 \rangle = \langle 10, -2 \rangle$.   ▲

Compass Directions for Vectors

We have used a coordinate system and directed line segments to identify vectors. It is often useful to describe the direction of a vector with compass directions, so a vector may have a given length in the direction $30°$ east of north, or $17.5°$ north of west. To represent such vectors in a coordinate plane, we usually take the positive y-axis as north and the positive x-axis as east.

EXAMPLE 5   Vector $\mathbf{u}$ has length 3.0 and direction $20°$ south of east; $\mathbf{v}$ has length 4.0 and direction $30°$ east of north. Find the length and direction of $\mathbf{u} + \mathbf{v}$.

Exercises

Looking Ahead to Calculus Some of the more difficult problems in calculus deal with related rates, where two or more quantities are changing simultaneously. A graphing calculator can make some very tricky problems quite tractable.

1. Two cars are approaching an overpass 20 ft high on highways at right angles to each other. Sherm is traveling on the interstate at 60 mph (88 ft/sec), and Teri is approaching the overpass at 45 mph (66 ft/sec). When they first see each other, Sherm is $\frac{1}{2}$ mile (2640 ft) from the overpass and Teri is $\frac{1}{3}$ mile away (1760 ft). At a time x seconds later, Sherm is $(2640 - 88x)$ feet away and Teri is $(1760 - 66x)$ feet away, at points S and T, respectively, in the diagram. Show that the distances in the diagram are given by the following formulas:

$$|\overline{SV}| = \sqrt{(2640 - 88x)^2 + 400}$$

$$|\overline{TU}| = \sqrt{(1760 - 66x)^2 + 400}$$

$$d(x) = |\overline{ST}|$$

$$= \sqrt{(2640 - 88x)^2 + (1760 - 66x)^2 + 400}.$$

2. Graph the function $y = d(x)$ from Exercise 1 in a window $[10, 40] \times [0, 1800]$. At what time are the two cars nearest each other? What is the minimum distance between Sherm's and Teri's cars?

3. Show that angle θ in the diagram is

$$\theta(x) = \text{Tan}^{-1}\left[\frac{\sqrt{(1760 - 66x)^2 + 400}}{2640 - 88x}\right].$$

4. Graph the function $y = \theta(x)$ from Exercise 3 in the window $[10, 40] \times [-2, 2]$. Make sure the calculator is in radian mode. What is the minimum angle, and when does it occur? Compare your answer with the time you obtained in Exercise 2.

5. Discuss the strange looking graph in Exercise 4. What is the physical meaning of the two portions of the graph, first as θ is decreasing, and then as it is increasing? What happens with the defining function to cause the graph to crash? What is happening with the two cars at the critical time?

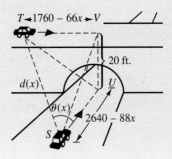

Solution

First draw a diagram (always an essential step) in the coordinate plane to show standard representations **OA** and **OB** for **u** and **v**. See Figure 7.35. The diagram shows **u** + **v** as the diagonal **OC** of the parallelogram *OACB*. Find the length and direction of **OC**. Both the length and direction can be described by solving the triangle *OAC* in the diagram, where $\alpha = \angle OAC = 100°$. (Why? See Develop Mastery Exercise 51.) If we let $\beta = \angle COA$, then the angle of inclination of segment $\overline{OC}$ is given by $\theta = \beta - 20°$. Let $d = |\overline{OC}|$. (See Figure 7.35b.)

By the Law of Cosines,

$$d^2 = 3^2 + 4^2 - 2 \cdot 3 \cdot 4 \cdot \cos 100° \approx 29.16756 \qquad d \approx 5.4.$$

Using either the Law of Sines or the Law of Cosines, $\beta \approx 47°$, from which $\theta \approx 27°$. Therefore **u** + **v** is the vector of length 5.4, directed 27° north of east (or 63° east of north). ▲

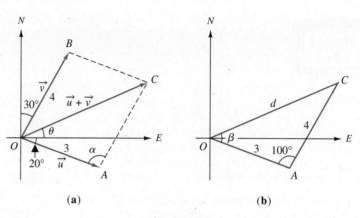

FIGURE 7.35

FIGURE 7.36

| EXAMPLE 6 |

A direct air route from Denver to Chicago runs about 10° north of east. An airplane flies at a constant airspeed of 500 mph at a heading of 15° north of east while the jet stream is blowing at a constant speed of 100 mph due east. What is the velocity (speed and direction) of the plane relative to the ground?

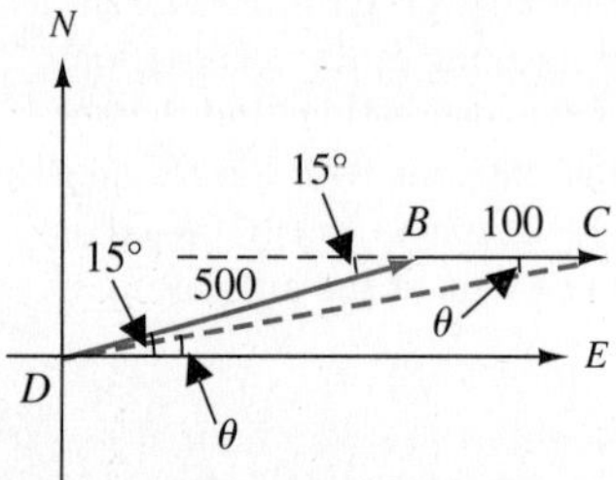

Solution

Represent the airspeed of the plane as vector **DB** of magnitude 500 in the direction 15° north of east. The jet stream contribution is vector **BC** of magnitude 100 directed due east. The ground speed of the plane is the vector sum **DB** + **BC**. The sum is represented by the directed line segment **DC** in Figure 7.36, of length c at a heading of θ north of east. By the Law of Cosines, the length is

$$c = \sqrt{500^2 + 100^2 - 2 \cdot 500 \cdot 100 \cdot \cos 165°} \approx 597.$$

Angle θ is also included in $\triangle BDC$, $\theta = \angle BCD$, and the Law of Sines is convenient:

$$\theta = \text{Sin}^{-1}\left(\frac{500 \sin 165°}{597}\right) \approx 12.5°.$$

The ground speed of the plane is nearly 600 mph, but the heading of 12.5° north of east will take the plane too far north, and a correction will be needed to reach Chicago. ▲

| EXERCISES 7.5 |

Check Your Understanding

Exercises 1–5   True or False. Give reasons for your conclusion.

1. For points $P(-1, 4)$ and $Q(-2, 3)$, vector **PQ** is equal to $\langle 1, 1 \rangle$.

2. Vectors $\langle 1, 0 \rangle$ and $\langle 0, -1 \rangle$ are perpendicular to each other.

3. If $\mathbf{v} = \langle -3, -4 \rangle$, then $|\mathbf{v}| = -5$.

4. If $\mathbf{u} = \langle 3, 0 \rangle$, $\mathbf{v} = \langle -1, 2 \rangle$, and $\mathbf{w} = \langle -2, -2 \rangle$, then $\mathbf{u} + \mathbf{v} + \mathbf{w}$ is the zero vector.

5. The angle between vectors $\langle 2, 2 \rangle$ and $\langle -1, 0 \rangle$ is 135°.

Exercises 6–10 Complete the sentence by selecting from the list below *all choices* that make the statement true. When compass directions are used, assume that north is in the positive *y*-direction and east is in the positive *x*-direction.

(a) $\langle 1, 4 \rangle$ (b) $\langle 5, 5 \rangle$
(c) $\langle -3, 4 \rangle$ (d) $-8\langle 1, \sqrt{3} \rangle$
(e) $16\langle -1, -2 \rangle$ (f) $-5\langle 1, 1 \rangle$
(g) $-8\langle \sqrt{3}, 1 \rangle$ (h) $\langle 16\sqrt{3}, 16 \rangle$

6. If $\mathbf{v} = \langle -1, 2 \rangle$ and $\mathbf{v} + \mathbf{w} = \langle 0, 6 \rangle$, then $\mathbf{w} =$ _____.

7. If $\mathbf{v} = \langle 0, 4 \rangle$ and $\mathbf{v} - \mathbf{w} = \langle -1, 0 \rangle$, then $\mathbf{w} =$ _____.

8. If **v** is directed 45° north of east, then $\mathbf{v} =$ _____.

9. If $|\mathbf{v}| = 16$ and **v** is directed 30° south of west, then $\mathbf{v} =$ _____.

10. If **v** is directed 45° north of west and **u** is perpendicular to **v**, then $\mathbf{u} =$ _____.

Explore and Discover

To get to their summer cottage on an island located 7 miles due east of the marina, the Hobsons must navigate around several intervening islands, as shown in the map. When they give guests directions for negotiating the island maze, the Hobsons use the vectors shown. For Exercises 1 through 5, refer to the map.

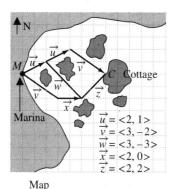

$\vec{u} = <2, 1>$
$\vec{v} = <3, -2>$
$\vec{w} = <3, -3>$
$\vec{x} = <2, 0>$
$\vec{z} = <2, 2>$

Map

1. Express each of the five vectors in terms of distance (to one decimal place) and compass heading in degrees measured counterclockwise from east (so that a vector directed 20° north of west has a heading of 160°).

2. Verify that each of the vector sums $2\mathbf{u} + \mathbf{v}$, $\mathbf{u} + \mathbf{w} + \mathbf{z}$, and $\mathbf{v} + \mathbf{x} + \mathbf{z}$ will take visitors from the marina to the Hobsons' cottage. (*Hint:* What are the components for each path?)

3. The length of the route indicated by $2\mathbf{u} + \mathbf{v}$ is not $|2\mathbf{u} + \mathbf{v}|$, but rather $|2\mathbf{u}| + |\mathbf{v}|$. Explain why $|2\mathbf{u} + \mathbf{v}| \neq |2\mathbf{u}| + |\mathbf{v}|$.

4. Find the length of the trip from the marina to the Hobsons' cottage by each of the routes indicated by the vector sums in Exercise 2. Which is the shortest route? Suggest some reasons (possibly nonmathematical) why the shortest route might not be Hobsons' choice for some guests.

5. In general which is greater, $|\mathbf{a} + \mathbf{b}|$ or $|\mathbf{a}| + |\mathbf{b}|$? Find examples of vectors **a** and **b** for which $|\mathbf{a} + \mathbf{b}| = |\mathbf{a}| + |\mathbf{b}|$. Draw pictures. Characterize such vectors and explain.

Develop Mastery

For the first 30 exercises, vectors **u**, **v**, and **w** are given by $\mathbf{u} = \mathbf{OP}$, $\mathbf{v} = \mathbf{OQ}$, and $\mathbf{w} = \mathbf{OR}$, where O is the origin and the other points are $P(1, 1)$, $Q(2, -5)$, and $R(-2, 1)$.

Exercises 1–10 Find the components of each vector and draw a diagram to show the vector as a directed line segment in standard position.

1. $4\mathbf{u}$ 2. $-2\mathbf{v}$
3. $3\mathbf{w}$ 4. $\mathbf{u} + \mathbf{v}$
5. $\mathbf{v} - \mathbf{u}$ 6. $\mathbf{u} - 2\mathbf{v}$
7. $-2\mathbf{v} + 3\mathbf{w}$ 8. $\mathbf{v} + \mathbf{u} + \mathbf{w}$
9. $2\mathbf{u} - \mathbf{v} + 3\mathbf{w}$ 10. $8\mathbf{u} + 3\mathbf{v} + 7\mathbf{w}$

11. Find a vector **x** that, when added to **u**, gives **w**.

12. Find a vector **x** that, when subtracted from $2\mathbf{v}$, gives **w**.

13. Find a vector **x** that, when added to $\mathbf{v} + \mathbf{w}$, gives **u**.

14. Find a vector **x** that, when added to $\mathbf{u} - \mathbf{v} + \mathbf{w}$, gives **0**.

Exercises 15–17 Find the angle (to the nearest degree) between the pair of vectors.

15. **u** and **v**   16. **u** and **w**   17. **w** and **v**

18. Find all unit vectors **OX** such that **OX** is perpendicular to **OP**.

19. Find all unit vectors **OX** such that **OX** is perpendicular to **OR**.

20. If $\mathbf{x} = 2\mathbf{u} + \mathbf{v} + \mathbf{w}$, show that **x** and **u** are perpendicular to each other.

Exercises 21–29 Find the lengths of the vectors.

21. **u** and $2\mathbf{u}$ 22. **v** and $-\mathbf{v}$
23. **w** and $-3\mathbf{w}$ 24. $\frac{1}{2}\mathbf{u}$ and $\frac{2}{3}\mathbf{u}$
25. **u**, **v** and $\mathbf{u} + \mathbf{v}$ 26. **w**, **v** and $\mathbf{w} - \mathbf{v}$
27. **u** and $k\mathbf{u}$, where $k > 0$.

28. **u** and k**u**, where $k < 0$.

29. **w**, **v** and $a\mathbf{w} + b\mathbf{v}$

30. Is there a positive integer n such that the vector $n\mathbf{u}$ has integer length? Explain your answer.

31. Find a vector **v** of length 4 whose first component is twice its second component.

32. Find all vectors **v** of length 8 whose components are equal in magnitude, but have opposite signs.

33. If $\mathbf{u} = \langle 3, -1 \rangle$, find all vectors $\mathbf{v} = \langle x, 2 \rangle$ for which $|\mathbf{v} - \mathbf{u}| = \sqrt{34}$.

34. If $\mathbf{u} = \langle 3, -1 \rangle$, find all vectors $\mathbf{v} = \langle x, 2 \rangle$ for which $|\mathbf{u} + \mathbf{v}| = \sqrt{17}$.

35. If $\mathbf{u} = \langle 3, -1 \rangle$, find all vectors $\mathbf{v} = \langle x, y \rangle$ for which $|\mathbf{u} + \mathbf{v}| = 2$.

36. Given point $P(-1, 2)$, find all points $Q(x, 2)$ for which the vector **PQ** has length 4.

37. Given point $P(-1, 2)$, find all points $Q(2, y)$ for which the vector **PQ** has length 5.

38. Given point $P(-1, 2)$, find all points $Q(x, y)$ for which the vector **PQ** has length 4.

39. Suppose A and B are points on opposite shores of a lake as shown in the diagram. A man starts at point A and reaches point B by walking from A to C ($48\sqrt{2}$ m 45° south of east), C to D (36 m east), D to B (72 m north). If he went directly by rowboat, how far and in what direction should he go? (*Hint:* Express each leg of his walk as a vector.)

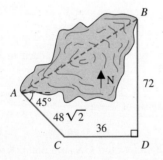

40. A boat sails from port 72 km due east, then turns 60° toward the south and travels 48 km in the new direction. How far, and in what direction, is the boat now located, relative to port?

41. In playing golf Patty takes two putts to get the ball into the hole. The first putt takes her ball 8.0 feet 30° north of east. She then sinks the ball by putting 1.5 feet due north. To execute the putt in one stroke how far and in what direction should she have hit the ball?

42. Patty's golfing partner (from Exercise 41) ended up on the green exactly 20 feet due north of Patty's ball before her first putt. How far and in what direction should he aim his putt to hole out in one stroke? Is his putt easier or more difficult than Patty's (assuming that the green is level in all directions)?

43. A small motorboat has a speed of 5.0 mph in still water. It heads perpendicularly across a river whose current is 3.5 mph. Find the true heading and speed of the boat. (*Hint:* Draw a diagram to show both the heading and speed of the boat and the direction and speed of the current as vectors.)

44. The instrument panel of a plane indicates a speed of 400 mph and a compass heading of due north. If there is a cross wind of 80 mph from the southwest (blowing 45° east of north), what is the actual velocity (speed and direction) of the plane relative to the ground?

45. An airplane has an airspeed of 500 mph in a northeasterly direction (45° north of east) and the jet stream is blowing at 100 mph due east. Find the velocity (speed and direction) of the plane relative to the ground.

46. Repeat Exercise 45 for an airplane with the same airspeed heading in a southwestern direction (45° south of west).

47. How much longer will it take the plane in Exercise 46 to travel 1000 miles than the plane in Exercise 45 (both measured in ground miles)?

48. Suppose an airplane has an airspeed of 500 mph and the jet stream is blowing at 100 mph due east. If the plane has to travel from Seattle to Salt Lake City (900 miles at a heading 45° south of east), in what direction should the plane head? How long will the flight take?

49. Repeat Exercise 48 for the return flight, from Salt Lake City to Seattle, with the same airspeed and jet stream.

50. Show that adjacent interior angles of a parallelogram have a sum of 180°. In the diagram show that $\alpha + \beta = 180°$. (*Hint:* Extend one of the sides and consider the resulting exterior angle.)

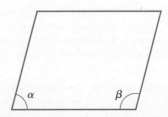

CHAPTER 7 REVIEW

Test Your Understanding

Determine the truth value (T or F) of the statement. Give reasons for your conclusion. For right triangles, assume that γ is the right angle.

1. In a right triangle suppose the hypotenuse c and angle β are given. Side b can be found by using $b = \frac{c}{\sin \beta}$.

2. In a right triangle the area A is given by $A = \frac{1}{2}c^2 \sin \alpha \sin \beta$.

3. In a right triangle the area A is given by $A = \frac{1}{4}c^2 \sin 2\alpha$.

4. Suppose angle β and the perimeter P of a right triangle are given. The hypotenuse c is given by $c = \frac{P}{1 + \sin \beta + \cos \beta}$.

5. If $\alpha = 2\beta$ in a right triangle, then $a = 2b$.

6. There is exactly one triangle for which $a = 3.2$, $b = 4.1$, and $\gamma = 24°$.

7. Exactly one triangle is determined by $b = 7.3$, $c = 8.7$, and $\gamma = 120°$.

8. There is no triangle with $a = 3.6$, $b = 3.6$, and $\gamma = 135°$.

9. A triangle with $a = 5, b = 12$, and $c = 13$ is a right triangle.

10. A triangle with $a = \sqrt{3}, b = \sqrt{5}$, and $c = 2\sqrt{2}$ is a right triangle.

11. If each side of a triangle is doubled, then its area is also doubled.

12. If $\alpha = 30°$ and $a = 16$, then $b = 32 \sin \beta$.

13. If $\beta = 45°$ and $b = 5\sqrt{2}$, then $c = 10 \sin \gamma$.

14. The area of a triangle with $a = \sqrt{3}, b = 8$, and $\gamma = 60°$ is a whole number.

15. If in a right triangle $a = \sqrt{3}$ and $\alpha = 30°$, then b is a whole number.

16. The area of a triangle with $a = 2$, $b = 4$, and $\gamma = 40°$ is twice that of a triangle with $a = 2$, $b = 4$, and $\gamma = 20°$.

17. The area of a triangle with $a = 4$, $b = 16$, and $\gamma = 43°$ is twice that of a triangle with $a = 2$, $b = 8$, and $\gamma = 43°$.

18. If the area of a triangle is 16 and $\gamma = 30°$, then the product $a \cdot b$ is equal to 32.

19. In a triangle with $a = 7.5, b = 5.3$, and $c = 5.6$, the largest angle is α.

20. The area of a triangle with $a = 4\sqrt{5}, b = \sqrt{15}$, and $\gamma = 60°$ is equal to 15.

21. If $c^2 > a^2 + b^2$, then $\cos \gamma$ is negative.

22. If $b^2 > a^2 + c^2$, then β is an obtuse angle.

23. If $a^2 = b^2 + c^2$, then γ is a right angle.

24. If γ is an obtuse angle, then $c > \sqrt{a^2 + b^2}$.

25. If $c > \sqrt{a^2 + b^2}$, then α must be an acute angle.

26. If b, β, and γ are given, then $c = \frac{b \sin \beta}{\sin \gamma}$.

27. If α, β, and c are given, then $b = \frac{c \sin \beta}{\sin (\alpha + \beta)}$.

28. If $a = 2b$, then $\alpha = 2\beta$.

29. If $b = 2c$, then $\sin \beta = 2 \sin \gamma$.

30. If $a = 2c$, then $\sin \alpha = \sin 2\gamma$.

31. If $\alpha = 2\beta$, then $a = 2b \cos \beta$.

32. In any triangle $\sin (\alpha + \beta) = \sin \gamma$.

33. Vectors $\langle -1, 1 \rangle$ and $\langle 1, -1 \rangle$ are perpendicular to each other.

34. The angle between vectors $\langle 1, -1 \rangle$ and $\langle 0, 1 \rangle$ is $135°$.

35. If $\mathbf{u} = \langle -1, 3 \rangle$ and $\mathbf{v} = \langle -2, 1 \rangle$ then $|\mathbf{u} + \mathbf{v}| = 5$.

36. If $\mathbf{u} = \langle 2, -1 \rangle$ and $\mathbf{u} + \mathbf{v} = \langle -2, 1 \rangle$ then $\mathbf{v} = \langle -4, 2 \rangle$.

Mastery Review

In the following exercises assume standard labeling of parts of a triangle where a, b, and c denote the lengths of the sides and α, β, and γ are the angles opposite the respective sides. For right triangles $\gamma = 90°$.

1. In a right triangle $c = 37.4$ and $\beta = 25°20'$. Find α, a, and b.

2. Find the area of a right triangle in which $c = 2.56$ and $\alpha = 34°10'$.

3. The area of a right triangle is 0.924 m^2 and one of the angles is $37°20'$. Find the length of the hypotenuse.

4. The hypotenuse of a right triangle is 6.5 cm and its area is 8.4 cm^2. Find the two acute angles.

5. Determine the area of an isosceles triangle with equal sides of length 8.6 cm and opposite (base) angles of $36°$.

6. Given $\alpha = 36°$, $\beta = 41°$, and $a = 7.6$, find c.

7. Given $a = 3.75$, $c = 5.76$, and $\beta = 137.4°$, find b.

8. If $a = 3.48$, $c = 5.63$, and $\gamma = 62.7°$, find b.

9. If $a = 3.7$, $b = 7.5$, and $c = 6.8$, determine angle α.

10. Given $a = 2.8$, $b = 3.7$, and $\beta = 54°$, find c and γ.

11. If $a = 1.53$, $b = 6.41$, and $\gamma = 37.4°$, find the area of the triangle.

12. If $b = 3.7$, $c = 5.3$, and $\alpha = 115°$, find the perimeter of the triangle and length of the altitude to side c.

13. An equilateral triangle is inscribed in a circle of radius 12.4 inches. What is the area of the triangle?

14. The area of triangle ABC is 427 m², $\gamma = 35.2°$ and $a = 23.5$ m. Find b.

15. The perimeter of a right triangle is 125 cm and one angle is 35.0°. Find the hypotenuse and the area of the triangle.

16. In the diagram, $|\overline{AC}| = 2.45$ km, $\alpha = 21.4°$, and $\gamma = 125.3°$. Find h, where $h = |\overline{BD}|$.

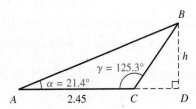

17. In the diagram the radius of the circle with center at C is 1.7 cm and the central angle $\theta = 43°$. Find the area of **(a)** triangle ABC, and **(b)** the shaded region.

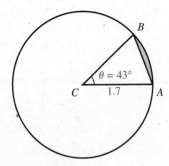

18. The perimeter of triangle ABC is 145 cm, $\alpha = 36.0°$, and $\beta = 77.0°$. Find the length of side c.

19. From the top of a building at point A, the angle of depression to point C on the ground is 56.0°, while from a point B, 48.0 feet directly below A, the angle of depression to point C is 41.0°. Find the height of the building. See the diagram.

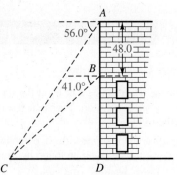

20. Point E is the midpoint of side $\overline{BC}$ of square $ABCD$. Find $\sin \theta$, where θ is the angle formed by $\overline{AE}$ and the diagonal $\overline{AC}$. (*Hint:* First draw a diagram.)

21. In the diagram show that $\cot \theta - \cot \phi = \frac{b}{c}$.

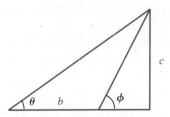

22. The CN Tower of Toronto is the world's tallest self-supporting structure. From a point on the ground 845.0 feet from the tower's base, the angle of elevation to the top is measured as 65.11°. What is the height of the tower?

23. A regular octagon is inscribed in a circle of radius 24 feet. **(a)** What is the perimeter of the octagon? **(b)** What is the area of the region bounded by the octagon?

24. Two cabins are located at points A and B on the shore of a lake (see the diagram). From the information in the diagram, find how far a boat would have to travel from A to B.

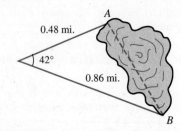

25. Points $A(12, 7)$, $B(7, 12)$, and $C(0, 0)$ are vertices of a triangle.
(a) Find the measure of angle $\theta = \angle ACB$ to the nearest tenth of a degree.
(b) What is the length of the altitude from C to $\overline{AB}$?
(c) What is the area of the region bounded by $\triangle ABC$?

26. For points $A(2, 1)$, $B(5, 5)$, and $C(6, 4)$ in the plane, find the measure of $\angle ABC$ **(a)** in degrees (to one decimal place) and **(b)** in radians (to one decimal place).

27. Find the measure to the nearest tenth of a degree of each angle of the parallelogram with vertices at $A(-2, 4)$, $B(2, 1)$, $C(5, 3)$, and $D(1, 6)$.

28. Find the largest angle to the nearest degree in the triangle with sides of lengths 39, 80, and 89.

29. Three mutually tangent circles with centers at A, B, and C have radii of 3.0, 4.0, and 5.0, respectively, as shown in the diagram. What is the area of the shaded region?

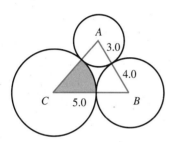

30. At a certain point A on the ground, the angle of elevation to the top of a building is $37.1°$. At a point 64.2 feet farther away, the angle of elevation is $30.2°$.
(a) What is the height of the building?
(b) How far from the base of the building is point A?

31. A tree stands vertically on a hill that slopes $35°$ from the horizontal. At a point 86 feet downhill from the tree, the angle of elevation to the top of the tree is $53°$. See the diagram. How tall is the tree?

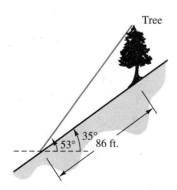

Tree

$53°$ $35°$ 86 ft.

32. The lengths of the diagonals of a parallelogram are 12 cm and 18 cm. If the smaller angle where the diagonals intersect is $32°$, what are the lengths of the sides?

Exercises 33–38 How many triangles (if any) have the given parts?

33. $a = 3.6$, $b = 7.5$, $\gamma = 75°$

34. $a = 5.6$, $b = 4.5$, $\beta = 24°$

35. $\alpha = 40°$, $\beta = 115°$, $\gamma = 25°$

36. $a = 7.3$, $b = 2.8$, $c = 5.4$

37. $b = 8.2$, $c = 3.7$, $\beta = 43°$

38. $\alpha = 47°$, $\beta = 65°$, $a = 24$

Exercises 39–44 Evaluate the expression. Give the answer in rectangular form for complex numbers, $a + bi$, where a and b are real numbers. Whenever reasonable, give the result in exact form; otherwise give a and b rounded off to two decimal places.

39. **(a)** $(1 + i)^5$ **(b)** $(3 - 2i)^6$

40. **(a)** $(1 + i)^{-2}$ **(b)** $(2 + 3i)^{-2}$

41. **(a)** $(\sqrt{3} + i)^6(1 + i)^{-4}$
(b) $(3 - 2i)^4(1 + 2i)^{-3}$

42. **(a)** $(\frac{1}{2} + \frac{\sqrt{3}}{2}i)^{12}$ **(b)** $(\frac{1}{\sqrt{5}} + \frac{2}{\sqrt{5}}i)^{-8}$

43. **(a)** $[2(\cos \frac{\pi}{12} + i \sin \frac{\pi}{12})]^6$
(b) $(\cos \frac{\pi}{8} + i \sin \frac{\pi}{8})^{-4}$

44. **(a)** $(\cos \frac{4\pi}{15} + i \sin \frac{4\pi}{15})^{10}$
(b) $(\cos \frac{2\pi}{15} + i \sin \frac{2\pi}{15})^{-10}$

45. Find the roots of **(a)** $z^2 - 2iz - 2 = 0$ and **(b)** $z^2 - (2 - i)z - i = 0$.

46. Find the cube roots of $\frac{\sqrt{3} - i}{2}$.

47. Find the fourth roots of $\frac{3 - 4i}{5}$.

48. Find the sixth roots of -729.

49. Find the fourth roots of $8\sqrt{2}(1 + i)$.

50. Find all complex number roots of the equation $x^5 + 1 = 0$.

Exercises 51–53 Vectors $\mathbf{u}$ and $\mathbf{v}$ are given by $\mathbf{u} = \langle -1, 3 \rangle$, $\mathbf{v} = \langle 0, -4 \rangle$.

51. Find **(a)** $\mathbf{u} + \mathbf{v}$ and **(b)** $2\mathbf{u} - \mathbf{v}$

52. Find **(a)** $|\mathbf{u}|$ and **(b)** $|\mathbf{u} - \mathbf{v}|$

53. Find the angle between **u** and **v**.

54. A boat travels 64 km due west from port, then turns 60° toward the north and travels 48 km in the new direction. How far and in what direction is the boat's location relative to the port?

55. An airplane has an airspeed of 400 mph in the direction 30° east of north. If there is a wind of 80 mph blowing due east, **(a)** what are the speed and direction of the plane relative to the ground? **(b)** How long will it take for the plane to fly a distance of 1000 ground miles?

8

DISCRETE MATHEMATICS
Functions on the Set of Natural Numbers

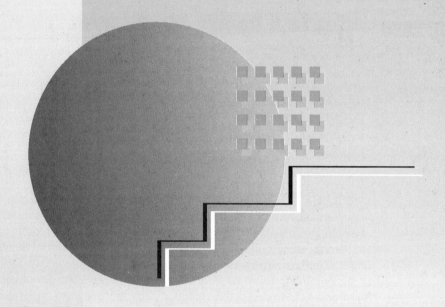

The unifying theme of this chapter is the set of natural numbers. Functions defined on that set, called *sequences,* are discussed in the first two sections. Throughout this book we have invited you to explore and discover mathematics yourself. Number patterns encourage this curiosity, and they are a primary source of the fascination mathematics has always had for humans. Section 8.3 is devoted to questions about patterns that illustrate where mathematical ideas come from and how theorems are discovered. Section 8.4 introduces mathematical induction, as both a productive way of thinking and a powerful tool to establish the validity of statements about the natural numbers. One such statement, the binomial theorem, is the focus of Section 8.5.

Introduction to Sequences; Summation Notation

In some cases such as the weather, the phenomenon always appears to be random but in other cases such as the dripping faucet, sometimes the dripping is periodic and other times each drip appears to be independent of the preceding one, thereby forming an irregular sequence.

   B. J. West

We live in a world largely ordered by numbers, most often by the natural numbers. Record books list many firsts; a runner in the Boston Marathon may be proud to come in 367th or 893rd. We sometimes use incredibly large numbers to identify things: nine digits suffice to provide unique Social Security numbers for 250 million Americans, but look at some of the numbers on insurance forms.

   A familiar example from mathematics is the sequence of prime numbers, where 2 is the first, 3 is the second, 5 is the third, and so on. This order defines a function, with the rule of correspondence

$$f(n) = \text{the } n\text{th prime number.}$$

Euclid proved that there are infinitely many primes, which means that the domain of the prime number function is infinite, the set N of all natural numbers. There is *no* last prime. We have no simple formula to compute the millionth prime, $f(1,000,000)$, but we know that it exists.

Sequences and Notation

A **sequence** (sometimes, for emphasis, an **infinite sequence**) can be thought of as a **list,** with a term for every natural number, even though we sometimes use sequences like $a_0, a_1, a_2, \ldots$ or $b_4, b_5, b_6, \ldots$. Each has a first term, a second term, and so on. It is convenient to define a sequence in terms of its domain, but equivalent domains could be used, as well.

By the time I was well enough to go back to school I had missed more than two years. My parents arranged to have me tutored by a retired elementary school teacher. One day she told me that you could never carry the square root of 2 to a point where the decimal began to repeat. She knew that his fact had been proved, although she did not know how.

Julia Robinson

> **Definition: Sequence**
>
> A **sequence** is a function whose domain is the set of natural numbers.

The rule that defines a sequence can be either given by a mathematical formula or stated in words. The terms of a sequence, the function values, can be listed as

$$f(1), f(2), f(3), \ldots, f(n), \ldots,$$

or we may use subscript notation, where $f(n)$, the nth term of the sequence, is denoted by a_n. We sometimes denote the whole list of sequence values by $\{a_n\}$:

$$a_1, a_2, a_3, \ldots, a_n, \ldots \text{ is equivalent to } \{a_n\}.$$

EXAMPLE 1   List the first four terms and the tenth term of the sequence **(a)** $f(n) = 2n - 1$, **(b)** $b_n = n^2 - 4$, and **(c)** $a_n = (-1)^n$.

Solution

(a) $f(1) = 2 \cdot 1 - 1 = 1$, $f(2) = 2 \cdot 2 - 1 = 3$, $f(3) = 2 \cdot 3 - 1 = 5$, $f(4) = 2 \cdot 4 - 1 = 7$, $f(10) = 2 \cdot 10 - 1 = 19$.

(b) $b_1 = 1^2 - 4 = -3$, $b_2 = 2^2 - 4 = 0$, $b_3 = 3^2 - 4 = 5$, $b_4 = 4^2 - 4 = 12$, $b_{10} = 10^2 - 4 = 96$. The sequence begins $-3, 0, 5, 12, \ldots$.

(c) $a_1 = (-1)^1 = -1$, $a_2 = (-1)^2 = 1$, $a_3 = (-1)^3 = -1$, and $a_4 = (-1)^4 = 1$. The sequence begins $-1, 1, -1, 1, \ldots$, and $a_{10} = (-1)^{10} = 1$. The same sequence is given by the rule

$$a_n = \begin{cases} -1 \text{ if } n \text{ is odd} \\ 1 \text{ if } n \text{ is even} \end{cases}.$$ ▲

EXAMPLE 2   List the first five terms.

(a) $a_n = 2n$

(b) $b_n = (n - 1)(n - 2)(n - 3) + 2n$

(c) $c_n = \begin{cases} 2n \text{ for } n = 1, 2, 3 \\ 0 \text{ for } n \geq 4 \end{cases}$

Solution

The sequences begin:

(a) $\{a_n\} = 2, 4, 6, 8, 10, \ldots$

(b) $\{b_n\} = 2, 4, 6, 14, 34, \ldots$

(c) $\{c_n\} = 2, 4, 6, 0, 0, \ldots$ ▲

Example 2 illustrates an important point. Giving a few terms does not define a sequence. Infinitely many sequences begin 2, 4, 6, ... Test makers sometimes ask for "the next term in the sequence 2, 4, 6, . . . ," expecting a response of "8," but as Example 2 shows, that question has no single correct response. Consider some less obvious sequences that begin 2, 4, 6, . . . :

Sequence Beginning	Rule (Function)
2, 4, 6, 10, 16, 26, . . .	Each term after the second is the sum of the two preceding terms.
2, 4, 6, 1, 3, 5, 0, . . .	The term a_n is the remainder when $9n$ is divided by 7.
2, 4, 6, 2, 3, 4, . . .	The sequence is taken from the decimal expansion for π starting in the 374th place, then listing every other digit.

Sequences Defined Recursively

We can define a sequence by stating the rule of correspondence, either by a formula or in words. Another useful method is to use **recursion,** continuing a sequence, based on known terms of the sequence, as illustrated in the following examples.

EXAMPLE 3   Evaluate several terms of the sequences

(a) $a_1 = 4$ and $a_n = a_{n-1} + 3$ for $n > 1$ (b) $b_n = 3n + 1$.

Solution

Strategy: (a) Evaluate the terms of a recursive sequence in order, using one term to get the next. In this case, given one term, we get the next one by adding 3.

(a) Start with $a_1 = 4$. The second part of the definition says that when n is greater than 1, each term is obtained by adding 3 to the preceding term, so $a_2 = a_1 + 3 = 4 + 3 = 7, a_3 = a_2 + 3 = 7 + 3 = 10$, and so on. The sequence begins 4, 7, 10, 13, 16, . . . , and continues by adding 3 each time.

(b) With a closed (explicit) formula, calculate the first few terms directly: 4, 7, 10, 13, 16. The sequence begins with exactly the same terms as those in part a. ▲

To be identical, two sequences must do more than agree for the first few terms; they must continue to agree. In Example 3, $\{a_n\}$ and $\{b_n\}$ have the same first five terms. Are they identical sequences? Notice how b_n is related to b_{n-1}. The formula gives $b_{n-1} = 3(n - 1) + 1 = 3n - 2$ and $b_n = 3n + 1 = (3n - 2) + 3$, so $b_n = b_{n-1} + 3$. The two sequences satisfy the same recursive relation, so they are identical sequences.

Example 3 also shows that a sequence defined recursively, $\{a_n\}$, may also be given by a formula in closed form, $\{b_n\}$. Both methods are useful. Recursive relations often occur naturally and they lend themselves to computer programming, but an explicit formula gives any particular term directly, without the need to calculate earlier terms. For example, the first sequence in the table above is

Fibonacci

Historical Note

THE FIBONACCI SEQUENCE

Among the many sequences that mathematicians have studied, surely none is more fascinating than the Fibonacci sequence that begins

1, 1, 2, 3, 5, 8, 13, 21, 34, 55, . . . ,

where each term after the second is the sum of the two preceding terms.

The sequence first appeared in print in the year 1202. Leonardo of Pisa, also known as Fibonacci, wrote a *Book of Counting (Liber Abaci)* that introduced the then modern mathematics of North Africa (including Arabic numerals) to Europe. The book was one of the most important sources of mathematical learning in Europe for several hundred years. One of the more trivial problems in the book dealt with the growth of a colony of rabbits and led to the sequence of numbers that now bears Fibonacci's name.

Once a person becomes aware of the numbers in the Fibonacci sequence, the numbers seem to pop up everywhere. All kinds of growth processes involve the sequence. As a simple example, the next time you pick up a pine cone or look at a sunflower head,

count the number of spirals at some fixed angle. They will turn out to be Fibonacci numbers. The golden rectangle of Greek architecture, the rectangle considered to have the most pleasing proportions, has sides whose ratio is approached by ratios of successive Fibonacci numbers. The Fibonacci numbers also occur as sums of binomial coefficients taken along diagonals of Pascal's triangle. An entire journal, *The Fibonacci Quarterly,* is devoted to discoveries related to Fibonacci numbers and the Fibonacci sequence.

The Fibonacci sequence is probably the only mathematical entity to have made the London stage. A recent play is based on the life of Alan Turing, the British mathematician who laid the theoretical foundations for modern computers and the study of artificial intelligence and who helped crack Germany's supersecret code in World War II. In the play Turing explains to the other characters the fascination of the Fibonacci sequence. You can explore some of that fascination in the Explore and Discover problems at the end of Section 8.3.

given recursively as:

$$f_1 = 2 \qquad f_2 = 4 \qquad \text{and} \qquad f_n = f_{n-1} + f_{n-2} \text{ for } n > 2.$$

To get f_{10}, we would need f_9 and f_8, for which we would need f_7 and f_6, etc. The term f_{64} is defined, but it requires considerable work to determine that

$$f_{64} = 21,220,419,715,446.$$

Factorials

An important sequence is often defined recursively as

$$F_0 = 1 \quad \text{and} \quad F_n = nF_{n-1} \quad \text{for } n > 0.$$

The first few items are easily calculated.

$$F_0 = 1 \qquad\qquad F_5 = 5 \cdot F_4 = 120$$
$$F_1 = 1 \cdot F_0 = 1 \qquad F_6 = 6 \cdot F_5 = 720$$
$$F_2 = 2 \cdot F_1 = 2 \qquad F_7 = 7 \cdot F_6 = 5,040$$
$$F_3 = 3 \cdot F_2 = 6 \qquad F_8 = 8 \cdot F_7 = 40,320$$
$$F_4 = 4 \cdot F_3 = 24 \qquad F_9 = 9 \cdot F_8 = 362,880$$

The terms of the sequence grow very rapidly. F_{10} exceeds 3 million, and F_{13} is nearly 8 billion.

This sequence is the sequence of **factorials;** we reserve a special notation for factorials:

$$F_n = n! \quad (\text{read "}n\text{ factorial"}).$$

The sequence has a recursive definition.

Factorial Sequence (Recursive Form)

Suppose n is any nonnegative integer. The factorial sequence $\{n!\}$ is given by

$$0! = 1$$
$$n! = n(n - 1)! \quad \text{for } n > 0.$$

A formula in closed form for $n!$ is suggested by the following examples.

$$2! = 2(1!) = 2 \cdot 1 \qquad 3! = 3(2!) = 3 \cdot 2 \cdot 1 \qquad 4! = 4(3!) = 4 \cdot 3 \cdot 2 \cdot 1.$$

It can be shown that for any positive integer n, $n!$ is the product of all the integers from 1 to n inclusive. This gives a closed-form definition.

Factorial Sequence (Closed Form)

If n is any nonnegative integer, then the factorial sequence is given by

$$0! = 1$$
$$n! = n(n - 1) \ldots 3 \cdot 2 \cdot 1 \text{ if } n \geq 1$$

| **EXAMPLE 4** | **(a)** Evaluate $\frac{8!}{4!4!}$. **(b)** Express the sum $\frac{7!}{2!5!} + \frac{7!}{3!4!}$

as a single fraction and then check by evaluating each expression.

Solution

Strategy: (b) To add fractions, find a common denominator that contains all factors of both given denominators. Since $5! = 5 \cdot 4!$ and $3! = 3 \cdot 2!$, the common denominator is $3!5!$; multiply the first term by $\frac{3}{3}$ and the second by $\frac{5}{5}$.

(a) Using the closed form for $n!$, write out each factorial as a product and then simplify.

$$\frac{8!}{4!4!} = \frac{8 \cdot 7 \cdot 6 \cdot 5 \cdot 4 \cdot 3 \cdot 2 \cdot 1}{4 \cdot 3 \cdot 2 \cdot 1 \cdot 4 \cdot 3 \cdot 2 \cdot 1} = \frac{8 \cdot 7 \cdot 6 \cdot 5}{4 \cdot 3 \cdot 2} = 70$$

(b) Follow the strategy.

$$\frac{7!}{2!5!} + \frac{7!}{3!4!} = \frac{3 \cdot 7!}{(3 \cdot 2!)5!} + \frac{5 \cdot 7!}{3!(5 \cdot 4!)} = \frac{3 \cdot 7!}{3!5!} + \frac{5 \cdot 7!}{3!5!}$$

$$= \frac{3 \cdot 7! + 5 \cdot 7!}{3!5!} = \frac{(3 + 5)7!}{3!5!} = \frac{8 \cdot 7!}{3!5!} = \frac{8!}{3!5!}$$

Thus

$$\frac{7!}{2!5!} + \frac{7!}{3!4!} = \frac{8!}{3!5!}.$$

As a check,

$$\frac{7!}{2!5!} + \frac{7!}{3!4!} = 21 + 35 = 56 \qquad \text{and} \qquad \frac{8!}{3!5!} = \frac{8 \cdot 7 \cdot 6}{1 \cdot 2 \cdot 3} = 56. \quad \blacktriangle$$

Partial Sums and Summation Notation

We will often be interested in the sum of certain terms of a given sequence. To illustrate, consider the sequence $\{b_n\}$ given by $b_n = 2n - 1$. This sequence begins $1, 3, 5, 7, \ldots$. There is a related sequence denoted by $\{S_n\}$, which we call the **sequence of partial sums,**

$$S_1 = b_1 = 1$$

$$S_2 = b_1 + b_2 = 1 + 3 = 4$$

$$S_3 = b_1 + b_2 + b_3 = 4 + 5 = 9$$

$$S_4 = b_1 + b_2 + b_3 + b_4 = 9 + 7 = 16.$$

The emerging pattern suggests that the general term is given by the formula $S_n = n^2$.

It is cumbersome to write out the partial sum for many terms of a sequence. For instance, S_{100} is the sum of 100 terms, $b_1 + b_2 + b_3 + \cdots + b_{100}$. We introduce some special notation to denote such sums, using the Greek letter sigma Σ:

$$S_{100} = \sum_{k=1}^{100} b_k = b_1 + b_2 + b_3 + \cdots + b_{100}$$

The summation notation is a convenient shorthand. We suggest frequent practice to become familiar with it.

Definition: Sequence of Partial Sums

Suppose $\{a_n\}$ is any sequence of real numbers. The corresponding sequence of partial sums is $\{S_n\}$ where

$$S_n = \sum_{k=1}^{n} a_k = a_1 + a_2 + a_3 + \cdots + a_n.$$

The sigma notation $\sum_{k=1}^{m} a_k$ simply means the sum of the first m terms of the sequence $\{a_n\}$. The letter k does not appear in the expanded form and is sometimes called a **dummy variable.** Any other letter would do as well. For example, $\sum_{k=1}^{3} a_k = a_1 + a_2 + a_3$, and the same sum is given by $\sum_{j=1}^{3} a_j$, which also equals $a_1 + a_2 + a_3$. In $\sum_{k=1}^{m} a_k$ the integer 1 is called the **lower limit** for the sum, and m is the **upper limit.**

The sigma notation is useful in many other contexts, including differences of partial sums. Suppose we are interested in $S_6 - S_3$. In expanded form,

$$S_6 - S_3 = (a_1 + a_2 + a_3 + a_4 + a_5 + a_6) - (a_1 + a_2 + a_3)$$

$$= a_4 + a_5 + a_6$$

$$= \sum_{k=4}^{6} a_k.$$

In general, for $m > n$,

$$S_m - S_n = \sum_{k=n+1}^{m} a_k.$$

It should also be clear that the sequence of partial sums has a recursive form.

Sequence of Partial Sums (Recursive Form)

Suppose $\{a_n\}$ is any sequence of real numbers. The corresponding sequence of partial sums $\{S_n\}$ is

$$S_1 = a_1 \qquad \text{and} \qquad S_n = S_{n-1} + a_n \qquad \text{for } n > 1.$$

EXAMPLE 5   Write out the sum in expanded form and evaluate.

$$\textbf{(a)} \sum_{k=1}^{4} k(k+2)^2 \qquad \textbf{(b)} \sum_{i=3}^{6} (i-2)i^2$$

Solution

(a) $\displaystyle \sum_{k=1}^{4} k(k+2)^2 = 1(1+2)^2 + 2(2+2)^2 + 3(3+2)^2 + 4(4+2)^2$

$$= 9 + 32 + 75 + 144 = 260.$$

(b) $\quad \sum_{i=3}^{6} (i - 2)i^2 = (3 - 2)3^2 + (4 - 2)4^2 + (5 - 2)5^2 + (6 - 2)6^2$

$$= 9 + 32 + 75 + 144 = 260. \quad \blacktriangle$$

Observe that the sums in Example 5 are identical even though they appear quite different in the compact sigma notation. We may write the same sum with any specified lower limit if we make appropriate adjustments in the upper limit and the defining formula. When rewriting a sum in sigma notation, always check at least the first and last terms to verify that your limits and formula give correct values.

EXAMPLE 6   Express the following in sigma notation.

$$\frac{1}{1 \cdot 2} + \frac{1}{2 \cdot 3} + \frac{1}{3 \cdot 4} + \frac{1}{4 \cdot 5} + \frac{1}{5 \cdot 6}$$

Solution

Sigma notation requires a formula that describes each term of the given sum. For this purpose it helps to identify what remains fixed and what changes from term to term. In each term the numerator is 1 and the denominator is the product of two consecutive integers, $k(k + 1)$. In the first term, $k = 1$, and in the last, $k = 5$. The desired sum may be written as

$$\sum_{k=1}^{5} \frac{1}{k(k + 1)}, \quad \text{or} \quad \sum_{n=2}^{6} \frac{1}{(n - 1)n}. \quad \blacktriangle$$

EXERCISES 8.1

Check Your Understanding

Exercises 1–5   True or False. Give reasons for your conclusion.

1. $\sum_{k=1}^{147} (-1)^k = 1.$

2. $\sum_{k=1}^{4} k^2 = \left(\sum_{k=1}^{4} k \right)^2.$

3. The sequence given by $b_n = 2n + 9 - n^2$ contains only positive integers.

4. For every positive integer n, $(n + 4)! = n! + 4!$.

5. $\sum_{k=1}^{4} \frac{1}{k} = \sum_{j=2}^{5} \frac{1}{j - 1}.$

Exercises 6–10   Complete the sentence by selecting from the list below *all choices* that make the statement true.

(a) equal to 6   **(b)** equal to 4
(c) a positive number   **(d)** a negative number
(e) equal to 1   **(f)** greater than 1   **(g)** less than 1

6. If $a_n = 2n + 1$, then $a_5 - a_2$ is _____ .

7. If $b_n = \frac{n! + 4}{n!}$, then b_4 is _____ .

8. If $a_n = 8 - 2n$, then a_5 is _____ .

9. $\sum_{k=1}^{4} (k - 2)^2$ is _____ .

10. If $a_n = (-1)^n (2n - 1)$, then $\sum_{k=1}^{4} a_k$ is _____ .

Explore and Discover

Exercises 1–3   The 3N + 1 Sequence   A curious sequence has been studied by many people; it is often called the *3N + 1 sequence* and is defined recursively as:

$$a_1 = \text{any positive integer}$$

$$a_{n+1} = \begin{cases} \dfrac{a_n}{2} & \text{if } a_n \text{ is an even integer} \\[2mm] 3a_n + 1 & \text{if } a_n \text{ is an odd integer} \end{cases}$$

1. (a) Find several terms for each of the sequences starting with $a_1 = 4, a_1 = 5, a_1 = 24, a_1 = 27$. In each case, continue the sequence until you observe something interesting happening.

   (b) Try different starting numbers of your own for a_1 and see if your observations in part a are still valid. Make a guess about what happens with any starting positive integer a_1.

2. It has been conjectured that starting with any positive integer a_1, the $3N + 1$ sequence eventually reaches 1, after which it repeats the loop 1, 4, 2, 1, 4, 2, ... Define a $3N - 1$ sequence in essentially the same way: begin with any positive integer a_1 and continue by defining $a_{n+1} = \frac{a_n}{2}$ if a_n is even, and $a_{n+1} = 3a_n - 1$ if a_n is odd.

   (a) Take several odd, positive integers for a_1 and write out enough terms of the $3N - 1$ sequence to reach a repeating loop.

   (b) Show that not every positive integer reaches the same loop (as appears to be the case for the $3N + 1$ sequence). How many different loops can you find?

3. Programs for computers or programmable calculators often use an IF . . . THEN . . . instruction that terminates the programs if certain conditions hold but branch to other instructions otherwise. Describe the kind of difficulties that we could conceivably encounter if we programmed a computer to run the $3N + 1$ sequence and print out the terms until reaching 1.

---

15. $b_1 = 2$ and $b_n = 3 \cdot b_{n-1}$ for $n \geq 2$

16. $b_1 = -1$ and $b_n = -2 \cdot b_{n-1}$ for $n \geq 2$

17. $a_1 = 1, a_2 = 2$ and $a_n = a_{n-1} \cdot a_{n-2}$ for $n \geq 3$

18. $a_1 = 2, a_2 = 3$ and $a_n = a_{n-1} + a_{n-2}$ for $n \geq 3$

19. $a_1 = 2, a_2 = 4$ and $a_n = a_{n-1} + a_{n-2}$ for $n \geq 3$

20. $a_1 = 700$ and $a_n = \frac{a_{n-1}}{10}$ for $n \geq 2$

21. $a_1 = 1, a_2 = 2$ and $a_n = \frac{a_{n-1} + a_{n-2}}{2}$ for $n \geq 3$

22. $a_1 = \frac{1}{2}, a_n = a_{n-1} + \frac{1}{2^n}$ for $n \geq 2$

23. $a_1 = 1, a_n = \frac{a_{n-1}}{n!}$ for $n \geq 2$

24. $a_1 = 2, a_n = \sqrt{(a_{n-1})^2 + 1}$ for $n \geq 2$.

Exercises 25–30 A formula for the kth term of a sequence is given. Find the first four terms of the corresponding partial sum sequence.

25. $a_k = 2k + 1$
26. $a_k = 5 - 2k$
27. $a_k = \frac{1}{2^k}$
28. $a_k = (\frac{3}{2})^k$
29. $a_k = \frac{1}{k}$
30. $a_k = \frac{1}{(k + 1)(k + 2)}$

Develop Mastery

Exercises 1–12 Find the first four terms and the eighth term.

1. $f(n) = 3n + 1$
2. $f(n) = 10 - 2n$
3. $g(n) = 5^{-n}$
4. $g(n) = (-1)^n \cdot 2^{-n}$
5. $f(n) = n^2 + n + 41$
6. $f(n) = 2^n - 1$
7. $a_n = 1 - \frac{1}{2^n}$
8. $a_n = \frac{1}{1 - 2^n}$
9. $b_n = \frac{(2n)!}{n!}$
10. $b_n = \frac{n!}{2^n}$
11. $c_n = 4n^2 - 10n + 8$
12. $c_n = (1 + \frac{1}{n})^n$

Exercises 13–24 Find the first four terms of the sequence defined recursively.

13. $a_1 = 3$ and $a_n = a_{n-1} - 4$ for $n \geq 2$
14. $a_1 = 5$ and $a_n = 3 - a_{n-1}$ for $n \geq 2$

Exercises 31–36 Write out the terms for the given summation and then evaluate the sum.

31. $\displaystyle\sum_{k=1}^{10} (k + 1)$

32. $\displaystyle\sum_{j=1}^{5} \frac{1}{j + 1}$

33. $\displaystyle\sum_{j=1}^{5} \left(\frac{1}{j + 1} - \frac{1}{j}\right)$

34. $\displaystyle\sum_{i=1}^{6} \frac{i + 1}{i}$

35. $\displaystyle\sum_{k=1}^{4} \left(1 - \frac{1}{2^k}\right)$

36. $\displaystyle\sum_{k=1}^{5} P_k$ where P_k is the kth prime number.

Exercises 37–42 The first few terms of a sequence are given. Determine a formula for the nth term. The answers are not unique, since many sequences could have the same starting terms. See Example 2.

37. $\frac{1}{2}, \frac{1}{4}, \frac{1}{8}, \frac{1}{16}, \ldots$

38. $\frac{1}{2}, -\frac{2}{3}, \frac{3}{4}, -\frac{4}{5}, \ldots$

39. $\frac{1}{4}, -\frac{2}{9}, \frac{3}{16}, -\frac{4}{25}, \ldots$

40. 5, 8, 11, 14, ...

41. 2, 3, 7, 25, 121, 721, ...
    (*Hint:* 1! = 1, 2! = 2, 3! = 6, 4! = 24.)

42. $\frac{1}{2}, \frac{3}{4}, \frac{7}{8}, \frac{15}{16}, \frac{31}{32}, \ldots$

Exercises 43–46 A formula for a sequence is given. Draw a graph to show the values of function f for $n = 1$, 2, 3, 4, and 5. (*Hint:* The graph consists of isolated points.)

43. $a_n = f(n) = (-1)^n$ 44. $a_n = f(n) = \frac{n}{n+1}$

45. $a_n = f(n) = \frac{(-1)^n(n+1)}{n}$

46. $a_n = f(n) = \frac{(-1)^n}{2^{n-1}}$

Exercises 47–52 Express the sum in sigma notation.

47. $\frac{1}{2} + \frac{1}{3} + \frac{1}{4} + \frac{1}{5} + \frac{1}{6} + \frac{1}{7}$

48. $1 + 4 + 9 + 16 + 25 + 36 + 49 + 64$

49. $\left(1 - \frac{1}{2}\right) + \left(\frac{1}{2} - \frac{1}{3}\right) + \left(\frac{1}{3} - \frac{1}{4}\right) + \left(\frac{1}{4} - \frac{1}{5}\right)$

50. $\frac{1}{2} - \frac{1}{4} + \frac{1}{6} - \frac{1}{8} + \frac{1}{10} - \frac{1}{12}$

51. $\frac{1}{1 \cdot 2} - \frac{1}{2 \cdot 3} + \frac{1}{3 \cdot 4} - \frac{1}{4 \cdot 5} + \frac{1}{5 \cdot 6}$

52. $\ln 2 + \ln 3 + \ln 4 + \ln 5 + \ln 6$

Exercises 53–56 Evaluate the expression.

53. $\frac{6!}{2!4!}$ 54. $\frac{12!}{8!}$ 55. $\frac{50!}{48!}$ 56. $\frac{15!}{5!10!}$

Exercises 57–58 Express each sum as a single fraction involving factorials. Do not evaluate. (*Hint:* See Example 4b.)

57. $\frac{8!}{3!5!} + \frac{8!}{4!4!}$ 58. $\frac{10!}{3!7!} + \frac{10!}{4!6!}$

59. The decimal expansion for $\frac{5}{33}$ is given by $\frac{5}{33} = 0.1515151515 \ldots$. A sequence is described by $a_n =$ the nth decimal digit of $\frac{5}{33}$. For instance, $a_1 = 1$, $a_2 = 5$, $a_3 = 1$.
    (a) Find a_{17} and a_{36}.
    (b) Evaluate $\displaystyle\sum_{k=1}^{6} a_k$ and $\displaystyle\sum_{k=1}^{60} a_k$.

60. A representation of the number $\frac{1}{7}$ is the repeating decimal $0.\overline{142857}$. The sequence $\{a_n\}$ is described by $a_n =$ the nth decimal digit of $\frac{1}{7}$. For instance, $a_1 = 1$, $a_2 = 4$, and $a_3 = 2$.
    (a) Find a_4, a_{17}, and a_{24}.
    (b) Evaluate $\displaystyle\sum_{k=1}^{6} a_k$ and $\displaystyle\sum_{k=1}^{25} a_k$.

Exercises 61–62 Write out the terms and compare the two sums. Are they identical?

61. (a) $\displaystyle\sum_{k=1}^{4} \frac{1}{k(k+1)}$ (b) $\displaystyle\sum_{j=3}^{6} \frac{1}{(j-1)(j-2)}$

62. (a) $\displaystyle\sum_{k=1}^{6} k \cdot 2^{k+1}$ (b) $\displaystyle\sum_{j=2}^{7} (j-1) \cdot 2^j$

Exercises 63–66 Evaluate several terms of the sequence and look for a pattern that will help you guess a formula for a_n in closed form.

63. $a_1 = 1$ $a_n = 2 + a_{n-1}$ for $n \geq 2$

64. $a_1 = 2$ $a_n = 2 \cdot a_{n-1}$ for $n \geq 2$

65. $a_n = \displaystyle\sum_{k=1}^{n} \frac{1}{2^k}$ 66. $a_n = \displaystyle\sum_{k=1}^{n} \left(\frac{1}{k} - \frac{1}{k+1}\right)$.

Exercises 67–70 Write out the first five terms of the sequence $\{a_n\}$ defined recursively.

67. $a_1 = 1$, $a_2 = 2$ $a_{n+2} = (a_{n+1})^2 + (a_n)^2$
    for $n \geq 1$

68. $a_1 = 2$ $a_{n+1} = \frac{n+1}{a_n}$ for $n \geq 1$

69. $a_1 = 1$, $a_2 = 2$ $a_{n+2} = (a_{n+1})(a_n)$
    for $n \geq 1$

70. $a_1 = 2$ $a_{n+1} = a_n^2$ for $n \geq 1$

71. Two sequences $\{a_n\}$ and $\{b_n\}$ are defined by $a_n = n^2 - n + 3$ and $b_1 = 3$, $b_{n+1} = b_n + 2n$ for $n \geq 1$. (a) Evaluate the first five terms of each sequence. (b) Are the sequences identical? Justify your answer. (c) Compute b_{60}.

72. A sequence $\{a_n\}$ is defined recursively by $a_1 = 1$, $a_2 = 4$, $a_{n+2} = a_{n+1} - a_n$ for $n \geq 1$.
    (a) Write out the first ten terms of the sequence.
    (b) What is the sum of the first 36 terms? Of the first 96 terms? Of the first 110 terms?

73. The increasing sequence 2, 3, 5, 6, 7, 8, 10, ... consists of all positive integers that are not squares of integers, that is, all natural numbers not in the sequence 1, 4, 9, ... (a) What is the 60th term of the sequence? (b) How many terms of the sequence precede the number 124?

Exercises 74–76   The sequence $\{a_n\}$ is defined recursively in terms of a function f.

(a) Find the first five terms.

(b) Find the sum of the first 20 terms.

(c) Explain why the sequence repeats as it does. [*Hint:* Find $f(f(x))$.]

74. $f(x) = \frac{2x}{x-2}$; $a_1 = f(1)$, $a_{n+1} = f(a_n)$, $n \geq 1$

75. $f(x) = \frac{-3x}{2x+3}$; $a_1 = f(3)$, $a_{n+1} = f(a_n)$, $n \geq 1$

76. $f(x) = \frac{3x}{x-3}$; $a_1 = f(4)$, $a_{n+1} = f(a_n)$, $n \geq 1$

77. The sequence $\{a_n\}$ is given by $a_n = x^n + x^{-n}$, where $x = \frac{-1 + \sqrt{3}i}{2}$.

(a) Use DeMoivre's theorem to evaluate $x^n + x^{-n}$, then show that $a_n = 2 \cos (n \cdot 120°)$.

(b) Write out the first six terms of the sequence and find their sum.

(c) What is the sum of the first 100 terms?

78. If $u = \sqrt[24]{24!}$ and $v = \sqrt[25]{25!}$, which is larger, u or v? (*Hint:* Compare u^{600} and v^{600}.)

Exercises 79–84   Use a calculator to evaluate the first five terms of the sequence. To efficiently use your calculator, store the term you just calculated and use it to get the next term, and then repeat. Look at your sequence of decimal answers and guess what number the sequence approaches. These exercises illustrate a technique for numerical approximations that is frequently used in practice.

79. $a_1 = 1$ $a_n = \frac{1}{2}(a_{n-1} + \frac{4}{a_{n-1}})$ for $n \geq 2$

80. $a_1 = 2$ $a_n = \frac{1}{2}(a_{n-1} + \frac{3}{a_{n-1}})$ for $n \geq 2$

81. $a_1 = 1$ $a_n = \frac{1}{2}(a_{n-1} + \frac{2}{a_{n-1}})$ for $n \geq 2$

82. $a_1 = \sqrt{2}$ $a_n = \sqrt{2 + a_{n-1}}$ for $n \geq 2$

83. $a_1 = \sqrt{6}$ $a_n = \sqrt{6 + a_{n-1}}$ for $n \geq 2$

84. $a_1 = 1$ $a_n = \frac{4}{a_{n-1}} - \sqrt{2}$ for $n \geq 2$

85. The factorial sequence $\{n!\}$ increases very rapidly. For instance,

$$10! \approx 3.6 \times 10^6 \qquad 20! \approx 2.4 \times 10^{18}$$

$$50! \approx 3.0 \times 10^{64} \qquad 70! \approx 1.2 \times 10^{100}$$

To get some idea of how large these numbers are, look at $20!$. Simple computation gives $20! \approx 2,432,902,008,176,690,000$. Now suppose a computer printer that operates at 100 characters per second were to print out a manuscript with $20!$ characters. How long would it take the printer to do the job?

86. For the manuscript described in Exercise 85, suppose each page contained about 4000 characters. How thick would the manuscript be? The thickness of a ream of paper (500 pages) is approximately 2 inches. For comparison, the distance from the earth to the sun is 93 million miles.

87. Evaluate the first five terms of $\{a_n\}$ and $\{b_n\}$ where

$$a_n = 2^{n-1}, \quad b_n = \frac{n^4 - 6n^3 + 23n^2 - 18n + 24}{24}.$$

Are the sequences identical?

88. (a) Evaluate the first six terms of $\{a_n\}$ where

$$a_n = \sqrt{n} + \sqrt{n + 9 - 6\sqrt{n}}.$$

Use your calculator to simplify each term. Is $a_n = 3$ for every $n \geq 1$? Explain.

(b) If $b_n = \sqrt{n} + |\sqrt{n} - 3|$, are the sequences $\{a_n\}$ and $\{b_n\}$ identical? Explain.

SECTION 8.2   **Arithmetic and Geometric Sequences**

Whenever you tell me that mathematics is just a human invention like the game of chess I would like to believe you. But I keep returning to the same problem. Why does the mathematics we have discovered in the past so often turn out to describe the workings of the Universe?
John Barrow

I remember that when I was about twelve I learned from [my uncle] that by the distributive law −1 times −1 equals +1. I thought that was great.

Peter Lax

Two kinds of regular sequences occur so often that they have specific names, **arithmetic** and **geometric sequences.** We treat them together because some obvious parallels between these kinds of sequences lead to similar formulas. This also makes it easier to learn and work with the formulas. The greatest value in this association is understanding how the ideas are related and how to derive the formulas from fundamental concepts. Anyone learning the formulas this way can recover them whenever needed.

Both arithmetic and geometric sequences begin with an arbitrary first term, and the sequences are generated by regularly adding the same number (the **common difference** in an arithmetic sequence) or multiplying by the same number (the **common ratio** in a geometric sequence). Definitions emphasize the parallel features, which examples will clarify.

Definition: Arithmetic and Geometric Sequences

Arithmetic Sequence

$$a_1 = a \quad \text{and} \quad a_n = a_{n-1} + d \quad \text{for } n > 1$$

The sequence $\{a_n\}$ is an arithmetic sequence with first term a and common difference d.

Geometric Sequence

$$a_1 = a \quad \text{and} \quad a_n = r \cdot a_{n-1} \quad \text{for } n > 1$$

The sequence $\{a_n\}$ is a geometric sequence with first term a and common ratio r.

The definitions imply convenient formulas for the nth term of both kinds of sequences. For an arithmetic sequence we get the nth term by adding d to the first term $n - 1$ times; for a geometric sequence, we multiply the first term by r, $n - 1$ times.

Formulas for the nth Terms of Arithmetic and Geometric

For an arithmetic sequence, a formula for the nth term of the sequence is

$$a_n = a + (n - 1)d. \tag{1}$$

For a geometric sequence, a formula for the nth term of the sequence is

$$a_n = a \cdot r^{n-1}. \tag{2}$$

The definitions allow us to recognize both arithmetic and geometric sequences. In an arithmetic sequence the difference between successive terms, $a_{n+1} - a_n$, is always the same, the constant d; in a geometric sequence the ratio of successive terms, $\frac{a_{n+1}}{a_n}$, is always the same.

EXAMPLE 1   The first three terms of a sequence are given. Determine if the sequence could be arithmetic or geometric. If it is an arithmetic sequence, find d; for a geometric sequence, find r.

Strategy: Calculate the differences and/or ratios of successive terms.

(a) 2, 4, 8, . . .   **(b)** ln 2, ln 4, ln 8, . . .   **(c)** $\frac{1}{2}, \frac{1}{3}, \frac{1}{4}, \ldots$

Solution

(a) $a_2 - a_1 = 4 - 2 = 2$, and $a_3 - a_2 = 8 - 4 = 4$. Since the differences are not the same, the sequence cannot be arithmetic. Checking ratios, $\frac{a_2}{a_1} = \frac{4}{2} = 2$, and $\frac{a_3}{a_2} = \frac{8}{4} = 2$, so the sequence could be geometric, with a common ratio $r = 2$. Without a formula for the general term, we cannot say anything more about the sequence.

(b) $a_2 - a_1 = \ln 4 - \ln 2 = \ln\left(\frac{4}{2}\right) = \ln 2$, and $a_3 - a_2 = \ln 8 - \ln 4 = \ln\left(\frac{8}{4}\right) = \ln 2$, so the sequence could be arithmetic, with ln 2 as the common difference. As in part **(a)**, we cannot say more because no general term is given.

(c) $a_2 - a_1 = \frac{1}{3} - \frac{1}{2} = -\frac{1}{6}$, and $a_3 - a_2 = \frac{1}{4} - \frac{1}{3} = -\frac{1}{12}$. The differences are not the same, so the sequence is not arithmetic. $\frac{a_2}{a_1} = \frac{\left(\frac{1}{3}\right)}{\left(\frac{1}{2}\right)} = \frac{2}{3}$, and

$\frac{a_3}{a_2} = \frac{\left(\frac{1}{4}\right)}{\left(\frac{1}{3}\right)} = \frac{3}{4}$, so the sequence is not geometric. Note that the sequence in part **(a)** *could be* geometric and the sequence in part **(b)** *could be* arithmetic, but in part **(c)** you can conclude unequivocally that the sequence cannot be either arithmetic or geometric. ▲

EXAMPLE 2   Determine whether the sequence is arithmetic, geometric, or neither.

(a) $\{3 - 1.6n\}$ **(b)** $\{2^n\}$ **(c)** $a_n = \ln n$

Solution

(a) $a_2 - a_1 = (3 - 1.6 \cdot 2) - (3 - 1.6 \cdot 1) = (-0.2) - 1.4 = -1.6$, and $a_3 - a_2 = (3 - 1.6 \cdot 3) - (3 - 1.6 \cdot 2) = -1.6$ From the first three terms, this could be an arithmetic sequence with $d = -1.6$. Check the difference $a_{n+1} - a_n$.

$$a_{n+1} - a_n = [3 - 1.6(n + 1)] - [3 - 1.6n] = 1.6.$$

The seqeunce is arithmetic, with $d = -1.6$.

(b) $a_2 - a_1 = 4 - 2 = 2$, and $a_3 - a_2 = 8 - 4 = 4$, so the sequence is not arithmetic. Using the formula for the general term,

$$\frac{a_{n+1}}{a_n} = \frac{2^{n+1}}{2^n} = 2.$$

The sequence $\{2^n\}$ is geometric, with 2 as the common ratio.

(c) $a_{n+1} - a_n = \ln(n+1) - \ln n = \ln\frac{n+1}{n}$. The difference depends on n, so the sequence is not arithmetic. Checking ratios, $\frac{a_{n+1}}{a_n} = \frac{\ln(n+1)}{\ln n}$, so the ratio also changes with n. The sequence is neither arithmetic or geometric. ▲

EXAMPLE 3   Show that the sequence is arithmetic; find the common difference and the twentieth term.

$$\textbf{(a) } a_n = 2n - 1 \qquad \textbf{(b) } 50, 45, 40, \ldots, 55 - 5n, \ldots$$

Solution

(a) The first few terms of $\{a_n\}$ are $1, 3, 5, 7, \ldots$, from which it is apparent that each term is 2 more than the preceding term; this is an arithmetic sequence with first term and common difference $a = 1$ and $d = 2$. Check to see that $a_{n+1} - a_n = 2$. To find a_{20}, use either the defining formula for the sequence or Equation 1 for the nth term:

$$a_{20} = 2 \cdot 20 - 1 = 39 \qquad \text{or} \qquad a_{20} = a + 19d = 1 + 19 \cdot 2 = 39.$$

(b) If $b_n = 55 - 5n$, then $b_{n+1} - b_n = [55 - 5(n+1)] = [55 - 5n] = -5$. This is an arithmetic sequence with $a = 50$, $d = -5$, and so $b_{20} = 55 - 5 \cdot 20 = -45$. ▲

Given the structure of arithmetic and geometric sequences, any two terms completely determine the sequence. Using Equation 1 or 2, two terms of the sequence give us a pair of equations from which we can find the first term and either the common difference or common ratio, as illustrated in the next example.

EXAMPLE 4   Suppose $\{a_n\}$ is an arithmetic sequence with $a_8 = 6$ and $a_{12} = -4$. Find a, d, and the three terms between a_8 and a_{12}.

Solution

From Equation 1, $a_8 = a + 7d$, and $a_{12} = a + 11d$, from which the difference is given by $a_{12} - a_8 = 4d$. Use the given values for a_8 and a_{12} to get $-4 - 6 = 4d$, or $d = -\frac{5}{2}$. Substitute $-\frac{5}{2}$ for d in $6 = a + 7d$ and solve for a, $a = \frac{47}{2}$. Find the three terms between a_8 and a_{12} by successively adding $-\frac{5}{2}$:

$$a_9 = a_8 - \frac{5}{2} = \frac{7}{2} \qquad a_{10} = a_9 - \frac{5}{2} = 1 \qquad a_{11} = a_{10} - \frac{5}{2} = -\frac{3}{2}. \quad ▲$$

Therefore, a_9 is $\frac{7}{2}$, a_{10} is 1, and a_{11} is $-\frac{3}{2}$.

EXAMPLE 5   Determine whether the sequence is geometric. If it is geometric, then find the common ratio and the terms a_1, a_3, and a_{10}.

$$\textbf{(a) } \{2^n\} \qquad \textbf{(b) } 2, -\frac{2}{3}, \frac{2}{9}, \ldots, 2\left(-\frac{1}{3}\right)^{n-1}, \ldots$$

Strategy: The property that identifies a geometric sequence is the common ratio: the values $\frac{a_2}{a_1}, \frac{a_3}{a_2}, \frac{a_4}{a_3},$ ... must all be the same. For a geometric sequence, use Equation 2.

Solution

(a) The first few terms are 2, 4, 8, 16, ... , each of which is twice the preceding term. This is a geometric sequence with first term $a = 2$, and common ratio given by $r = \frac{a_{n+1}}{a_n} = \frac{2^{n+1}}{2^n} = 2$. Using $a_n = 2^n$,

$$a_1 = 2 \qquad a_3 = 2^3 = 8 \qquad \text{and} \qquad a_{10} = 2^{10} = 1024.$$

(b) Consider the ratio

$$\frac{a_{n+1}}{a_n} = \frac{2\left(-\frac{1}{3}\right)^n}{2\left(-\frac{1}{3}\right)^{n-1}} = -\frac{1}{3},$$

so the sequence is geometric with $a = 2$ and $r = -\frac{1}{3}$. Using $a_n = 2(-\frac{1}{3})^{n-1}$, we get $a_1 = 2$, $a_3 = ar^2 = \frac{2}{9}$, and $a_{10} = ar^9 = 2(-\frac{1}{3})^9 = -\frac{2}{19683}$. ▲

Partial Sums of Arithmetic Sequences

There is a charming story told about Carl Freidrich Gauss, one of the greatest mathematicians of all time. Early in Gauss' school career, the schoolmaster assigned the class the task of summing the first hundred positive integers, $1 + 2 + 3 + \ldots + 99 + 100$. That should have occupied a good portion of the morning, but while other class members busied themselves at their slates calculating $1 + 2 = 3, 3 + 3 = 6, 6 + 4 = 10$, and so on, Gauss sat quietly for a few moments, wrote a single number on his slate, and presented it to the teacher. Young Gauss observed that 1 and 100 add up to 101, as do the pair 2 and 99, 3 and 98, and so on up to 50 and 51. There are fifty such pairs, each with a sum of 101, for a total of $50 \cdot 101 = 5050$, the number he wrote on his slate.

This approach works for the partial sum of any arithmetic sequence, and we will use the method to derive some useful formulas. However, the ideas are more valuable than memorizing formulas. If you understand the idea, you can recreate the formula when needed.

To find a formula for the nth partial sum of an arithmetic sequence, that is, the sum of n consecutive terms, pair the first and last terms, the second and next-to-last, and so on; *each pair has the same sum*. In fact, it is easier to pair all terms twice, as illustrated with Gauss' sum:

$$
\begin{array}{rccccccc}
S_{100} = & 1 + & 2 + & \cdots + & 99 + & 100 \\
S_{100} = & 100 + & 99 + & \cdots + & 2 + & 1 \\
\hline
2S_{100} = & 101 + & 101 + & \cdots + & 101 + & 101
\end{array}
$$

The sum on the right has 100 terms, so $2S_{100} = 100(101)$. Dividing by 2, $S_{100} = 50(101) = 5050$.

For the the general case, pairing the terms in S_n and adding gives $2S_n = n(a_1 + a_n)$ because there are n pairs, each with the same sum. Dividing by 2 yields the desired formula.

Partial Sums of an Arithmetic Sequence

Suppose $\{a_n\}$ is an arithmetic sequence. The sum S_n of the first n terms is given by

$$S_n = \frac{n(a_1 + a_n)}{2}$$

(3)

The formula is probably most easily remembered as n times the average of the first and last terms.

EXAMPLE 6 For the sequence $\{a_n\} = \{2n - 1\}$, **(a)** evaluate the sum $S_{25} = \sum_{k=1}^{25} (2k - 1)$ and **(b)** find a formula for S_n.

Solution

Strategy: Let $a_n = 2n - 1$. To find S_{25} from Equation 3 requires a_1 and a_{25}, which the formula for a_n can provide. For **(b)**, substitute 1 for a_1 and $2n - 1$ for a_n in Equation 3 and simplify.

Follow the strategy.

(a) By equation 3, $S_{25} = \frac{25(a_1 + a_{25})}{2}$. Now, find a_1 and a_{25}.

$$a_1 = 2 \cdot 1 - 1 = 1 \quad \text{and} \quad a_{25} = 2 \cdot 25 - 1 = 49$$

Thus, $S_{25} = \dfrac{25(1 + 49)}{2} = 625$.

(b) In general,

$$S_n = \frac{n(a_1 + a_n)}{2} = \frac{n[1 + (2n - 1)]}{2} = \frac{n(2n)}{2} = n^2.$$

Hence, $S_n = n^2$. ▲

EXAMPLE 7 The sum of the first eight terms of an arithmetic sequence $\{a_n\}$ is 24; the sixth term is 0. Find a formula for a_n.

Solution

For a_n, first find a and d. Since $a_6 = a + 5d$, $a + 5d = 0$. Express S_8 in terms of a and d,

$$S_8 = \frac{8[a + (a + 7d)]}{2} = 4(2a + 7d).$$

Since we are given $S_8 = 24$, Equation 3 states that $4(2a + 7d) = 24$. This gives a pair of equations to solve for a and d.

$$\begin{cases} a + 5d = 0 \\ 2a + 7d = 6 \end{cases}$$

We find $d = -2$ and $a = 10$. Therefore, the nth term is

$$a_n = a + (n - 1)d = 10 + (n - 1)(-2) = 12 - 2n. \quad ▲$$

Partial Sums of Geometric Sequences

The idea of pairing terms, which works so well for arithmetic sequences, does not help with a geometric sequence. Another idea does make the sum easy to calculate though. Multiply both sides by r and subtract:

$$S_n = a + ar + ar^2 + \cdots + ar^{n-1}$$
$$rS_n = \quad\; ar + ar^2 + \cdots + ar^{n-1} + ar^n$$
$$\overline{S_n - rS_n = a - ar^n}$$

Thus,

$$S_n(1 - r) = a(1 - r^n).$$

If $r \neq 1$, dividing both sides by $(1 - r)$ yields a formula for S_n.

Partial Sums of a Geometric Sequence

Suppose $\{a_n\}$ is a geometric sequence with $r \neq 1$. The sum of the first n terms is

$$S_n = \frac{a(1 - r^n)}{1 - r} \tag{4}$$

In the special case where $r = 1$, the geometric sequence is also an arithmetic sequence, and $S_n = a + a + a + \cdots + a = na$.

EXAMPLE 8   Find a_n and S_n for the geometric sequence $\frac{1}{3}, \frac{1}{6}, \frac{1}{12}, \ldots$.

Solution

Strategy: Since it is given that the sequence is geometric, find the common ratio $r = \frac{a_2}{a_1}$ and then use Equations 2 and 4.

Follow the strategy. We know that $a_1 = \frac{1}{3}$ and a_2 is $\frac{1}{6}$. The common ratio is $r = \frac{a_2}{a_1} = \frac{\left(\frac{1}{6}\right)}{\left(\frac{1}{3}\right)} = \frac{1}{2}$. From Equation 2,

$$a_n = ar^{n-1} = \left(\frac{1}{3}\right)\left(\frac{1}{2}\right)^{n-1} = \frac{1}{3 \cdot 2^{n-1}}.$$

Since $r = \frac{1}{2}$, $1 - r = \frac{1}{2}$ and $(1 - r^n) = 1 - \left(\frac{1}{2}\right)^n$. Applying Equation 4 gives

$$S_n = \frac{a(1 - r^n)}{1 - r} = \frac{\left(\frac{1}{3}\right)\left[1 - \left(\frac{1}{2}\right)^n\right]}{1 - \left(\frac{1}{2}\right)} = \frac{2}{3}\left(1 - \frac{1}{2^n}\right).$$

Therefore,

$$a_n = \frac{1}{3 \cdot 2^{n-1}} \quad \text{and} \quad S_n = \frac{2}{3}\left(1 - \frac{1}{2^n}\right)$$

EXAMPLE 9   Find the sum of the first 5, 10, and 100 terms of the geometric sequence $\{\frac{1}{3 \cdot 2^{n-1}}\}$ from Example 8.

Solution

In Example 8 we found a formula for the nth partial sum. $S_n = \frac{2}{3}[1 - (\frac{1}{2})^n]$. Substituting 5, 10, and 100 for n,

$$S_5 = \left(\frac{2}{3}\right)\left(\frac{31}{32}\right) = \frac{31}{48}$$

$$S_{10} = \left(\frac{2}{3}\right)\left(\frac{1023}{1024}\right) = \frac{1023}{1536}$$

$$S_{100} = \left(\frac{2}{3}\right)\left[1 - \frac{1}{2^{100}}\right]$$

The last factor of S_{100} is so near 1 that a calculator shows it as 1. The term $(\frac{1}{2})^{100}$ has 30 zeros immediately following the decimal point (about 7.89×10^{-31}). Thus $S_{100} \approx \frac{2}{3}$. ▲

Looking Ahead to Calculus: Infinite Series

As indicated above, each sequence $\{a_n\}$ is associated with a sequence of partial sums $\{S_n\}$, where $S_n = a_1 + a_2 + \cdots + a_n$. What happens to S_n as n gets larger and larger, that is, as we add more and more terms? We are considering an "infinite sum" written as $a_1 + a_2 + a_3 + \cdots$, or in summation notation,

$$\sum_{n=1}^{\infty} a_n.$$

This is called an **infinite series.**

Since we cannot add an infinite set of numbers, we need instead the notion of a limit. In one sense, calculus is the study of limits. It is beyond the scope of this book to deal with infinite series in general, but for a geometric sequence $\{a_n\}$, we can at least get an intuitive feeling for what happens to S_n as n becomes large.

In Examples 8 and 9, where $a_n = \frac{1}{3 \cdot 2^n}$ and $S_n = \frac{2}{3}[1 - (\frac{1}{2})^2]$, it is reasonable to assume that $(\frac{1}{2})^n$ gets close to 0 as n becomes large. In calculus notation

$$\lim_{n \to \infty} \left(\frac{1}{2}\right)^n = 0, \qquad \text{from which} \qquad \lim_{n \to \infty} S_n = \frac{2}{3}.$$

We say that the infinite series, $\sum_{n=1}^{\infty} \frac{1}{3 \cdot 2^n}$ **converges** to $\frac{2}{3}$, and we write

$$\sum_{n=1}^{\infty} \frac{1}{3 \cdot 2^n} = \frac{1}{3} + \frac{1}{6} + \frac{1}{12} + \cdots = \frac{2}{3}.$$

In general, we associate each geometric sequence $\{ar^{n-1}\}$ with an infinite geometric series

$$\sum_{n=1}^{\infty} ar^{n-1} = a + ar + ar^2 + \cdots + ar^{n-1} + \cdots.$$

The only meaning we give to this infinite sum is the limit of the sequence of partial sums,

$$\lim_{n \to \infty} S_n = \lim_{n \to \infty} \frac{a(1 - r^n)}{1 - r},$$

which depends on $\lim_{n \to \infty} r^n$. Looking at different values of r, we conclude that if r is any number between -1 and 1, then $\lim_{n \to \infty} r^n = 0$, from which

$$\lim_{n \to \infty} S_n = \lim_{n \to \infty} \frac{a(1 - r^n)}{1 - r} = \frac{a}{1 - r}.$$

Infinite Geometric Series

Associated with every geometric sequence $\{ar^{n-1}\}$ is an infinite geometric series

$$\sum_{n=1}^{\infty} ar^{n-1} = a + ar + ar^2 + \cdots + ar^{n-1} + \cdots.$$

If $-1 < r < 1$, then the series converges to $\frac{a}{1-r}$, and we write

$$\sum_{n=1}^{\infty} ar^{n-1} = a + ar + ar^2 + \cdots + ar^{n-1} + \cdots = \frac{a}{1 - r}. \quad \textbf{(5)}$$

If $|r| \geq 1$, then the infinite series does not have a sum, and it diverges.

Repeating Decimals   In Section 1.2 we said that the decimal representation of any rational number is a repeating decimal. The following example illustrates how we can use an infinite geometric series to express a repeating decimal as a fraction of integers.

EXAMPLE 10   Write $1.2454545 \cdots (= 1.2\overline{45})$ in terms of an infinite geometric series, then use Equation 5 to express $1.2\overline{45}$ in the form $\frac{p}{q}$, where p and q are integers.

Solution

$$1.2454545 \cdots = 1.2 + 0.045 + 0.00045 + \cdots = \frac{12}{10} + \frac{45}{10^3} + \frac{45}{10^5} + \cdots$$

The terms following $\frac{12}{10}$ form an infinite geometric series with $a = 0.045 = \frac{45}{1000}$ and $r = 0.01 = \frac{1}{100}$. Since r is between -1 and 1, we may use Equation 5 to express the sum as

$$\frac{6}{5} + \frac{0.045}{1 - 0.01} = \frac{6}{5} + \frac{45}{990} = \frac{137}{110}.$$

Therefore, $\frac{137}{110}$ and $1.2\overline{45}$ represent the same number.   ▲

Functions Represented by Infinite Series   The infinite series $1 + x + x^2 + \cdots$ is geometric (with $a = 1$ and $r = x$), so if x is any number between -1 and 1, the series converges:

$$1 + x + x^2 + x^3 + \cdots = \frac{1}{1 - x}.$$

Hence the function $f(x) = \frac{1}{1-x}$, where $-1 < x < 1$, can be represented by the infinite series $1 + x + x^2 + \cdots$.

An important topic arises in calculus when we represent functions by infinite series. For instance, it can be shown that the function $F(x) = \sin x$ is also given by

$$\sin x = x - \frac{x^3}{3!} + \frac{x^5}{5!} - \frac{x^7}{7!} + \cdots.$$

The representation for $\sin x$ is not a geometric series, but it does converge for every real number x. It follows that $\sin x$ can be approximated by polynomial functions of the first few terms of the infinite series. For example, if we let $p(x)$ be the sum of the first four terms,

$$p(x) = x - \frac{x^3}{3!} + \frac{x^5}{5!} - \frac{x^7}{7!}, \qquad \text{then} \qquad p(x) \approx \sin x.$$

Evaluating at $x = 0.5$,

$$\sin 0.5 \approx p(0.5) = 0.5 - \frac{(0.5)^3}{6} + \frac{(0.5)^5}{120} - \frac{(0.5)^7}{5040} \approx 0.4794255332.$$

To see how good this approximation is, use your calculator to evaluate $\sin 0.5$ (in radian mode). In fact, your calculator is probably designed to use polynomial approximations to evaluate most of its built-in functions.

Following are series representations for some other important functions we have studied in Chapters 4 and 5.

$$\sin x = x - \frac{x^3}{3!} + \frac{x^5}{5!} - \frac{x^7}{7!} + \cdots \qquad \cos x = 1 - \frac{x^2}{2!} + \frac{x^4}{4!} - \frac{x^6}{6!} + \cdots$$

$$e^x = 1 + x + \frac{x^2}{2!} + \frac{x^3}{3!} + \cdots \qquad e^{-x} = 1 - x + \frac{x^2}{2!} - \frac{x^3}{3!} + \cdots$$

EXERCISES 8.2

Check Your Understanding

Exercises 1–6   True or False. Give reasons for your conclusion.

1. If $\{a_n\}$ is an arithmetic sequence, then $a_6 - a_3 = a_8 - a_5$.

2. The sequence beginning $\frac{1}{2}, \frac{1}{4}, \frac{1}{6}, \frac{1}{8}, \ldots$ could be an arithmetic sequence.

3. If $\{c_n\}$ is a geometric sequence, then $\frac{c_5}{c_2} = r^3$.

4. The sequences $\{a_n\}$ and $\{b_n\}$ given by $a_n = 2n$ and $b_n = \log(100^n)$ are identical.

5. In a geometric sequence if the common ratio is negative, then after a certain point in the sequence, all the terms will be negative.

6. In an arithmetic sequence if the common difference is negative, then after a certain point in the sequence, all the terms will be negative.

Exercises 7–10 Complete the sentence by selecting from the list below *all choices* that make the statement true.

(a) 0   **(b)** 1   **(c)** -8 **(d)** 8   **(e)** 14
(f) a negative number   **(g)** none of the above

7. $14 + \sum\limits_{k=1}^{5} (-2)^k =$ _____.

8. $\sum\limits_{k=1}^{15} (8 - k) =$ _____.

9. $0.999 \ldots = 0.\overline{9} =$ _____.

10. $11(0.727272 \ldots) = 11(0.\overline{72}) =$ _____.

Explore and Discover

1. Square S_1 has vertex A_1 as shown in the diagram and each side of S_1 has length 1. Join the midpoints of the sides of S_1 to get another square S_2 with vertex A_2. Now join the midpoints of the sides of S_2 to get square S_3 with a vertex at A_3. Continue this process to obtain a sequence of squares $S_1, S_2, S_3, \ldots$.
  (a) Suppose $K_1, K_2, K_3, \ldots$ are the areas of the squares $S_1, S_2, S_3, \ldots$, respectively. Evaluate $K_1, K_2,$ and K_3. Make a guess about a formula for K_n, the area of the nth square. What type of sequence is $\{K_n\}$?
  (b) Let $a_1 = |\overline{A_1A_2}|$, $a_2 = |\overline{A_2A_3}|$, $a_3 = |\overline{A_3A_4}|$, $\ldots$. Evaluate $a_1, a_2,$ and a_3 and guess a formula for a_n. What type of sequence is $\{a_n\}$?
  (c) Does it make sense to talk about the total length of the path from A_1 to A_2 to A_3, and so on? That is, what is the sum of the infinite series $a_1 + a_2 + a_3 + \ldots$?

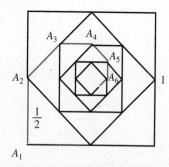

2. Follow a procedure similar to that in Exercise 1, taking points a third of the way along the side of the square rather than the midpoints, as suggested in the diagram. Answer questions **a, b,** and **c**.

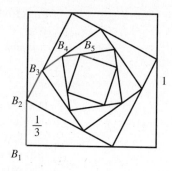

3. Consider a situation similar to that in Exercise 1, but using equilateral triangles instead of squares, as suggested in the diagram.

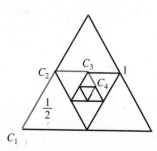

Develop Mastery

Exercises 1–10 The first three terms of an arithmetic sequence are given. Find **(a)** the common difference, **(b)** the sixth and tenth terms, and **(c)** the sum of the first ten terms.

1. $3, 6, 9, \ldots$ **2.** $-18, -11, -4, \ldots$
3. $4, -1, -6, \ldots$ **4.** $\frac{1}{2}, \frac{2}{3}, \frac{5}{6}, \ldots$
5. $20, \frac{52}{3}, \frac{44}{3}, \ldots$ **6.** $0.24, 0.32, 0.40, \ldots$
7. $1 + \sqrt{2}, 1 - \sqrt{2}, 1 - 3\sqrt{2}, \ldots$
8. $1 + \sqrt{5}, 1, 1 - \sqrt{5}, \ldots$
9. $\ln 2, \ln 4, \ln 8, \ldots$ **10.** $\ln e, 4, 7, \ldots$

Exercises 11–20 The first three terms of a geometric sequence are given. Find **(a)** the common ratio, **(b)** the sixth and eighth terms, and **(c)** the sum of the first five terms.

11. $1, -\frac{1}{3}, \frac{1}{9}, \ldots$ **12.** $2, 1, \frac{1}{2}, \ldots$
13. $18, 6, 2, \ldots$ **14.** $1, -0.5, 0.25, \ldots$
15. $1, \sqrt{2}, 2, \ldots$ **16.** $1, \frac{1}{\sqrt{2}}, \frac{1}{2}, \ldots$
17. $3, 1.5, 0.75, \ldots$ **18.** $\frac{4}{9}, -\frac{2}{3}, 1, \ldots$
19. $\sqrt{2} - 1, 1, \sqrt{2} + 1, \ldots$ **20.** $\frac{3}{2}, 1, \frac{2}{3}, \ldots$

Exercises 21–28   The first three terms of a sequence are given. Determine whether the sequence could be arithmetic, geometric, or neither. If arithmetic, find the common difference; if geometric, give the common ratio.

21. $3, -1, -4, \ldots$ **22.** $-2, -4, -8, \ldots$

23. $\frac{1}{2}, \frac{1}{3}, \frac{1}{4}, \ldots$ **24.** $\frac{4}{9}, -\frac{2}{3}, 1, \ldots$

25. $\ln \sqrt{3}, \ln 3, \ln 3\sqrt{3}, \ldots$ **26.** $1, 4, 9, \ldots$

27. $0.21, 0.0021, 0.000021, \ldots$

28. $e^{-1}, e^{-2}, e^{-3}, \ldots$

Exercises 29–36   Assume that the given information refers to an arithmetic sequence. Find the indicated quantities.

29. $a_3 = 5, a_6 = 0; d, a_1$

30. $a_2 = 5, d = \frac{3}{2}; a_1, a_{10}$

31. $a_1 = 1, a_8 = 15; d, S_8$

32. $a_8 = 1, a_9 = 1; S_4, S_{16}$

33. $a_8 = 15, S_8 = 64; a_1, S_4$

34. $a_6 = -1, S_{16} = 8; a_1, S_6$

35. $a_5 = \frac{\pi}{3}, d = \frac{\pi}{3}, a_4, a_{16}, S_{16}$

36. $a_5 = \sqrt{2}, a_8 = 4\sqrt{2}; a_1, a_{12}, S_{12}$

Exercises 37–44   Assume that the given information refers to a geometric sequence. Determine the indicated quantities.

37. $a_1 = 4, a_2 = 6; r, a_6$

38. $a_2 = 3, a_3 = -\sqrt{3}; a_4, a_7$

39. $a_5 = \frac{1}{4}, r = \frac{3}{2}; a_1, S_5$

40. $a_4 = 6, a_7 = 48; r, a_{10}$

41. $a_1 = 18, S_2 = 24; a_5, S_5$

42. $a_4 = \frac{1}{3}, a_7 = -\frac{1}{81}; r, S_7$

43. $a_3 = -\frac{8}{5}, a_{10} = \frac{1}{80}; a_1, S_8$

44. $a_1 = \frac{1}{2}, S_2 = \frac{2}{3}; a_6, S_6$

Exercises 45–50   Determine the value(s) of x for which the given expressions will form the first three terms of the indicated type of sequence.

45. $2, x, x^2 - 1$; arithmetic

46. $x - 2, x + 2, x + 6$; arithmetic

47. $2, x, x^2 - 1$; geometric

48. $x - 2, x + 2, x + 6$; geometric

49. $x + 1, 3x - 1, 3x + 3$; arithmetic

50. $2, 2^x, 2^{x-4}$; geometric

Exercises 51–56   Three expressions are given. Determine whether they are the first three terms of an arithmetic sequence or a geometric sequence for every real number x.

51. $x + 1, x + 3, x + 5$

52. $2 - x, 3 - 2x, 4 - 3x$

53. $2^x, 2^{x-1}, 2^{x-2}$

54. $2^{x-1}, 2^{2x-2}, 2^{3x-3}$

55. $(1 + x), (1 + x)^2, (1 + x)^3$

56. $\frac{1}{x^2 + 1}, \frac{2}{x^2 + 1}, \frac{4}{x^2 + 1}$

Exercises 57–60   For the infinite series, **(a)** write out the first four terms and find the common ratio and **(b)** evaluate the sum of the series, that is, find the number to which the series converges.

57. $\displaystyle\sum_{n=1}^{\infty} \left(-\frac{1}{3}\right)^{n-1}$ **58.** $\displaystyle\sum_{n=1}^{\infty} \frac{3}{2^n}$

59. $\displaystyle\sum_{n=1}^{\infty} \frac{3^n}{4^{n+1}}$ **60.** $\displaystyle\sum_{n=1}^{\infty} 4\left(\frac{1}{5}\right)^{n-1}$

61. Find the sum of the infinite geometric series
$3 - 2 + \frac{4}{3} - \frac{8}{9} + \ldots$.

62. For each of the following values of a common ratio r, calculate $r, r^2, r^4, r^8, \ldots$, squaring repeatedly. Count the number of squaring operations until your calculator displays 0 or an error message for the first time. What does an error message indicate?

(a) $r = \frac{1}{3}$ **(b)** $r = \frac{98}{99}$

(c) $r = 1.04$ **(d)** $r = \frac{99}{98}$

Exercises 63–66   Express as a quotient of two integers in reduced form.

63. (a) 1.24, **(b)** $1.\overline{24}$ **64. (a)** 1.45, **(b)** $1.\overline{45}$

65. (a) 1.125, **(b)** $1.\overline{125}$ **66.** 0.72, **(b)** $0.\overline{72}$

67. Evaluate the sum $\frac{\pi}{2} + \pi + \frac{3\pi}{2} + 2\pi + \frac{5\pi}{2} + \ldots + \frac{31\pi}{2} + 16\pi$.

68. (a) How many integers between 200 and 1000 are divisible by 11?
(b) What is their sum?

69. Find the sum of all odd positive integers less than 200.

70. Find the sum of all positive integers between 400 and 500 that are divisible by 3.

71. If $1 < a < b < c$ and a, b, and c are the first three terms of a geometric sequence, show that the numbers $\frac{1}{\log_a 4}$, $\frac{1}{\log_b 4}$, and $\frac{1}{\log_c 4}$ are three consecutive terms of an arithmetic sequence. (*Hint:* Use the change of the base formula from Section 4.4.)

72. In a geometric sequence $\{a_n\}$ of positive terms, $a_2 - a_1 = 12$ and $a_5 - a_4 = 324$. Find the first five terms of the sequence.

73. If the sum of the first 60 odd positive integers is subtracted from the sum of the first 60 even positive integers, what is the result?

74. The measures of the four interior angles of a quadrilateral form four terms of an arithmetic sequence. If the smallest angle is 72°, what is the largest angle?

75. In a right triangle with legs a, b, and hypotenuse c, suppose that a, b, and c are three consecutive terms of a geometric sequence. Find the common ratio r.

76. The seats in a theater are arranged in 31 rows with 40 seats in the first row, 42 in the second, 44 in the third and so on.
   (a) How many seats are in the thirty-first row? In the middle row?
   (b) How many seats are in the theater?

77. A rubber ball is dropped from the top of the Washington Monument, which is 170 meters high. Suppose each time it hits the ground it rebounds $\frac{2}{3}$ of the distance of the preceding fall.
   (a) What total distance does the ball travel up to the instant when it hits the ground for the third time?
   (b) What total distance does it travel before it essentially comes to rest?

78. Suppose we wish to create a vacuum in a tank that contains 1000 cubic feet of air. Each stroke of the vacuum pump removes half of the air that remains in the tank.

(a) How much air remains in the tank after the fourth stroke?

(b) How much air was removed during the fourth stroke?

(c) How many strokes of the pump are required to remove at least 99 percent of the air?

79. From a helicopter hovering at 6400 feet above ground level an object is dropped. The distance s it falls in t seconds after being dropped is given by the formula $s = 16t^2$.
   (a) How far does the object fall during the first second?
   (b) Let a_n denote the distance that the object falls during the nth second, that is, $a_n = f(n) - f(n-1)$. Find a formula for a_n. What kind of sequence is a_n?
   (c) Evaluate the sum $a_1 + a_2 + \cdots + a_{12}$, and they find s when $t = 12$. Compare these two numbers.
   (d) Clearly this is a finite sequence since the object cannot fall more than 6400 feet. How many terms are there in the sequence? What is the sum of these terms?

Exercises 80–83 Looking Ahead to Calculus The polynomial function g approximates the given function f. Evaluate both $g(x)$ and $f(x)$ when x is **(a)** -0.2, **(b)** 0.4, and **(c)** 1. Give results rounded off to four decimal places.

80. $g(x) = x - \frac{x^3}{3!} + \frac{x^5}{5!}$; $f(x) = \sin x$

81. $g(x) = 1 - \frac{x^2}{2!} + \frac{x^4}{4!} - \frac{x^6}{6!}$; $f(x) = \cos x$

82. $g(x) = 1 + x + \frac{x^2}{2!} + \frac{x^3}{3!} + \frac{x^4}{4!}$; $f(x) = e^x$

83. $g(x) = x - \frac{x^3}{5} + \frac{x^5}{5} - \frac{x^7}{7} + \frac{x^9}{9}$; $f(x) = \text{Arctan } x$

SECTION 8.3 | Patterns, Guesses, and Formulas

What humans do with the language of mathematics is to describe patterns. Mathematics is an exploratory science that seeks to understand every kind of pattern—patterns that occur in nature, patterns invented by the human mind, and even patterns created by other patterns.

Lynn Arthur Steen

Arithmetic and geometric sequences are highly structured, and it is precisely because we can analyze the regularity of their patterns that we can do so much with them. The formulas developed in the preceding section are examples of what can be done when patterns are recognized and used appropriately.

One of the strongest urges of the human mind is to discover, seek out, or impose some kind of order in the world around us. If we can organize new information into some kind of recognizable pattern, we can learn more efficiently and remember more accurately.

Patterns and mathematical formulas to describe patterns permeate mathematics. Where did all these formulas come from? All too often people have the impression that mathematics just is, that it has always been around in precisely its current form. Students frequently get the feeling that their main responsibility is just to learn the wisdom that has passed down through the ages.

Mathematics should be seen as an experimental, growing, changing science. It has never been limited to professional mathematicians. Some very important discoveries have been made by amateurs, ordinary people who became involved in the fascinating questions that are always at the heart of mathematics. Mathematics has grown from discoveries that excited those who found answers in patterns they were investigating. It has been strengthened by vigorous disagreements and arguments between different investigators. It has grown in much the same way as other scientific disciplines and it continues to develop today as much as ever before.

Our goal in this section is not to make a mathematician of every reader, but we do want to *involve* you in the discovery process, to provide some opportunity to experience the feeling of creation that drives mathematics. Someone who sees what appears to be a relationship and then can work through to an understanding of why it is valid is truly doing mathematics, whether or not someone else may have made a similar discovery before.

As a first step, we will always need raw data, numbers we can look at to search for patterns or regularity. On the basis of our search, we will try to formulate a guess as to what is happening. A good guess will allow us to predict what should happen in the next case. Such a prediction allows us to test our guess. On the basis of checking a guess, we either strengthen our confidence that we have a good explanation, or we find out that some modification is necessary. We want to emphasize that there is no such thing as a bad guess if it explains something we have observed. Guesses may later turn out to be inadequate or incorrect, but any hope of finding new knowledge depends on a willingness to risk wrong guesses that can be corrected.

In many situations there may be several ways to write formulas, and there are almost always different ways to verify their correctness. In general, there is no single correct response. As you look for patterns, guess freely. Examine possible solutions. Try to understand what is happening. A guess remains just a guess until it is proven to be correct or shown to be incorrect. Proofs generally are much more difficult, and there is never any guarantee that a proof even exists. Some guesses that appear to be sound have not yet been established, even years after they were made. We illustrate some typical procedures in the following examples.

In the 1970s Penrose's lifelong passion for geometric puzzles yielded a bonus. He found that as few as two geometric shapes, put together in jigsaw-puzzle fashion, can cover a surface in patterns that never repeat themselves. "To a small extent I was thinking about how simple structures can force complicated arrangements, but mainly I was doing it for fun."

Roger Penrose

EXAMPLE 1 For what positive integers n is $2^n - 1$ divisible by 3?

Strategy: Evaluate $2^n - 1$
for the first few values of n
and see which are divisible
by 3. Use enough values of n
to see a pattern.

Solution

Follow the strategy. Substituting $n = 1, 2, 3, \ldots$, calculate some numbers.

$$2^1 - 1 = 1 \qquad 2^2 - 1 = 3 \qquad 2^3 - 1 = 7 \qquad 2^4 - 1 = 15$$

This indicates that $2^n - 1$ is divisible by 3 when n is 2 or 4. On the basis of this very small sample, we should probably hesitate to make a guess with much confidence, but it appears that every even value of n may give a number that is divisible by 3.

GUESS: $2^n - 1$ is divisible by 3 for every even positive integer n.

Now test the guess. The next even number for n is 6, and $2^6 - 1 = 63$, which does have a factor of 3, reinforcing confidence in the guess. Also check what happens when $n = 5$, to see if $2^5 - 1 (= 31)$ is not divisible by 3. The next even values for n yield $2^8 - 1 = 255$ and $2^{10} - 1 = 1023$, both of which are divisible by 3.

To prove that the guess is correct, we can use mathematical induction, which is discussed in the next section. ▲

Often one guess about a pattern leads to recognition of a related pattern. After evaluating $2^n - 1$ for several values of n, other patterns may emerge. For convenience, let us use function notation $f(n) = 2^n - 1$:

$$f(1) = 1 \qquad f(2) = 3 \qquad f(3) = 7 \qquad f(4) = 15$$
$$f(5) = 31 \qquad f(6) = 63 \qquad f(7) = 127$$

A natural question is, For what n is $f(n)$ a prime number? We leave the question to the exercises, as well as another related question. If function g is given by $g(n) = 2^n + 1$, then ask when is $g(n)$ divisible by 3, or when is $g(n)$ a prime? For what values of n are $f(n)$ or $g(n)$ divisible by other numbers?

Pascal's Triangle

One marvelous source for pattern observation, called **Pascal's triangle,** is a triangular array of numbers named after Blaise Pascal (1623–1687). Pascal may be considered the father of modern probability theory, in which these numbers play an important role. The numbers in Pascal's triangle are also called **binomial coefficients,** a name we will justify in Section 8.5. Pascal was not the first, or only, discoverer of some of the properties of binomial coefficients. A beautiful representation of the triangle appeared in China as early as 1303, but Pascal did a great deal of work with the numbers we now associate with his name.

We shall examine binomial coefficients in greater detail in Section 8.5. At the moment, we are concerned primarily with the way the triangle is generated, one row at a time. Figure 8.1 shows only the first six rows, but the triangle can be continued as needed. The first and last entries on each row are always ones, and every other entry is obtained by adding the two adjacent entries immediately above.

Figure 8.1 shows the numbers themselves. In order to refer to specific entries in the triangle, we need to identify entries by location. The rows are

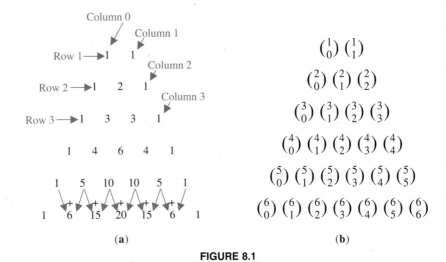

(a)   **(b)**

FIGURE 8.1

numbered in obvious fashion; the columns are numbered diagonally, starting with column 0, not column 1. The entry in the nth row and the cth column is denoted by $\binom{n}{c}$. Figure 8.1b shows addresses of the corresponding entries in Figure 8.1a. For example, in the sixth row, the figure shows the following.

$$\binom{6}{0} = 1 \qquad \binom{6}{1} = 6 \qquad \binom{6}{2} = 15 \qquad \binom{6}{3} = 20 \qquad \binom{6}{4} = 15, \text{ etc.}$$

The rule for generating each row of Pascal's triangle from the one just above it is indicated by the arrows in Figure 8.1a, showing how the fifth row generates the sixth row. In address notation,

$$\binom{5}{0} + \binom{5}{1} = \binom{6}{1} \qquad \binom{5}{1} + \binom{5}{2} = \binom{6}{2} \qquad \binom{5}{2} + \binom{5}{3} = \binom{6}{3} \qquad \text{etc.}$$

This rule may be stated recursively.

Binomial Coefficients (Recursive Form)

The symbol $\binom{n}{c}$ denotes the entry in the nth row and the cth column of Pascal's triangle. The end entries (where c is 0 or n) are 1 on each row. If $0 < c < n$, then adding adjacent entries in the nth row gives the entry between them in the next row.

$$\binom{n}{0} = \binom{n}{n} = 1 \qquad \text{and} \qquad \binom{n}{c} + \binom{n}{c+1} = \binom{n+1}{c+1}$$

EXAMPLE 2   Guess a formula for the sum of the entries on the nth row of Pascal's triangle.

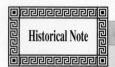

Historical Note

COMPUTERS AND PATTERN RECOGNITION

Pulitzer Prize-winning computer scientist Douglas Hofstadter

Researchers in the area of artificial intelligence marvel at the capacity of the human mind to see patterns and discover relationships. As Douglas Hofstadter has said, "An inherent property of intelligence [is] that it is always looking for, and often finding, patterns."

How can a machine be instructed to recognize that a set of data points lie along some line, that they are essentially linear? Such judgments require the ability to ignore exceptional cases and to consider others in clusters. Recent applications of pattern recognition routines are as diverse as space probes that can make midcourse corrections using star patterns for guidance, computer programs in medicine that can make probable diagnoses from patient responses to programmed questions, and programs to identify insect pests by analyzing the patterns in which leaves are chewed.

Now investigators are exploring ways to connect large numbers of computer chips into neural networks to more closely simulate the way they think the brain may work. Some results are very promising. Neural nets are proving to be remarkably adept at predicting the biological activity of comparatively short fragments of DNA. They can find patterns in sequences that appear to be random. While we do not clearly understand just how these networks operate, they seem to take functions that describe the given numbers and combine the functions to predict the next terms. Scientists still cannot approach the capabilities of the human mind with machines, but, in some instances, the neural nets can now recognize patterns more complicated than human brains can handle.

Solution

We first begin by looking at some specific cases that will help us understand the problem, and from which we may be able to recognize patterns. From Figure 8.1a, we add the numbers across each row and get the following sums.

Row	Sum
1	$1 + 1 = 2 \,(= 2^1)$
2	$1 + 2 + 1 = 4 \,(= 2^2)$
3	$1 + 3 + 3 + 1 = 8 \,(= 2^3)$
4	$1 + 4 + 6 + 4 + 1 = 16 \,(= 2^4)$

The sums appear to be doubling at each stage, suggesting an obvious guess.

GUESS: The sum of the entries on the nth row of Pascal's triangle is 2^n.

The sum of the entries on the fifth row is 32, which is 2^5, and for the sixth row, the sum is 64, which is 2^6. The guess still looks good.

The key to understanding why the guess is correct is the way each row is derived from the row above it. Look at the arrows from the fifth to the sixth row in Figure 8.1a. The first 6 comes from adding the 1 and 5 above, and the same 5 with the 10 gives 15. Similarly, the same 10 is used again for the next entry. Thus each entry on the fifth row is added twice to get the sixth row, including the outside 1s to get the outside 1s on the sixth row. It follows that the sum of the entries on Row 6 is twice the sum of the entries on Row 5. Since 2^5 is the sum for Row 5, the sum of Row 6 must equal $2(2^5) = 2^6$. ▲

This argument is essentially a proof by mathematical induction, which we will discuss formally in the next section.

EXAMPLE 3   Find a formula for the sum of the first n positive integers in terms of the entries in Pascal's triangle.

Solution

Let $f(n)$ denote the sum of the first n positive integers,

$$f(n) = 1 + 2 + 3 + \cdots + n.$$

Express $f(n)$ in terms of entries in Pascal's triangle. First get some data:

$$f(1) = 1 \qquad f(2) = 1 + 2 = 3 \qquad f(3) = 1 + 2 + 3 = 6$$
$$f(4) = 1 + 2 + 3 + 4 = 10.$$

The numbers 1, 3, 6, and 10 are successive entries in Column 2 of Pascal's triangle in Figure 8.1a. In address notation,

$$f(1) = \binom{2}{2} \qquad f(2) = \binom{3}{2} \qquad f(3) = \binom{4}{2} \qquad f(4) = \binom{5}{2}.$$

Based on the data we gathered, we arrive at the following guess.

$$\text{GUESS: } f(n) = \binom{n+1}{2} \text{ for every positive integer } n.$$

If we look at the way each entry is obtained from the two immediately above it, we may see that we are adding precisely what is needed for the pattern to continue. Therefore, our guess must be correct. ▲

EXAMPLE 4   Given n points on a circle, consider two functions:

$C(n)$ is the number of chords determined by connecting each pair of these points.

$R(n)$ is the number of regions into which the chords divide the interior of the circle, where no three chords have a common point of intersection inside the circle.

Guess a formula for **(a)** $C(n)$ and **(b)** $R(n)$.

Solution

Strategy: From a table showing the first few values of $C(n)$ and $R(n)$, look for numbers that may be related to obvious powers of numbers or to entries in Pascal's triangle.

For each value of n, make a sketch from which we can get the information needed for the table (see Figure 8.2).

n	$C(n)$	$R(n)$
1	0	1
2	1	2
3	3	4
4	6	8
5	10	16

(a) For $n \geq 2$, the values of $C(n)$ are numbers in Column 2 of Pascal's triangle. In address notation

$$C(2) = \binom{2}{2} \qquad C(3) = \binom{3}{2} \qquad C(4) = \binom{4}{2} \qquad C(5) = \binom{5}{2}$$

A pattern emerges on which to base a reasonable guess.

$$\text{GUESS: } C(n) = \binom{n}{2} \text{ for } n \geq 2.$$

To see why the guess for $C(n)$ continues to give the correct values, see what happens when you add one more point (going from n to $n + 1$). Check to see that you get n new chords. Compare the resulting values with the values predicted by the formulas.

(b) From the table of values of $R(n)$, the number of pieces appears to be a power of 2, doubling with each new point:

$$R(1) = 1 = 2^0 \qquad R(2) = 2 = 2^1 \qquad R(3) = 4 = 2^2$$
$$R(4) = 8 = 2^3 \qquad \text{and} \qquad R(5) = 16 = 2^5.$$

Make the obvious guess: $R(n) = 2^{n-1}$ for every positive integer n.

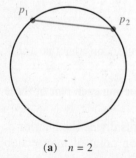

(a) $n = 2$

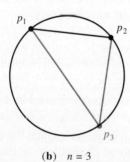

(b) $n = 3$

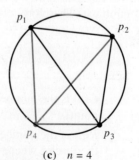

(c) $n = 4$

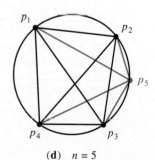

(d) $n = 5$

FIGURE 8.2

Draw circles with 6 and 7 points and carefully count the number of regions. According to the guess $R(n) = 2^{n-1}$, we should get $R(6) = 32$ and $R(7) = 64$. What numbers do you get?

This is an excellent guess based on a beautiful pattern that simply happens to be wrong. Sometimes people speak of a pattern "breaking down." The pattern does not break down; we have failed to find the right pattern. The correct formula is more complicated and may be expressed in terms of the entries in Pascal's triangle.

$$R(n) = \binom{n}{0} + \binom{n}{2} + \binom{n}{4}.$$

For instance, when n is 5, from Figure 8.1

$$\binom{5}{0} + \binom{5}{2} + \binom{5}{4} = 1 + 10 + 5 = 16$$

which is the value of $R(5)$. Evaluate

$$\binom{n}{0} + \binom{n}{2} + \binom{n}{4}$$

when n is 6 and when n is 7. (Extend Pascal's triangle to include row seven.) Compare your results with the actual count of the number of regions, $R(6)$ and $R(7)$.

In Section 8.5 we will see how to evaluate binomial coefficients to get

$$R(n) = \frac{n^4 - 6n^3 + 23n^2 - 18n + 24}{24}.$$

EXERCISES 8.3

Check Your Understanding

Exercises 1–10. True or False. Give reasons for your conclusion.

1. When n is 1, 2, 3, 4, or 5, the sum of the first n odd positive integers is equal to n^2.

2. When n is 1, 2, 3, 4, or 5, the sum of the first n even positive integers is equal to $n(n + 1)$.

3. If $f(n) = n^2 - n + 17$, then $f(n)$ is a prime number for $n = 1, 2, 4, 8,$ and 17.

4. If $f(n) = n^2 + n$, then $f(n)$ is an even number for every positive integer n.

5. Evaluating the expressions $(n + 1)^2$ and 2^n for $n = 1, 2, 3, 4, 5,$ and 6, it is reasonable to conclude that $(n + 1)^2 > 2^n$ for every positive integer.

6. For every positive integer n, $3^n + 1$ is an even number.

7. For every positive integer n, the units digit of $5^n - 1$ is 4.

8. When n is 1, 2, 3, or 4, $5^n + 1$ is not divisible by 4.

9. For every positive integer n, the units digit of 2^n is 2, 4, or 8.

10. For every positive integer n, the units digit of $4^n - 1$ is 3 or 5.

Explore and Discover

The following exercises refer to the sequence of Fibonacci numbers (see the Historical Note, "The Fibonacci Sequence," in Section 8.1) defined recursively as follows:

$$F_1 = F_2 = 1 \quad \text{and} \quad F_n = F_{n-1} + F_{n-2}$$

$$\text{for } n \geq 3.$$

The first eight terms of the sequence are 1, 1, 2, 3, 5, 8, 13, and 21. Make a table with the values of n and corresponding values of F_n for at least the first 15 Fibonacci numbers.

1. For what values of n is F_n even? Odd? Describe the pattern of even and odd numbers in the sequence, and explain why the pattern must continue.

2. Guess a pattern that describes which F_n values are (a) multiples of 3 or (b) multiples of 5.

Exercises 3–4 Guess a formula that gives $f(n)$ in simpler form. First evaluate $f(n)$ for several values of n and look for patterns.

3. $f(n) = F_1 + F_3 + F_5 + \cdots + F_{2n-1}$. For example, $f(3) = F_1 + F_3 + F_5 = 1 + 2 + 5 = 8 = F_8$.

4. $f(n) = F_2 + F_4 + F_6 + \cdots + F_{2n}$. For example, $f(4) = F_2 + F_4 + F_6 + F_8 = 33 = F_9 - 1$.

5. We have previously explored sets of Pythagorean triples $[a, b, c]$ such that $a^2 + b^2 = c^2$. By extension $[a, b\ c, d]$ is a Pythagorean quadruple if $a^2 + b^2 + c^2 = d^2$. Since $3^2 + 4^2 = 5^2$ and $5^2 + 12^2 = 13^2$, it follows that $[3, 4, 12, 13]$ is a Pythagorean quadruple.
    (a) Show that if $[a, b, c]$ and $[c, d, e]$ are Pythagorean triples, then $[a, b, d, e]$ is a Pythagorean quadruple. How many other examples than $[3, 4, 12, 13]$ can you find?
    (b) Find formulas for another family of Pythagorean quadruples that contain $[3, 4, 12, 13]$, and have the form $[a, a + 1, b, b + 1]$.

Develop Mastery

In these exercises, n always denotes a natural number.

Exercises 1–5 As a first step for each exercise, complete the following table by entering the values of $f(n)$ for the given function. In order to see patterns, it is very important that computations be correct. As a check, one of the values of $f(n)$ is given.

n	1	2	3	4
$f(n)$				

n	5	6	7
$f(n)$			

1. $f(n) = 5^n - 1$. Check: $f(4) = 5^4 - 1 = 624$.
    (a) For what values of n in your table is $f(n)$ a multiple of 3? Of 4? Of 12?
    (b) Based on these observations, make a guess that describes all natural numbers n for which $f(n)$ is a multiple of 3, of 4, and of 12. State your guess in complete sentences.

2. $f(n) = 5^n + 1$. Check: $f(5) = 5^5 + 1 = 3126$.
    (a) For what values of n in your table is $f(n)$ a multiple of 6? Of 7?
    (b) Make a guess that describes all natural numbers n for which $f(n)$ is a multiple of 6. Express your guess in complete sentences.
    (c) For additional information: Is $f(9)$ a multiple of 7? Is $f(15)$ a multiple of 7? Is $f(18)$ a multiple of 7? For which n is $f(n)$ a multiple of 7?

3. $f(n) = 9 + 9^2 + 9^3 + \cdots + 9^n$. Check: $f(3) = 9 + 9^2 + 9^3 = 819$. Based on the data in your table, make a guess that describes all natural numbers n for which the units digit of $f(n)$ is a zero, a one, a nine. Convince your teacher that your guess is correct.

4. $f(n) = n^2 - n + 11$. Check: $f(5) = 5^2 - 5 + 11 = 31$.
    (a) For what values of n in your table is $f(n)$ a prime number? Is $f(n)$ a prime number for every natural number n?
    (b) Make a guess concerning the units digit of $f(n)$.
    (c) To lead to a recursive formula, enter appropriate numbers in each of the blank spaces:

    $$f(2) = f(1) + \underline{\hspace{2cm}}$$
    $$f(3) = f(2) + \underline{\hspace{2cm}}$$
    $$f(4) = f(3) + \underline{\hspace{2cm}} \cdots$$

    Now guess the quantity that should be entered in the general case:

    $$f(n + 1) = f(n) + \underline{\hspace{2cm}}.$$

    Prove that your guess is valid (or not valid) by actually evaluating $f(n + 1)$ and $f(n) + \underline{\hspace{1cm}}$ to see if they are equal.
    (d) Evaluate $f(11)$, $f(22)$, and $f(33)$. Now check your conclusion in (a).

5. $f(n) = n^2 - n + 41$. Check: $f(5) = 5^2 - 5 + 41 = 61$.
    (a)–(c) Same as in Exercise 4.
    (d) Evaluate $f(41)$ and $f(82)$. Are these primes?

Exercises 6–14 Function f is defined as a sum.
(a) Make a table that shows the values of $f(n)$ for $n = 1$, 2, 3, 4, 5, and 6.

(b) Based on the data in the table, guess a simpler formula for f. The value of $f(4)$ is also given, which should serve as a check on your computations and also possibly as a hint to help you recognize patterns.

6. $f(n) = 1 + 3 + 5 + \cdots + (2n - 1)$

$$= \sum_{k=1}^{n} (2k - 1); \qquad f(4) = 16.$$

7. $f(n) = 2 + 4 + 6 + \cdots + 2n = \sum_{j=1}^{n} 2j;$

$f(4) = 4 \cdot 5.$

8. $f(n) = \frac{1}{1 \cdot 2} + \frac{1}{2 \cdot 3} + \frac{1}{3 \cdot 4} + \cdots + \frac{1}{n(n + 1)}$

$$= \sum_{i=1}^{n} \frac{1}{i(i + 1)}; \qquad f(4) = \frac{4}{5}.$$

9. $f(n) = \frac{1}{2} + \frac{1}{4} + \frac{1}{8} + \cdots + \frac{1}{2^n} = \sum_{k=1}^{n} \frac{1}{2^k};$

$f(4) = \frac{16 - 1}{16}.$

10. $f(n) = 2(\frac{1}{3} + \frac{1}{9} + \frac{1}{27} + \cdots + \frac{1}{3^n})$

$$= 2 \cdot \left(\sum_{k=1}^{n} \frac{1}{3^k}\right); \qquad f(4) = \frac{80}{81}.$$

11. $f(n) = 1 + 2(3^0 + 3^1 + 3^2 + \cdots + 3^{n-1})$

$$= 1 + 2 \sum_{k=1}^{n} 3^{k-1}; \qquad f(4) = 3^4.$$

(c) Use the result in **(b)** to get a formula for $\sum_{k=1}^{n} 3^{k-1}$.

12. $f(n) = \frac{1}{2!} + \frac{2}{3!} + \frac{3}{4!} + \cdots + \frac{n}{(n + 1)!}$

$$= \sum_{k=1}^{n} \frac{k}{(k + 1)!}; \qquad f(4) = \frac{119}{120}.$$

(Hint: Keep in mind the values of factorials, such as $6 = 3!$, $24 = 4!$, $120 = 5!$, $\cdots$)

13. $f(n) = 1 + (1 + 2 + 4 + \cdots + 2^{n-1})$

$$= 1 + \sum_{j=1}^{n} 2^{j-1}; \qquad f(4) = 2^4.$$

(c) Use your results in **(b)** to get a simpler formula for $g(n) = 1 + 2 + 4 + \cdots + 2^{n-1}$.

14. $f(n) = 1 + 2 + 3 + \cdots + (n - 1) + n$
$+ (n - 1) + \cdots + 3 + 2 + 1$
$f(4) = 1 + 2 + 3 + 4 + 3 + 2 + 1 = 16.$

15. For $f(n) = 2[1 - \frac{1}{2^2}][1 - \frac{1}{3^2}][1 - \frac{1}{4^2}] \cdots$
$[1 - \frac{1}{(n + 1)^2}]$, evaluate $f(n)$ for $n = 1, 2, 3, 4,$
$5,$ and 6. For instance, $f(4) = \frac{6}{5} = \frac{4 + 2}{4 + 1}$. Based on your data, guess a simpler formula for $f(n)$.

Exercises 16–18 For the functions defined recursively,

(a) Make a table that shows the values of $f(n)$ for $n = 1, 2, 3, 4, 5,$ and 6.

(b) Using the data from this table, guess a closed form formula for f.

16. $f(1) = 2$ and $f(n) = 2f(n - 1)$ for $n \geq 2$;
$f(5) = 2^5.$

17. $f(1) = 2$ and $f(n) = f(n - 1) + 2n$ for $n \geq 2$;
$f(5) = 5 \cdot 6.$

18. $f(1) = 3$ and $f(n) = f(n - 1) + (2n + 1)$ for $n \geq 2$; $f(4) = 4 \cdot 6.$

19. *Number of Handshakes* Suppose that each of the n people at a party shakes hands with every other person exactly once. Let $f(n)$ denote the total number of handshakes, so that $f(1) = 0$ (one person, no handshakes), $f(2) = 1$ (two people, one handshake), $f(3) = f(2) + 2$ (adding a person adds two more handshakes). A newcomer shakes hands with each of the k people present and so $f(k + 1) = f(k) + k$. Find a formula for f.

20. In Example 4 let $D(n)$ be the number of diagonals of the polygon obtained by connecting the points on the circle. For example, $D(1) = D(2) = D(3) = 0$, $D(4) = 2$, and $D(5) = 5$. Guess a formula for $D(n)$. *(Hint:* Count the number of new diagonals when adding a point.)

Exercises 21–24 Extend Pascal's triangle, shown in Figure 8.1, for a few more rows. When you are asked to find a number in the triangle, express it in address notation, $\binom{n}{c}$.

21. How many entries appear on row n?

22. On what rows of the triangle are the two middle entries the same?

23. Each row in Figure 8.1 is symmetrical. (Each reads the same forward and backward.) Explain how you can know that Row 7 is symmetrical without computing any entries in Row 7? How about Row 8? Row n?

24. In Example 2, we showed that the sum of all the entries on Row n is 2^n (symbolically, $\sum_{c=0}^{n} \binom{n}{c} = 2^n$). Let $f(n)$ be the sum of the entries in the even-numbered columns of Row n. That is,

$$f(n) = \binom{n}{0} + \binom{n}{2} + \binom{n}{4} + \cdots + \binom{n}{m}$$

where m is the last even-numbered column on Row n.

For instance,

$$f(4) = \binom{4}{0} + \binom{4}{2} + \binom{4}{4} = 1 + 6 + 1 = 8$$

$$f(5) = \binom{5}{0} + \binom{5}{2} + \binom{5}{4} = 1 + 10 + 5 = 16.$$

Evaluate $f(n)$ for several other values of n and then use the information to help you guess a simpler formula for f.

25. Follow the instructions for Exercise 24, but let $f(n)$ denote the sum of all the entries in odd-numbered columns on Row n, that is

$$f(n) = \binom{n}{1} + \binom{n}{3} + \binom{n}{5} + \cdots + \binom{n}{m}$$

where m is the last odd-numbered column in Row n.

Exercises 26–29   Find the sums of entries in Columns 0, 1, 2, and 3 of Pascal's triangle.

(a) Evaluate $f(n)$ for several values of n [with $f(4)$ given as a check].

(b) Locate these sums in the triangle, and then guess a simpler formula for f in terms of address notation.

26. *Column 0*

$$f(n) = \binom{1}{0} + \binom{2}{0} + \binom{3}{0} + \cdots + \binom{n}{0}$$

$$f(4) = \binom{4}{1}.$$

27. *Column 1*

$$f(n) = \binom{1}{1} + \binom{2}{1} + \binom{3}{1} + \cdots + \binom{n}{1}$$

$$f(4) = \binom{5}{2}.$$

28. *Column 2*

$$f(n) = \binom{2}{2} + \binom{3}{2} + \binom{4}{2} + \cdots + \binom{n+1}{2}$$

$$f(4) = \binom{6}{3}.$$

29. *Column 3*

$$f(n) = \binom{3}{3} + \binom{4}{3} + \binom{5}{3} + \cdots + \binom{n+2}{3}$$

$$f(4) = \binom{7}{4}.$$

30. Let $f(n)$ denote the sum of the squares of the first n natural numbers:

$$f(n) = 1^2 + 2^2 + 3^2 + \cdots + n^2.$$

(a) Evaluate $f(n)$ for $n = 1, 2, 3, 4, 5,$ and 6. For instance, $f(4) = 30$.

(b) Now look in Column 3 of Pascal's triangle and find two consecutive entries whose sum is $f(n)$. For instance,

$$f(4) = 30 = 10 + 20 = \binom{5}{3} + \binom{6}{3}.$$

Use this information to help you guess a formula that gives $f(n)$ as the sum of two consecutive entries in Column 3. Use address notation in your answer.

31. Let $P(n)$ denote the number of pieces (regions) into which n lines divide the plane. Assume that no two lines are parallel, and that no three lines contain a common point. Draw figures to illustrate the cases for $n = 1, 2, 3, 4,$ and 5. By actually counting the pieces in each case, evaluate $P(n)$ for $n = 1, 2, 3, 4,$ and 5. Guess a formula for $P(n)$. (*Hint:* Look for $P(n) - 1$ in Pascal's triangle.)

32. Function f is defined recursively by

$$f(1) = 1 \qquad f(2) = 5 \qquad \text{and}$$
$$f(n) = f(n-1) + 2f(n-2) \qquad \text{for } n \geq 3.$$

Functions g and h are given in closed form by

$$g(n) = 2^n + 1 \qquad h(n) = 2^n - 1.$$

(a) Complete the following table:

n	1	2	3
$f(n)$			
$g(n)$			
$h(n)$			

n	4	5	6
$f(n)$			
$g(n)$			
$h(n)$			

As a check, you should have $f(4) = 17$, $g(4) = 17$, $h(4) = 15$.

(b) Based on the data in the table, make a guess about the values of n for which $f(n) = g(n)$ and for which $f(n) = h(n)$.

(c) Using your guess in (b), is $f(n) = 2^n + (-1)^n$ for every natural number n?

33. At the end of Example 4, we indicated that $R(n)$ is given by the formula:

$$R(n) = \frac{n^4 - 6n^3 + 23n^2 - 18n + 24}{24}.$$

Evaluate $R(n)$ for $n = 4, 5, 6,$ and 7. For each value of n draw an appropriate diagram and actually count the number of regions to see if there is agreement with the formula prediction.

SECTION 8.4   **Mathematical Induction**

The idea of mathematical induction is simply that if something is true at the beginning of the series, and if this is "inherited" as we proceed from one number to the next, then it is also true for all *natural numbers. This has given us a method to prove something for* all *natural numbers, whereas to try out all such numbers is impossible with our finite brains. We need only prove two things, both conceivable by means of our finite brains: that the statement in question is true for 1, and that it is the kind that is "inherited."*
        Rózsa Péter

In Section 1.4 we discussed statements (sentences that are either true or false) and open sentences, whose truth value depends on replacing a variable or placeholder with a number. In this section we consider sentences of the type

$$n! < 8n \text{ for every positive integer } n. \qquad \textbf{(1)}$$

Such a sentence involves a quantifier : for every positive integer. Looking at the first few statements, we get

$1! < 8 \cdot 1$	$4! < 8 \cdot 4$	$6! < 8 \cdot 6$
$1 < 8$ (True)	$24 < 32$ (True)	$720 < 48$ (False)

Since $n! < 8n$ does not yield a true statement for every positive integer n, sentence 1 is false. To show that a sentence of the type of sentence 1 is false, all we need is one value of n ($n = 6$ in this case) that yields a false statement; any such value of n is a counterexample.
        A statement of the form

$$P(n) \text{ for every positive integer } n, \qquad \textbf{(2)}$$

means that the infinite set of statements $P(1)$, $P(2)$, $P(3)$, . . . are all true. Establishing the truth of such a statement requires a special method of proof called **mathematical induction.** Consider an example of a statement of the type given in statement 2. An appeal to intuition leads us to the formal statement of the Principle of Mathematical Induction.
        Suppose $P(n)$ is

$P(n)$: The sum of the first n odd positive integers is n^2.

It is difficult to work mathematically with a statement given verbally. We can restate $P(n)$ in mathematical terms.

$$P(n): 1 + 3 + 5 + \cdots + (2n - 1) = n^2$$

In sigma notation

$$P(n): \sum_{m=1}^{n} (2m - 1) = n^2.$$

If we claim that $P(n)$ is true for every positive integer n, then we must somehow show that each of the statements $P(1)$, $P(2)$, $P(3)$, . . . is true. We list a few of these:

$$P(1): \sum_{m=1}^{1} (2m - 1) = 1^2 \quad \text{or} \quad 1 = 1^2 \qquad \text{True}$$

$$P(2): \sum_{m=1}^{2} (2m - 1) = 2^2 \quad \text{or} \quad 1 + 3 = 2^2 \qquad \text{True}$$

$$P(3): \sum_{m=1}^{3} (2m - 1) = 3^2 \quad \text{or} \quad 1 + 3 + 5 = 3^2 \qquad \text{True}$$

So far we have verified that $P(1)$, $P(2)$, and $P(3)$ are all true. Clearly we cannot continue with the direct verification for the remaining positive integers n, but suppose we can accomplish two things:

(a)   Verify that $P(1)$ is true.

(b)   For any arbitrary positive integer k, show that the truth of $P(k + 1)$ follows from the truth of $P(k)$.

If **(a)** and **(b)** can be done, then we reason as follows: $P(1)$ is true by **(a)**; since $P(1)$ is true, then by **(b)** it follows that $P(1 + 1)$, or $P(2)$, must be true; now since $P(2)$ is true then by **(b)** it follows that $P(3)$ is true; and so on. Therefore, it is intuitively reasonable to conclude that $P(n)$ is true for every positive integer n. This type of reasoning is the basis for the idea of mathematical induction.

Having done **(a)** for the example, let use see if we can accomplish **(b)**. We can state **(b)** in terms of a hypothesis and a conclusion and argue that the conclusion follows from the induction hypothesis:

Hypothesis $P(k)$: $1 + 3 + 5 + \cdots + (2k - 1) = k^2$ **(3)**

Conclusion $P(k + 1)$: $1 + 3 + 5 + \cdots + (2k - 1) +$ **(4)**
$(2k + 1) = (k + 1)^2$

Now use Equation 3 and argue that Equation 4 follows from it. To get to Equation 4 from Equation 3, add $2k + 1$ to both sides.

$$[1 + 3 + 5 + \cdots + (2k - 1)] + (2k + 1) = k^2 + (2k + 1) \qquad \textbf{(5)}$$

The right side of Equation 5 can be written as

$$k^2 + (2k + 1) = k^2 + 2k + 1 = (k + 1)^2.$$

Therefore, Equation 5 is equivalent to

$$1 + 3 + 5 + \cdots + (2k - 1) + (2k + 1) = (k + 1)^2$$

This is precisely the form of Equation 3, so we have accomplished **(b)**. Hence we can conclude that the statement

$$1 + 3 + 5 + \cdots + (2n - 1) = n^2 \text{ for every positive integer } n$$

is true.

The mathematical basis for our conclusion follows from the Principle of Mathematical Induction.

Principle of Mathematical Induction

Suppose $P(n)$ is an open sentence that gives statements $P(1)$, $P(2)$, $P(3)$, ... If we can accomplish the following two things:

(a) verify that $P(1)$ is true,

(b) for any arbitrary positive integer k, show that the truth of $P(k + 1)$ follows from the truth of $P(k)$,

then $P(n)$ is true for every positive integer n.

EXAMPLE 1 For the open sentence, write out $P(1)$, $P(2)$, and $P(5)$. Determine the truth value of each.

(a) $P(n)$: $n^3 + 11n = 6(n^2 + 1)$.

(b) $P(n)$: $5^n - 1$ is divisible by 4.

Solution

(a) $P(1)$: $1^3 + 11 \cdot 1 = 6(1^2 + 1)$ or $1 + 11 = 6(1 + 1)$ True

$P(2)$: $2^3 + 11 \cdot 2 = 6(2^2 + 1)$ or $8 + 22 = 6(5)$ True

$P(5)$: $5^3 + 11 \cdot 5 = 6(5^2 + 1)$ or $125 + 55 = 6(26)$ False

(b) $P(1)$: $5^1 - 1$ is divisible by 4, $5^1 - 1 = 4$ True

$P(2)$: $5^2 - 1$ is divisible by 4, $5^2 - 1 = 24$ True

$P(5)$: $5^5 - 1$ is divisible by 4, $5^5 - 1 = 3124$ True

▲

EXAMPLE 2 Let $P(n)$ be the open sentence

$$P(n)\text{: } 5^n - 1 \text{ is divisible by 4.}$$

Prove that $P(n)$ is true for every positive integer n.

Strategy: After verifying that $P(1)$ is true, for mathematical induction, show that $P(k)$ implies $P(k + 1)$; relate $5^{k+1} - 1$ to $5^k - 1$.

Solution

Proof will follow if we can accomplish **(a)** and **(b)** of the Principle of Mathematical Induction. For **(a)** we must show that $P(1)$ is true. This has already been done in Example 1b.

For **(b)**, state the induction hypothesis and conclusion.

$$\text{Hypothesis } P(k): \qquad 5k - 1 \text{ is divisible by 4.} \qquad \textbf{(6)}$$

$$\text{Conclusion: } P(k + 1): \qquad 5^{k+1} - 1 \text{ is divisible by 4.} \qquad \textbf{(7)}$$

Since by hypothesis, $5^k - 1$ is divisible by 4, there is an integer m such that

$$5^k - 1 = 4m \qquad \text{or} \qquad 5^k = 4m + 1.$$

Therefore,

$$5^{k+1} - 1 = 5 \cdot 5^k - 1 = 5(4m + 1) - 1$$
$$= 20m + 4 = 4(5m + 1).$$

Hence if $5^k - 1$ is divisible by 4, then $5^{k+1} - 1$ is also divisible by 4. This establishes **(b)**, and proves that $5^n - 1$ is divisible by 4 for every positive integer n. ▲

EXAMPLE 3   Show that $2^{n+1} > n + 2$ for every positive integer n.

Solution

(a)   When n is 1, $2^{1+1} > 1 + 2$, or $4 > 3$, which is true.

(b)   Hypothesis $P(k)$: $2^{k+1} > k + 2$

   Conclusion $P(k + 1)$: $2^{k+2} > k + 3$

Begin with the hypothesis and multiply both sides of the inequality by 2.

$$2 \cdot 2^{k+1} > 2k + 4 \qquad \text{or} \qquad 2^{k+2} > 2k + 4$$

We would like $k + 3$ on the right-hand side, but $2k + 4 = (k + 3) + (k + 1)$, and since k is a positive integer, $k + 1 > 0$, so $2k + 4 > k + 3$. Therefore,

$$2^{k+2} > 2k + 4 > k + 3.$$

By the Principle of Mathematical Induction, we conclude that $2^{n+1} > n + 2$ for every positive integer n. ▲

EXERCISES 8.4

Check Your Understanding

Exercises 1–10   True or False. Give reasons for your conclusion.

1. There is no positive integer n such that $(n + 1)! = n! + 1!$.

2. There is no positive integer n such that $n^2 + n = 6$.

3. For every positive integer n, $(n + 1)^2 \geq 2^n$.

4. For every positive integer n, $\sin n\pi = 0$.

5. For every positive integer n, $(2n - 1)(2n + 1)$ is an odd number.

6. For every positive integer n, $n^2 + n$ is an even number.

7. For every positive integer n, $n^2 + 1 \geq 2n$.

8. For every positive integer n, $(n + 1)^3 - n^3 - 1$ is divisible by 6.

9. For every positive integer n, $n^2 - n + 17$ is a prime number.

10. For every integer n greater than 1, $\log_2 n \geq \log_n 2$.

Explore and Discover

Exercises 1–2 **(a)** Evaluate the sum when n is 1, 2, 3, and 4. **(b)** Guess a formula for the sum. **(c)** Prove that your formula is valid for every positive integer n.

1. $\frac{1}{1 \cdot 2} + \frac{1}{2 \cdot 3} + \frac{1}{3 \cdot 4} + \cdots + \frac{1}{n(n + 1)}$

2. $1 + 2 + 3 + \cdots + n + \cdots + 3 + 2 + 1$

3. Let $f(n) = 5^n - 4$.
  (a) Evaluate f when n is 1, 2, 3, 4, and 5.
  (b) For what positive integers n is $f(n)$ divisible by 3? Prove that your guess is correct.
  (c) For what positive integers n is $f(n)$ divisible by 24? Prove that your guess is correct.

Develop Mastery

Exercises 1–8 Denote the given open sentence as $P(n)$. Write out $P(1)$, $P(2)$, and $P(5)$, and determine the truth value of each.

1. $n^2 - n + 11$ is a prime number.

2. $4n^2 - 4n + 1$ is a perfect square.

3. $n^2 < 2n + 1$

4. $3^n > n^2$

5. $n! \leq n^2$

6. $4^n - 1$ is a multiple of 3.

7. $1^3 + 2^3 + 3^3 + \cdots + n^3$ is a perfect square.

8. The sum of the first n even positive integers is equal to $n(n + 1)$.

Exercises 9–12 Find the smallest positive integer n for which $P(n)$ is false.

9. $P(n)$: $n! \leq n^3$

10. $P(n)$: $n^2 - n + 5$ is a prime number.

11. $P(n)$: $n^3 < 3^n$ **12.** $P(n)$: $n! < 3^n$

Exercises 13–18 Step **(b)** of the Principle of Mathematical Induction involves an induction hypothesis and a conclusion. Write out the hypothesis and the conclusion.

13. $1^3 + 2^3 + 3^3 + \cdots + n^3 = \frac{n^2(n + 1)^2}{4}$

14. $2 + 5 + 8 + \cdots + (3n - 1) = \frac{n(3n + 1)}{2}$

15. $1 \cdot 2 + 2 \cdot 3 + 3 \cdot 4 + \cdots + n(n + 1)$
$= \frac{n(n + 1)(n + 2)}{3}$

16. $3^n > n^2$

17. $4^n - 1$ is a multiple of 3.

18. The sum of the first n even positive integers equals $n(n + 1)$.

Exercises 19–32 Use mathematical induction to prove that the given formula is valid for every positive integer n.

19. $2 + 5 + 8 + \cdots + (3n - 1) = \frac{n(3n + 1)}{2}$

20. $1 \cdot 2 + 2 \cdot 3 + 3 \cdot 4 + \cdots + n(n + 1)$
$= \frac{n(n + 1)(n + 2)}{3}$

21. The sum of the first n positive integers is equal to $\frac{n(n + 1)}{2}$.

22. The sum of the first n even positive integers is equal to $n(n + 1)$.

23. $2 \cdot 1 + 2 \cdot 4 + 2 \cdot 7 + \cdots + 2(3n - 2)$
$= 3n^2 - n$.

24. $1^2 + 2^2 + 3^2 + \cdots + n^2 = \frac{n(n + 1)(2n + 1)}{6}$.

25. $1^3 + 2^3 + 3^3 + \cdots + n^3 = \frac{n^2(n + 1)^2}{4}$.

26. $\frac{1}{1 \cdot 2} + \frac{1}{2 \cdot 3} + \frac{1}{3 \cdot 4} + \cdots + \frac{1}{n(n + 1)} = \frac{n}{n + 1}$.

27. $2 + 2^2 + 2^3 + \cdots + 2^n = 2(2^n - 1)$.

28. $1 \cdot 1! + 2 \cdot 2! + 3 \cdot 3! + \cdots + n \cdot n!$
$= (n + 1)! - 1$

29. $\sum_{m=1}^{n} (3m^2 + m) = n(n + 1)^2$

30. $\sum_{m=1}^{n} (2m - 3) = n(n - 2)$

31. $\sum_{m=1}^{n} (2^{m-1} - 1) = 2^n - n - 1$

32. $\sum_{m=1}^{n} \ln m = \ln (n!)$

Exercises 33–40 Prove that $P(n)$ yields a true statement when n is replaced by any positive integer.

33. $P(n)$: $4^n - 1$ is divisible by 3.

34. $P(n)$: $(\cos \theta + i \sin \theta)^n = \cos n\theta + i \sin n\theta$

35. $P(n)$: $n^3 + 2n$ is divisible by 3.

36. $P(n)$: $2^{2n-1} + 1$ is divisible by 3.

37. $P(n)$: $2^n \leq (n + 1)!$

38. $P(n)$: $3^n \leq (n + 2)!$

39. $P(n)$: $2^n \geq n + 1$

40. $P(n)$: $2^{n+1} > 2n + 1$

Exercises 41–49   Let $P(n)$ denote the open sentence. Either find the smallest positive integer n for which $P(n)$ is false, or prove $P(n)$ is true for every positive integer n.

41. $n(n^2 - 1)$ is divisible by 6.

42. $n^2 + n$ is an even number.

43. $n^2 - n + 41$ is an odd number.

44. $5n^2 + 1$ is divisible by 3.

45. $5n^2 + 1$ is not a perfect square.

46. $2^n < (n + 1)^2$.

47. $n^2 - n + 41$ is a prime number.

48. $n^4 + 35n^2 + 24 = 10n(n^2 + 5)$.

49. $(1 + \frac{1}{1})(1 + \frac{1}{2})(1 + \frac{1}{3}) \cdots (1 + \frac{1}{n}) = n + 1$.

50. *Towers of Hanoi*   There are three pegs on a board. Start with n disks on one peg, as suggested in the drawing. Move all disks from the starting peg onto another peg, one at a time, placing no disk atop a smaller one. (You can experiment yourself without pegs; use coins of different sizes, for example, a dime on top of a penny, on top of a nickle, on top of a quarter. It may take some patience to find the minimum number of moves required.)

   (a) What is the minimum number of moves required if you start with 1 disk? 2 disks? 3 disks? 4?

   (b) Based on your results for **(a)**, guess the minimum number of moves required if you start with an arbitrary number of n disks. (*Hint:* Add 1 to the number of moves for $n = 1, 2, 3, 4$.)

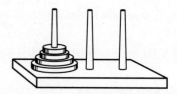

   (c) A legend claims that monks in a remote monastery are working to move a set of 64 disks, and that the world will end when they complete their sacred task. Moving one disk per second without error, 24 hours a day, 365 days a year, how long would it take to move all 64 disks?

51. Suppose there are n people at a party and that each person shakes hands with every other person exactly once. Let $f(n)$ denote the total number of handshakes. See Section 8.3, Develop Mastery Exercise 19. Show

$$f(n) = \frac{n(n - 1)}{2} \quad \text{for every positive integer } n.$$

52. Suppose n is an odd positive integer not divisible by 3. Show that $n^2 - 1$ is divisible by 24. (*Hint:* Consider the three consecutive integers $n - 1, n, n + 1$. Explain why the product $(n - 1)(n + 1)$ must be divisible by 3 and by 8.)

53. If $a_n = \sqrt{24n + 1}$, **(a)** write out the first five terms of the sequence $\{a_n\}$. **(b)** What odd integers occur in $\{a_n\}$? **(c)** Explain why $\{a_n\}$ contains all primes greater than 3. (*Hint:* Use Exercise 52.)

SECTION 8.5   **The Binomial Theorem**

We remake nature by the act of discovery, in the poem or in the theorem. And the great poem and the great theorem are new to every reader, and yet are his own experiences, because he himself recreates them. [And] in the instant when the mind seizes this for itself, in art or in science, the heart misses a beat.

   J. Bronowski

In this section we derive a general formula to calculate an expansion for $(a + b)^n$ for any positive integer power n, or to find any particular term in such an expansion. We begin by calculating the first few powers directly and then look for significant patterns. To go from one power of $(a + b)$ to the next, we simply multiply by $(a + b)$:

$$(a + b)^1 = a + b$$
$$(a + b)^2 = a^2 + 2ab + b^2$$
$$(a + b)^3 = a^3 + 3a^2b + 3ab^2 + b^3$$

(×) $\quad \underline{a + b}$
$\qquad a^4 + 3a^3b + 3a^2b^2 + ab^3$
$\qquad\qquad\quad a^3b + 3a^2b^2 + 3ab^3 + b^4$

Add like terms

$$(a + b)^4 = a^4 + 4a^3b + 6a^2b^2 + 4ab^3 + b^4$$

(×) $\quad \underline{a + b}$
$\qquad a^5 + 4a^4b + \ 6a^3b^2 + \ 4a^2b^3 + \ ab^4$
$\qquad\qquad\quad a^4b + \ 4a^3b^2 + \ 6a^2b^3 + 4ab^4 + b^5$

Add like terms

$$(a + b)^5 = a^5 + 5a^4b + 10a^3b^2 + 10a^2b^3 + 5ab^4 + b^5$$

When we look at these expansions of $(a + b)^n$ for $n = 1, 2, 3, 4,$ and 5, several patterns become apparent.

1. There are $n + 1$ terms, from a^n to b^n.
2. Every term has essentially the same form: some coefficient times the product of a power of a times a power of b.
3. In each term the sum of the exponents on a and b is always n.
4. The powers (exponents) on a decrease, term by term, from n down to 0 where the last term is given by $b^n = a^0b^n$, and the exponents on b increase from 0 to n.

The thing that started it all was this silly newspaper puzzle that asked you to count up the total number of ways you could spell the words "Pyramid of Values" from a triangular array of letters. This led my friend and me to discover Pascal's triangle. This happened in grade 10 or 11.

Bill Gosper

Knowing the form of the terms in the expansion and that the sum of the powers is always n, we will have the entire expansion when we know how to calculate the coefficients of the terms. If we display the coefficients from the computations above, we find precisely the numbers in the first few rows of Pascal's triangle:

$$1 \ \ 1$$
$$1 \ \ 2 \ \ 1$$
$$1 \ \ 3 \ \ 3 \ \ 1$$
$$1 \ \ 4 \ \ 6 \ \ 4 \ \ 1$$
$$1 \ \ 5 \ \ 10 \ \ 10 \ \ 5 \ \ 1$$

Using the address notation for Pascal's triangle that we introduced in Section 8.3, the last row of coefficients in the triangle is $\binom{5}{0}, \binom{5}{1}, \binom{5}{2}, \binom{5}{3}, \binom{5}{4}, \binom{5}{5},$

and we may write the expansion for $(a + b)^5$:

$$(a + b)^5 = \binom{5}{0}a^5b^0 + \binom{5}{1}a^4b^1 + \binom{5}{2}a^3b^2 + \binom{5}{3}a^2b^3$$

$$+ \binom{5}{4}a^1b^4 + \binom{5}{5}a^0b^5$$

Each term exhibits the same form. For $n = 5$, each coefficient has the form $\binom{5}{r}$, where r is also the exponent on b. For each term the sum of the exponents on a and b is always 5, so that when we have b^r, we must also have a^{5-r}. Finally, since the first term has $r = 0$, the second term has $r = 1$, etc., the $(r + 1)$st term involves r.

This leads to a general conjecture for the expansion of $(a + b)^n$ which we state as a theorem that can be proved using mathematical induction. (See the end of this section.)

Binomial Theorem

Suppose n is any positive integer. The expansion of $(a + b)^n$ is given by

$$(a + b)^n = \binom{n}{0}a^nb^0 + \binom{n}{1}a^{n-1}b^1 + \cdots + \binom{n}{r}a^{n-r}b^r$$

$$+ \cdots + \binom{n}{n}a^0b^n \tag{1}$$

where the $(r + 1)$st term is $\binom{n}{r}a^{n-r}b^r$, $0 \le r \le n$. In summation notation,

$$(a + b)^n = \sum_{r=0}^{n}\binom{n}{r}a^{n-r}b^r. \tag{2}$$

At this point, we have established only that the form of our conjecture is valid for the first five values of n, and we have not completely justified our use of the name Pascal's triangle of **binomial coefficients**. Nonetheless, the multiplication of $(a + b)^4$ by $(a + b)$ to get the expansion for $(a + b)^5$ contains all the essential ideas of the proof.

We still lack a closed-form formula for the binomial coefficients. We know, for example, that the fourth term of the expansion of $(x + 2y)^{20}$ is $\binom{20}{3}x^{17}(2y)^3$, but we cannot complete the calculation without the binomial coefficient $\binom{20}{3}$. This would require writing at least the first few terms of 20 rows of Pascal's triangle.

Pascal himself posed and solved the problem of computing the entry at any given address within the triangle. He observed that to find $\binom{n}{r}$, we can take the product of all the numbers from 1 through r, and divide it into the product of the same number of integers, from n downward. This leads to the following formula.

> **Pascal's Formula for Binomial Coefficients**
>
> Suppose n is a positive integer and r is an integer that satisfies $0 < r \leq n$. The binomial coefficient $\binom{n}{r}$ is given by
>
> $$\binom{n}{r} = \frac{n(n-1)\cdots(n-r+1)}{1 \cdot 2 \cdot 3 \cdots r} \qquad (3)$$

We leave it to the reader to verify that the last factor in the numerator, $(n - r + 1)$, is the rth number counting down from n. This gives the same number of factors in the numerator as in the denominator.

EXAMPLE 1   Find the first five binomial coefficients on the tenth row of Pascal's triangle, and hence the first five terms of the expansion of $(a + b)^{10}$.

Solution

Strategy: We know $\binom{10}{0} = 1$. Use Equation (3) to get the remaining coefficients.

Follow the strategy.

$$\binom{10}{1} = \frac{10}{1} = 10, \quad \binom{10}{2} = \frac{10 \cdot 9}{1 \cdot 2} = 45, \quad \binom{10}{3} = \frac{10 \cdot 9 \cdot 8}{1 \cdot 2 \cdot 3} = 120, \text{ and}$$

$$\binom{10}{4} = \frac{10 \cdot 9 \cdot 8 \cdot 7}{1 \cdot 2 \cdot 3 \cdot 4} = 210.$$

Therefore the first five terms in the expansions of $(a + b)^{10}$ are

$$a^{10} + 10ab^9 + 45a^8b^2 + 120a^7b^3 + 210a^6b^4. \quad \blacktriangle$$

There is another very common formula for binomial coefficients that uses factorials. Equation 3 has a factorial in the denominator, and we can get a factorial in the numerator if we multiply numerator and denominator by the product of the rest of the integers from $n - r$ down to 1:

$$\binom{n}{r} = \frac{n(n-1)\ldots(n-r+1)}{1 \cdot 2 \cdot \ldots \cdot r}$$

$$= \frac{n(n-1)\ldots(n-r+1)}{r!} \cdot \frac{(n-r)\ldots 2 \cdot 1}{(n-r)\ldots 2 \cdot 1} = \frac{n!}{r!(n-r)!}.$$

While Equation 3 does not give a formula for $\binom{n}{0}$, the formulation in terms of factorials does apply.

$$\binom{n}{0} = \frac{n!}{0!(n-0)!} = \frac{n!}{1 \cdot n!} = \frac{n!}{n!} = 1.$$

Historical Note

BLAISE PASCAL

Blaise Pascal made significant contributions to the study of mathematics before deciding to devote his life to religion.

Pascal's triangle is named after Blaise Pascal, born in France in 1623. Pascal was an individual of incredible talent and breadth who made basic contributions in many areas of mathematics, but who died early after spending much of life embroiled in bitter philosophical and religious wrangling.

For some reason, Pascal's father decided that his son should not be exposed to any mathematics. All mathematics books in the home were locked up and the subject was banned from discussion. We do not know if the appeal of the forbidden was at work, but young Pascal approached his father directly and asked what geometry was. His father's answer so fascinated the 12-year-old boy that be began exploring geometric relationships on his own. He apparently rediscovered much of Euclid completely on his own. When Pascal was introduced to conic sections (see Chapter 10) he quickly absorbed everything available; he submitted a paper on conic sections to the French academy when he was only 16 years of age.

At the age of 29, Pascal had a conversion experience that led to a vow to renounce mathematics for a life of religious contemplation. Before that time, however, in addition to his foundational work in geometry, he

- built a mechanical computing machine (in honor of which the structured computer language Pascal is named)
- explored relations among binomial coefficients so thoroughly that we call the array of binomial coefficients Pascal's triangle even though the array had been known, at least in part, several hundred years earlier
- proved the binomial theorem
- gave the first published proof by mathematical induction
- invented (with Fermat) the science of combinatorial analysis, probability, and mathematical statistics.

Before his death ten years later, Pascal spent only a few days on mathematics. During a night made sleepless by a toothache, he concentrated on some problems about the cycloid curve that had attracted many mathematicians of the period. The pain subsided, and, in gratitude, Pascal wrote up his work for posterity.

This gives an alternative to Pascal's formula.

Alternative Formula for Binomial Coefficients

Suppose n is a positive integer and r an integer that satisfies $0 \le r \le n$. The binomial coefficient $\binom{n}{r}$ is given by

$$\binom{n}{r} = \frac{n!}{r!(n-r)!} \tag{4}$$

EXAMPLE 2   Show that

$$\textbf{(a) } \binom{6}{2} = \binom{6}{4} \qquad \textbf{(b) } \binom{n}{r} = \binom{n}{n-r}.$$

Solution

Strategy: Use Equation 4 to evaluate both sides of the given equations to show that the two sides of each equation are equal.

Follow the strategy.

(a) $\binom{6}{2} = \dfrac{6!}{2!(6-2)!} = \dfrac{6!}{2!4!}$ and $\binom{6}{4} = \dfrac{6!}{4!(6-4)!} = \dfrac{6!}{4!2!}.$

(b) $\binom{n}{r} = \dfrac{n!}{r!(n-r)!}$ and

$$\binom{n}{n-r} = \frac{n!}{(n-r)![n-(n-r)]!} = \frac{n!}{(n-r)!r!}$$

Thus

$$\binom{n}{r} = \binom{n}{n-r}. \quad \triangle$$

EXAMPLE 3   Show that $\binom{8}{3} + \binom{8}{4} = \binom{9}{4}$. Get a common denominator and add fractions, but do not evaluate any of the factorials or binomial coefficients.

Solution

Use Equation 3 to get $\binom{8}{3}$ and $\binom{8}{4}$, then add.

$$\binom{8}{3} + \binom{8}{4} = \frac{8 \cdot 7 \cdot 6}{1 \cdot 2 \cdot 3} + \frac{8 \cdot 7 \cdot 6 \cdot 5}{1 \cdot 2 \cdot 3 \cdot 4} = \frac{(8 \cdot 7 \cdot 6) \cdot 4}{(1 \cdot 2 \cdot 3) \cdot 4} + \frac{8 \cdot 7 \cdot 6 \cdot 5}{1 \cdot 2 \cdot 3 \cdot 4}$$

$$= \frac{8 \cdot 7 \cdot 6(4 + 5)}{1 \cdot 2 \cdot 3 \cdot 4} = \frac{9 \cdot 8 \cdot 7 \cdot 6}{1 \cdot 2 \cdot 3 \cdot 4} = \binom{9}{4}.$$

Thus

$$\binom{8}{3} + \binom{8}{4} = \binom{9}{4}. \quad \blacktriangle$$

Example 3 focuses more on the process than the particular result, hence the instruction to add fractions without evaluating. When we write out the binomial coefficients as fractions, we can identify the extra factors we need to get a common denominator and then add. By a similar process, we can prove a corresponding general result. (See Exercise 61.)

In Example 2, we proved that $\binom{n}{r} = \binom{n}{n-r}$, giving a symmetry property for the nth row of Pascal's triangle. Example 3 illustrates the essential steps to prove the following additivity property (see Exercise 61):

$$\binom{n}{r} + \binom{n}{r+1} = \binom{n+1}{r+1}$$

Symmetry and Additivity Properties

Binomial coefficients have the following properties:

Symmetry $\qquad\qquad \binom{n}{r} = \binom{n}{n-r}$ $\qquad\qquad$ **(5)**

Additivity $\qquad\qquad \binom{n}{r} + \binom{n}{r+1} = \binom{n+1}{r+1}$ $\qquad\qquad$ **(6)**

Notice that we used the additivity property from Equation 6 in Section 8.3 to get the $(n+1)$st row from the nth row in Pascal's triangle. This justifies our claim that the entries in Pascal's triangle are binomial coefficients.

EXAMPLE 4 Use the binomial theorem to write out the first five terms of the binomial expansion of $(x + 2y^2)^{20}$ and simplify.

Solution

Use Equation 1 with $a = x$, $b = 2y^2$, and $n = 20$. The first five terms of $(x + 2y^2)^{20}$ are

$$x^{20} + \binom{20}{1}x^{19}(2y^2) + \binom{20}{2}x^{18}(2y^2)^2 + \binom{20}{3}x^{17}(2y^2)^3 + \binom{20}{4}x^{16}(2y^2)^4.$$

Before simplifying, find the binomial coefficients using Equation 3.

$$\binom{20}{1} = \frac{20}{1} = 20 \qquad\qquad \binom{20}{2} = \frac{20 \cdot 19}{1 \cdot 2} = 190$$

$$\binom{20}{3} = \frac{20 \cdot 19 \cdot 18}{1 \cdot 2 \cdot 3} = 1140 \qquad \binom{20}{4} = \frac{20 \cdot 19 \cdot 18 \cdot 17}{1 \cdot 2 \cdot 2 \cdot 4} = 4845$$

Therefore, the first five terms of $(x + 2y^2)^{20}$ are

$$x^{20} + 20 \cdot 2x^{19}y^2 + 190 \cdot 4x^{18}y^4 + 1140 \cdot 8x^{17}y^6 + 4845 \cdot 16x^{16}y^8, \text{ or}$$

$$x^{20} + 40x^{19}y^2 + 760x^{18}y^4 + 9120x^{17}y^6 + 77520x^{16}y^8. \quad \blacktriangle$$

EXAMPLE 5   In the expansion of $(2x^2 - \frac{1}{x})^{10}$, find the middle term.

Solution

There are $10 + 1$ or 11 terms in the expansion of a tenth power, so the middle term is the sixth (five before and five after). The sixth term is given by $r = 5$.

$$\binom{10}{5}(2x^2)^5\left(-\frac{1}{x}\right)^5 = \frac{10 \cdot 9 \cdot 8 \cdot 7 \cdot 6}{1 \cdot 2 \cdot 3 \cdot 4 \cdot 5}(32x^{10})\left(-\frac{1}{x}\right)^5 = -8064x^5$$

The middle term is $-8064x^5$. $\quad \blacktriangle$

EXAMPLE 6   In the expansion of $(2x^2 - \frac{1}{x})^{10}$, find the term whose simplified form involves $\frac{1}{x}$.

Solution

Strategy: First find the general term, then simplify. Finally, find the value of r that gives -1 as the exponent of x.

Follow the strategy. The general term given in Equation 2 is

$$\binom{10}{r}(2x^2)^{10-r}\left(-\frac{1}{x}\right)^r = \binom{10}{r}2^{10-r}x^{20-2r}(-1)^r x^{-r}$$

$$= \binom{10}{r}(-1)^r 2^{10-r}x^{20-3r}.$$

For the term that involves $\frac{1}{x}$ or x^{-1}, find the value of r for which the exponent on x is -1: $20 - 3r = -1$, or $r = 7$. The desired term is given by

$$\binom{10}{7}(2x^2)^3\left(-\frac{1}{x}\right)^7 = -\frac{120(8)x^6}{x^7} = -\frac{960}{x}. \quad \blacktriangle$$

Proof of the Binomial Theorem

We can use mathematical induction to prove that Equation 1 holds for every positive integer n.

(a)   For $n = 1$, Equation 1 is $(a + b)^1 = \binom{1}{0}a^1b^0 + \binom{1}{1}a^0b^1 = a + b$, so Equation 1 is valid when n is 1.

(b)   Hypothesis: $(a + b)^k = \binom{k}{0}a^k + \binom{k}{1}a^{k-1}b + \cdots$

$$+ \binom{k}{r}a^{k-r}b^4 + \cdots + \binom{k}{k}b^k \tag{7}$$

Conclusion: $(a + b)^{k+1} = \binom{k + 1}{0}a^{k+1} + \binom{k + 1}{1}a^k b + \cdots$ $\tag{8}$

$$+ \binom{k + 1}{r}a^{k+1-r}b^r + \cdots + \binom{k + 1}{k + 1}b^{k+1}$$

Since $(a + b)^{k+1} = (a + b)^k(a + b) = (a + b)^k a + (a + b)^k b$, multiply the right side of Equation 7 by a, then by b, and add, combining like terms. It is also helpful to replace $\binom{k}{0}$ by $\binom{k+1}{0}$ and $\binom{k}{k}$ by $\binom{k+1}{k+1}$, since all are equal to 1.

$$(a + b)^k(a + b) = \binom{k+1}{0}a^{k+1} + \left[\binom{k}{0} + \binom{k}{1}\right]a^k b + \left[\binom{k}{1}\right]$$

$$+ \binom{k}{2}\right] a^{k-1}b^2 + \cdots$$

$$+ \left[\binom{k}{r-1} + \binom{k}{r}\right]a^{k+1-r}b^r + \cdots$$

$$+ \binom{k+1}{k+1}b^{k+1}.$$

Apply the additive property given in Equation 6 to the expressions in brackets to get Equation 8, as desired. Therefore, by the Principle of Mathematical Induction, Equation 1 is valid for every position integer n.

EXERCISES 8.5

Check Your Understanding

Exercises 1–6 True or False. Give reasons for your conclusion.

1. For every positive integer n, $(3n)! = (3!)(n!)$.
2. There are ten terms in the expression of $(1 + x)^{10}$.
3. The middle term of the expansion of $(x + \frac{1}{x})^8$ is 70.
4. The expansion of $(x^2 + 2x + 1)^8$ is the same as the expansion of $(x + 1)^{16}$.
5. $\binom{8}{1} + \binom{8}{2} - \binom{9}{2} = 0$.
6. For every positive number x, $(\sqrt{x} + \frac{1}{x})^4 = x^2 + \frac{1}{x^4}$.

Exercises 7–10 Complete the sentence by selecting from the list below *all* choices that make the statement true.

(a) a positive number (b) a negative number
(c) -20 (d) 10 (e) 20 (f) 25
(g) 28 (h) 56 (i) greater than 30

7. After simplifying the expansion of $(x^2 - \frac{1}{x})^5$, the coefficient of x^4 is _____.
8. In the expansion of $(\sqrt{x} - \frac{1}{\sqrt{x}})^6$, the middle term is _____.
9. $\binom{8}{3} - \binom{8}{2}$ is _____.
10. The number of terms in the expansion of $(x^2 + 4x + 4)^{12}$ is _____.

Explore and Discover

1. Let $S_n = 1 \cdot 1! + 2 \cdot 2! + \cdots + n \cdot n! + 1$.
   $S_1 = 1 \cdot 1! + 1 = 2 = 2!$ and
   $S_2 = 1 \cdot 1! + 2 \cdot 2! + 1 = 6 = 3!$
   (a) Evaluate S_3, S_4, and S_5 and look for a pattern. On the basis of your data, guess the value of S_8. Verify your guess by evaluating S_8 directly.
   (b) Guess a formula for S_n and use mathematical induction to prove that your formula is correct.

2. Suppose $f_n(x) = (x + \frac{1}{x})^{2n}$ and let a_n be the middle term of the expansion of $f_n(x)$.
   (a) Find a_1, a_2, a_3, and a_4.
   (b) Guess a formula for the general term a_n. Is $a_n = \frac{(2n)!}{n!n!}$?

3. Write a brief explanation about how the additive property of the binomial coefficients (Equation 6) relates to Pascal's triangle .

Develop Mastery

Exercises 1–18 Evaluate and simplify.

1. (a) $\binom{9}{3}$ (b) $\binom{9}{6}$
2. (a) $\binom{14}{3}$ (b) $\binom{14}{11}$
3. (a) $\binom{8}{5}$ (b) $\binom{8}{3}$
4. (a) $\binom{100}{98}$ (b) $\binom{100}{2}$
5. (a) $\binom{20}{2} + \binom{20}{3}$ (b) $\binom{21}{3}$

6. (a) $\binom{7}{3} + \binom{7}{4}$ **(b)** $\binom{8}{4}$

7. (a) $\frac{5}{6} \cdot \binom{10}{5}$ **(b)** $\binom{10}{6}$

8. (a) $\frac{9}{4} \cdot \binom{12}{3}$ **(b)** $\binom{12}{4}$

9. (a) $\binom{10}{6} \cdot \binom{6}{3}$ **(b)** $\binom{10}{7} \cdot \binom{7}{3}$

10. (a) $\binom{12}{10} \cdot \binom{10}{4}$ **(b)** $\binom{8}{5} \cdot \binom{5}{3}$

11. (a) $\frac{10!}{7!}$ **(b)** $\frac{10!}{7!3!}$

12. (a) $8! + 2!$ **(b)** $10!$

13. (a) $\frac{6! + 4!}{3!}$ **(b)** $\frac{8! - 5!}{3!}$

14. (a) $6! - 3!$ **(b)** $(6 - 3)!$

15. (a) $2(4!)$ **(b)** $(2 \cdot 4)!$

16. (a) $\frac{(2 \cdot 4)!}{4!}$ **(b)** $(2 \cdot 4)! - 4!$

17. (a) $\frac{\binom{12}{7}}{\binom{12}{6}}$ **(b)** $\frac{\binom{14}{9}}{\binom{14}{8}}$

18. (a) $\frac{\binom{9}{5}}{\binom{8}{4}}$ **(b)** $\frac{\binom{11}{7}}{\binom{10}{6}}$

Exercises 19–24   Evaluate and simplify.

19. $\binom{n}{n-1}$ **20.** $\binom{n}{n-2}$ **21.** $\binom{n+1}{n-1}$

22. $\frac{(n+1)!}{(n-1)!}$ **23.** $\frac{\binom{n}{k+1}}{\binom{n}{k}}$ **24.** $\frac{\binom{n+1}{r}}{\binom{n}{r-1}}$

Exercises 25–30   Use the binomial theorem formula to expand the expression, then simplify your result.

25. $(x - 1)^5$ **26.** $(x - 3y)^4$

27. $(\frac{1}{x} - 2y^2)^4$ **28.** $(x^2 + \frac{2}{x})^6$

29. $(3x + \frac{1}{x^2})^5$ **30.** $(x - 1)^7$

Exercises 31–34   Use the formula in Equation 2.

(a) Write the expansion in sigma form.

(b) Expand and simplify.

31. $(2 - x)^5$ **32.** $(2x + \frac{y}{2})^5$

33. $(x^2 + \frac{2}{x})^5$ **34.** $(x^2 - 2)^6$

Exercises 35–38

(a) How many terms are there in the expansion of the given expression?

(b) If the answer in **(a)** is odd, then find the middle term. If it is even, find the two middle terms.

35. $(x^2 - 3)^8$ **36.** $(x^2 - \frac{1}{x})^{15}$

37. $(1 + \sqrt{x})^5$ **38.** $(x + 2\sqrt{x})^{10}$

Exercises 39–40   Find the first three terms in the expansion of

39. $(x + \frac{1}{x})^{20}$ **40.** $(x - \frac{3}{x})^{25}$

Exercises 41–44   If the expression is expanded using equation 1, find the indicated term and simplify.

41. $(x^3 - \frac{2}{x})^5$; third term

42. $(\frac{x}{2} - 2y)^{12}$; tenth term

43. $(2x - \frac{y}{2})^{10}$; fourth term

44. $(x^{-1} + 2x)^8$; fourth term

Exercises 45–52   If the expression is expanded and each term is simplified, find the coefficient of the term that contains the given power of x. (See Example 6.)

45. $(x^3 - \frac{2}{x})^4$; x^4 **46.** $(2x - \frac{1}{3})^{10}$; x^7

47. $(x^2 + 2)^{11}$; x^8 **48.** $(x^2 - \frac{2}{x})^{10}$; x^8

49. $(x^3 - \frac{1}{x})^{15}$; x^{25} **50.** $(x^2 - \frac{3}{x})^{12}$; x^9

51. $(x^2 - 2x + 1)^3$; x^4 **52.** $(x^2 + 4x + 4)^3$; x^2

Exercises 53–60   Find all positive integers n that satisfy the equation.

53. $(2n)! = 2(n!)$ **54.** $(3n)! = (3!)(n!)$

55. $2(n - 2)! = n!$ **56.** $(3n)! = 3(n + 1)!$

57. $\binom{n}{3} = \binom{n}{5}$ **58.** $\binom{n}{3} + \binom{n}{4} = \binom{8}{4}$

59. $\binom{n}{2} = 15$ **60.** $\binom{n}{2} = 28$

61. (a) Show that $\binom{10}{6} + \binom{10}{7} = \binom{11}{7}$ by carrying out the following steps. Using Equation 3, express each term of $\binom{10}{6} + \binom{10}{7}$ as a fraction with factorials; then, without expanding, get a common denominator and express the result as a fraction involving factorials. By Equation 3, show that the result is equal to $\binom{11}{7}$. See Example 3.

(b) Following a pattern similar to that described in part **(a)**, prove the additivity property for the binomial coefficients

$$\binom{n}{r} + \binom{n}{r+1} = \binom{n+1}{r+1}.$$

62. By expanding the left- and right-hand sides, verify that

$$\binom{n}{k+1} = \frac{n-k}{k+1} \cdot \binom{n}{k}.$$

63. Observe that 5! (= 120) ends with one zero (meaning that 5! is a multiple of 10). Find the smallest positive integer n such that $n!$ is a multiple of **(a)** 100, **(b)** 1000, and **(c)** 10^6.

64. Find the smallest positive integer n such that $n!$ exceeds **(a)** 1 billion, **(b)** 1 trillion, and **(c)** 10^{15}.

65. Show that $\binom{5}{0} - \binom{5}{1} + \binom{5}{2} - \binom{5}{3} + \binom{5}{4} - \binom{5}{5}$ is equal to 0. (*Hint:* Expand $[1 + (-1)]^5$ using Equation 1.)

66. Show that $\binom{5}{0} + \binom{5}{1} + \binom{5}{2} + \binom{5}{3} + \binom{5}{4} + \binom{5}{5}$ is equal to 2^5. (*Hint:* Expand $(1 + 1)^5$ using Equation 1.)

CHAPTER 8 REVIEW

Test Your Understanding

Determine the truth value (T or F) of the statement. Give reasons for your conclusion.

1. If $a_n = n^2 - n + 17$, then all terms of the sequence $\{a_n\}$ are prime numbers.

2. In an arithmetic sequence the common difference d equals $a_8 - a_7$.

3. In an arithmetic sequence, if d is negative, then all terms of the sequence must be negative from some point on.

4. The numbers $5, -\frac{5}{2}, \frac{5}{4}, -\frac{5}{6}$, are four consecutive terms of a geometric sequence.

Exercises 5–8   Assume that $\{a_n\}$ is an arithmetic sequence and that each term is a positive integer.

5. The common difference d cannot be a negative number.

6. If a_1 is even and d is even, then every a_n is even.

7. If a_1 is odd and d is odd, then every a_n is odd.

8. If a_1 is odd and d is even, then every a_n is odd.

9. The terms $x + 1, x - 2$, and $x - 3$ constitute three consecutive terms of an arithmetic sequence for every real number x.

10. There is no real number x for which $x, x + 1, x + 2$ will be three consecutive terms of a geometric sequence.

11. There is no sequence that is both arithmetic and geometric.

12. The sequence whose nth term is $\ln(2n)$ is neither arithmetic nor geometric.

13. The sequence whose nth term is $n \ln 2$ is arithmetic.

14. The sequence whose nth term is $\ln 2^n$ is geometric.

15. If $a_{n+1} = a_n - 3$ for $n = 1, 2, 3, \ldots$, then $\{a_n\}$ is an arithmetic sequence.

16. If $a_1 < 0$ and $a_{n+1} = -a_n$, then $\{a_n\}$ is a geometric sequence.

17. In a geometric sequence if a_1 is an irrational number, then every term of the sequence must be an irrational number.

18. If $a_n = 2n - 1$ and $b_m = 3m + 1$, then no number is in both sequences $\{a_n\}$ and $\{b_m\}$.

19. The eleventh term of the sequence $\{2n + 3\}$ is the same as the ninth term of $\{3n - 2\}$.

20. The numbers $\frac{1}{2}, \frac{1}{4}, \frac{1}{6}$, are the first three terms of an arithmetic sequence.

21. $\displaystyle\sum_{k=1}^{15} (2k - 1) = 15^2$.   **22.** $\displaystyle\sum_{k=1}^{4} \left(-\frac{1}{2}\right)^k = -\frac{5}{16}$

23. The numbers e, e^2, e^3 are the first three terms of a geometric sequence.

24. If $a_n = \frac{1}{n^2}$, then $\{a_n\}$ is a geometric sequence.

25. If $a_n = \sin\left[(2n - 1)\frac{\pi}{2}\right]$, then $\{a_n\}$ is a geometric sequence.

26. If $a_n = \cos n\pi$, then $\{a_n\}$ is a geometric sequence.

27. If $a_k = \cos k\pi$, then $\sum_{k=1}^{n} a_k$ equals 0 whenever n is even.

28. $1.\overline{21} = \frac{40}{33}$.

29. $n^2 - n + 3$ is an odd number for every positive integer n.

30. $n^2 - 2n + 4$ is an even number for every positive integer n.

31. $\frac{(n+1)!}{(n-1)!} = n^2 + n$ for every positive integer n.

32. $\binom{8}{5} = \binom{8}{3}$

33. $\binom{7}{4} + \binom{7}{5} = \binom{8}{5}$

34. $\frac{16!}{2!14!} = 240$

35. $\frac{3! + 6!}{3!} = 1 + 2!$

36. There are eight terms in the expansion of $(x - \frac{1}{x})^8$.

37. In the expansion of $(x + \frac{1}{x})^6$ the fourth term is a constant.

38. $\binom{n}{n-1} = n$ for every positive integer n.

39. $\binom{2n}{n} = \frac{2n!}{n!n!}$ for every positive integer n.

40. $2\binom{n}{2} + \binom{n}{1} = n^2$ for every positive integer n.

Mastery Review

Exercises 1–4 For the sequence whose nth term is given, **(a)** find the first four terms, and **(b)** evaluate $\sum_{k=1}^{4} a_k$.

1. $a_n = 1 - \frac{1}{2^n}$

2. $a_n = 1 - \frac{1}{2^{n-1}}$

3. $a_n = 3n - 1$

4. $a_n = \frac{1}{n(n+2)}$

5. If $a_1 = 3$ and $a_n = 2a_{n-1}$ for $n \geq 2$, find the first five terms of the sequence $\{a_n\}$.

6. If $a_1 = 1$, $a_2 = 2$, and $a_n = 2a_{n-1} + 3a_{n-2}$ for $n \geq 3$, find the first five terms of the sequence $\{a_n\}$.

Exercises 7–12 The first four terms of a sequence $\{a_n\}$ are given. Guess a formula for a_n that could generate the sequence. There is no unique correct answer. (Why?)

7. $3, 8, 13, 18, \ldots$

8. $\sqrt{2}, 2, 2\sqrt{2}, 4, \ldots$

9. $1, 3, 7, 15, \ldots$

10. $3, 5, 9, 17, \ldots$

11. $-1, 1, -1, 1, \ldots$

12. $\frac{1}{2}, -\frac{1}{6}, \frac{1}{12}, -\frac{1}{20}, \ldots$

13. The first three terms of an arithmetic sequence are 3, 8, 13. Find **(a)** the twenty-fourth term, and **(b)** the sum of the first 24 terms.

14. In an arithmetic sequence $a_4 = 16$ and $a_{13} = -2$. Find **(a)** a_{20}, **(b)** $\sum_{k=1}^{20} a_k$, and **(c)** the number n of terms such that $\sum_{k=1}^{n} a_k = -140$.

15. Find all values of x such that $x^2, x, -3$ are three consecutive terms of arithmetic sequence.

16. The first three terms of a geometric sequence are $3, \frac{3}{2}, \frac{3}{4}$. Find **(a)** the fifth term, and **(b)** the sum of the first five terms.

17. Suppose a sequence $\{a_n\}$ is given by $a_n = 1 + \frac{1}{2^n}$.
   (a) Write out the first four terms.
   (b) Is this a geometric sequence?
   (c) Find the sum of the first four terms.

18. In a geometric sequence $a_1 = \frac{2}{3}$ and $r = \frac{1}{3}$. Find the number of terms n such that the sum S_n equals $\frac{6560}{6561}$.

19. Find the repeating decimal expansion for **(a)** $\frac{4}{15}$, **(b)** $\frac{18}{11}$, and **(c)** $\frac{3}{14}$.

20. Express the repeating decimal $0.727272\ldots$ (that is, $0.\overline{72}$) as a quotient of two integers.

Exercises 21–27 Evaluate the sum.

21. $\sum_{k=1}^{15} (2k - 1)$

22. $\sum_{k=1}^{50} (3k + 2)$

23. $\sum_{k=1}^{\infty} (\frac{1}{3})^k$

24. $\sum_{k=1}^{\infty} (\frac{1}{4})^k$

25. $\sum_{k=1}^{5} (2^k - k)$

26. $\sum_{k=1}^{10} (-1)^k (2k - 1)$

27. $\sum_{k=1}^{10} (\frac{1}{k} - \frac{1}{k+1})$

Exercises 28–31 The sequence $\{a_n\}$ is either arithmetic or geometric. Find the indicated term.

28. $5, 8, 11, 14, \cdots$ a_{16}

29. $3, \frac{5}{2}, 2, \frac{3}{2}, \cdots$ a_{24}

30. $2, 3, \frac{9}{2}, \frac{27}{4}, \cdots$ a_8

31. $4, -2, 1, -\frac{1}{2}, \cdots$ a_{10}

Exercises 32–33 Find the sum of the infinite geometric series.

32. $\frac{2}{5} + \frac{2}{25} + \frac{2}{125} + \cdots$

33. $\frac{1}{3} - \frac{1}{9} + \frac{1}{27} - \frac{1}{81} + \cdots$

Exercises 34–36 Use the Principle of Mathematical Induction to prove that $P(n)$ yields a true statement for every positive integer n.

34. $P(n)$: $3 + 9 + 15 + \cdots + (6n - 3) = 3n^2$

35. $P(n)$: $\frac{1}{2} + \frac{1}{4} + \frac{1}{8} + \cdots + \frac{1}{2^n} = 1 - \frac{1}{2^n}$

36. $P(n)$: $7^n - 1$ is divisible by **(a)** 2 **(b)** 3 **(c)** 6.

37. Is it true that $3n^3 + 6n$ is divisible by 9 for every positive integer n? Give reasons for your answer.

38. Is this a true statement: $3^n \le (n + 3)^2$ for every positive integer n? If so, give a proof; if not, give a counterexample.

39. Evaluate **(a)** $\frac{6!}{2!4!}$ **(b)** $\binom{15}{3}$ **(c)** $\binom{8}{2} + \binom{8}{3}$.

Exercises 40–45 Use the binomial theorem to expand the expression.

40. $(2x - \frac{1}{x})^5$

41. $(3 + 2x)^4$

42. $(4 - 3x)^5$

43. $(1 - \sqrt{2})^6$

44. $(1 - \frac{1}{x})^5$

45. $(x^{-1} + \sqrt{y})^6$

46. Find the fourth term in the expansion of $(x + 2y)^8$.

47. In the expansion of $(2 - \frac{x}{3})^{10}$, write out the term that contains x^8.

48. In the expansion of $(1 - \sqrt{x})^8$, write out the term that contains x^3.

49. Suppose $(x^2 + \frac{1}{x})^{15}$ is expanded and the resulting terms are simplified. Find the term that involves x^6.

50. Find the sum of all positive integers less than 400 that are divisible by both 2 and 3.

51. Suppose a sequence $\{a_n\}$ is given by $a_n = (1 - \frac{1}{n})^n$. Find the term and give results rounded off to five decimal places.
(a) a_{10} **(b)** a_{100} **(c)** $a_{1,000}$ **(d)** $a_{10,000}$
(e) Evaluate e^{-1} and compare with a_n for large n.

52. Expand $(1 + 2\sqrt{x} + x)^3$. [*Hint:* First show that $1 + 2\sqrt{x} + x = (1 + \sqrt{x})^2$.]

53. Evaluate
(a) $\binom{1}{0}^2 + \binom{1}{1}^2$ **(b)** $\binom{2}{0}^2 + \binom{2}{1}^2 + \binom{2}{2}^2$
(c) $\binom{3}{0}^2 + \binom{3}{1}^2 + \binom{3}{2}^2 + \binom{3}{3}^2$.

9

SYSTEMS OF EQUATIONS AND INEQUALITIES

A consistent theme throughout this book is **solving equations.** So far, our equations have involved a single variable or unknown. In this chapter we explore methods for solving *systems* of equations, where the equations involve more than one variable.

When we look at a given problem, it is often natural to label more than one variable. Then we try to relate the variables. For example, suppose we know that the hypotenuse of a right triangle is 17, the perimeter is 40, and we want to find the lengths of the two legs. If x and y represent the lengths of the legs as shown in Figure 9.1, then equations relating x and y are

$$x + y + 17 = 40 \quad \text{or} \quad x + y = 23$$
$$x^2 + y^2 = 17^2 \quad \text{or} \quad x^2 + y^2 = 289. \tag{1}$$

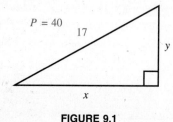

FIGURE 9.1

The two equations in (1) form a **system of equations** in two variables. It is simple to verify that the solutions are given by $x = 8$, $y = 15$, or $x = 15$, $y = 8$. In either case, the lengths of the legs are 8 and 15.

In the first two sections of this chapter, we will concentrate on systems of **linear** equations and introduce nonlinear equations in Section 9.3. In Section 9.4 we consider systems of inequalities and the vital application of linear programming. In the last sections we give a brief introduction to matrix algebra and determinants, including Cramer's rule.

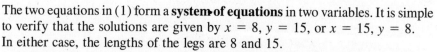

Systems of Linear Equations; Gaussian Elimination

Mathematics is effective precisely because a relatively compact mathematical scheme can be used to predict over a relatively long period of time the future behavior of some physical system to a certain level of accuracy, and thereby generate more information about the system than is contained in the mathematical scheme to begin with.
    P. W. C. Davies

Our focus in this section is **linear equations** in several variables, such as

$$3x - 4y + 2z + w = 5 \quad \text{and} \quad -3s + 2t = 1.$$

The following equations are not linear:

$$x^2 - y = 4 \qquad \text{Not linear in } x$$
$$x + 3|y| - z = 7 \qquad \text{Not linear in } y$$
$$uv + \ln w = 0 \qquad \text{Not linear in } u, v, \text{ and } w$$

I also engaged in wild mathematical discussions, formulating vast and new projects, new problems, theories and methods bordering on the fantastic . . . . .

    Stan Ulam

For a *system* of linear equations, we indicate both the number of equations and the number of variables. A 2×2 system consists of two equations in two

478

variables, and a 3×3 system has three equations in three variables:

$$\begin{cases} -3x + 4y = 11 \\ 2x - 3y = -8 \end{cases} \tag{2}$$

$$\begin{cases} 2a - 5b + 3c = 8 \\ a + 5b - c = 4 \\ 3a + 2c = 12 \end{cases} \tag{3}$$

A **solution** to a system of linear equations consists of a value for each variable such that when we substitute the replacement values, every equation becomes a true statement. For system (2) above, the values $x = -1$, and $y = 2$ satisfy both equations in the system. A solution to system (3) can be written $(a, b, c) = (6, -1, -3)$, which means that $a = 6$, $b = -1$, and $c = -3$. The ordered pair of numbers $(-1, 2)$ is the only solution to system (2), but $(a, b, c) = (8, -2, -6)$ is another of many solutions to system (3).

Equivalent Systems

We need a systematic procedure to find all solutions to a system of equations. There are several methods, some of which you may have seen in previous courses. We will describe a technique that replaces a system of equations in turn by other, simpler systems with the same solutions until we get a system simple enough that we can read off the solution. For example, consider these 3×3 systems:

$$\begin{cases} 2x - 5y + 3z = -4 \\ x - 2y - 3z = 3 \\ -3x + 4y + 2z = -4 \end{cases} \tag{4}$$

$$\begin{cases} 2x - 5y + 3z = -4 \\ y - 9z = 10 \\ -z = 1 \end{cases} \tag{5}$$

It is simple to solve system (5) by starting with the last equation to get $z = -1$. Substitute into the second equation and find $y = 1$, and then substitute both y and z values into the first equation to get $x = 2$. In fact, it is easy to see that $(x, y, z) = (2, 1, -1)$ is the only solution for system (5). In Example 1 we will show that the two systems have the same solution, and hence that our solution for system (5) is the solution for system (4). Two systems of linear equations are **equivalent** if they have identical solutions.

In the process of going from system (4) to system (5), we successively eliminate variables. So x has been eliminated from the second equation in system (5), and both x and y have been eliminated in the third equation. System (5) is called an **echelon,** or **upper triangular,** form of system (4).

Definition: Echelon (Upper Triangular) Form

A system of three linear equations in variables x, y, z is said to be in echelon form if it can be written as

$$a_1 x + a_2 y + a_3 z = d_1$$
$$b_2 y + b_3 z = d_2$$
$$c_3 z = d_3$$

where all coefficients a, b, c, and d are given numbers, some of which may be zero.

Elementary Operations and Gaussian Elimination

The systematic elimination of variables to change a system of linear equations into an equivalent system in echelon form from which we can read the solution is called **Gaussian elimination** in honor of Carl Friedrich Gauss, one of the most brilliant mathematicians of all time.

The key to Gaussian elimination (which can be done efficiently on computers) is the idea of **elementary operation,** the replacement of one equation in a system by another in a way that leaves the solution unchanged. Each of the following operations gives an equivalent system, that has the same solution set. E_k denotes the kth equation of the system and $-2E_1 + E_2$ is what we get when we multiply both sides of equation E_1 by -2 and add the result to equation E_2.

Elementary Operations

Operation	*Notation and Meaning*
1. Interchange two rows	$E_2 \leftrightarrow E_3$ means interchange equation E_2 and E_3.
2. Multiply by a nonzero constant	$4E_3 \rightarrow E_3$ means replace equation E_3 with $4E_3$.
3. Add a multiple of one equation to another equation	$4E_2 + E_3 \rightarrow E_3$ means replace E_3 with $4E_2 + E_3$.

Equivalent Systems

Performing any of the elementary operations on a system of linear equations gives an equivalent system.

Follow the next example closely, performing each operation as indicated, to be certain that you understand both the process by which we reduce the original system to echelon form and the notation by which we keep track of and check each step.

> **EXAMPLE 1**   Reduce the following system to echelon form and then find the solution.

$$E_1 \qquad 2x - 5y + 3z = -4$$
$$E_2 \qquad x - 2y - 3z = 3$$
$$E_3 \qquad -3x + 4y + 2z = -4$$

Solution

Strategy: Since the coefficient of x in E_2 is 1, first interchange E_1 and E_2, then eliminate x from the other two equations without involving fractions.

Follow the strategy. We will not repeatedly write the equation numbers, simply assuming in each system that the equations are numbered E_1, E_2, and E_3, from top to bottom. Beginning with the given system, we perform elementary operations as indicated:

$$E_1 \longleftrightarrow E_2 \quad \begin{cases} x - 2y - 3z = 3 \\ 2x - 5y + 3z = -4 \\ -3x + 4y + 2z = -4 \end{cases}$$

$$\begin{array}{c} -2E_1 + E_2 \longrightarrow E_2 \\ \text{and} \\ 3E_1 + E_3 \longrightarrow E_3 \end{array} \quad \begin{cases} x - 2y - 3z = 3 \\ -y + 9z = -10 \\ -2y - 7z = 5 \end{cases}$$

$$(-2)E_2 + E_3 \longrightarrow E_3 \quad \begin{cases} x - 2y - 3z = 3 \\ -y + 9z = -10 \\ -25z = 25 \end{cases}$$

We now have a system in echelon form that is equivalent to the given system.

To solve the echelon-form system, start with the last equation and solve for z: $z = \frac{25}{-25} = -1$. Substitute -1 for z into E_2 and solve for y: $-y + 9(-1) = -10$, or $y = 1$. Substitute -1 for z and 1 for y into E_1 and solve for x: $x - 2(1) - 3(-1) = 3$, or $x = 2$. The solution is given by $x = 2$, $y = 1$, $z = -1$. ▲

The process of solving a system of equations in echelon form has the name **back-substitution.** This suggests the procedure of starting at the bottom and working toward the top, substituting into each successive equation.

> **EXAMPLE 2**   Use elementary operations to get an equivalent system, eliminating the x-variable from E_2 and E_3.

$$2x - 3y + z = -1$$
$$-3x + 4y - z = 2$$
$$2x - y + 2z = -3$$

Strategy: We can easily use E_1 to eliminate x in E_3, but to avoid fractions for E_2, first multiply E_2 by 2, then add $3E_1$ to eliminate x.

Solution

Carry out the elementary operations suggested in the strategy:

$$(-1)E_1 + E_3 \longrightarrow E_3 \quad \begin{cases} 2x - 3y + z = -1 \\ -3x + 4y - z = 2 \\ \qquad\quad 2y + z = -2 \end{cases}$$

$$2E_2 \longrightarrow E_2 \quad \begin{cases} 2x - 3y + z = -1 \\ -6x + 8y - 2z = 4 \\ \qquad\quad 2y + z = -2 \end{cases}$$

$$3E_1 + E_2 \longrightarrow E_2 \quad \begin{cases} 2x - 3y + z = -1 \\ \qquad -y + z = 1 \\ \qquad\quad 2y + z = -2 \end{cases}$$

Complete the solution and verify that $z = 0$, $y = -1$, and $x = -2$.   ▲

> **EXAMPLE 3**   Solve the system by using Gaussian elimination.

$$\textbf{(a)} \quad \begin{cases} x + 2y - 2z = 3 \\ 2x + 3y - 3z = 1 \\ -4x - 5y + 5z = 3 \end{cases}$$

$$\textbf{(b)} \quad \begin{cases} x + 2y - 2z = 3 \\ 2x + 3y - 3z = 1 \\ -4x - 5y + 5z = 5 \end{cases}$$

Solution

(a) The following elementary operations lead to an echelon form, from which we find x, y, and z.

$$(-2)E_1 + E_2 \longrightarrow E_2 \quad \begin{cases} x + 2y - 2z = 3 \\ \quad - y + z = -5 \\ -4x - 5y + 5z = 3 \end{cases}$$

$$4E_1 + E_3 \longrightarrow E_3 \quad \begin{cases} x + 2y - 2z = 3 \\ \quad - y + z = -5 \\ \qquad 3y - 3z = 15 \end{cases}$$

$$3E_2 + E_3 \longrightarrow E_3 \quad \begin{cases} x + 2y - 2z = -3 \\ \quad - y + z = -5 \\ \qquad\quad 0 \cdot z = 0 \end{cases}$$

We now have an echelon form system in which E_3, $0 \cdot z = 0$, is satisfied by any number z. Therefore, we have infinitely many solutions.

Let $z = t$, where t is any number. E_2 implies $y = z + 5 = t + 5$. Finally, we get x from E_1.

$$x = 3 - 2y + 2z = 3 - 2(t + 5) + 2t = 3 - 2t - 10 + 2t = -7.$$

Infinitely many solutions are given by

$$x = -7, y = t + 5, z = t,$$

where t is any number. For instance,

$$t = 0 \text{ gives } x = -7, y = 5, z = 0$$
$$t = -3 \text{ gives } x = -7, y = 2, z = -3.$$

(b) Note that the system of equations given here is the same as that in part **(a)** except for the right side of E_3. The same elementary operations performed in the solution to Example 3a yield the echelon form for the system.

$$x + 2y - 2z = 3$$
$$-y + z = -5$$
$$0 \cdot z = 2$$

Since no number z satisfies the equation $0 \cdot z = 2$, the system has no solution. ▲

A system of linear equations that has infinitely many solutions is said to be **dependent,** while a system with no solutions is called **inconsistent.** The system in Example 3a is dependent and that in 3b is inconsistent. Another advantage of echelon form is that the last equation tells us the nature of the solutions, which must be one of the following possibilities.

Nature of Solutions for a System of Linear Equations

1. There is exactly one solution; the solution is unique.
2. There are no solutions; the system is inconsistent.
3. There are infinitely many solutions; the system is dependent.

The next example illustrates the three possibilities for 2×2 systems. It shows geometrically a unique solution, a dependent system, and an inconsistent system.

EXAMPLE 4 Graph the pair of equations on the same coordinate system, then solve the system.

(a) $\begin{cases} -3x + y = 5 \\ 2x - 3y = -8 \end{cases}$

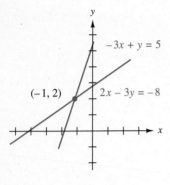

(a)   Unique solution

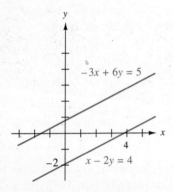

(b)   Inconsistent system

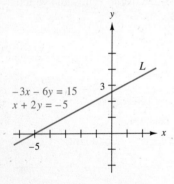

(c)   Dependent system

FIGURE 9.2

(b) $\begin{cases} -3x + 6y = 5 \\ x - 2y = 4 \end{cases}$

(c) $\begin{cases} -3x + 6y = 15 \\ x - 2y = -5 \end{cases}$

Solution

The graphs are shown in Figure 9.2. Use Gaussian elimination to verify the following solutions.

(a) Unique solution; $x = -1$, $y = 2$. The two lines intersect at $(-1, 2)$.

(b) No solution; the system is inconsistent. The two lines are parallel; they have no intersection.

(c) Infinitely many solutions; the system is dependent. Both equations determine the same line; every point of the line satisfies both equations.   ▲

A system of any number of linear equations must have either a unique solution, no solution, or be dependent, just as the 2 × 2 systems in Example 4. Unfortunately, we cannot see the geometry as easily with larger systems as we can with 2 × 2 systems. In the next example we illustrate how linear systems occur in applications.

EXAMPLE 5   Dessert consists of chocolate pudding and whipped cream. We are interested in the energy (calories) and vitamin A content. The necessary information in the table is taken from a handbook on nutrition.

Food	Energy (calories)	VitaminA (units)
Pudding (1 cup)	385	390
Cream (1 tablespoon)	26	220

How much pudding (in cups) and cream (in tablespoons) will give a dessert with 283 calories and 674 units of vitamin A?

Strategy: To find the numbers of cups and tablespoons, assign variables and write equations for the number of calories ($= 283$) and units of vitamin A ($= 674$).

Solution

Follow the strategy. Let x = number of cups of pudding and y = number of tablespoons of cream.

Since each cup of pudding contains 385 calories (see the table), x cups must contain $385x$ calories. Similarly, y tablespoons of cream contain $26y$ calories. Set the sum of these two equal to 283 calories: $385x + 26y = 283$. In

For Graphers 9.1

GRAPHICAL SOLUTION OF 2 × 2 LINEAR SYSTEMS

There are several different ways to solve linear systems, some of which are better adapted to technology than others. For systems of two equations in two unknowns, we can use the zoom capabilities of graphing calculators to locate the solution with considerable accuracy.

EXAMPLE Find the solution set for the system
$$374x + 15y = 792$$
$$64x - 275y = 493$$

Solution The graph of each of the equations in the system is a line. From the two lines we can locate the point whose coordinates satisfy both equations. Since the calculator plots graphs of functions of the form $y = f(x)$, we must solve each equation for y. Graph the functions

$$y = \frac{-374x + 792}{15} \quad \text{and} \quad y = \frac{64x - 493}{275}$$

in the Familiar Window. We can trace to see that the intersection of the two lines is near $(2.2, -1.3)$. If we then zoom in on the intersection a couple of times by drawing small boxes around the intersection, we can identify the point of intersection to three decimal places as $(2.169, -1.288)$, which we can check, if we wish, by substitution into the original equations. ▲

Exercises 1–6 Solve the system graphically, to an accuracy of three decimal places. Hint: For Exercises 5 and 6, the solution does not appear in the Familiar Window. Begin with a larger window and then make adjustments as necessary to locate the intersection.

1. $\begin{aligned} 15x + 37y &= 43 \\ 17x + 14y &= 36 \end{aligned}$

2. $\begin{aligned} 192x - 135y &= 140 \\ 64x + 83y &= 127 \end{aligned}$

3. $\begin{aligned} 72x + 43y &= 293 \\ 129x - 22y &= 341 \end{aligned}$

4. $\begin{aligned} 429x - 362y &= 527 \\ 611x + 243y &= 385 \end{aligned}$

5. $\begin{aligned} 17x + 43y &= 293 \\ 12x - 28y &= 341 \end{aligned}$

6. $\begin{aligned} 42x - 36y &= 293 \\ 61x - 24y &= 869 \end{aligned}$

a similar manner, to get 674 units of vitamin A, $390x + 220y = 674$. Therefore, solve the following system of equations.

$$E_1: \quad 385x + 26y = 283 \quad \text{Calories}$$

$$E_2: \quad 390x + 220y = 674 \quad \text{Vitamin A}$$

To eliminate x from E_2, first multiply E_1 by 390 ($390E_1 \to E_1$) and E_2 by -385 ($-385E_2 \to E_2$). Then add the resulting equations ($E_1 + E_2 \to E_2$). This gives for the last equation

$$-74{,}560y = -149{,}120 \quad \text{or} \quad y = 2. \quad \text{Check!}$$

Substitute 2 for y in one of the original equations to get $x = 0.6$. Hence $\frac{3}{5}$ cup of pudding with 2 tablespoons of cream will give the desired proportions of calories and vitamin A. ▲

Check Your Understanding

Exercises 1–7   True or False. Give reasons for your conclusion.

1. The equation $3x - \sqrt{2}y = 5$ is linear in x and y.
2. The equation $3\sqrt{x^2} + 4y = 7$ is linear in x and y.
3. The graphs of $2x - 3y = 3$ and $x + y = 3$ intersect in the first quadrant.
4. Both $(0, 0, 0)$ and $(-3, 2, 1)$ are solutions to the system

$$x + y + z = 0$$
$$y - 2z = 0$$
$$x - 2y - z = 0$$

5. The solution to the system

$$2x + y = 5$$
$$x + 3y = -4$$

consists of a pair of positive integers.

6. The system

$$2x + y = 0$$
$$x - 3y = 5$$

is dependent.

7. In the solution to the following system, x and y are negative and z is positive.

$$x + y - z = 4$$
$$y + 2z = 0$$
$$3x + y = 5$$

Exercises 8–10   Complete the sentence by selecting from the list below *all choices* that make the statement true. Lines L_1, L_2, and L_3 are given by L_1: $x - 3y = 0$, L_2: $x + 3y = 6$, L_3: $x - 9y = 6$.

(a) $(-3, -1)$ (b) $(3, 1)$
(c) $(6, 0)$ (d) a point in QI
(e) a point in QII   (f) a point in QIII
(g) a point in QIV

8. Lines L_1 and L_2 intersect at _____ .
9. Lines L_1 and L_3 intersect at _____ .
10. Lines L_3 and L_2 intersect at _____ .

Develop Mastery

Exercises 1–6   Solve the system of equations and graph the pair of lines on the same system of coordinates. (See Example 4.)

1. $x + y = 4$
   $3x - 2y = -3$

2. $3x + y = -5$
   $-x + 2y = 4$

3. $3x + 4y = -1$
   $-3x + 5y = -2$

4. $3x - 2y = 4$
   $-5x + 2y = 8$

5. $4x - 2y = 3$
   $-2x + y = 5$

6. $2x + 4y = 3$
   $x + 2y = 1.5$

Exercises 7–36   Solve the system of equations.

7. $2x - y + z = 6$
   $3y + 2z = 3$
   $-z = 3$

8. $x + 3y - z = 4$
   $2y - 3z = 8$
   $3z = -6$

9. $x + y + z = 1$
   $2x - y - z = 5$
   $-x + 2y - 3z = -4$

10. $2x - 3y + z = 6$
    $x + 2y + 2z = -5$
    $-3x - y - z = 6$

11. $2x - y + 3z = 1$
    $x + y - 5z = 2$
    $3x - 2z = 3$

12. $x + 3y - z = 1$
    $-2x + y + 3z = 0$
    $-4x + 9y + 7z = 3$

13. $3.1x - 2.5y = 13.7$
    $1.7x + 2.4y = -3.8$

14. $\frac{3}{4}x + \frac{1}{3}y = \frac{1}{12}$
    $2x - y = 5$

15. $371x + 258y = 2710$
    $137x + 125y = 971$

16. $325x - 175y = -625$
    $173x - 276y = 33$

17. $2x - y = -7$
    $3x - 4z = -1$
    $3x + y - 4z = 0$

18. $x - y = -4$
    $x + z = 1$
    $3x + y + 2z = 4$

19. $x + y + z = 0$
    $x + 2y + z = 0$
    $2x + 3y + 2z = 0$

20. $2x + y + z = 0$
    $3x + 2y + 4z = 0$
    $x - 2y - 3z = 0$

21. $x - y + 2z = 4$
    $2x + 3y - z = 5$
    $3x + 2y + z = 8$

22. $x + 5y + 3z = -3$
    $4x + 3y + 2z = 2$
    $3x + y + z = 3$

23. $x + 3y + z = 0$
    $-2x + y = -4$
    $8x + 3y + 2z = 12$

24. $x - 3y - 3z = -5$
    $5x - 7y - 3z = 15$
    $4x - 4y - 3z = 8$

25. $2x - 4y + 3z = 0$
$\qquad x - y - 2z = -6$
$\qquad 6x - 4y + z = -8$

26. $5x + 6y + 3z = -1$
$\qquad x + 4y - 2z = 8$
$\qquad x + 3y + 2z = 2$

27. $\quad -x + 6y + 2z = 1$
$\qquad 2x - 7y + z = 13$
$\qquad -5x + 7y + 3z = 0$

28. $\quad x - 4y + \;\; z = -14$
$\qquad 3x - \;\; y + 3z = 2$
$\qquad -x + 4y - \;\; z = 12$

29. $x - 2y + 2z = -3$
$\qquad x - 2y + 7z = -13$
$\qquad 3x - 2y + 7z = -3$

30. $\quad x + 3y + 2z = 0$
$\qquad 6x + 3y + 2z = 10$
$\qquad 3x + \;\; y + 3z = 17$

31. $x + y - 2z = 9$ $\qquad$ **32.** $2x - y + z = 4$
$\qquad 2x - y = 0$ $\qquad\qquad\quad\;\; x - y = 0$
$\qquad 3x + z = 0$ $\qquad\qquad\;\; 2x + z = 0$

33. $6x - 4y + z = -24$ $\qquad$ **34.** $\qquad\qquad x - 2y = 0$
$\qquad 7x - 4y + z = -26$ $\qquad\qquad -3x - 4y + z = 0$
$\qquad 6x - 3y + z = -20$ $\qquad\qquad\qquad\quad 2y + z = 0$

35. $2x - 3y + z = 11$
$\qquad 3x - y + 2z = 10$
$\qquad 5x + 4y - z = 1$

36. $-2x + y - 3z = 14$
$\qquad 3x - 2y - z = -5$
$\qquad 2x + 2y - 3z = 7$

Exercises 37–40 $\quad$ Solve for x and y. (*Hint:* First let $\frac{1}{x} = u$ and $\frac{1}{y} = v$.)

37. $\frac{1}{x} + \frac{1}{y} = 4$ $\qquad$ **38.** $\frac{3}{x} + \frac{1}{y} = -5$
$\quad\;\; \frac{3}{x} - \frac{2}{y} = -3$ $\qquad\qquad \frac{1}{x} - \frac{2}{y} = -4$

39. $\frac{3}{x} - \frac{2}{y} = 4$ $\qquad$ **40.** $\frac{1}{x} - \frac{3}{y} = 0$
$\quad\;\; \frac{-5}{x} + \frac{2}{y} = 8$ $\qquad\qquad \frac{4}{x} + \frac{1}{y} = 6$

41. Find the point of intersection of the two lines given by $2x - 3y = 4$ and $3x + y = -5$.

42. Find the point of intersection of the two lines given by $y = 2x - 5$ and $2y = 3x - 8$.

Exercises 43–46 $\quad$ One vertex of a triangle is the point of intersection of lines L_1 and L_2, and the other two vertices are the x-intercept points of L_1 and L_2. Find (**a**) the perimeter of the triangle and (**b**) the area of the triangular region.

43. $\quad L_1: x + y = 6$ $\qquad$ **44.** $L_1: x + 2y = 4$
$\qquad L_2: x - 3y = -2$ $\qquad\qquad L_2: 3x - y = -9$

45. $L_1: y = -0.5x + 2.5$ $\qquad$ **46.** $L_1: y = x - 2$
$\qquad L_2: y = -3x$ $\qquad\qquad\qquad\quad L_2: y = 0.5x + 0.5$

Exercises 47–52 $\quad$ Solve the system of equations.

47. $\frac{xy}{x+y} = 3, \frac{xz}{x+z} = 4, \frac{yz}{z+y} = 6$
(*Hint:* If $\frac{xy}{x+y} = 3$, then
$\frac{x+y}{xy} = \frac{1}{y} + \frac{1}{x} = \frac{1}{3}$.)

48. $\log(xyz) = 2, \log\left(\frac{xy}{z}\right) = 0, \log\left(\frac{yz}{x}\right) = 0$
(*Hint:* $\log(xyz) = \log x + \log y + \log z$.)

49. $\ln(xyz) = 0.5, \ln(x^2 y) = 1, \ln\left(\frac{yz}{x}\right) = -1.5$
(*Hint:* See Exercise 48.)

50. $2^{2x+2y} = 4^z \qquad 4 \cdot 2^{x-y} = 8^z \qquad 32 \cdot 2^{y+z} = 4^x$
(*Hint:* Use properties of exponents.)

51. $4^x = 8 \cdot 2^{x+2y}$
$\qquad 9^{x-6y} = 9 \cdot 3^{-4y}$

52. $\log(x - 2y) + \log 5 = 1$
$\qquad \log x - \log y = 0$

53. Suppose lines L_1, L_2, L_3 are given by the equations:

$$L_1: -x + 2y = 1$$
$$L_2: x + 2y = 3 \qquad L_3: 3x + 2y = 13.$$

(**a**) Draw a graph to show lines L_1, L_2, and L_3.
(**b**) Find the points of intersection for each pair of the three lines.
(**c**) For the triangle formed by the three lines in (**a**), find the largest angle to the nearest degree.

54. The area of a rectangle remains unchanged if its width is increased by 2 and its length is decreased by 2, or if its width is decreased by 2 and its length is increased by 3. What is the perimeter of the rectangle?

55. The perimeter of a rectangle is 24 cm. If its length is 2 cm greater than its width, what is the area of the rectangular region?

56. A gardener wants to buy two kinds of flowers to plant a border. Ajugas are $1.10 each, and Lilliput Zinnias are $0.85 each. The gardener wants to spend exactly $200 dollars to purchase exactly 200 plants. Can some combination of ajugas and zinnias meet this need? If so, how many of each should be bought?

57. A total of $2500 is invested at simple interest in two accounts. The first pays 8 percent interest and the second pays 10 percent interest per year. The total interest earned from the two accounts after one year is $234. How much is invested in each account?

58. A mixture of 36 pounds of peanuts and cashew costs a total of $33. If peanuts cost $0.80 per pound and cashews cost $1.10 per pound, how many pounds of each does the mixture contain?

59. The sum of two numbers is 63 and the first is twice the second. What is the product of the two numbers?

60. A rectangular lot has a length-to-width ratio of 4 to 3. If 168 meters of fence will enclose it, what are the dimensions of the lot?

61. Suppose x grams of food A and y grams of food B are mixed and the total weight is 2000 grams. Food A contains 0.25 units of vitamin D per gram, and food B contains 0.50 units of vitamin D per gram. Suppose the final mixture contains 900 units of vitamin D. How many grams of each type of food does the mixture contain?

62. Two pipelines A and B are used to fill a tank with water. The tank can be filled by running A for three hours and B for six hours, or it can be filled by having both of the supply lines open for four hours. How long would it take for A to fill the tank alone? How long would it take for B to fill the tank alone? (*Hint:* If x is the number of hours it takes A to fill the tank alone, then in one hour, A will fill $\frac{1}{x}$ of the total capacity of the tank.)

63. When flying with the wind, it takes a plane 1 hour and 15 minutes to travel 600 kilometers; when flying against the wind it takes 1 hour 40 minutes to travel 600 kilometers. What is the airspeed of the plane and the speed of the wind?

64. One cup of half-and-half cream contains 28 g of fat and 7 g of protein, while one cup of low-fat milk contains 5 g of fat and 8 g of protein. How many cups of half-and-half and how many cups of low-fat milk should be combined to get a mixture that contains 71 g of fat and 38 g of protein?

65. The cost of a sandwich, a drink, and a piece of pie is $2.50. The sandwich costs a dollar more than the pie, and the pie costs twice as much as the drink. What is the cost of each?

66. A total of $3600 is invested in three different accounts. The first account earns interest at a rate of 8 percent, the second at 10 percent, and the third at 12 percent. The amount invested in the first account is twice as much as that in the second account. If the total amount of simple interest earned in one year is $388, how much is invested in each account?

67. Suppose x grams of food A, y grams of food B, and z grams of food C are mixed together for a total weight of 2400 grams. The vitamin D and calorie content of each food is given in the table.

Food	Units of Vitamin D per Gram	Calories per Gram
A	0.75	1.4
B	0.50	1.6
C	1.00	1.5

The 2400-gram mixture contains a total of 1725 units of vitamin D and 3690 calories. How many grams of each type of food does it contain?

68. (a) Find an equation for the quadratic function whose graph passes through the three points $(-1, 8)$, $(0, 5)$, and $(1, -4)$. (*Hint:* Let the parabola have equation $y = Ax^2 + Bx + C$, substitute coordinates of the given points, and solve for A, B, and C.)

(b) What is the distance between the x-intercept points of the parabola?

69. A large tank full of water has three outlet pipes, A, B, and C. If only A and B are opened, the tank empties in three hours. If only A and C are open, the tank drains in four hours. If only pipes B and C are open, the tank drains in six hours. How long does it take to empty the tank if all three pipes are open? (*Hint:* If outlet A can empty the tank in x hours, how much drains through A in one hour?)

SECTION 9.2   Systems of Linear Equations as Matrices

If you have a thousand equations in a thousand unknowns, you know there exists a solution, but how do you compute it?

Garrett Birkhoff

A close inspection of Gaussian elimination shows that the method combines application of elementary operations together with careful bookkeeping. We streamline the entire process by noting that it makes no difference what letters we use for the variables. For instance, if we used u, v, and w, in place of x, y, and z, the problem and technique for solving the system would be the same. However, if we altered any of the coefficients or constants in the equations, the problem would change. The coefficients of the variables and the numbers on the right side completely describe the system.

Therefore, we may consider a system of linear equations in terms of a rectangular array of numbers consisting of the coefficients and constants on the right side, arranged in the same order as they appear in the equations. Then Gaussian elimination becomes a matter of operating on rows of numbers. We refer to the rectangular array of numbers as a **matrix.**

To illustrate the notion of a matrix let us consider the system of equations given in Example 1 of the preceding section.

$$
\begin{aligned}
E_1 && 2x - 5y + 3z &= -4 \\
E_2 && x - 2y - 3z &= 3 \\
E_3 && -3x + 4y + 2z &= -4
\end{aligned}
\tag{1}
$$

System (1) can be described in terms of matrix M:

$$
M = \begin{bmatrix} 2 & -5 & 3 & -4 \\ 1 & -2 & -3 & 3 \\ -3 & 4 & 2 & -4 \end{bmatrix}
\begin{array}{l} \longleftarrow R_1 \\ \longleftarrow R_2 \\ \longleftarrow R_3 \end{array}
\tag{2}
$$

Array (2) consists of three rows and four columns of numbers; it is a 3×4 matrix. We refer to the rows as R_1, R_2, and R_3.

Gaussian elimination can now be described as a process of elementary operations on rows of a matrix to obtain a sequence of matrices that correspond to equivalent systems of equations, until we get one in echelon form. This process is referred to as **row reduction to echelon form.**

Elementary Row Operations

The elementary operations on equations of a system of linear equations listed in the preceding section translate into corresponding elementary row operations on matrices as follows.

1. Interchange any two rows.
2. Replace any row by a nonzero multiple of itself.
3. Replace any row by the sum of itself and a multiple of some other row.

When we apply any elementary row operation to a matrix we get an **equivalent matrix.**

To describe row operations, we shall use notation analogous to that in the preceding section. For instance, $R_1 \leftrightarrow R_2$ means interchange rows one and two; $3R_1 + R_2 \rightarrow R_2$ means multiply R_1 by 3 and add to R_2 to get the new R_2. We

I applied the matrix tower idea to the Ramanujan series for pi. You are evaluating the series exactly. In other words if you evaluate a million terms of this series and that's worth say eight million digits of pi, what you actually have is the exact rational fraction which is the sum of those million terms, which is something massively larger than eight million digits. I must have a hundred million digits of stuff in there.

Bill Gosper

MATRICES

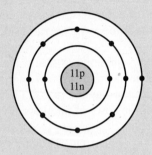

The atomic structure of sodium

In this section we introduce a matrix as a single array that carries all the significant information about a system of linear equations. As one mathematician described the process, "strip the linear functions of every piece of clothing and there remain the matrices."

Matrices have been around in one form or another for a long time. Cauchy (France, 1789–1857) seems to have been the first to use such arrays, but the British mathematician Arthur Cayley was the first to study them systematically, considering sums and products of matrices. He announced to the Royal Society of London in 1858 a "peculiarity" of matrix multiplication: if A and B are square matrices of the same size, then the products AB and BA are also square, but, in general, *they are not equal; $AB \neq BA$.*

In 1925 Werner Heisenberg, trying to keep track of the characteristic states of orbiting electrons in the atomic nucleus, entered the data in square arrays. He then worked out ways to

combine these arrays to describe subatomic interactions and developed the first successful quantum mechanics.

Heisenberg appears to have been embarrassed by the discovery that his multiplication of arrays is not generally commutative ($AB \neq BA$). He mentions it casually in one sentence and immediately gives an example without the noncommutativity. Heisenberg's teacher and collaborator, Max Born, was apparently one of the few European physicists who knew anything about matrix analysis. He recognized Heisenberg's matrices for what they were and explored all kinds of applications of the new physics. Interestingly, both Heisenberg and Born were later awarded the Nobel prize in physics.

Today matrices are indispensable throughout mathematics and physics. Most calculus sequences are followed by a linear algebra course in which matrices are a powerful and indispensable tool for analysis of all kinds of linear systems.

illustrate elementary row operations and related notation in the following example which uses matrices to solve the system given in Example 1 of the preceding section.

EXAMPLE 1   Express the system of equations in terms of a matrix, and then get an equivalent matrix in echelon form that can be used to get the solution.

$$2x - 5y + 3z = -4$$
$$x - 2y - 3z = 3$$
$$-3x + 4y + 2z = -4$$

Solution

Strategy: Since the coefficient of x in E_2 is 1, first interchange R_1 and R_2 in order to avoid working with fractions.

The matrix M that corresponds to the system of equations is

$$M = \begin{bmatrix} 2 & -5 & 3 & -4 \\ 1 & -2 & -3 & 3 \\ -3 & 4 & 2 & -4 \end{bmatrix}$$

The following steps are analogous to those in the solution of Example 1 in Section 9.1.

$$\begin{bmatrix} 2 & -5 & 3 & -4 \\ 1 & -2 & -3 & 3 \\ -3 & 4 & 2 & -4 \end{bmatrix} \quad R_1 \longleftrightarrow R_2 \quad \begin{bmatrix} 1 & -2 & -3 & 3 \\ 2 & -5 & 3 & -4 \\ -3 & 4 & 2 & -4 \end{bmatrix} \quad \begin{array}{l} -2R_1 + R_2 \longrightarrow R_2 \\ 3R_1 + R_3 \longrightarrow R_3 \end{array}$$

$$\begin{bmatrix} 1 & -2 & -3 & 3 \\ 0 & -1 & 9 & -10 \\ 0 & -2 & -7 & 5 \end{bmatrix} \quad -2R_2 + R_3 \longrightarrow R_3 \quad \begin{bmatrix} 1 & -2 & -3 & 3 \\ 0 & -1 & 9 & -10 \\ 0 & 0 & -25 & 25 \end{bmatrix}$$

The final matrix corresponds to a system of equations in echelon form. Use it for back-substitution to get the desired solution. The last row represents the equation $-25z = 25$ and so $z = -1$. Similarly from rows 2 and 1, y and x are given by $y = 1$, $x = 2$. ▲

EXAMPLE 2 Solve the system of equations using matrix notation and row reduction to echelon form.

$$\begin{aligned} x + 3y - z &= 0 \\ -2x + y &= -4 \\ 8x + 3y - 2z &= 12 \end{aligned}$$

Solution

The matrix that corresponds to the system is

$$M = \begin{bmatrix} 1 & 3 & -1 & 0 \\ -2 & 1 & 0 & -4 \\ 8 & 3 & -2 & 12 \end{bmatrix}$$

Find a sequence of equivalent matices:

$$\begin{bmatrix} 1 & 3 & -1 & 0 \\ -2 & 1 & 0 & -4 \\ 8 & 3 & -2 & 12 \end{bmatrix} \quad \begin{array}{l} 2R_1 + R_2 \longrightarrow R_2 \\ -8R_1 + R_3 \longrightarrow R_3 \end{array}$$

$$\begin{bmatrix} 1 & 3 & -1 & 0 \\ 0 & 7 & -2 & -4 \\ 0 & -21 & 6 & 12 \end{bmatrix} \quad 3R_2 + R_3 \longrightarrow R_3 \quad \begin{bmatrix} 1 & 3 & -1 & 0 \\ 0 & 7 & -2 & -4 \\ 0 & 0 & 0 & 0 \end{bmatrix}$$

The equation that corresponds to R_3 of the final matrix is $0 \cdot x + 0 \cdot y + 0 \cdot z = 0$, which is satisfied by any numbers for x, y, and z. We want x, y, and z that satisfy the equations for R_1 and R_2. Thus the system reduces to

$$\begin{aligned} x + 3y - z &= 0 \\ 7y - 2z &= -4 \end{aligned}$$

If $z = k$ (any number), then from the second equation $y = \frac{2k - 4}{7}$. Substitute $\frac{2k - 4}{7}$ for y and k for z in the first equation and solve for x.

$$x + \frac{3(2k - 4)}{7} - k = 0 \quad \text{or} \quad x = \frac{k + 12}{7}$$

The system of equations is dependent and has infinitely many solutions given by

$$x = \frac{k + 12}{7} \qquad y = \frac{2k - 4}{7} \qquad z = k,$$

where k is any number.   ▲

Partial Fractions

Elementary algebra courses devote considerable time to learning to add and subtract fractions to get a single fraction. Here we consider the problem of going in the opposite direction. Suppose we have a given rational expression in which the denominator can be expressed in factored form with linear or quadratic factors. What fractions could have been added or subtracted to get the given rational expression? The following examples illustrate a method to answer this question. The technique demonstrated here is called the **method of partial fractions.**

EXAMPLE 3

Express $\frac{6x^2 + 3x + 1}{x^3 - x}$ as a sum of fractions.

Solution

Strategy: To add fractions, we need a common denominator. To reverse the process, identify the factors that make up the denominator. Begin by factoring, $x^3 - x = x(x + 1)(x - 1)$. Look for fractions with denominators of x, $x + 1$, and $x - 1$ which can be added to get the given fraction.

Follow the strategy. The given fraction can be written as

$$\frac{6x^2 + 3x + 1}{x^3 - x} = \frac{6x^2 + 3x + 1}{x(x + 1)(x - 1)}.$$

It seems reasonable to expect that the given rational expression must have come from adding three fractions whose denominators are x, $x + 1$, and $x - 1$. Find three numbers a, b, and c (the unknowns) for which the following is an identity:

$$\frac{6x^2 + 3x + 1}{x(x + 1)(x - 1)} = \frac{a}{x} + \frac{b}{x + 1} + \frac{c}{x - 1} \tag{3}$$

Add the fractions on the right side and collect like terms in the numerator to get:

$$\frac{6x^2 + 3x + 1}{x(x + 1)(x - 1)} = \frac{(a + b + c)x^2 + (-b + c)x - a}{x(x + 1)(x - 1)} \quad \text{Check this.}$$

The two fractions in the last equation will be identically equal if we choose a, b, and c so that the corresponding coefficients in the numerators are the same, that is, if

$$a + b + c = 6$$
$$-b + c = 3$$
$$-a = 1$$

We solve this system of equations and get $a = -1$, $b = 2$, and $c = 5$. Replacing

a, b, and c by -1, 2, and 5, respectively, in equation 3 gives the desired result.

$$\frac{6x^2 + 3x + 1}{x(x + 1)(x - 1)} = -\frac{1}{x} + \frac{2}{x + 1} + \frac{5}{x - 1} \quad \blacktriangle$$

In the next example we consider a denominator that contains a quadratic factor.

EXAMPLE 4

Express $\frac{3x^2 - 2x + 5}{x^3 - 1}$ as a sum of fractions with simpler denominators.

Solution

Strategy: Begin by factoring the denominator as a difference of cubes.

Follow the strategy. Note that $x^3 - 1 = (x - 1)(x^2 + x + 1)$. It is reasonable to assume that the given fraction can be written as a sum of fractions of the form

$$\frac{3x^2 - 2x + 5}{(x - 1)(x^2 + x + 1)} = \frac{A}{x - 1} + \frac{Bx + C}{x^2 + x + 1}$$

Add the two functions on the right side and collect like terms in the numerator to get (*Check!*):

$$\frac{3x^2 - 2x + 5}{(x - 1)(x^2 + x + 1)} = \frac{(A + B)x^2 + (A - B + C)x + (A - C)}{(x - 1)(x^2 + x + 1)}$$

Equating corresponding coefficients in the numerator gives a system of linear equations.

$$A + B = 3$$
$$A - B + C = -2$$
$$A - C = 5$$

Solving the system, $A = 2$, $B = 1$, and $C = -3$. Therefore

$$\frac{3x^2 - 2x + 5}{(x - 1)(x^2 + x + 1)} = \frac{2}{x - 1} + \frac{x - 3}{x^2 + x + 1} \quad \blacktriangle$$

Up to this point we have not had any repeated linear factors in a denominator. Check this addition:

$$\frac{2}{x - 2} + \frac{3}{(x - 2)^2} = \frac{2x - 1}{(x - 2)^2}$$

This sets the pattern for the next example.

EXAMPLE 5

Express $\frac{5x^2 - 8x + 2}{x^3 - 2x^2 + x}$ as a sum of fractions with simpler denominators.

Strategy: The denominator factors as $x(x - 1)^2$, so try x, $x - 1$, $(x - 1)^2$ as denominators.

Solution

Follow the strategy. The given fraction may be expressible as a sum of fractions as follows.

$$\frac{5x^2 - 8x + 2}{x(x - 1)^2} = \frac{A}{x} + \frac{B}{x - 1} + \frac{C}{(x - 1)^2}$$

Add the fractions on the right side and collect like terms in the numerator to get

$$\frac{5x^2 - 8x + 2}{x(x - 1)^2} = \frac{(A + B)x^2 + (-2A - B + C)x + A}{x(x - 1)^2}$$

Equating corresponding coefficients in the numerator gives us the following system of linear equations:

$$A + B = 5$$
$$-2A - B + C = -8$$
$$A = 2$$

Solving the system, we find that $A = 2$, $B = 3$, and $C = -1$. Therefore

$$\frac{5x^2 - 8x + 2}{x(x - 1)^2} = \frac{2}{x} + \frac{3}{x - 1} - \frac{1}{(x - 1)^2}. \quad \blacktriangle$$

EXERCISES 9.2

Check Your Understanding

Exercises 1–6   True or False. Give reasons for your conclusion.

1. The matrix for the system

$$2x - y = 5$$
$$x + 2y = 3$$

is

$$\begin{bmatrix} 2 & -1 & 5 \\ 1 & 2 & 3 \end{bmatrix}.$$

2. The system of linear equations that correspond to the matrix

$$\begin{bmatrix} 3 & -1 & 0 \\ 0 & 1 & 0 \end{bmatrix}$$

is

$$3x - y = 0$$
$$y = 0.$$

3. For the system of equations in x and y that correspond to the matrix

$$\begin{bmatrix} 2 & -1 & 0 \\ 0 & 3 & 6 \end{bmatrix},$$

the solution is given by $x = 1$, $y = 2$.

4. The systems of linear equations that correspond to the following matrices are equivalent.

$$\begin{bmatrix} 1 & -2 & -3 & 3 \\ 0 & 1 & -9 & 10 \\ 0 & 0 & 1 & -1 \end{bmatrix} \quad \begin{bmatrix} 1 & 0 & 0 & 2 \\ 0 & 1 & 0 & 1 \\ 0 & 0 & 1 & -1 \end{bmatrix}$$

5. The triangle formed by the three lines $2x - 3y = 1$, $2x + 3y = 4$, and $3x + 2y = 3$ is a right triangle. (*Hint:* Consider the slopes of the lines.)

6. The triangle formed by the three lines $x + 2y = 3$, $2x - 2y = 5$, and $x - 2y = 4$ is a right triangle. (*Hint:* Consider the slopes of the lines.)

Exercises 7–10 Complete the sentence by selecting from the list below *all choices* that make the statement true. Solve the system of equations that correspond to the matrix.

(a) $x = 2, y = -4$ **(b)** $x = 1, y = -2$
(c) $x = -2, y = 4$ **(d)** $x = -2, y = 3$
(e) $x = 3, y = 2, z = -1$
(f) $x = -3, y = 1, z = 2$
(g) $x = 5, y = 2, z = -2$ **(h)** None of the above

7. $\begin{bmatrix} 1 & -1 & 3 \\ 0 & -1 & 2 \end{bmatrix}$; solution is _____.

8. $\begin{bmatrix} 2 & 0 & -4 \\ 1 & 2 & 6 \end{bmatrix}$; solution is _____.

9. $\begin{bmatrix} 1 & -2 & 0 & -3 \\ 0 & 1 & -1 & 4 \\ 0 & 0 & -3 & 6 \end{bmatrix}$; solution is _____.

10. $\begin{bmatrix} 1 & 0 & -1 & 4 \\ -1 & 0 & 0 & -3 \\ 0 & 2 & -1 & 5 \end{bmatrix}$; solution is _____.

Develop Mastery

Exercises 1–4 For the given matrix, write the corresponding system of linear equations.

1. $\begin{bmatrix} 1 & 2 & -1 \\ 1 & -3 & 2 \end{bmatrix}$ **2.** $\begin{bmatrix} -2 & 0 & 3 \\ 1 & -4 & 1 \end{bmatrix}$

3. $\begin{bmatrix} 1 & -1 & 0 & 1 \\ 2 & 3 & -4 & 1 \\ -1 & -2 & 3 & 5 \end{bmatrix}$ **4.** $\begin{bmatrix} 0 & 1 & 3 & 2 \\ -1 & -2 & 0 & 0 \\ 3 & 2 & 1 & -1 \end{bmatrix}$

Exercises 5–8 Write the matrix that corresponds to the system of equations.

5. $2x - y = 3$
$\quad x + 2y = -1$

6. $-3x + 2y = 1$
$\quad 5x - y = -3$

7. $\quad x + y - z = 1$
$\quad\quad 2x - y = 3$
$\quad -x + 2y - z = 0$

8. $3x - y + z = -4$
$\quad x + y = 3$
$\quad y - z = 5$

Exercises 9–12 Solve the system of linear equations given in matrix form. Use x, y, and z as the variables.

9. $\begin{bmatrix} 1 & 1 & 2 & -1 \\ 0 & 1 & 0 & 2 \\ 0 & 0 & -2 & 4 \end{bmatrix}$ **10.** $\begin{bmatrix} 2 & -1 & 3 & 0 \\ 0 & 1 & 1 & 3 \\ 0 & 0 & 3 & -6 \end{bmatrix}$

11. $\begin{bmatrix} 0 & 0 & 2 & -4 \\ 1 & 2 & -1 & 0 \\ 2 & 1 & 0 & -1 \end{bmatrix}$ **12.** $\begin{bmatrix} 0 & 2 & 2 & 5 \\ 1 & 2 & -3 & 1 \\ 0 & 1 & 1 & 2 \end{bmatrix}$

Exercises 13–24 Solve the system of equations by expressing it in terms of a matrix, and then complete row reduction to achieve echelon form.

13. $3x + y = -1$
$\quad\quad x - y = 3$

14. $x - 3y = 5$
$\quad 3x + y = 5$

15. $\quad 0.4x - 0.5y = 2.8$
$\quad -1.5x + 0.6y = -5.4$

16. $6x - 12y = 7$
$\quad 4x - 8y = -5$

17. $\quad 4x - 8y = -5$
$\quad -2x + 4y = 2.5$

18. $\frac{x}{3} - \frac{y}{2} = 4$
$\quad \frac{x}{2} - y = 7$

19. $x + 2y + z = 3$
$\quad -3x + 4z = 5$
$\quad\quad -3y + 2z = 1$

20. $\quad x + 2y + z = 1$
$\quad -2x + y - 2z = -2$
$\quad -x + 8y - z = 2$

21. $\quad x + y + 3z = -1$
$\quad\quad 3x - 4z = -4$
$\quad -x + 2y + 2z = 2$

22. $3x + 4y - 4z = -1$
$\quad 6x - 2y - 2z = -2$
$\quad\quad y - 3z = -3$

23. $\quad -x + y = 2$
$\quad\quad 3x + 4z = 5$
$\quad 4x - y + 4z = 3$

24. $2x - y - 3z = 1$
$\quad x + y + 5z = 2$
$\quad 3x + 2z = 3$

Exercises 25–32 Use the method of partial fractions to express the rational expression as a sum or difference of fractions with simpler denominations.

25. $\dfrac{-8}{3x^2 - 4x - 4}$ **26.** $\dfrac{14x}{3x^2 + 5x - 2}$

27. $\dfrac{-10x - 4}{x^3 - 4x}$ **28.** $\dfrac{5x^2 + x}{2x^3 + x^2 - 2x - 1}$

29. $\dfrac{5x^2 - 3x + 2}{x^3 - x^2 + x - 1}$ **30.** $\dfrac{3x^2 - 3x + 5}{(x - 1)(x^2 + 2x + 2)}$

31. $\dfrac{x^2 + 5x - 12}{x^3 - 4x^2 + 4x}$ **32.** $\dfrac{x^2 - 6x - 13}{(x - 1)(x + 2)^2}$

33. The average of three numbers is 8. The first is three greater than twice the second, and the third is the sum of the first two. What are the numbers?

34. A grocery store sells two kinds of candy, A and B, each at a certain price per pound. When these are combined in a ratio of 3 to 1 (by weight) of A to B, then the price per pound of the mixture is $1.10. However, if the corresponding ratio is 3 to 2, then the price per pound is $1.04. If a ratio of 4 to 1 were made, what should be the price per pound of the resulting mixture?

35. A breakfast menu is to consist of oatmeal, whole milk, and fresh orange juice. We are interested in the protein, calcium, and vitamin C content. The following table gives the pertinent information.

Food	Protein (grams)	Calcium (milligrams)	Vitamin C (milligrams)
Oatmeal (1 cup; 245g)	5	22	0
Milk (1 cup; 244 g)	8	291	2
Orange juice (1 cup; 248 g)	2	27	124

How many cups of each (oatmeal, milk, and orange juice) are required to get a breakfast with 9 grams of protein, 185.7 milligrams of calcium, and 125 milligrams of vitamin C?

36. A mixture of 50 pounds of peanut, cashews, and walnuts costs a total of $49. If peanuts cost $0.80 per pound, cashews cost $1.10 per pound, and walnuts cost $1.20 per pound, and if the mixture contains twice as many pounds of peanuts as walnuts, how many pounds of each does the mixture contain?

SECTION 9.3 **Systems of Nonlinear Equations**

In economics and psychology, linear least squares or constant input–output matrices are often used, and indeed, sometimes used automatically by means of canned programs, when fundamental force interactions are nonlinear. Unfortunately, linear models may be very poor approximations for nonlinear models.
        Donald Greenspan

Gaussian elimination and matrix methods are well-suited for systems of linear equations. However, we often have to deal with systems that include nonlinear equations. Such systems can sometimes be difficult to solve, but one method that is often useful, the **method of substitution,** is illustrated in the following examples. In Example 1 we revisit the system we saw in the introduction to this chapter.

Strategy: Draw a triangle and label the legs, say x and y. The perimeter is known and the Pythagorean theorem relates the legs and hypotenuse of a right triangle.

EXAMPLE 1 The hypotenuse of a right triangle is 17 and its perimeter is 40. Find the lengths of the two legs.

Solution

Follow the strategy, referring to Figure 9.3.

Perimeter is 40 $x + y + 17 = 40$ or $x + y = 23$

Pythagorean theorem $x^2 + y^2 = 17^2$ or $x^2 + y^2 = 289.$ **(1)**

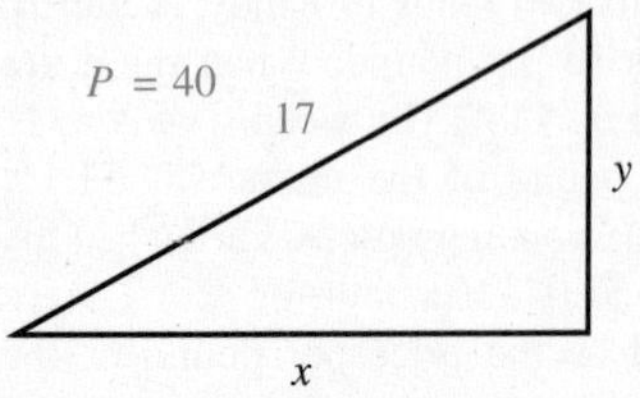

The first equation in system (1) is linear; the second is not. The method of substitution can eliminate a variable. We solve one equation for one of the variables and substitute the result into the other equation. Solving the first equation for y gives $y = 23 - x$. Substituting this for y in the second equation, we obtain a quadratic equation in x:

$$x^2 + (23 - x)^2 = 289 \quad \text{or} \quad 2x^2 - 46x + 240 = 0.$$

FIGURE 9.3

Simplify and factor, or use the quadratic formula to get $x = 8$ or $x = 15$. If $x = 8$, then $y = 15$, and if $x = 15$, then $y = 8$. In either case, the legs of the triangle are 8 and 15. ▲

Strategy: Eliminate either x or y by substituting from the first equation into the second, and then solving a quadratic.

| **EXAMPLE 2** | Solve the system of equations and show the solutions graphically.

$$x + 2y = -4$$
$$y = x^2 - 2x - 3$$

Solution

Follow the strategy. Solving the first equation for x gives $x = -2y - 4$. Substitute into the second equation and solve for y.

$$y = (-2y - 4)^2 - 2(-2y - 4) - 3$$
$$y = 4y^2 + 16y + 16 + 4y + 8 - 3$$
$$4y^2 + 19y + 21 = 0$$
$$(4y + 7)(y + 3) = 0$$

Therefore, $y = -\frac{7}{4}$ or $y = -3$. Now use $x = -2y - 4$ to get the corresponding values of x. For $y = -\frac{7}{4}$, $x = -\frac{1}{2}$; for $y = -3$, $x = 2$.

The graph of the first equation is a line and that of the second is a parabola that opens upward with vertex at $(1, -4)$. See Figure 9.4. The points of intersection are $\left(-\frac{1}{2}, -\frac{7}{4}\right)$ and $(2, -3)$, which correspond to the two solutions. ▲

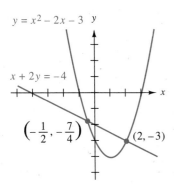

FIGURE 9.4

| **EXAMPLE 3** | Solve the system of equations and interpret the solution graphically.

$$2x + y = 3$$
$$x^2 + y = 1$$

Solution

Solve the second equation for y to get $y = 1 - x^2$. Substitute into the first equation and solve for x.

$$2x + (1 - x^2) = 3$$
$$x^2 - 2x + 2 = 0$$

To solve the quadratic equation, apply the quadratic formula.

$$x = \frac{2 \pm \sqrt{4 - 8}}{2} = \frac{2 \pm \sqrt{-4}}{2} = \frac{2 \pm 2i}{2} = 1 \pm i.$$

We find the coordinates of the points of intersection, if any, of the parabola and the line by solving the system for real number solutions only. Since we have imaginary number solutions, there are no points of intersection, as we see in the graphs in Figure 9.5. ▲

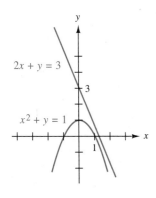

FIGURE 9.5

| **EXAMPLE 4** | Find the solution set for the system of equations

$$x^2 - y^2 = 3$$
$$2x^2 + y^2 = 9.$$

For Graphers 9.3	SYSTEMS OF NONLINEAR EQUATIONS

A graphing calculator makes some nonlinear equations as easy to graph as linear equations, but we are still limited to graphs that can be described by equations of the form $y = f(x)$. When we can get reasonable graphs, however, the solutions can usually be found quite accurately with the Trace feature. Still, we must recognize the limitations of graphical solutions. Pixel size and location affect the interpretation of any graph.

EXAMPLE   Graph the two equations in the system

$$x + 2y = -4$$
$$y = x^2 - 2x - 3$$

(from Example 2) in

(a)   the window $[-10, 10] \times [-10, 10]$ and

(b)   the Familiar Window and find the solutions in each window.

Solution   To graph the first equation, write it in the form $y = \frac{-4 - x}{2}$.

(a)   With the two graphs in the $[-10, 10] \times [-10, 10]$ window, locate one intersection near $(2, -3)$. The closest we can come to the intersection in Quadrant III is about $(-0.526, -1.7)$. If we ZOOM IN, the intersection appears to be near $(-0.5, -1.8)$.

(b)   In the Familiar Window, in Trace, when $x = -0.5$, $y = -1.75$ *on both curves*. (See this using the up or down arrow.) The other intersection is at $(2, -3)$, as in part a.

Exercises

1.   Graph the system

$$y = 2 \cos x$$
$$y = x^3 - 2x$$

in the Familiar Window. How many intersections do you see? Zoom in at least twice on the intersection in Quadrant II. Explain what you see.

2.   Review the suggestions for graphing circles in Section 1.6 and use your calculator to approxi-mate the solution to the system in Develop Mastery Exercise 2.

3.   Compare your results in Exercise 2 with the exact solution you obtain by the method of substitution.

4.   Decide how to graph the equations in Develop Mastery Exercise 15. Find a window on which you can read the solutions exactly.

5.   Use your calculator to get three-place accuracy for the solutions to the following Develop Mastery Exercises: **(a)** 17   **(b)** 19   **(c)** 23.

Strategy: The domain of $y = 2 \ln x$ is $(0, \infty)$ while that of $y = \ln (4 - x)$ is $(-\infty, 4)$. Thus any solution will be such that x is in $(0, 4)$. To draw graphs, use properties of the ln function from Chapter 4.

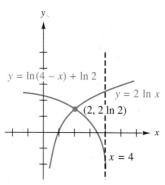

FIGURE 9.6

Solution

Eliminate y by adding the two equations and then solve for x.

$$3x^2 = 12 \qquad x^2 = 4 \qquad x = \pm 2.$$

To get the corresponding values of y, substitute 2 or -2 into either of the given equations, say the first.

$$4 - y^2 = 3 \qquad y^2 = 1 \qquad y = \pm 1.$$

This gives four solutions. The solution set is $\{(2, 1), (2, -1), (-2, 1), (-2, -1)\}$. ▲

EXAMPLE 5 Find the points of intersection of the graphs of $y = 2 \ln x$ and $y = \ln (4 - x) + \ln 2$. Draw the graphs.

Solution

Follow the strategy. Eliminate y from the equations.

$$2 \ln x = \ln (4 - x) + \ln 2$$

Now use properties of logarithms from Chapter 4 and then solve for x.

$$\ln x^2 = \ln [2(4 - x)]$$
$$x^2 = 2(4 - x)$$
$$x^2 + 2x - 8 = 0$$
$$(x - 2)(x + 4) = 0$$

Therefore, we get two possible solutions for x: $x = 2$ or $x = -4$, but -4 is not a solution. See the Strategy. To find the corresponding values of y use either of the given equations, say $y = 2 \ln x$. For $x = 2$, $y = 2 \ln 2 = \ln 4$. The graphs of the two equations intersect at only one point $(2, \ln 4) \approx (2, 1.39)$. See Figure 9.6. ▲

EXERCISES 9.3

Check Your Understanding

Exercises 1–6 True or False. Give reasons for your conclusion.

1. The system of equations

$$\sqrt{2}x - \sqrt{5}y = 4$$
$$\sqrt{3}x + \sqrt{7}y = 3$$

is a nonlinear system.

2. The graphs of $y = x^2$ and $y = -x - 1$ intersect at two points.

3. The graphs of $y = |x|$ and $y = x$ have in common only one point, $(0, 0)$.

4. The system of equations

$$x - y = 0$$
$$x^2 + y^2 = 8$$

has exactly two solutions.

5. The system

$$x - 2y - 1 = 0$$

$$x^2 + y^2 + 1 = 0$$

has no solutions.

6. The system

$$x^2 + y = 0$$

$$x^2 - y = 0$$

has no solutions.

Exercises 7–10 Complete the sentence by selecting from the list below *all choices* that make the statement true.

(a) at $(0, -1)$ and $(0, 1)$ **(b)** at $(4, -3)$ and $(-4, 3)$
(c) at $(1, 0)$ and $(-1, 0)$ **(d)** at $(-3, 4)$ and $(3, -4)$
(e) in QI **(f)** in QII **(g)** in QIII **(h)** in QIV

7. The graphs of $y = x^2 - 1$ and $y = 1 - x^2$ intersect _____ .

8. The graphs of $x^2 + y^2 = 25$ and $4x + 3y = 0$ intersect _____ .

9. The graphs of $|x| + y = 0$ and $y + 2 = 0$ intersect _____ .

10. The graphs of $y = |x| - 1$ and $y = 1 - |x|$ intersect _____ .

Explore and Discover

1. Find all pairs of real numbers (if any) such that
  (a) their difference is 1 and their product is 1.
  (b) their sum is 1 and their product is 1.
  (c) their difference is 1 and their quotient is 1.
  (d) their sum is 1 and their quotient is 1.

2. In each part of Exercise 1 replace 1 with **(a)** 2 **(b)** 3 **(c)** 4.

3. In each part of Exercise 1 replace 1 by an arbitrary number k. What values of k will give real number solutions?

Develop Mastery

Exercises 1–16 Find all pairs of real numbers x, y that satisfy the system of equations. Draw graphs and show points of intersection (if any).

1. $y = 3x + 4$
  $y = x^2$

2. $2x - y + 2 = 0$
  $x^2 + y^2 = 169$

3. $3x + y = 0$
  $2x^2 + 4x + y = 0$

4. $2x - y = -2$
  $xy = 4$

5. $2x + 3y = -3$
  $xy = -3$

6. $5x - y = 10$
  $x^2 + x - y = 6$

7. $2x - y = 0$
  $x^2 - y = -3$

8. $x + y = 2$
  $x^2 + y^2 = 2$

9. $3x - y = 5$
  $x^2 + y^2 = 25$

10. $y = x^2 - 4x + 4$
  $y = -2x^2 + x + 16$

11. $x - y = 2$
  $x^2 + y = 2$

12. $y = \sqrt{x}$
  $y = 2x - 6$

13. $\dfrac{x}{\sqrt{x}} - y = 2$
  $\sqrt{x} - y = 0$

14. $2x - y = 0$
  $xy - y = 2$

15. $x^2 - y^2 = 0$
  $x^2 + y^2 = 8$

16. $x - y = 0$
  $x^3 - 3x + y = 0$

Exercises 17–30 Solve the system of equations. If results involve irrational numbers, give approximations rounded off to two decimal places.

17. $y = \ln x$
  $y = \ln (2 - x)$

18. $y = e^x$
  $x + \ln y = 0$

19. $y = 2 \ln x$
  $y = \ln (3 - x) + \ln 4$

20. $y = \ln x^2$
  $y = \ln (3 - x) + \ln 4$

21. $x - \ln y = 2$
  $x - \ln (y - 3) = 3$

22. $x + \ln (y + 1) = 2$
  $x - \ln y = 1$

23. $2^x + y = 16$
  $2^{x+1} - y = 8$

24. $3^x + 3y = 10$
  $3^{x-1} - y = 8$

25. $x^2 y = 2$
  $y = 2x^2$

26. $xy = 2$
  $y = \sqrt{x} + 1$

27. $x^2 + 2y^2 = 6$
  $xy = 2$

28. $x^2 y = 1$
  $y = -x^2 + 2$

29. $x^2 + y^2 - xy = 3$
  $x^2 + y^2 = 5$

30. $2x^2 + 5xy + 3y^2 = 4$
  $xy = -2$

Exercises 31–34 Solve the system of equations. Assume that $0 \le x \le 2\pi$; for Exercises 33 and 34, $0 \le y \le 2\pi$.

31. $\sin x - y = 0$
  $\cos x - y = 0$

32. $\sin x + y = 0$
  $\sin 2x - y = 0$

33. $2 \sin x + \cos y = 2$
  $\sin x - \cos y = -0.5$

34. $\sin x + \cos y = 0$
  $2 \sin x - 4 \cos y = 3\sqrt{2}$

Exercises 35–42 Solve the system of equations.

35. $3|x| - 2|y| = -2$
  $|x| + 3|y| = 14$

36. $2|x| - 3|y| = 0$
  $4|x| + 3|y| = 18$

37. $6e^x - e^y = 1$
$3e^x + e^y = 8$

38. $e^x + 2e^y = 8$
$2e^x - e^y = 1$

39. $\ln x + \ln y = 0$
$2 \ln x + \ln y = 1$

40. $\ln x + \ln y = 0$
$3 \ln x + 4 \ln y = 2$

41. $x + y + |x| = 9$ (*Hint:* If $x < 0$, what does
$x - y + |y| = 12$ that say about possible
solutions?)

42. $x + y + \sqrt{x^2} = 6$
$x + \sqrt{y^2} - y = 8$

43. The perimeter of a rectangle is 40 cm and the area is 96 cm². Find the dimensions of the rectangle.

44. Find the dimensions of a rectangle that has a diagonal of length 13 cm and a perimeter of 34 cm.

45. One side of a rectangle is 3 cm longer than twice the shorter side, and the area is 230 cm². Find the perimeter of the rectangle.

46. An altitude of a triangle is twice as long as the corresponding base and the area of the triangle is 36 cm². Find the altitude and the base. Does the given information determine a unique triangle? Suppose the problem states that one of the other sides is $4\sqrt{10}$. What is the perimeter of the triangle?

47. Find an equation for the line that passes through the points of intersection of the graphs of $y = x^2 + 2x$ and $y = -x^2$.

48. Find an equation for the line that passes through the points of intersection of the graphs of $y = x^2 - 4x - 5$ and $y = -x^2 + 2x + 3$.

49. A rectangle is inscribed in a circle of radius $\sqrt{10}$. If the area of the rectangle is 16, find its dimensions.

SECTION 9.4 **Systems of Linear Inequalities; Linear Programming**

Consider the problem of assigning 70 men to 70 jobs. Unfortunately there are 70 factorial permutations, or ways to make the assignments. The problem is to compare 70 factorial ways and to select the one which is optimal, or "best" by some criterion. Even if the Earth were filled with nano-speed computers, all programmed in parallel from the time of the Big Bang until the sun grows cold, it would [be] impossible to examine all the possible solutions. The remarkable thing is that the simplex method with the aid of a modern computer can solve this problem in a split second.
George P. Dantzig

In earlier chapters we solved inequalities that involved single variables. We noted that the solution sets could be shown on a number line. In this section we are interested in solving inequalities in which two variables are involved. We shall see that the solution set may be shown as a region of the plane.

Linear Inequalities

In Section 9.1 we studied linear equations that can be written in the form $ax + by = c$. If we replace the equal sign by one of the inequality symbols, $\leq$, $<$, $\geq$, or $>$, we have a **linear inequality.** The example that follows illustrates a technique for representing the solution set for a linear inequality.

EXAMPLE 1   Show all points in the plane that satisfy
(a) $-x + 2y = 4$, **(b)** $-x + 2y < 4$, and **(c)** $-x + 2y > 4$.

Solution

(a)   The points (x, y) that satisfy the equation are on line L whose equation may also be written $y = \frac{1}{2}x + 2$. This appears in Figure 9.7, which also shows some typical points M, P, and Q, where M is on the line, P is below M, and Q is above M. Since $y_2 < y_1$ and $y_1 = \frac{1}{2}x_1 + 2$, then $y_2 < \frac{1}{2}x_1 + 2$. Similarly, $y_3 > \frac{1}{2}x_1 + 2$.

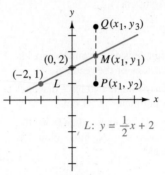

FIGURE 9.7

(b)   The inequality can be written $y < \frac{1}{2}x + 2$. The diagram in Figure 9.8 shows that the coordinates of any point below the line L, such as $P(x_1, y_2)$, will satisfy the given inequality. Any point on or above the line will not. Therefore, the set of points (x, y) that satisfy $-x + 2y < 4$ consists of all points below L. This is the shaded region (or half-plane) in Figure 9.8, where L is shown as a broken line to indicate that the points on L are not included in the solution set.

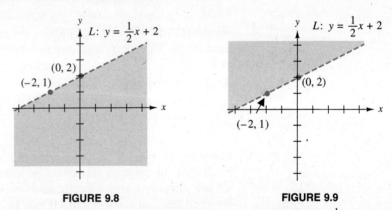

FIGURE 9.8   **FIGURE 9.9**

(c)   In a similar manner, the given inequality is equivalent to $y > \frac{1}{2}x + 2$, and the solution set consists of all points in the half-plane above L. See Figure 9.9.   ▲

Parts b and c of Example 1 suggest the following observation.

> The solution set for a linear inequality, such as $ax + by < c$, consists of all points on one side of a defining line, $ax + bx = c$. The graph of the linear inequality is a **half-plane.**

Strategy: Begin with the boundary line L ($3x - 2y = 6$), and choose a test point that is not on the line. If the coordinates satisfy the desired inequality, the solution is the half-plane that contains the test point; if not, choose the other half-plane.

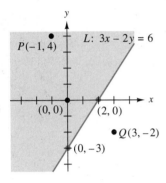

FIGURE 9.10

My earliest recollection of feeling that mathematics might some day be something special was perhaps in the fourth grade when I showed the arithmetic teachers that the squares always end in—well, whatever it is that they end in.

Irving Kaplansky

EXAMPLE 2 Graph the inequality $3x - 2y \le 6$.

Solution

We want all points (x, y) that satisfy $3x - 2y < 6$ and all those that satisfy $3x - 2y = 6$. The graph will consist of all points in a half-plane together with the points *on* the boundary line.

Follow the strategy, referring to Figure 9.10. We must decide which half-plane (above or below L) satisfies the inequality. To do this, take a test point not on L, say $(0, 0)$, and see if it satisfies the inequality.

$$3 \cdot 0 - 2 \cdot 0 \le 6 \quad \text{or} \quad 0 \le 6$$

Since $0 \le 6$ is a true statement, the half-plane that contains $(0, 0)$ is the one we want, the portion of the plane above and to the left of L. The shaded region in Figure 9.10 including the line L (drawn solid) is the graph of the inequality. ▲

The technique for determining the solution set by drawing a graph of a linear inequality, as illustrated in the above example, can be expressed in algorithmic form.

Algorithm for Solving a Linear Inequality

1. Replace the inequality symbol by an equal sign and graph the corresponding line L (broken, for a strict inequality, solid otherwise).

2. Take a test point P not on line L and see if it satisfies the inequality. If it does, then the desired solution set includes all points in the half-plane that contains P; if not, then the solution set consists of the half-plane on the other side of L.

Systems of Inequalities

A **system of linear inequalities** consists of two or more linear inequalities that must be satisfied simultaneously. The following two examples illustrate techniques for determining the solution set or the graph of such a system.

EXAMPLE 3 Solve the system of inequalities and show the solution set as a graph in the plane.

$$x + 2y \le 3$$
$$-3x + y < 5$$
$$-3x + 8y \ge -23$$

Strategy: Each inequality defines a half-plane, so the solution set for the system is the intersection of three half-planes. Draw each boundary line, find the coordinates of the intersections, and identify the correct half-planes by taking test points.

Solution

Follow the strategy. First draw graphs of the three lines L_1, L_2, and L_3:

$$L_1: x + 2y = 3 \qquad L_2: -3x + y = 5 \qquad L_3: -3x + 8y = -23.$$

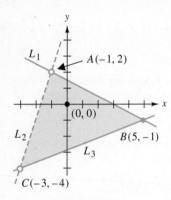

FIGURE 9.11

The points of intersection of these three lines, called **corner points,** are obtained by solving the equations in pairs.

$$A \begin{cases} x + 2y = 3 \\ -3x + y = 5 \end{cases} \quad B \begin{cases} x + 2y = 3 \\ -3x + 8y = -23 \end{cases} \quad C \begin{cases} -3x + y = 5 \\ -3x + 8y = -23 \end{cases}$$

The three corner points are $A(-1, 2)$, $B(5, -1)$, and $C(-3. -4)$. In Figure 9.11 L_2 is shown as a broken line, and points A and C are indicated by open circles, since the points on L_2 are not in the solution set.

Returning to the inequalities, identify the points that belong to all three half-planes. Using $(0, 0)$ as a test point, the desired half-planes are below L_1, below L_2, and above L_3. The intersection of the three half-planes, the solution set, is shown as the shaded region in the figure. Any other test point not on any of the three lines would serve as well to identify the three half-planes and their intersection. ▲

EXAMPLE 4   A dietitian wishes to combine two foods, A and B, to make a mixture that contains at least 50 g of protein, at least 130 mg of calcium, and not more than 550 calories. The nutrient values of foods A and B are given in the table.

	Protein (g/cup)	Calcium (mg/cup)	Calories (per cup)
A	20	20	100
B	10	50	150

How many cups of each of the foods should the dietitian use?

Strategy: We want numbers of cups of A and B, so assign letters (variables). Write inequalities for grams of protein (≥ 50), milligrams of calcium (≥ 130), and number of calories (≤ 550), then draw a graph to show the solution set.

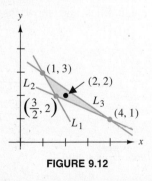

FIGURE 9.12

Solution

Follow the strategy. Let x be the number of cups of food A and y be the number of cups of food B. The three conditions to be met can be written as inequalities:

Protein: $20x + 10y \geq 50$

Calcium: $20x + 50y \geq 130$

Calories: $100x + 150y \leq 550$.

Simplify the inequalities by dividing each of the first two by 10 and the third by 50, and then graph the three lines L_1, L_2, and L_3,

$$L_1: 2x + y = 5 \qquad L_2: 2x + 5y = 13 \qquad L_3: 2x + 3y = 11.$$

Find the points of intersection of L_1, L_2, and L_3 and draw the lines, as shown in Figure 9.12. The solution set for the system of inequalities is the region shown. Therefore, any point in the region will give a combination of foods A and B that will satisfy the given constraints. For instance, point $(2, 2)$ is in the region. Taking two cups of each type of food will provide 60 g of protein, 140 mg of calcium, and 500 calories. ▲

Historical Note

SIMPLEX AND KARMARKAR ALGORITHMS FOR LINEAR PROGRAMMING

Algorithms for linear programming are used to solve complex problems that face oil companies and firms in other industries

Example 5 illustrates a kind of problem that modern industry and government face all the time—that of maximizing or minimizing some function subject to constraints or restrictions. An oil refinery, for example, may produce a dozen products (grades of engine oil, gasoline, diesel, and so on), each of which requires different crude oil purchases, refining processes, and storage. Transportation costs and customer demand vary. Refinery and storage capacity and raw material availability also affect what can be produced and the profitability of the whole operation.

The constraints can usually be described by a set of linear inequalities such as those in Example 5. The set of points satisfying the system of inequalities forms some kind of polyhedral region in a high dimensional space like the regions pictured in Figure 9.13. It turns out that the desired maximum or minimum always occurs at a corner point of the graph. Many industrial or economic applications may present dozens or even hundreds of variables, and locating and testing corner points becomes a staggering problem.

In 1947 an American mathematician, George B. Dantzig, developed a new method for dealing with such problems called the *simplex algorithm for linear programming.* The algorithm uses computers to manipulate matrices in a way that essentially moves from one corner to the next, improving the result at each step. The simplex algorithm has saved untold billions of dollars for industries and consumers worldwide.

Now a new algorithm under investigation promises to deal with even larger problems in less time. This new algorithm, named for its developer, Narendra Karmarkar of Bell Laboratories, intuitively takes shortcuts through the polyhedron, instead of moving along the edges. Scientists, engineers, and economists are working and experimenting to see if computer utilization of the Karmarkar algorithm can significantly improve on the simplex algorithm.

Linear Programming

The Historical Note at the end of this section describes some applications of linear programming. For most such problems we want to maximize or minimize a function, called the **objective function,** subject to conditions (linear inequalities) called **constraints.** The constraints define a set (the set satisfying the system of inequalities) referred to as the **feasible set.** The remarkable fact that makes it possible to solve such optimization problems effectively is the following theorem.

Linear Programming Theorem

If the objective function of a linear programming problem has a maximum or minimum value on the feasible set, then the extreme value must occur at a corner point of the feasible set.

Some of the problems that linear programming helps solve can include dozens of variables and even more constraints. Such complex problems require sophisticated computer techniques, but we can illustrate all of the key ideas with much simpler problems. We begin by outlining the basic ideas for solving a linear programming problem.

Solving a Linear Programming Problem

1. Name the variables; express the constraints and the objective function in terms of the variables.
2. Sketch the boundaries of the feasible set (one boundary for each constraint).
3. Find the corners of the feasible set.
4. Evaluate the objective function at each corner point to identify maximum and minimum values.

EXAMPLE 5   A farmer planning spring planting has decided to plant up to a total of 120 acres in corn and soybeans. An estimate of the investment required and the expected return per acre for each appears in the table.

	Investment	Return
Corn	$20	$50
Soybeans	$35	$80

Because corn is needed for feed purposes on the farm, the farmer needs at least 38 acres of corn, and the budget can cover at most $3000 for both corn and soybeans. How many acres of corn and how many acres of soybeans should be planted to maximize the return from these two crops?

Solution

Let x be the number of acres to be planted in soybeans and y the number of acres of corn. Then we must have $x \geq 0$ and the need for corn as feed implies $y \geq 38$. The total allowable acreage for the two crops is 120 acres, so $x + y \leq 120$. The investment required by x acres of soybeans and y acres of corn is $35x + 20y$, so $35x + 20y \leq 3000$. Finally, the objective function is the expected return, which is $R(x, y) = 80x + 50y$.

We want to maximize the function $R(x, y)$ on the feasible set, which is defined by the inequalities

$$x \geq 0 \qquad y \geq 38 \qquad x + y \leq 120 \qquad 35x + 20y \leq 3000.$$

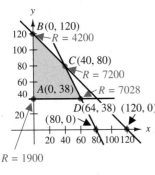

$R = 1900$

FIGURE 9.13

Draw a diagram and shade the feasible set. See Figure 9.13. To find coordinates of the corner points, find the intersections of the boundary lines. The corner points are: $A(0, 38)$, $B(0, 120)$, $C(40, 80)$, and $D(64, 38)$. Finally, determine the estimated return for each choice, that is, evaluate the objective function $R(x, y) = 80x + 50y$ at each corner point:

$$R(0, 38) = 1900 \qquad R(0, 120) = 6000$$

$$R(40, 80) = 7200 \qquad R(64, 38) = 7020.$$

The farmer will get the greatest return, subject to the given constraints, by planting 40 acres of soybeans and 80 acres of corn, for a return of $7200. ▲

EXERCISES 9.4

Check Your Understanding

Exercises 1–6   True or False. Give reasons for your conclusion.

1. The point $(-1, 2)$ is in the solution set for $2x + 3y < 4$.

2. The solution set for the system $x < 0$, $y > 0$, $x + y > 1$ contains only points in the second quadrant.

3. The solution set for the system $x < 0$, $y > 0$, $x + y > 1$ is the empty set.

4. The solution set for the system $x < 0$, $x - y > 1$ contains points in the third quadrant only.

5. The solution set for the system $x < 1$, $y < x$ contains no points in the foruth quadrant.

6. Point $(2, -3)$ is a corner point for the system of inequalities, $2x + 3y \leq -5$, $3x - y \geq 9$, $x - y \leq 1$.

Exercises 7–10   Complete the sentence by selecting from the list below *all choices* that make the statement true.

(a) Quadrant I   (b) Quadrant II
(c) Quadrant III   (d) Quadrant IV
(e) None of the above

7. The solution set for $y > x + 2$ contains no points in _____ .

8. The solution set for $y \geq 2x + 1$ contains points in _____ .

9. The solution set for the system $y \geq x$, $y \leq -x$ contains points in _____ .

10. The expression $\sqrt{x - y - 2}$ is a real number for some points (x, y) in _____ .

Develop Mastery

Exercises 1–4   Determine whether or not the given pair of numbers (x, y) belongs to the solution set of the system of inequalities.

1. $x - 3y < 4$ (a) $(1, 1)$
   $2x + y < 3$ (b) $(\sqrt{2}, -0.5)$

2. $-2x + y > -3$ (a) $(-1, 2)$
   $5x + 2y < 1$ (b) $(1, -5)$

3. $x - 3y \geq 1$ (a) $(1, -1)$
   $4x - y \leq \pi$ (b) $(\sqrt{2}, \pi)$

4. $y \leq 2x$ (a) $(0, 0)$
   $3x + y > 0$ (b) $(-1, 3)$

Exercises 5–12

(a) Draw a graph showing all points (x, y) in the solution set of the given inequality.

(b) Give coordinates of any two specific pairs (x, y) that satisfy the inequality.

5. $x + 2y < 4$ **6.** $-x + y > 3$

7. $2x - 3y \geq 6$ **8.** $4x - 2y \leq 9$

9. $x + y + 4 < 0$ **10.** $2x > y - 4$

11. $y \geq 2x$ **12.** $2y < 3x - 4$

Exercises 13–24   Draw a graph showing the solution set for the system of inequalities. Determine the coordinates of any corner points and show them on your diagram. Indicate which boundary curves and corner points belong and which do not belong to the solution set.

13. $x + y < 4$ **14.** $3x - 2y > 5$
$\quad\;\; 2x - y < -1$ $\quad\;\; -x - y < -5$

15. $x - 2y \geq 4$ **16.** $3x - 4y < 6$
$\quad\;\; |x| > 2$ $\quad\;\; |x| < 2$
$\quad\;\;\;\;\;\;\;\;\;\;\;$ $\quad\;\; |y| < 3$

17. $-x + 2y < 5$ **18.** $4x + 3y \leq 16$
$\quad\;\; 2x + y > 0$ $\quad\;\; -x + y > -4$
$\quad\;\; 3x - y < 5$ $\quad\;\; 6x + y \geq 10$

19. $\quad y > 0$ **20.** $\quad x < 0$
$\quad\;\; x + y > 1$ $\quad\;\; x + y > 1$

21. $\quad x < 0$ **22.** $-1 < x - y \leq 2$
$\quad\;\; y > 0$ $\quad\;\; -2 < x + y \leq 2$
$\quad\;\; x + y > 1$

23. $\quad x > 2$ **24.** $|x - y| \leq 2$
$\quad\;\; y > -1$ $\quad\;\; |x + y| \leq 2$
$\quad\;\; x + y < 3$

Exercises 25–28   For the system of inequalities, determine which quadrants contain points in the solution set.

25. $y > 2x$ **26.** $x > 1$
$\quad\;\; y > 4 - x$ $\quad\;\; y > x$

27. $x + y \leq 1$ **28.** $x - y \geq 2$
$\quad\;\; x - y \leq -1$ $\quad\;\; 2x + y \geq 4$

Exercises 29–36   Show on a graph all points (x, y) for which the expression will be a real number.

29. $\sqrt{2x - y - 4}$ **30.** $\sqrt{x - y + 1}$

31. $\ln (2x + y - 2)$ **32.** $\log (x - 2y - 4)$

33. $\text{Arcsin} (y - x)$ **34.** $\text{Arcsin} (x + y + 1)$

35. $\ln x + \ln (y - x)$

36. $\log (x + y) - \log (2x - y)$

Exercises 37–39   Write a linear equality whose solution set is the shaded region in the diagram.

37.

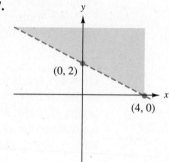

38.

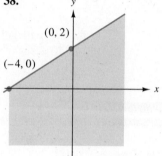

39.

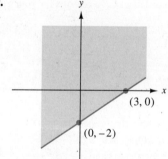

Exercises 40–42   Find a system of inequalities whose solution set is the shaded region in the diagram and give the coordinates of the corner points.

40.

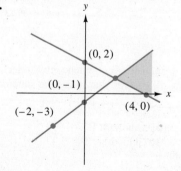

41.

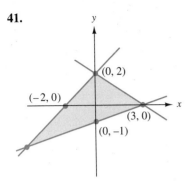

42.

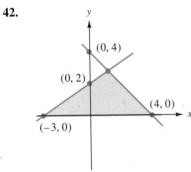

Exercises 43–46 **(a)** Draw a diagram showing the set of all points inside the triangle whose vertices are the points A, B, and C. **(b)** Find a system of inequalities whose solution set consists of all points inside the triangle.

43. $A(-2, 0)$ $B(0, 4)$ $C(4, -2)$

44. $A(-3, 2)$ $B(3, -2)$ $C(5, 2)$

45. $A(-3, 0)$ $B(0, 4)$ $C(2, 0)$

46. $A(0, 0)$ $B(-2, 2)$ $C(4, 2)$

Exercises 47–48 Sketch a graph for the set described and find a system of inequalities for which the set described is the solution set.

47. All points above the line $2x - y = 1$ and below the line $x + 2y = 4$.

48. All points above the line $y = 2x$ and below the line $x + 2y = 5$.

Exercises 49–54 Find the minimum and maximum values of the objective function subject to the given constraints. (*Hint:* First draw a diagram showing the feasible set and use the linear programming theorem.)

49. Objective function: $T = 48x + 56y + 120$
$x + y \geq 4, y \leq 2x + 1, 4x + y \leq 13$

50. Objective function: $T = 36x + 73y - 16$
$x \geq 1, y \leq x, y \geq 3x - 8$

51. Objective function: $T = 67x + 35y$
$y \leq 2, y \leq 2x, y \geq x - 4$

52. Objective function: $T = 65x + 124y - 200$
$x + y \geq 3, y \leq 2x, 4x + y \leq 12$

53. Objective function: $T = 84x + 73y - 78$
$y \geq 0, 2x - y \geq 0,$
$2x + y \geq 4, 3x + y \leq 15$

54. Objective function: $T = 47x + 56y - 24$
$x - 3y + 11 \geq 0, 4x + y \leq 21, 3x + 4y \geq 6$

55. A concert is to be presented in an auditorium that has a seating capacity of 800. The price per ticket for 200 of the seats is $6, and for the remaining 600 seats costs $3. The total cost for putting on the concert will be $2100. Draw a graph to show the various possible pairs of numbers of $6 and $3 tickets that must be sold for the concert to avoid financial loss.

56. A rancher wants to purchase some lambs and goats—at least five lambs and at least four goats—but cannot spend more than $800. Each lamb costs $80, and goats cost $50 each. How many of each can the rancher buy? Draw a graph to list all possible pairs, keeping in mind that lambs and goats come in whole numbers.

57. A sheep rancher raises two different kinds of sheep for market, Rambis and Eustis, with only enough summer range to support 3000 animals for sale each year. To satisfy loyal customers, the rancher must have at least 750 of each breed available, and because of different range demands, at least a third of the herd should be Rambis. The average profit for the Rambis breed is $8 per animal, while each Eustis should yield an average of $10. How many of each breed should the rancher raise to maximize the profit? (*Hint:* If x is the number of Rambis sheep and y is the number of Eustis, the condition that at least a third should be Rambis can be expressed as $x \geq \frac{(x + y)}{3}$ or $y \leq 2x$.)

58. A fish cannery packs tuna in two ways, chunk style and solid pack. Limits on storage space and customer demand lead to these constraints:

> The total number of cases produced per day must not exceed 3000.
>
> The number of cases of chunk style must be at least twice the number of cases of solid pack.
>
> At least 600 cases of solid pack must be produced each day.

How many cases of each type can be produced per day if all constraints are to be satisfied? Draw a graph of the solution set and show the coordinates of the corner points.

Exercises 58–60   Use the information from the following table, which gives nutrient values for four foods, A, B, C, and D. Each unit is 100 grams.

Food	Energy (calories/unit)	Vitamin C (mg/unit)	Iron (mg/unit)
A	200	2	0.5
B	100	3	1.5
C	300	0	2.0
D	400	1	0.0

Food	Calcium (mg/unit)	Protein (g/unit)	Carbohydrate (g/unit)
A	10	2	15
B	4	3	30
C	20	9	10
D	5	3	10

59. In preparing a menu, determine how many units of A and of B can be included so that the combined nutrient values will satisfy the following constraints:

At least 8 milligrams of vitamin C

At least 18 milligrams of calcium

Not more than 800 calories

60. How many units of A and C can be included in a menu to contribute:

At least 3 milligrams of vitamin C

At least 40 milligrams of calcium

Not more than 60 grams of carbohydrates

61. How many units of C and D will give a combined total that satisfies these constraints:

At least 2 milligrams of vitamin C

At least 15 grams of protein

Not more than 6 milligrams of iron

Not more than 2100 calories

62. Would the farmer's decision in Example 5 be different if there were no minimum acreage to be alotted to corn?

63. What would be the optimal planting scheme for Example 5 if the expected return on soybeans were **(a)** $100 per acre? **(b)** $110 per acre?

64. In Example 5 how many acres should be planted to corn and how many to soybeans if the return of corn were to drop to $25 per acre?

65. A commercial gardener wants to feed plants a very specific mix of nitrates and phosphates. Two kinds of fertilizer, Brand A and Brand B, are available, each sold in 50 pound bags, with the following quantities of each mineral per bag:

	Phosphate	Nitrate
Brand A	2.5 lbs	10 lbs
Brand B	5.0	5

The gardener wants to put at least 30 lbs of nitrates and 15 lbs of phosphates on the gardens and not more than 250 lbs of fertilizer altogether. If Brand A costs $8.50 a bag and Brand B costs $4.50 a bag, how many bags of each would minimize fertilizer costs?

66. Repeat Exercise 65 if the cost of Brand B fertilizer increases to $6.00 a bag.

SECTION 9.5	Determinants

. . . A staggering paradox hits us in the teeth. For abstract mathematics happens to work. It is the tool that physicists employ in working with the nuts and bolts of the universe! There are many examples from the history of science of a branch of pure mathematics which, decades after its invention, suddenly finds a use in physics.
        F. David Peat

In Section 9.2 we introduced matrices as convenient tools for keeping track of coefficients and handling the arithmetic required to solve systems of linear equations. Matrices are being used today in more and more applications. A matrix presents a great deal of information in compact, readable form. Finding optimal solutions to linear programming problems requires extensive use of matrices. The properties and applications of matrices are studied in *linear algebra,* a discipline that includes much of the material of this chapter. In this section we introduce the determinant of a square matrix as another tool to help solve systems of linear equations.

Dimension (Size) of a Matrix and Matrix Notation

A matrix is a rectangular array arranged in horizontal **rows** and vertical **columns.** The number of rows and columns give the dimension, or size, of the matrix. A matrix with m rows and n columns is called an m **by** n $(m \times n)$ **matrix.** Double subscripts provide a convenient system of notation for labeling or locating matrix entries.

Here are some matrices of various sizes:

$$A = \begin{bmatrix} a_{11} & a_{12} & a_{13} \\ a_{21} & a_{22} & a_{23} \\ a_{31} & a_{32} & a_{33} \end{bmatrix} \qquad B = \begin{bmatrix} b_{11} \\ b_{21} \\ b_{33} \end{bmatrix} \qquad C = \begin{bmatrix} 1 & 0 \\ 0 & 1 \end{bmatrix}$$

Matrix A is 3×3, B is 3×1, and C is 2×2. A and B show the use of double subscripts: a_{ij} is the entry in the ith row and the jth column. The first subscript identifies the row, the second tells the column; virtually all references to matrices are given in the same order, row first and then column. A matrix with the same number of rows and columns is a **square matrix.**

Determinants

Every square matrix A has an associated number called its **determinant,** denoted by $\det(A)$ or $|A|$. To evaluate determinants, we begin by giving a recursive definition, starting with the determinant of a 2×2 matrix.

Determinant of a 2 × 2 matrix For 2×2 matrix A, we obtain $|A|$ by multiplying the entries along each diagonal and subtracting.

Definition: Determinant of a 2 × 2 Matrix

For the 2×2 matrix

$$A = \begin{bmatrix} a_{11} & a_{12} \\ a_{21} & a_{22} \end{bmatrix},$$

the determinant is given by $|A| = a_{11}a_{22} - a_{12}a_{21}$. Multiply along each arrow, then subtract.

Thus, for example, if

$$A = \begin{bmatrix} 3 & 2 \\ -4 & 1 \end{bmatrix},$$

then $|A| = (3)(1) - (2)(-4) = 3 + 8 = 11$.

For larger square matrices, the determinant definition uses determinants of smaller matrices within the given matrix. The determinant of a 3×3 matrix uses 2×2 determinants, the determinant of a 4×4 matrix uses 3×3 determinants, and so on.

Minors and Cofactors   We associate with each entry a_{ij} of square matrix A a **minor determinant** M_{ij} and a **cofactor** C_{ij}. The minor determinant, more commonly called simply the **minor,** of an entry is the determinant obtained by deleting the row and column of the entry, so M_{ij} is the determinant we get by crossing out the ith row and the jth column. The cofactor C_{ij} is the signed minor given by

$$C_{ij} = (-1)^{i+j} M_{ij}.$$

EXAMPLE 1   Find the cofactor for each element in the first row of the matrix.

$$A = \begin{bmatrix} 1 & -3 & -2 \\ 3 & 2 & -1 \\ -1 & 5 & 0 \end{bmatrix}$$

Solution

Strategy: The elements of the first row are a_{11}, a_{12}, a_{13}. Apply the definition of cofactor for each set of subscripts.

Follow the strategy. In the first row $a_{11} = 1$, $a_{12} = -3$, and $a_{13} = -2$. For the minor M_{11}, delete row 1 and column 1 and then use $C_{11} = (-1)^{1+1} M_{11}$.

$$C_{11} = (-1)^{1+1} \begin{vmatrix} 2 & -1 \\ 5 & 0 \end{vmatrix} = (-1)^2 [0 - (-5)] = 5.$$

To obtain M_{12}, delete row 1 and column 2 and then use $C_{12} = (-1)^{1+2} M_{12}$.

$$C_{12} = (-1)^{1+2} \begin{vmatrix} 3 & -1 \\ -1 & 0 \end{vmatrix} = -[0 - (1)] = 1$$

In a similar manner C_{13} is given by

$$C_{13} = (-1)^{1+3} \begin{vmatrix} 3 & 2 \\ -1 & 5 \end{vmatrix} = [15 - (-2)] = 17 \quad \blacktriangle$$

Determinant of a 3×3 Matrix   The determinant of a 3×3 matrix can be obtained using the elements of the first row.

Definition: Cofactor Expansion by the First Row

Let A be a 3×3 matrix with entries a_{ij}. If C_{ij} and M_{ij} are the cofactor and minor, respectively, of a_{ij} as defined above, then the determinant of A is given by

$$|A| = a_{11}C_{11} + a_{12}C_{12} + a_{13}C_{13} = a_{11}M_{11} - a_{12}M_{12} + a_{13}M_{13}. \quad (1)$$

Determinants of any size have a remarkable property. We get the same number using the entries and cofactors of *any* row or column. For example, each of the following gives the same value for $|A|$ as equation 1.

Expansion by second row $\quad |A| = a_{21}C_{21} + a_{22}C_{22} + a_{23}C_{23}$

Expansion by third column $\quad |A| = a_{13}C_{13} + a_{23}C_{23} + a_{33}C_{33}$

To illustrate that the cofactor expansion is independent of the row or column chosen, we return to the matrix from Example 1, for which we already have some cofactors.

EXAMPLE 2 Evaluate the determinant of matrix A by

(a) the first row **(b)** the second column.

$$A = \begin{bmatrix} 1 & -3 & -2 \\ 3 & 2 & -1 \\ -1 & 5 & 0 \end{bmatrix}$$

Solution

Strategy: (a) Since matrix A is the same as the matrix in Example 1, we already have the cofactors for expansion by the first row. Multiply each cofactor by its entry, and add.

Follow the strategy.

(a) Using $C_{11} = 5$, $C_{12} = 1$, and $C_{13} = 17$ from Example 1, then by Equation 1,

$$|A| = 1 \cdot 5 + (-3) \cdot 1 + (-2) \cdot 17 = 5 - 3 - 34 = -32.$$

(b) Expansion by the second column gives

$$|A| = a_{12}C_{12} + a_{22}C_{22} + a_{32}C_{32}$$

$$= (-3)(-1)^{1+2}M_{12} + (2)(-1)^{2+2}M_{22} + (5)(-1)^{3+2}M_{32}$$

$$= 3\begin{vmatrix} 3 & -1 \\ -1 & 0 \end{vmatrix} + 2\begin{vmatrix} 1 & -2 \\ -1 & 0 \end{vmatrix} - 5\begin{vmatrix} 1 & -2 \\ 3 & -1 \end{vmatrix}$$

$$= 3(-1) + 2(-2) - 5 \cdot 5 = -32,$$

the same value as for the first-row expansion. ▲

Determinant of an $n \times n$ Matrix Since we know how to evaluate 3×3 determinants, we can use a similar cofactor expansion for a 4×4 determinant. Choose any row or column and take the sum of the products of each entry with the corresponding cofactor. The determinant of a 4×4 matrix involves four 3×3 determinants, one for each of the four entries in the chosen row or column. Similarly, the determinant of a 5×5 matrix uses five 4×4 determinants. We give no formal definition of the procedure to evaluate the determinant of an $n \times n$ matrix, but it should be clear from the form of Equation 1. It should also be clear that the number of arithmetic operations required to evaluate a determinant grows staggeringly large as the size of the matrix increases.

Elementary Row (Column) Operations and Determinants One way to simplify the evaluation of determinants is to recognize that certain elementary matrix operations leave the determinant unchanged.

> **Elementary Operation Property**
>
> Given a square matrix A, if the entries of one row (column) are multiplied by a constant and added to the corresponding entries of another row (column), then the determinant of the resulting matrix is still equal to $|A|$.

Applying the Elementary Operation Property (EOP) may give some zero entries that make the evaluation of a determinant much easier, as illustrated in the next example.

EXAMPLE 3   Evaluate the determinant of the matrix

$$A = \begin{bmatrix} -2 & 2 & 0 & 1 \\ 2 & -1 & 3 & 0 \\ -1 & 0 & 2 & -4 \\ 0 & -3 & 5 & 3 \end{bmatrix}$$

Solution

Strategy: Use the EOP to get a matrix with three zeros in a row or column and use that row or column for the cofactor expansion.

Follow the strategy. Several choices seem reasonable, including using the last 1 in the first row to get three zeros in the first row, or using the -1 in the first column to get zeros in the first column or in the third row. To get zeros in the first column, perform the following elementary row operations: $-2R_3 + R_1 \rightarrow R_1$ and $2R_3 + R_2 \rightarrow R_2$. The result is matrix B. Evaluate its determinant through expansion by the first column.

$$|B| = \begin{vmatrix} 0 & 2 & -4 & 9 \\ 0 & -1 & 7 & -8 \\ -1 & 0 & 2 & -4 \\ 0 & -3 & 5 & 3 \end{vmatrix} = 0 \cdot C_{11} + 0 \cdot C_{21} + (-1)C_{31} + 0 \cdot C_{41}.$$

Thus

$$|A| = |B| = (-1)(1) \begin{vmatrix} 2 & -4 & 9 \\ -1 & 7 & -8 \\ -3 & 5 & 3 \end{vmatrix}$$

Apply elementary row operations $2R_2 + R_1 \rightarrow R_1$ and $-3R_2 + R_3 \rightarrow R_3$ to get a matrix with two zeros in the first column:

$$|B| = (-1) \begin{vmatrix} 0 & 10 & -7 \\ -1 & 7 & -8 \\ 0 & -16 & 27 \end{vmatrix} = (-1)(-1)(-1)^3 \begin{vmatrix} 10 & -7 \\ -16 & 27 \end{vmatrix}$$

$$= -(270 - 112) = -158.$$

Since $|A| = |B|$, $|A| = -158$. ▲

DETERMINANTS

English mathematician
Arthur Cayley

Most students of mathematics today learn about determinants only in connection with matrices. Historically, though, determinants had a lively role of their own long before matrices were recognized. Matrices as such have been studied only for a little more than one hundred years, and were not widely known even into the first third of this century (see "Matrices" in Section 9.2). Determinants are numbers rather than arrays, and it probably should not be surprising that they have been recognized more than twice as long as matrices.

At least three important mathematicians independently developed and used some properties of determinants. Leibnitz, best known for his part in the invention of calculus, wrote letters in 1693 that described how to determine whether a given system of homogeneous equations is consistent by calculating a single number, which we now call a determinant. Maclaurin probably used Cramer's rule twenty years before Cramer published it in 1750.

We would probably not recognize Cramer's rule in its original form. It used none of the special notation we use today. There were also formulas for the solution of three by three systems, but it is likely that neither Maclaurin nor Cramer extended the rule to larger systems—with good reason. A formula for quotients of two 24-term expressions is too complicated to be worth much.

By 1773 Lagrange was using essentially modern notation for certain problems. He is responsible for the formula given in the Explore and Discover exercises of this section for the area of a triangle as a determinant. Cauchy applied the name *determinant* to a class of functions including those that we now call determinants, and Jacobi broadened Cauchy's usage to a determinant consisting of derivatives. Cayley finally related determinants and matrices in 1858, when he used them to describe points and lines in higher-dimensional geometry.

Cramer's Rule

We now consider a method for solving systems of linear equations using determinants. The technique is known as **Cramer's Rule.** We state the rule for $n \times n$ systems, but while Cramer's Rule is handy for small systems, the difficulty of evaluating determinants of larger matrices makes it a very inefficient technique for large values of n.

Cramer's Rule

Given a system of n linear equations in variables $x_1, x_2, \ldots x_n$, where A is the coefficient matrix and B is the column of constants, let $D = |A|$ and let D_i be the determinant of the matrix obtained by replacing the ith column of A by column B. If $D \neq 0$, the system has a unique solution given by

$$x_1 = \frac{D_1}{D}, \qquad x_2 = \frac{D_2}{D}, \ldots, x_n = \frac{D_n}{D}.$$

EXAMPLE 4   Solve the system of equations using Cramer's Rule.

$$x - 2y - 3z = 3$$
$$2x - 5y + 3z = -4$$
$$-3x + 4y + 2z = -4$$

Solution

The coefficient matrix is

$$A = \begin{bmatrix} 1 & -2 & -3 \\ 2 & -5 & 3 \\ -3 & 4 & 2 \end{bmatrix}$$

Check that $D = |A| = 25$.

Since $D \neq 0$, proceed with Cramer's Rule and find $D_1, D_2,$ and D_3 by replacing each column of A, in turn, with the column of constants.

$$D_1 = \begin{vmatrix} 3 & -2 & -3 \\ -4 & -5 & 3 \\ -4 & 4 & 2 \end{vmatrix} \qquad D_2 = \begin{vmatrix} 1 & 3 & -3 \\ 2 & -4 & 3 \\ -3 & -4 & 2 \end{vmatrix} \qquad D_3 = \begin{vmatrix} 1 & -2 & 3 \\ 2 & -5 & -4 \\ -3 & 4 & -4 \end{vmatrix}$$

Evaluating determinants, we find that $D_1 = 50, D_2 = 25,$ and $D_3 = -25$. Then by Cramer's rule, we find

$$x = \frac{D_1}{D} = \frac{50}{25} = 2 \qquad y = \frac{D_2}{D} = \frac{25}{25} = 1 \qquad z = \frac{D_3}{D} = -\frac{25}{25} = -1.$$

This system of equations is the same as that in Example 1 of Section 9.1, which used Gaussian elimination to obtain the same solution.   ▲

EXERCISES 9.5

Check Your Understanding

Exercises 1–6 True or False. Give reasons for your conclusion.

1. The determinant of
$$\begin{bmatrix} 2 & -1 \\ 3 & -5 \end{bmatrix}$$
is equal to -7.

2. The only solution of the equation
$$\begin{vmatrix} x & -2 \\ 4 & 2 \end{vmatrix} = 6$$
is given by $x = -1$.

3.
$$\begin{vmatrix} 1 & 3 & -2 \\ 0 & 1 & 4 \\ 0 & 1 & 1 \end{vmatrix} = \begin{vmatrix} 1 & 4 \\ 1 & 1 \end{vmatrix}.$$

4. The solution of the equation
$$\begin{vmatrix} x & 3 & -2 \\ 0 & 1 & 4 \\ 0 & 1 & 1 \end{vmatrix} = 3$$
is given by $x = -1$.

5. The solution set for the equation
$$\begin{vmatrix} \sin x & \cos x \\ -\cos x & \sin x \end{vmatrix} = 1$$
is the empty set.

6. If every element of 2×2 matrix A is a positive number, then the determinant of A is a positive number.

Exercises 7–10 Complete the sentence by selecting from the list below *all choices* that make the statement true. All questions refer to the matrix
$$A = \begin{bmatrix} 0 & -1 & 1 \\ 1 & 1 & -1 \\ -1 & 0 & 2 \end{bmatrix}.$$

(a) 1   **(b)** -1 **(c)** 2   **(d)** -2 **(e)** 3
(f) -3 **(g)** 0   **(h)** None of the above

7. The determinant of A is equal to _____ .

8. The minor M_{31} is equal to _____ .

9. The cofactor C_{11} is equal to _____ .

10. The cofactor C_{12} is equal to _____ .

Explore and Discover

1.
$$A = \begin{bmatrix} 1 & x & y \\ 1 & 2 & 3 \\ 1 & -2 & 4 \end{bmatrix}$$

Show that if the determinant of matrix A is expanded, then an equation for the line that contains the points $P(2, 3)$ and $Q(-2, 4)$ is given by $|A| = 0$. (*Hint:* Expand $|A|$ and verify that $|A| = 0$ is an equation for a line and is satisfied by the coordinates of P and Q.)

2. Find a 3×3 matrix B such that $|B| = 0$ is an equation for the line that contains the points $P(5, -1)$ and $Q(0, 0)$. See Exercise 1.

3. Find a 3×3 matrix C such that $|C| = 0$ is an equation for the line that contains two arbitrary points $P(x_1, y_1)$ and $Q(x_2, y_2)$. See Exercises 1 and 2.

4. Let $A(3, 1)$, $B(5, -2)$, and $C(7, 4)$ be the vertices of a triangle. Show that the area of the triangle is given by $\frac{1}{2}|K|$, where K is the matrix
$$K = \begin{bmatrix} 1 & 3 & 1 \\ 1 & 5 & -2 \\ 1 & 7 & 4 \end{bmatrix}$$

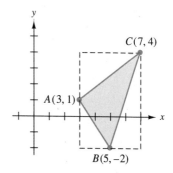

(*Hint:* In the diagram find the area of the rectangle and subtract the sum of the areas of the three right triangles.)

5. Suppose a triangle has the three points $A(x_1, y_1)$, $B(x_2, y_2)$, and $C(x_3, y_3)$ as vertices, as shown in the diagram. Find a 3×3 matrix K such that the area of the triangle is given by $\frac{1}{2}|K|$. (If $|K|$ is negative, take the absolute value.) See Exercise 4.

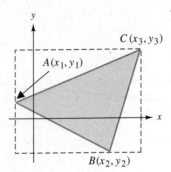

Develop Mastery

Exercises 1–4   Evaluate the indicated cofactors.

1. $\begin{vmatrix} 2 & -1 & 3 \\ 3 & 2 & -5 \\ 1 & 0 & -2 \end{vmatrix}$ Find C_{12}, C_{31}.

2. $\begin{vmatrix} -1 & 0 & 0 \\ 2 & 5 & 3 \\ 2 & -1 & 4 \end{vmatrix}$ Find C_{23}, C_{32}.

3. $\begin{vmatrix} 0 & -2 & \sqrt{3} \\ 5 & \sqrt{3} & 2 \\ -2 & 0 & 1 \end{vmatrix}$ Find C_{22}, C_{33}.

4. $\begin{vmatrix} 2 & -1 & e \\ 3 & e & -1 \\ 5 & 2 & -3 \end{vmatrix}$ Find C_{11}, C_{13}.

Exercises 5–16   Evaluate the determinant of the given matrix.

5. $A = \begin{bmatrix} 3 & -5 \\ 2 & 5 \end{bmatrix}$ **6.** $A = \begin{bmatrix} 0 & 4 \\ -3 & 2 \end{bmatrix}$

7. $B = \begin{bmatrix} 6 & -4 & 1 \\ 7 & -4 & 1 \\ 6 & -3 & 1 \end{bmatrix}$ **8.** $A = \begin{bmatrix} 1 & 0 & 2 \\ 0 & 3 & 3 \\ 0 & 1 & 5 \end{bmatrix}$

9. $B = \begin{bmatrix} 2 & 5 & 2 \\ 6 & 2 & -1 \\ 2 & 2 & 1 \end{bmatrix}$ **10.** $C = \begin{bmatrix} 1 & 1 & 0 \\ 0 & 1 & 1 \\ 1 & 0 & 1 \end{bmatrix}$

11. $C = \begin{bmatrix} 3 & -2 & 2 \\ 4 & -1 & 1 \\ 1 & -1 & 1 \end{bmatrix}$

12. $A = \begin{bmatrix} 0.3 & 0.7 & 1.2 \\ -0.8 & -1.3 & 0.4 \\ 0.0 & 1.0 & 2.1 \end{bmatrix}$

13. $A = \begin{bmatrix} 2 & -1 & 0 \\ \sqrt{3} & \sqrt{12} & \sqrt{27} \\ \sqrt{75} & \sqrt{48} & -\sqrt{3} \end{bmatrix}$

14. $B = \begin{bmatrix} 1 & 3 & 0 & 0 \\ -1 & 0 & 1 & 1 \\ 2 & 0 & 4 & -2 \\ 0 & 1 & 2 & 1 \end{bmatrix}$

15. $C = \begin{bmatrix} 1 & 0 & 2 & -1 \\ 3 & -1 & 2 & 1 \\ -2 & 1 & 4 & -1 \\ -1 & -2 & 3 & 1 \end{bmatrix}$

16. $A = \begin{bmatrix} -1 & 0 & -2 & 0 \\ -3 & 2 & 1 & -3 \\ 1 & -2 & -1 & 3 \\ 2 & 1 & 4 & -2 \end{bmatrix}$

Exercises 17–25   The equation involves the variable x. **(a)** Expand the determinant and **(b)** solve for x.

17. $\begin{vmatrix} 2x & -4 \\ 3x & 2 \end{vmatrix} = 3$ **18.** $\begin{vmatrix} 3 & -4x \\ x & -5 \end{vmatrix} = 6$

19. $\begin{vmatrix} e^x & e \\ e & 1 \end{vmatrix} = 0$ **20.** $\begin{vmatrix} 1 & 0 & x \\ 3 & -1 & 2 \\ -5 & 3 & 0 \end{vmatrix} = -2$

21. $\begin{vmatrix} -2x & 1 & 0 \\ 0 & 3 & 2 \\ -x & 1 & 5 \end{vmatrix} = 4$ **22.** $\begin{vmatrix} x & 4 & 0 \\ 2 & 2 & -x \\ 1 & 1 & 1 \end{vmatrix} = 0$

23. $\begin{vmatrix} x & -2x & 1 \\ 3x & 1 & -2 \\ 2x & 2x+1 & -3 \end{vmatrix} = 0$

24. $\begin{vmatrix} e^x & 0 & 1 \\ -1 & 2 & -3 \\ 0 & 2 & -1 \end{vmatrix} = 4$

25. $\begin{vmatrix} 4\sin x & 1 & 0 \\ -1 & 1 & 3 \\ 2 & -1 & -1 \end{vmatrix} = -3$

26. Let A_θ be the matrix

$$A_\theta = \begin{bmatrix} \cos\theta & \sin\theta \\ -\sin\theta & \cos\theta \end{bmatrix}.$$

Show that the determinant of A_θ is not zero for any value of θ.

Exercises 27–36 Use Cramer's Rule to solve the system of equations. If the determinant of the coefficient matrix is zero, use Gaussian elimination.

27. $6.3x + 2.1y = 18.9$
 $1.5x + 3.4y = -4.2$

28. $2.4x - 5.2y = -8.0$
 $1.6x + 2.4y = 6.4$

29. $371x + 285y = 2726$
 $137x + 125y = 977$

30. $325x - 175y = -625$
 $173x - 276y = 33$

31. $2x + y - 3z = 11$
 $3x + 2y - z = 10$
 $5x - y + 4z = 1$

32. $6x + 5y + 3z = -1$
 $4x + y - 2z = 8$
 $3x + y + 2z = 2$

33. $6x + 2y + 3z = 10$
 $3x + 3y + z = 17$
 $x + 2y + 3z = 0$

34. $3x - y - 2z = -5$
 $-2x - 3y + z = 14$
 $2x - 3y + 2z = 7$

35. $3x - 2y + z = 14$
 $x + y - 3z = 12$
 $5x - 2y + 7z = 25$

36. $5x - 4y - z = -22$
 $x - 2y + 3z = 5$
 $4x + y - 5z = -26$

37. Using the slope intercept form of an equation for a line ($y = mx + b$), find m and b if the line passes through the points $A(-2, 4)$ and $B(3, 5)$.

38. Find the point of intersection of the two lines with equations $2x - 3y = 4$ and $5x - y = 7$.

Exercises 39–41 For the circle that passes through the three points **(a)** write an equation in the form $x^2 + y^2 + bx + cy = d$ and **(b)** find the radius and the coordinates of the center.

39. $(-1, -2), (5, 6), (6, 5)$

40. $(-1, -1), (0, 2), (2, 2)$

41. $(0, 2), (7, 1), (8, -2)$

Exercises 42–44 For the parabola that passes through the three points, **(a)** write an equation in the form $y = ax^2 + bx + c$ and **(b)** find the coordinates of the x-intercept points and the vertex.

42. $(0, 1), (1, -2), (2, -3)$

43. $(-1, -1), (0, 2), (2, 2)$

44. $(0, 7), (1, 1), (2, -1)$

45. The height from ground level of an object is given by an equation of the form $h(t) = at^2 + bt + c$, where t is the time in seconds and h is measured in feet.
   (a) Find a, b, and c, if $h(1) = 240, h(2) = 246$, and $h(3) = 248$.
   (b) At what time will the object be at ground level?

| **SECTION 9.6** | **Matrix Algebra (Optional)** |

A genuine discovery should do more than merely conform to the facts: it should feel right, it should be beautiful. Aesthetic qualities are important in science, and necessary, I think, for great science.
   Roger Penrose

In Sections 9.2 and 9.5 we introduced some ideas related to matrices, but we did not discuss the algebra of matrices themselves. In this section we present a small portion of matrix algebra for solving systems of linear equations. We will limit most of our discussion to 2×2 or 3×3 systems, but all of the essential ideas can be applied to larger systems, as well.

Matrix Equality
Since matrices have many entries, we need to know when two matrices are equal. Equality requires not only that the matrices contain the same numbers, but that all corresponding entries be the same.

> **Definition: Equality of Matrices**
>
> Matrices A and B are equal, written $A = B$, if and only if
>
> 1. A and B have the same size, and
> 2. Each entry in A is equal to the corresponding entry in B: $a_{ij} = b_{ij}$.

Matrix Product

The product of two matrices is probably most easily introduced with an example.

[In college] there were no women teaching mathematics but I remember women teaching biology and psychology. Naturally I elected to major in mathematics. [Most math] students [were] planning to be engineers. There were also girls who were going to be teachers. At that time I had no idea that such a thing as a mathematician (as opposed to math teacher) existed.

Julia Robinson

EXAMPLE 1   A bicycle dealer has three outlets, one downtown, one in a mall, and one at a nearby resort. A special mountain bike sale features three brands of bikes with these sale prices: Hoppit ($375), Runner ($425), Climber ($315). The numbers of bikes sold at the three outlets during the special promotion are displayed in a matrix:

$$\begin{array}{c} \\ \text{Downtown} \\ \text{Mall} \\ \text{Resort} \end{array} \begin{array}{ccc} H & R & C \\ \left[\begin{array}{ccc} 8 & 7 & 12 \\ 4 & 14 & 9 \\ 5 & 8 & 16 \end{array}\right. \end{array}$$

Find the sales total in dollars at each outlet.

Solution

We could find the desired information without using matrices. The dollar total from the downtown store is $8(\$375) + 7(\$425) + 12(\$315) = \$9,755$, and the same operations will give us the gross sales figures for the mall store ($10,285) and the resort store ($10,315). Matrix multiplication is defined to do precisely these operations. Let A and B be matrices.

$$A = \begin{bmatrix} 8 & 7 & 12 \\ 4 & 14 & 9 \\ 5 & 8 & 16 \end{bmatrix} \quad \text{and} \quad B = \begin{bmatrix} 375 \\ 425 \\ 315 \end{bmatrix}$$

The product AB is a 3×1 matrix C:

$$AB = \begin{bmatrix} 8 & 7 & 12 \\ 4 & 14 & 9 \\ 5 & 8 & 16 \end{bmatrix} \cdot \begin{bmatrix} 375 \\ 425 \\ 315 \end{bmatrix}$$

$$= \begin{bmatrix} 8 \cdot 375 + 7 \cdot 425 + 12 \cdot 315 \\ 4 \cdot 375 + 14 \cdot 425 + 9 \cdot 315 \\ 5 \cdot 375 + 8 \cdot 425 + 16 \cdot 315 \end{bmatrix} = \begin{bmatrix} 9,755 \\ 10,285 \\ 10,315 \end{bmatrix} = C$$

From the matrix C, read off sales totals: $c_{11} = \$9,755$ (downtown), $c_{21} = \$10,285$ (mall), and $c_{31} = \$10,315$ (resort). ▲

The matrix product in Example 1 is sometimes called a *row by column product*. Each entry in product AB is obtained by multiplying the entries of one row of A by the entries of a column of B, and each entry c_{ij} of the product is the sum of the products of the entries in the ith row of A with the corresponding entries of the jth column of B. More specifically, c_{11} is given by $c_{11} = a_{11}b_{11} + a_{12}b_{21} + a_{13}b_{31}$. Similarly, c_{21} comes from the second row of A and the first column of B: $c_{21} = a_{21}b_{11} + a_{22}b_{21} + a_{23}b_{31}$, and $c_{31} = a_{31}b_{11} + a_{32}b_{21} + a_{33}b_{31}$.

The row-by-column idea defines the product of two matrices in general. The product AB requires that the number of entries in each row of A matches the number of entries in each column of B. It is easy to see in a particular example whether or not A and B allow multiplication, but we can also read the information from the dimensions of A and B.

Definition: Product of Two Matrices

Let A be an $m \times k$ matrix and B be a $k \times n$ matrix. The product AB is an $m \times n$ matrix C, where the entry c_{ij} is obtained by multiplying the entries of the ith row of A by the corresponding entries of the jth column of B and then adding the resulting products:

$$c_{ij} = a_{i1}b_{1j} + a_{i2}b_{2j} + a_{i3}b_{3j} + \cdots + a_{ik}b_{kj}.$$

Strategy: (a) Using the row-by-column definition, if $AB = C$, then $c_{11} = 1 \cdot 4 + (-2)0 + 0(-2) = 4$, and so on.

EXAMPLE 2 Find the products AB and BA if matrices A and B are given by

$$A = \begin{bmatrix} 1 & -2 & 0 \\ 3 & 2 & -1 \\ 2 & 0 & -1 \end{bmatrix} \quad B = \begin{bmatrix} 4 & -1 & 2 \\ 0 & 1 & 3 \\ -2 & 1 & -1 \end{bmatrix}.$$

Solution

Follow the strategy.

$$AB = \begin{bmatrix} 1 & -2 & 0 \\ 3 & 2 & -1 \\ 2 & 0 & -1 \end{bmatrix} \cdot \begin{bmatrix} 4 & -1 & 2 \\ 0 & 1 & 3 \\ -2 & 1 & -1 \end{bmatrix}$$

$$= \begin{bmatrix} 1 \cdot 4 + (-2)0 + 0(-2) & 1(-1) + (-2)1 + 0 \cdot 1 & 1 \cdot 2 + (-2)3 + 0(-1) \\ 3 \cdot 4 + 2 \cdot 0 + (-1)(-2) & 3(-1) + 2 \cdot 1 + (-1)1 & 3 \cdot 2 + 2 \cdot 3 + (-1)(-1) \\ 2 \cdot 4 + 0 \cdot 0 + (-1)((-2) & 2(-1) + 0 \cdot 1 + (-1)1 & 2 \cdot 2 + 0 \cdot 3 + (-1)(-1) \end{bmatrix}$$

$$= \begin{bmatrix} 4 & -3 & -4 \\ 14 & -2 & 13 \\ 10 & -3 & 5 \end{bmatrix}$$

$$BA = \begin{bmatrix} 4 & -1 & 2 \\ 0 & 1 & 3 \\ -2 & 1 & -1 \end{bmatrix} \begin{bmatrix} 1 & -2 & 0 \\ 3 & 2 & -1 \\ 2 & 0 & -1 \end{bmatrix} = \begin{bmatrix} 5 & -10 & -1 \\ 9 & 2 & -4 \\ -1 & 6 & 0 \end{bmatrix} \quad \blacktriangle$$

In the solution to Example 2 note that $AB \neq BA$, which implies that matrix multiplication is not necessarily commutative.

EXAMPLE 3   Matrices A, B, and C are

$$A = \begin{bmatrix} -1 & 2 \\ 3 & -5 \end{bmatrix} \qquad B = \begin{bmatrix} 1 & 4 \\ -1 & 2 \end{bmatrix} \qquad C = \begin{bmatrix} -1 & 0 \\ 2 & 3 \end{bmatrix}.$$

Find the matrix products **(a)** $(AB)C$ and **(b)** $A(BC)$

Solution

Follow the strategy.

Strategy: (a) First find AB, then multiply the result by C (with C on the right) to get $(AB)C$.

(a) $(AB)C = \left(\begin{bmatrix} -1 & 2 \\ 3 & -5 \end{bmatrix} \begin{bmatrix} 1 & 4 \\ -1 & 2 \end{bmatrix} \right) \begin{bmatrix} -1 & 0 \\ 2 & 3 \end{bmatrix}$

$\qquad = \begin{bmatrix} -3 & 0 \\ 8 & 2 \end{bmatrix} \begin{bmatrix} -1 & 0 \\ 2 & 3 \end{bmatrix} = \begin{bmatrix} 3 & 0 \\ -4 & 6 \end{bmatrix}$

(b) $A(BC) = \begin{bmatrix} -1 & 2 \\ 3 & -5 \end{bmatrix} \left(\begin{bmatrix} 1 & 4 \\ -1 & 2 \end{bmatrix} \begin{bmatrix} -1 & 0 \\ 2 & 3 \end{bmatrix} \right)$

$\qquad = \begin{bmatrix} -1 & 2 \\ 3 & -5 \end{bmatrix} \begin{bmatrix} 7 & 12 \\ 5 & 6 \end{bmatrix} = \begin{bmatrix} 3 & 0 \\ -4 & 6 \end{bmatrix}.$ ▲

The solution to Example 3 illustrates a general property of matrix multiplication: matrix multiplication is associative. Whenever the products are defined, $(AB)C = A(BC)$.

EXAMPLE 4   Matrices A and B are given by

$$A = \begin{bmatrix} -1 & 2 \\ 3 & -1 \end{bmatrix} \qquad B = \begin{bmatrix} 1 & 0 \\ 0 & 1 \end{bmatrix}.$$

Find the matrix products **(a)** AB and **(b)** BA.

Solution

(a) $AB = \begin{bmatrix} -1 & 2 \\ 3 & -1 \end{bmatrix} \begin{bmatrix} 1 & 0 \\ 0 & 1 \end{bmatrix} = \begin{bmatrix} -1 & 2 \\ 3 & -1 \end{bmatrix}$

(b) $BA = \begin{bmatrix} 1 & 0 \\ 0 & 1 \end{bmatrix} \begin{bmatrix} -1 & 2 \\ 3 & -1 \end{bmatrix} = \begin{bmatrix} -1 & 2 \\ 3 & -1 \end{bmatrix}$ ▲

The solution to Example 4 shows that $AB = BA = A$, so the matrix B acts much like the number 1 in ordinary arithmetic ($a \cdot 1 = 1 \cdot a = a$). The matrix B has the same property for any 2×2 matrix, and we call B the **identity matrix** for the set of 2×2 matrices. It is customary to denote the identity matrix by the letter I. There is an identity matrix of size $n \times n$ for every dimension n. The 3×3 identity is the matrix

$$I = \begin{bmatrix} 1 & 0 & 0 \\ 0 & 1 & 0 \\ 0 & 0 & 1 \end{bmatrix}.$$

The same letter I can denote the identity matrix of any size under discussion, but the context should make it clear which size identity is intended.

EXAMPLE 5   Find matrix products AB and BA, where

$$A = \begin{bmatrix} 1 & 0 & 1 \\ -5 & 1 & -5 \\ -2 & 1 & -1 \end{bmatrix} \quad B = \begin{bmatrix} 4 & 1 & -1 \\ 5 & 1 & 0 \\ -3 & -1 & 1 \end{bmatrix}$$

Solution

$$AB = \begin{bmatrix} 1 & 0 & 1 \\ -5 & 1 & -5 \\ -2 & 1 & -1 \end{bmatrix}\begin{bmatrix} 4 & 1 & -1 \\ 5 & 1 & 0 \\ -3 & -1 & 1 \end{bmatrix} = \begin{bmatrix} 1 & 0 & 0 \\ 0 & 1 & 0 \\ 0 & 0 & 1 \end{bmatrix}$$

$$BA = \begin{bmatrix} 4 & 1 & -1 \\ 5 & 1 & 0 \\ -3 & -1 & 1 \end{bmatrix}\begin{bmatrix} 1 & 0 & 1 \\ -5 & 1 & -5 \\ -2 & 1 & -1 \end{bmatrix} = \begin{bmatrix} 1 & 0 & 0 \\ 0 & 1 & 0 \\ 0 & 0 & 1 \end{bmatrix} \quad \blacktriangle$$

The product of the two matrices in Example 5 (in either order) is the identity matrix. In the set of real numbers two numbers whose product is 1 are called *reciprocals* or *multiplicative inverses* of each other. We use the same terms in matrix algebra. If $AB = BA = I$, then A and B are inverses of each other, $B = A^{-1}$. In general, $AA^{-1} = A^{-1}A = I$. Not all matrices have inverses, but every square matrix with a nonzero determinant does have an inverse.

We sum up our discussion so far in a list of some properties of matrix algebra.

Properties of Matrix Algebra

1. In general, matrix multiplication is *not* commutative: $AB \neq BA$.
2. Matrix multiplication is associative: $(AB)C = A(BC)$.
3. The square matrix I with 1s on the main diagonal and 0s everywhere else is an identity matrix: $AI = IA = A$.
4. Any square matrix A with a nonzero determinant has an inverse: $AA^{-1} = A^{-1}A = I$.

Finding the Inverse of a Square Matrix

Matrix inverses have several important applications. Among them is another technique for solving systems of linear equations. To use the technique we need a method for finding the inverse of a matrix. The following algorithm is simple and relatively efficient.

Algorithm to Find the Inverse of a Square Matrix

Suppose A is a square matrix with a nonzero determinant.

1. Adjoin the identity matrix to the right of A, getting a matrix with the structure $[A\,|\,I]$.

> 2. Use elementary row operations on $[A\,|\,I]$ to get a matrix of the form $[I\,|\,B]$.
> 3. The inverse of A is the matrix B.

We illustrate the algorithm with matrix A of Example 5.

$$[A\,|\,I] = \begin{bmatrix} 1 & 0 & 1 & | & 1 & 0 & 0 \\ -5 & 1 & -5 & | & 0 & 1 & 0 \\ -2 & 1 & -1 & | & 0 & 0 & 1 \end{bmatrix} \quad \begin{matrix} 5R_1 + R_2 \to R_2 \\ 2R_1 + R_3 \to R_3 \end{matrix} \quad \begin{bmatrix} 1 & 0 & 1 & | & 1 & 0 & 0 \\ 0 & 1 & 0 & | & 5 & 1 & 0 \\ 0 & 1 & 1 & | & 2 & 0 & 1 \end{bmatrix}$$

$$(-1)R_2 + R_3 \to R_3 \quad \begin{bmatrix} 1 & 0 & 1 & | & 1 & 0 & 0 \\ 0 & 1 & 0 & | & 5 & 1 & 0 \\ 0 & 0 & 1 & | & -3 & -1 & 1 \end{bmatrix}$$

$$(-1)R_3 + R_1 \to R_1 \quad \begin{bmatrix} 1 & 0 & 0 & | & 4 & 1 & -1 \\ 0 & 1 & 0 & | & 5 & 1 & 0 \\ 0 & 0 & 1 & | & -3 & -1 & 1 \end{bmatrix}$$

The last matrix has the form $[I\,|\,B]$, so

$$A^{-1} = B = \begin{bmatrix} 4 & 1 & -1 \\ 5 & 1 & 0 \\ -3 & -1 & 1 \end{bmatrix},$$

as we found in Example 5, which showed that $AB = I$.

Solving Systems of Linear Equations

We stated that a goal of this section was to develop the matrix algebra needed to express an $n \times n$ system of linear equations as a matrix equation and then to use matrix algebra to solve the system. Two examples illustrate this process.

EXAMPLE 6   For the matrices

$$A = \begin{bmatrix} 1 & 0 & 1 \\ -5 & 1 & -5 \\ -2 & 1 & -1 \end{bmatrix} \quad X = \begin{bmatrix} x \\ y \\ z \end{bmatrix} \quad \text{and} \quad C = \begin{bmatrix} 3 \\ -2 \\ 4 \end{bmatrix},$$

(a) write the matrix product AX, and

(b) write the system of linear equations that result if $AX = C$.

Solution

(a)
$$AX = \begin{bmatrix} 1 & 0 & 1 \\ -5 & 1 & -5 \\ -2 & 1 & -1 \end{bmatrix} \cdot \begin{bmatrix} x \\ y \\ z \end{bmatrix} = \begin{bmatrix} x + z \\ -5x + y - 5z \\ -2x + y - z \end{bmatrix}$$

(b) If $AX = C$, then

$$\begin{bmatrix} x + z \\ -5x + y - 5z \\ -2x + y - z \end{bmatrix} = \begin{bmatrix} 3 \\ -2 \\ 4 \end{bmatrix} \quad \text{so} \quad \begin{matrix} x + z = 3 \\ -5x + y - 5z = -2 \\ -2x + y - z = 4 \end{matrix} \quad \blacktriangle$$

For Graphers 9.6

MATRICES AND SOLVING LINEAR SYSTEMS

Graphing calculators handle reasonable matrix calculations easily. Given a system of linear equations in matrix form $AX = B$, where A is $n \times n$ and X and B are both $n \times 1$ column matrices, the solution of the system is given by $X = A^{-1}B$. (We use the notation $AX = B$ rather than $AX = C$ because of the way the matrix registers work in the graphing calculator.) Here we use a matrix inverse to solve a system of linear equations, using the system from Example 7.

EXAMPLE 1   Use your graphing calculator to solve

$$x \qquad + z = 3$$
$$-5x + y - 5z = -2$$
$$-2x + y - z = 4$$

Solution   As in Example 7, the matrix form for the system is $AX = B$, where

$$A = \begin{bmatrix} 1 & 0 & 1 \\ -5 & 1 & -5 \\ -2 & 1 & -1 \end{bmatrix}.$$

First, enter matrix A in the matrix register A of the calculator (review the Using a Graphing Calculator section). Then enter the column of constants as matrix B.

TI

Return to the home screen (2nd QUIT). Matrices A, B, and C are located above the numerical keys 1–3. Press 2nd [A] x⁻¹ 2nd [B], and then ENT.

Casio

Press PRE to return to the previous screen, with menu keys A, B, +, −, ×, C. Press A and F4 for A⁻¹, which appears in register C. F1 puts A⁻¹ back as matrix A. PRE (×) calculates the product AB and displays it as C.

The solution is a matrix, from which $x = 6$, $y = 13$, $z = -3$. We can check our results by multiplication: on the TI, A* ANS returns the original matrix B. On the Casio, the answer $A^{-1}B$ appears in register C. Press F2 to put the answer back as B and then multiply by A. ▲

Exercises

Find the solution of the system, and check by matrix multiplication.

1. $2x - 3y + 5z = -5$
$\quad 4x + y - 2z = 7$
$\quad -x - 2y + 2z = -3$

2. $5x + y - z = 26$
$\quad 2x - y + 3z = 36$
$\quad 3x + 2y + 5z = 38$

3. $x + 2y + 4z = \frac{15}{2}$
$\quad 2x + 7y - 13z = -\frac{57}{2}$
$\quad 4x + 6y - 5z = -11$

4. $2x - y - z = -1$
$2x + y - z = 3$
$3x + 6y + z = 12$

5. $2x + y = 1$
$3x + 2y + 4z = 1$
$-4x + 6y + 9z = 0$

6. $x + 3y + 3z = 1$
$2x - y + 2z = -1$
$-3x + 2y - 2z = 2$

7. Neither the TI-81 nor the Casio fx 7700G is programmed to directly evaluate a matrix power like A^{24}, as needed for Develop Mastery Exercises 39–51, although the TI will compute A^2 ($\boxed{\text{2nd}}$ $[A]$ $\boxed{x^2}$ $\boxed{\text{ENT}}$). Experiment with your calculator and find ways to evaluate A^3 for a matrix A of your choosing.

Example 6 shows how a system of linear equations can be written as a matrix equation. Building on this result, we can use properties of matrix algebra to find the solution to a system of equations.

EXAMPLE 7 Using Example 6, solve the system

$$x \qquad + z = 3$$
$$-5x + y - 5z = -2$$
$$-2x + y - z = 4$$

as a matrix equation.

Solution

Example 6 demonstrated that the system is equivalent to the matrix equation $AX = C$, where A, X, and C are as given in that example. To solve the matrix equation $AX = C$, multiply both sides by the matrix A^{-1} and use the associative property of matrix multiplication:

$$A^{-1}(AX) = A^{-1}C \qquad (A^{-1}A)X = A^{-1}C \qquad IX = A^{-1}C \qquad \text{or}$$
$$X = A^{-1}C.$$

Matrix A is the matrix of Example 5, whose inverse we have already found. The solution of the system (in matrix form) is

$$X = A^{-1}C = \begin{bmatrix} 4 & 1 & -1 \\ 5 & 1 & 0 \\ -3 & -1 & 1 \end{bmatrix} \begin{bmatrix} 3 \\ -2 \\ 4 \end{bmatrix} = \begin{bmatrix} 6 \\ 13 \\ -3 \end{bmatrix} \qquad \text{from which}$$

$$\begin{bmatrix} x \\ y \\ z \end{bmatrix} = \begin{bmatrix} 6 \\ 13 \\ -3 \end{bmatrix},$$

and so $x = 6$, $y = 13$, and $z = -3$. ▲

The procedure outlined in Examples 6 and 7 can be stated as an algorithm for using matrix algebra to solve an $n \times n$ system of linear equations.

Algorithm for Solving an $n \times n$ System of Linear Equations

1. Express the system in matrix form as $AX = C$, where A is the coefficient matrix.
2. Evaluate $|A|$. If $|A| = 0$, then the system is either dependent or inconsistent. Use Gaussian elimination.
3. If $|A| \neq 0$, then find A^{-1}.
4. The solution to the system is given by $X = A^{-1}C$.

EXERCISES 9.6

Check Your Understanding

Exercises 1–5 True or False. Give reasons for your conclusion.

1. If $A = \begin{bmatrix} -1 & 0 \\ 0 & -1 \end{bmatrix}$, then $A \cdot A = \begin{bmatrix} 1 & 0 \\ 0 & 1 \end{bmatrix}$.

2. The inverse of $\begin{bmatrix} 1 & 4 \\ 1 & 5 \end{bmatrix}$ is $\begin{bmatrix} 5 & -4 \\ -1 & 1 \end{bmatrix}$.

3. If $A = \begin{bmatrix} 0 & 1 & 0 \\ 1 & 0 & 0 \\ 0 & 0 & 1 \end{bmatrix}$, then $A^{-1} = A$.

4. If $A = \begin{bmatrix} 1 & -1 \\ 0 & 1 \end{bmatrix}$ and $B = \begin{bmatrix} -1 & 1 \\ -1 & 0 \end{bmatrix}$,

   then $BA = AB$.

5. If $A = \begin{bmatrix} 2 & -3 \\ -1 & 2 \end{bmatrix}$ and $B = \begin{bmatrix} 2 & 3 \\ 1 & 2 \end{bmatrix}$,

   then $BA = AB$.

Exercises 6–10 Fill in the blank with A, B, C, D or *None* to make the statement true. Matrices A, B, C, and D are

$$A = \begin{bmatrix} 1 & 0 \\ 0 & 1 \end{bmatrix} \qquad B = \begin{bmatrix} 1 & 0 \\ 0 & -1 \end{bmatrix}$$

$$C = \begin{bmatrix} -1 & 0 \\ 0 & 1 \end{bmatrix} \qquad D = \begin{bmatrix} -1 & 0 \\ 0 & -1 \end{bmatrix}$$

6. $CD =$ _____ .

7. $BC =$ _____ .

8. $CB =$ _____ .

9. $AB =$ _____ .

10. $DB =$ _____ .

Develop Mastery

Exercises 1–4 **(a)** Give the dimension of matrix A and **(b)** find a_{12} and a_{21} when possible. If this is not possible, explain why.

1. $A = \begin{bmatrix} 2 & -3 \\ -1 & -4 \end{bmatrix}$

2. $A = \begin{bmatrix} 0 & -1 \\ 2 & 0 \end{bmatrix}$

3. $A = \begin{bmatrix} 1 & 1 & -1 \\ 0 & 0 & 2 \\ 1 & 2 & 4 \end{bmatrix}$

4. $A = \begin{bmatrix} -2 \\ 5 \\ 1 \end{bmatrix}$

Exercises 5–12 Evaluate the matrix product when possible; if the product is not defined, explain why. Use the matrices

$$A = \begin{bmatrix} 2 & -3 \\ -1 & -4 \end{bmatrix} \qquad B = \begin{bmatrix} 3 \\ -1 \end{bmatrix}$$

$$C = \begin{bmatrix} -1 & 0 & 2 \\ 3 & -1 & 4 \\ -2 & 0 & 1 \end{bmatrix} \qquad D = \begin{bmatrix} -1 \\ 5 \\ 2 \end{bmatrix}$$

$$E = \begin{bmatrix} 0 & 1 \\ -1 & 2 \end{bmatrix} \qquad F = \begin{bmatrix} 0 & -1 & 2 \\ 3 & -2 & 1 \\ 4 & 0 & 2 \end{bmatrix}$$

5. AB
6. BA
7. CD
8. AE
9. EA
10. CF
11. FC
12. $A(EA)$

Exercises 13–26 Find the inverse of the matrix if it has an inverse; if it has no inverse, explain how you know.

13. $A = \begin{bmatrix} 5 & -3 \\ -3 & 2 \end{bmatrix}$

14. $B = \begin{bmatrix} 3 & 5 \\ -1 & -2 \end{bmatrix}$

15. $C = \begin{bmatrix} 1 & 0 \\ 6 & 2 \end{bmatrix}$

16. $A = \begin{bmatrix} -2 & 1 \\ -4 & 3 \end{bmatrix}$

17. $B = \begin{bmatrix} -1 & 0 \\ 0 & 2 \end{bmatrix}$ **18.** $C = \begin{bmatrix} 0 & -1 \\ -1 & 1 \end{bmatrix}$

19. $B = \begin{bmatrix} 3 \\ -1 \end{bmatrix}$ **20.** $A = \begin{bmatrix} 0 \\ 2 \\ 0 \end{bmatrix}$

21. $A = \begin{bmatrix} 1 & 2 & 4 \\ 1 & 3 & 3 \\ 1 & 2 & 3 \end{bmatrix}$ **22.** $B = \begin{bmatrix} 1 & -1 & 0 \\ 0 & -1 & 1 \\ -2 & 6 & -3 \end{bmatrix}$

23. $C = \begin{bmatrix} -4 & 2 & -3 \\ 10 & -5 & 8 \\ -1 & 1 & -1 \end{bmatrix}$

24. $A = \begin{bmatrix} -3 & -1 & 1 \\ 2 & 1 & 2 \\ 5 & 2 & 0 \end{bmatrix}$

25. $B = \begin{bmatrix} 4 & 1 & -1 \\ 5 & 1 & 0 \\ -3 & -1 & 1 \end{bmatrix}$

26. $C = \begin{bmatrix} 1 & 0 & 1 \\ -4 & 1 & -4 \\ -2 & 1 & -1 \end{bmatrix}$

Exercises 27–34

(a) Give the matrices A, X, and C for which the system of equations can be written in matrix form as $AX = C$. (See Examples 6 and 7.)

(b) Evaluate $|A|$.

(c) If A has an inverse, find A^{-1} and solve the system of equations by solving the matrix equation $AX = C$.

27. $3x + 4y = 2$
$-7x - 9y = 3$

28. $x + 3y = 4$
$3x + 5y = -2$

29. $-3x + 2y = 4$
$5x - 3y = -1$

30. $-2x + y = 3$
$-5x + 3y = 1$

31. $x - y = 0$
$-y + z = 4$
$-2x + 6y - 3z = 1$

32. $x + 2y + 4z = -1$
$x + 3y + 3z = 2$
$x + 2y + 3z = -4$

33. $-3x - y + z = 2$
$2x + y + 2z = -1$
$-x + 3z = 0$

34. $x + 2y + 2z = -1$
$x + 3y + 2z = -2$
$2x + 6y + 5z = 3$

Exercises 35–38 For matrices A and B, find **(a)** AB, **(b)** A^{-1}, and **(c)** B^{-1}.

35. $A = \begin{bmatrix} 2 & -3 \\ -1 & 2 \end{bmatrix}$ $B = \begin{bmatrix} 2 & 3 \\ 1 & 2 \end{bmatrix}$

36. $A = \begin{bmatrix} 1 & 4 \\ 1 & 5 \end{bmatrix}$ $B = \begin{bmatrix} 5 & -4 \\ -1 & 1 \end{bmatrix}$

37. $A = \begin{bmatrix} -4 & 2 & -3 \\ 10 & -5 & 8 \\ -1 & 1 & -1 \end{bmatrix}$ $B = \begin{bmatrix} -3 & -1 & 1 \\ 2 & 1 & 2 \\ 5 & 2 & 0 \end{bmatrix}$

38. $A = \begin{bmatrix} 3 & 2 & -2 \\ -1 & 1 & 0 \\ 0 & -2 & 1 \end{bmatrix}$ $B = \begin{bmatrix} 1 & 2 & 2 \\ 1 & 3 & 2 \\ 2 & 6 & 5 \end{bmatrix}$

Exercises 39–44 For matrix A, find **(a)** $A^2 (= A \cdot A)$, **(b)** A^3, **(c)** A^{16}, and **(d)** A^{48}.

39. $A = \begin{bmatrix} 4 & 5 \\ -3 & -4 \end{bmatrix}$ **40.** $A = \begin{bmatrix} -2 & -1 \\ 3 & 2 \end{bmatrix}$

41. $A = \begin{bmatrix} \frac{1}{4} & \frac{5}{4} \\ \frac{3}{4} & -\frac{1}{4} \end{bmatrix}$ **42.** $A = \begin{bmatrix} 1 & 0 & 0 \\ 0 & 0 & 1 \\ 0 & 1 & 0 \end{bmatrix}$

43. $A = \begin{bmatrix} 1 & 0 & 0 \\ 0 & 4 & -3 \\ 0 & 5 & -4 \end{bmatrix}$ **44.** $A = \begin{bmatrix} 1 & 4 & 2 \\ 3 & 5 & 3 \\ -6 & -12 & -7 \end{bmatrix}$

Exercises 45—51 For matrix A, find **(a)** $A^2 (= A \cdot A)$, **(b)** A^3, **(c)** A^{24}, and **(d)** A^{100}.

45. $A = \begin{bmatrix} -2 & -6 \\ 1 & 3 \end{bmatrix}$ **46.** $A = \begin{bmatrix} 6 & 10 \\ -3 & -5 \end{bmatrix}$

47. $A = \begin{bmatrix} 2 & -1 \\ 4 & -2 \end{bmatrix}$ **48.** $A = \begin{bmatrix} 0 & 2 & -1 \\ 0 & 0 & 3 \\ 0 & 0 & 0 \end{bmatrix}$

49. $A = \begin{bmatrix} -2 & 1 & -3 \\ 6 & -3 & 9 \\ 4 & -2 & 6 \end{bmatrix}$ **50.** $A = \begin{bmatrix} -6 & 8 & 2 \\ -3 & 4 & 1 \\ -9 & 12 & 3 \end{bmatrix}$

51. $A = \begin{bmatrix} 2 & 6 & 2 \\ -1 & -3 & -1 \\ -1 & -1 & 1 \end{bmatrix}$

CHAPTER 9 REVIEW

Test Your Understanding

True or False. Give reasons for your conclusion.

1. The equation $3x - 4y + z = 7$ is linear in x, y, and z.

2. The equation $\sqrt{3}x - \sqrt{5}y = \sqrt{6}$ is not a linear equation in x and y.

3. The system

$$2x - 3y = 5$$
$$-4x + 6y = 7$$

has infinitely many solutions. It is dependent.

4. The solution for the system

$$x - 2y - 3z = 4$$
$$y - 2z = 6$$
$$3z = -9$$

is given by $x = -5$, $y = 0$, $z = -3$.

Exercises 5–8 Refer to the system of inequalities:

$$2x - y \le 0$$
$$2x + y \ge 4$$

5. Point $(0, 1)$ is in the solution set.

6. Point $(2, 4)$ is not in the solution set.

7. Point $(1, 2)$ is a corner point.

8. The solution set contains no points in Quadrants III or IV.

Exercises 9–12 Lines L_1 and L_2 are given by

$$L_1: \quad x + 2y = 0 \qquad L_2: \quad 3x - 4y = -5$$

9. Point $(-2, 1)$ is on both L_1 and L_2.

10. Point $(-1, \frac{1}{2})$ is on both L_1 and L_2.

11. Point $(1, 2)$ is on L_2, but not on L_1.

12. Point $(0, 1)$ is above L_1 and below L_2.

Exercises 13–18 Let G be the set of all points (x, y) that satisfy the system

$$x - 2y \ge -6$$
$$x + y \ge -3$$
$$7x - 2y \le 6$$

13. Point $(0, 3)$ is in G.

14. Point $(0, 0)$ is in G.

15. Point $(0, -3)$ is a corner point of G.

16. Point $(-4, 1)$ is not a corner point of G.

17. Point $(2, 4)$ is not in G.

18. There is no point on the line $2x + y = 0$ that is also in G.

Exercises 19–23 Line L and parabola P are given by

$$L: \quad x - 2y = -1 \qquad P: \quad y = x^2 - 1$$

19. There is exactly one point that is on both L and P.

20. There are exactly two points that are on both L and P.

21. Point $(1, 1)$ is on both L and P.

22. Point $(-1, 0)$ is not on both L and P.

23. Point $(0, -1)$ is on L, but not on P.

24. If $A = \begin{bmatrix} 2 & -3 \\ -1 & 2 \end{bmatrix}$, then $A^{-1} = \begin{bmatrix} 2 & 3 \\ 1 & 2 \end{bmatrix}$.

25. If $A = \begin{bmatrix} 1 & 4 \\ 1 & 5 \end{bmatrix}$ and $B = \begin{bmatrix} 5 & -4 \\ -1 & 1 \end{bmatrix}$, then $AB = I$.

Exercises 26–31 Let G be the graph of the equation given by

$$\begin{vmatrix} x & y & 1 \\ 2 & 3 & 1 \\ 1 & 1 & 1 \end{vmatrix} = 0.$$

26. G is a line.

27. Point $(2, 3)$ is on G.

28. Point $(-1, -1)$ is on G.

29. G is a line with slope $\frac{4}{3}$.

30. The x-intercept point of G is $(\frac{1}{2}, 0)$.

31. The y-intercept point of G is $(0, -\frac{2}{3})$.

32. The equation $\begin{vmatrix} x^2 & 3 \\ -1 & 1 \end{vmatrix} = 4$ has two real solutions.

33. The equation $3 + \begin{vmatrix} x & 1 \\ -1 & 1 \end{vmatrix} = 4$ has no real solutions.

Mastery Exercises

Exercises 1–9   Solve the system of equations. If it is dependent (has infinitely many solutions), describe all solutions and then give two specific ones.

1. $3x - 2y = 5$
$x - y = -1$

2. $-2x + y = 3$
$5x - 3y = -4$

3. $\frac{x}{2} - \frac{y}{3} = 4$
$\frac{x}{4} + \frac{y}{2} = -2$

4. $0.4x + 0.6y = 0$
$0.8x - 1.2y = 2$

5. $x - 2y + z = 3$
$-2x + y - z = 0$
$4x - 3y + 2z = 1$

6. $x + 2y = 2$
$3x - 4y + z = -2$
$x + 3z = -8$

7. $x + 2y - 5z = 1$
$3x + 2y + z = -2$
$3x - 2y + 17z = -7$

8. $x - y + z = 3$
$5x - 4y + 3z = 2$
$x - 2y + 3z = 16$

9. $\frac{1}{x} - \frac{2}{y} = \frac{1}{3}$
$\frac{2}{x} - \frac{5}{y} = -\frac{2}{5}$

Exercises 10–15   Solve the system of equations and draw a graph to illustrate the solution graphically.

10. $y = -3x + 4$
$y = x^2$

11. $2x - 3y = -26$
$x^2 + y^2 = 169$

12. $y = -2x$
$y = -x^2 - 3x$

13. $2y = x + 2$
$xy = 4$

14. $x + y = 4$
$x^2 + y^2 = 4$

15. $y = x^2 - 4x + 4$
$y = -2x^2 + 5x + 4$

Exercises 16–19   Draw a graph of the set of points (x, y) that satisfy the inequality or inequalities.

16. $2x - y < 1$

17. $x + y > 1$ and $2x - y < 5$

18. $y \le x$ and $x - y < 2$

19. $2x + y < 4$ and $x - 2y \ge 1$

Exercises 20–22   Draw a graph of the region described by the system of inequalities, identifying all corner points.

20. $x - y \le 4$
$2x + y \ge 2$
$x + 2y \le 4$

21. $2x - y \ge 8$
$2x + y \le 4$
$x - y \le 8$

22. $y \ge x - 1$
$x + 2y \le 10$

Exercises 23–25   Evaluate the determinant of the matrix.

23. $A = \begin{bmatrix} 3 & -4 \\ 2 & 5 \end{bmatrix}$

24. $B = \begin{bmatrix} \sqrt{3} - 1 & 2 + \sqrt{5} \\ 2 - \sqrt{5} & \sqrt{3} + 1 \end{bmatrix}$

25. $C = \begin{bmatrix} 1 & -2 & 0 \\ 3 & 2 & -1 \\ 5 & 4 & 2 \end{bmatrix}$

Exercises 26–31   Use the matrices:

$$A = \begin{bmatrix} 7 & 3 \\ 2 & 1 \end{bmatrix} \qquad B = \begin{bmatrix} 4 & 1 \\ 3 & 1 \end{bmatrix}$$

$$C = \begin{bmatrix} -2 \\ 3 \end{bmatrix} \qquad X = \begin{bmatrix} x \\ y \end{bmatrix}$$

26. Find **(a)** AB **(b)** BA.

27. Find **(a)** A^{-1} **(b)** B^{-1}.

28. Find **(a)** $(AB)^{-1}$ **(b)** $B^{-1}A^{-1}$.

29. Find **(a)** $(BA)^{-1}$ **(b)** $A^{-1}B^{-1}$.

30. **(a)** Express the matrix equation $AX = C$ as a system of equations
(b) Solve the system using $X = A^{-1}C$.

31. Solve the matrix equation $BX = C$ for X.

32. Find the inverse of the matrix A where

$$A = \begin{bmatrix} 4 & 5 & -3 \\ 1 & 1 & -1 \\ -1 & 0 & 1 \end{bmatrix}$$

33. Use the result in Exercise 32 to solve the system of equations

$$4x + 5y - 3z = 1$$
$$x + y - z = 3$$
$$-x + z = -4$$

Exercises 34–37   A system of linear constraints is given. **(a)** Draw a graph to show the feasible set F and determine the corner points. **(b)** For the given objective function, determine the point in F that will give the indicated optimal solution.

34. Constraints: $x - y \ge 0$, $4x + 2y \le 5$, $y \ge 0$.
Objective function: $z = 5x - 2y$; maximum.

35. Constraints: $x - y \ge 0$, $4x + 2y \le 5$, $y \ge 0$.
Objective function: $z = 5x + 4y$; maximum.

36. Constraints: $y \le x + 2$, $y \ge 2x - 1$, $y \ge -x + 2$. Objective function: $z = 2x + 3y$; maximum.

37. Constraints: $y \le x + 2$, $y \ge 2x - 1$, $y \ge -x + 2$. Objective function: $z = 3x + 4y$; minimum.

Exercises 38–39   Use Cramer's Rule to find the value of *y* in the solution of the system of equations.

38. $x - y + z = 3$
$\quad 2x + y = 1$
$\quad x - 3z = -2$

39. $3x - y + 2z = 0$
$\quad x + y = 2$
$\quad y - 2z = 1$

40. If 1 cup of oatmeal contains 5 grams of protein and 20 milligrams of calcium, and 1 cup of milk contains 8 grams of protein and 300 milligrams of calcium, determine the amount (in cups) of oatmeal and milk that will give a serving that contains 12 grams of protein and 383 milligrams of calcium.

41. A musical sponsored by the student association is to be held in the school auditorium, which seats 1500. Ticket prices are $5 each for the 500 reserved seats and $3 each for the remaining 1000 general admission seats. The cost to present the musical will be $3700. How many reserved seat tickets and how many general admission tickets must be sold to cover the cost of the production?

42. A producer of lawn fertilizer makes two different kinds. Type A contains 20 percent nitrogen and 10 percent potash, while type B contains 10 percent nitrogen and 4 percent potash. The firm has a sufficient supply of each and wishes to put together a mixture that contains a total of at least 240 kg. The mixture should also contain at least 15 percent nitrogen and not more than 8 percent potash. The costs per kilogram of A and B are 20 cents and 15 cents, respectively.
(a) Draw a graph showing the amounts of each that will give the desired mixture.
(b) For each corner point of the graph, find the corresponding cost of the mixture.

43. Two pipelines, *A* and *B*, supply water to a reservoir, while pipeline *C* (located at the bottom) drains the reservoir. When all three pipelines are open it takes 18 hours to fill the reservoir. If *A* and *B* are open and *C* is closed, it takes 12 hours to fill the reservoir. If *A* and *C* are open and *B* is closed, it takes 24 hours to fill the reservoir. How many hours does it take to fill the reservoir if only A is open?

44. A computer manufacturer has orders from two retail stores, one in Harmony and one in Gladstone. The Harmony store has ordered 50 computers and the Gladstone store needs 60. The manufacturer has supplies of computers in two warehouses, 80 computers in Salem and 40 in Trent. Shipping costs (in dollars per computer) are shown in the table.

	Harmony	Gladstone
Salem	$20	$12
Trent	$16	$10

Let *x* be the number of computers shipped from the Salem warehouse to the Harmony store and let *y* be the number shipped from Salem to Gladstone. How many must be shipped from Trent to each retail store? If the manufacturer wants to minimize shipping costs, how many computers should be sent from each warehouse to each retailer?

45. Solve the problem in Exercise 44 if the shipping costs are

	Harmony	Gladstone
Salem	$10	$16
Trent	$12	$ 8

10 ANALYTIC GEOMETRY

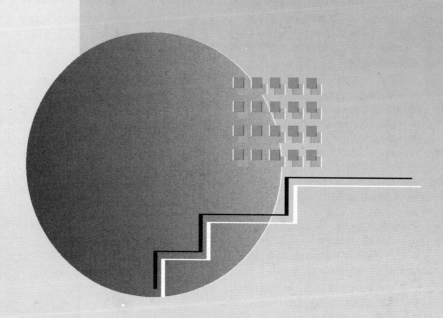

Analytic geometry is the name given to the marriage of algebra and geometry. The early Greeks developed a rich geometry, but their algebra was limited. The algebra-free geometry that came through Euclid is called **synthetic geometry.** Algebra developed independently, with little connection to geometry. Not until the early 1600s were the two melded, primarily by René Descartes (after whom Cartesian coordinates are named) and Pierre de Fermat.

The idea that a geometric picture can illuminate an equation is not new. Graphs are an integral part of our thinking, learning, and understanding. Most of our work has started with an equation or functional relation; in this chapter we more often begin with a geometric property and use algebra to interpret the geometry.

In the first section we review and extend our understanding of lines and circles. Later sections explore conic sections and some applications. The last two sections of the chapter deal with alternative ways to describe sets of points in the plane, using polar coordinates or parametric equations.

Lines and Circles

The man who breaks out into a new era of thought is usually himself still a prisoner of the old. Even Isaac Newton, who invented the calculus as a mathematical vehicle for his epoch-making discoveries in physics and astronomy, preferred to express himself in archaic geometrical terms.

Freeman Dyson

We introduced lines and circles early in the book, but they have many useful properties we have not yet touched, and some of the important techniques of analytic geometry make use of these familiar figures. Let us begin by recalling some familiar properties and equation forms.

Lines

A standard form for an equation of a line is $Ax + By + C = 0$ where not both A and B are zero.

A line containing the points (x_1, y_1) and (x_2, y_2) where $x_2 \neq x_1$, has slope

$$m = \frac{y_2 - y_1}{x_2 - x_1}.$$

There are two other useful forms for equations of lines:

Point-slope form: $\qquad y - y_0 = m(x - x_0)$

Slope-intercept form: $\qquad y = mx + b$

Parallel and Perpendicular Lines   Any vertical line is perpendicular to any horizontal line, and all vertical lines are parallel to each other. Lines with slopes m_1 and m_2 are parallel if and only if $m_1 = m_2$, or perpendicular if, and only if, $m_1 m_2 = -1$.

Circles

A standard form for an equation of a circle is any equation of the form $x^2 + y^2 + Ax + By + C = 0$ where $A^2 + B^2 > 4C$.

A circle with center at point (h, k) and radius r has an equation $(x - h)^2 + (y - k)^2 = r^2$.

. . . [B]y the time I was in the sixth grade I understood algebra and geometry fairly well. I knew the rudiments of calculus and a smattering of number theory, which I liked very much. I felt rather isolated. A lot of teachers are very threatened when they find a child is studying advanced things. And I was reluctant at that time to talk to other children because I felt they found my interest in math somewhat strange.

Paul Cohen

Deriving Equations for Geometric Figures

One of the key goals of analytic geometry is to find a convenient equation to describe a given geometric figure. A circle, for instance, is the set of all points that are equidistant from a given point. By an equation for such a figure or set of points we mean an equation that is satisfied by the coordinates of precisely the points that belong to the figure. The set of points 1 unit from the origin is the unit circle, and a familiar equation describes the set: $x^2 + y^2 = 1$. Since many geometric descriptions involve distance, the distance formula is often the tool needed to derive an equation for the set. The distance formula involves a square root, so we frequently need to square both sides of an equation. While such an operation can introduce extraneous points, we have the following useful property.

Squaring Property

If U and V are expressions in x and y and both are nonnegative for the x, y values being considered, then these are equivalent equations:

$$U = V \qquad \text{and} \qquad U^2 = V^2$$

EXAMPLE 1   Given points $A(1, 2)$ and $B(3, -2)$, show that the set of points that are equidistant from A and B is the perpendicular bisector of the segment $\overline{AB}$.

Strategy: Draw a diagram to visualize the problem, including a typical point P (x, y) that is equidistant from A and B. Get an equation by setting the distances from P to A and P to B equal and simplifying.

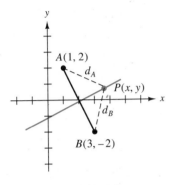

$A(1, 2)$

d_A

$P(x, y)$

d_B

$B(3, -2)$

FIGURE 10.1

Solution

Follow the strategy. First draw the diagram shown in Figure 10.1, where d_A and d_B denote the distances from P to A and P to B, respectively. Let S be the set of all points for which $d_A = d_B$. The distance formula for d_A and d_B gives:

$$\sqrt{(x - 1)^2 + (y - 2)^2} = \sqrt{(x - 3)^2 + (y + 2)^2} \qquad \textbf{(1)}$$

To simplify Equation 1, since both sides are nonnegative, we can use the squaring property.

$$(x - 1)^2 + (y - 2)^2 = (x - 3)^2 + (y + 2)^2 \qquad \textbf{(2)}$$

Expanding and simplifying, Equation 2 reduces to $x - 2y - 2 = 0$, an equation of a line L. Thus all points in S are on the line L. Reversing the above steps would also show that every point on the line L satisfies Equation 1 and hence is equidistant from A and B.

To show that L is the perpendicular bisector of $\overline{AB}$, show that **(a)** L contains the midpoint M of $\overline{AB}$ and **(b)** L is perpendicular to the line through A and B.

(a) The coordinates of the midpoint M are

$$x_m = \frac{1 + 3}{2} = 2 \quad \text{and} \quad y_m = \frac{2 + (-2)}{2} = 0,$$

so M is point $(2, 0)$. Substituting into the equation for L shows that M is a point on L.

(b) The slope m_1 of the line through A and B is given by

$$m_1 = \frac{-2 - 2}{3 - 1} = -2.$$

The slope m_2 of line L can be found by putting the equation for L into point-slope form (that is, by solving for y): $y = \frac{1}{2}x - 1$, so $m_2 = \frac{1}{2}$. Since $m_1 m_2 = -1$, line L is perpendicular to the line through A and B. ▲

EXAMPLE 2 For the given points $A(-4, -1)$ and $B(2, 5)$, let K be the set of points P such that the distance $|\overline{AP}|$ is twice the distance $|\overline{BP}|$. Find an equation for K and sketch the graph.

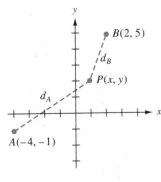

$B(2, 5)$

d_B

$P(x, y)$

d_A

$A(-4, -1)$

FIGURE 10.2

Solution

We begin with a figure showing A and B and a typical point $P(x, y)$ belonging to K (see Figure 10.2). The condition that must be satisfied for P to belong to K is that $d_A = 2d_B$. Expressing d_A and d_B in terms of coordinates, we get the following equation:

$$\sqrt{(x + 4)^2 + (y + 1)^2} = 2\sqrt{(x - 2)^2 + (y - 5)^2}.$$

Applying the squaring property, expanding, and simplifying, we have

$$(x^2 + 8x + 16) + (y^2 + 2y + 1) = 4[(x^2 - 4x + 4) + (y^2 - 10y + 25)]$$

$$3x^2 - 24x + 3y^2 - 42y + 99 = 0.$$

A NEW VIEW OF THE WORLD

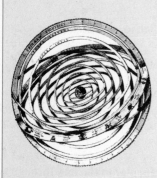

Astronomers used principles of analytic geometry to disprove the Ptolemaic view of the universe, in which the planets orbited in circles around a stationary earth.

Analytic geometry and the curves it describes have profoundly affected the way we think about our universe. To the ancient Greeks with their love of beauty and ideal form, it was unthinkable that the motion of the sun and planets could involve anything except circles. Careful observations, however, revealed that the planets do not move around the earth in smooth circular paths. At least from the earth, some planets even occasionally move backward! To harmonize observations with the perfection of circles, elaborate schemes were developed. Ptolemy (150 A.D.) described circles rolling around on circles, all rotating about an ideal point somewhere off in space.

By the middle ages, dogma was more important than observation and dictated circular orbits centered about the earth. Copernicus proposed (1543) that the earth and planets orbited a stationary sun, but the idea was heretical. When Galileo reported (1610) that through his newly invented telescope he had *seen* the moons of Jupiter orbiting a heavenly body other than the

earth, he was forced to recant, but not before his widely read "Dialogue" spread Copernicanism.

Johannes Kepler, a "closet Copernican," was invited to assist the Danish astronomer Tyche Brahe, undoubtedly the most patient and accurate observer of his (or most any) age. At Brahe's death (1601), Kepler inherited the mountains of data Brahe had collected in over 20 years of watching the night sky. More than ten years of prodigious calculations with Brahe's data forced Kepler to the conclusion that the orbit of Mars is not a circle but an ellipse having the sun at one focus. Ten years of further computation with Brahe's observations ultimately yielded Kepler's laws about times of revolution and distances from the sun.

By Newton's time, mathematics had progressed to the point that when Halley (of Halley's comet) asked Newton about the curve that would describe the motion of planets, assuming Newton's formulation of gravitational force. Newton immediately replied, "An ellipse." And how did he know it? "Why I have calculated it."

Now we divide through by 3 and complete squares.

$$(x^2 - 8x + 16) + (y^2 - 14y + 49) = -33 + 16 + 49 \qquad \textbf{(3)}$$

$$(x - 4)^2 + (y - 7)^2 = 32$$

We recognize Equation 3 as an equation for the circle C with center at $C(4, 7)$ and radius $4\sqrt{2}$ (see Figure 10.3). Thus every point in K is on the circle. Conversely, we leave it to the reader to show that by reversing the above steps,

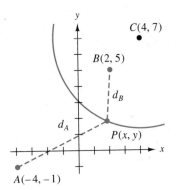

FIGURE 10.3

Strategy: Choose a convenient location for an arbitrary parallelogram, say with a vertex at the origin and one side along the positive *x*-axis. Give coordinates to the other vertices and finally try to show that the diagonals have the same midpoints.

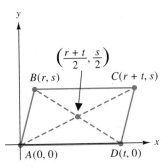

FIGURE 10.4

every point P on the circle C has the property that $|\overline{AP}| = 2|\overline{BP}|$ and hence belongs to the set K. Therefore K consists precisely of those points on the circle. ▲

Examples 1 and 2 were stated in terms of specific points, which assumes a given coordinate system. The next example shows how a judicious choice of a coordinate system can simplify the proof of a geometric theorem.

EXAMPLE 3   Show that the diagonals of a parallelogram bisect each other.

Solution

Follow the strategy and draw a typical parallelogram like the one in Figure 10.4. Assuming coordinates $A(0, 0)$ and $D(t, 0)$ makes it easy to get coordinates for B and C. With no special assumption about the *x*-coordinate of B, $\overline{BC}$ is parallel to $\overline{AD}$, so B and C must have the same *y*-coordinate, and the lengths of $\overline{AD}$ and $\overline{BC}$ are the same, so the difference between *x*-coordinates of B and C must be the same as the difference between A and D, namely t. Thus, if B has coordinates (r, s), then C must have coordinates $(r + t, s)$, as shown in Figure 10.4.

In terms of the coordinates shown in Figure 10.4, find the midpoints of the diagonals $\overline{AC}$ and $\overline{BD}$. Denote the midpoints of $\overline{AC}$ and $\overline{BD}$ by M_{AC} and M_{BD}, respectively.

$$M_{AC} = \left(\frac{0 + r + t}{2}, \frac{0 + s}{2}\right) = \left(\frac{r + t}{2}, \frac{s}{2}\right) \quad \text{and} \quad M_{BD} = \left(\frac{r + t}{2}, \frac{s}{2}\right)$$

Since the midpoints are the same point, the diagonals bisect each other. ▲

Slopes, Angles, and Distance

The amount of information a single equation can provide may be surprising. Changing the form slightly can reveal additional information. For example, starting with an equation for a line L, say $3x - 2y = 6$, we can solve for y and obtain the slope-intercept form.

$$y = \frac{3}{2}x - 3$$

The slope-intercept form shows that L has slope $\frac{3}{2}$ and crosses the *y*-axis at point $(0, -3)$.

Other relations and forms of equations for lines are also useful.

Slope and Normal Form of a Line

1. Suppose L is a line with slope m $(m \neq 0)$. The **angle of inclination** of L is the smallest positive angle θ measured from a ray in the positive direction of the *x*-axis to line L. The slope of L equals the tangent of the angle of inclination of L. See Figure 10.5.

$$m = \tan \theta \qquad\qquad \textbf{(4)}$$

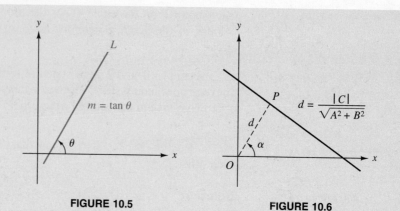

FIGURE 10.5   FIGURE 10.6

2. Suppose L is a line that does not contain the origin. There is a line segment $\overline{OP}$ from the origin perpendicular to L. See Figure 10.6. The length of $\overline{OP}$, the distance from L to the origin, is called the **normal distance** to the line; the **normal angle** is angle α in Figure 10.6. If an equation for L is written in the form $Ax + By = C$, then a **normal form** for the line is the equation obtained by dividing through by $\sqrt{A^2 + B^2}$.

$$\frac{A}{\sqrt{A^2 + B^2}}x + \frac{B}{\sqrt{A^2 + B^2}}y = \frac{C}{\sqrt{A^2 + B^2}} \qquad \text{(5)}$$

The normal distance d is

$$d = \frac{|C|}{\sqrt{A^2 + B^2}} \qquad \text{(6)}$$

and the normal angle α satisfies the equations:

$$\cos \alpha = \frac{A}{\sqrt{A^2 + B^2}} \qquad \text{and} \qquad \sin \alpha = \frac{B}{\sqrt{A^2 + B^2}}$$

It is a simple matter to justify Equation 4. Consider Figure 10.7, which shows an arbitrary line L and the line L_0 that contains the origin and is parallel to L. L and L_0 have the same slope m and the same angle of inclination θ. If we take any point $P_0(x_0, y_0)$ of L_0 on the terminal side of θ, then we can use P_0 to compute both $\tan \theta$ and slope m. By the definition of the tangent of an angle in standard position, $\tan \theta = \frac{y_0}{x_0}$. Using the coordinates of P_0 and the origin O, the slope is given by

$$m = \frac{y_0 - 0}{x_0 - 0} = \frac{y_0}{x_0}.$$

Thus for L_0, and hence for L, $m = \tan \theta$.

To justify Equation 6, consider the case where L has an equation of the form $Ax + By = C$, where A, B, and C are all positive. The graph of L looks

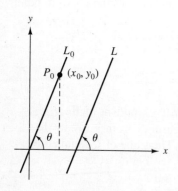

FIGURE 10.7

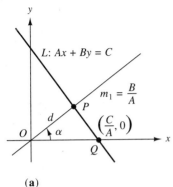

something like Figure 10.8a. The slope of L is given by $m = \frac{-A}{B}$, so the slope of any line perpendicular to L is given by $m_1 = \frac{B}{A}$. The line through the origin perpendicular to L thus has equation $y = (\frac{B}{A})x$ and an angle of inclination α, where $\tan \alpha = \frac{B}{A}$. Figure 10.8b shows α in standard position, which indicates that

$$\cos \alpha = \frac{A}{\sqrt{A^2 + B^2}} \quad \text{and} \quad \sin \alpha = \frac{B}{\sqrt{A^2 + B^2}}.$$

Returning to Figure 10.8a, since the x-intercept of L is $\frac{C}{A}$, the hypotenuse of right triangle OPQ has length $\frac{C}{A}$ and $\cos \alpha = \frac{d}{C/A}$, from which,

$$d = \frac{C}{A} \cos \alpha = \frac{C}{A} \frac{A}{\sqrt{A^2 + B^2}} = \frac{C}{\sqrt{A^2 + B^2}}.$$

Cases where A, B, and C are not all positive are handled similarly, and the results can differ at most by a sign. Since the normal distance d must be positive, the absolute value in Equation 6 takes care of all possibilities.

Distance Between Parallel Lines

The distance between two parallel lines L and K is defined to be the length of a line segment perpendicular to both lines, with one endpoint on L and one endpoint on K. We can use the normal form of lines to derive information about distances between lines, as illustrated in the next example.

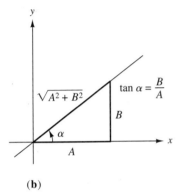

(b)

FIGURE 10.8

| **EXAMPLE 4** | Show that lines L: $3x - 2y = 6$ and K: $6x - 4y = -5$ are parallel, and find the distance between the two lines.

Solution

Strategy: Draw a diagram. To show the lines are parallel we need their slopes. For the distance between lines, write the equations in normal form, and use the distances from the lines to the origin (Equation 6).

Follow the strategy. Write the lines in point-slope form to see that they have the same slope:

$$L: \quad y = \frac{3}{2}x - 3 \qquad K: \quad y = \frac{3}{2}x + \frac{5}{4}$$

Since each line has slope $\frac{3}{2}$, the lines are parallel. See Figure 10.9.

From the figure, it is apparent that the lines are on opposite sides of the origin and the distance between them is the sum of the normal distances, d_1 and d_2, which we can identify from the normal forms of lines L and K. To find the normal distances, write equations for lines L and K in normal form. For line L, divide through by $\sqrt{3^2 + (-2)^2}$, or $\sqrt{13}$, and for K, by $\sqrt{36 + 16}$, or $2\sqrt{13}$.

$$L: \quad \frac{3}{\sqrt{13}}x - \frac{2}{\sqrt{13}}y = \frac{6}{\sqrt{13}}$$

$$K: \quad \frac{6}{2\sqrt{13}}x - \frac{4}{2\sqrt{13}}y = \frac{-5}{2\sqrt{13}} \quad \text{or} \quad \frac{3}{\sqrt{13}}x - \frac{2}{\sqrt{13}}y = \frac{-5}{2\sqrt{13}}$$

Thus the normal distances are

$$d_1 = \frac{6}{\sqrt{13}} \quad \text{and} \quad d_2 = \frac{|-5|}{2\sqrt{13}} = \frac{5}{2\sqrt{13}}$$

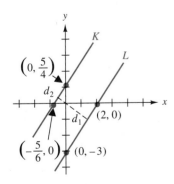

FIGURE 10.9

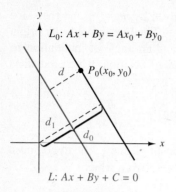

$L_0: Ax + By = Ax_0 + By_0$

d $P_0(x_0, y_0)$

d_1

d_0

$L: Ax + By + C = 0$

FIGURE 10.10

and the distance between L and K is the sum

$$d = d_1 + d_2 = \frac{17}{2\sqrt{13}}. \quad \blacktriangle$$

Distance from a Point to a Line

We define the distance from a point P to a line L as the length of the line segment perpendicular to L that has P as one endpoint and the other endpoint on L. Example 4 illustrates how to use the normal distance from the origin to a line to determine the distance between two parallel lines.

Consider an arbitrary line $L: Ax + By + C = 0$, and a fixed point $P_0(x_0, y_0)$, as in Figure 10.10. If we denote by L_0 the line that is parallel to L and contains P_0, then the distance from P_0 to L is the distance between the parallel lines L and L_0. Any line parallel to L has an equation of the form $Ax + By + E = 0$, for some constant E. To get an equation for L_0, substitute in the coordinates of the point P_0:

$$Ax_0 + By_0 + E = 0.$$

It follows that $E = -Ax_0 - By_0$, and an equation for L_0 is

$$Ax + By - Ax_0 - By_0 = 0.$$

The distance between L and L_0 in Figure 10.10 is given by $d = d_0 - d_1$, where d_0 and d_1 are the normal distances shown in the figure. For the line and point shown in Figure 10.10, A and B are positive and C is negative; hence $|C| = -C$. Writing the equations for both L and L_0 in normal form, we can find the normal distances.

$$L: \quad d_1 = \frac{-C}{\sqrt{A^2 + B^2}} \qquad L_0: \quad d_0 = \frac{Ax_0 + By_0}{\sqrt{A^2 + B^2}}$$

The distance is given by

$$d = d_0 - d_1 = \frac{Ax_0 + By_0 + C}{\sqrt{A^2 + B^2}}.$$

To allow for the fact that P_0 could be on either side of L, we must take the absolute value of the final expression. You might try some other diagrams to convince yourself of the validity of the following theorem.

Distance from a Point to a Line

Suppose we are given a point $P_0(x_0, y_0)$ and a line $L: Ax + By + C = 0$. The distance d from P_0 to L is given by

$$d = \frac{|Ax_0 + By_0 + C|}{\sqrt{A^2 + B^2}}. \tag{7}$$

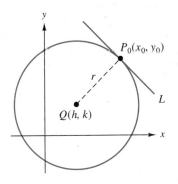

FIGURE 10.11

Lines Tangent to a Circle

Geometrically, it is clear that a line and a circle can intersect in exactly two points, exactly one point, or not at all. When a line and a circle have only one point P_0 in common, the line is **tangent** to the circle at P_0, and point P_0 is the **point of tangency**. Figure 10.11 shows line L tangent at point $P_0(x_0, y_0)$ to the circle with center at $Q(h, k)$ and radius r. Recall from geometry that the line through P_0 and Q is perpendicular to L and the length of the line segment $\overline{P_0 Q}$ is equal to r. We have the following theorem.

> **Tangent Line Theorem**
>
> A line L is tangent to the circle with center $Q(h, k)$ and radius r if and only if the distance from the center $Q(h, k)$ to line L is equal to r.

Strategy: A general line through $(-2, 8)$ can be written $y - 8 = m(x + 2)$. Rewrite this in standard form and use Equation 7 to find the slope m for which the distance to the center of C equals 2.

| **EXAMPLE 5** | Line L: $3x + 4y = 26$ contains point $(-2, 8)$.

a. Show that L is tangent to circle C: $(x - 8)^2 + (y - 3)^2 = 4$.

b. Find the other line that contains $(-2, 8)$ and is tangent to C.

Solution

a. We could find the intersection of the line and circle by solving the equations simultaneously. If there is only one solution, then L is tangent to C. It is easier, however, to calculate the distance from the center of the circle, $C(8, 3)$, to L. By the Tangent Line theorem, L is tangent if the distance equals the radius, 2.

Use Equation 7 for the distance d from $C(8, 3)$ to L, first writing the equation for L in standard form.

$$d = \frac{|3 \cdot 8 + 4 \cdot 3 - 26|}{\sqrt{9 + 16}} = \frac{|24 + 12 - 26|}{5} = 2$$

Since $d = 2$ and $r = 2$, L is tangent to C.

b. The other line L' contains $(-2, 8)$ and is tangent to C, as shown in Figure 10.12. In terms of the slope m, write an equation for L' as $y - 8 = m(x + 2)$, or in standard form,

$$L': mx - y + (2m + 8) = 0$$

Again by the Tangent Line theorem, for L' to be tangent to C the distance from the center $C(8, 3)$ to the line must equal 2. Express d in terms of the slope m, and then find the values of m for which the distance from C to the line equals 2. Substitute the coordinates $(8, 3)$ into Equation 7 and divide by $\sqrt{A^2 + B^2}$ ($= \sqrt{m^2 + 1}$),

$$d = \frac{|m \cdot 8 + (-1) \cdot 3 + (2m + 8)|}{\sqrt{m^2 + 1}} = 2.$$

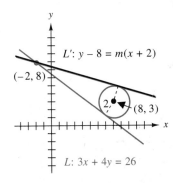

FIGURE 10.12

Square, clear fractions, and simplify:

$$(10m + 5)^2 = 4(m^2 + 1)$$

$$96m^2 + 100m + 21 = 0$$

$$(4m + 3)(24m + 7) = 0.$$

Thus $m = \frac{-3}{4}$ or $m = \frac{-7}{24}$. Line L in part a has slope $\frac{-3}{4}$, so the slope of the other line is $\frac{-7}{24}$. An equation for L' is

$$y - 8 = \left(-\frac{7}{24}\right)(x + 2) \qquad \text{or} \qquad 7x + 24y - 178 = 0. \quad \blacktriangle$$

EXERCISES 10.1

Check Your Understanding

Exercises 1–10 True or False. Give reasons for your conclusion.

1. The distance from point $(3, -4)$ to line $y - 2 = 0$ is equal to 6.

2. Line $3x + 4y + 25 = 0$ is tangent to circle $x^2 + y^2 = 25$ at point $(3, 4)$.

3. Line $y = 2x$ is not tangent to circle $(x - 10)^2 + y^2 = 80$.

4. The distance from point $(-2, 4)$ to line $y = 2x$ is greater than 3.7.

5. Line $y = x$ is a perpendicular bisector of the line segment with endpoints at $(4, 0)$ and $(0, 4)$.

6. If line $3x - 2y = 4$ is tangent to a circle with center at $(0, 6)$ then the radius of the circle must equal 4.

7. The distance between the parallel lines $y = x$ and $y = x + 2$ equals 2.

8. The distance between the x-intercept points of the circle $(x - 2)^2 + y^2 = 4$ is equal to 4.

9. If A is the point $(-3, 0)$ and B is the point $(7, 0)$, then the line segment $\overline{AB}$ is a diameter of the circle $(x - 2)^2 + y^2 = 25$.

10. Two lines both contain the point $(4, 4)$ and are tangent to circle $x^2 + y^2 = 16$.

Explore and Discover

1. Sketch the circles C_1: $x^2 + y^2 - 14x - 2y + 25 = 0$ and C_2: $x^2 + y^2 - 25 = 0$ on the same axes and find the points of intersection. **(a)** Find an equation for line L_c through the centers of the two circles. **(b)** Find an equation for line L_i through the intersections of the two circles. How are lines L_c and L_i related? **(c)** If we subtract the equation of C_1 from the equation of C_2, we obtain equation E: $14x + 2y - 50 = 0$. Add the graph of equation E to your sketch.

2. Repeat Exercise 1 with circles C_1: $(x - 1)^2 + y^2 = 1$ and C_2: $x^2 + (y + 1)^2 = 1$, or with another pair of intersecting circles of your choice.

Develop Mastery

Exercises 1–8 Find an equation for the set of points $P(x, y)$ that satisfy the condition.

1. Equidistant from $A(-3, 0)$ and $B(0, 3)$.

2. Equidistant from $A(-3, 0)$ and $B(3, 0)$.

3. Equidistant from $A(3, -1)$ and $B(1, 5)$.

4. $|\overline{PA}| = 2|\overline{PB}|$, for $A(6, 0)$ and $B(0, 0)$.

5. $|\overline{PA}| = 2|\overline{PB}|$, for $A(-1, -4)$ and $B(5, 8)$.

6. $|\overline{PA}| = 3|\overline{PB}|$, for $A(-8, 5)$ and $B(8, -3)$.

7. $|\overline{PA}| = 3|\overline{PB}|$, for $A(6, 4)$ and $B(2, 0)$.

8. The distance $|\overline{PA}|$ for $A(0, \frac{1}{4})$ equals the distance from P to line $y + \frac{1}{4} = 0$. (*Hint:* What are the coordinates of point B in the diagram?)

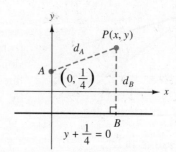

Exercises 9–16 For the geometric theorem, first draw a figure and then prove the theorem analytically. See Example 3.

9. The medians to the equal sides of an isosceles triangle are equal in length. (*Hint:* Locate the base on the *x*-axis with the opposite vertex on the positive *y*-axis.)

10. The midpoint of the hypotenuse of a right triangle is equidistant from all vertices of the triangle.

11. The line segment that joins the midpoints of two sides of a triangle is parallel to the third side and half the length of the third side.

12. The diagonals of a square are perpendicular to each other.

13. If the diagonals of a rectangle are perpendicular to each other, then the rectangle is a square.

14. The line segments that join midpoints of opposite sides of a quadrilateral bisect each other.

15. Given a quadrilateral $ABCD$, let R, S, T, and U be the midpoints of sides $\overline{AB}, \overline{BC}, \overline{CD}$, and $\overline{DA}$, respectively. Segments $\overline{RS}$ and $\overline{TU}$ are parallel.

16. The medians of any triangle are concurrent. That is, given $\triangle ABC$ with midpoints of opposite sides M_a, M_b, M_c as in the diagram, the segments $\overline{AM_a}, \overline{BM_b}$, $\overline{CM_c}$ all have a common point.

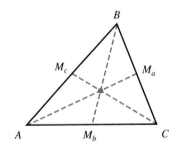

Exercises 17–25 Find an equation for the circle that satisfies the conditions. (*Hint:* Draw a figure.)

17. Center (3, 2), contains the origin.

18. Center (3, 2), tangent to the *x*-axis.

19. Center (3, 2), tangent to the *y*-axis.

20. Center (3, 2), tangent to the line $x + y = 0$.

21. Contains (2, 9), tangent to both axes.

22. A diameter is the line segment that joins $A(1, 1)$ and $B(7, -5)$.

23. Center on the *x*-axis, contains $A(3, 5)$ and $B(-1, 7)$.

24. Center on line $x - y = 0$, contains $A(3, 5)$ and $B(-1, 7)$.

25. Center on line $3x - 2y + 3 = 0$, tangent to lines $x = 1$ and $x = 5$.

Exercises 26–29 Find an equation for the circle that circumscribes the triangle whose vertices are the points of intersection of the given three lines. (*Hint:* First check to see if the triangle is a right triangle. The hypotenuse of a right triangle inscribed in a circle is a diameter of the circle.)

26. The coordinate axes and line $3x + 4y = 12$

27. $5x + y = 22, x - 5y + 6 = 0$, and $2x + 3y = 1$

28. $2x - y = 0, x + 2y = 0$, and $3x - 4y + 10 = 0$

29. $3x - 4y = 6, 7x - y = 39$, and $x + 7y + 23 = 0$

Exercises 30–35 Find an equation for the line or lines that are tangent to the circle as specified.

30. $x^2 + y^2 = 17$, at $A(-4, 1)$

31. $x^2 + y^2 - 6x - 2y + 8 = 0$, where the circle meets the *x*-axis.

32. $x^2 + y^2 = 8$, perpendicular to $y = x + 2$.

33. $x^2 + y^2 = 1$, contains point $A(4, 1)$.

34. $x^2 + y^2 = 10$, where the circle meets $x^2 + y^2 - 12x - 4y + 30 = 0$.

35. $x^2 + y^2 = 2$, contains the intersection of lines $x - 2y = 1$ and $x + y = 4$.

Exercises 36–39 (a) Express L in normal form, and (b) find the distance from the origin to L.

36. $L: 3x - 4y = 5$ 37. $L: 2x + 3y = 6$

38. $2x - y = 4$ 39. $5x + 12y = 26$

Exercises 40–43 (a) Draw a graph of L and of line L_0 that passes through the origin and is perpendicular to L. (b) Find the angle of inclination of L_0 (to the nearest degree).

40. $L: 3x - 4y = 12$ 41. $L: 2x + 3y = 6$

42. $2x + y = 4$ 43. $3x - y = 6$

Exercises 44–47 Find the distance from the point to the line.

44. $P(1, 3); x - 4y + 5 = 0$

45. $P(2, -1): 3x + y - 2 = 0$

46. Origin; line through $A(3, 2)$ and $B(6, -4)$.

47. Origin; line through $A(-1, 3)$ and $B(-2, -4)$.

Exercises 48–51   **(a)** For $\triangle ABC$, find the length of the altitude from the vertex A to side $\overline{BC}$, and **(b)** find the area of the triangle.

48. $A(0, 0)$, $B(1, 8)$, $C(6, -2)$

49. $A(1, -3)$, $B(2, -3)$, $C(6, 5)$

50. $A(-2, -4)$, $B(1, -2)$, $C(3, 6)$

51. $A(-1, 2)$, $B(2, -1)$, $C(6, 3)$

SECTION 10.2   **Parabolas**

And perhaps the greatest scientific impact of these new geometries was that the geometry of Riemann laid the groundwork for the geometry utilized in Einstein's theory of relativity. Thus mathematical history shows that until some freedom of choice with regard to the selection of axioms was realized, the development of the theory of relativity simply was not possible.

Donald Greenspan

The circle is the first of the **conic sections** we encountered. The ancient Greeks defined all the conic sections, including the parabola, as sets of points that satisfied some distance condition. In Chapter 2, we called the graph of a quadratic function a parabola; we justify our use of the term later in this section.

> **Definition: Parabola**
>
> A **parabola** is the set of all points equidistant from a given point F and a line D that does not contain F. Point F is the **focus** and line D is the **directrix** of the parabola.

Analytic geometry was great. It began with a description of Descartes' great victory, the insight that made algebra out of geometry and vice versa. It was all about graphs, and mainly about conics. I thought it was all great stuff and in my letters home I wrote enthusiastically about my mathematics course; it was a beauty, I said.

Paul Halmos

Equation of a Parabola

To get a simple equation for the parabola, we choose to put the origin midway between F and D, with D parallel to one of the axes. If $2p$ denotes the distance from F to D and we put F on the positive y-axis, then we get the diagram shown in Figure 10.13, where F has coordinates $(0, p)$ and D has the equation $y = -p$. If a point $P(x, y)$ falls on the parabola, the distances d_1 and d_2 in the diagram must be equal:

$$d_1 = \sqrt{(x - 0)^2 + (y - p)^2} \quad \text{and} \quad d_2 = \sqrt{(x - x)^2 + (y + p)^2}.$$

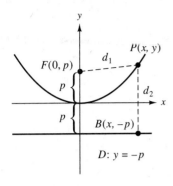

FIGURE 10.13

Setting d_1 equal to d_2, squaring both sides (according to the Squaring Property in Section 10.1), and simplifying, gives

$$x^2 + y^2 - 2py + p^2 = y^2 + 2py + p^2 \qquad \text{or} \qquad x^2 = 4py. \qquad \textbf{(1)}$$

Figure 10.13 clearly shows that the parabola is symmetric about a line through the focus and perpendicular to the directrix (in this case, the y-axis). This line of symmetry is the **axis** of the parabola. The **vertex** is the point midway between the focus and the directrix, where the parabola meets its axis.

Standard Forms

With the vertex at $(0, 0)$, Equation 1 is one of four standard forms for an equation of a parabola. As long as $2p$ denotes the distance between the focus and the directrix (so that p is positive), we can keep the vertex at the origin (and one of the coordinate axes as the parabola's axis) if we locate F at either $(0, \pm p)$ or $(\pm p, 0)$. The four standard forms are shown with their graphs in Figure 10.14.

If the vertex is at some other point $V(h, k)$ but the axis of symmetry remains vertical or horizontal and the distance $(2p)$ between F and D remains the same, essentially the same derivation we used to get Equation 1 will give us one of the standard forms, where both F and D are p units from the vertex.

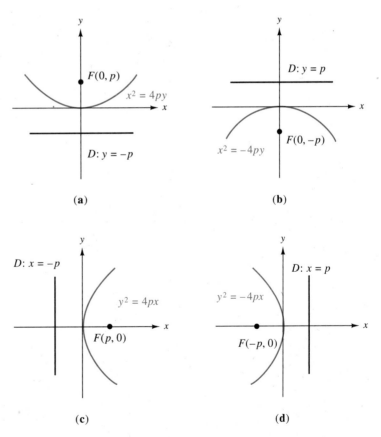

FIGURE 10.14

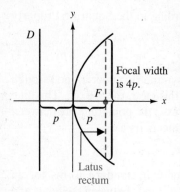

FIGURE 10.15

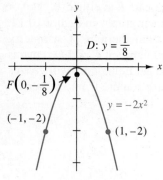

FIGURE 10.16

Strategy: All specified items are defined in terms of the number p in Equations 2 and 3. Begin with each equation in standard form by solving for the squared term and reading off p. $x^2 = -\frac{1}{2}y$; $p = \frac{1}{8}$, and $y^2 = -2x$; $p = \frac{1}{2}$.

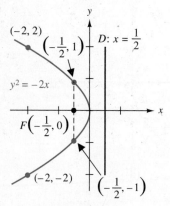

FIGURE 10.17

> ### Standard-Form Equations for Parabolas with Vertex V(h, k)
>
> Vertical Axis, $x = h$: $(x - h)^2 = \pm 4p(y - k)$ (2)
>
> With a plus sign, the parabola opens upward; with a minus sign, the parabola opens downward.
>
> Horizontal Axis, $y = k$: $(y - k)^2 = \pm 4p(x - h)$ (3)
>
> With a plus sign, the parabola opens to the right; with a minus sign, the parabola opens to the left.

The number $4p$ that appears in the standard form for parabolas has geometric significance. For a given curve we define a **chord** as any line segment that has both endpoints on the curve. A **focal chord** of a parabola is a chord that contains the focus. The focal chord parallel to the directrix is the **latus rectum.** The length of the latus rectum is $4p$. (See Figure 10.15 and Exercise 20.) The length of the latus rectum is also called the **focal width** of the parabola because it measures the width of the parabola opening, as illustrated in the following example.

| **EXAMPLE 1** | For each parabola, find the focus, directrix, and focal width, and sketch the graph.

$$\textbf{(a) } y = -2x^2 \qquad \textbf{(b) } y^2 = -2x$$

Solution

a.   The equation $y = -2x^2$ is a quadratic function of the type we graphed in Section 2.4. The vertex is at $(0, 0)$ and the parabola opens downward. We locate a point on the parabola, say $(1, -2)$, and by symmetry $(-1, -2)$ is also on the graph (see Figure 10.16). Identify p from a standard form. First express the equation in standard form (Equation 2 with a minus sign) by dividing both sides by -2,

$$x^2 = -\frac{1}{2}y.$$

Thus $h = 0$, $k = 0$, and $-4p = -\frac{1}{2}$. Hence $p = \frac{1}{8}$ and the length of the latus rectum, the focal width, is $4p(= \frac{1}{2})$. Since the parabola opens downward, the focus is $\frac{1}{8}$ unit *below* the vertex, at point $F(0, -\frac{1}{8})$, and an equation for the directrix is $D: y = \frac{1}{8}$.

b.   Comparing standard forms, $y^2 = -2x$ is already in the form of Equation 3 with $h = 0$, $k = 0$, and $4p = 2$. Thus $p = \frac{1}{2}$ and the focal width is 2. The parabola opens to the left and has its vertex at the origin. The focus is $F(-\frac{1}{2}, 0)$, and the directrix is $D: x = \frac{1}{2}$. See Figure 10.17.   ▲

In Figures 10.16 and 10.17 the latus rectum visually indicates the focal width. For the parabola $y = -2x^2$, the focal width is $\frac{1}{2}$ and the parabola is quite narrow. In contrast, the wider parabola $y^2 = -2x$ has a focal width of 2.

Strategy: First complete the square on the y terms and write the equation in the form of Equation 3, from which find p and the vertex. The focus is on the axis, p units from the vertex.

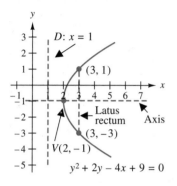

FIGURE 10.18

EXAMPLE 2   Find the focus, the directrix, and the ends of the latus rectum for the parabola with equation $y^2 + 2y - 4x + 9 = 0$ and sketch the graph.

Solution

Follow the strategy.

$$y^2 + 2y = 4x - 9$$
$$y^2 + 2y + 1 = 4x - 8$$
$$(y + 1)^2 = 4(x - 2)$$

This equation has the form of Equation 3 with a plus sign, so the vertex is at $(2, -1)$, the parabola opens to the right, and $4p = 4$, $p = 1$. The focus is 1 unit to the right of the vertex, at $F(3, -1)$, and the directrix is the vertical line D: $x = 1$. The focal width is 4, so the ends of the latus rectum are at $(3, 1)$ and $(3, -3)$. The graph is shown in Figure 10.18. ▲

EXAMPLE 3   Find an equation for the parabola with a vertical axis, vertex at $(2, -2)$, and focus on the line $x + y = 1$.

Solution

Begin with a diagram that shows the vertex and the line $x + y = 1$. See Figure 10.19a. The vertical line $x = 2$ intersects line $x + y = 1$ at point $(2, -1)$, so that is the focus of the parabola. Since the focus is 1 unit from the vertex, $p = 1$, the vertex is at $(2, -2)$, and the parabola opens upward. Using Equation 2 with a plus sign, an equation for the parabola is $(x - 2)^2 = 4(y + 2)$. ▲

Strategy: The vertex lies on the axis, so the axis is the vertical line $x = 2$. The focus must be the point where the line $x + y = 1$ crosses the axis. The distance from the vertex to the focus is p, from which we can write an equation in the form of Equation 2.

Quadratic Functions and Parabolas

In Chapter 2 we considered quadratic functions and their graphs. We called the graph of a quadratic function a parabola. Now that we have a formal definition for a parabola, we need to justify our statement that the graph of any quadratic function is a parabola.

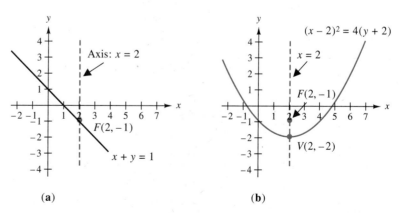

(a)   (b)

FIGURE 10.19

Consider a function defined by an equation of the form

$$f(x) = ax^2 + bx + c, \text{ where } a \neq 0.$$

To show that the graph of $y = f(x)$ is a parabola, it is sufficient to rewrite the equation in one of the standard forms for a parabola. The argument is most easily presented in terms of a specific example.

EXAMPLE 4   Consider the function $f(x) = 2x^2 - 4x - 3$. Show that the graph of the equation $y = f(x)$ is a parabola, identify the vertex, and sketch the graph.

Solution

Begin by completing the square in x:

$$y = 2x^2 - 4x - 3 = 2(x^2 - 2x) - 3$$
$$= 2(x^2 - 2x + 1 - 1) - 3$$
$$= 2(x - 1)^2 - 5.$$

Add 5 to both sides, rearrange, and divide by 2:

$$(x - 1)^2 = \tfrac{1}{2}(y + 5).$$

The last equation has the form of Equation 2 with the plus sign, which indicates a parabola that opens upward with vertex at $(1, -5)$, as shown in Figure 10.20. ▲

Any quadratic function can be handled in a manner similar to Example 4. See Exercise 33.

Applications of Parabolas

The name *focus* comes from one of the properties that makes parabolas important in physical applications. A basic law of physics states that the angle of reflection of light or sound is the same as the angle of incidence. It is proved in calculus that all light rays parallel to the axis of a parabola will be reflected through the focus of the parabola. See Figure 10.21. This is the principle on which telescopes work. A parabolic mirror gathers light waves from a distance at the focus where the eyepiece is located. The light source of an automobile headlight is located near the focus of the parabolic reflector to send the light in essentially parallel rays. Using a similar principle, a parabolic antenna picks up sounds from a distance (as from a football huddle) or signals from an orbiting satellite.

The path of an object moving near the surface of the earth under the influence of gravity, such as a kicked ball or a thrown baseball, is very nearly parabolic.

EXAMPLE 5   The diameter of a parabolic mirror of a telescope is 200 centimeters, and the mirror is 10 centimeters deep at its center. How far is the focus of the vertex, that is, how far above the vertex should the eyepiece be located?

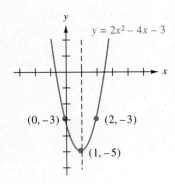

FIGURE 10.20

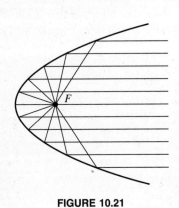

FIGURE 10.21

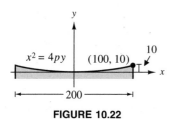

FIGURE 10.22

Solution

The cross section of the mirror is part of a parabola, as shown schematically in Figure 10.22. On the coordinate system, $(100, 10)$ is a point on the parabola whose equation in standard form is $x^2 = 4py$. Substituting the coordinates $(100, 10)$ into the equation,

$$4p \cdot 10 = 100^2 \qquad \text{or} \qquad p = \frac{10,000}{4 \cdot 10} = 250.$$

The focus is at $(0, 250)$, or 250 centimeters above the center of the mirror. ▲

EXERCISES 10.2

Check Your Understanding

Exercises 1–6 True or False. Give reasons for your conclusion.

1. Point $(2, 1)$ is on the parabola with a focus at $(1, 0)$ and directrix given by $x = -1$.

2. If the directrix of a parabola is a horizontal line and the focus is below the directrix, then the parabola opens downward.

3. If $(1, 3)$ is the focus of a parabola and $(1, -1)$ is its vertex, then the directrix is the horizontal line $y = -3$.

4. The vertex of the parabola $(y - 2)^2 = 4(x + 1)$ is a point in the fourth quadrant.

5. The graph of $y^2 = 4(x - 2)$ contains points in the first and fourth quadrants.

6. The graph of $y^2 = 2(1 - x)$ contains points in all four quadrants.

Exercises 7–10 Complete the sentence by selecting from the list below *all choices* that make the statement true.

(a) Quadrant I   **(b)** Quadrant II
(c) Quadrant III   **(d)** Quadrant IV

7. The vertex of the parabola $x^2 + 2x + 4y - 7 = 0$ is in _____ .

8. The vertex of the parabola $y^2 - 2y - 4x - 3 = 0$ is in _____ .

9. The graph of the parabola $y = x^2 + 2x + 1$ contains points in _____ .

10. The graph of the parabola $(y - 1)^2 - 4(x - 2) = 0$ contains points in _____ .

Explore and Discover

1. All our work with equations for parabolas in this section has assumed either vertical or horizontal axes.
   (a) Find an equation for the set of points that are equidistant from $F(1, 1)$ and D: $x + y + 1 = 0$ (see the diagram). (*Hint:* Use the formula for the distance from a point to a line; see Equation 7 in Section 10.1.)
   (b) Choose another focus and a directrix that is neither horizontal or vertical. Find an equation for the parabola thus determined.
   (c) On the basis of your equations for **(a)** and **(b)**, would you expect to have a nonzero xy term any time the directrix is not parallel to a coordinate axis? Why or why not?

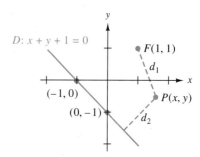

2. **(a)** Draw a reasonably accurate graph of each equation:

   (i) $x^2 = 2y$ **(ii)** $y^2 = 8x$
   (iii) $(x - 1)^2 = 4(y + 2)$
   (iv) $(y + 1)^2 = 4(x - 3)$

   (b) On each of your graphs, let A and B be the endpoints of the latus rectum and C be the point at which the directrix meets the axis of the parabola. Based on your diagrams, make a guess about what kind of triangle ABC is. What is the area of triangle ABC?

3. Based on your work in Exercise 2, write a brief paragraph to describe your conclusions about triangle ABC, where A and B are the endpoints of the latus rectum of a general parabola and C is the point where the directrix meets the axis of the parabola.

Develop Mastery

Exercises 1–8   An equation for a parabola is given. Give the coordinates of the vertex and focus, and an equation for the directrix. Sketch the graph.

1. $y^2 - 8x = 0$

2. $x^2 + 8y = 0$

3. $4x + y^2 - 2y + 9 = 0$

4. $x^2 + 2x - 8y + 9 = 0$

5. $x^2 - 2x + 2y - 3 = 0$

6. $9y^2 + 24y - 12x + 28 = 0$

7. $x^2 + 2x - 6y - 17 = 0$

8. $x^2 - 6x - 2y + 1 = 0$

Exercises 9–19   The given conditions determine one or more parabolas, each with axis parallel to one of the coordinate axes. Find an equation in the form of Equation 2 or 3 for each parabola and sketch a graph.

9. $F(2, 0)$; $D: x = -2$

10. $F(0, -3)$; $D: y = 3$

11. $F(0, -\frac{1}{2})$; $D: y = \frac{1}{2}$

12. $F(1, 2)$; $D: x = 3$

13. Vertex $(2, -1)$; $D: x = 1$

14. Vertex $(2, -1)$; $D: y = 0$

15. Vertex $(-1, -2)$; contains $(1, 3)$

16. Vertex $(0, 0)$; contains $(3, -2)$

17. Vertex $(2, 1)$; focus on the line $x + y = 1$

18. Vertex $(2, 1)$; focus on the line $y = 2x + 1$

19. Contains points $(1, 3)$, $(1, -1)$, and $(7, 5)$

20. Show that the latus rectum of the parabola $x^2 = 4py$ has length $4p$. (*Hint:* Draw the parabola with its latus rectum. Each endpoint of the latus rectum is equidistant from F and D.)

Exercises 21–25   Find an equation for the parabola or parabolas satisfying the conditions.

21. $D: x = 2$; bottom endpoint of latus rectum at $(6, 2)$

22. $D: x = 2$; upper endpoint of the latus rectum at $(6, 2)$

23. $F(1, 2)$; one endpoint of latus rectum at $(-1, 2)$

24. The latus rectum is the common chord of the two circles $x^2 + y^2 - 4x + 2 = 0$ and $x^2 + y^2 - 4x - 6y + 8 = 0$.

25. The latus rectum is the vertical diameter of the circle $x^2 + y^2 - 2x + 2y = 2$.

26. Given parabola $4py = x^2$, let T_p be the triangle with vertices at the origin and at the ends of the latus rectum.
    (a) Find the area of triangle T_p for parabola $y = x^2$.
    (b) For what focal width does the area of T_p equal 2? 1?

27. Find an equation for the circle that contains the ends of the latus rectum of the parabola $2x = -y^2$ and that is tangent to the directrix of the parabola.

28. The parabolic mirror for the Mount Palomar telescope is 200 inches in diameter; the mirror is 3.75 inches deep at the center. How far from the center of the mirror is the focal point?

29. A parabolic headlight is 4 inches deep and has a maximum diameter of 4 inches. How far from the vertex should the light source be placed to produce a beam of light parallel to the axis of the parabola?

30. Suppose a golf ball driven off the tee travels 200 meters down the fairway, and during its flight it reaches a maximum height of 50 meters. Taking the tee as the origin of a coordinate system with positive x-axis along the ground in the direction of the drive, find an equation that describes the ball's parabolic path.

31. (a) Write an equation in point-slope form for line L_m with slope m and containing point $(1, 1)$.
    (b) For what positive slope m is the line in part (a) tangent to the parabola $y = x^2$? (For what value of m does L_m intersect the parabola in a single point?) Note that a line parallel to the axis of the parabola is not a tangent line.

32. (a) Find the coordinates of the right endpoint R of the latus rectum of the parabola $y = x^2$.
    (b) Find the slope of the line tangent to the parabola $y = x^2$ at point R. See Exercise 31.

33. Show that the equation $y = ax^2 + bx + c$, where $a \neq 0$, can be written in the form $(y - k) = a(x - h)^2$, where $h = \frac{-b}{2a}$ and $k = c - \frac{b^2}{4a}$.

Ellipses and Hyperbolas

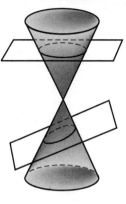

(a)

(b)

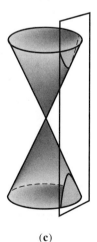

(c)

FIGURE 10.23

Let's take . . . a step up the ladder from the circle. I mean the conic sections, especially the ellipse. These curves were studied by Apollonius of Perga (262–200 B.C) as the "sections" of a right circular cone. This is "pure mathematics" in the sense that it has no contact with science or technology. The interesting thing is that nearly 2000 years later, Kepler announced that the planetary orbits are ellipses.
  Reuben Hersh

The conic sections (see Figure 10.23) mentioned in the epigraph above have influenced human ideas about the universe (see the Historical Note, "Conic Sections" p. 554). The two remaining conics (after circles and parabolas) are the ellipse and the hyperbola. By treating them together in this section, we emphasize both similarities and differences. Both the ellipse and the hyperbola involve two focus points, called **foci**. In Figure 10.24, F_1 and F_2 are the fixed focus points and P is an arbitrary point. In terms of the distances shown, we can define the ellipse and hyperbola.

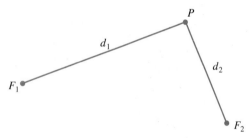

FIGURE 10.24

Definition: Ellipse and Hyperbola

Given two points F_1 and F_2 and a fixed positive number k.

An **ellipse** is the set of all points P such that the *sum* of the distances from P to F_1 and from P to F_2 is equal to k, that is, if $d_1 = |\overline{PF_1}|$ and $d_2 = |\overline{PF_2}|$, then

$$d_1 + d_2 = k.$$

A **hyperbola** is the set of all points P such that the *difference* of the distances from P to F_1 and from P to F_2 is equal to k, that is, if $d_1 = |\overline{PF_1}|$ and $d_2 = |\overline{PF_2}|$, then either

$$d_1 - d_2 = k \quad \text{or} \quad d_2 - d_1 = k.$$

Together, $|d_1 - d_2| = k.$

It just came to me that I could use this technique, this theorem, in connection with these curves in Hilbert space that I was dealing with—and get the answer! It just came to me out of the blue one day. It has always struck me as so amazing. One half of me had been bouncing around with this theorem a lot and the other half had been doing this problem, and they had never gotten together.

Andrew Gleason

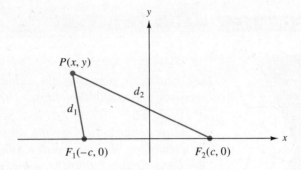

ellipse: $d_1 + d_2 = 2a$
hyperbola: $d_1 - d_2 = \pm 2a$

FIGURE 10.25

To get equations for the ellipse and hyperbola, we need a coordinate system. The standard equations assume both foci are on a line parallel to one of the coordinate axes. Take the focus points on the x-axis, symmetric to the origin, say at $F_1(-c, 0)$ and $F_2(c, 0)$. For convenience, take the constant k as $2a$. (See Figure 10.25.) Then we want equations that must be satisfied for a point $P(x, y)$ to lie on an ellipse or a hyperbola. We organize the derivations in parallel columns to make them easier to compare.

Ellipse $(a > c)$	**Hyperbola** $(a < c)$
$d_1 + d_2 = 2a$	$d_1 - d_2 = \pm 2a$
$\sqrt{(x + c)^2 + y^2} + \sqrt{(x - c)^2 + y^2} = 2a$	$\sqrt{(x + c)^2 + y^2} - \sqrt{(x - c)^2 + y^2} = \pm 2a$
First separate the radicals	First separate the radicals
$\sqrt{(x + c)^2 + y^2} = 2a - \sqrt{(x - c)^2 + y^2}$	$\sqrt{(x + c)^2 + y^2} = \pm 2a + \sqrt{(x - c)^2 + y^2}$
Square both sides and simplify; isolate the radical	Square both sides and simplify; isolate the radical
$a\sqrt{(x - c)^2 + y^2} = a^2 - cx$	$\pm a\sqrt{(x - c)^2 + y^2} = cx - a^2$
Square both sides, simplify, and rearrange	Square both sides, simplify, and rearrange
$(a^2 - c^2)x^2 + a^2y^2 = a^2(a^2 - c^2)$	$(c^2 - a^2)x^2 - a^2y^2 = a^2(c^2 - a^2)$
Substitute b^2 for $a^2 - c^2$	Substitute b^2 for $c^2 - a^2$
$b^2x^2 + a^2y^2 = a^2b^2$	$b^2x^2 - a^2y^2 = a^2b^2$
Divide through by a^2b^2	Divide through by a^2b^2
$\dfrac{x^2}{a^2} + \dfrac{y^2}{b^2} = 1 \qquad \textbf{(1)}$	$\dfrac{x^2}{a^2} - \dfrac{y^2}{b^2} = 1 \qquad \textbf{(2)}$

Note that we introduced no extraneous points by squaring both sides (see the Squaring Property discussed in Section 10.1).

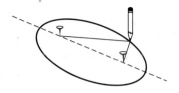

FIGURE 10.26

The Ellipse

The definition suggests a simple way to draw a very good ellipse. Stick two tacks into a drawing board and tie an end of a piece of string to each tack. Moving a pencil around so as to keep the string taut defines a set of points such that the sum of the distances to the two foci (the tacks) equals the constant string-length. See Figure 10.26. If the foci are located at $(\pm c, 0)$, the graph of Equation 1 is clearly symmetric with respect to both axes and the origin.

Choosing our coordinate system so that the foci are at $F_1(-c, 0)$ and $F_2(c, 0)$ reveals the significance of the constants in the equation. When $y = 0$, $\frac{x^2}{a^2} = 1$ or $x = \pm a$ and the x-intercept points are $(-a, 0)$ and $(a, 0)$. Setting $x = 0$, we find that the y-intercept points are $(0, -b)$ and $(0, b)$. Since b was defined by $b^2 = a^2 - c^2$, we always have $b < a$.

The chord through the foci is called the **major axis** (length $2a$) and its midpoint is the **center** of the ellipse. The endpoints of the major axis are called the **vertices** of the ellipse. The chord that runs perpendicular to the major axis through the center is called the **minor axis** (length $2b$). Because $b < a$, the minor axis is always shorter than the major axis. Each focal chord (that is, each chord that passes through a focus) perpendicular to the major axis is called a **latus rectum.** These relations are shown in Figure 10.27.

Had we chosen the coordinate system with the foci on the y-axis at $F_1(0, c)$ and $F_2(0, -c)$, then the major axis would fall on the y-axis. The same derivation would lead to an equation of the form

$$\frac{x^2}{b^2} + \frac{y^2}{a^2} = 1 \tag{3}$$

and the terminology shown in Figure 10.28. Ellipses whose equations can be written in the form of either Equation 1 or Equation 3 are in standard position, and those equations are in standard form for ellipses.

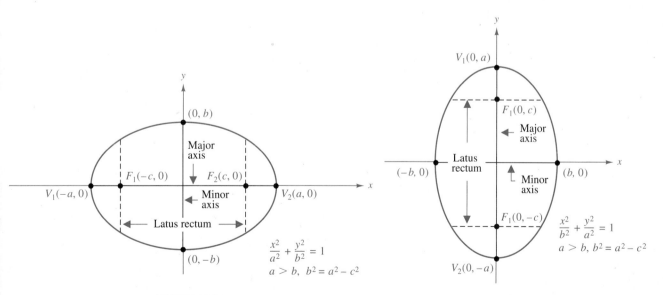

FIGURE 10.27   **FIGURE 10.28**

Historical Note

Note how the direction of the light source creates increasingly elongated shadows.

CONIC SECTIONS

The name *conic section* comes from the idea of sections or slices of a right, circular cone. If you could take slices through an ice cream cone at various angles, each slice would result in a conic section, as for instance, the circular section at the top of the cone where the ice cream rests.

The shadows in the photo are examples of conic sections. You can also observe models of conic sections created by the cone of light coming from the top of a lamp. The shadow of the lampshade on the wall forms conic sections. When the top is pointed directly at the wall the shadow is a circle. As the lamp is tipped, the shadow becomes a more and more elongated ellipse, until finally the shadow is no longer closed and becomes a parabola. Tipped further, the shadow becomes a branch of a hyperbola.

At least as far back as Euclid, the Greeks recognized and studied the conics. Apollonius wrote a treatise on conics (200 B.C.) that included our modern definitions in terms of distances from foci. His work remained essentially the last word on conics through the Middle Ages. At age 16 (in 1640), Pascal announced a remarkable theorem regarding what he called "mystic hexagons": Any six points on a conic section determine a hexagon with three pairs of opposite sides. If opposite sides are extended so that they intersect, then the three points of intersection all lie on one line.

Nature seems to like conic sections; we observe conic sections all about us. Without conics, Kepler's discovery that planetary orbits are elliptical would have been unlikely. It is impossible to guess what effect that might have had on Sir Isaac Newton's physics and mathematics. Space exploration would be impossible without an understanding of conic sections.

EXAMPLE 1   Identify the vertices and foci, find the lengths of the major and minor axes, and sketch the graph.

$$\text{(a) } \frac{x^2}{16} + \frac{y^2}{9} = 1 \qquad \text{(b) } \frac{x^2}{6} + \frac{y^2}{16} = 1 \qquad \text{(c) } x^2 + 9y^2 = 144.$$

Solution

Strategy: (c) First divide through by 144 to get an equation in the form of Equation 1, from which we get a and b. From $c^2 = a^2 - b^2$, get c and the foci.

(a) Since $16 > 9$, the given equation is in the form of Equation 1; the foci and major axis are on the x-axis. Comparing with Equation 1 $a^2 = 16$ and $b^2 = 9$, and since $b^2 = a^2 - c^2$, $c^2 = a^2 - b^2 = 7$. Therefore $a = 4, b = 3$, and $c = \sqrt{7}$. The vertices are at $(\pm 4, 0)$ and the foci are at $(\pm\sqrt{7}, 0)$. The y-intercepts are $(0, \pm 3)$ as shown in Figure 10.29. The major and minor axes have lengths 8 and 6, respectively.

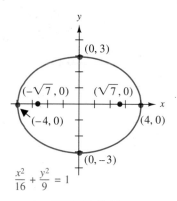

$$\frac{x^2}{16} + \frac{y^2}{9} = 1$$

FIGURE 10.29

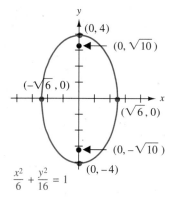

$$\frac{x^2}{6} + \frac{y^2}{16} = 1$$

FIGURE 10.30

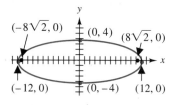

FIGURE 10.31

(b) Since $6 < 16$, the equation has the form of Equation 3. The major axis is on the y-axis and $a^2 = 16$. Thus $a = 4$, and the vertices are $(0, \pm 4)$. Since $b^2 = 6$, $b = \sqrt{6}$, and $c^2 = a^2 - b^2 = 16 - 6 = 10$. The foci are also on the y-axis, at $(0, \pm\sqrt{10})$, and the x-intercepts are $(\pm\sqrt{6}, 0)$. See Figure 10.30. Lengths of major and minor axes are, respectively, 8 and $2\sqrt{6}$.

(c) The equation $x^2 + 9y^2 = 144$ does not have the form of either Equation 1 or 3. Following the strategy,

$$\frac{x^2}{144} + \frac{y^2}{16} = 1.$$

This equation has the form of Equation 1 with $a^2 = 144$, $b^2 = 16$, and $c^2 = 128$. Thus $a = 12$, $b = 4$, and $c = 8\sqrt{2}$. With x-intercept points $(\pm 12, 0)$ and y-intercept points $(0, \pm 4)$, the ellipse is long and thin (see Figure 10.31). The foci are $(\pm 8\sqrt{2}, 0)$, near the ends of the major axis. The major axis is 24 units long, while the minor axis is 8. ▲

The ellipse is something of a "squashed circle," the shape we see when looking at a circular disk from an angle. The three ellipses in Example 1 demonstrate the considerable variation possible in the amount of distortion from a circle. One measure of the distortion is the ratio $\frac{b}{a}$. When a is much larger than b, the ellipse is long and narrow; when the ratio $\frac{b}{a}$ is near 1, the lengths of the major and minor axes are more nearly equal and the ellipse more closely resembles a circle. Indeed, when $\frac{b}{a} = 1$, the equation

$$\frac{x^2}{a^2} + \frac{y^2}{b^2} = 1$$

reduces to

$$x^2 + y^2 = a^2,$$

an equation for a circle. Historically, however, rather than the ratio $\frac{b}{a}$, the measure used to indicate the distortion of an ellipse is called the **eccentricity**, defined by $\epsilon = \frac{c}{a}$.

Strategy: Drawing diagrams of ellipses through $(2, 3)$ suggests two solutions, one with a horizontal major axis and one with a vertical major axis. Using the form of Equation 1 with $a = 4$ and substituting the coordinates $(2, 3)$ into the equation should set up the problem to solve for b for the horizontal case. Use Equation 3 for the vertical case.

| **EXAMPLE 2** | Find an equation for the ellipse in standard position that has a major axis of length 8 and that passes through point $(2, 3)$.

Solution

Since the major axis can lie on either coordinate axis, we expect two solutions. See Figure 10.32. For each ellipse, $2a = 8$, or $a = 4$. If the major axis is on the x-axis, then use Equation 1 with $a = 4$:

$$\frac{x^2}{16} + \frac{y^2}{b^2} = 1.$$

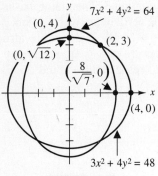

FIGURE 10.32

Substitute the coordinates of the given point into the equation,

$$\frac{2^2}{16} + \frac{3^2}{b^2} = 1$$

and solve for b^2. We get $b^2 = 12$, $b = \sqrt{12} = 2\sqrt{3}$. Therefore an equation for the ellipse is

$$\frac{x^2}{16} + \frac{y^2}{12} = 1 \qquad \text{or} \qquad 3x^2 + 4y^2 = 48.$$

Similarly, if the major axis is on the y-axis, use Equation 3:

$$\frac{x^2}{b^2} + \frac{y^2}{16} = 1, \qquad \frac{2^2}{b^2} + \frac{3^2}{16} = 1, \qquad b^2 = \frac{64}{7}.$$

Thus, the desired equation becomes

$$\frac{x^2}{64/7} + \frac{y^2}{16} = 1 \qquad \text{or} \qquad 7x^2 + 4y^2 = 64. \quad \blacktriangle$$

Hyperbolas

The derivation of the first standard equation for the hyperbola places the foci at $F_1(-c, 0)$ and $F_2(c, 0)$. Setting $y = 0$ in Equation 2,

$$\frac{x^2}{a^2} - \frac{y^2}{b^2} = 1$$

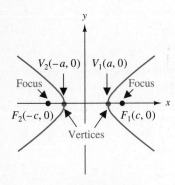

FIGURE 10.33

Hyperbola with vertices
and foci

we find the x-intercept points at $(-a, 0)$ and $(a, 0)$. Since $a < c$ for the hyperbola, the intercepts, called the **vertices** of the hyperbola, are between the foci. See Figure 10.33. From the form of Equation 2, the graph has symmetry similar to that of the ellipse. When we know the graph in one quadrant, the rest of the graph comes from reflections through the coordinate axes and the origin. The **center** of the hyperbola is the midpoint of the segment that joins the vertices.

If we solve Equation 2 for y, we obtain

$$y = \pm\frac{b}{a}\sqrt{x^2 - a^2} \tag{4}$$

Equation 4 demonstrates that there is no y-value when x is between $-a$ and a. Furthermore, we may rewrite equation 4 in the form

$$y = \pm\frac{bx}{a}\sqrt{1 - \frac{a^2}{x^2}}$$

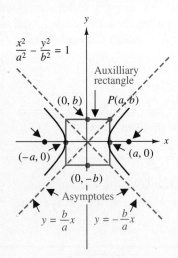

FIGURE 10.34

Clearly, as $|x|$ becomes larger, the quantity $\frac{a^2}{x^2}$ approaches 0, and y approaches $\frac{\pm bx}{a}$. This shows that lines $y = \frac{bx}{a}$ and $y = \frac{-bx}{a}$ are oblique **asymptotes** for the hyperbola. The vertices and the asymptotes make graphing the hyperbola simple. Point $P(a, b)$ in the first quadrant is one corner of what is called the **auxiliary rectangle.** The other corners are symmetric to $P(a, b)$, as shown in Figure 10.34. The auxiliary rectangle is not part of the graph of the hyperbola, but it aids graphing. The lines that contain the diagonals of the rectangle are the

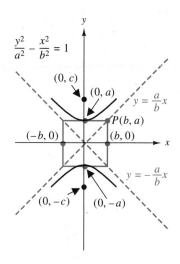

$$\frac{y^2}{a^2} - \frac{x^2}{b^2} = 1$$

FIGURE 10.35

asymptotes, and the vertices of the hyperbola are the midpoints of opposite sides of the rectangle. The hyperbola is shown in Figure 10.34.

If the foci are on the y-axis, at $F_1(0, -c)$ and $F_2(0, c)$, then, by interchanging the roles of x and y, we obtain the other standard form for a hyperbola,

$$\frac{y^2}{a^2} - \frac{x^2}{b^2} = 1. \tag{5}$$

Again $b^2 = c^2 - a^2$. The vertices are at $(0, a)$ and $(0, -a)$, and the asymptotes are $y = \frac{\pm ax}{b}$. The same kind of auxiliary rectangle facilitates drawing this graph, shown in Figure 10.35.

EXAMPLE 3 Find the coordinates of the foci and the vertices, give equations for the asymptotes, and sketch the graph.

$$\textbf{(a)}\ \frac{y^2}{25} - \frac{x^2}{9} = 1 \qquad \textbf{(b)}\ \frac{x^2}{9} - \frac{y^2}{25} = 1$$

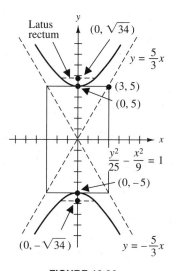

FIGURE 10.36

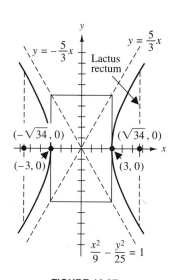

FIGURE 10.37

Solution

(a) The first equation has the form of Equation 5, where $a = 5, b = 3$, and the foci are on the y-axis. Since $b^2 = c^2 - a^2$, $c^2 = a^2 + b^2 = 25 + 9 = 34$, or $c = \sqrt{34}$. Thus the foci are at $(0, \pm\sqrt{34})$ and the vertices are at $(0, \pm 5)$. The asymptotes are $y = \frac{\pm ax}{b} = \frac{\pm 5x}{3}$, and the graph is shown in Figure 10.36.

(b) The given equation has the form of Equation 2, so the foci and vertices are on the x-axis, even through the denominator of the y^2-term is larger. Since $a = 3$, and $b = 5$, $c = \sqrt{a^2 + b^2} = \sqrt{34}$. The asymptotes are $y = \pm\frac{bx}{a} = \pm\frac{5x}{3}$. The vertices, foci, and graph are shown in Figure 10.37. ▲

Note that the hyperbola in Figure 10.36 has a much narrower opening than the one in Figure 10.37. This is conveniently measured by a latus rectum, as for parabolas and ellipses. A latus rectum is a chord through a focus perpendicular to the line that contains the foci and vertices. As with parabolas and ellipses, a latus rectum is easily drawn (see Figures 10.36 and 10.37) and indicates the width of the hyperbola at the focus. We leave it to the reader to show that the length of the latus rectum in Figure 10.36 is $\frac{18}{5}$, while that in Figure 10.37 is $\frac{50}{3}$.

EXAMPLE 4   Find **(a)** the foci and endpoints of the right latus rectum of the hyperbola $\frac{x^2}{16} - \frac{y^2}{9} = 1$, and **(b)** an equation for the parabola in standard position (with its vertex at the origin) that passes through the endpoints of the right latus rectum of the hyperbola.

Solution

Strategy: (b) Standard form for the equation of the parabola is $y^2 = 4px$, so substitute coordinates of the endpoints into the equation.

(a) For the given hyperbola, $a = 4$, $b = 3$, from which $c^2 = 16 + 9 = 25$. Thus $c = 5$ and the foci of the hyperbola are at $(\pm 5, 0)$. The right latus rectum is the vertical chord through the right focus, $(5, 0)$. When $x = 5$,

$$\frac{25}{16} - \frac{y^2}{9} = 1 \qquad \text{or} \qquad y = \pm \frac{9}{4}.$$

The ends of the right latus rectum are thus $(5, \pm \frac{9}{4})$, as in Figure 10.38.

(b) Follow the strategy. Substituting the coordinates $(5, \frac{9}{4})$ into the equation $y^2 = 4px$, we find, $4p = \frac{81}{80}$. Therefore an equation for the parabola shown in Figure 10.38 is $y^2 = \frac{81}{80}x$. ▲

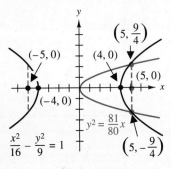

FIGURE 10.38

Applications of Ellipses and Hyperbolas

The fact that the angle of incidence equals the angle of reflection makes parabolic reflectors useful in many settings. Elliptical reflectors also have applications. An ellipse reflects sound or light from one focus back to the other focus. Buildings in the shape of elliptical domes are often called *whispering galleries*. The Mormon Tabernacle in Salt Lake City and the Statuary Hall in the capitol building in Washington, D.C. are both whispering galleries. A whisper or a dropped pin near one focus can be heard clearly at the other focus. Historical rumor suggests that John C. Calhoun was aware of this property in Statuary Hall, where the House of Representatives met in his time, and he used the knowledge to eavesdrop on his adversaries.

Elliptical paths determine the most efficient changes in the orbits of spacecraft about the earth. Knowledge of conic sections has been profoundly significant in understanding orbiting bodies.

Hyperbolas provide the basis for location and navigation instruments. If three receivers in different places all record the times when a sound is heard from a common source, then the time differences determine hyperbolas on which the source must be located. Plotting the intersection of the hyperbolas allows observers to pinpoint the location. The same principle, in reverse, allows a submarine, say, to locate itself relative to three known sound beacons, which underlies LORAN navigation.

A summary of the significant relations and properties for ellipses and hyperbolas in standard position may be useful.

**For Graphers
10.3**

ELLIPSES AND HYPERBOLAS

Of the conic sections, parabolas are the most easily described by equations of the form $y = f(x)$, and hence the most easily graphed on calculators. Nevertheless, with simple preparations, we can use graphing calculators to visualize important relationships among the conic sections. For example, given the ellipse $\frac{x^2}{a^2} + \frac{y^2}{b^2} = 1$, we can solve for y: $y = \pm\frac{b}{a}\sqrt{a^2 - x^2}$. (Check!) Similarly, for the hyperbola $\frac{x^2}{a^2} - \frac{y^2}{b^2} = 1$, $y = \pm\frac{b}{a}\sqrt{x^2 - a^2}$.

EXAMPLE **(a)** Graph the ellipse $\frac{x^2}{16} + \frac{y^2}{9} = 1$ and $\frac{x^2}{9} + \frac{y^2}{16} = 1$ on the same axes. **(b)** Graph the hyperbola $\frac{x^2}{16} - \frac{y^2}{9} = 1$ and its asymptotes $y = \pm\frac{3}{4}x$ on the same axes.

Solution **(a)** For the ellipse $\frac{x^2}{16} + \frac{y^2}{9} = 1$, solve for y to get $y = 0.75\sqrt{16 - x^2}$ and $y = -0.75\sqrt{16 - x^2}$, both of which we can graph. The Familiar Window will not quite show all of the second ellipse, but it should give a good feeling for the two together.

TI

On the [Y=] menu, enter Y1= 0.75[$\sqrt{\ }$]$(16 - x^2)$. For the bottom half of the graph, either type out $Y2 = -0.75$[$\sqrt{\ }$]$(16 - x^2)$ or use $Y2 = -Y1$([2nd] [Y-VARS] 1). For the second ellipse, $Y3 = (\frac{4}{3})$[$\sqrt{\ }$]$(9 - x^2)$ and $Y4 = -Y3$.

Casio

Type Graph $Y = 0.75$[$\sqrt{\ }$]$(16 - x^2)$ for the top of the ellipse and : (or a line return) Graph $Y = -0.75$[$\sqrt{\ }$]$(16 - x^2)$. For the second ellipse, : Graph $Y = (\frac{4}{3})$[$\sqrt{\ }$]$(9 - x^2)$:Graph $Y = -(\frac{4}{3})$[$\sqrt{\ }$]$(9 - x^2)$. Press [EXE].

(b) We need a larger window to see the hyperbola; a convenient equal scale window is $[-9.4, 9.6] \times [-6.3, 6.3]$ on the TI, or $[-9.4, 9.4] \times [-6.2, 6.2]$ on the Casio. As for part (a), graph the two halves of the hyperbola separately: $y = 0.75$[$\sqrt{\ }$]$(x^2 - 16)$ and $y = -0.75$[$\sqrt{\ }$]$(x^2 - 16)$, along with the two asymptotes $y = 0.75x$ and $y = -0.75x$. Press [EXE] to see the top half of each branch of the hyperbola, followed by the bottom half, and then the asymptotes. Observe how well the hyperbola fits into the asymptotes. ▲

Exercises

1. Graph the ellipse $\frac{x^2}{16} + \frac{y^2}{9} = 1$ and the hyperbola $\frac{x^2}{16} - \frac{y^2}{9} = 1$ on the same set of axes.

2. Find another pair (an ellipse and a hyperbola with foci on the x-axis) whose graphs are related to each other as the pair in Exercise 1.

3. Find another pair with foci on the y-axis whose graphs are related to each other in the same way as the pair in Exercise 1.

4. Graph the conjugate hyperbolas $\frac{x^2}{16} - \frac{y^2}{9} = 1$ and $\frac{x^2}{9} - \frac{y^2}{16} = 1$ on the same set of axes.

5. Add the asymptotes for the hyperbolas in Exercise 2. (*Hint:* On the Casio, either overwrite the graph by toggling back to the home screen and adding the asymptote equations, or replay and add additional graphing instructions to those for Exercise 2. The TI offers only four functions, so graph only the top halves of the hyperbolas from Exercise 2 and then add the asymptotes.)

6. Repeat Exercise 4 for the conjugate hyperbolas $\frac{x^2}{144} - \frac{y^2}{9} = 1$ and $\frac{x^2}{9} - \frac{y^2}{144} = 1$. (*Hint:* What kind of window will you need?)

Ellipses and Hyperbolas in Standard Position

Ellipse: $\dfrac{x^2}{a^2} + \dfrac{y^2}{b^2} = 1,$

$a > c,\quad b^2 = a^2 - c^2$

Latus rectum length $\dfrac{2b^2}{a}$

Major axis length $2a$

Minor axis length $2b$

Hyperbola: $\dfrac{x^2}{a^2} - \dfrac{y^2}{b^2} = 1,$

$c > a,\quad b^2 = c^2 - a^2$

Latus rectum length $\dfrac{2b^2}{a}$

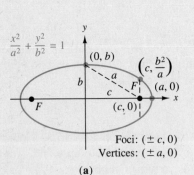

Foci: $(\pm c, 0)$
Vertices: $(\pm a, 0)$

(a)

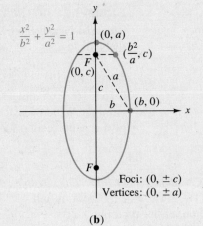

Foci: $(0, \pm c)$
Vertices: $(0, \pm a)$

(b)

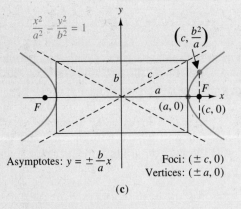

Asymptotes: $y = \pm \dfrac{b}{a}x$ Foci: $(\pm c, 0)$
Vertices: $(\pm a, 0)$

(c)

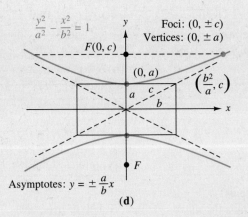

Asymptotes: $y = \pm \dfrac{a}{b}x$

(d)

EXERCISES 10.3

Check Your Understanding

Exercises 1–6   True or False. Give reasons for your conclusion.

1. The graph of $x^2 = y^2 + 4$ is an ellipse.

2. The graph of $x^2 = 5 - y^2$ is a hyperbola.

3. The graph of $x^2 + 2x + 1 = y^2 - 8y$ is a circle.

4. If P and Q are any two points on an ellipse with its foci at F_1 and F_2, then $|F_1P| - |F_2Q| = |F_1Q| - |F_2P|$.

5. One of the foci for the ellipse $x^2 + 4y^2 = 4$ is the point $(\sqrt{3}, 0)$.

6. The graph of $y^2 = x^2 + 1$ is a hyperbola with foci on the y-axis.

Exercises 7–10 Complete the sentence by selecting from the list below *all choices* that make the statement true.

(a) $(2, 0)$ **(b)** $(0, 2)$ **(c)** $(3, 0)$ **(d)** $(0, 3)$

7. One of the foci for the graph $x^2 = 2y^2 + 6$ is the point _____ .

8. A vertex for the graph of $2x^2 + y^2 = 4$ is the point _____ .

9. A point inside the ellipse $4x^2 + 9y^2 = 36$ is _____ .

10. A vertex for the graph of $25x^2 - 9y^2 = 225$ is _____ .

Explore and Discover

1. **(a)** Show that line $\frac{-4x}{18} + \frac{1y}{9} = 1$ is tangent to the ellipse $\frac{x^2}{18} + \frac{y^2}{9} = 1$ at the point $(-4, 1)$.

 (b) Show that line $\frac{2x}{8} + \frac{5y}{50} = 1$ is tangent to the ellipse $\frac{x^2}{8} + \frac{y^2}{50} = 1$ at point $(2, 5)$.

 (c) Make a guess for an equation of the line tangent to the ellipse $\frac{x^2}{a^2} + \frac{y^2}{b^2} = 1$ at point (m, n). Test your guess for point $(3, \frac{-8}{5})$ on the ellipse $\frac{x^2}{25} + \frac{y^2}{4} = 1$.

 (d) Does your guess also work for hyperbolas?

2. Suppose the foci for a hyperbola are at $F_1(\sqrt{2}, \sqrt{2})$, $F_2(-\sqrt{2}, -\sqrt{2})$. For a given point $P(x, y)$, show that the equation $|\overline{PF_2}| - |\overline{PF_1}| = \pm 2\sqrt{2}$ reduces to $xy = 1$. Graph the equation $xy = 1$ and identify the asymptotes.

3. Given points $F_1(1, 0)$ and $F_2(-1, 0)$ and an arbitrary point $P(x, y)$, let m_1 and m_2 be the slopes of the lines that contain $\overline{PF_2}$ and $\overline{PF_2}$, respectively. Find an equation for the set of all points such that $m_1 m_2 = 1$ and identify the graph.

Develop Mastery

1. Given points $F_1(-3, 0)$ and $F_2(3, 0)$ and $P(x, y)$, suppose that the sum of the distances from P to F_1 and from P to F_2 is 10. From the equation $|\overline{PF_1}| + |\overline{PF_2}| = 10$, show that coordinates of $P(x, y)$ must satisfy the equation $\frac{x^2}{25} + \frac{y^2}{16} = 1$.

2. Given points $F_1(0, -3)$ and $F_2(0, 3)$ and $P(x, y)$, suppose that the differences of the distances $|\overline{PF_1}| - |\overline{PF_2}|$ is ± 4. From the equation $|\overline{PF_1}| -$

$|\overline{PF_2}| = \pm 4$, show that the coordinates of $P(x, y)$ must satisfy the equation $\frac{y^2}{4} - \frac{x^2}{5} = 1$.

Exercises 3–12 An equation is given for either an ellipse or a hyperbola in standard position.

(a) Identify the curve, and find the coordinates of the vertices and the foci.

(b) For an ellipse give the lengths of the major and minor axes; for a hyperbola, find equations for the asymptotes.

(c) Sketch the graph.

3. $\frac{x^2}{9} + \frac{y^2}{4} = 1$ **4.** $\frac{x^2}{4} + \frac{y^2}{9} = 1$

5. $\frac{x^2}{9} - \frac{y^2}{4} = 1$ **6.** $\frac{x^2}{4} - \frac{y^2}{9} = 1$

7. $4x^2 + 5y^2 = 20$ **8.** $4x^2 - 5y^2 = 20$

9. $5x^2 - 4y^2 = 20$ **10.** $5x^2 + 4y^2 = 20$

11. $x^2 = 9y^2 - 144$ **12.** $x^2 = 144 - 9y^2$

Exercises 13–19 Find an equation in standard form for the ellipse satisfying the given conditions.

13. Foci $(\pm 3, 0)$, vertices $(\pm 5, 0)$

14. Foci $(0, \pm 2)$, vertices $(0, \pm 4)$

15. Foci $(\pm 2, 0)$, major axis 6

16. Vertices $(\pm 5, 0)$, minor axis 4

17. Vertices $(\pm 5, 0)$, contains $(4, -1)$

18. Contains $(2, 1)$ and $(1, -\frac{\sqrt{7}}{2})$

19. Minor axis 12, contains $(5, 4)$ (Two solutions)

Exercises 20–26 Find an equation for the hyperbola in standard position satisfying the given conditions.

20. Foci $(\pm 3, 0)$, vertices $(\pm 2, 0)$

21. Foci $(0, \pm 4)$, vertices $(0, \pm 2)$

22. Foci $(\pm 3, 0)$, asymptote $y = x$

23. Vertices $(\pm 1, 0)$, asymptote $y = 2x$

24. Vertices $(0, \pm 1)$, asymptote $y = \frac{3}{2}x$

25. Contains $(2, -1)$ and $(\sqrt{10}, 5)$

26. Vertices $(0, \pm 4)$, asymptotes are perpendicular to each other

27. Show that the length of each latus rectum of an ellipse is $\frac{2b^2}{a}$. (*Hint:* Find the coordinates of the endpoints of the vertical chord through the focus.)

28. Show that the length of each latus rectum of a hyperbola is $\frac{2b^2}{a}$. (*Hint:* Find the coordinates of the endpoints of the vertical chord through the focus.)

At top of right column (continuation):
$|\overline{PF_2}| = \pm 4$, show that the coordinates of $P(x, y)$ must satisfy the equation $\frac{y^2}{4} - \frac{x^2}{5} = 1$.

Exercises 29–32   Find the coordinates of all intersection points of each pair of curves, and show the solutions graphically.

29. $4x^2 + 3y^2 = 12$, with the line containing $(\frac{3}{2}, -1)$ and the upper focus point of the ellipse.

30. $x^2 - y^2 = 8$, with the line containing $(-3, 1)$ and the right focus point of the hyperbola.

31. $x^2 + 3y^2 = 1$; $3x^2 + y^2 = 1$

32. $4y^2 - x^2 = 36$; $32y = x^2 + 96$

33. Find an equation for the parabola with vertex at the left focus of the ellipse $9x^2 + 25y^2 = 900$ and that contains the endpoints of the right latus rectum of the same ellipse.

34. Let C be the circle having as diameter the segment with ends at the foci of the hyperbola $5x^2 - 4y^2 = 9$. Show that C also contains the foci of the conjugate hyperbola $4y^2 - 5x^2 = 9$.

35. An elliptical garden is to be laid out in a rectangular area 16 feet by 20 feet by driving stakes at the foci and tying an end of a rope to each stake. Where should the stakes be placed, and how long a rope is needed to make the largest possible ellipse in the available area?

36. "The Ellipse" in Washington, D.C., is an elliptical grassy area between the White House and the Washington Monument. The major axis is approximately 500 yards and the minor axis is approximately 425 yards. How far are the foci from the vertices of the ellipse?

37. Suppose an auditorium is to be built with cross sections in the shape of a half-ellipse, as in the diagram. The building is to be 250 feet long and 75 feet high. If a speaking platform is located at one focus of the ellipse, how far from the nearest end of the building should it be?

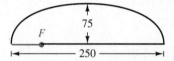

| **SECTION 10.4** | **Translation of Axes** |

. . . [T]his is . . . a mathematical form that has survived several scientific revolutions! Cartesian coordinates imply continuity, as well as the notion of space as a backdrop against which objects move.
    F. David Peat

Early in Chapter 2 we considered the effects of various translations and reflections on core graphs, an idea we have revisited throughout the study of functions and graphs. From the graph G of an equation $y = f(x)$, we can get graphs of equations such as $y = f(x) \pm c$ or $y = f(x \pm b)$ by translating G vertically or horizontally, as suggested in Figure 10.39.

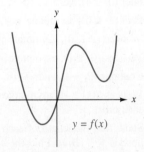

(a)

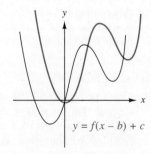

(b)   Graph translated c units upward

(c)   Graph translated upward and to the right

FIGURE 10.39

In this section we explore the use of translations to simplify equations, to change coordinates, and as an aid in graphing.

An equation that describes a given plane curve depends on the coordinate system we choose. Ordinarily we try to choose coordinates that give us a simple equation. A given equation may be easier to graph, however, in a different coordinate system.

We recognize $(x - 1)^2 + (y + 2)^2 = 9$ as an equation for the circle with center $(1, -2)$ and radius 3. We can simplify the equation by substituting X for $x - 1$ and Y for $y + 2$. The given equation becomes $X^2 + Y^2 = 9$, which is an equation for a circle with center at the origin of the XY-coordinate system. The circle has not changed, but the equation is simpler.

Suppose we have two systems of rectangular coordinates, an xy system and an XY system, positioned so that the x-axis and the X-axis are parallel, and the y-axis and the Y-axis are parallel, both oriented in the same directions, as shown in Figure 10.40. A change from one system to the other *translates* the axes horizontally and vertically.

Each point in the plane then has coordinates relative to the xy-system, and different coordinates relative to the XY system. To avoid confusion as to which coordinates we intend, we shall use round parentheses, (x, y), to denote coordinates in the xy system, and square brackets, $[X, Y]$, for coordinates relative to the XY system.

To translate from the xy system to a new system centered at point (h, k), as in Figure 10.40, we can derive transformation formulas to determine the coordinates of a point in one system based on its coordinates in the other system. Let P be any point in the plane. From the diagram

$$x = X + h \qquad \text{and} \qquad y = Y + k$$
$$X = x - h \qquad \text{and} \qquad Y = y - k$$

Although these equations come from a diagram in which the new origin is in the first quadrant of the old system, it is easy to verify that the same equations hold wherever the new origin is located.

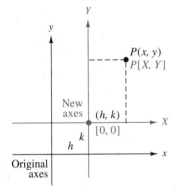

FIGURE 10.40

Coordinate Equations for Translation of Axes

Assume a given xy-coordinate system and a new XY-coordinate system, with axes parallel to the given axes, centered at the point (h, k). Coordinates in the two systems are related by these equations:

$$\begin{cases} x = X + h \\ y = Y + k \end{cases} \tag{1}$$

$$\begin{cases} X = x - h \\ Y = y - k \end{cases} \tag{2}$$

EXAMPLE 1   Suppose the xy-coordinate system is translated to a new system centered at point $(-2, 3)$.

(a)   Draw the new coordinate axes and give the translation equations.

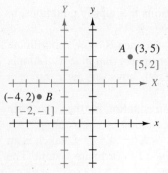

FIGURE 10.41

(b) Locate points $A(3, 5)$ and $B[-2, -1]$ in your figure and label each with the appropriate names in both coordinate systems.

Solution

(a) The two coordinate systems are shown in Figure 10.41, with the new axes indicated in color. Substituting -2 for h and 3 for k into translation Equations 1 and 2 gives

$$\begin{cases} x = X - 2 \\ y = Y + 3 \end{cases} \quad \text{and} \quad \begin{cases} X = x + 2 \\ Y = y - 3 \end{cases}$$

(b) For point $A(3, 5)$ substituting 3 for x and 5 for y in the translation equations gives $X = 5$ and $Y = 2$. Thus point A has the names $(3, 5)$ and $[5, 2]$. The XY name for B is $[-2, -1]$. Substituting $X = -2$ and $Y = -1$ into the translation equations gives $x = -4$ and $y = 2$. Both points are shown in the figure. ▲

We have learned that $x^2 + y^2 + Ax + By + C = 0$ is an equation for a circle whenever $A^2 + B^2 - 4C > 0$. To identify the center and radius, complete the squares in x and y and then translate coordinates. Other conic sections also may have simpler equations in translated coordinate systems. By completing the square in one or both variables, we can identify the vertex of a parabola or the center of an ellipse or a hyperbola. The procedure is illustrated in the next example.

EXAMPLE 2   Complete the squares in x and y and identify the graph of the equation $4x^2 + 9y^2 + 16x - 54y + 61 = 0$ as a conic section by translating axes. Sketch the graph.

Solution

Strategy: After completing the squares, find the values of h and k for transformation Equations 2. The conic section will be in standard position relative to the new coordinate system, and hence easy to graph.

First collect the x terms and y terms and factor out the coefficients of x^2 and y^2.

$$4(x^2 + 4x) + 9(y^2 - 6y) = -61$$

Now complete the squares by adding the same quantities to both sides of the equation. Note that this implies adding $4 \cdot 4$ and $9 \cdot 9$, not just 4 and 9.

$$4(x^2 + 4x + 4) + 9(y^2 - 6y + 9) = -61 + 4 \cdot 4 + 9 \cdot 9$$

$$4(x + 2)^2 + 9(y - 3)^2 = 36$$

Translate axes to a new system in which $X = x + 2$, $Y = y - 3$:

$$4X^2 + 9Y^2 = 36.$$

Dividing through by 36 gives an equation for an ellipse in standard form.

$$\frac{X^2}{9} + \frac{Y^2}{4} = 1$$

The equation is that of an ellipse in standard position relative to the XY-coordinate system. Comparing the translation equations $X = x + 2$, $Y = y - 3$ with Equations 2 gives the values $h = -2$, $k = 3$. Therefore the origin

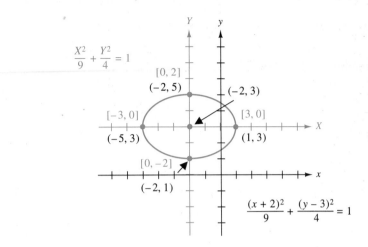

FIGURE 10.42

of the new coordinate system (the XY system) is at point $(-2, 3)$ in the old system. In the new system, draw the ellipse shown in Figure 10.42. The coordinates of the vertices are $[\pm3, 0]$, and the ends of the minor axis are at $[0, \pm2]$. Relative to the original axes, these points have the coordinates $(-5, 3),(1, 3)$, and $(-2, 1), (-2, 5)$ as shown in the figure. ▲

EXAMPLE 3 Find an equation for the hyperbola shown in Figure 10.43 with center at $(2, 1)$, vertices at $(0, 1)$, $(4, 1)$ and foci at $(-1, 1)$, $(5, 1)$.

Solution

Strategy: From the figure, the hyperbola is in standard position relative to the coordinate system centered at $(2, 1)$, so $h = 2, k = 1$. Knowing $a = 2$ and $c = 3$, find b.

Follow the strategy. With respect to the XY-system centered at $(2, 1)$, the equation has the form $\frac{X^2}{a^2} - \frac{Y^2}{b^2} = 1$ with vertices at $[\pm2, 0]$ and foci at $[\pm3, 0]$. With

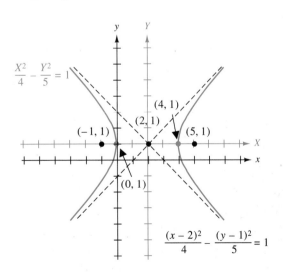

FIGURE 10.43

$c = 3$, $a = 2$, $b^2 = 3^2 - 2^2 = 5$. The XY equation is

$$\frac{X^2}{4} - \frac{Y^2}{5} = 1.$$

Translation Equation 2 with $h = 2$, $k = 1$ give $X = x - 2$, $Y = y - 1$. Making these substitutions, the desired equation becomes

$$\frac{(x - 2)^2}{4} - \frac{(y - 1)^2}{5} = 1. \quad \blacktriangle$$

Examples 2 and 3 show a consistent pattern in equations for the entire family of conic sections.

Conic Section Standard Form Equations

Suppose a conic section is in standard position relative to a translated coordinate system centered at (h, k). The conic section has an equation in one of these standard forms:

Circle: $(x - h)^2 + (y - k)^2 = r^2$

Parabola: $(x - h)^2 = \pm 4p(y - k)$

or $(y - k)^2 = \pm 4p(x - h)$

Ellipse: $\dfrac{(x - h)^2}{a^2} + \dfrac{(y - k)^2}{b^2} = 1$

or $\dfrac{(x - h)^2}{b^2} + \dfrac{(y - k)^2}{a^2} = 1$

Hyperbola: $\dfrac{(x - h)^2}{a^2} - \dfrac{(y - k)^2}{b^2} = 1$

or $\dfrac{(y - k)^2}{a^2} - \dfrac{(x - h)^2}{b^2} = 1$

Expanding, collecting terms, and simplifying notation, all of the standard form conic section equations can be written in the same general form,

$$Ax^2 + Cy^2 + Dx + Ey + F = 0, \tag{3}$$

where not both A and C are zero. The type of curve represented in Equation 3, except for degenerate cases such as a point-circle with radius 0, is determined by the values of the coefficients A and C. The condition for each conic section is:

Circle: $A = C$

Parabola: $A \cdot C = 0$ (One of A or C is zero.)

Ellipse: $A \cdot C > 0$ (A and C have the same sign, and are unequal.)

Hyperbola: $A \cdot C < 0$ (A and C have opposite signs.)

If Equation 3 has Bxy as a term, where B is not zero, then rotate axes. See Develop Mastery Exercises 39 through 46.

EXERCISES 10.4

Check Your Understanding

Exercises 1–6 True or False. Give reasons for your conclusion. The xy system of coordinates is translated so the origin $[0, 0]$ for the new XY system is at point $(-2, 4)$. Continue the notation used in the text: (x, y) is a point relative to the original coordinate system, and $[x, y]$ is the same point relative to the new, translated coordinate system.

1. The same point has the names $(2, -3)$ and $[4, -7]$.
2. The graph of $x + y = 1$ is the same as that of $X + Y + 1 = 0$.
3. The graph of $(x - 2)^2 + (y + 4)^2 = 9$ is the same as that of $X^2 + Y^2 = 9$.
4. The graph of $y = 4x^2 + 16x + 20$ is the same as that of $Y = 4X^2$.
5. The origin of the xy system has the name $[2, -4]$.
6. Point $[1, -1]$ is in the fourth quadrant of the original xy system.

Exercises 7–10 The XY system of coordinates is a translation of the xy system so that $(-2, 3)$ is the same point as $[0, 0]$. Complete the sentence by selecting form the list below *all choices* that make the statement true. (*Hint:* First draw a diagram.)

(a) QI of the xy system **(b)** QII of the xy system
(c) QIII of the xy system **(d)** QIV of the xy system
(e) QI of the XY system **(f)** QII of the XY system
(g) QIII of the XY system **(h)** QIV of the XY system

7. Point $[0, -4]$ is in ————.
8. Point $(-3, 1)$ is in ————.
9. Line $3x + 2y = 0$ contains no points in ————.
10. Circle $x^2 + y^2 = 1$ contains no points in ————.

Explore and Discover

In Section 10.2 a parabola was defined as the set of points that are equidistant from a fixed point and a fixed line.

1. Find an equation for the set of points that are equidistant from point $(1, 0)$ and line $x = -1$ [in the diagram the set of points $P(x, y)$ such that $d_1 = d_2$].
2. Referring to the figure, find an equation for the set of points $P(x, y)$ such that $d_1 = 2d_2$. Identify and sketch the graph, then find an equation for the set of points

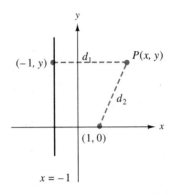

$P(x, y)$ such that $d_1 = \frac{1}{2}d_2$. Identify and sketch the graph.

3. On the basis of your results from Exercise 2, make a guess about the kind of curve defined as the set of points whose distance from a fixed line is some constant multiple (greater than 1) of the distance from a fixed point. What if the multiple is less than 1?

Develop Mastery

Exercises 1–2 Find the translation equations and the new coordinates of each point when the axes have been translated to the new origin centered as indicated. Sketch the points and show both sets of coordinates.

1. $A(3, 2)$; $B(-4, 1)$; $C[0, -2]$; $D[-3, 1]$; center $(4, 5)$
2. $A(3, 2)$; $B(-4, 1)$ $C[0, -2]$; $D[-3, 1]$; center $(-1, 2)$

Exercises 3–6 Find the new equation that corresponds to the given equation when the axes are translated to a new coordinate system centered at the given point.

3. $x^2 + y^2 - 4x - 2y = 0$; center $(2, 1)$
4. $xy + 3x - y = 4$; center $(1, -3)$
5. $y^2 - 8x + 24 = 0$; center $(3, 0)$
6. $4x^2 - y^2 - 8x + 4y + 4 = 0$; center $(1, 2)$

Exercises 7–20 Identify and sketch the graph of the conic section that corresponds to the equation.

7. $\dfrac{(x - 1)^2}{4} - \dfrac{(y + 1)^2}{9} = 1$
8. $\dfrac{(x - 1)^2}{4} + \dfrac{(y + 1)^2}{16} = 1$

9. $\frac{x^2}{8} + \frac{(y-1)^2}{9} = 1$

10. $\frac{(x+2)^2}{4} - \frac{(y-2)^2}{16} = 1$

11. $(x + \frac{1}{2})^2 + 16(y - \frac{3}{2})^2 = 16$

12. $4(x + 1.25)^2 - (y - 2.5)^2 = 4$

13. $x^2 + 6x - y + 4 = 0$

14. $y^2 + 4y - 3x + 1 = 0$

15. $9x^2 + 4y^2 - 18x - 27 = 0$

16. $4x^2 + 9y^2 - 8x + 54y + 49 = 0$

17. $x^2 + y^2 + 6x - 2y + 6 = 0$

18. $x^2 + 4y^2 - 4x - 8y - 8 = 0$

19. $x^2 - 4y^2 + 2x + 16y - 19 = 0$

20. $8x^2 - 4y^2 + 8x + 12y - 23 = 0$

Exercises 21–25   Find an equation in x and y for the ellipse specified by the given conditions.

21. Foci $(3, 2)$, $(3, -2)$; major axis 6

22. Vertices $(1, 5)$, $(1, 1)$; minor axis 2

23. Vertices $(3, -1)$, $(-1, -1)$, contains $(1, 0)$

24. Center $(3, -1)$, vertex $(5, -1)$, focus $(\frac{9}{2}, -1)$

25. Center $(-3, 0)$, vertex $(-3, 3)$, minor axis 4

Exercises 26–30   Find an equation in x and y for the hyperbola specified by the given conditions.

26. Vertices $(3, 2)$, $(3, -2)$, contains $(4, 4)$

27. Center $(-2, 1)$, vertex $(-2, 3)$, focus $(-2, 4)$

28. Center $(0, -1)$, vertex $(2, -1)$, focus $(3, -1)$

29. Foci $(4, 2)$, $(-4, 2)$, vertex $(2, 2)$

30. Vertex $(1, 1)$, asymptotes $y = x - 1$, $y = -x + 3$

Exercises 31–38   **(a)** Complete the square on the x and y terms and then write the equation in standard form for a conic section. **(b)** Find the translation equations needed to get an equation of the conic section in standard position relative to the XY axes. Find the resulting XY equation and draw its graph. **(c)** Give the coordinates of foci (if any) or of the center (for a circle) relative to both the xy and XY systems. See Example 2.

31. $x^2 - 6x - y + 4 = 0$

32. $x^2 + 4x - 3y + 1 = 0$

33. $4x^2 + y^2 - 8x + 4y - 8 = 0$

34. $4x^2 + 9y^2 - 18y - 27 = 0$

35. $x^2 + y^2 - 6x + 2y + 6 = 0$

36. $x^2 - 4y^2 - 2x - 16y - 19 = 0$

37. $x^2 - y^2 - 4x - 6y - 9 = 0$

38. $y^2 - x^2 + 6x + 4y - 9 = 0$

Exercises 39–46   *Rotation of Axes*   For given constants A, B, C, and D, graphs of second-degree equations of the form $Ax^2 + Bxy + Cy^2 + D = 0$, are conic sections (including some degenerate cases). If $B \neq 0$, the axes of the conic section are neither horizontal or vertical. By rotating the axes through an angle θ to get a new set of XY axes, it can be shown that the transformation equations are

$$x = X \cos \theta - Y \sin \theta \qquad (5)$$
$$y = X \sin \theta + Y \cos \theta.$$

Draw a diagram and use it to see how Equations 5 are derived. If θ is selected so that $\tan 2\theta = \frac{B}{A - C}$, then the resulting XY equation will contain no XY term. In the following exercises **(a)** select an angle θ between $0°$ and $90°$ such that $\tan 2\theta = \frac{B}{A - C}$ and then find $\cos 2\theta$. **(b)** Use the identities $\sin \theta = \sqrt{\frac{1 - \cos 2\theta}{2}}$ and $\cos \theta = \sqrt{\frac{1 + \cos 2\theta}{2}}$ to write out transformation Equations 5.

(c) Determine an equation for the curve relative to the XY coordinate system, identify the type of conic section, and draw a graph.

39. $x^2 + 4xy - 2y^2 - 6 = 0$

40. $x^2 - 4xy - 2y^2 - 6 = 0$

41. $x^2 - \sqrt{3}xy + 2y^2 - 10 = 0$

42. $4x^2 - 3xy - 18 = 0$

43. $x^2 + 8xy + 7y^2 - 1 = 0$

44. $x^2 + \sqrt{3}xy + 2y^2 - 5 = 0$

45. $9x^2 - 6xy + 17y^2 - 72 = 0$

46. $x^2 + 3xy + y^2 - 10 = 0$

Exercises 47–48   Suppose the xy axes are rotated through angle θ.

(a) Write out the transformation Equations 5.

(b) What is the name of point A relative to the XY system of coordinates? (*Hint:* Solve a system of equations.)

47. $\theta = 30°$, $A(2, 2)$ 48. $\theta = 45°$, $A(0, 2)$

SECTION 10.5	Polar Coordinates

*In such examples as Lobachevsky's non-Euclidean geometry, or
Cayley's matrix theory, or Galois' and Jordan's group theory, or the
algebraic topology of the mid-twentieth century, pure mathematics
seemed to have left far behind any physical interpretation or utility.
And yet, in the cases mentioned here, and many others, physicists later
found in these "useless" mathematical abstractions just the tools they
needed.*
        Reuben Hersh

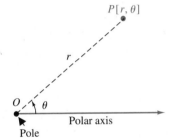

FIGURE 10.44

In Section 10.4 we considered alternative ways to get equations for given plane
curves by changing coordinate systems from one rectangular system to another.
Now we consider an entirely different way to name points using distances and
angles: **polar coordinates.**

As with rectangular coordinates, polar coordinates begin with a single
point that serves as an origin O, which we call the **pole.** From the pole we take
an initial ray called the **polar axis,** as shown in Figure 10.44. To each point P
in the plane we assign an ordered pair $[r, \theta]$, where r is the **directed distance**
from O to P, and θ is a **directed angle** from the polar axis to $\overline{OP}$. We use the
convention for positive and negative angles from Chapter 5 (counterclockwise is
positive, clockwise is negative). We may use either radian- or degree-measure for
θ. The ray OP from the pole through P is the **θ-ray.**

Rectangular coordinates allow precisely one ordered pair (x, y) for every
point in the plane. Polar coordinates for a given point are never unique. For
instance, if P is the point 3 units from O along the 60° ray, then both $[3, 60°]$ (or
in radian measure $[3, \frac{\pi}{3}]$) and $[3, -300°]$ are names for P. See Figure 10.45. In
fact, because infinitely many different angles are coterminal with $\overline{OP}$, there are
infinitely many polar coordinate names for P.

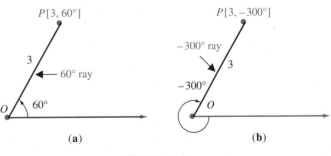

FIGURE 10.45

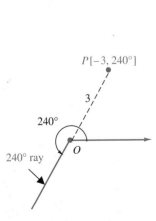

FIGURE 10.46

Furthermore, in addition to multiple angle names, another option arises.
We said that r is a *directed* distance, implying that r can assume positive or
negative values. For a negative number r, to reach the point $[r, \theta]$, we go r units
in the opposite direction. We can reach the point $P[3, 60°]$ by going -3 units
along the 240° ray, so that $[-3, 240°]$ is yet another name for P. See Figure
10.46. For the pole, $[0, \theta]$ names the pole, for any angle θ.

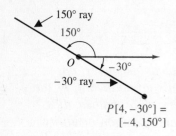

$P[4, -30°] =$
$[-4, 150°]$

FIGURE 10.47

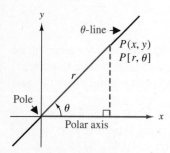

FIGURE 10.48

Strategy: Begin with a
diagram that shows P and Q
and one for A and B, as a
check on Equations 1 and 2.

EXAMPLE 1   Point P is 4 units from the pole O along the $-30°$ ray. Describe all possible polar coordinate names (using degree measure) for P.

Solution

First draw a diagram to show P. See Figure 10.47. Clearly, one name for P is $[4, -30°]$, but an angle name can be any angle coterminal with $-30°$, so P can be named by any of the pairs $[4, -30° + k \cdot 360°,]$ where k is any integer. We can also reach P by going 4 units in the opposite direction on the 150° ray. Hence P can be named as well by $[-4, 150° + k \cdot 360°]$ for any integer k. ▲

Relating Polar Coordinates and Rectangular Coordinates

If we want the option of choosing either polar or rectangular coordinate equations for a given curve, we must be able to relate the two systems. Take the pole O at the origin of the xy system and the positive x axis as the polar axis. With the diagram in Figure 10.48, we can read off the relations between polar and rectangular coordinates for a given point P.

Polar–Rectangular Coordinate Transformation Equations

$$x = r \cos \theta \quad \text{and} \quad y = r \sin \theta \qquad (1)$$

$$r^2 = x^2 + y^2 \quad \text{and} \quad \tan \theta = \frac{y}{x} \qquad (2)$$

EXAMPLE 2   Use the polar–rectangular coordinate transformation equations to **(a)** express $P[4, \frac{\pi}{6}]$ and $Q[-2, 90°]$ in rectangular coordinates, and **(b)** express $A(-2, 2)$ and $B(-1, 0)$ in polar coordinates.

Solution

(a)   Follow the strategy. See Figure 10.49a. From transformation Equations 1, for P

$$x = 4 \cos\left(\frac{\pi}{6}\right) = 4 \cdot \frac{\sqrt{3}}{2} = 2\sqrt{3} \qquad y = 4 \sin\left(\frac{\pi}{6}\right) = 4 \cdot \frac{1}{2} = 2.$$

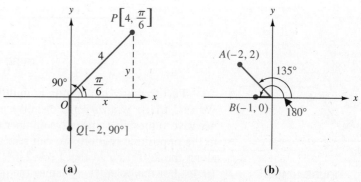

(a)   (b)

FIGURE 10.49

Similarly, for Q,

$$x = -2 \cos 90° = -2(0) = 0 \qquad y = -2 \sin 90° = -2(1) = -2.$$

Thus both $[4, \frac{\pi}{6}]$ and $(2\sqrt{3}, 2)$ are names for point P, while $[-2, 90°]$ and $(0, -2)$ both represent point Q.

(b) From transformation Equations 2, for A choose r and θ to satisfy

$$r^2 = (-2)^2 + 2^2 = 8 \qquad \text{and} \qquad \tan \theta = (-2)/2 = -1.$$

One such pair is $r = 2\sqrt{2}$ and $\theta = 135°$, so point A has names $(-2, 2)$ and $[2\sqrt{2}, 135°]$. For B,

$$r^2 = (-1)^2 + 0^2 = 1 \qquad \text{and} \qquad \tan \theta = 0/(-1) = 0.$$

We can take $r = 1$ and $\theta = 180°$, or take r to be -1 and any value of θ that is coterminal with $0°$, so $(-1, 0)$, $[1, 180°]$, and $[-1, 0°]$ are all names for B. See Figure 10.49b. ▲

EXAMPLE 3 Express the equation $x^2 + y^2 - 2y = 0$ in polar coordinates.

Solution

Strategy: Use $x = r \cos \theta$ and $y = r \sin \theta$. Simplify.

Follow the strategy. Using the identity $\cos^2 \theta + \sin^2 \theta = 1$,

$$(r \cos \theta)^2 + (4 \sin \theta)^2 - 2(r \sin \theta) = 0,$$

$$r^2(\cos^2 \theta + \sin^2 \theta) - 2r \sin \theta = 0 \qquad r^2 - 2r \sin \theta = 0.$$

Simplifying and dividing by r,

$$r = 2 \sin \theta.$$

Since we cannot divide by 0, check to see that we do not lose the point where $r = 0$ (the pole) when we divide by r. In particular, see if there is still a value of θ for which the pole is on the graph. When $\theta = 0$, then $r = 2 \sin 0 = 0$, so $[0, 0]$ is still on the graph. ▲

EXAMPLE 4 Express the polar equation $r = \frac{4}{2 \sin \theta - \cos \theta}$ in terms of rectangular coordinates.

Solution

Write the given equation as $r(2 \sin \theta - \cos \theta) = 4$, or as $2(r \sin \theta) - (r \cos \theta) = 4$. Using transformation Equations 1, replace $r \sin \theta$ by y and $r \cos \theta$ by x to get

$$2y - x = 4.$$

Since the graph of $2y - x = 4$ is a line, the graph of $r = \frac{4}{2 \sin \theta - \cos \theta}$ is the same line. ▲

Polar Functions and Graphs

So far in this course we have devoted considerable attention to drawing graphs of functions in rectangular coordinates. The analogous situation in polar coordinates is graphing functions expressible as $r = f(\theta)$. In many cases we can express the polar equation in rectangular form and draw the graph using familiar techniques. For many polar functions, though, the equation in x and y is difficult

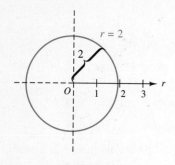

FIGURE 10.50

Graph of $r = 2$

to handle and it is easier to draw the graph directly from the polar equation. We will look at examples of both kinds of equations, those that are fairly easy to translate into recognizable rectangular equivalents, and those where it is easier to draw the graph directly in polar form.

EXAMPLE 5   Draw a graph of the equation $r = 2$.

Solution

Since the r-coordinate of a point measures the distance from the pole, the equation $r = 2$ is satisfied by all points that are 2 units from the pole, precisely the condition for the circle centered at the origin with radius 2. See Figure 10.50. In this case, we can also translate to rectangular coordinates. Squaring both sides of the equation and using Equation 2,

$$r^2 = 4 \quad \text{or} \quad x^2 + y^2 = 4,$$

the familiar form for the equation of the circle. We must be careful about introducing extraneous points when squaring both sides, but in this instance we already saw that all points of the circle satisfy the original equation. ▲

Strategy: Try some equivalent forms, looking for $r \cos \theta$, $r \sin \theta$, or r^2.

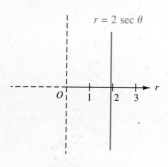

FIGURE 10.51

Graph of $r = 2 \sec \theta$

EXAMPLE 6   Draw a graph of the function $r = 2 \sec \theta$.

Solution

The transformation equations involve certain expressions listed in the strategy. Since $\sec \theta = \frac{1}{\cos \theta}$, multiply through by $\cos \theta$:

$$r(\cos \theta) = (2 \sec \theta)(\cos \theta) \quad \text{or} \quad r \cos \theta = 2.$$

For this equation, the transformation Equations 1 yield

$$x = 2,$$

an equation that describes the vertical line in Figure 10.51. ▲

EXAMPLE 7   Draw a graph of the function $r = 2 \sin \theta$.

Solution

We saw in Example 3 that the equation $r = 2 \sin \theta$ is equivalent to $x^2 + y^2 - 2y = 0$, the equation a circle. Without having that example at hand, how could we change to rectangular coordinates? As in the strategy for Example 6, the most convenient expressions involve $r \cos \theta$, $r \sin \theta$, or r^2. In this case, multiply both sides by r, to get two such expressions:

$$r^2 = 2r \sin \theta \quad \text{from which} \quad x^2 + y^2 = 2y.$$

Completing the square in the y terms, $x^2 + (y - 1)^2 = 1$, the circle shown in Figure 10.52. As a partial check, note that the points with polar coordinates $[0, 0]$, $[1, \frac{\pi}{6},]$ and $[2, \frac{\pi}{2}]$ all satisfy the equation $r = 2 \sin \theta$. ▲

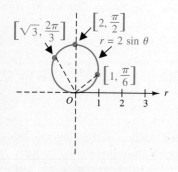

FIGURE 10.52

Graph of $r = 2 \sin \theta$

Sometimes the expressions in the transformation equations do not lead to a rectangular from that is any better than the polar form, as shown in the following example.

GRAPHING IN POLAR COORDINATES

The TI-81 and the Casio *fx-7700G* handle polar coordinate graphing quite differently, but for both, be sure you are in radian mode before starting.

TI

The calculator uses the transformation equations $x = r \cos \theta$ $y = r \sin \theta$ in parametric mode, so to graph the function $r = f(\theta)$, first go to the MODE screen and select "Param" and "Polar." On Y= enter $X_{1T} = f(T) \cos T$, and $Y_{2T} = f(T) \sin T$.

Casio

SHIFT MODE − (POL) puts the calculator in polar mode, so Graph displays "Graph r=" and X,θ,T enters θ. To graph the function $r = f(\theta)$, press Graph and then enter $f(\theta)$ directly.

EXAMPLE   Graph the function $r = \sin 2\theta$.

Solution

TI

On Y= , $X_{1T} = \sin 2T(\cos T)$, and $Y_{2T} = \sin 2T(\sin T)$. Set range values at T:[0, 6.3], 0.1, X:[−1.5, 1.5], 1, Y:[−1, 1], 1, then GRAPH .

Casio

Set range values X:[−1.5, 1.5], 1, Y:[−1, 1], 1, $T{:}\theta$:[0, 6.3], 0.1, and then on the home screen Graph sin 2 X,θ,T .

The four-petaled rose shown in Figure 10.56 should be traced out in precisely the manner described in Example 9, first in QI, then in QIV (where θ is in QII and r is negative), then in QIII, and finally QII (from θ in QIV). Trace along the curve again, watching both the cursor and the r and θ values displayed at the bottom of the screen. Note where the r values are positive and negative. ▲

Exercises

1. (a) Add the graph of the function $r = 1$ to the graph of $r = \sin 2\theta$ from the example. (*Hint:* On the TI, $X_{2T} = 1 \cos T$, $Y_{2T} = 1 \sin T$.)
   (b) Trace around both curves, using the up arrow to jump back and forth between the curves for several values of θ. At each jump, the θ value remains the same (because the cursor stays on the same θ-ray). For what values of θ are the curves in different quadrants?

2. Graph the functions (a) $r = \cos 2\theta$ and (b) $r = \cos 3\theta$. (c) Explain why there are four petals for $r = \cos 2\theta$, but only three petals for $r = \cos 3\theta$. (*Hint:* Trace the complete curve for $r = \cos 3\theta$.)

3. Graph the limaçons and cardioids: (a) $r = 1 + 2 \cos \theta$, (b) $r = 2 + 2 \cos \theta$, (c) $r = 3 + 2 \cos \theta$. You will need to choose an appropriate window.

4. On the basis of your graphs in Exercise 3, predict how the graphs of $r = 1 + 2 \sin \theta$, $r = 2 + 2 \sin \theta$, and $r = 3 + 2 \sin \theta$ should be related. Check your predictions by graphing all three curves on the same set of axes.

5. Graph the lemniscates shown in the Brief Catalog of Polar Curves (p. 576).

For Graphers
10.5

EXAMPLE 8

Express the equation $r = \sin 2\theta$ in rectangular coordinates.

Solution

Replace $\sin 2\theta$ by $2 \sin \theta \cos \theta$ (double-angle identity) and then multiply both sides by r^2 to make the right side easily expressible in xy terms:

$$r^3 = 2(r \cos \theta)(r \sin \theta).$$

Since $r = \sqrt{x^2 + y^2}$, the equation becomes

$$(x^2 + y^2)^{3/2} = 2xy. \quad \blacktriangle$$

Quick Graphing from Rectangular Coordinates

We have no experience with an equation of the form in Example 8, and rectangular coordinates are not helpful in graphing $r = \sin 2\theta$. We could make a table of values and hope to identify enough points to get an accurate picture, but experience teaches that point plotting is tedious and can miss important graphical features (unless a calculator or computer can plot hundreds of points). The graphing method illustrated in the next example is useful for a wide variety of polar functions.

Recall that a point with polar coordinates $[r, \theta]$ is located r units from the pole along the θ-ray. To graph a function $r = f(\theta)$, simply show how the r-distance varies as θ changes. Experience with rectangular coordinates can help.

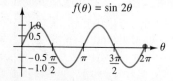

$f(\theta) = \sin 2\theta$

FIGURE 10.53

Rectangular coordinate graph of $f(\theta) = \sin 2\theta$

EXAMPLE 9

Graph the function $r = \sin 2\theta$.

Solution

Treating $r = \sin 2\theta$ as an equation in rectangular coordinates would give the familiar sine curve in Figure 10.53. The sine curve serves as a guide for polar graphing. Observe that as θ goes through first-quadrant values from 0 to $\frac{\pi}{2}$, the r values start at 0, increase to 1, and then return to 0. Plotting the same behavior in polar coordinates, the r values shown by arrows in Figure 10.54a correspond to the r values in Figure 10.54b. Just as the arch of the sine curve is symmetric,

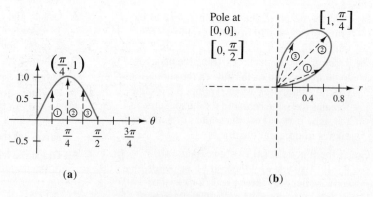

(a)   (b)

FIGURE 10.54

Graph of $r = \sin 2\theta$ (r is positive if $0 < \theta < \frac{\pi}{2}$)

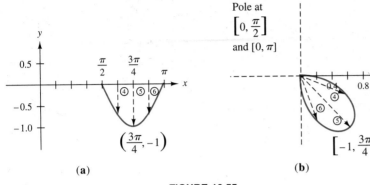

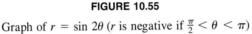

(a)

FIGURE 10.55

Graph of $r = \sin 2\theta$ (r is negative if $\frac{\pi}{2} < \theta < \pi$)

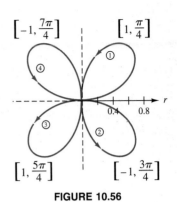

(b)

FIGURE 10.56

Graph of $r = \sin 2\theta$

the corresponding piece of the polar graph is symmetric about the ray $\theta = \frac{\pi}{4}$. When θ is in the second quadrant, $\frac{\pi}{2} < \theta < \pi$, the r values are all negative and hence are plotted in the opposite direction along each θ-ray, with the pairing shown in Figure 10.55. Continuing through the θ-interval $[0, 2\pi]$ produces the "four-petal rose" shown in Figure 10.56. Thereafter the curve simply repeats. ▲

Other Polar Graphs

No brief introduction can do more than touch on the tremendous variety of useful polar graphs. The kinds of polar curves you are most likely to encounter in calculus are illustrated in the Brief Catalog. All of the graphs in the catalog can be sketched as illustrated in this section.

Brief Catalog of Curves and Graphs in Polar Coordinates

Assume that a, b, d, and α are given constants.

Line: $r \cos(\theta - \alpha) = d$
$\quad\quad \theta = a$

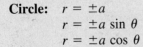

Circle: $r = \pm a$
$\quad\quad\quad r = \pm a \sin \theta$
$\quad\quad\quad r = \pm a \cos \theta$

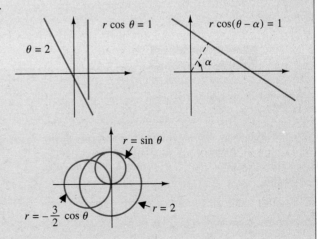

Rose: $r = a \sin n\theta$
       $r = a \cos n\theta$

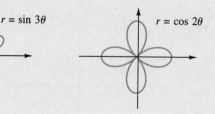

For $0 \le \theta \le 2\pi$, there are n petals if n is odd (each traced twice); $2n$ petals if n is even (each traced once).

Limaçon and cardioid:
$r = a \pm b \sin \theta$
$r = a \pm b \cos \theta$
There is an inside loop if $a < b$, just an indentation if $a > b$, and if $a = b$, the curve is a cardioid (heart-shaped).

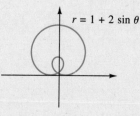

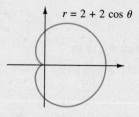

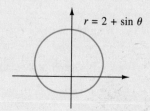

Lemniscate:
$r^2 = \pm a^2 \sin 2\theta$
$r^2 = \pm a^2 \cos 2\theta$

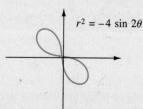

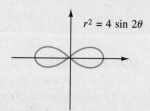

Spiral: $r = \pm a\theta$

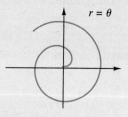

EXERCISES 10.5

Check Your Understanding

Exercises 1–5   True or False. Give reasons for your conclusion. Throughout, the notation is the same as in the text: (x, y) is the name of a point relative to the rectangular coordinate system and $[r, \theta]$ names a point in polar coordinates.

1. Another name for $(\frac{1}{2}, \frac{\sqrt{3}}{2})$ is $[1, \frac{\pi}{3}]$.
2. Another name for $[-2, \frac{5\pi}{4}]$ is $(-\sqrt{2}, \sqrt{2})$.

3. Point $[1, -\frac{\pi}{3}]$ belongs to the graphs of both $r = 1$ and $r^2 - 4r \cos \theta + 1 = 0$.
4. The graph of $r^2 - 4r \cos \theta = 0$ is a circle.
5. The graph of $r = 2 \sin \theta$ contains points in all four quadrants of the rectangular coordinate system.

Exercises 6–10 Complete the sentence by selecting from the list below *all choices* that make the statement true.

(a) $(1, 1)$ (b) $[1, \pi]$ (c) $[1, 1]$ (d) $(-2, 0)$
(e) $[2, -\pi]$ (f) $[-2, 0]$ (g) $[2\sqrt{2}, \frac{7\pi}{4}]$
(h) $[2\sqrt{2}, \frac{-\pi}{4}]$

6. Another name for point $[2, \pi]$ is _____.
7. Another name for point $(2, -2)$ is _____.
8. The center of circle $r = -4 \cos \theta$ is _____.
9. The graph of $r(\cos \theta - \sin \theta) = 4$ is a line that passes through point _____.
10. The graph of $\theta = \frac{\pi}{4}$ is a line that passes through the point _____.

Explore and Discover

1. (a) Convert each equation to rectangular coordinates and identify the conic section:

$$r = \frac{2}{1 - \cos \theta} \qquad r = \frac{2}{1 + \cos \theta}$$

   (b) Do the same for

$$r = \frac{2}{1 + (\frac{1}{2})\cos \theta} \qquad r = \frac{2}{1 + 2 \cos \theta}$$

2. What conic section is represented by the equation

$$r = \frac{2}{1 + b \cos \theta}$$

for various values of b? Write a brief paragraph to give your guess and describe your reasons. What is the effect of using a different numerator, say 1 or -2? What would happen if $\sin \theta$ replaced $\cos \theta$?

Develop Mastery

Exercises 1–4 Draw a diagram that shows the given points. Give both rectangular coordinates and two different sets of polar coordinates for each point.

1. $A[2, \frac{\pi}{3}]$; $B[-2, \frac{\pi}{3}]$ 2. $A(0, -2)$; $B(-2, 0)$
3. $A(\sqrt{3}, -1)$; $B[2, -\frac{\pi}{4}]$ 4. $A(1, 1)$; $B[1, 1]$

Exercises 5–8 Draw a diagram that shows the points described. Give both rectangular coordinates and two different sets of polar coordinates. O denotes the pole.

5. P is 2 units from O on the $\frac{5\pi}{6}$ line; Q is the reflection of P through O.

6. P is -4 units from O on the π-line; Q is the reflection of P through the $\frac{\pi}{4}$ line.

7. A, B, and C are the vertices of the equilateral triangle with sides of length 2, A on the positive y-axis, and the side opposite on the x-axis.

8. P and Q are the points of intersection of the circles $x^2 + y^2 = 1$ and $(x - 2)^2 + y^2 = 3$.

Exercises 9–15 Express the equation in polar coordinates. If the pole is on the graph, find the smallest nonnegative value of θ for which $[0, \theta]$ satisfies the equation, then sketch the graph.

9. $x^2 + y^2 = 4$ 10. $x^2 + y^2 - 4x = 0$
11. $x = 3$ 12. $\sqrt{x^2 + y^2} - 2 = 0$
13. $y = 3x$ 14. $x^2 + y^2 - \sqrt{x^2 + y^2} = y$
15. $x^2 + y^2 - 2x + 2y = 0$

Exercises 16–25 Express the equation in rectangular coordinates and sketch the graph.

16. $r = 3$ 17. $r = -2$
18. $r = 3 \cos \theta$ (*Hint*: Multiply by r.)
19. $r \sec \theta = -4$ 20. $\theta = \frac{-\pi}{4}$
21. $\theta = \frac{3\pi}{4}$ 22. $r(\cos \theta - \sin \theta) = 1$
23. $r = \sin^2 \theta + \cos^2 \theta$
24. $r = 2\sqrt{2} \sin (\theta + \frac{\pi}{4})$
25. $r^2 - 2\sqrt{3}r \cos \theta - 2r \sin \theta = 12$

Exercises 26–32 Graph the equation. Use the Catalog of Polar Curves for reference. Keep graphs of the basic sine and cosine curves handy (see Example 9), and plot a few key points.

26. $r = 3 \cos \theta$ (circle)
27. $r = \cos 3\theta$ (rose)
28. $r = 2 - \cos \theta$ (limaçon)
29. $r = 2 + 2 \cos \theta$ (cardioid)
30. $r^2 = \sin 2\theta$ (lemniscate)
31. $r = \cos^2 \theta - \sin^2 \theta$ (rose)
32. $r + \theta = 0$ (spiral)

Exercises 33–39 Compare the graphs of the pair of equations.

33. $r = 2$ 34. $r = 3 \cos \theta$
    $r = -2$ $r = \cos 3\theta$
35. $r = \sin \theta$ 36. $r = 1 + \cos \theta$
    $r = \sin \theta + 1$ $r = 1 - \cos \theta$
37. $r = 2 + 2 \cos \theta$ 38. $r = 1 + 2 \sin \theta$
    $r = 3 + 2 \cos \theta$ $r = 2 + 1 \sin \theta$
39. $r = \theta$
    $r = -\theta$

Exercises 40–42   First sketch the graphs of the pair of equations and observe that the graphs intersect. Find polar coordinates for each intersection by first solving the pair of equations simultaneously and then checking for common points that have different names in polar coordinates (for instance, the pole).

40. $r = \cos \theta$
$r = -\sin \theta$

41. $r = 1 + \cos \theta$
$r = 1 - \cos \theta$

42. $r = 2 \sin 2\theta$
$r = 1$

43. Use an identity to convert the polar equation $r \cos \left(\theta + \frac{\pi}{6} \right) = 2$ to rectangular coordinates in the form $ax + by = c$. Sketch the graph.

44. Use an identity to convert the polar equation $r \cos (\theta - \alpha) = d$ into rectangular coordinates. Show that the result is an equation for a line in normal form (recall Equation 4 from Section 10.1).

45. By converting to rectangular coordinates, show that $r = a \cos \theta + b \sin \theta$ is an equation for a circle. Find the center and the radius.

Parametric Equations

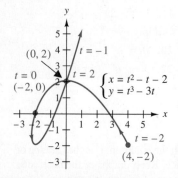

FIGURE 10.57

Graph of $x = t^2 - t - 2$, $y = t^3 - 3t$ for $t \geq 2$

Our experience hitherto justifies us in believing that nature is the realization of the simplest conceivable mathematical ideas.
    Albert Einstein

The path shown in Figure 10.57 fails both the horizontal line test and the vertical line test, so we cannot hope to describe the curve in the form $y = f(x)$ or $x = g(y)$ where f and g are functions. The graph can, however, show the path of a point moving in the plane in the direction indicated by the arrows. As the point moves, its location and coordinates are functions of t. These equations describe the motion:

$$x = t^2 - t - 2 \quad \text{and} \quad y = t^3 - 3t. \tag{1}$$

Equations 1 are **parametric equations** for the curve in Figure 10.57 and the variable t is called a **parameter.**

Definition: Parametric Equations for a Curve

If f and g are functions defined on an interval $[a, b]$, then

$$x = f(t) \quad \text{and} \quad y = g(t) \qquad t \in [a, b] \tag{2}$$

are parametric equations for the curve C which consists of all points $P(t)$ where

$$P(t) = (f(t), g(t)) \text{ for } t \in [a, b].$$

So there was one year spent largely on ordinary differential equations. I had a taste of real life and found that mathematics could actually be used for something.

    Irving Kaplansky

In the above definition the interval for t may be the set of all real numbers, but if the interval is finite, then $P(a)$ is the **initial point** and $P(b)$ is the **terminal point** of the curve.

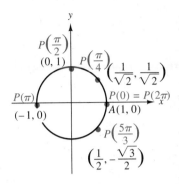

FIGURE 10.58

EXAMPLE 1 Describe the curve C defined by the parametric equations $x = \cos t$ and $y = \sin t$, $0 \le t \le 2\pi$.

Solution

First plot a few points as given by $P(t) = (\cos t, \sin t)$.

$P(0) = (\cos 0, \sin 0) = (1, 0)$, $\qquad P(\frac{\pi}{4}) = (\cos \frac{\pi}{4}, \sin \frac{\pi}{4}) = (\frac{1}{\sqrt{2}}, \frac{1}{\sqrt{2}})$

$P(\frac{\pi}{2}) = (\cos \frac{\pi}{2}, \sin \frac{\pi}{2}) = (0, 1)$ $\qquad P(\pi) = (\cos \pi, \sin \pi) = (-1, 0)$.

$P(\frac{3\pi}{2}) = (\cos \frac{3\pi}{2}, \sin \frac{3\pi}{2}) = (0, -1)$ $\qquad P(2\pi) = (\cos 2\pi, \sin 2\pi) = (1, 0)$.

In this case the initial point and the terminal point of curve C coincide (both have coordinates $(1, 0)$, and all of these points are on the unit circle. See Figure 10.58. Since every point on the unit circle has coordinates $(\cos t, \sin t)$ where t measures either the distance of a point $P(t)$ moving along the curve from the point $A(1, 0)$, or the central angle in radians, curve C is precisely the unit circle. ▲

Sometimes it is helpful to relate x and y directly by eliminating the parameter between the equations $x = f(t)$, $y = g(t)$. It may be possible to eliminate the parameter by solving one equation for the parameter and substituting into the other equation, or, perhaps, using trigonometric identities. One advantage of parametric equations, however, is that they can define a specified portion of a given curve. Different parametric representations may describe different portions of the same curve, or portions traversed in different directions, as illustrated in the following example.

EXAMPLE 2 Show that each of the following parametric equations represents a portion of the circle $x^2 + y^2 = 4$. In each case identify the portion of the circle and the direction in which the point $P(x, y)$ traverses the curve as the parameter increases.

(a) $x = 2 \cos t$ $\qquad 0 \le t \le \dfrac{\pi}{2}$ $\qquad$ **(b)** $x = 2 \cos \pi t$ $\qquad 0 \le t \le 1$

$\quad\ y = 2 \sin t$ $\qquad\qquad\qquad\qquad\qquad\ \ y = -2 \sin \pi t$

(c) $x = \dfrac{2}{\sqrt{m^2 + 1}}$ $\qquad y = \dfrac{2m}{\sqrt{m^2 + 1}}$ $\qquad -\infty < m < \infty$

Solution

Strategy: To verify that the given parametric equations satisfy the equation of the circle, calculate the quantity $x^2 + y^2$ to verify that $x^2 + y^2 = 4$. For the direction and portion of the circle, identify the starting and ending points [for **(a)** and **(b)**] and plot some points.

Follow the strategy.

(a) $\qquad x^2 + y^2 = (2 \cos t)^2 + (2 \sin t)^2$

$\qquad\qquad\qquad = 4 \cos^2 t + 4 \sin^2 t = 4(\cos^2 t + \sin^2 t) = 4 \cdot 1 = 4.$

Thus each point $P(x, y)$ whose coordinates are given by

$$x = 2 \cos t \qquad y = 2 \sin t$$

lies on the circle $x^2 + y^2 = 4$. Parts **(b)** and **(c)** can be treated in a similar manner. See Exercises 39 and 40.

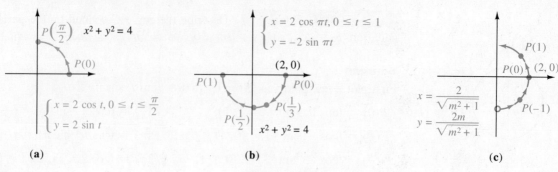

FIGURE 10.59

To identify the portion of the curve in each case, plot some points and examine what happens as the parameter changes. In **(a)** the parameter is restricted to the interval $[0, \frac{\pi}{2}]$, so plot $P(t)$ for values such as $t = 0$, $\frac{\pi}{4}$, and $\frac{\pi}{2}$, as shown in Figure 10.59a. It should be clear that as t increases from 0 to $\frac{\pi}{2}$, $P(t)$ moves counterclockwise around a quarter-circle.

(b)   Again, plot $P(t)$ for several values of t in the interval $[0, 1]$:

$$P(0) = (2 \cos 0, -2 \sin 0) = (2, 0)$$

$$P\left(\frac{1}{3}\right) = \left(2 \cos \frac{\pi}{3}, -2 \sin \frac{\pi}{3}\right) = (1, -\sqrt{3})$$

$$P\left(\frac{1}{2}\right) = \left(2 \cos \frac{\pi}{2}, -2 \sin \frac{\pi}{2}\right) = (0, -2)$$

$$P(1) = (2 \cos \pi, -2 \sin \pi) = (-2, 0)$$

As t varies from 0 to 1, point $P(t)$ moves clockwise around the lower half-circle shown in Figure 10.59b.

(c)   The parameter m in **(c)** is not restricted, but the x-coordinate, the quantity $\frac{2}{\sqrt{m^2 + 1}}$, can never be negative, so $P(m)$ must be on the right half of the circle. Furthermore, as m gets large and positive or large and negative, the x-coordinate approaches (but never equals) zero. Thus as m varies over all real numbers, it traces the right half of the circle, not including the endpoints. Plotting $P(-1)$, $P(0)$ and $P(1)$ shows that $P(m)$ moves counterclockwise with increasing m, as indicated by the arrow in Figure 10.59c.   ▲

The sets of parametric equations in Example 2 give no indication of where they came from or how to interpret parameters. It is easy to think of the pairs of equations in **(a)** and **(b)** as functions of a time variable t. In **(a)** t could as easily represent the radian measure of the central angle. The equations in **(c)** are expressed in terms of the variable m, which we have often associated with the slope of a line. As a matter of fact, these equations can be derived in terms of slope. The point of intersection of line $y = mx$ with the right half of circle $x^2 + y^2 = 4$ (see Exercise 40) has coordinates given by

$$x = \frac{2}{\sqrt{m^2 + 1}} \qquad y = \frac{2m}{\sqrt{m^2 + 1}}.$$

EXAMPLE 3   For each of the curves stated parametrically, eliminate the parameter to find an equation in rectangular coordinates that represents the curve, then sketch the graph.

(a) $x = 2 + t$ (b) $x = \sin t$

       $y = 1 - 3t$ $y = \cos^2 t$

Solution

Strategy: (a) Solve one equation for t and substitute into the other equation, checking for limitations in the parametric form that are not apparent in rectangular form.

(b) With sines and cosines, the Pythagorean identity is often helpful for eliminating the parameter. Note that sines and cosines have limited ranges, so x and y will also be limited.

(a)   Follow the strategy. From $x = 2 + t$, $t = x - 2$. By substitution, $y = 1 - 3(x - 2) = 1 - 3x + 6$, or $y = -3x + 7$. Therefore curve C is all or part of line $3x + y = 7$. Since there is no restriction on t, both x and y take on all real values as t varies over the set of all real numbers; consequently the given parametric equations give the entire line (see Figure 10.60).

(b)   Follow the strategy. Since $x = \sin t$ and $y = \cos^2 t$,

$$x^2 + y = \sin^2 t + \cos^2 t = 1.$$

Therefore, the curve contains points $P(t)$ on the parabola $y = -x^2 + 1$. However, whatever the value of t,

$$-1 \le \sin t \le 1 \quad \text{and} \quad 0 \le \cos^2 t \le 1.$$

Thus $P(t)$ is restricted to the portion of the parabola where

$$-1 \le x \le 1 \quad \text{and} \quad 0 \le y \le 1.$$

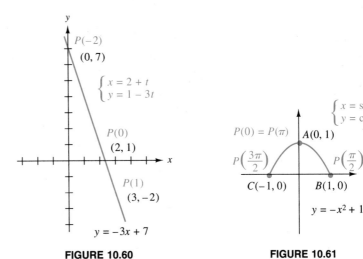

FIGURE 10.60   **FIGURE 10.61**

The curve for the parametric equations is the arc of the parabola shown in Figure 10.61. Think of $P(t)$ moving in time when $t \ge 0$; visualize the point starting at $A(0, 1)$ ($t = 0$), and moving along the parabola to $B(1, 0)$ at time $t = \frac{\pi}{2}$, then back to A at $t = \pi$, and on to $C(-1, 0)$ when $t = \frac{3\pi}{2}$, reversing direction again, and continuing indefinitely. ▲

THE WITCH OF AGNESI

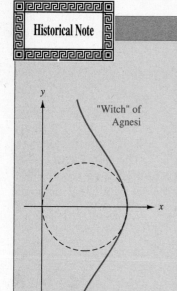

"Witch" of Agnesi

Women today play an important part in the growth and development of mathematics. Throughout much of history, however, circumstances and the attitudes of society have severely limited the role of women. One notable exception to the repression of women occurred in renaissance Italy. An atmosphere of encouragement resulted in many women making contributions to all areas of learning, including mathematics.

One of the most remarkable of these women was Maria Gaetana Agnesi, whose name, through an unfortunate twist, is forever linked in English with the word *witch*.

Agnesi began work at the age of 20 on a comprehensive treatment of calculus. Her two-volume work, *Instituzioni Analitiche (Analytic Institutions),*

appeared ten years later, in 1748. It was the first major text to pull together the calculus of both Newton and Leibnitz. The book was translated into French and English and it influenced European mathematicians for much of the century.

One curve that Agnesi treated in the analytic geometry portion of her text is shown in the diagram. (See also the Explore and Discover exercises in this section.) The curve was called the *versieri,* from the Latin word that means turning. The word *versieri* is similar to the Italian word *avversieri* (which means wife of the devil). Whether a pun or simply a mistranslation, an 1801 translation of Agnesi's book into English rendered the name of the curve as *witch,* and the curve has become widely known as the Witch of Agnesi.

EXAMPLE 4   Find two pairs of parametric equations for the line L that contains point $(3, 1)$ and has slope 2.

Solution

Strategy: Start with an equation for L in rectangular coordinates. Among many different choices, you could let either x or y equal t and then solve for the other variable.

Using the point-slope formula for a line, an equation for L is $y - 1 = 2(x - 3)$. One set of parametric equations can be found by setting $x - 3$ equal to t, from which $x = 3 + t$. By substitution, $y - 1 = 2t$, or $y = 1 + 2t$. Thus one set of parametric equations for L is

$$x = 3 + t$$
$$y = 1 + 2t.$$

As in the strategy, let $y = t$, then substituting t for y and solving for x gives $x = \frac{t + 5}{2}$. Another set of equations for L is thus

$$x = \frac{t + 5}{2}$$
$$y = t. \qquad \blacktriangle$$

For Graphers 10.6

PARAMETRIC CURVE GRAPHING

One of the great advantages of parametric equations is that we can see the graph (literally, with a graphing calculator) as the path of a moving point. The final set of points included in a curve C may not be as meaningful as watching the curve being traced. We illustrate with two parametrizations describing parts of the same ellipse.

EXAMPLE Let C_1 and C_2 be the curves given parametrically by C_1: $x = 3 \cos t, y = 2 \sin t$ and C_2: $x = 3 \sin t, y = 2 \cos t$, both on the interval $0 \le t \le \pi$. (Set the Familiar Window with $[0, 3.14]$ for T.) **(a)** Graph C_1, clear the graphics screen (F5 EXE on the Casio, 2nd DRAW 1 ENT on the TI), and then graph C_2. **(b)** Describe how curves C_1 and C_2 are related.

Solution If necessary, review the instructions on graphing in parametric mode in the section Using the Graphing Calculator. C_1 is the top half of the ellipse $4x^2 + 9y^2 = 36$ traced out counterclockwise. (Check to verify that the parametric equations satisfy the equation for the ellipse.) C_2 is the right half of the same ellipse traced out clockwise. ▲

Exercises

1. Let C_1 and C_2 be the curves in the example, but on the interval $0 \le t \le 6.3$. **(a)** Graph C_1 and C_2. **(b)** Describe how curves C_1 and C_2 are related. If you did not clear the screen between C_1 and C_2, how could you distinguish the two?

2. **(a)** Graph the curve C given by $x = (0.2t)\cos t$, $y = (0.2t)\sin t$, $-20 \le t \le 20$.
   (b) What information do you get from watching the curve being drawn that you could not observe from the finished graph?
   (c) The finished graph appears to intersect itself several times. Does it really, or is the appearance misleading? Explain.

3. **(a)** Graph the curves given parametrically by C_1:
   $x = 2 - t, \ y = -1 + 2t, \ t \in [0, 2]$, and C_2: $x = 2 + t, \ y = -1 - 2t, \ t \in [0, 2]$.
   (b) Show that C_1 and C_2 describe different portions of the same line, and find a standard equation for that line.
   (c) Find parametric equations for the curve C_3 that contains exactly the same portion of the line as C_1 but such that C_3 is traced out in the opposite direction from C_1.

4. Graph the path of the ladybug in Develop Mastery Exercises 44 and 45.

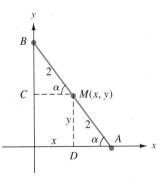

FIGURE 10.62

It should be clear from Example 4 that from an equation in rectangular coordinates there are many different substitutions we could make to express one variable in terms of a parameter. Solving for the variable then yields a pair of parametric equations. Parametric representations are never unique.

EXAMPLE 5   Suppose a line segment $\overline{AB}$ of length 4 is moving in such a way that point B is always on the positive y-axis and A is always on the positive x-axis. Think of a ladder propped against a wall with the lower end being pulled away from the wall. Use angle α in Figure 10.62 to find parametric equations for the midpoint $M(x, y)$ of line segment $\overline{AB}$.

Strategy: To express x and y as functions of α, note that x is a side of $\triangle MCB$ and y is a side of $\triangle ADM$, and both right triangles have a hypotenuse of 2.

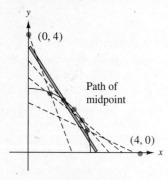

FIGURE 10.63

Midpoint spot on a sliding ladder

Solution

Follow the strategy. In $\triangle MCB$, $\cos \alpha = \frac{x}{2}$, and in $\triangle ADM$ $\sin \alpha = \frac{y}{2}$. Therefore, the equations

$$x = 2 \cos \alpha \qquad \text{and} \qquad y = 2 \sin \alpha$$

express the coordinates of M in terms of the parameter α. In the first quadrant, α varies from $\frac{\pi}{2}$ (when A is at the origin) to 0 (when B is at the origin). Parametric equations are

$$x = 2 \cos \alpha$$
$$y = 2 \sin \alpha$$

α decreases from $\frac{\pi}{2}$ to 0. ▲

If we think of Example 5 in terms of a sliding ladder, the conclusion of the example indicates that the midpoint of the ladder moves in the curve given by

$$x = 2 \cos \alpha$$
$$y = 2 \sin \alpha$$
$$0 \leq \alpha \leq \frac{\pi}{2}.$$

In Example 2 the same parametric equations defined a quarter-circle. Thus a spot by the middle rung of the ladder would move in a quarter-circle path from the wall to the ground. See Figure 10.63. Exercises 41–43 ask you to consider other questions related to the same setting.

EXERCISES 10.6

Check Your Understanding

Exercises 1–4 True or False. Give reasons for your conclusion.

1. The graph of $x = 1 - t$, $y = 3 + t$ is a line.

2. The graph of $x = 1 - \cos t$, $y = \cos t$ is a line segment with endpoints $(0, 0)$ and $(2, -1)$.

3. The graph of $x = \sin t$, $y = \cos^2 t$ is a parabola.

4. Point $(2, 0)$ is on the graph of $x = 1 + t$, $y = 1 - t^2$.

Exercises 5–10 Complete the sentence by selecting from the list below *all choices* that make the statement true.

(a) a line   (b) a half-line   (c) a line segment
(d) a circle   (e) a half-circle   (f) a quarter-circle
(g) a parabola   (h) part of a parabola

5. The graph of $x = \sqrt{t}$, $y = \sqrt{1 - t}$ is _____.

6. The graph of $x = \sin t$, $y = -\cos t$ is _____.

7. The graph of $x = 2^t$, $y = 4^t$ is _____.

8. The graph of $x = 1 + t^2$, $y = 1 - t^2$ is _____.

9. The graph of $x = \cos t$, $y = -\cos t$ is _____.

10. The graph of $x = e^t$, $y = -e^t$ is _____.

Explore and Discover

1. The motion of a particle in the xy plane is given parametrically by $x = 1 + \cos t$, $y = 1 - \cos t$, where t is a time variable ($t \geq 0$). Describe the motion in words, that is, tell where the particle begins and in what direction it moves as t increases.

2. Repeat Exercise 1, but replace $\cos t$ by $\sin t$, so that the motion is given by $x = 1 + \sin t$, $y = 1 - \sin t$.

3. The curve called the *versieri* in Maria Agnesi's 1748 calculus treatise (see the Historical Note, "The Witch of Agnesi") can be most easily described parametrically. Take a circle of radius a as shown in the diagram, tangent to the y-axis and to line $x = 2a$. A line through the origin intersects the circle at point A and the vertical line at point B. Point P has the same x-coordinate as A and the same y-coordinate as B. The *versieri* is the set of all such points P.

(a) Using the line through the origin, $y = mx$, find the coordinates of point A in terms of parameter m.

(b) Find the coordinates of point B in terms of m.

(c) Give parametric equations for the *versieri* (that is, express coordinates of point P in terms of m).

(d) The usual equation for the *versieri* is $xy^2 = d^2(d - x)$, where d is the diameter of the circle.

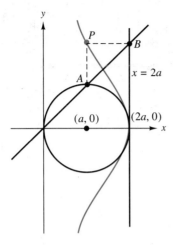

Show that the values of x and y given by your parametric equations satisfy this equation.

(e) If x and y are interchanged and the radius of the circle is $\frac{1}{2}$, show that the *versieri* is given by the equation $y = \frac{1}{1 + x^2}$.

Develop Mastery

Exercises 1–18   Sketch the graph of the curve defined by the parametric equations. Find an equation in rectangular coordinates for each curve and give any restrictions on x and y.

1. $x = t,\ y = 4 - t^2$
2. $x = t,\ y = 2 - \sqrt{t}$
3. $x = t,\ y = \sqrt{4 - t^2}$
4. $x = \sqrt{t},\ y = \sqrt{t} - 2$
5. $x = \sqrt{t},\ y = \sqrt{4 - t}$
6. $x = t,\ y = \sqrt{t^2 - 4}$
7. $x = 5 - t,\ y = 2 + t$
8. $x = 3t,\ y = -\frac{1}{2}t - 1$
9. $x = 1 - 3t,\ y = 5t + 2$
10. $x = 3 \cos t,\ y = -3 \sin t$
11. $x = 1 + \sin t,\ y = 1 - \cos t$
12. $x = 2 \cos t,\ y = 3 \sin t$
13. $x = \sin t,\ y = -\sin t$
14. $x = 1 + \cos t,\ y = 1 - \cos t$
15. $x = 1 + e^t,\ y = 1 - e^t$
16. $x = \cos t,\ y = \sin^2 t$
17. $x = -\cos t,\ y = -\sin^2 t$
18. $x = 2^t,\ y = -2^t$

Exercises 19–26   The parametric equations in **(a)** and **(b)** define portions of the same curve. Sketch the graph and indicate the portion of the curve defined and the direction in which the point $P(t)$ moves as t increases.

19. **(a)** $x = \sin t,\ y = -\sin t$
    (b) $x = \cos^2 t,\ y = -\cos^2 t$
20. **(a)** $x = e^t,\ y = -e^t$
    (b) $x = -e^t,\ y = e^t$
21. **(a)** $x = e^t,\ y = e^{-t}$
    (b) $x = -e^t,\ y = -e^{-t}$
22. **(a)** $x = 2^t,\ y = 4^t$
    (b) $x = -2^t,\ y = 4^t$
23. **(a)** $x = -\cos t,\ y = \sin t,\ 0 \le t \le \pi$
    (b) $x = \sin \frac{\pi}{2} t,\ y = \cos \frac{\pi}{2} t,\ 0 \le t \le 2$
24. **(a)** $x = \sqrt{1 - t^2},\ y = -t,\ -1 \le t \le 1$
    (b) $x = \sqrt{t},\ y = \sqrt{1 - t},\ 0 \le t \le 1$
25. **(a)** $x = 1 - t,\ y = 3t - 2,\ 0 \le t \le 2$
    (b) $x = t - 2,\ y = 7 - 3t,\ 1 \le t \le 3$
26. **(a)** $x = t,\ y = \ln t,\ t > 1$
    (b) $x = e^t,\ y = t,\ t > 0$

Exercises 27–34   Eliminate the parameter and give an equation in rectangular coordinates to describe the curve. Indicate any restrictions if the parametric equations define only a portion of the curve.

27. $x = 1 + \cos t,\ y = 2 - \sin t$
28. $x = -\cos t,\ y = 3 \sin t$
29. $x = 1 + \cos t,\ y = 2 - \cos t$
30. $x = 2 \cos^2 t,\ y = 1 + 3 \sin t$
31. $x = 4 \sec t,\ y = 5 \tan t$
32. $x = 2 \tan t,\ y = \sec^2 t$
33. $x = 1 + 4 \sec t,\ y = 5 \tan t$
34. $x = \cos t,\ y = \cos 2t$

Exercises 35–38   Find two sets of parametric equations for the curve. See Example 4. Answers are not unique.

35. The line that contains $A(-2, 4)$ and is parallel to $3x - y = 4$.
36. The line that contains $(0, 0)$ and is perpendicular to $3x - y = 4$.
37. The line that is tangent to $x^2 + y^2 = 25$ at the point $(-3, 4)$.
38. The line that contains the left latus rectum of $x^2 - y^2 = 1$.
39. Verify (by substitution) that each pair of parametric equations in Example 2 satisfies the equation $x^2 + y^2 = 4$.

40. Find parametric equations for the right half of the circle $x^2 + y^2 = 4$ by finding the coordinates of the intersection of line $y = mx$ with the right half of the circle. Your parametric equations should agree with those in Example 2.

41. Given the line segment $\overline{AB}$ of Example 5, let $P(x, y)$ be the point that is always 1 unit from A. Find parametric equations (using angle α in Figure 10.62) for the curve traced out by point P as the segment moves from vertical to horizontal. What kind of curve is traced out by P?

42. Let $Q(x, y)$ be the point that is always 1 unit from B on the line segment $\overline{AB}$ of Example 5. Find parametric equations for the curve traced out by Q. See Exercise 41.

43. Let $T(x, y)$ be the point at some fixed distance a from A on line segment $\overline{AB}$ of Example 5. Find parametric equations for the curve traced out by T. See Exercises 41 and 42. For what values of a is the path of T part of a circle?

44. A 20-foot ladder is resting against a vertical wall with a ladybug at the lower end. Suppose the lower end of the ladder is being pulled horizontally away from the wall at the rate of 1 foot per minute, while at the same time the ladybug is crawling upward on the ladder at the rate of 1 foot per minute until it reaches the other

end. If the bug is located at point $B(x, y)$ at time t minutes (see the diagram), find formulas that give x and y as functions of t. Find the position of the bug at time $t = 2, 5, 10,$ and 20. For what values of t are your formulas valid?

45. Suppose the ladder in Exercise 44 is being pulled from the wall at the rate of 2 feet per minute while the bug still crawls 1 foot per minute. Answer the same questions as Exercise 44.

46. Given the two concentric circles in the diagram, a line at angle θ from the positive x-axis intersects the circles in points A and B. Point $P(x, y)$ has the same y-coordinate as A and the same x-coordinate as B. Using the right triangles, find parametric equations in terms of θ for the curve traced out by P.

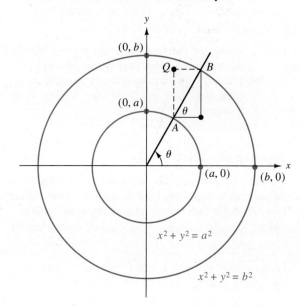

47. Let Q be the point shown in the diagram for Exercise 46. Find parametric equations in terms of θ for the curve traced out by Q.

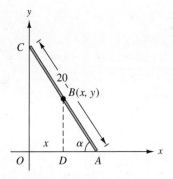

CHAPTER 10 REVIEW

Test Your Understanding

Exercises   Determine the truth value (T or F). Give reasons for your conclusion. Drawing a graph first will be helpful.

1. The graph of $x^2 + y^2 - 4 = 0$ is a circle.

2. The graph of $y^2 = x^2 - 1$ is a hyperbola.

3. The graph of $y^2 = 9 + 4x^2$ is an ellipse.

4. The graph of $x^2 + y + 4 = 0$ is a parabola.

5. The graph of $x^2 + y^2 = -1$ is a circle.

6. The graph of $x^2 - y^2 = 0$ is a hyperbola.

7. The graph of $9x^2 - y^2 = 0$ consists of two intersecting lines.

8. The graph of $y = \sqrt{4 - x^2}$ is a semicircle.

9. The graph of $y = \sqrt{1 + 4x^2}$ is half of an ellipse.

10. The graph of $y = -\sqrt{1 - 4x^2}$ is half of an ellipse.

11. The graph of $x^2 + y^2 - 2x + 4y + 6 = 0$ is a circle.

12. The graph of $0.5x^2 + 0.5y^2 = 2$ is a circle of radius 2.

13. The graph of $xy = 4$ is a hyperbola.

14. The graph of $x^2 + 2y^2 - 2x + 4y - 8 = 0$ is an ellipse.

15. Every hyperbola has two asymptotes that intersect at the point midway between the foci of the hyperbola.

16. The line $y = x$ is an asymptote for the hyperbola $(x - 1)^2 - (y - 1)^2 = 1$.

17. Every point inside the circle $x^2 + y^2 = 4$ is also inside the ellipse $x^2 + 2y^2 = 2$.

18. Every point inside the ellipse $x^2 + 4y^2 = 4$ is also inside the circle $x^2 + y^2 = 4$.

19. The graphs of $x^2 + 4y^2 = 4$ and $4x^2 + y^2 = 4$ intersect in four points.

20. Point $(1, 2)$ is inside the graph of $3x^2 + 4y^2 = 12$.

21. The graph of $r = \cos \theta$ is a circle of radius 0.5.

22. The graph of $r = |\cos \theta|$ is a semicircle.

23. The graph of $r = \frac{1}{\sin \theta + \cos \theta}$ is a line.

24. The polar coordinates $[-1, \frac{\pi}{4}]$ and $[1, -\frac{3\pi}{4}]$ represent the same point.

25. Point $[-1, \pi]$ is inside circle $r = 2 \cos \theta$.

26. The graph of $\begin{cases} x = \sin t \\ y = \cos^2 t \end{cases}$ is part of a parabola.

27. The graph of $\begin{cases} x = \sin t \\ y = |\cos t| \end{cases}$ is a circle with its center at the origin.

28. The graph of $\begin{cases} x = |\sin t| \\ y = |\cos t| \end{cases}$ is a quarter-circle.

29. The graph of $\begin{cases} x = 2t \\ y = t^2 \end{cases}$ is a parabola with its focus at $(-1, 0)$.

30. The graph of $\begin{cases} x = 2 + \sin t \\ y = 1 + 2 \cos t \end{cases}$ is an ellipse with its center at $(2, 1)$.

Mastery Review

Exercises 1–6 Find the vertices and foci for the conic section.

1. $\frac{x^3}{9} + \frac{y^2}{25} = 1$ 2. $\frac{x^2}{25} + \frac{y^2}{9} = 1$

3. $\frac{x^2}{9} - \frac{y^2}{25} = 1$ 4. $\frac{y^2}{9} - \frac{x^2}{25} = 1$

5. $\frac{(x - 1)^2}{9} + \frac{(y + 2)^2}{25} = 1$

6. $\frac{x^2}{9} - \frac{(y + 1)^2}{16} = 1$

Exercises 7–17 For the conic section specified by the given information, write an equation in standard form. Some may have more than one solution.

7. Circle: center $(-2, 1)$, radius 3

8. Circle: center $(0, -3)$, radius $\sqrt{5}$

9. Parabola: focus $(3, 0)$, vertex $(0, 0)$

10. Parabola: directrix $x = 5$, axis $y = 1$, contains $(0, 4)$

11. Ellipse: center $(1, 4)$, focus $(1, 2)$, vertex $(1, 0)$

12. Ellipse: foci $(4, -1)$ and $(0, -1)$ vertex $(5, -1)$

13. Hyperbola: center $(1, -1)$, focus $(4, -1)$, vertex $(3, -1)$

14. Hyperbola: vertices $(1, 3)$ and $(1, -1)$, focus $(1, -2)$

15. Parabola: focus $(3, 1)$, directrix $x = 2$

16. Parabola: focus $(3, 1)$, directrix $y = 2$

17. Parabola: vertex $(3, -1)$, contains the ends of a diameter of the circle $x^2 + y^2 - 6x - 4y + 9 = 0$

Exercises 18–23 Identify the type of conic section defined by the equation and sketch the graph. For a circle, give the center and radius; for a parabola, give the focus and vertex; for an ellipse, give the center and the lengths of the major and minor axes; for a hyperbola, give the center, vertices, and asymptotes.

18. $x^2 + y^2 + 2x - 4y + 1 = 0$

19. $x^2 - 2x + 2y = 5$

20. $9x^2 + 4y^2 - 8y - 32 = 0$

21. $x^2 + y^2 = 2y + 2$

22. $x^2 - 9y^2 - 4x - 5 = 0$

23. $x^2 = 2x + y$

24. Find an equation for the set of points $P(x, y)$ such that the distance $|\overline{PF}| = ed$, where F is point $(1, 2)$ and d is the distance from P to the x-axis, for the values of e: (a) $e = 1$, (b) $e = 2$, (c) $e = \frac{2}{3}$.

25. Given the ellipse $\frac{x^2}{a^2} + \frac{y^2}{b^2} = 1$ labeled as shown in the diagram, show that $\frac{|\overline{AB}|}{|\overline{CF}|} = \frac{|\overline{CF}|}{|\overline{BE}|}$.

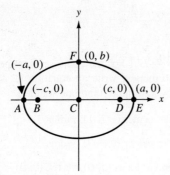

Exercises 26–30   Sketch the graph of the curve defined by the polar coordinate equation.

26. $r^2 = 4 \cos 2\theta$

27. $r = 2 - \sqrt{3} \cos \theta$

28. $r = \sqrt{3} - 2 \cos \theta$

29. $r = \sqrt{3} + \sqrt{3} \sin \theta$

30. $r = \sqrt{3} - \sqrt{3} \sin \theta$

Exercises 31–32   Sketch the two curves and find their points of intersection.

31. $r = 2 \cos \theta$; $r = \sin \theta + \cos \theta$

32. $r^2 = 2 \sin 2\theta$; $r = 1$

Exercises 33–38   Sketch the graph of the curve determined by the parametric equations.

33. $x = 2t, y = \sqrt{4 - 4t^2}$

34. $x = 2t - 1, y = 3 - 6t$

35. $x = \sqrt{t - 1} - 1, y = 2\sqrt{t - 1} + 3$

36. $x = \cos t, y = -\cos t$

37. $x = 4^t, y = 2^t$

38. $x = 1 + \sin t, y = 1 - \sin t$

How They Came to Mathematics

The quotations included in the margins throughout the book are all from prominent contemporary mathematicians, most of them still active professionally. Too often we get the impression that mathematics somehow sprang full-blown from the brow of Zeus, without human intervention or participation. Quite to the contrary—mathematics is an intensely human creation, requiring the passionate involvement of people who find satisfaction (and fun) in thinking about its puzzles. The field is growing today faster than at any time in the past. The people who contribute to the creation of mathematics vary as much as those engaged in any other human endeavor. No one has succeeded very well in defining mathematical talent, but it is clear that talent is not limited to individuals of any particular gender or race, and mathematical discoveries have been made by high school students as well as by mature professionals.

The statements we quote are all taken from larger contexts, from interviews or from writings. They are intended to give just a flavor of the variety of backgrounds and interests of those who decided to spend much of their lives with mathematics. Each person came to mathematics differently; some got caught almost accidentally, others found the subject fascinating from the beginning. The capsule biographies that follow cannot do justice to the rich and complex lives of the individuals quoted, but they may give an idea of the stature of people who began significant careers in ordinary ways. Many of our quotations were taken from a series of interviews conducted by Donald J. Albers and Gerald L. Alexanderson, now available in two books: *Mathematical People* (published by Birkhaüser Boston) and *More Mathematical People* (Harcourt, Brace, Jovanovich, with Constance Reid as coeditor).

Lipman Bers was born in what is now Latvia. He fled fascism several times in his life, first to study mathematics in Germany and then in Czechoslovakia, and ultimately to the United States. He taught for years at Columbia University and wrote technical books (*Partial Differential Equations, Mathematical Aspects of Subsonic and Transonic Gas Dynamics*) as well as *Calculus.* He was president of the American Mathematical Society and was a member of the American Academy of Arts and Sciences.

Garrett Birkhoff is the son of one of the first American mathematicians to achieve international recognition. The younger Dr. Birkhoff became a world-renowned mathematician in his own right and taught at Harvard for 45 years. His book, *A Survey of Modern Algebra,* co-authored with Saunders MacLane, placed an indelible stamp on mathematics curricula and affected the training offered by colleges and universities throughout the nation.

David Blackwell planned originally to be an elementary school teacher but earned instead a Ph.D. in mathematics. After a dozen years at Howard University, he was invited to teach mathematical statistics at the University of California at Berkeley. He is deeply interested in understanding ideas thoroughly enough to communicate them to his students, who have responded by making Dr. Blackwell one of the most honored teachers at Berkeley.

Ralph P. Boas, Jr. was born in Walla Walla, Washington. He "drifted" into mathematics because, he claimed, he "was too clumsy to be a chemist." He did his doctoral work at Harvard, with postdoctoral study at Princeton. In addition to chairing the Mathematics Department at Northwestern University in Chicago for many years, he edited both *Math Reviews* and the *American Mathematical Monthly* and served as president of the Mathematical Association of America.

Paul Cohen grew up in Brooklyn. He was one of four national Westinghouse Science Talent Search winners from his high school graduating class. Now at Stanford, Dr. Cohen has won two of the most prestigious awards available to mathematicians: the Bôcher Prize and the Fields Medal (the mathematical equivalent of the Nobel Prize). Much of his international reputation comes from his proof of the independence of the continuum hypothesis, one of the most fundamental problems in set theory, where he showed that we can neither prove nor disprove Cantor's conjecture.

John Horton Conway is at home on two continents (at Cambridge and Princeton universities). His delight in mathematics as a glorious game infects almost everyone who works with him. An accomplished Rubik's cubologist, he analyzes the mathematical games of others as well as inventing his own. He loves to sit in the Commons Room and lock horns with all comers. Much of his serious mathematics grows out of his interest in recreational mathematics, where his contributions are, according to Martin Gardner, "unique in their combination of depth, elegance, and humor."

George B. Dantzig is best known as the inventor of the simplex method, which makes linear programming such an incredibly powerful tool for management and production. While the simplex method and linear programming are among the most important of all applied mathematics, Dr. Dantzig doesn't believe there is any real difference between applied and pure mathematics. He was just 33 when he developed the simplex algorithm, but his fame as the "Father of Linear Programming" led people to expect a much older man. He was given the Presidential Medal of Science by former President Gerald Ford.

Freeman Dyson has one of the widest ranging imaginations among current physicists and mathematicians. Growing up in Britain, he worked for its War Office during World War II doing statistical analysis of the effectiveness of bombing. (He learned that aerial bombing is *very* inefficient.) One of his earliest mathematical memories is of adding up the infinite geometric series $1 + \frac{1}{2} + \frac{1}{4} + \frac{1}{8} \ldots$ (and getting a sum of 2). He writes widely on public policy and disarmament issues (*Disturbing the Universe*), has spent considerable time at the Institute for Advanced Study (Princeton), and has made fundamental contributions to both physics and mathematics.

Richard Feynman has been called "perhaps the most original genius produced in theoretical physics [in] his generation." He worked on the Manhattan Project in the development of the atomic bomb and won the Nobel Prize for physics in 1965 for his work in the fundamental nature of matter. He was deeply concerned with how we learn physics and developed a radically new approach to teach introductory physics during his years at Cal Tech. A delightful and very personal book is *"Surely You're Joking, Mr. Feynman!"*

Andrew Gleason finished his master's degree at Yale and immediately went into the Navy to work on cryptanalysis. After the war ended, he was appointed as a Junior Fellow at Harvard. He remained at Harvard for the next forty years, without a Ph.D., while directing a number of doctoral students of his own. Some of his early reputation was established by his part in the solution of Hilbert's Fifth Problem, one of a famous list of twenty challenges posed by David Hilbert at the beginning of the twentieth century.

Bill Gosper was one of the original MIT "hackers", who were fascinated by computers and convinced that they should have access to any and all information about the way the world works. His approach to computing millions of decimals of the number π used new techniques of continued fractions. He continues to be fascinated by all kinds of "toys," from the Aerobie to supercomputers, which he says will never be "big enough or fast enough."

Paul Halmos grew up in Hungary but received most of his schooling in America. A gifted research mathematician and expositor, he taught for many years in the midwest (at the universities of Chicago, Indiana, Illinois, Michigan, and Syracuse) as well as in California and Hawaii. As editor of the *American Mathematical Monthly* and in his own writing (he calls his life story, *I Want to be A Mathematician,* an "Automathography"), he has worked tirelessly to improve the quality of writing both of and about mathematics.

Mark Kac went to high school in Poland but became "profoundly American." Less than a year after he came to America, "the world exploded and much of my part of it was consumed by flames. Millions, including my parents and my brother, were murdered by the Germans and many disappeared without a trace. . . ." Dr. Kac made basic and profound contributions to probability theory and inspired hundreds of students during his years of teaching at Cornell and Rockefeller University. Many thousands more have seen his Mathematical Association of America film, "Can One Hear the Shape of a Drum?"

Irving Kaplansky grew up and went to college in Toronto, Canada, before going to Harvard for his Ph.D. in algebra. Complementing his years of research at the University of Chicago are many books, including the very readable *Matters Mathematical.* More recently he moved to Berkeley to direct the Mathematical Sciences Research Institute. He is a member of the National Academy of Sciences and served as president of the American Mathematical Society.

Peter Lax was born in Hungary. He emigrated to New York when he was fifteen. While he was still a student in high school, Paul Erdös introduced him to Albert Einstein. Dr. Lax has also been president of the American Mathematical Society and was the director of the Courant Institute at New York University, where he still teaches. His wife Anneli is also a professor of mathematics (they met in a graduate course in complex variables), and they work together to improve mathematics education.

Lucien Le Cam grew up in rural France before World War II. He interrupted his schooling to join the French underground in resisting the Nazis. After the war he worked with the organization that set up the modern electric system of France. He came to Berkeley to work with the statistician Jerzy Neyman, completed his doctorate in less than two years, and has remained at Berkeley ever since. Called "brilliant" by colleagues, he sometimes refuses to share his discoveries. When he claimed in a colloquium that he had proved the speaker's result years earlier, the speaker said, "Ah, but you didn't publish it!"

Saunders MacLane has been a "towering figure in American mathematics for over half a century." The University of Gottingen in Germany attracted students from all over the world, from the latter part of the nineteenth century until the rise of the Nazis before World War II. Saunders MacLane was one of the last Americans to study at Gottingen before the war. Some of his best-known work has been done in collaboration with others, including Garrett Birkhoff. A long-time professor at the University of Chicago, MacLane is one of only five people who have served as president of both the American Mathematical Society and the Mathematical Association of America.

Cathleen S. Morawetz is of Irish parentage and is a grand-niece of the Irish playwright J. M. Synge. She grew up in Toronto before leaving for her graduate study at the Massachusetts Institute of Technology. She got her Ph.D. in partial differential equations at New York University, where she has taught for many years and where she also directed the Courant Institute of Mathematical Sciences. She is the only woman to have been invited to give the Gibbs Lecture to the American Mathematical Society and is a member of the National Academy of Sciences.

Frederick Mosteller was trained as a mathematician and statistician with a Ph.D. from Princeton, but he considers himself a "scientific generalist." Reflecting his concern for public education, he designed and taught a statistics course for the Continental Classroom, a long-running and popular program on public television. He also co-authored the popular text that has also been used in hundreds of college classes, *Probability, A First Course*. He has been president of both the American Statistical Association and the American Association for the Advancement of Science.

Ivan Niven grew up in the northwest, going to high school and college in British Columbia. He went on to his Ph.D. in number theory at the University of Chicago, but after a few years in the midwest he returned to Oregon for the rest of his professional career. He received considerable attention early for his one-page *Simple Proof that π Is Irrational*—simple in that it only uses calculus. He wrote *Mathematics of Choice* for the Mathematical Association of America's New Mathematical Library series. Dr. Niven has been president of the Mathematical Association of America and was recognized by the association for Distinguished Service to Mathematics.

Roger Penrose claims to be unable to decide whether he is a mathematician or a physicist, but he makes important contributions to both fields. He and Stephen Hawking together showed that black holes are an inevitable part of our universe. His fascination with patterns led to his discovery of two shapes of tiles that together can cover the plane without any repetition. Long an Oxford don, he has given much thought to computers and the human mind. In his book *The Emperor's New Mind,* he asserts that the mind is forever beyond the capabilities of any computer.

I. I. Rabi grew up on the Lower East Side of New York and went to Cornell to study chemistry and physics. He earned a doctorate in physics from Columbia but had to go to Europe to learn about quantum mechanics. He returned to teach at Columbia, where he earned the prestigious rank of University Professor. He won the Nobel Prize in 1944 and during World War II was a key player at the Massachusetts Institute of Technology Radiation Laboratory in the development of radar. A recent biography is titled *Rabi, Scientist and Citizen.*

Julia Robinson's life was a series of "only" or "first" accomplishments. She was the only girl taking mathematics, the only one taking physics in her high school (San Diego), the only woman taking a number theory course at Berkeley (from Rafael Robinson, who later became her husband). She was one of the three people who collectively solved Hilbert's Tenth Problem. She was elected to the National Academy of Sciences and served as president of the American Mathematical Society (the first woman mathematician in both instances). She died of leukemia in 1985.

Mary Ellen Rudin is another mathematician who married a mathematician. She was recruited in college by the famous "Texas topologist," R. L. Moore. Like many Moore students, she went on to a remarkably productive career. She lives in a house designed by Frank Lloyd Wright. While her husband Walter does some of his mathematics in his well-appointed study, she works on hers in the living room where, over the years, she has simultaneously been able to watch over their children. After years of doing mathematics without formal academic affiliation, she was recognized with an endowed chair at the University of Wisconsin.

Claude Shannon is known as the father of information theory, the mathematical theory of communication. Widely respected as a creative engineer of daring imagination for his work at Bell Laboratories, Dr. Shannon laid the groundwork for the improvement of signal tranmission, especially telephone and television communication. He pioneered the programming of machines for complicated tasks (including chess playing and juggling). His love of toys (e.g., a two-seated unicycle) and games of imagination is reflected in his work, keeping him young at heart while he continues to do serious mathematics and engineering.

William Thurston is a Princeton topologist who deals with high-level geometry. He is known around Princeton for his "uniform" of jeans and plaid shirts, and his friends wondered if he would conform to formal dress standards when he received an international award in Finland. Bill did appear formal (for him); he had pressed his plaid shirt. Many people are surprised by how much use he makes of the computer in very abstract mathematics. The quality of his research is reflected in the number of awards he has won, including the Fields Medal and the Veblen Prize.

Stanislaw (Stan) Ulam is internationally known for his work with the Manhattan Project in World War II and for his contributions to the design of the "super," as the fusion H-bomb was known. He grew up in Poland but spent his professional life in America, teaching for many years at Colorado, Florida, and California. Before he received his doctorate, he studied number theory, topology, and set theory. He later broadened the scope of his studies to contribute to the fields of probability, computers, biology, and coding theory. According to Gian-Carlo Rota, "to generations of mathematicians, Ulam's problems were the door that led them into the new, to the first sweet taste of discovery."

Robin Wilson is the son of a two-time Prime Minister of England. He spends much of his time as a mathematician at the Open University. This national university serves thousands of adults all over Britain who have never done university work or who have been away from it for many years. Much of his teaching is done on camera or over the air, and he writes supporting materials for his students. He also devotes time to his love of music, both as a performer and as an author of books as diverse as *Graph Theory* and *Gilbert and Sullivan.*

ACKNOWLEDGMENTS

Pages 18, 186, 202, 427, 520; from interview with Julia B. Robinson from *More Mathematical People: Contemporary Conversations,* edited by Donald J. Albers, Gerald L. Alexanderson and Constance Reid, pages 266, 267 and 269. Reprinted by permission of Raphael M. Robinson.

Pages 25, 112, 394; from interview with William P. Thurston from *More Mathematical People: Contemporary Conversations,* edited by Donald J. Albers, Gerald L. Alexanderson and Constance Reid, pages 326, 327 and 328–329. Reprinted by permission of William P. Thurston.

Pages 34, 128, 398; from interview with Mary Ellen Rudin from *More Mathematical People: Contemporary Conversations,* edited by Donald J. Albers, Gerald L. Alexanderson and Constance Reid, pages 286 and 288. Reprinted by permission of Mary Ellen Rudin.

Pages 161, 276, 315; from interview with Saunders MacLane from *More Mathematical People: Contemporary Conversations,* edited by Donald J. Albers, Gerald L. Alexanderson and Constance Reid, page 198. Reprinted by permission of Saunders MacLane.

Pages 55, 237, 563; from interview with Ralph P. Boas, Jr. from *More Mathematical People: Contemporary Conversations,* edited by Donald J. Albers, Gerald L. Alexanderson and Constance Reid, pages 24 and 41. Reprinted by permission of the estate of Ralph P. Boas, Jr.

Pages 252, 350; from interview with Frederick Mosteller from *More Mathematical People: Contemporary Conversations,* edited by Donald J. Albers, Gerald L. Alexanderson and Constance Reid, pages 245–246. Reprinted by permission of Frederick Mosteller.

Pages 202, 300, 334; reprinted from *"Surely You're Joking, Mr. Feynman!" Adventures of a Curious Character,* by Richard P. Feynman, as told to Ralph Leighton, edited by Edward Hutchings. Copyright © 1985 by Richard P. Feynman and Ralph Leighton. Reprinted by permission of W. W. Norton & Company, Inc.

Page 437; from interview with Peter D. Lax from *More Mathematical People: Contemporary Conversations,* edited by Donald J. Albers, Gerald L. Alexanderson and Constance Reid, page 140. Reprinted by permission of Peter D. Lax.

Pages 120, 324, 345, 412, 488; from *Mathematical People: Profiles and Interviews* by Donald J. Albers and Gerald L. Alexanderson, pages 3, 20, 24, and 43. Reprinted by permission of the authors.

Pages 33, 93, 460; from interview with Lipman Bers from *More Mathematical People: Contemporary Conversations,* edited by Donald J. Albers, Gerald L. Alexanderson and Constance Reid, page 5. Reprinted by permission of Lipman Bers.

Pages 76, 153, 266, 534; from interview with Paul J. Cohen from *More Mathematical People: Contemporary Conversations,* edited by Donald J. Albers, Gerald L. Alexanderson and Constance Reid, pages 44, 46 and 47. Reprinted by permission of Paul J. Cohen.

Pages 3, 228, 383, 501; from interview with George B. Dantzig from *More Mathematical People: Contemporary Conversations,* edited by Donald J. Albers, Gerald L. Alexanderson and Constance Reid, pages 63–64 and 72. Reprinted by permission of George B. Dantzig.

Pages 222, 552; from interview with Andrew M. Gleason from *More Mathematical People: Contemporary Conversations,* edited by Donald J. Albers, Gerald L. Alexanderson and Constance Reid, pages 83 and 92. Reprinted by permission of Andrew M. Gleason.

Pages 503, 578; Irving Kaplansky from *More Mathematical People: Contemporary Conversations,* edited by Donald J. Albers, Gerald L. Alexanderson and Constance Reid, pages 124 and 127. Reprinted by permission of Irving Kaplansky.

Page 570; from interview with Lucien Le Cam from *More Mathematical People: Contemporary Conversations,* edited by Donald J. Albers, Gerald L. Alexanderson and Constance Reid, page 162. Reprinted by permission of Lucien Le Cam.

Page 358; from interview with Cathleen S. Morawetz from *More Mathematical People: Contemporary Conversations,* edited by Donald J. Albers, Gerald L. Alexanderson and Constance Reid, page 223. Reprinted by permission of Cathleen S. Morawetz.

Pages 46, 69, 154; from interview with Robin Wilson from *More Mathematical People: Contemporary Conversations,* edited by Donald J. Albers, Gerald L. Alexanderson and Constance Reid, pages 345–346 and 348. Reprinted by permission of Robin Wilson.

Pages 11, 465, 489; from interview with Bill Gosper from *More Mathematical People: Contemporary Conversations,* edited by Donald J. Albers, Gerald L. Alexanderson and Constance Reid, pages 106 and 111–112. Reprinted by permission of Bill Gosper.

Pages 315, 371, 374, 402; from I WANT TO BE A MATHEMATICIAN: AN AUTOMATHOGRAPHY IN THREE PARTS, by Paul R. Halmos, copyright © 1985 by Springer/Verlag, NY, Inc. Reprinted by permission.

Page 214; from interview with Ivan Niven in THE COLLEGE MATHEMATICS JOURNAL, November 1991. Copyright © 1991 by the Mathematical Association of America, Inc. Reprinted by permission.

CHAPTER 1

Exercises 1.1
Check Your Understanding   **1.** F   **3.** F   **5.** T   **7. (a)** c, **(b)** b, **(c)** b   **9.** e, f

Develop Mastery   **17. (a)** 3,200, **(b)** 0.00506, **(c)** 0.08400   **19. (a)** 1.73, **(b)** 0.628, **(c)** 8.86,
(d) 4.88   **21. (a)** 95.7, **(b)** 44.3, **(c)** 4.64   **23. (a)** 22.9 ft., **(b)** 41.6 sq. ft.   **25.** 1.30×10^5 in^3
27. (a) 9.33 ft./sec., **(b)** 560 ft./min., **(c)** 6.36 mi./hr.   **29.** 1,040 mi./hr.   **31.** 15,600 mi./hr.
33. 4.7 miles   **35.** 89 miles   **37.** 8 miles compared to 9.8 miles

Exercises 1.2
Check Your Understanding   **1.** F   **3.** T   **5.** a, d   **7.** a, d   **9.** a, c, d

Develop Mastery   **1. (a)** F, **(b)** F   **3. (a)** T, **(b)** F   **5. (a)** T, **(b)** T   **7. (a)** F, **(b)** F
9. (a) Q, **(b)** N, I, E, Q, **(c)** H, **(d)** N, I, E, Q   **11. (a)** 0.625, **(b)** $0.41\overline{6}$ **13. (a)** $0.8\overline{2}$, **(b)** $0.\overline{769230}$
15. (a) $\frac{63}{100}$, **(b)** $\frac{7}{11}$ **17. (a)** $\frac{5}{6}$, **(b)** $\frac{83}{99}$ **19. (a)** 0.344, **(b)** 0.344   **21. (a)** 3.118, **(b)** 3.118
23. 6.928203   **25.** 1.366025   **27.** 3.162278   **29.** 3.968119   **31.** 169   **33. (a)** F, **(b)** T, **(c)** T
35. (a) $\sqrt{2} + \sqrt{3}$, **(b)** $(3 + \sqrt{2}) + (1 - \sqrt{2})$, **(c)** $(2 + \sqrt{2})(2 - \sqrt{2})$, **(d)** $\frac{\sqrt{3}}{\sqrt{3}}$ **37.** $x = \sqrt{6}$; irrational
39. (a) 3.142857143, **(b)** 3.141509434 **(c)** 3.141592920   **41.** 80 characters per line of length 4 inches;
1,783 miles

Exercises 1.3
Check Your Understanding   **1.** T   **3.** F   **5.** F   **7.** c, d, f   **9.** d

Develop Mastery   **1.**   **3.**   **5.**

7. (a) $\frac{5}{4} = 1.25$, **(b)** $\frac{3}{2} = 1.5$ **9. (a)** $\pi - 3 \approx 0.1416$, **(b)** $\frac{22}{7} - \pi \approx 0.0013$ **11. (a)** >, **(b)** <
13. (a) =, **(b)** >   **15.** $y < z < x$ **17.** $y < x < z$ **19. (a)** T, **(b)** F   **21.**

23.   **25.**   **27.**
29. 5   **31.** 16   **33.** $8 - 4i$ **35.** $3 + 3i$ **37.** $7 + i$ **39.** 10   **41.** $3 - i$ **43.** $-2 + 2\sqrt{3}i$
45. (a) -1, **(b)** -1, **(c)** 1, **(d)** -1 **47.** $-5 + 2i$ **49.** $-1 - 3i$ **51.** $-1.2 - 0.6i$
53. (a) $(-3, 2)$, **(b)** $(-2, -1)$, **(c)** $(-3, -2)$, **(d)** $(-5, 1)$, **(e)** $(8, -1)$ **55. (a)** $(5, -1)$, **(b)** $(-1, 1)$
(c) $(5, 1)$, **(d)** $(4, 0)$, **(e)** $(-4, 6)$ **57.** All points are on the circle of radius 1 and center at $(0, 0)$.

Exercises 1.4
Check Your Understanding   **1.** T   **3.** F   **5.** F   **7.** c   **9.** e

Develop Mastery   **1.** F   **3.** Not a statement **5.** Not a statement   **7.** T   **9.** T   **11.** T   **13.** T
15. T   **17.** F   **19. (a)** F, **(b)** T, **(c)** T   **21. (a)** T, **(b)** T, **(c)** F   **23. (a)** T, **(b)** T, **(c)** T
25. There is a positive integer n for which $n (n + 1)$ is not an even number. False.   **27.** There is a positive
integer n such that $4n - 1$ is not a prime. True.   **29.** There is no rational number between 1 and 2. False
31. False   **33.** True   **35.** False   **37.** Any negative x **39.** Any multiple of 41   **41. (a)** True,
(b) False, **(c)** True, **(d)** True, **(e)** True   **43. (a)** True, **(b)** True, **(c)** True   **45. (a)** True,
(b) True, **(c)** True   **47.** Any x between 0 and 1   **49.** Any negative x

Exercises 1.5

Check Your Understanding   **1.** F   **3.** T   **5.** F   **7.** e   **9.** b

Develop Mastery   **1.** $-\frac{1}{2}$ **3.** $\frac{3}{2}$ **5.** $-1, \frac{1}{3}$ **7.** $-\frac{2}{3}, \frac{4}{3}$ **9.** $-\frac{5}{2}, \frac{3}{2}$ **11.** $x > 2$
13. $-0.55 \le x \le -0.45$ **15.** $-1 \le x \le 2$ **17.** $x < -3$ or $-2 \le x \le 2$ **19.** $1 \le x \le 3$
21. $x < 0$ **23.** $x > 4$ or $x < -1$ **25.** $x \le 2$ **27.** $(-\infty, -2)$ **29.** $(-3, -2) \cup (3, \infty)$
31. $(-1, 3)$ **33.** $(1 - \sqrt{2}, \sqrt{2} - 1)$ **35.** Two real roots   **37.** $\pm\sqrt{2}$ **39.** $-3, 13$ **41.** ± 3
43. No solution   **45.** ± 3 **47.** $\{0, 1, 2\}$ **49.** $\{0, \pm 1, \pm 2\}$ **51.** $-3 \le x \le -1$
53. $x < -3$ or $x > -2$ **55.** $\{-2, 3\}$ **57.** $\{x \mid -5 < x < 1\}$ **59.** $x^2 + 6x + 8 = 0$
61. $x^2 - 2x - 1 = 0$ **63.** Seven   **65.** $\{-3, 2, 3\}$ **67.** Six   **69.** -6 **71.** 4   **73.** 17
75. $5 + \sqrt{69}$ **77.** $41° < F < 68°$ **79.** 2 hours and 24 minutes   **81.** 16.2 minutes
83. $A = 100x - x^2; 0 < x < 100$ **85. (b)** $V = 4x^3 - 40x^2 + 96x; 0 < x < 4$

Exercises 1.6

Check Your Understanding   **1.** T   **3.** F   **5.** T   **7.** f   **9.** c

Develop Mastery   **1. (a)** $\sqrt{10}$,   **(b)** $(-\frac{1}{2}, \frac{7}{2})$ **3. (a)** $\frac{\sqrt{277}}{6}$,   **(b)** $(\frac{1}{4}, \frac{5}{6})$ **5. (a)** 8,   **(b)** $(0, -\sqrt{2})$
7. Right triangle   **9.** Isosceles triangle   **11.** Right triangle   **13.** $x^2 + y^2 - 2x - 2y - 1 = 0$
15. $4x^2 + 4y^2 + 8x - 40y + 103 = 0$ **17.** $x^2 + y^2 + 4x + 2y + 1 = 0$
19. $x^2 + y^2 - 8x - 2y + 7 = 0$ **21.** $x^2 + y^2 - 8x - 5y + 16 = 0$ **23. (a)** $(3, 4), (3, -2),$
(b) $(6, 1), (0, 1)$ **25. (a)** $(3 \pm 2\sqrt{2}, 0), (0, 1),$ **(b)** $4\sqrt{2}$,   **(c)** 0   **27. (a)** $(-4, 0); (0, 3),$ **(b)** 5
29. (a) Line,   **(b)** $(4, 0); (0, 4)$ **31. (a)** Line,   **(b)** $(\frac{2}{3}, 0), (0, -2)$ **33. (a)** Circle,   **(b)** $(0, 0), \sqrt{7}$
35. (a) Circle,   **(b)** $(-1, 0), 1$ **37. (a)** Circle,   **(b)** $(2, -1), 2$ **39. (a)** Circle,   **(b)** $(-2, -2), 2\sqrt{3}$
41. $(1, 4), (3, 5)$; Not unique   **43.** Answer not unique; **(a)** $(-2, 3), (4, -1),$ **(b)** $(-3, 4), (1, -2),$
(c) $(-6, 1), (4, -3),$ **(d)** $(-3, 3), (3, -3)$ **45.** $(1, 4), (4, 3), (7, 2), (10, 1)$ **47.** $(1, 2), (2, 1)$
49. $(-5, 1), (3, -3), (5, 5)$ **51.** $(\frac{13}{2}, \frac{9}{2})$ **53.** $(7, 2), (7, -3), (-3, -3)$ **55. (a)** $(4, 0),$ **(b)** $(0, 3),$
(c) $(-3, -4),$ **(d)** $(3, 4)$ **57.** 3π **59.** $\frac{3\pi + 2}{\pi - 2}$ **61.** $\sqrt{5} < r < \sqrt{8}$

Exercises 1.7

Check Your Understanding   **1.** T   **3.** T   **5.** T   **7.** a   **9.** c

Develop Mastery   **1.** $\frac{1}{12}$ **3.** 64   **5.** 2.4 hours   **7. (a)** Runs 6 miles, walks 14 miles,   **(b)** Runs 1 hour,
walks 3.5 hours   **9.** 1.5 sq. mi.   **11.** $\frac{-1 \pm \sqrt{5}}{2}$ **13.** Yes   **15.** $4\sqrt{3}$ **19.** 2   **21.** 37.5 mph
23. 200 mph   **25.** $\frac{4\pi}{3}$ **27.** 192 sq. cm.   **29.** 32   **31.** Any point $(u, 1)$ where u is a positive integer;
area is 3   **33.** All triangles have an area of 12   **35.** 6 ft.   **37. (a)** $2\sqrt{2}, 2\sqrt{3}, 2\sqrt{4}, 2\sqrt{5},$ **(b)** h
39. Two

Chapter 1 Review

Test Your Understanding   **1.** F   **3.** T   **5.** T   **7.** F   **9.** F   **11.** F   **13.** F   **15.** F   **17.** F
19. T   **21.** F   **23.** F   **25.** F   **27.** T   **29.** F   **31.** T   **33.** F   **35.** T   **37. (a)** T,   **(b)** T,
(c) T   **39. (a)** F,   **(b)** T,   **(c)** T

Review for Mastery   **1.** No   **3.** No   **5. (a)** $\frac{1}{7}$,   **(b)** $3 - 2\sqrt{2}$,   **(c)** $\frac{1}{275}$ **7. (a)** >,   **(b)** >,   **(c)** =

9. (a)   **(b)**   **(c)**

11. $x \le 3$ **13.** $\{\frac{8}{3}\}$ **15.** $\{0, -2\}$ **17.** $\{(2 \pm \sqrt{14})/2\}$ **19.** $\{-3, 1\}$ **21.** $\{-1, 4\}$
23. $\{-3, 3\}$ **25.** $5i$ **27.** $-2\sqrt{6}$ **29. (a)** F,   **(b)** T   **31. (a)** T,   **(b)** F   **33.** $\{x \mid x < 3\}$
35. $\{x \mid x < -2$ or $x > \frac{1}{2}\}$ **37.** $\{x \mid -1 < x < 0$ or $x > \frac{5}{2}\}$ **39.** $\{x \mid -3 \le x \le 1\}$
41. (a) $\{-1\}$,   **(b)** $\{x \mid x > -1\}$ **43. (a)** $\{x \mid x \ge 0\}$,   **(b)** $\{x \mid x < 0\}$ **45.** $-5 \le x \le 1$

47. $x^2 + y^2 + 6x - 4y + 12 = 0$ **49. (a)** Line,   **(b)** $(2, 0)$,   **(c)** $(0, -3)$ **51. (a)** Circle, C $(3, -1)$, $r = 2$,   **(b)** $(3 \pm \sqrt{3}, 0)$,   **(c)** None   **53. (a)** Line,   **(b)** $(\sqrt{3}, 0)$,   **(c)** $(0, 3)$ **55. (a)** Circle, C $(3, 2)$, $r = 2$,   **(b)** A is outside, B is inside, C is on the circle   **57. (a)** 40 percent,   **(b)** 2.5 quarts   **59.** 3 seconds **61.** $64\pi - 48\sqrt{3}$ **63.** $4\sqrt{7}$ **65. (a)** $8\sqrt{3}$ ft.,   **(b)** 12 sq. ft.

CHAPTER 2

Exercises 2.1

Check Your Understanding   **1.** F   **3.** F   **5.** T   **7.** b, c, d, g   **9.** a, c

Develop Mastery   **1.** $\{-4, 0, 4\}$ **3.** $\{\frac{2}{3}, \frac{9}{11}\}$ **5. (a)** 1,   **(b)** R **7. (a)** $\frac{5}{17}$,   **(b)** R **9. (a)** -2, **(b)** $\{x \mid 1 \le 1$ and $x \ne -2\}$ **11. (a)** $\sqrt{6}$,   **(b)** $\{x \mid x \le -4$ or $x \ge 1\}$ **13.** $(x + 2)/x^2$ **15.** $-x/\sqrt{x^2 + 4}$ **17.** -18.27; 0   **19.** 3; 4.83   **21.** 3   **23.** $2x + h - 2$ **25.** $-1/x(x + h)$ **27.** Triple x and add 4 to the result.   **29.** Take square root of x and subtract from 4.   **31.** 9; 4; $\sqrt{5} - 2$ **33.** 1; -1; -1 **35. (a)** 7,   **(b)** 3,   **(c)** 3,   **(d)** $2\sqrt{2} + 3$; $g(x) = \begin{cases} 1 - 2x & \text{if } x \le -\frac{1}{2} \\ 2x + 3 & \text{if } x > -\frac{1}{2} \end{cases}$ **37. (a)** 5, **(b)** -1,   **(c)** $x^4 - 4$,   **(d)** $x^2 - 2x - 3$ **39. (a)** 2,   **(b)** 5,   **(c)** 5,   **(d)** 43   **41. (a)** $\frac{2}{3}$,   **(b)** $\frac{5}{8}$, **(c)** 12,   **(d)** $(1 \pm \sqrt{41})/4$ **43. (a)** $C = 2\pi r$,   **(b)** $C = \pi d$ **45.** $P = 4s$ **47.** $A = \frac{p^2}{16}$ **49. (a)** $\sqrt{99}$; $25\sqrt{3}$; $9\sqrt{19}$,   **(b)** $A = x\sqrt{100 - x^2}$ **51. (a)** $d = |x|$,   **(b)** 1; 3,   **(c)** R **53. (a)** \$576; \$936, **(b)** $W = \begin{cases} 18x \text{ if } 0 \le x \le 40 \\ 27x - 360 \text{ if } 40 < x \le 168 \end{cases}$ **55. (a)** $L = \frac{3x}{5}$,   **(b)** 10 ft.   **57.** $A = 8x - \frac{8x^2}{15}, 0 < x < 15$

Exercises 2.2

Check Your Understanding   **1.** T   **3. (a)** F,   **(b)** T   **5.** T   **7.** b   **9.** f, g

Develop Mastery   **1.** Graph consists of three points: $(-1, -3)$, $(2, 3)$, $(3, 5)$. $R = \{-3, 3, 5\}$ **3.** Graph consists of five points: $(-2, -6)$, $(-1, 0)$, $(0, 0)$, $(1, 0)$, $(2, 6)$. $R = \{-6, 0, 6\}$

5.
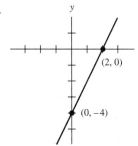

7.
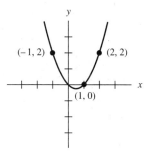

9. Even   **11.** Neither   **13.** Translate graph in **a** (of Figure 2.9) 2 units to the left.   **15.** Translate graph in **e** (of Figure 2.9) 2 units to the left.   **17.** Reflect graph in **f** (of Figure 2.9) about the *y*-axis.   **19.** Use 4 for a in **g** (of Figure 2.9), then compress toward the x axis by a factor of $\frac{1}{2}$.   **21.** Use 2 for a in **g** (of Figure 2.9), then stretch upward by a factor of 2, and then reflect about the *x*-axis.   **23.** Translate graph in **e** (of Figure 2.9) 2 units to the left, then upward 1 unit.   **25.** Reflect graph in **b** (of FIgure 2.9) about the *x*-axis, then translate upward 2 units.   **27.** $g(x) = -\frac{1}{x - 1}$. Translate graph in **d** (of Figure 2.9) 1 unit to the right, then reflect about the *x*-axis.   **29.** $f(x) = \sqrt{9 - (x - 1)^2}$ Use 3 for a in **g** (of Figure 2.9), translate graph 1 unit to the right. **31.** $f(x) = \sqrt{-(x - 2)}$. Reflect graph in **e** (of Figure 2.9) about the *y*-axis, then translate to the right 2 units. **33.** $y = (x + 2)^2 - 1$ **35.** $y = -\frac{1}{x} + 1$ **37.** $y = -\sqrt{x} - 1$ **39.** $y = |x - 1| - 2$

41. (a)

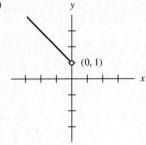

43. (a)

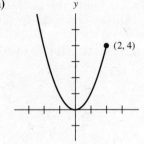

45.

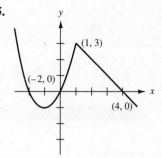

(b) $\{y \mid y > 1\}$ **(b)** $\{y \mid y \geq 0\}$

47. (i)   **49.** (c)   **51.** (f)   **53.** (d)   **55.** (h)

57. $f(3) < f(4.5) < f(-1) < f(0.5)$ **59.** $(1, 3)$; $(3, -2)$ **61. (a)** $-2 < x < -1$ or $2 < x < 5$,

    (b) $-1 < x < 2$ or $5 < x < 6$ **63.** a, d, and e

65. (a) R,   **(b)** Even,

    (c) $0 \leq y < 1$,

(d)

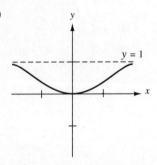

67.

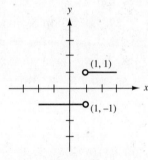

71.

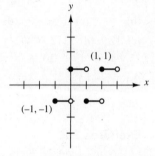

$$D = \{x \mid x \neq 1\}, R = \{-1, 1\}$$

69. Translate graph of $y = [x]$ 1 unit downward.   **73. (a)** $\{x \mid 2 \leq x < 3\}$,   **(b)** $\{x \mid 5 \leq x < 6\}$

75. (a) $\{x \mid -3 \leq x < -2\}$,   **(b)** $\{x \mid 0 \leq x < 1\}$ **77. (b)** $\{x \mid 4 \leq x < 5\}$,   **(c)** $(4, 9)$, $(4.1, 9)$, $(4.5, 9)$, $(4.8, 9)$

79.

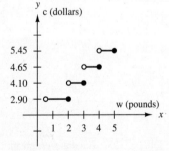

81. $(x + y)(x - y)(y + 3)$;

Graph consists of
three lines: $y = x$,
$y = -x$, $y = -3$.

Exercises 2.3

Check Your Understanding   **1.** F   **3.** T   **5.** T   **7.** e, f   **9.** a, c

Develop Mastery   **1.** $-\frac{3}{2}$ **3.** $\frac{5}{9}$ **5.** 0   **7.** $y = -2x - 2$ **9.** $y = -\frac{2x}{3}$ **11.** $y = -\frac{3}{2}$

13. $-\frac{3}{2}$; $(2, 0)$, $(0, 3)$ **15.** -2; $(2, 0)$, $(0, 4)$ **17.** -3; $(2, 0)$, $(0, 6)$ **19. (b)** $y = \frac{x}{2} + \frac{7}{2}$,

(c) $y = -2x + 1$ **21. (b)** $y = -\frac{2x}{3} - 2$,   **(c)** $y = \frac{3x}{2} - 2$ **23. (b)** $y = 2$,   **(c)** $x = -1$

25. Not collinear   **27.** Collinear   **29.** I, III, IV   **31.** II, IV

33. (a) 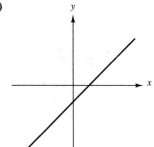   **(b)** 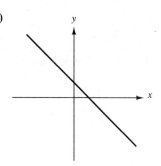   **(c)**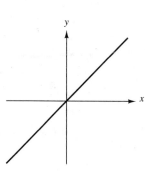

35. (a) $(0, 4)$,   **(b)** $y = -2x + 4$ **37. (a)** $(0, 2)$,   **(b)** $y = \frac{3x}{2} + 2$ **39.** $y = -\frac{x}{4} + \frac{3}{2}$
41. $y = \frac{x}{3} + \frac{10}{3}$ **43.** Yes   **45.** No   **47.** 2   **49. (a)** $m_{AC} = -\frac{1}{2}$, $m_{BC} = 2$,
(b) $x^2 + y^2 - 12x - 13y + 62 = 0$ **51. (a)** $C = 60 + 0.20x$,   **(b)** Not more than 200 mi.
53. (a) $C = 1{,}200 + 10x$,   **(b)** $R = 16x$,   **(c)** $P = 6x - 1{,}200$, $x > 200$ **55.** 4   **57. (a)** \$64,000,
(b) \$4,000   **59. (a)** $L = 0.002T + 124.91$,   **(b)** 124.95 cm,   **(c)** $130°$ C   **61.** $\pm\sqrt{3}$ **63.** $\frac{2}{3}$
65. π **67.** $4 - 2\sqrt{2}$

Exercises 2.4
Check Your Understanding   **1.** T   **3.** F   **5.** T   **7.** b   **9.** c, e, f

Develop Mastery   **1.** Translate graph of $y = x^2$ downward 3 units.   **3.** Translate graph of $y = x^2$ to the right
1 unit, then stretch it upward by a factor of 2.   **5.** Translate graph of $y = x^2$ to the left 1 unit, then downward
3 units.   **7.** Translate graph of $y = x^2$ to the left 1 unit, then reflect it about the x-axis.
9. (a) $f(x) = (x - 1)^2 + 3$,   **(b)** $V(1, 3)$; $(0, 4)$,   **(c)** Graph is a parabola opening up from $(1, 3)$.
11. (a) $f(x) = -(x + 1)^2 + 3$,   **(b)** $V(-1, 3)$; $(-1 \pm \sqrt{3}, 0)$, $(0, 2)$,   **(c)** Graph is a parabola opening down from
$(-1, 3)$.   **13. (a)** $f(x) = 2(x - 1)^2$,   **(b)** $V(1, 0)$; $(1, 0)$, $(0, 2)$,   **(c)** Graph is a parabola opening up from
$(1, 0)$.   **15. (a)** $f(x) = \frac{(x + 2)^2}{2} - 2$,   **(b)** $(-2, -2)$; $(0, 0)$, $(-4, 0)$,   **(c)** Graph is a parabola opening up
from $(-2, -2)$. **17. (a)** $f(x) = (x - \frac{3}{2})^2 - \frac{25}{4}$,   **(b)** $V(\frac{3}{2}, -\frac{25}{4})$; $(-1, 0)$, $(4, 0)$, $(0, -4)$, **(c)** Graph is a parabola
opening up from $(\frac{3}{2}, -\frac{25}{4})$.   **19. (a)** $f(x) = -2(x + 1)^2 + 3$,   **(b)** $V(-1, 3)$; $(\frac{-2 \pm \sqrt{6}}{2}, 0)$, $(0, 1)$,   **(c)** Graph
is a parabola opening down from $(-1, 3)$.   **21.** $y = -\frac{x}{2}$ **23.** $y = -x$ **25.** $y = -2x + 1$
27. $y = -4x + 3$ **29.** $V(1, 1)$; no x-intercept points   **31.** $V(-\frac{3}{2}, \frac{3}{2})$; two x-intercept points   **33.** I, II, and IV
35. I and II   **37.** $2\sqrt{7}$ **39.** $\sqrt{2}$ **41.** 15   **43.** 24   **45. (a)** Translate graph of $y = x^2$ to the right
2 units, then up 1 unit.,   **(b)** $y = x^2 - 4x + 5$ **47. (a)** Reflect graph of $y = x^2$ about the x-axis, then
translate down 2 units.   **49.** $f(x) = -x^2 + 4x + 5$ **51.** $f(x) = x^2 + 6x + 7$ **53. (a)** $A = (\frac{\sqrt{15}}{4})x^2$,
(b) $A = (\frac{\sqrt{15}}{100})$ P^2 **55. (a)** $A = x(18 - x)$,   **(b)** $0 < x < 18$ **57.** $(-3, 5)$, $(-2, 12)$, $(-1, 17)$ **59.** ten
61. $A = -x^2 + 410x$; $D = \{x \mid 0 < x \le 390\}$ **63.** $T = \begin{cases} 1{,}400x & \text{if } 0 \le x \le 120 \\ 2{,}600x - 10x^2 & \text{if } 120 < x \le 150 \end{cases}$
65. (a) $K = (\frac{\pi}{2})(4 - u^2)$,   **(b)** $K = 4 - u^2$,   **(c)** $K = \sqrt{3}(4 - u^2)$,   **(d)** $K = 2(4 - u^2)$

Exercises 2.5
Check Your Understanding   **1.** F   **3.** F   **5.** F   **7.** c   **9.** a

Develop Mastery   **1.** $\{x \mid x < 1 \text{ or } x > 3\}$ **3.** $\{x \mid -1 < x < \frac{3}{2}\}$
5. $\{x \mid x \le 1 - \sqrt{5} \text{ or } x \ge 1 + \sqrt{5}\}$ **7.** $\{2\}$ **9. (a)** $\{y \mid y \ge -4\}$,   **(b)** $[-4, \infty)$
11. (a) $\{y \mid y \le 3\}$,   **(b)** $(-\infty, 3]$ **13. (a)** $\{y \mid y \ge -4\}$,   **(b)** $[-4, \infty)$ **15. (a)** $\{y \mid y \ge -3\}$,
(b) $[-3, \infty)$ **17.** $\{y \mid 4 \le y \le 8\}$ **19.** $\{y \mid -1 < y \le 8\}$ **21.** Min is $-\frac{25}{4}$, no max
23. Max is 5, no min   **25.** Min is -5, no max   **27.** Min is $-\frac{1}{4}$, max is 12   **29.** Max is 9, no min

31. (a)

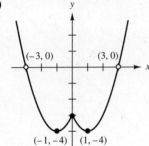

33. (a)

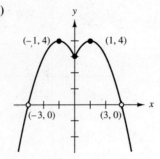

(b) $\{y \mid y \geq -4\}$,
(c) $\{x \mid -3 < x < 3\}$

(b) $\{y \mid y \leq 4\}$,
(c) $\{x \mid x < -3 \quad \text{or} \quad x > 3\}$

35. Max is 2, min is 0   **37.** Min is $\sqrt{2}$, no max   **39. (a)** Min is 2, no max,   **(b)** Max is -2, no min,
(c) Min is -1, no max   **41.** $\{x \mid x \leq 2 - \sqrt{6} \quad \text{or } x \geq 2 + \sqrt{6}\}$ **43.** $\{x \mid -\sqrt{5} \leq x \leq \sqrt{5}\}$ **45.** $\sqrt{10}$
47. $\sqrt{5}$ **49.** $\sqrt{24.2}$ **51.** $(3, -1)$ **53.** $(3, 3)$ **55.** $(2.4, 5.2)$ **57. (a)** 131 ft.   **(b)** 3 seconds, 147 ft.

59. (a)

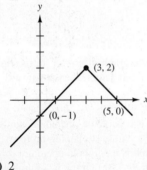

61.

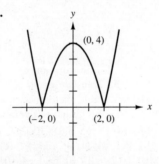

(b) 2

63. (a) $A = 2u - \frac{u^2}{2}$,   **(b)** $(2, 2)$,   **(c)** 2   **65. (a)** $A = 10x - 2x^2$, $D = \{x \mid 0 < x < 5\}$,   **(b)** $\frac{5}{2}$
67. (a) $T = \begin{cases} 2,400x & \text{if } 0 \leq x \leq 100 \\ 3,900x - 15x^2 & \text{if } 100 < x \leq 180 \end{cases}$ **(b)** $\{0, 1, 2, 3, \ldots, 180\}$,   **(c)** 130
69. 5 ft. when t is 10 minutes

Exercises 2.6

Check Your Understanding   **1.** F   **3.** F   **5.** T   **7.** g   **9.** f

Develop Mastery   **1. (a)** -5,   **(b)** 0   **3. (a)** 3,   **(b)** 2.25   **5. (a)** $(f + g)(x) = 2x - \frac{1}{x}$, $x \neq 0$
(b) $(\frac{f}{g})(x) = 1 - \frac{1}{x^2}$, $x \neq 0$ **7. (a)** $(f + g)(x) = -1$, $x \geq 0$,   **(b)** $(\frac{f}{g})(x) = \frac{\sqrt{x} - 2}{1 - \sqrt{x}}$, $x \geq 0$ and $x \neq 1$
9. (a) 5,   **(b)** 15,   **(c)** 8   **11. (a)**   **(b)** $\{-3, -1, 1, 3\}$,   **(c)** $\{0, 3\}$

x	-3	-1	0	1	3
$(g \circ f)(x)$	-2	-1	u	3	4

13. $(g \circ f)(x) = x - 4$, $D = \{x \mid x \geq 0\}$ **15.** $0, -1$ **17.** $-1, \frac{9}{2}$ **19.** $\frac{2 \pm \sqrt{31}}{3}$
21. $\{x \mid -\sqrt{2} \leq x \leq \sqrt{2}\}$ **23.** $\{x \mid x \geq \frac{11}{7}\}$ **25.** $\mathbb{R}$ **27. (a)** $(f \circ g)(x) = -3x - 1$,
(b) Graph is a line through $(-\frac{1}{3}, 0)$ and $(0, -1)$.   **29. (a)** $(f \circ g)(x) = -x^2 - 4x - 1$,
(b) Graph is a parabola opening down from $(-2, 3)$.   **31. (a)** $(f \circ g)(x) = x$, $(g \circ f)(x) = x$,   **(b)** Yes
33. (a) $(f \circ g)(x) = x$ for $x \geq 1$; $(g \circ f)(x) = |x|$ for x in $\mathbb{R}$,   **(b)** No   **35.** $g(x) = \frac{x + 5}{2}$ **37.** $g(x) = \frac{2x}{x - 2}$
39. 3.68   **41.** 1.81   **43.** $f(x) = \frac{1}{x}$, $g(x) = x^2 + 5$ **45.** $f(x) = |x|$, $g(x) = 5x + 3$ **47.** $f(x) = [x]$,
$g(x) = x^2 - 1$ **49.** $f(x) = \sqrt{x}$, $g(x) = x^2 + 1$ **51.** $F(x) = (f \circ k)(x)$ **53.** $H(x) = (g \circ h)(x)$
55. 5   **57.** 3   **59. (a)** $3, -1, 3, -1$,   **(b)** $-1, 3$ **61. (a)** $-1, 0, -1, 0$,   **(b)** $0, -1$

63. (a) $C = 80 + 192t - 16t^2$, **(b)** \$592 **(c)** 6 hrs. **65. (a)** $V = (\frac{\pi}{48})t^3$, **(b)** 6.74 sec.
67. (a) $A = \frac{\pi}{(t+1)^2}$, **(b)** $\frac{\pi}{4}$ sq. ft.; $\frac{\pi}{9}$ sq. ft., **(c)** 4 min. **69. (a)** 3 ft., **(b)** $V = (\frac{4\pi}{3})(0.25t + 3)^3$,
(c) 697 cu. ft., **(d)** 6.3 sec. **71. (a)** $12x(x^2 - 1)^2$, **(b)** -216

Exercises 2.7

Check Your Understanding **1.** F **3.** F **5.** T **7.** e **9.** h

Develop Mastery **1. (a)** $\{(-1, 0), (3, 1), (5, 2)\}$, **(b)** Yes
3. (a) $\{(4, -3), (2, -1), (1, 1), (2, 3)\}$, **(b)** No
5. Yes **7.** No

9. (a)

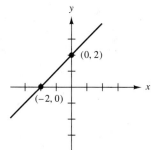

(b)

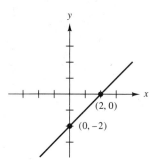

11. (a)

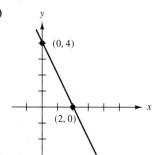

(b)

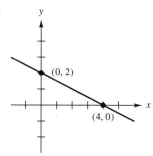

13. (a)

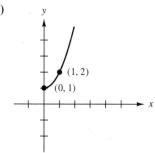

(b)

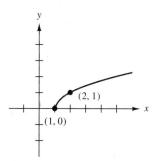

15. $f^{-1}(x) = \frac{x-5}{2}$ **17.** $f^{-1}(x) = \frac{1}{x-1}$ **19.** $f^{-1}(x) = \frac{2}{x+1}$ **21.** $f^{-1}(x) = x$ **23.** $f^{-1}(x) = 1 + \sqrt{x}$
25. (b) f is one–one, **(c)** Yes **27. (b)** f is not one–one, **(c)** No **29. (b)** f is one–one, **(c)** Yes
31. (a) Decreasing, **(b)** Yes **33. (a)** Decreasing, **(b)** Yes **35. (a)** Increasing, **(b)** Yes **39.** $y = -x$
41. (a) $f^{-1}(-3) = 0$, **(b)** $f(1) = 2, f^{-1}(2) = 1; f(-1) = -8, f^{-1}(-8) = -1$ **43. (b)** 2 **47.** Graph is
the line segment with endpoints **(a)** $(-2, -1)$, and $(7, 2)$, **(b)** $(0, -3)$ and $(3, 6)$, **(c)** $(-3, 1)$ and $(6, 4)$,
(d) $(-1, -1)$ and $(2, 8)$ **49. (a)** $r = \sqrt[3]{\frac{3V}{4\pi}}$, **(b)** 0.94, 1.05, 1.11 **51. (a)** $K = \sqrt{2}(2x - x^2)$,
(b) $D = \{x \mid 0 < x < 2\}, R = \{y \mid 0 < y \le \sqrt{2}\}$, **(c)** f is not one–one., **(d)** 0.196, 1.804 **53.** $r = \sqrt{\frac{V}{3\pi}}$

Exercises 2.8

Check Your Understanding   **1.** T   **3.** T   **5.** T   **7.** T   **9.** T

Develop Mastery   **1.** $\sqrt{10} \approx 3.16$ sec.   **3. (a)** 6.31 sec.   **(b)** 177 ft./sec.   **5. (a)** 42 ft.,   **(b)** 3.12 sec.
7. (a) $s(t) = 128t - 16t^2$,   **(b)** 192 ft.,   **(c)** 256 ft.   **9. (c)** 287 ft.   **11. (a)** 9.6 sec.,   **(b)** 307 ft./sec.
13. $8\sqrt{2.4} \approx 12.4$ ft./sec.   **15.** 80 ft.   **17. (a)** 80 ft./sec.,   **(b)** 80 ft./sec.   **19.** 42.1 sec.   **21.** 178 ft.
23. 320 ft.   **25. (a)** $R = 36x - 0.2x^2$,   **(b)** 90 calculators   **27. (a)** \$6,000; \$6,300; \$6,400,   **(b)** \$40
rental rate gives \$6,400   **29. (a)** $V = -312.5t + 3,000$,   **(b)** 9.6 yrs.   **31.** 40 by 60 ft.   **33. (a)** 1,000
cu. in.,   **(b)** 38.2 sec.,   **(c)** $\{t \mid 0 \le t \le 38.2\}$,   **(d)** 17.7 sec.; 20.5 sec.   **35. (a)** $r = \frac{d}{3}; V = (\frac{\pi}{27})d^3$,
(b) $V = (\frac{\pi}{27})(30 - 5\sqrt{t})^3$,   **(c)** $\frac{1,000\pi}{27} \approx 116$ cu. ft.,   **(d)** 36 min.   **37. (a)** $C = 4,000(40 - 2x + 3\sqrt{x^2 + 36})$,
(b) 216,498; 213,722; 213,823; 216,000; 219,943; 233,866,   **(c)** When x is about 5.4 mi., then $C \approx \$213,666$.

Chapter 2 Review

Test Your Understanding   **1.** F   **3.** F   **5.** T   **7.** F   **9.** T   **11.** T   **13.** T   **15.** T   **17.** T
19. F   **21.** T   **23.** F   **25.** T   **27.** F   **29.** T   **31.** F   **33.** F   **35.** F   **37.** F   **39.** T
41. T   **43.** T

Mastery Exercises   **1.** Yes   **3.** $\mathbb{R}$ **5.** $\{x \mid x \le 2\}$ **7.** $\{x \mid x \ne -2, x \ne 2\}$ **9.** $2x - 3y + 11 = 0$
11. $3x + 2y = 1$ **13.** Graph is a line through $(2, 0)$ and $(0, -4)$.   **15.** Graph is a parabola opening up from
lowest point $(2, -1)$ and passing through $(1, 0)$, $(3, 0)$, $(0, 3)$.   **17.** Graph consists of two half-lines: $y = x$ for
$x \ge 1$ and $y = -x + 2$ for $x < 1$.   **19.** $\{x \mid x < 3\}$ **21.** $\{x \mid x < 0 \text{ or } x > 2\}$ **23.** $\{x \mid -1 \le x \le 4\}$
25. $\{-2\}$ **27.** 3   **29.** -7 **31.** 1   **33.** $0, -2$ **35.** $0, 1$ **37. (a)** Neither,   **(b)** Not one–one
39. (a) Increasing,   **(b)** Is one–one   **41.** $f^{-1}(x) = \frac{x+4}{2}; D = \mathbb{R}, R = \mathbb{R}$ **43.** $f^{-1}(x) = x^2 + 1$;
$D = \{x \mid x \ge 0\}, R = \{y \mid y \ge 1\}$

45. (a)

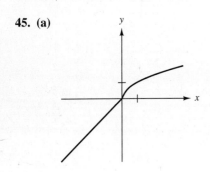

47. (a) Graph is a parabola opening up with lowest point at $(1, 1)$,
(b) Min is 1, no max   **49. (a)** Translate graph of $y = \sqrt{x}$ up 1 unit,
(b) Min is 1, no max   **53. (a)** $s = 160 + 48t - 16t^2$, **(b)** 5 sec.,
(c) 196 ft.   **55.** 32 min. and 44 sec. after 12 o'clock   **57.** -1
59. 2   **61.** -4 **63. (a)** 1,200 cu. in., **(b)** 1,043.2; 820;
480 cu. in., **(c)** 36.75 sec.   **65.** 3.35 sec.   **67.** 30 min.

CHAPTER 3

Exercises 3.1

Check Your Understanding   **1.** T   **3.** F   **5.** a   **7.** b, d   **9.** i

Develop Mastery   **1.** Yes; one   **3.** No   **5.** No   **7. (a)** $(f + g)(x) = 2x + 7$,   **(b)** deg. 1, l.c. 2, c.t. 7
9. (a) $(fg)(x) = -3x^2 + 13x + 10$,   **(b)** deg. 2, l.c. -3, c.t. 10   **11. (a)** $(h \circ f)(x) = 18x^2 + 21x + 6$,
(b) deg. 2, l.c. 18, c.t. 6   **13. (a)** $(\frac{f}{g})(x) = \frac{3x + 2}{5 - x}$,   **(b)** Not a polynomial function
15. (a) $p(x) = x^3 + x^2 - 2x$,   **(b)** $(0, 0)$, $(1, 0)$, $(-2, 0)$ **17. (a)** $p(x) = 2x^3 - x^2 - 2x + 1$,
(b) $(-1, 0)$, $(0.5, 0)$, $(1, 0)$, $(0, 1)$ **19. (a)** $p(x) = 3x^4 + 6x^3 - 3x^2 - 6x$,   **(b)** $(0, 0)$, $(-2, 0)$, $(-1, 0)$, $(1, 0)$
21. (a) $f(x) = (x + 1)(x - 1)$,   **(b)** $-1, 1$,   **(c)** $-1, 1$ **23. (a)** $p(x) = (x - 2)(x^2 + 2x + 4)$,
(b) 2,   **(c)** $2, -1 \pm \sqrt{3}i$ **25. (a)** $g(x) = x(x - 1)(x - 2)$,   **(b)** 0, 1, 2,   **(c)** 0, 1, 2

27. (a) $f(x) = (x + 1)(x - 1)(x^2 + 4)$, (b) ± 1, (c) $\pm 1, \pm 2i$ **29.** (a) $f(x) = x^2(2x + 5)$, (b) $0, 0, -\frac{5}{2}$,
(c) $0, 0, -\frac{5}{2}$ **31.** (a) $p(x) = (3x - 2)(x - 1)(x^2 + x + 1)$, (b) $1, \frac{2}{3}$, (c) $1, \frac{2}{3}, \frac{-1 \pm \sqrt{3}i}{2}$
33. $\{x \mid -2 < x < 1 \quad \text{or} \quad x > 3\}$ **35.** $\{x \mid x < -3 \quad \text{or} \quad -1 < x < 1\}$
37. (a) $p(x) = (x - 1)(x^2 + x + 1)$, (b) 1, **39.** (a) $p(x) = x(2 + x)(2 - x)$, (b) $0, \pm 2$,

(c)

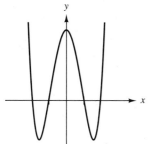

(c)

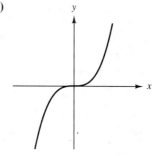

41. (a) $p(x) = (x + 2)(x - 2)(x + 1)(x - 1)$, **43.** (a)
(b) $\pm 1, \pm 2$,

(c)

(b) Reflect graph of $y = x^3$ about x-axis,
(c) Translate graph of $y = -x^3$ up 1 unit.

45. (a)

(b) Translate graph of $y = x^3 - 4x$ down 1 unit.
(c) Translate graph of $y = x^3 - 4x$ up 2 units.

47. $x \to \infty, f(x) \to -\infty; x \to -\infty, f(x) \to -\infty$
49. $x \to \infty, h(x) \to -\infty; x \to -\infty, h(x) \to \infty$
51. $x \to \infty, g(x) \to \infty; x \to -\infty, g(x) \to \infty$ **53.** m
55. mn **57.** mn **59.** e **61.** b
63. f does not have an inverse. **65.** No, f is not one–one.

Exercises 3.2

Check Your Understanding   **1.** T   **3.** F   **5.** T   **7.** d, i   **9.** c, d

Develop Mastery   **1.** $[-2, -0.5]$ **3.** $[-0.5, 0]$ **5.** $[0.25, 0.5]$ **7.** $[-1, 0], [0, 1], [3, 4]$ **9.** $[-2, -1]$
11. $[0, 1], [3, 4]$ **13.** 2.18   **15.** -2.10 **17.** 1.32   **19.** $p(x) = (x - 1)(2x^2 + 5x + 4) + 2; p(1) = 2$
21. $p(x) = (x + 1)(3x^3 - 2x^2 + 1) - 2; p(-1) = -2$ **23.** $p(x) = (x - 0.5)(2x^2 - 2x + 8); p(0.5) = 0$
25. $p(x) = (x - 1)(x^4 + x^3 + x^2 + x - 3) - 1; p(1) = -1$
27. $p(x) = (x - 0.5)(4x^2 + 2x + 4) - 1; p(0.5) = -1$ **29.** 11   **31.** 0
33. Yes; $x^9 - 2x^8 + 4x^7 - 8x^6 + 8x^5$ **35.** No   **37.** $-\frac{3}{2}$ **39.** $-\frac{4}{3}$ **41.** 1
43. $p(x) = (x - 1)(x + 1)(3x + 1)$ **45.** $p(x) = (x - 1)(3x + 1)(x + 2)$
47. $p(x) = (3x + 1)(x - 3)(x + 3)$ **49.** $p(x) = (x + 1)(x - 3)^2$ **51.** $-\frac{3}{2}$ **53.** $-\frac{15}{2}$ **55.** 0
57. **(a)** $[-2, -1], [-1, 0], [0, 1], [1, 2]$,   **(b)** $\pm\sqrt{2 - \sqrt{3}}, \pm\sqrt{2 + \sqrt{3}}$,   **59.** 2.8   **61.** 2.55 by 2.75 in.
63. **(a)** 60 cu. ft.,   **(b)** 2.74 ft.
65. **(a)** $(1, 4), (3, 0)$,   **67.** **(a)** $(-0.73, 3.4), (2.73, -17.4)$,   **69.** **(a)** No turning points; decreasing,

(b)   **(b)**   **(b)**

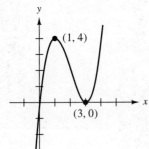 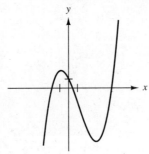 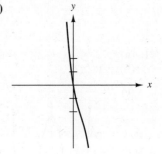

71. f is increasing. **(a)** -0.4,   **(b)** -0.9 **73.** f is decreasing **(a)** 0.3,   **(b)** 1.1

Exercises 3.3

Check Your Understanding   **1.** T   **3.** F   **5.** b, e, f   **7.** c, e, f   **9.** c, e, f

Develop Mastery   **1.** $\pm[1, \frac{1}{2}, \frac{1}{3}, \frac{1}{6}]$ **3.** $\pm[1, 2, \frac{1}{2}]$ **5.** $\pm[1, \frac{1}{2}, \frac{1}{3}, \frac{1}{6}]$ **7.** $\pm[1, 3, \frac{1}{2}, \frac{3}{2}]$
9. 1 is an upper bound; -2 is a lower bound.   **11.** 2 is an upper bound; -2 is a lower bound.
13. $4, \pm\sqrt{2}i$ **15.** $-\frac{3}{2}, 2 \pm \sqrt{5}$ **17.** $-1, -2, -\frac{2}{3}$ **19.** $-1, 2, \frac{5}{2}$ **21.** $\frac{3}{2}, \frac{5}{3}, -\frac{1 \pm \sqrt{3}i}{2}$
23. $1, \frac{3}{2}, -1, -\frac{1}{2}$ **25.** $\frac{1}{3}, \pm\sqrt{1.5}$ **27.** $-1, -1, 1, 2$ **29.** $1, 1, -2$ **31.** $-3, -1, -\frac{2}{3}$
33. $-\frac{1}{3}, 1 \pm \sqrt{5}$ **35.** $-1, -1, 2, 2$ **37.** $p(x) = x^3 + x^2 - 2x$ **39.** $p(x) = x^4 + 2x^3 - 3x^2$
41. $p(x) = x^3 + 4x^2 + 2x - 4$ **43.** $p(x) = x^4 - 3x^3 + 2x$ **45.** 2 and $1 + \sqrt{2}$
47. $\frac{1}{2}$ and $2 + \sqrt{5}$ **49.** $p(x) = (x - 1)(x + 4)(2x + 1)$ **51.** $p(x) = (2x - 1)(2x + 1)(4x - 5)$
53. $p(x) = (2x - 1)(x + 1)(x + 3)(2x + 1)$ **55.** $p(x) = (x - 1)(3x + 2)(x + 1)^2$
57. **(a)** $\{0, 4\}$,   **(b)** $\varnothing$ **59.** 2   **61.** -2

63.

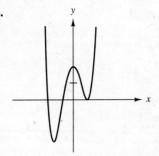

65. **(a)** $\{-1, \frac{1}{2}, 2\}$,   **(b)** $\{0, \frac{3}{2}, 3\}$,   **(c)** $\{x | x \le -1$ or $\frac{1}{2} \le x \le 2\}$
67. **(a)** $\{-2, 1\}$,   **(b)** $\{-1, 2\}$,   **(c)** $\{x | x \le -2$ or $x = 1\}$
69. $f^{-1}(16) = 2, f^{-1}(-12) = -2$ **71.** $f^{-1}(31) = -1, f^{-1}(-4) = -2$
73. **(a)** $-1, 3, 5$,   **(b)** 5   **75.** $-1 + \sqrt{2}$ is a root of $x^2 + 2x - 1 = 0$.
77. 6 ft. by 8 ft.   **79.** 5 in.

Exercises 3.4

Check Your Understanding   **1.** F   **3.** F   **5.** T   **7.** b   **9.** d, f

Develop Mastery   **1. (a)** $f(0.92) \approx 122, f(0.97) \approx 1,014,$ **(b)** $f(1.11) \approx 113, f(1.03) \approx 1,214$
3. Within 0.01 when $x < -51$ or $x > 49$. Within 0.0001 when $x < -5,001$ or $x > 4,999$.

5. (a)

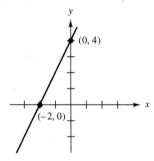

(b)

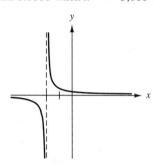

7. (a)

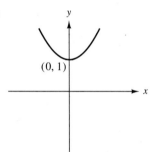

(b)

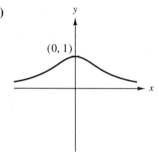

9. (a)

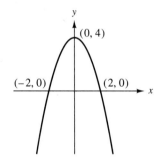

(b)

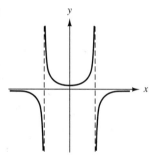

11. (a)

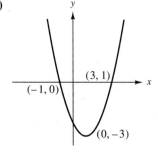

(b)

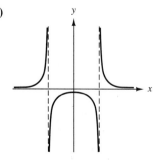

13. (a)

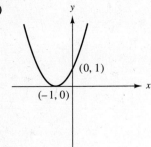

(b)

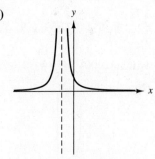

15. $y = -\frac{1}{x-1}$. Reflect graph of $y = \frac{1}{x}$ about the x-axis, then translate to the right 1 unit.   **17.** $y = -\frac{2}{x-3}$. Reflect graph of $y = \frac{1}{x}$ about the x-axis, translate to the right 3 units, and then stretch vertically away from the x-axis by a factor of 2.   **19.** $y = 1 - \frac{1}{x}$. Reflect graph of $y = \frac{1}{x}$ about the x-axis, then translate up 1 unit.

21. *V.A.* $x = -2$; *H.A.* $y = 0$

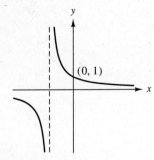

23. *V.A.* $x = -2$; *H.A.* $y = 2$

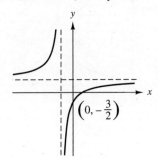
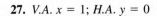

25. *V.A.* $x = -2$, $x = 2$; *H.A.* $y = 1$

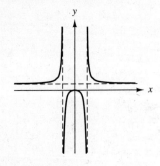

27. *V.A.* $x = 1$; *H.A.* $y = 0$

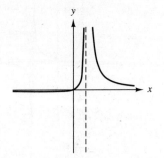
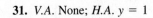

29. *V.A.* None; *H.A.* $y = 0$

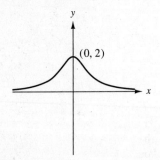

31. *V.A.* None; *H.A.* $y = 1$

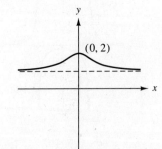

33. *V.A.* $x = 0$, $x = -1$, $x = 4$; *H.A.* $y = 0$

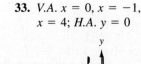
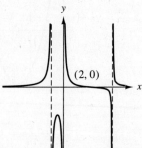

35. Graph $y = \frac{1}{x+2}$ with point $(0, \frac{1}{2})$ missing   **37.** Graph $y = \frac{x-1}{x+3}$ with point $(1, 0)$ missing
39. $y = 1$; $(3, 1)$ **41.** $y = 1$; $(-1, 1)$ **43.** $y = x + 1$; graph does not cross asymptote
45. $y = 2x + 3$, graph does not cross asymptote   **47.** d   **49.** f   **51.** b   **53.** c   **55.** $f(x) = 2$ for
every x except 0   **57.** $y = x - 1$ is a slant asymptote; turning points are $(-2, -5)$ and $(2, 3)$.
59. $f(x) = (x - \frac{1}{x})^2 + 3$; minimum value is 3 when $x = \pm 1$.   **61.** $f(x) = (2x - \frac{1}{x})^2 + 5$; minimum value is 5
when $x = \pm \frac{1}{\sqrt{2}}$.   **63.** $y = 0.5x + 10$ is a slant asymptote; minimum value of A is $2\sqrt{6} + 10$ when x is $2\sqrt{6}$.

Chapter 3 Review
Test Your Understanding   **1.** F   **3.** T   **5.** T   **7.** F   **9.** F   **11.** F   **13.** F   **15.** F   **17.** T
19. T   **21.** T   **23.** T   **25.** T   **27.** F   **29.** T   **31.** T   **33.** T   **35.** F   **37.** F   **39.** F
41. T   **43.** T   **45.** T   **47.** T   **49.** T   **51.** F

Mastery Review   **1.** -2.5; 2   **3.** $q(x) = 3x^2 - 7x + 6$; $r = -5$ **5.** 12
7. $(-2, 0)$, $(1, 0)$, $(1, 0)$, $(0, 2)$; $x \to \infty$, $f(x) \to \infty$; $x \to -\infty$, $f(x) \to -\infty$ **9.** 0, 1, 4   **11.** $-3, -2, \frac{1}{2}$
13. **(a)** $[-3, -2]$, $[0, 1]$, $[1, 2]$,   **(b)** $[-2.5, -2.4]$, $[0.6, 0.7]$, $[1.8, 1.9]$,   **(c)** 1.83   **15.** **(a)** 0, 0, $\pm\sqrt{3}$
(b) Graph is tangent to the x-axis at $(0, 0)$ and crosses at $(-\sqrt{3}, 0)$ and $(\sqrt{3}, 0)$.   **17.** $f(x) = x^4 - 8x^2 + 16$
19. $y = (x + 1)(x - 1)(x - 3)$; $(-1, 0)$, $(1, 0)$, $(3, 0)$, $(0, 3)$ **21.** **(a)** Function is odd; $(-2, 0)$, $(0, 0)$, $(2, 0)$,
(b) Translate graph in (a) down 1 unit.,   **(c)** Translate graph in (a) to the right 1 unit.   **23.** **(a)** $(-3, 0)$, $(0, 1.5)$,
(b) *V.A.* $x = 2$; *H.A.* $y = -1$ **25.** **(a)** $(1, 0)$, $(1, 0)$, no y-intercept,   **(b)** *V.A.* $x = 0$, $x = 4$; *H.A.* $y = 1$
27. $\{x \,|\, x \geq 3\}$ **29.** $\{x \,|\, x \leq -1$ or $x = 2$ or $x > 3\}$ **31.** **(a)** 2,   **(b)** -2 **33.** **(a)** $\{-1, 0.5, 3\}$,
(b) $\{0, 1.5, 4\}$,   **(c)** $\{-3, -1.5, 1\}$ **35.** **(a)** $\{x \,|\, -3 \leq x \leq -0.5$ or $x \geq 1\}$,
(b) $\{x \,|\, -2 \leq x \leq 0.5$ or $x \geq 2\}$

CHAPTER 4

Exercises 4.1
Check Your Understanding   **1.** F   **3.** T   **5.** T   **7.** a, c   **9.** e, h

Develop Mastery   **1.** $\frac{7}{2}$ **3.** $\frac{1}{8}$ **5.** -140 **7.** 1   **9.** -6.240 **11.** 0.5664   **13.** 36.55
15. 4.160   **17.** **(a)** $(2\sqrt{5} - 1)$,   **(b)** $\sqrt{x} + 2$ **19.** $|x|$ **21.** x **23.** 3^{9x-5} **25.** $\{\frac{1}{2}, 1\}$ **27.** $\{\frac{2}{5}\}$
29. $\{x \,|\, x \neq 1, x \neq -1\}$ **31.** Yes   **33.** No   **35.** **(a)** -0.37,   **(b)** 5.82   **37.** $3^{\sqrt{3}}$ **39.** $(\sqrt{5})^5$
41. **(a)** $\{y \,|\, y < 0\}$,   **(b)** Decreasing   **43.** **(a)** $\{y \,|\, y > 0\}$,   **(b)** Increasing   **45.** **(a)** $\{y \,|\, y < 1\}$,
(b) Decreasing   **47.** $f(0.01) = 2.7048$, $f(0.0001) = 2.7181$, $f(-0.01) = 2.7320$, $f(-0.0001) = 2.7184$
49. $\{8\}$ **51.** $\{1, 2\}$ **53.** $\{\frac{\sqrt{3}}{2}\}$ **55.** **(a)** $\{4\}$,   **(b)** $\{x \,|\, x < 0$ or $x \geq 4\}$,
(c) $\{x \,|\, x < 0$ or $x \geq 0.25\}$,   **(d)** $\{-2, 2\}$ **57.** $f(x) = e^{x+2}$; translate graph of $y = e^x$ to the left 2 units.
59. $f(x) = 2$; Graph is a horizontal line.   **61.** $b = c$ **63.** $c > b$ **65.** Zero of $f(x) = x^2 - 2x - 4$.
67. $\{x \,|\, x < -\sqrt{5}$ or $x > \sqrt{5}\}$ **69.** 34; 309   **71.** 1   **75.** **(a)** $V = (\frac{4\pi}{3})(1 + 2\sqrt{t})^3$, $0 \leq t \leq 49$,
(b) When $t = 4$, $V \approx 524$ cm.^{3}; When $t = 60$, no value of V.   **77.** **(a)** 39.7 sec.,   **(b)** 28.3 sec.,   **(c)** 16.6 sec.
79. **(a)** \$4.87,   **(b)** \$1,869.16   **81.** **(a)** 11.6 days; 11,600 days,   **(b)** 31.7 yrs.; 129,000 yrs.   **83.** 442,000 mi.
85. 57 pp. (assuming 4,000 characters per page)

Exercises 4.2
Check Your Understanding   **1.** T   **3.** T   **5.** T   **7.** b   **9.** b, g

Develop Mastery   **1.** **(a)** $\log_5 125 = 3$,   **(b)** $\log_4(\frac{1}{16}) = -2$,   **(c)** $\log_3 5 = x - 1$ **3.** **(a)** 2,   **(b)** -2
5. **(a)** -2,   **(b)** 5   **7.** **(a)** 0,   **(b)** $\frac{1}{3}$ **9.** **(a)** $\sqrt{e}$,   **(b)** 1   **11.** **(a)** 16,   **(b)** 17   **13.** $\frac{9}{4}$ **15.** **(a)** x;
for any real number,   **(b)** $x + 1$; for $x > -1$ **17.** $2x$; for any real number,   **(b)** $5x$; for $x > 0$ **19.** 5
21. $-1, 3$ **23.** $\frac{5}{3}$ **25.** $\pm\sqrt{5}$ **27.** $\frac{1}{3}$, 27   **31.** $b = (\frac{2}{3})c$ **33.** **(a)** $\sqrt{2}$,   **(b)** $\frac{1}{49}$ **35.** **(a)** 2 and 3,
(b) 3 and 4   **37.** $\log_2 6$ **39.** $\log_2 0.4$ **41.** 4   **43.** 4   **45.** Four   **47.** Four

49. (a)

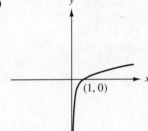

$(1, 0)$

(b)

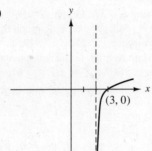

$(3, 0)$

51. (a)

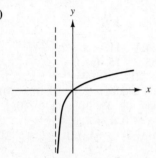

(b)

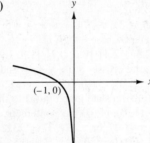

$(-1, 0)$

53. (a) $D = \mathbb{R}$, **(b)** $y = -x^2$,

(c)

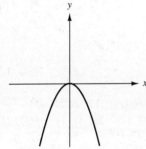

55. (a) $D = \{x \mid x < 2\}$, **(b)** $y = 2 - x, x < 2$,

(c)

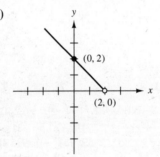

$(0, 2)$

$(2, 0)$

57. $D = \{x \mid x < -1 \ \text{ or } \ x > 1\}$ **59.** $D = \{x \mid x > 0\}$ **61.** $D = \{x \mid x < 0 \ \text{ or } \ x > 2\}$
63. (a) $(0, 0)$, **(b)** $\{x \mid -1 < x < 0\}$ **65. (a)** $(4, 0)$, **(b)** $\{x \mid 0 < x < 4\}$ **67.** a **69.** c
71. $f^{-1}(x) = 3^{x-1}$ **73.** $f^{-1}(x) = 3^{x-1}$ **75. (a)** $D = \mathbb{R}, R = \{y \mid 0 < y < 1\}$, **(b)** $f^{-1}(x) = \log_3(\frac{x}{1-x})$,
(c) $D = \{x \mid 0 < x < 1\}, R = \mathbb{R}$

Exercises 4.3
Check Your Understanding **1.** F **3.** T **5.** F **7.** a, d, i, j, l **9.** a, c

Develop Mastery **1.** $\frac{3}{2}$ **3.** $\frac{5}{2}$ **5.** 1 **7.** $\log_3 8$ **9.** $\log_{10} 2$ **11.** $\log_3 2 + 3 \log_3 x$
13. $\log_5 x + (\frac{1}{2}) \log_5(x^2 + 4)$ **15.** $3 + 2 \log_2 x - (\frac{1}{2}) \log_2(x^2 + 1)$ **17.** $\log_3[\frac{x^2}{(x + 2)}]$ **19.** $\log_3(\frac{4}{x})$
21. (a) 0.631, **(b)** 2.096 **23. (a)** 0.529, **(b)** 1.780 **25. (a)** $1 - u$, **(b)** $u - 1$
27. (a) $(\frac{1}{3})(u + 2v)$, **(b)** $(\frac{1}{2})(3u + v)$ **29. (a)** $v - u$, **(b)** $(\frac{1}{3})(v - u)$ **31. (a)** $2u$, **(b)** $(\frac{1}{2})(3v - u)$
33. $\frac{1}{2}$ **35.** $\frac{3}{14}$ **37.** 2 **39.** 1 **41.** $1 + \sqrt{3}$ **43.** $\{x \mid x > 3\}$ **45.** $\{x \mid 0 < x < 4\}$
47. $\{x \mid x > 0\}$ **51.** $x > 4$ **55.** $\log_2(ab) = 7, (\log_2 a)(\log_2 b) = 12$ **57.** $\log_2 c^n = 6, (\log_2 c)^n = 8$
59. (a) $\varnothing$, **(b)** $\mathbb{R}$ **61.** $\sqrt{3} + \sqrt{2} = \frac{1}{\sqrt{3} - \sqrt{2}}$ **63.** $\sqrt{k + 1} + \sqrt{k} = \frac{1}{\sqrt{k+1} - \sqrt{k}}$ **65.** $D = \mathbb{R}$;
$f^{-1}(x) = (\frac{1}{2})(3^{-x} - 3^x)$

Exercises 4.4

Check Your Understanding   **1.** F   **3.** F   **5.** F   **7.** c   **9.** e

Develop Mastery   **1. (a)** 1.6094,   **(b)** 1.1931   **3. (a)** 0.6826,   **(b)** -0.5108,   **(c)** 1.5440   **5. (a)** 0.3466,
(b) 0.8326,   **(c)** 0.6931   **7. (a)** 0.4136,   **(b)** Undefined,   **(c)** 0.5774   **9.** $\sqrt{5}$; 2.24,   **(b)** $\frac{1}{\sqrt{5}}$; 0.45
11. (a) $\sqrt{3}$; 1.73,   **(b)** $\frac{1}{6}$; 0.17   **13.** $>$ **15.** $=$ **17.** $>$ **19.** $\sqrt[3]{e}$; 1.396   **21.** $(e+10)/15$; 0.848
23. $\frac{10}{29}$; 0.345   **25.** $\frac{(10+\sqrt{10})}{9}$; 1.462   **27.** $\frac{\ln 4}{\ln 3}$; 1.262   **29.** $-\ln(0.56)$; 0.580   **31.** $\frac{\ln(\ln 4)}{\ln 3}$; 0.297
33. $\frac{\ln 3}{(1-\ln 4)}$; -2.844 **35.** $-\ln(\ln 8 - 1)$; -0.076.   **37.** $(1.72, 0)$, $(0, -1)$ **39.** $(0.66, 0)$, $(0, -3)$
41. $(-0.42, 0)$, $(0, -0.31)$ **43. (a)** Translate graph of $y = \ln x$ to the right 1 unit and then 1 unit down; crosses
x-axis at $(1 + e, 0)$.   **(b)** $\{x \mid x \geq 1 + e\}$ **45. (a)** Translate graph of $y = e^x$ down 2 units; crosses x-axis at
$(\ln 2, 0)$.   **(b)** $\{x \mid x \geq \ln 2\}$ **47.** $\ln 2$ **49.** 1, $\frac{\ln 2}{\ln 5}$ **51.** 1, $e \approx 2.718$ **53.** $\ln 2 \approx 0.693$
55. $\frac{\ln 3}{\ln 2} \approx 1.585$ **57.** $\{2\}$ **59.** $\mathbb{R}$ **61.** $\{\frac{1}{12}\}$ **63. (a)** $\{10\}$ **(b)** $\{e^{-2}, e^2\}$ **65.** $\{x \mid x > 0 \text{ and } x \neq 1\}$
67. $\{x \mid x > 0 \text{ and } x \neq 1\}$ **69.** $\frac{10^{-3}w}{m^2}$ **71. (a)** 95 dB,   **(b)** 27 percent   **73.** $g^{-1}(x) = (e^x - e^{-x})/2 = \sinh x$

Exercises 4.5

Check Your Understanding   **1.** f   **3.** a   **5.** c   **7.** a   **9.** b

Develop Mastery   **1. (a)** 16,000,   **(b)** 25,000,   **(c)** 5 hrs.   **3. (a)** 6.4 billion,   **(b)** Year 2005
5. 270 million   **7.** 6 percent   **9.** $8\frac{2}{3}$ percent   **11.** $1,934.79   **13. (a)** 9.69 gm.,   **(b)** 6.2 gm.
15. 7.3 lb.   **17.** 3.9 yrs.   **19.** 7,500 yrs.   **21.** 1,340 yrs.   **23.** 250 times as great   **25.** 7.7
27. 19.5 km.   **29.** 7.35, slightly basic   **31.** 26 yrs.   **33. (a)** 111 lb., **(b)** 110 min.   **35. (a)** 16,800,
(b) 17 days

Chapter 4 Review

Test Your Understanding   **1.** F   **3.** F   **5.** F   **7.** T   **9.** F   **11.** T   **13.** F   **15.** T
17. F   **19.** F   **21.** T   **23.** F   **25.** T   **27.** F   **29.** T   **31.** T   **33.** T   **35.** F   **37.** F
39. F   **41.** T   **43.** T   **45.** F   **47.** T   **49.** F   **51.** F   **53.** T   **55.** T   **57.** T   **59.** c
61. i   **63.** e

Mastery Review   **1.** $\frac{6}{5}$ **3.** $\frac{3}{2}$ **5.** 0   **7.** $\frac{1}{49}$ **9.** $\frac{1}{2}$ **11.** 3.850   **13.** 0.235   **15.** 23.141
17. $\sqrt{2}$ **19.** 2.08; -0.54 **21.** -2.35; 23.10   **23.** $\frac{9}{2}$ **25.** 4   **27.** 1   **29.** $\frac{e}{(e-1)}$ **31.** 0.86
33. 1.20   **35.** 0.29   **37.** 3.72   **39.** 0   **41.** $\{x \mid x < 0 \text{ or } x > 2\}$ **43.** $\{x \mid x > 0\}$
45. $\{x \mid x > 1\}$ **47.** Translate graph of $y = \ln x$ up 1 unit.   **49.** Reflect graph of $y = e^x$ about the y-axis,
then translate up 1 unit.   **51.** Draw graph of $y = x$ for $x > 0$.   **53.** $(\ln 2, 0)$ **55.** $(\frac{5}{2}, 0)$ **57.** No;
domains are different   **61.** $2,246.64   **63.** 2,400 yrs.   **65.** 87 dB

CHAPTER 5

Exercises 5.1

Check Your Understanding   **1.** F   **3.** T   **5.** F   **7.** e   **9.** a, b, c, d

Develop Mastery

1. (a)   **(b)**   **(c)**

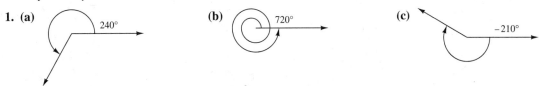

3. (a) 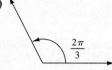 **(b)**  **(c)**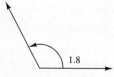

5. (a) 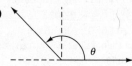 **(b)** 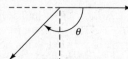 **(c)**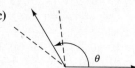

7. (a) 23.633°, **(b)** 143.273°, **(c)** −95.517°
9. (a) $\frac{\pi}{3}$, 1.05, **(b)** $\frac{11\pi}{6}$; 5.76, **(c)** $\frac{\pi}{8}$; 0.39, **(d)** $\frac{7\pi}{12}$; 1.83 **11. (a)** 120°, **(b)** 75°, **(c)** 720°, **(d)** 206.3°
13. (a) $\frac{\pi}{4}$, **(b)** 60°, **(c)** $\frac{3\pi}{4}$, **(d)** 105° **15.** $\gamma < \alpha < \beta$ **17.** $\gamma < \beta < \alpha$ **19.** 49° **21.** $\frac{\pi}{3}$
23. (a) 4π, **(b)** 48π **25. (a)** 733, **(b)** 60,100 **27. (a)** 150, **(b)** 2,800 **29. (a)** 1.5; 1.9,
(b) 0.26; 4.3, **(c)** 9.0; 34, **(d)** 214°; 420 **31. (a)** 2.33, **(b)** 133.5° **33. (a)** 1.26, **(b)** 117 million mi.
35. (a) 105°, **(b)** 172.5° **37. (a)** 9.42 in., **(b)** 311 in. **39. (a)** 0.009 rad./min., **(b)** 0.105 rad./min.
41. $r = 11.25$ inches, $V \approx 1,315$ cu. in. **43. (a)** 11 in., **(b)** 190 cu. in. **45. (a)** $144\sqrt{3}$ cm.²,
(b) 96π cm.², **(c)** 192π cm.² **47. (a)** $\frac{2}{5}$ rev./hr.; $\frac{4\pi}{5}$ rad./hr., **(b)** 10,300 mi./hr. **49.** 2,290 mi./hr.
51. (a) $\frac{8}{3}$ rev./min., **(b)** 200 in./min. **53.** 2.6 mi./hr. **55. (a)** 148 rev./hr., **(b)** 3,260 ft./min., **(c)** 205 mi.

Exercises 5.2

Check Your Understanding **1.** F **3.** T **5.** F **7.** b **9.** f, i

Develop Mastery

1. (a)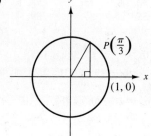

(b) All are positive.

3. (a)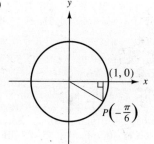

(b) $\cos(-\frac{\pi}{6})$ is positive,
the other two are negative.

5. (a)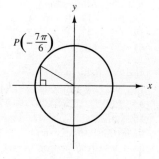

(b) $\sin(-\frac{7\pi}{6})$ is positive;
the other two are negative.

7. (a)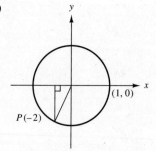

(b) $\tan(-2)$ is positive;
the other two are negative.

9. (a)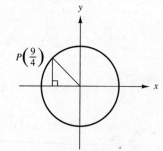

(b) $\sin(\frac{9}{4})$ is positive;
the other two are negative.

11. $P(\frac{5\pi}{2})$ is $(0, 1)$; $\cos(\frac{5\pi}{2}) = 0$; $\sin(\frac{5\pi}{2}) = 1$, $\csc(\frac{5\pi}{2}) = 1$, $\cot(\frac{5\pi}{2}) = 0$ **13.** $P(-3\pi)$ is $(-1, 0)$; $\cos(-3\pi) = -1$, $\sin(-3\pi) = 0$, $\sec(-3\pi) = -1$, $\tan(-3\pi) = 0$ **15.** $P(-\frac{15\pi}{2})$ is $(0, 1)$; $\cos(-\frac{15\pi}{2}) = 0$, $\sin(-\frac{15\pi}{2}) = 1$, $\csc(-\frac{15\pi}{2}) = 1$, $\cot(-\frac{15\pi}{2}) = 0$

Exercise	t	$\sin t$	$\cos t$	$\tan t$	$\cot t$	$\sec t$	$\csc t$
17	$\frac{5\pi}{6}$	$\frac{1}{2}$	$-\frac{\sqrt{3}}{2}$	$-\frac{1}{\sqrt{3}}$	$-\sqrt{3}$	$-\frac{2}{\sqrt{3}}$	2
19	$\frac{7\pi}{4}$	$-\frac{1}{\sqrt{2}}$	$\frac{1}{\sqrt{2}}$	-1	-1	$\sqrt{2}$	$-\sqrt{2}$
21	$-\frac{11\pi}{6}$	$\frac{1}{2}$	$\frac{\sqrt{3}}{2}$	$\frac{1}{\sqrt{3}}$	$\sqrt{3}$	$\frac{2}{\sqrt{3}}$	2
23	$\frac{13\pi}{3}$	$\frac{\sqrt{3}}{2}$	$\frac{1}{2}$	$\sqrt{3}$	$\frac{1}{\sqrt{3}}$	2	$\frac{2}{\sqrt{3}}$

25. $\{t \mid t = k \cdot 2\pi\}$ **27.** $\{t \mid t = \frac{\pi}{3} + k \cdot 2\pi$ or $t = \frac{5\pi}{3} + k \cdot 2\pi\}$ **29.** $\{t \mid t = \frac{\pi}{6} + k \cdot \pi\}$
31. $\{t \mid t = \frac{3\pi}{4} + k \cdot \pi\}$ **33.** $\{t \mid t = \frac{5\pi}{6} + k \cdot 2\pi\}$ **35.** $\{t \mid t = \frac{3\pi}{4} + k \cdot 2\pi\}$ **37.** IV   **39.** II or III
41. (a) negative, **(b)** negative   **43. (a)** negative, **(b)** positive   **45.** $P(t) = (-\frac{3}{5}, \frac{4}{5})$; $\sin t = \frac{4}{5}$,
$\cos t = -\frac{3}{5}$, $\tan t = -\frac{4}{3}$, $\cot t = -\frac{3}{4}$, $\sec t = -\frac{5}{3}$, $\csc t = \frac{5}{4}$ **47.** $P(t) = (\frac{7}{25}, -\frac{24}{25})$; $\sin t = -\frac{24}{25}$, $\cos t = \frac{7}{25}$,
$\tan t = -\frac{24}{7}$, $\cot t = -\frac{7}{24}$, $\sec t = \frac{25}{7}$, $\csc t = -\frac{25}{24}$ **49. (a)** $y = \pm\frac{\sqrt{3}}{2}$, **(b)** $\cos t = \frac{1}{2}$, $\sin t = \pm\frac{\sqrt{3}}{2}$
51. (a) $x = \pm\frac{1}{\sqrt{2}}$, **(b)** $\cos t = \pm\frac{1}{\sqrt{2}}$, $\sin t = \mp\frac{1}{\sqrt{2}}$ **53. (a)** $y = \pm\frac{1}{\sqrt{5}}$, **(b)** $\cos t = \pm\frac{2}{\sqrt{5}}$, $\sin t = \pm\frac{1}{\sqrt{5}}$
55. $-\frac{\pi}{6}$ **57.** $\frac{7\pi}{6}$ **59.** $-\frac{3\pi}{2}$ **61.** $\frac{5\pi}{4}$ **63.** $\frac{\pi}{4}$ **65.** $\cos t = -\frac{\sqrt{7}}{4}$, $\sin t = -\frac{3}{4}$ **67.** $\cos t = -\frac{3}{5}$,
$\sin t = \frac{4}{5}$ **69.** 1   **71.** 1   **73. (a)** -1, **(b)** $\sqrt{2}$, **(c)** -1; $\sin 2t = 2 \sin t \cos t$ **75. (a)** 0, **(b)** 2,
(c) 0; $\sin 2t = 2 \sin t \cos t$ **77.** The weight oscillates between 3 and -3 for y and makes a complete oscillation
every $\frac{1}{2}$ second.

Exercises 5.3

Check Your Understanding   **1.** F   **3.** T   **5.** F   **7.** b   **9.** f, g, i

Develop Mastery

1. $\sin \theta = \frac{4}{5}$, $\cos \theta = -\frac{3}{5}$, $\tan \theta = -\frac{4}{3}$ **3.** $\sin \theta = \frac{12}{13}$, $\cos \theta = \frac{5}{13}$, $\tan \theta = \frac{12}{5}$ **5.** $\sin \theta = -\frac{24}{25}$,
$\cos \theta = -\frac{7}{25}$, $\tan \theta = \frac{24}{7}$ **7.** $\sin \theta = -\frac{1}{\sqrt{2}}$, $\cos \theta = \frac{1}{\sqrt{2}}$, $\tan \theta = -1$ **9.** $\sin \theta = -\frac{2}{\sqrt{5}}$, $\cos \theta = -\frac{1}{\sqrt{5}}$,
$\tan \theta = 2$ **11.** $\sin \theta = \frac{3}{\sqrt{13}}$, $\cos \theta = \frac{2}{\sqrt{13}}$, $\tan \theta = \frac{3}{2}$ **13.** $\sin \theta = -\frac{2}{3}$, $\cos \theta = \frac{\sqrt{5}}{3}$, $\tan \theta = -\frac{2}{\sqrt{5}}$
15. $\sin \theta = \frac{4}{5}$, $\cos \theta = -\frac{3}{5}$, $\tan \theta = -\frac{4}{3}$ **17.** $\sin \phi \approx -0.45$, $\cos \phi \approx -0.89$, $\tan \phi = 0.50$
19. $\sin \phi \approx 0.40$, $\cos \phi \approx -0.92$, $\tan \phi \approx -0.44$ **21.** $\sin \phi \approx -0.60$, $\cos \phi = 0.80$, $\tan \phi \approx -0.75$
23. $\sin \phi \approx -0.87$, $\cos \phi = 0.50$, $\tan \phi \approx -1.73$ **25.** $\sin \phi \approx -0.98$, $\cos \phi \approx 0.20$, $\tan \phi = -5.00$
27. 0.595   **29.** 0.972   **31.** -0.130 **33.** -3.381 **35.** 1.110   **37.** -1.323 **39. (a)** $(-0.15, 0.99)$,
(b) $\sin t \approx 0.99$, $\cos t \approx -0.15$, $\tan t \approx -6.80$ **41. (a)** $(0.81, -0.59)$ **(b)** $\sin t \approx -0.59$, $\cos t \approx 0.81$,
$\tan t \approx -0.73$ **43. (a)** $(-0.54, -0.84)$, **(b)** $\sin t \approx -0.84$, $\cos t \approx -0.54$, $\tan t \approx 1.56$
45. (a) $(-0.91, 0.41)$, **(b)** $\sin t \approx 0.41$, $\cos t \approx -0.91$, $\tan t \approx -0.45$ **47. (a)** 0.416, **(b)** 7.750
49. (a) -0.909, **(b)** 1.342   **51.** $\sin(\theta + \frac{\pi}{2}) = \cos \theta$ **53.** $1 + (\tan \theta)^2 = (\sec \theta)^2$
55. $\cos 2\theta \neq 2 \cos \theta$, but $\cos 2\theta = (\cos \theta)^2 - (\sin \theta)^2 = 2(\cos \theta)^2 - 1$ **57. (a)** $x = 4 \cos(\frac{2\pi t}{15})$, $y = 4\sin(\frac{2\pi t}{15})$,
(b) $Q(x, y)$; $(-2, -3.46)$, $(-2, 3.46)$ $(-2, -3.46)$, $(-2, -3.46)$ **59. (a)** 1.04, **(b)** -5.36, **(c)** 0.703
61. $\cos 0.1 \approx 0.9950$, $C(0.1) \approx 0.9950$; $\cos 0.2 \approx 0.9801$, $C(0.2) \approx 0.9801$; $\cos 6.6 \approx 0.8253$, $C(6.6) \approx 0.8254$

Exercises 5.4

Check Your Understanding   **1.** T   **3.** T   **5.** T   **7.** c   **9.** h, i

Develop Mastery   **1.** The graph should be a portion of the graph in Figure 5.41 for $0 \leq x \leq \frac{\pi}{2}$.
3. The graph should be a portion of the graph in Figure 5.49 (a) for $\frac{\pi}{4} \leq x \leq \frac{3\pi}{4}$.   **5.** $\tan(\theta + \frac{\pi}{2}) = -\cot \theta$;
$\cot(\theta + \frac{\pi}{2}) = -\tan \theta$, $\sec(\theta + \frac{\pi}{2}) = -\csc \theta$, $\csc(\theta + \frac{\pi}{2}) = \sec \theta$ **7.** $\cos(t - \frac{\pi}{2}) = \sin t$

9. $\sin\left(t - \frac{3\pi}{2}\right) = \cos t$ **11.** $\cot\left(t - \frac{\pi}{2}\right) = -\tan t$ **13.** $\sin(\theta + \pi) = -\frac{4}{5}$, $\cos(\theta + \pi) = \frac{3}{5}$, $\tan(\theta + \pi) = -\frac{4}{3}$ **15.** $\sin\left(\theta - \frac{\pi}{2}\right) = -\frac{12}{13}$, $\cos\left(\theta - \frac{\pi}{2}\right) = -\frac{5}{13}$, $\tan\left(\theta - \frac{\pi}{2}\right) = \frac{12}{5}$
17. $\sin\left(-\theta + \frac{\pi}{2}\right) = -\frac{8}{17}$, $\cos\left(-\theta + \frac{\pi}{2}\right) = \frac{-15}{17}$, $\tan\left(-\theta + \frac{\pi}{2}\right) = \frac{8}{15}$ **19.** $y = \frac{12}{13}$; $\sin\theta = -\frac{12}{13}$, $\cos\theta = -\frac{5}{13}$, $\tan\theta = \frac{12}{5}$ **21.** $x = \frac{4}{5}$; $\sin\theta = \frac{3}{5}$, $\cos\theta = \frac{4}{5}$, $\tan\theta = \frac{3}{4}$ **23.** $x = -\frac{24}{25}$; $\sin\theta = -\frac{7}{25}$, $\cos\theta = \frac{24}{25}$, $\tan\theta = -\frac{7}{24}$ **25.** $y = -\frac{7}{25}$; $\sin\theta = \frac{24}{25}$, $\cos\theta = \frac{7}{25}$, $\tan\theta = \frac{24}{7}$ **27.** $\cos t \approx 0.315$, $\sin t \approx 0.949$; $\cos s \approx -0.949$, $\sin s \approx 0.315$ **29.** $\cos\theta \approx -0.743$, $\sin\theta \approx 0.669$; $\cos\alpha \approx -0.669$, $\sin\alpha \approx -0.743$
31. No   **33.** No   **35.** Yes   **37.** Draw the graph of $y = \sin x$, $-2\pi \leq x \leq 2\pi$.   **39.** Draw the graph of $y = \tan x$, $-2\pi \leq x \leq 2\pi$.   **41.** Stretch the graph of $y = \sin x$ vertically away from the x-axis by a factor of 2.
43. Reflect the graph of $y = \tan x$ about the x-axis.   **45.** $f(x) = -1$, $D = \{x \mid x \neq (2k - 1)(\frac{\pi}{2})\}$
47. $f(x) = 1$, $D = \{x \mid x \neq k(\frac{\pi}{2})\}$ **49.** $f(x) = \cos x$, $D = \mathbb{R}$ **51.** Graph is the horizontal line segment with holes at $(-\pi, -1)$, $(0, -1)$, and $(\pi, -1)$.   **53.** Draw a graph of $y = \sin x$ for $-\pi \leq x \leq \pi$.
55. f is even, periodic with period π **57.** f is even, periodic with period 2π.

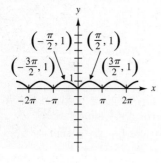 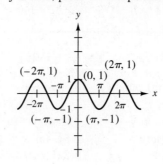

59. f is even, periodic with period π.   **61.** f is neither even nor odd.   **63.** Three   **65.** Seven

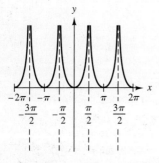 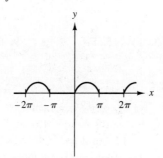

Exercises 5.5
Check Your Understanding   **1.** F   **3.** F   **5.** T   **7.** e   **9.** h, i

Develop Mastery   **1.** $\frac{\pi}{6}$ **3.** $\frac{\pi}{3}$ **5.** $\frac{\pi}{4}$ **7.** $-\frac{\pi}{4}$ **9.** $\frac{\pi}{2}$ **11.** $-\frac{\pi}{2}$ **13.** 1.160   **15.** -0.808
17. -0.853 **19.** 0.779   **21.** Undefined   **23.** -0.092 **25.** 0.3   **27.** 2   **29.** 0   **31.** $\frac{2}{3}$
33. $-\frac{3\sqrt{5}}{7}$ **35.** $\frac{1}{3}$ **37.** 1.471   **39.** 0.707   **41.** 1.374   **43.** -0.35 **45.** No solution
47. No solution   **49. (a)** Reflect the graph of $y = \text{Cos}^{-1}x$ (Figure 5.53b) about the x-axis, **(b)** Translate graph of $y = \text{Cos}^{-1}x$ to the left 1 unit. **(c)** Translate graph of $y = \text{Cos}^{-1}x$ down $\frac{\pi}{2}$ units.

51. (a)

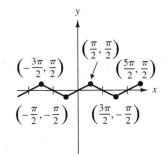

(b)

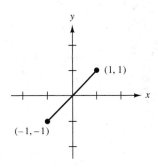

53. (a) Draw graphs (Figures 5.42 and 5.53(b)).   **(b)** One,   **(c)** 0.7
55. (a) For graph see Figure 5.53(a).   **57. (a)** See Figure 5.53(c) for graph.

(b)

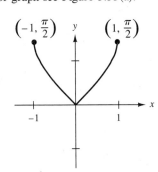

(b)

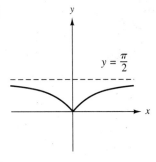

59. $f(x) = \dfrac{x}{\sqrt{x^2 + 1}}$ **61.** $f(x) = \dfrac{1}{\sqrt{x^2 + 1}}$ **67. (a)** 0.79,   **(b)** 0.32,   **(c)** 1.89
69. (a) 0.52,   **(b)** 1.05,   **(c)** 2.24

Chapter 5 Review

Test Your Understanding   **1. (a)** T,   **(b)** F,   **(c)** F,   **(d)** T   **3.** F   **5. (a)** F,   **(b)** T,   **(c)** T,   **(d)** T
7. F   **9.** T   **11.** T   **13.** F   **15.** T   **17.** T   **19. (a)** F,   **(b)** F   **21. (a)** F,   **(b)** F
23. F   **25.** T   **27.** T   **29.** T   **31.** T   **33.** F   **35.** T   **37.** F   **39.** T   **41.** F

Mastery Review   **1.** $s \approx 13$ cm., $A \approx 150$ cm.^{2} **3.** $r \approx 9.8$, $\theta \approx 1.3$ **5. (a)** $P(t) = (-\frac{\sqrt{2}}{2}, \frac{\sqrt{2}}{2})$,
(b) $\sin t = \frac{\sqrt{2}}{2}$, $\cos t = -\frac{\sqrt{2}}{2}$, $\tan t = -1$ **7. (a)** $P(t) = (-\frac{\sqrt{3}}{2}, \frac{1}{2})$,   **(b)** $\sin t = \frac{1}{2}$, $\cos t = -\frac{\sqrt{3}}{2}$,
$\tan t = -\frac{\sqrt{3}}{3}$ **9. (a)** $P(t) = (0.81, -0.59)$,   **(b)** $\sin t = -0.59$, $\cos t = 0.81$, $\tan t = -0.73$
11. $(2k + 1)\pi$ where k is any integer.   **13. (a)** Two points,   **(b)** $(\frac{1}{4}, \pm\frac{\sqrt{15}}{4})$ **15.** $-\cos t$ **17.** $-\sec t$
19. (a) $\frac{5\pi}{4}$,   **(b)** $\frac{2\pi}{3}$,   **(c)** π **21. (a)** 0.682,   **(b)** -0.532,   **(c)** 0.541   **23. (a)** $-\frac{3}{5}$,   **(b)** $\frac{3}{5}$
25. (b) $(-\frac{5}{13}, \frac{12}{13})$,   **(c)** $\frac{12}{13}$; $-\frac{12}{5}$ **27.** $\sin \theta = \frac{4}{5}$, $\cos \theta = \frac{3}{5}$, $\tan \theta = \frac{4}{3}$; $\theta \approx 0.93$ **29.** $\sin \theta = -\frac{3}{5}$,
$\cos \theta = -\frac{4}{5}$, $\tan \theta = \frac{3}{4}$; $\theta \approx 3.79$ **31. (a)** $\frac{\pi}{4}$,   **(b)** $\frac{5\pi}{6}$ **33. (a)** $\frac{1}{\sqrt{5}}$,   **(b)** $\frac{\pi}{4}$ **35. (a)** $-\frac{\pi}{6}$,   **(b)** $-\sqrt{5}$
37. (a) $-\frac{5}{7}$,   **(b)** $-\frac{12}{13}$ **39. (a)** 0.49,   **(b)** 1.82   **41.** $\frac{\sqrt{3}}{2}$ **43.** None   **45.** See graph in Figure 5.42.
47. Translate graph of $y = \cos x$ up 1 unit.   **49.** Draw graph of $y = -\cot x$ by reflecting the graph in Figure
5.49b about the x-axis.   **51.** Graph is the line segment with endpoints $(-1, -1)$ and $(1, 1)$.
$D = \{x \mid -1 \le x \le 1\}$, $R = \{y \mid -1 \le y \le 1\}$ **53.** Translate graph of $y = \text{Cos}^{-1}x$ in Figure 5.53b down $\frac{\pi}{2}$
units. $D = \{x \mid -1 \le x \le 1\}$, $R = \{y \mid -\frac{\pi}{2} \le y \le \frac{\pi}{2}\}$ **55. (a)** Locate point $(-\frac{1}{2}, \frac{2\pi}{3})$ on the graph.
(b) $\{x \mid -1 \le x \le -\frac{1}{2}\}$

CHAPTER 6

Exercises 6.1

Check Your Understanding   **1.** T   **3.** T   **5.** F   **7.** b   **9.** f

Develop Mastery   **1. (a)** Identity; $\mathbb{R}$,   **(b)** Not an identity,   **(c)** Identity; $\{x \mid x > 0\}$ **41.** $f(x) = \sin x$
43. $f(x) = \sec x$ **45.** $f(x) = \sin x \cos x$ **47.** $f(x) = \sin x$ **49.** $f(x) = \sec x$ **51.** Identity
53. Not an identity   **55.** Not an identity   **57.** Identity   **59.** Identity   **61.** Identity   **63.** Identity
65. $(f \circ g)(x) = |\sin x|$ **67.** $(f \circ g)(x) = |\cot x|$ **69. (b)** Graph is the same as the graph of $y = \cos x$
with holes at points such as $(-2\pi, 1), (-\pi, -1), (0, 1), (\pi, -1), (2\pi, 1), \dots$ **(c)** No   **71.** False
73. (b) $\{x \mid x \neq 0, \frac{\pi}{2}, \pi, \frac{3\pi}{2}, 2\pi\}$ **75. (b)** $\{x \mid 0 \leq x < \frac{\pi}{2} \text{ or } \frac{3\pi}{2} < x \leq 2\pi\}$ **77. (b)** $\{x \mid 0 < x < \pi\}$

Exercises 6.2

Check Your Understanding   **1.** F   **3.** T   **5.** T   **7.** g, h   **9.** c

Develop Mastery   **5.** $\frac{(\sqrt{6} - \sqrt{2})}{4}$, 0.2588   **7.** $\frac{(\sqrt{2} - \sqrt{6})}{4}$, -0.2588 **9. (a)** $\frac{(\sqrt{2} + \sqrt{6})}{4}$,   **(b)** $-2 - \sqrt{3}$
11. (a) $\frac{(-\sqrt{2} - \sqrt{6})}{4}$,   **(b)** $\sqrt{2} - \sqrt{6}$ **13.** $-\frac{33}{65}$ **15.** $\frac{63}{16}$ **17.** $-\frac{119}{169}$ **19.** $\frac{7}{25}$ **21.** $-\frac{17}{31}$ **23.** -8
25. $\frac{(4\sqrt{3} - 3\sqrt{7})}{5}$ **27.** $\frac{(3 - \sqrt{21})}{8}$ **29.** $\frac{1}{8}$ **31. (a)** $\frac{\sqrt{3}}{2}$, **(b)** 0   **33. (a)** $\frac{1}{2}$, **(b)** 2   **45.** $\frac{1}{7}$
47. (a) $\sqrt{2} \sin x$,   **(b)** $\sqrt{2} \cos x$ **51.** $\frac{\pi}{2}$ **53.** $\frac{\pi}{4}$ **55.** $\frac{6}{7}$ **57.** No solution   **61.** $\frac{1}{2}$ **63.** $\frac{1}{2}$, 1

Exercises 6.3

Check Your Understanding   **1.** F   **3.** T   **5.** T   **7.** b   **9.** d, g

Develop Mastery   **1. (a)** $\frac{\sqrt{2 - \sqrt{3}}}{2}$; 0.25882,   **(b)** $-\frac{\sqrt{2 - \sqrt{2}}}{2}$; -0.38268 **3. (a)** $-\frac{\sqrt{2 + \sqrt{2}}}{2}$; -0.92388,
(b) $\frac{\sqrt{2 - \sqrt{2}}}{2}$; 0.38268   **5. (a)** $-\frac{2}{\sqrt{2 - \sqrt{3}}}$; -3.86370,   **(b)** $-\frac{1}{2 + \sqrt{3}}$; -0.26795 **7. (a)** $\frac{5}{\sqrt{26}}$,   **(b)** $\frac{1}{\sqrt{26}}$,
(c) 5   **9. (a)** $-\frac{2}{\sqrt{5}}$,   **(b)** $-\frac{1}{\sqrt{5}}$,   **(c)** 2   **11. (a)** $\frac{3}{\sqrt{10}}$,   **(b)** $-\frac{1}{\sqrt{10}}$,   **(c)** -3

Exercise	$\sin x$		$\cos x$		$\sin\left(\frac{x}{2}\right)$		$\cos\left(\frac{x}{2}\right)$		$\sin 2x$		$\cos 2x$	
	(a)	(b)	(a)	(b)	(a)	(b)	(a)	(b)	(a)	(b)	(a)	(b)
13.	$-$	$-$	$-$	$-$	$+$	$+/-$	$-$	$+/-$	$+$	$+$	$+/-$	$+/-$
15.	$+$	$-$	$-$	$-$	$+$	$+$	$+$	$-$	$-$	$+$	$+$	$+$

17. (a) $\sin\left(\frac{\theta}{2}\right)$ is positive, $\cos\left(\frac{\theta}{2}\right)$ and $\tan\left(\frac{\theta}{2}\right)$ are negative.   **(b)** $\cos\left(\frac{\theta}{2}\right)$ is positive, $\sin\left(\frac{\theta}{2}\right)$ and $\tan\left(\frac{\theta}{2}\right)$ are negative.
19. (a) $\frac{\sqrt{2 - \sqrt{3}}}{2}$,   **(b)** $\frac{\sqrt{6} - \sqrt{2}}{4}$ **21. (a)** $2 + \sqrt{3}$,   **(b)** $\frac{\sqrt{3} + 1}{\sqrt{3} - 1}$ **35.** Not an identity   **37.** Identity
39. Identity   **41.** Not an identity   **43.** Identity   **45. (a)** 0.368,   **(b)** 0.183,   **(c)** 0.449   **47. (a)** 5.260,
(b) -0.561,   **(c)** 0.967   **49. (a)** $-\frac{3}{4}$,   **(b)** $\frac{1}{\sqrt{10}}$,   **(c)** $-\frac{3}{\sqrt{10}}$,   **(d)** $-\frac{1}{3}$ **51. (a)** $\frac{13}{5\sqrt{10}}$,   **(b)** $-\frac{13}{9}$ **53.** $\frac{\sqrt{6}}{2}$
55. $\frac{(2 + \sqrt{3})}{4}$ **57.** $\frac{(\sqrt{3} - 2)}{4}$ **61.** $\frac{(\sin x + \sin 5x)}{2}$ **63.** $\frac{(\cos x - \cos 5x)}{2}$ **65.** $\frac{(\cos x + \cos 2x)}{2}$ **69.** $2 \cos x \cos 2x$
71. $-2 \sin 2x \sin 3x$ **73.** $\tan\left(\frac{5x}{2}\right)$ **75.** $\cot 2x$ **77. (a)** $\cos x = \frac{1 - u^2}{1 + u^2}$, $\tan x = \frac{2u}{1 - u^2}$,   **(b)** $\frac{u(1 - u^2)}{1 + u^2}$

Exercises 6.4

Check Your Understanding   **1.** F   **3.** F   **5.** T   **7.** a, d, j, k   **9.** a, c, d, h, j, k

Develop Mastery   **1.** $\frac{\pi}{3}, \frac{5\pi}{3}$ **3.** $\frac{2\pi}{3}, \frac{4\pi}{3}$ **5.** $0, \frac{2\pi}{3}, 2\pi$ **7.** $0, \pi, 2\pi$ **9.** $0, \pi, \frac{7\pi}{6}, \frac{11\pi}{6}, 2\pi$
11. $\frac{\pi}{4}, \frac{3\pi}{4}, \frac{5\pi}{4}, \frac{7\pi}{4}$ **13.** $\frac{\pi}{6}, \frac{5\pi}{6}$ **15.** $\frac{\pi}{2}$ **17.** $\frac{\pi}{3}, \frac{2\pi}{3}$ **19.** $-\frac{7\pi}{12}, \frac{5\pi}{12}$ **21.** $\pm\frac{\pi}{3}, \pm\frac{2\pi}{3}$ **23.** $\pm\frac{\pi}{6}, \pm\frac{5\pi}{6}$
25. $\frac{\pi}{6}, \frac{5\pi}{6}$ **27.** $0, \pm\pi$ **29.** $\{x \mid x = \pm\frac{\pi}{4} + k \cdot 2\pi\}$ **31.** $\{x \mid x = \pm\frac{\pi}{3} + k \cdot \pi\}$
33. $\{x \mid x = \frac{7\pi}{6} + k \cdot 2\pi \text{ or } x = \frac{11\pi}{6} + k \cdot 2\pi\}$ **35.** $\{x \mid x = k \cdot \pi \text{ or } x = \frac{\pi}{2} + k \cdot 2\pi\}$

37. $\{x \mid x = \frac{\pi}{2} + k \cdot 2\pi\}$ **39.** 0.73, 2.41 **41.** 3.96, 5.46 **43.** 1.18, 2.75, 4.32, 5.89 **45.** 0.34, 2.80
47. $\frac{2}{5}$ **49.** $\frac{33\pi}{2}$ **51.** $\frac{199\pi}{4}$ **53.** (a) three, (b) six, (c) four **55.** (a) six, (b) twelve, (c) seven
57. (a) six, (b) twelve, (c) eight **59.** (a) 2, (b) $\frac{\pi}{2}$ **61.** (a) 3, (b) $\frac{\pi}{2}$ **63.** (a) 6, (b) π
65. (a) $A = 16\pi \sec \theta$, (b) $0 \le \theta \le \text{Tan}^{-1}1.2$

Exercises 6.5
Check Your Understanding **1.** T **3.** T **5.** F **7.** a, f **9.** b, d

Develop Mastery **1.** $\frac{\pi}{6}, \frac{5\pi}{6}$ **3.** $\frac{7\pi}{6}, \frac{11\pi}{6}$ **5.** $\frac{\pi}{2}, \frac{3\pi}{2}$ **7.** $0, \frac{\pi}{6}, \frac{5\pi}{6}, \pi, 2\pi$ **9.** $\frac{\pi}{3}, \frac{4\pi}{3}$ **11.** $\frac{\pi}{6}, \frac{\pi}{2}, \frac{5\pi}{6}, \frac{3\pi}{2}$
13. $0, \frac{2\pi}{3}, \pi, \frac{4\pi}{3}, 2\pi$ **15.** $\frac{\pi}{4}, \frac{3\pi}{4}, \frac{5\pi}{4}, \frac{7\pi}{4}$ **17.** $0, \frac{\pi}{2}, \pi, \frac{3\pi}{2}, 2\pi$ **19.** $\frac{3\pi}{4}, \frac{7\pi}{4}$ **21.** π **23.** $\frac{\pi}{2}$
25. $\frac{\pi}{2}, \pi$ **27.** $\frac{\pi}{6}$ **29.** $\frac{\pi}{12}, \frac{17\pi}{12}$ **31.** $\{\pm \frac{\pi}{2}\}$ **33.** $\{-\frac{5\pi}{6}, \frac{\pi}{6}\}$ **35.** $\{-\frac{5\pi}{6}, -\frac{\pi}{2}, -\frac{\pi}{6}, \frac{\pi}{2}\}$ **37.** 0.46, 3.61
39. 0.25, 2.89 **41.** 0.84, 5.44 **43.** $0, \frac{\pi}{2}, \pi, \frac{3\pi}{2}, 2\pi$ **45.** $0, \frac{\pi}{4}, \frac{3\pi}{4}, \pi, \frac{5\pi}{4}, \frac{7\pi}{4}, 2\pi$
47. (a) $f(x) = 2\sin(x + \frac{\pi}{3})$, (b) 2, (c) $\frac{\pi}{6}$ **49.** (a) $f(x) = 2\sqrt{2}\sin(x + \frac{\pi}{4})$, (b) $2\sqrt{2}$, (c) $\frac{\pi}{4}$
51. $\{\frac{\pi}{4}, \frac{3\pi}{4}\}$ **53.** $\{\frac{\pi}{6}\}$ **55.** $\{0, \frac{2\pi}{3}, 2\pi\}$ **57.** $\{\frac{\pi}{2}, \frac{3\pi}{2}\}$ **59.** $\{\frac{\pi}{8}, \frac{5\pi}{8}, \frac{9\pi}{8}, \frac{13\pi}{8}\}$ **61.** $\{x \mid 0 \le x \le 2\pi\}$
63. $\frac{3}{4}, \frac{7}{4}$ **65.** $0, 1, 2, \frac{1}{3}, \frac{5}{3}$ **67.** $\frac{1}{6}, \frac{5}{6}, \frac{3}{2}$ **69.** $\frac{1}{3}, 1, \frac{5}{3}$ **71.** $\mathbb{R}$ **73.** $\mathbb{R}$ **75.** $\{x \mid x$ is in the first
quadrant$\}$ **77.** (a) 3, (b) 0 **79.** (a) 4, (b) -6 **81.** (a) 13, (b) -4 **83.** $\{x \mid x = (2k + 1)(\frac{\pi}{2})\}$
85. $\{x \mid x = \frac{\pi}{4} + k \cdot \pi\}$ **87.** $x = \frac{\pi}{4} + k \cdot 2\pi$

Exercises 6.6
Check Your Understanding **1.** T **3.** F **5.** F **7.** f **9.** e

Develop Mastery **1.** $[0, \frac{2\pi}{3}]$ **3.** $[-\frac{3}{4}, \frac{5}{4}]$ **5.** $[-3, 2\pi - 3]$ **7.** $[\frac{\pi}{6}, \frac{7\pi}{6}]$ **9.** (a) $y = -\cos 2x$,
(b) $[0, \pi], A = 1, p = \pi$ **11.** (a) $y = -2\sin x$, (b) $[0, 2\pi], A = 2, p = 2\pi$ **13.** (a) $y = -4\sin 2x$,
(b) $[0, \pi], A = 4, p = \pi$ **15.** (a) $y = \sqrt{3}\sin 2x$, (b) $[0, \pi], A = \sqrt{3}, p = \pi$

Exercises 17–29 Use algorithm steps of this section.
17. (1) $y = \sin \frac{\pi x}{2}$, (2) $FI = [0, 4]$, (3) $(0, 0), (2, 0), (4, 0)$, (4) $(1, 1), (3, -1)$, No phase shift
19. (1) $y = 2\cos 3x$, (2) $FI = [0, \frac{2\pi}{3}]$, (3) $(\frac{\pi}{6}, 0), (\frac{5\pi}{6}, 0)$, (4) $(0, 2), (\frac{2\pi}{3}, 2), (\frac{\pi}{3}, -2)$, No phase shift
21. (1) $y = -2\cos(\frac{x}{2})$, (2) $FI = [0, 4\pi]$, (3) $(\pi, 0), (3\pi, 0)$, (4) $(0, -2), (2\pi, 2), (4\pi, -2)$, No phase shift
23. (1) $y = 2\sin(x + \frac{\pi}{3})$, (2) $FI = [-\frac{\pi}{3}, \frac{5\pi}{3}]$, (3) $(-\frac{\pi}{3}, 0), (\frac{2\pi}{3}, 0), (\frac{5\pi}{3}, 0)$, (4) $(\frac{\pi}{6}, 2), (\frac{7\pi}{6}, -2)$. Phase shift $\frac{\pi}{3}$
to the left **25.** (1) $y = -3\sin(2x - \frac{\pi}{4})$, (2) $FI = [\frac{\pi}{8}, \frac{9\pi}{8}]$, (3) $(\frac{\pi}{8}, 0), (\frac{5\pi}{8}, 0), (\frac{9\pi}{8}, 0)$, (4) $(\frac{3\pi}{8}, -3), (\frac{7\pi}{8}, 3)$,
Phase shift $\frac{\pi}{8}$ to the right **27.** (1) $y = \sqrt{3}\cos(x - \frac{3\pi}{4})$, (2) $FI = [\frac{3\pi}{4}, \frac{11\pi}{4}]$, (3) $(\frac{5\pi}{4}, 0), (\frac{9\pi}{4}, 0)$,
(4) $(\frac{3\pi}{4}, \sqrt{3}), (\frac{7\pi}{4}, -\sqrt{3}), (\frac{11\pi}{4}, \sqrt{3})$, Phase shift $\frac{3\pi}{4}$ to the right **29.** (1) $y = 4\sin(\frac{x}{2} - \frac{\pi}{4})$, (2) $FI = [\frac{\pi}{2}, \frac{9\pi}{2}]$,
(3) $(\frac{\pi}{2}, 0), (\frac{5\pi}{2}, 0), (\frac{9\pi}{2}, 0)$, (4) $(\frac{3\pi}{2}, 4), (\frac{7\pi}{2}, -4)$, Phase shift $\frac{\pi}{2}$ to the right **31.** $y = \sqrt{2}\sin(x + \frac{\pi}{4})$,
$FI = [-\frac{\pi}{4}, \frac{7\pi}{4}]$ **33.** $y = 2\sin(x + \frac{\pi}{3})$, $FI = [-\frac{\pi}{3}, \frac{5\pi}{3}]$ **35.** $y = 4\sin(x - \frac{\pi}{6})$, $FI = [\frac{\pi}{6}, \frac{13\pi}{6}]$
37. $A = 4, p = \frac{1}{3}, F = 3, f(0) = 0$ **39.** $A = 3, p = 4, F = \frac{1}{4}, f(0) = -3$ **41.** $A = \frac{2\sqrt{26}}{5}, p = 3, F = \frac{1}{3}$,
$E(0) = 2$ **43.** $A = \sqrt{13}, p = \frac{1}{60}, F = 60, V(0) = 2$ **45.** Draw graph of $y = \sin \pi x$ with $FI = [0, 2]$,
then translate it down 2 units. **47.** Draw graph of $y = \cos 2x$ with $FI = [0, \pi]$, reflect about the x-axis, then
translate up 3 units. **49.** Graph is the same as the graph of $y = 1 + \sin x$. **51.** Graph is the same as the
graph of $y = 2 + \sin 2x$. **53.** Graph is the same as the graph of $y = \cos 2x$. **55.** Graph is the same as the
graph of $y = \sin 2x - 1$. **57.** Graph is the same as the graph of $y = 2 + 2\cos x$. **59.** Graph is the same
as the graph of $y = \cos x$ with points missing at $(0, 1), (\pm \pi, -1), (\pm 2\pi, 1), \dots$ **61.** Graph is the same as
the graph of $y = \cos x$ where the domain is $\{x \mid \cos x > 0\}$ or $\{x \mid -\frac{\pi}{2} < x < \frac{\pi}{2}, \frac{3\pi}{2} < x < \frac{5\pi}{2}, \dots\}$
63. Draw a graph of $y = |\sin x|$, where $x \ne 0, \pm \pi, \pm 2\pi, \dots$ **65.** $d(t) = 4\cos 8\pi t$

Chapter 6 Review
Test Your Understanding **1.** T **3.** T **5.** T **7.** T **9.** F **11.** T **13.** F **15.** F **17.** T
19. F **21.** T **23.** T **25.** T **27.** T **29.** T **31.** F **33.** F

Mastery Review   **17.** Identity   **19.** Not an identity

21. $f(x) = \cos x$, $x \neq (2k - 1)(\frac{\pi}{2})$ **23.** $f(x) = 1$ for every real number x.   **25.** $-\frac{4}{3}$ **27.** $-\frac{1}{\sqrt{26}}$

29. $\frac{33}{56}$ **31.** $-\frac{3}{5}$ **33.** $\frac{837}{845}$ **35.** $\frac{\pi}{4}, \frac{3\pi}{4}, \frac{5\pi}{4}, \frac{7\pi}{4}$ **37.** $\frac{\pi}{2}, \frac{7\pi}{6}, \frac{11\pi}{6}$ **39.** $\frac{3\pi}{4}$ **41.** $\frac{\pi}{6}, \frac{5\pi}{6}, \frac{7\pi}{6}, \frac{11\pi}{6}$

43. $\frac{\pi}{2}, \frac{3\pi}{2}$ **45.** $-1.11, 2.03$ **47.** $-0.97, -2.18$ **49.** Graph is a sine curve with $FI = [\frac{\pi}{4}, \frac{9\pi}{4}]$, amplitude 2, period 2π, and phase shift $\frac{\pi}{4}$ to the right   **51.** Draw a sine curve with $FI = [0, 2]$, $A = 2$, $p = 2$, reflect about the x-axis.   **53.** Draw a graph of $y = 2 \sin (x - \frac{\pi}{4})$.   **55.** Graph is the same as the graph of $y = \cos x$ with points missing at $(0, 1)$, $(\pm\pi, -1)$, $(\pm 2\pi, 1)$, ...

CHAPTER 7

Exercises 7.1

Check Your Understanding   **1.** T   **3.** F   **5.** F   **7.** e   **9.** h, j

Develop Mastery   **1.** $\beta = 54°$, $b = 5.1$, $c = 6.3$ **3.** $\beta = 63°$, $a = 18$, $c = 39$ **5.** $\alpha = 24°40'$, $a = 9.89$, $b = 21.5$ **7.** $c = 92$, $\alpha = 53°$, $\beta = 37°$ **9.** $b = 29.9$, $\alpha = 35.6°$, $\beta = 54.4°$ **11.** 0.078   **13.** 0.588   **15.** 1.45   **17.** 63°   **19.** 5.3   **21.** 16.66 cm. and 8.397 cm.   **23.** 3.55 cm., 42.0°   **25.** 15 ft.   **27.** 17   **29. (a)** 8.3, **(b)** 24   **31.** $P = 47.5$ cm., $A = 109$ cm.^{2} **33. (a)** 750 cm.^{2}, **(b)** 1,200 cm.^{2}, **(c)** 1,500 cm.^{2}, **(d)** 1,700 cm.^{2} **35.** 51 ft.   **39.** $|\overline{AD}| = 227$ ft., $|\overline{CD}| = 179$ ft.   **41.** 6,280 cm.^{3} **43.** $\frac{3}{4}$ **45.** 47.16°   **47.** 32°   **49. (a)** $\sin \theta = \frac{3}{\sqrt{9 + 4x^2}}$, **(b)** $\cos \theta = \frac{2x}{\sqrt{9 + 4x^2}}$, **(c)** $\theta = \mathrm{Tan}^{-1}(\frac{3}{2x})$ **51. (c)** $\sin 15° = \frac{1}{2\sqrt{2 + \sqrt{3}}}$, $\cos 15° = \frac{\sqrt{2 + \sqrt{3}}}{2}$ **53.** $d = \sqrt{1.5h + (\frac{h}{5,280})^2}$, h in feet, d in miles.   **55.** 1,070 mi.

Exercises 7.2

Check Your Understanding   **1.** T   **3.** T   **5.** T   **7.** e   **9.** h

Develop Mastery   **1.** $\gamma = 81.0°$, $b = 35.6$, $c = 36.4$ **3.** $\gamma = 21.0°$, $a = 158$, $b = 208$ **5.** $\alpha = 92° 15'$, $a = 14.2$, $c = 11.9$ **7.** $\gamma = 90.0°$, $a = 28.0$, $c = 53.0$ **9.** Two solutions: $\beta_1 = 82°$, $\gamma_1 = 42°$, $c_1 = 46$; $\beta_2 = 98°$, $\gamma_2 = 26°$, $c_2 = 30$ **11.** $\alpha = 32°$, $\gamma = 24°$, $a = 2.1$ **13.** $\alpha = 38°$, $\beta = 86°$, $b = 78$ **15.** $\alpha = 39°10'$, $\gamma = 77°20'$, $c = 25.3$ **17.** 364   **19.** 630   **21.** 12   **23.** 298 ft.   **25.** 374 yds.   **27.** 437 ft.   **29.** $|\overline{BC}| = 5.5$, $|\overline{CD}| = 2.8$ **31.** 41.4°   **33. (a)** 240, **(b)** 50   **35.** 5.26°   **37.** 30.2   **39. (a)** 63 million mi.; 120 million mi., **(b)** 23°, one solution

Exercises 7.3

Check Your Understanding   **1.** T   **3.** T   **5.** F   **7.** a, e   **9.** g

Develop Mastery   **1.** $c = 52$, $\alpha = 30°$, $\beta = 102°$ **3.** $b = 114$, $\alpha = 39.5°$, $\gamma = 25.1°$ **5.** $\alpha = 41°$, $\beta = 91°$, $\gamma = 48°$ **7.** $\alpha = 51.3°$, $\beta = 38.6°$, $\gamma = 90.0°$ **9.** $a = 6.30$, $\beta = 72.4°$, $\gamma = 53.9°$ **11.** $c = 21.1$, $\alpha = 102°00'$, $\beta = 43°30'$ **13.** $\alpha = 90°$, $\beta = 58°$, $\gamma = 32°$ **15.** $\alpha = 47°$, $\beta = 40°$, $\gamma = 93°$ **17.** $c = 53$, $\alpha = 58°$, $\beta = 32°$ **19.** $a = 86$, $\beta = 48°$, $\gamma = 42°$ **21. (a)** 4.4, **(b)** 16   **23. (a)** 6.95, **(b)** 18.9   **25. (a)** 36.2°, **(b)** 26.6°, **(c)** 825   **27. (a)** 34.1°, **(b)** 2.44, **(c)** 4.16   **29.** $\beta = 86°$ **31.** 18   **33. (a)** 28, **(b)** 98°   **35. (a)** $(-1, 5)$, **(b)** 13°, 30°   **37.** 2.0   **41.** No solution   **43.** 9.24   **47. (a)** 15, **(b)** 90   **49. (a)** $d = \begin{cases} 4t & \text{if } 0 \leq t \leq 1 \\ \sqrt{9t^2 - 30t + 37} & \text{if } t > 1 \end{cases}$, **(b)** 7.8 mi., **(c)** 1:30 P.M.   **51.** 30°   **53. (a)** 0.769, **(b)** 221   **55.** 78°   **57.** $2\sqrt{43}$ **59.** 58 m.   **61.** $20 + 16\sqrt{2}$

Exercises 7.4

Check Your Understanding   **1.** F   **3.** T   **5.** T   **7.** b   **9.** g, h

Develop Mastery   **1. (a)** $(-3, 0)$; $3(\cos 180° + i \sin 180°)$, **(b)** $(0, -1)$; $\cos 270° + i \sin 270°$ **3. (a)** $(3, 5)$; $\sqrt{34} (\cos \theta + i \sin \theta)$, $\theta = \mathrm{Tan}^{-1}(\frac{5}{3})$, **(b)** $(2, -3)$; $\sqrt{13} (\cos \theta + i \sin \theta)$, $\theta = \mathrm{Tan}^{-1}(-1.5)$ **5. (a)** $(\sqrt{3}, 2)$; $\sqrt{7} (\cos \theta + i \sin \theta$, $\theta = \mathrm{Tan}^{-1}(\frac{2}{\sqrt{3}})$, **(b)** $(1, 1)$; $\sqrt{2} (\cos 45° + i \sin 45°)$

7. (a) $(0, -1)$; $\cos 270° + i \sin 270°$, **(b)** $(\frac{1}{2}, -\frac{1}{2})$; $(\frac{1}{\sqrt{2}})(\cos 315° + i \sin 315°)$ **9.** $\sqrt{2} + \sqrt{2}i$
11. $4i$ **13.** $-\frac{1}{2} - (\frac{\sqrt{3}}{2})i$ **15.** $2(\cos 315° + i \sin 315°)$ **17.** $4(\cos 270° + i \sin 270°)$
19. $\cos(-30°) + i \sin(-30°)$ **21.** $\cos 60° + i \sin 60° = \frac{1}{2} + (\frac{\sqrt{3}}{2})i$ **23.** $\cos 60° + i \sin 60° = \frac{1}{2} + (\frac{\sqrt{3}}{2})i$
25. $2(\cos 150° + i \sin 150°) = -\sqrt{3} + i$ **27.** $2(\cos 270° + i \sin 270°) = -2i$
29. $2(\cos 150° + i \sin 150°) = -\sqrt{3} + i$ **31.** $8(\cos 90° + i \sin 90°) = 8i$
33. $8(\cos 90° + i \sin 90°) = 8i$ **35.** $8(\cos 90° + i \sin 90°) = 8i$
37. $\cos 120° + i \sin 120° = -\frac{1}{2} + (\frac{\sqrt{3}}{2})i$ **39.** $\cos 240° + i \sin 240° = -\frac{1}{2} - (\frac{\sqrt{3}}{2})i$
41. $\cos 180° + i \sin 180° = -1$ **43.** $16(\cos 60° + i \sin 60°) = 8 + 8\sqrt{3}\,i$
45. $16(\cos 0° + i \sin 0°) = 16$ **47.** $(\frac{1}{4})(\cos 90° + i \sin 90°) = (\frac{1}{4})i$
49. $\frac{1}{64}$ **51.** $i, -\frac{\sqrt{3}}{2} - (\frac{1}{2})i, \frac{\sqrt{3}}{2} - (\frac{1}{2})i$ **53.** $-1, \frac{1}{2} + (\frac{\sqrt{3}}{2})i, \frac{1}{2} - (\frac{\sqrt{3}}{2})i$
55. $1, 0.31 \pm 0.95i, -0.8i \pm 0.59i$ **57.** $\pm(0.38 + 0.92i), \pm(0.92 - 0.38i)$ **59.** $\pm(2 - i)$
61. $\pm(1.10 + 0.38i), \pm(1.10 - 0.38i)$ **63.** $1 + i, -1 + i$ **67.** $1, -1, -2, -1, 1, 2$ (repeat cycle of 6)

Exercises 7.5
Check Your Understanding   **1.** F   **3.** F   **5.** T   **7.** a   **9.** g

Develop Mastery   **1.** $\langle 4, 4 \rangle$ **3.** $\langle -6, 3 \rangle$ **5.** $\langle 1, -6 \rangle$ **7.** $\langle -10, 13 \rangle$ **9.** $\langle -6, 10 \rangle$ **11.** $\langle -3, 0 \rangle$
13. $\langle 1, 5 \rangle$ **15.** $113°$ **17.** $138°$ **19.** $(\frac{1}{\sqrt{5}})\langle 1, 2 \rangle, (\frac{1}{\sqrt{5}})\langle -1, -2 \rangle$ **21.** $\sqrt{2}, 2\sqrt{2}$ **23.** $\sqrt{5}, 3\sqrt{5}$
25. $\sqrt{2}, \sqrt{29}, 5$ **27.** $\sqrt{2}, k\sqrt{2}$ **29.** $\sqrt{5}, \sqrt{29}, \sqrt{5a^2 - 18ab + 29b^2}$
31. $\langle \frac{8}{\sqrt{5}}, \frac{4}{\sqrt{5}} \rangle$ or $\langle -\frac{8}{\sqrt{5}}, -\frac{4}{\sqrt{5}} \rangle$ **33.** $\langle 8, 2 \rangle$ or $\langle -2, 2 \rangle$ **35.** Any x, y for which (x, y) is a point on the circle with center $(-3, 1)$ and radius 2   **37.** $(2, 6)$ or $(2, -2)$ **39.** 87.4 m., 16° north of east
41. 8.8 ft., 38° north of east   **43.** Downstream at 6 mph, at an angle of 55° from direction of current.
45. 575 mph, 38° north of east   **47.** 34 min.   **49.** 37° north of west, 2 hrs., and 7 min.

Chapter 7 Review
Test Your Understanding   **1.** F   **3.** T   **5.** F   **7.** T   **9.** T   **11.** F   **13.** T   **15.** T   **17.** F
19. T   **21.** T   **23.** F   **25.** T   **27.** T   **29.** T   **31.** T   **33.** F   **35.** T

Mastery Review   **1.** $\alpha = 64°40', a = 33.8, b = 16.0$ **3.** 1.96 cm.   **5.** 35 cm.^{2} **7.** 8.89   **9.** 29°
11. 2.98   **13.** 200 in.^{2} **15.** 52.2 cm., 641 cm.^{2} **17. (a)** 0.99 cm.^{2}, **(b)** 0.099 cm.^{2} **19.** 116 ft.
23. (a) 150 ft., **(b)** 1,600 sq. ft.   **25. (a)** 29.5°, **(b)** 13.4, **(c)** 47.5   **27. (a)** 70.6°, **(b)** 109.4°
29. 11   **31.** 44 ft.   **33.** One   **35.** Infinitely many   **37.** One   **39. (a)** $-4 - 4i$, **(b)** $-2,035 + 828i$
41. (a) 16, **(b)** $12.39 + 8.66i$ **43. (a)** $64i$, **(b)** $-i$ **45. (a)** $i \pm 1$, **(b)** $\frac{(2 \pm \sqrt{3})}{2} - \frac{i}{2}$
47. $\pm(0.97 - 0.23i), \pm(0.23 + 0.97i)$ **49.** $\pm(1.96 + 0.39i), \pm(0.39 - 1.96i)$ **51. (a)** $\langle -1, -1 \rangle$,
(b) $\langle -2, 10 \rangle$ **53.** 162°   **55. (a)** 445 mph, 51° north of east, **(b)** 2 hrs. and 15 min.

CHAPTER 8

Exercises 8.1
Check Your Understanding   **1.** F   **3.** F   **5.** T   **7.** c, f   **9.** a, c, f

Develop Mastery   **1.** 4, 7, 10, 13; 25   **3.** $\frac{1}{5}, \frac{1}{25}, \frac{1}{125}, \frac{1}{625}; \frac{1}{390,625}$ **5.** 43, 47, 53, 61; 113   **7.** $\frac{1}{2}, \frac{3}{4}, \frac{7}{8}; \frac{15}{16}; \frac{255}{256}$
9. 2, 12, 120, 1680; 518,918,400   **11.** 2, 4, 14, 32; 184   **13.** 3, $-1, -5, -9$ **15.** 2, 6, 18, 54
17. 1, 2, 2, 4   **19.** 2, 4, 6, 10   **21.** 1, 2, $\frac{3}{2}, \frac{7}{4}$ **23.** 1, $\frac{1}{2}, \frac{1}{12}, \frac{1}{288}$ **25.** 3, 8, 15, 24   **27.** $\frac{1}{2}, \frac{3}{4}, \frac{7}{8}, \frac{15}{16}$
29. 1, $\frac{3}{2}, \frac{11}{6}, \frac{25}{12}$ **31.** 65   **33.** $-\frac{5}{6}$ **35.** $\frac{49}{16}$ **37.** $a_n = \frac{1}{2^n}$ **39.** $a_n = (-1)^{n+1} \frac{n}{(n+1)^2}$
41. $a_n = n! + 1$ **43.** $(1, -1), (2, 1), (3, -1), (4, 1), (5, -1)$ **45.** $(1, -2), (2, \frac{3}{2}), (3, -\frac{4}{3}), (4, \frac{5}{4}), (5, -\frac{6}{5})$
47. $\Sigma^6_{k=1} \frac{1}{k+1}$ **49.** $\Sigma^4_{k=1} \frac{1}{k(k+1)}$ **51.** $\Sigma^5_{k=1} \frac{(-1)^{k+1}}{k(k+1)}$ **53.** 15   **55.** 2,450   **57.** $\frac{9!}{4!5!}$ **59. (a)** 1, 5,
(b) 18, 180   **61.** Yes   **63.** $a_n = 2n - 1$ **65.** $a_n = 1 - \frac{1}{2^n}$ **67.** 1, 2, 5, 29, 866   **69.** 1, 2, 2, 4, 8

71. (a) a_n: 3, 5, 9, 15, 23, b_n: 3, 5, 9, 15, 23, **(b)** Yes, **(c)** 3,543   **73. (a)** 68, **(b)** 112 terms
75. (a) $-1, 3, -1, 3, -1$, **(b)** 20, **(c)** $f(f(x)) = x$ **77. (b)** $-1, -1, 2, -1, -1, 2$; $S_6 = 0$,
(c) $S_{100} = -1$ **79.** 2   **81.** $\sqrt{2}$ **83.** 3   **85.** 770 million yrs.

Exercises 8.2

Check Your Understanding   **1.** T   **3.** T   **5.** F   **7.** c, f   **9.** b

Develop Mastery   **1. (a)** 3, **(b)** 18, 30, **(c)** 165   **3. (a)** -5, **(b)** $-21, -41$, **(c)** -185 **5. (a)** $-\frac{8}{3}$,
(b) $\frac{20}{3}, -4$, **(c)** 80   **7. (a)** $-2\sqrt{2}$, **(b)** $1 - 9\sqrt{2}, 1 - 17\sqrt{2}$, **(c)** $10 - 80\sqrt{2}$ **9. (a)** $\ln 2$,
(b) $6 \ln 2, 10 \ln 2$, **(c)** $55 \ln 2$ **11. (a)** $-\frac{1}{3}$, **(b)** $-\frac{1}{243}, -\frac{1}{2.187}$, **(c)** $\frac{61}{81}$ **13. (a)** $\frac{1}{3}$, **(b)** $\frac{2}{27}, \frac{2}{243}$, **(c)** $\frac{242}{9}$
15. (a) $\sqrt{2}$, **(b)** $4\sqrt{2}, 8\sqrt{2}$, **(c)** $7 + 3\sqrt{2}$ **17. (a)** $\frac{1}{2}$, **(b)** $\frac{3}{32}, \frac{3}{128}$, **(c)** $\frac{93}{16}$ **19. (a)** $1 + \sqrt{2}$,
(b) $17 + 12\sqrt{2}, 99 + 70\sqrt{2}$, **(c)** $11 + 9\sqrt{2}$ **21.** Neither   **23.** Neither   **25.** Arithmetic, $d = \ln \sqrt{3}$
27. Geometric, $r = 0.01$ **29.** $d = -\frac{5}{3}, a_1 = \frac{25}{3}$ **31.** $d = 2, S_8 = 64$ **33.** $a_1 = 1, S_4 = 16$
35. $a_4 = 0, a_{16} = 4\pi, S_{16} = 24\pi$ **37.** $r = \frac{3}{2}, a_6 = \frac{243}{8}$ **39.** $a_1 = \frac{4}{81}, S_5 = \frac{211}{324}$ **41.** $a_5 = \frac{2}{9}, S_5 = \frac{242}{9}$
43. $a_1 = -\frac{32}{5}, S_8 = -\frac{17}{4}$ **45.** 1   **47.** $\pm\sqrt{2}$ **49.** 3   **51.** Arithmetic   **53.** Geometric
55. Geometric   **57. (a)** $r = -\frac{1}{3}$, **(b)** $\frac{3}{4}$ **59. (a)** $r = \frac{3}{4}$, **(b)** $\frac{3}{4}$ **61.** $\frac{9}{5}$ **63. (a)** $\frac{31}{25}$, **(b)** $\frac{41}{33}$
65. (a) $\frac{9}{8}$, **(b)** $\frac{1,124}{999}$ **67.** 264π **69.** 10,000   **73.** 60   **75.** $\sqrt{\frac{1 + \sqrt{5}}{2}}$ **77. (a)** 548 m., **(b)** 850 m.
79. (a) 16 ft., **(b)** $a_n = 32n - 16$, arithmetic, **(c)** 2,304, **(d)** 20 terms, sum = 6,400
81. $f(-0.2) \approx 0.9801, f(0.4) \approx 0.9211, f(1) \approx 0.5403, g(-0.2) \approx 0.9801, g(0.4) \approx 0.9211, g(1) \approx 0.5403$
83. $f(-0.2) \approx -0.1974, f(0.4) \approx 0.3805, f(1) \approx 0.7854, g(-0.2) \approx -0.1974, g(0.4) \approx 0.3805, g(1) \approx 0.8349$

Exercises 8.3

Check Your Understanding   **1.** T   **3.** F   **5.** F   **7.** T   **9.** F

Develop Mastery   **1. (b)** $f(n)$ is divisible by 4 for every n, and is divisible by 3 and 12 for every even number n.
3. The units digit of $f(n)$ is 0 for every even n and it is 9 for every odd n. The units digit is never 1.   **5. (a)** $f(n)$
is prime for all n in the table. **(b)** The units digit of $f(n)$ is 1, 3, or 7. **(c)** $f(n + 1) = f(n) + 2n$, **(d)** $f(n)$ is
not prime when n is 41 or 82.   **7. (b)** $f(n) = n(n + 1)$ **9. (b)** $f(n) = \frac{2^n - 1}{2^n}$ **11. (b)** $f(n) = 3^n$
(c) $\sum_{k=1}^{n} 3^{k-1} = \frac{(3^n - 1)}{2}$ **13. (b)** $f(n) = 2^n$, **(c)** $g(n) = 2^n - 1$ **15.** $f(n) = \frac{n + 2}{n + 1}$ **17. (b)** $f(n) = n(n + 1)$
19. $f(n) = \frac{n(n - 1)}{2}$ **21.** Row n has $n + 1$ entries.   **25.** $f(n) = 2^{n-1}$ **27.** $f(n) = \binom{n + 1}{2}$
29. $f(n) = \binom{n + 3}{4}$ **31.** $P(n) = 1 + \binom{n + 1}{2}$ **33.** $R(4) = 8, R(5) = 16, R(6) = 31, R(7) = 57$

Exercises 8.4

Check Your Understanding   **1.** F   **3.** F   **5.** T   **7.** T   **9.** F

Develop Mastery   **1.** All are true.   **3.** $P(1)$ and $P(2)$ are true; $P(5)$ is false.   **5.** $P(1)$ and $P(2)$ are true;
$P(5)$ is false.   **7.** All are true.   **9.** 6   **11.** 3   **13.** Hyp: $1^3 + 2^3 + \ldots + k^3 = \frac{k^2(k + 1)^2}{4}$;
Concl: $1^3 + 2^3 + \ldots + k^3 + (k + 1)^3 = \frac{(k + 1)^2(k + 2)^2}{4}$
15. Hyp: $1 \cdot 2 + 2 \cdot 3 + \ldots + k(k + 1) = \frac{k(k + 1)(k + 2)}{3}$;
Concl: $1 \cdot 2 + 2 \cdot 3 + \ldots + k(k + 1) + (k + 1)(k + 2) = \frac{(k + 1)(k + 2)(k + 3)}{3}$
17. Hyp: $4^k - 1$ is a multiple of 3; Concl: $4^{k+1} - 1$ is a multiple of 3.   **41.** True for every n
43. True for every n **45.** $P(4)$ is false.   **47.** $P(41)$ is false.   **49.** True for every n **53. (b)** All odd
integers greater than 3 and not a multiple of 3; the sequence includes all prime numbers greater than 3.

Exercises 8.5

Check Your Understanding   **1.** F   **3.** T   **5.** T   **7.** a, d   **9.** a, g

Develop Mastery   **1. (a)** 84, **(b)** 84   **3. (a)** 56, **(b)** 56   **5. (a)** 1,330, **(b)** 1,330
7. (a) 210, **(b)** 210   **9. (a)** 4,200, **(b)** 4,200   **11. (a)** 720, **(b)** 120   **13. (a)** 124,
(b) 6,700   **15. (a)** 48, **(b)** 40,320   **17. (a)** $\frac{6}{7}$, **(b)** $\frac{2}{3}$ **19.** n **21.** $\frac{n(n + 1)}{2}$ **23.** $\frac{n - k}{k + 1}$

25. $x^5 - 5x^4 + 10x^3 - 10x^2 + 5x - 1$ **27.** $\frac{1}{x^4} - 8\frac{y^2}{x^3} + 24\frac{y^4}{x^2} - 32\frac{y^6}{x} + 16y^8$
29. $243x^5 + 405x^2 + \frac{270}{x} + \frac{90}{x^4} + \frac{15}{x^7} + \frac{1}{x^{10}}$ **31. (b)** $32 - 80x + 80x^2 - 40x^3 + 10x^4 - x^5$
33. (b) $x^{10} + 10x^7 + 40x^4 + 80x + \frac{80}{x^2} + \frac{32}{x^5}$ **35. (a)** Nine, **(b)** $5{,}670x^8$ **37. (a)** Six, **(b)** $10x + 10x\sqrt{x}$
39. $x^{20} + 20x^{18} + 190x^{16}$ **41.** $40x^7$ **43.** $-1{,}920x^7y^3$ **45.** 24 **47.** 42,240 **49.** $-3{,}003$
51. 15 **53.** 1 **55.** 2 **57.** 8 **59.** 6 **63. (a)** 10, **(b)** 15, **(c)** 30

Chapter 8 Review
Check Your Understanding **1.** F **3.** T **5.** T **7.** F **9.** F **11.** F **13.** T **15.** T
17. F **19.** T **21.** T **23.** T **25.** T **27.** T **29.** T **31.** T **33.** T **35.** F
37. T **39.** F

Mastery Review **1. (a)** $\frac{1}{2}, \frac{3}{4}, \frac{7}{8}, \frac{15}{16}$, **(b)** $\frac{49}{16}$ **3. (a)** 2, 5, 8, 11, **(b)** 26 **5.** 3, 6, 12, 24, 48
7. $a_n = 5n - 2$ **9.** $a_n = 2^n - 1$ **11.** $a_n = (-1)^n$ **13. (a)** 118, **(b)** 1,452 **15.** -1 or 3
17. (a) $\frac{3}{2}, \frac{5}{4}, \frac{9}{8}, \frac{17}{16}$, **(b)** No, **(c)** $\frac{79}{16}$ **19. (a)** $0.2\overline{6}$, **(b)** $1.\overline{63}$, **(c)** $0.\overline{214857}$ **21.** 225 **23.** $\frac{1}{2}$
25. 47 **27.** $\frac{10}{11}$ **29.** $-\frac{17}{2}$ **31.** $-\frac{1}{128}$ **33.** $\frac{1}{4}$ **37.** Yes **39. (a)** 15, **(b)** 455, **(c)** 84
41. $81 + 216x + 216x^2 + 96x^3 + 16x^4$ **43.** $99 - 70\sqrt{2}$
45. $\frac{1}{x^6} + 6\frac{y^{1/2}}{x^5} + 15\frac{y}{x^4} + 20\frac{y^{3/2}}{x^3} + 15\frac{y^2}{x^2} + 64\frac{y^{5/2}}{x} + y^3$ **47.** $\left(\frac{20}{729}\right)x^8$ **49.** $6435x^6$
51. (a) 0.34868, **(b)** 0.36603, **(c)** 0.36770, **(d)** 0.36786, **(e)** 0.36788 **53. (a)** 2, **(b)** 6, **(c)** 20

CHAPTER 9

Exercises 9.1
Check Your Understanding **1.** T **3.** T **5.** F **7.** F **9.** a, f

Develop Mastery **1.** $x = 1, y = 3$ **3.** $x = \frac{1}{9}, y = -\frac{1}{3}$ **5.** Inconsistent **7.** $x = 6, y = 3, z = -3$
9. $x = 2, y = -1, z = 0$ **11.** Dependent $x = \frac{2k+3}{3}, y = \frac{13k+3}{3}, z = k$ (any number) **13.** $x = 2, y = -3$
15. $x = 8, y = -1$ **17.** $x = -3, y = 1, z = -2$ **19.** Dependent $x = -k, y = 0, z = k$ (any number)
21. Inconsistent **23.** Dependent $x = \frac{12-k}{7}, y = \frac{-4-2k}{7}, z = k$ (any number) **25.** $x = -1, y = 1, z = 2$
27. $x = 1, y = -1, z = 4$ **29.** $x = 5, y = 2, z = -2$ **31.** $x = 1, y = 2, z = -3$ **33.** $x = -2,$
$y = 4, z = 4$ **35.** $x = 2, y = -2, z = 1$ **37.** $x = 1, y = \frac{1}{3}$ **39.** $x = -\frac{1}{6}, y = -\frac{1}{11}$ **41.** $(-1, -2)$
43. (a) $8 + 2\sqrt{2} + 2\sqrt{10}$, **(b)** 8 **45. (a)** $5 + 3\sqrt{5} + \sqrt{10}$, **(b)** 7.5 **47.** $x = \frac{24}{5}, y = 8, z = 24$
49. $x = e, y = \frac{1}{e}, z = \sqrt{e}$ **51.** $x = 5, y = 1$ **53. (b)** $(1, 1), (3, 2) (5, -1)$, **(c)** 97° **55.** 35 cm.²
57. $800 and $1,700 **59.** 882 **61.** $x = 400$ gm., $y = 1{,}600$ gm. **63.** Plane 420 km./hr., wind 60 km./hr.
65. Sandwich $1.60, drink $0.30, pie $0.60 **67.** $x = 300$ gm., $y = 1{,}200$ gm., $z = 900$ gm.
69. 2 hrs. and 40 min.

Exercises 9.2
Check Your Understanding **1.** T **3.** T **5.** T **7.** b **9.** h

Develop Mastery **1.** $\begin{aligned}x + 2y &= -1\\ x - 3y &= 2\end{aligned}$ **3.** $\begin{aligned}x - y &= 1\\ 2x + 3y - 4z &= 1\\ -x - 2y + 3z &= 5\end{aligned}$ **5.** $\begin{bmatrix} 2 & -1 & 3 \\ 1 & 2 & -1 \end{bmatrix}$ **7.** $\begin{bmatrix} 1 & 1 & -1 & 1 \\ 2 & -1 & 0 & 3 \\ -1 & 2 & -1 & 0 \end{bmatrix}$
9. $x = 1, y = 2, z = -2$ **11.** $x = 0, y = -1, z = -2$ **13.** $x = \frac{1}{2}, y = -\frac{5}{2}$ **15.** $x = 2, y = -4$
17. Dependent, $x = \frac{(8k-5)}{4}, y = k$ (any number) **19.** $x = \frac{3}{11}, y = \frac{7}{11}, z = \frac{16}{11}$ **21.** $x = -\frac{4}{3}, y = \frac{1}{3}, z = 0$
23. Dependent, $x = \frac{(5-4k)}{3}, y = \frac{(11-4k)}{3}, z = k$ (any number) **25.** $\frac{3}{3x+2} - \frac{1}{x-2}$ **27.** $\frac{1}{x} + \frac{2}{x+2} - \frac{3}{x-2}$
29. $\frac{2}{x-1} + \frac{3x}{x^2+1}$ **31.** $\frac{4}{x-2} + \frac{1}{(x-2)^2} - \frac{3}{x}$ **33.** 9, 3, 12 **35.** Oatmeal 0.6 cup, milk 0.5 cup,
orange juice 1 cup

Exercises 9.3

Check Your Understanding **1.** F **3.** F **5.** T **7.** c **9.** g, h

Develop Mastery **1.** $(-1, 1), (4, 16)$ **3.** $(0, 0), (-0.5, 1.5)$ **5.** $(-3, 1), (1.5, -2)$ **7.** No solution
9. $(0, -5), (3, 4)$ **11.** $(-2.56, -4.56), (1.56, -0.44)$ **13.** $(4, 2)$ **15.** $(-2, -2), (-2, 2), (2, -2), (2, 2)$
17. $x = 1, y = 0$ **19.** $x = 2, y = 1.39$ **21.** $x = 3.56, y = 4.75$ **23.** $x = 3, y = 8$
25. $(-1, 2), (1, 2)$ **27.** $(2, 1), (-2, -1), (\sqrt{2}, \sqrt{2}), (-\sqrt{2}, -\sqrt{2})$
29. $(1, 2), (-1, -2), (2, 1), (-2, -1)$ **31.** $(\frac{\pi}{4}, \frac{1}{\sqrt{2}}), (\frac{5\pi}{4}, -\frac{1}{\sqrt{2}})$ **33.** $(\frac{\pi}{6}, 0), (\frac{\pi}{6}, 2\pi), (\frac{5\pi}{6}, 0), (\frac{5\pi}{6}, 2\pi)$
35. $(2, 4), (2, -4), (-2, 4), (-2, -4)$ **37.** $(0, \ln 5)$ **39.** $(e, \frac{1}{e})$ **41.** $(6, -3)$ **43.** 8 cm. by 12 cm.
45. 66 cm. **47.** $y = x$ **49.** $2\sqrt{2}$ by $4\sqrt{2}$

Exercises 9.4

Check Your Understanding **1.** F **3.** F **5.** F **7.** d **9.** b, c

Develop Mastery **1.** (a) No, (b) Yes **3.** (a) No, (b) No **5.** (a) All points below line $x + 2y = 4$
(broken), (b) $(0, 0), (1, 1)$ **7.** (a) All points on or below line $2x - 3y = 6$ (solid), (b) $(2, -1), (4, 0)$
9. (a) All points below line $x + y = -4$ (broken), (b) $(-3, -2), (-6, 0)$ **11.** (a) All points on or above line
$y = 2x$ (solid), (b) $(0, 0), (0, 1)$ **13.** All points below line $x + y = 4$ and above line $2x - y = -1$ (both
broken), corner point $(1, 3)$, open circle **15.** All points on or below line $x - 2y = 4$ (solid) and to the right of $x = 2$
or to the left of $x = -2$, corner points $(2, -1), (-2, -3)$, open circles **17.** All points inside the triangle with
vertices $(-1, 2), (3, 4)$, and $(-1, 2)$, all open circles. **19.** All points above the x-axis and above line $x + y = 1$,
corner point $(1, 0)$, open circle **21.** All points to the left of the y-axis and above the line $x + y = 1$, corner point $(0,$
$1)$, open circle **23.** All points inside the traingle with vertices $(2, -1), (2, 1)$, and $(4, -1)$, all open circles
25. I and II **27.** II and III **29.** All points on or below line $2x - y = 4$ (solid) **31.** All points above line
$2x + y = 2$ (broken) **33.** All points on or between lines $y = x + 1$ and $y = x - 1$ (both solid) **35.** All points
to the right of the y-axis and above line $y = x$ (broken) **37.** $x + 2y > 4$ **39.** $2x - 3y \le 6$
41. $2x + 3y \le 6$ **43.** (b) $x + 3y > -2$ **45.** (b) $y > 0$ **47.** $2x - y < 1$
$\quad\;\; x - 3y \le 3$ $\qquad\quad\; 3x + 2y < 8$ $\qquad\quad 2x + y < 4$ $\qquad\;\; x + 2y < 4$
$\quad\;\; x - y \ge -2$ $\qquad\quad\; 2x - y > -4$ $\qquad\quad 4x - 3y > -12$
49. Minimum 320 at $(3, 1)$; maximum 496 at $(2, 5)$ **51.** Minimum -548 at $(-4, -8)$; maximum 472 at $(6, 2)$
53. Minimum 90 at $(2, 0)$; maximum 612 at $(3, 6)$ **55.** Let x, y denote numbers of $6 and $3 seats, respectively:
$0 \le x \le 200, 0 \le y \le 600, 6x + 3y \ge 2{,}100$. All lattice points (x, y) that satisfy the constraints.
57. 1,000 Rambis, 2,000 Eustis; profit $28,000 **59.** x units of A, y units of B: $x \ge 0, y \ge 0, 2x + 3y \ge 8$,
$5x + 2y \ge 9, 2x + y \le 8$ **61.** x units of C, y units of D: $0 \le x \le 3, y \ge 2, 3x + y \ge 5, 3x + 4y \le 21$
63. (a) 64 acres of soybeans and 38 acres of corn for a return of $8,300,
(b) 64 acres of soybeans and 38 acres of corn for a return of $8940 **65.** Two bags of each, cost of $26

Exercises 9.5

Check Your Understanding **1.** T **3.** T **5.** F **7.** c **9.** c

Develop Mastery **1.** $c_{12} = 1, c_{31} = -1$ **3.** $c_{22} = 2\sqrt{3}, c_{33} = 10$ **5.** 25 **7.** 1 **9.** -16 **11.** 0
13. -132 **15.** 45 **17.** (a) $16x$, (b) $\frac{3}{16}$ **19.** (a) $e^x - e^2$, (b) 2 **21.** (a) $-28x$, (b) $-\frac{1}{7}$
23. (a) $0 \cdot x$, (b) Any real number **25.** (a) $8 \sin x + 5$, (b) $\frac{3\pi}{2} + k \cdot 2\pi$ **27.** $x = 4, y = -3$
29. $x = 8.5, y = -1.5$ **31.** $x = 2, y = 1, z = -2$ **33.** $x = 2, y = 5, z = -4$ **35.** $x = 7.075,$
$y = 3.35, z = -0.525$ **37.** $m = \frac{1}{5}, b = \frac{22}{5}$ **39.** (a) $x^2 + y^2 - 4x - 4y = 17$, (b) Center $(2, 2)$,
radius 5 **41.** (a) $x^2 + y^2 - 6x + 4y = 12$, (b) Center $(3, -2)$, radius 5 **43.** (a) $y = -x^2 + 2x + 2$,
(b) $(1 - \sqrt{3}, 0), (1 + \sqrt{3}, 0); V(1, 3)$ **45.** (a) $a = -2, b = 12, c = 230$, (b) 14.1 sec.

Exercises 9.6

Check Your Understanding   **1.** T   **3.** T   **5.** T   **7.** d   **9.** b

Develop Mastery   **1. (a)** 2 by 2, **(b)** $a_{12} = -3, a_{21} = -1$ **3. (a)** 3 by 3, **(b)** $a_{12} = 1, a_{21} = 0$

5. $\begin{bmatrix} 9 \\ 1 \end{bmatrix}$ **7.** $\begin{bmatrix} 5 \\ 0 \\ 4 \end{bmatrix}$ **9.** $\begin{bmatrix} -1 & -4 \\ -4 & -5 \end{bmatrix}$ **11.** $\begin{bmatrix} -7 & 1 & -2 \\ -11 & 2 & -1 \\ -8 & 0 & 10 \end{bmatrix}$ **13.** $\begin{bmatrix} 2 & 3 \\ 3 & 5 \end{bmatrix}$ **15.** $\begin{bmatrix} 1 & 0 \\ -3 & 0.5 \end{bmatrix}$

17. $\begin{bmatrix} -1 & 0 \\ 0 & 0.5 \end{bmatrix}$ **19.** No inverse   **21.** $\begin{bmatrix} -3 & -2 & 6 \\ 0 & 1 & -1 \\ 1 & 0 & -1 \end{bmatrix}$ **23.** $\begin{bmatrix} -3 & -1 & 1 \\ 2 & 1 & 2 \\ 5 & 2 & 0 \end{bmatrix}$ **25.** $\begin{bmatrix} 1 & 0 & 1 \\ -5 & 1 & -5 \\ -2 & 1 & -1 \end{bmatrix}$

27. (a) $A = \begin{bmatrix} 3 & 4 \\ -7 & -9 \end{bmatrix}, X = \begin{bmatrix} x \\ y \end{bmatrix}, c = \begin{bmatrix} 2 \\ 3 \end{bmatrix}$,   **(b)** $|A| = 1$,   **(c)** $x = -30, y = 23$

29. (a) $A = \begin{bmatrix} -3 & 2 \\ 5 & -3 \end{bmatrix}, X = \begin{bmatrix} x \\ y \end{bmatrix}, c = \begin{bmatrix} 4 \\ -1 \end{bmatrix}$,   **(b)** $|A| = -1$,   **(c)** $x = 10, y = 17$

31. (b) $|A| = -1$,   **(c)** $x = 13, y = 13, z = 17$ **33. (b)** $|A| = 0$,   **(c)** Inconsistent

35. (a) $\begin{bmatrix} 1 & 0 \\ 0 & 1 \end{bmatrix}$, **(b)** $\begin{bmatrix} 2 & 3 \\ 1 & 2 \end{bmatrix}$, **(c)** $\begin{bmatrix} 2 & -3 \\ -1 & 2 \end{bmatrix}$

37. (a) $\begin{bmatrix} 1 & 0 & 0 \\ 0 & 1 & 0 \\ 0 & 0 & 1 \end{bmatrix}$, **(b)** $\begin{bmatrix} -3 & -1 & 1 \\ 2 & 1 & 2 \\ 5 & 2 & 0 \end{bmatrix}$, **(c)** $\begin{bmatrix} -4 & 2 & -3 \\ 10 & -5 & 8 \\ -1 & 1 & -1 \end{bmatrix}$

39. (a) $\begin{bmatrix} 1 & 0 \\ 0 & 1 \end{bmatrix}$, **(b)** $\begin{bmatrix} 4 & 5 \\ -3 & -4 \end{bmatrix}$, **(c)** $\begin{bmatrix} 1 & 0 \\ 0 & 1 \end{bmatrix}$, **(d)** $\begin{bmatrix} 1 & 0 \\ 0 & 1 \end{bmatrix}$

41. (a) I, **(b)** A, **(c)** I, **(d)** I **43. (a)** I, **(b)** A, **(c)** I, **(d)** I **45. (a)** A, **(b)** A, **(c)** A, **(d)** A

47. $A^n = \begin{bmatrix} 0 & 0 \\ 0 & 0 \end{bmatrix}$ for $n = 2, 3, 4, \ldots$ **49.** $A^n = A$ for $n = 1, 2, 3, \ldots$

51. (a) $\begin{bmatrix} -4 & -8 & 0 \\ 2 & 4 & 0 \\ 2 & -4 & 0 \end{bmatrix}$ $A^n = \begin{bmatrix} 0 & 0 & 0 \\ 0 & 0 & 0 \\ 0 & 0 & 0 \end{bmatrix}$ for $n = 3, 4, 5, \ldots$

Chapter 9 Review

Test Your Understanding   **1.** T   **3.** F   **5.** F   **7.** T   **9.** F   **11.** T   **13.** T   **15.** T
17. F   **19.** F   **21.** F   **23.** F   **25.** T   **27.** T   **29.** F   **31.** F   **33.** F

Mastery Review   **1.** $x = 7, y = 8$ **3.** $x = 4, y = -6$ **5.** $x = -2, y = -1, z = 3$
7. Dependent, $x = \frac{-6k - 3}{2}, y = \frac{16k + 5}{4}, z = k$ (any number)   **9.** $x = \frac{15}{37}, y = \frac{15}{16}$
11. A line and a circle intersecting at $(-13, 0)$ and $(5, 12)$ **13.** Graphs intersect at $(2, 2)$ and $(-4, -1)$
15. Two parabolas intersecting at $(0, 4)$ and $(3, 1)$ **17.** All points above line $x + y = 1$ and above line
$2x - y = 5$ (both broken), lines intersect at $(2, -1)$ **19.** All points below line $2x + y = 4$ (broken) and
on or below line $x - 2y = 1$ (solid), intersection point $(\frac{9}{5}, \frac{2}{5})$ not in the graph
21. All points on or inside the traingle with vertices at $(0, -8)$, $(4, -4)$, and $(3, -2)$ **23.** 23   **25.** 30

27. (a) $\begin{bmatrix} 1 & -3 \\ -2 & 7 \end{bmatrix}$, **(b)** $\begin{bmatrix} 1 & -1 \\ -3 & 4 \end{bmatrix}$ **29. (a)** $\begin{bmatrix} 10 & -13 \\ -23 & 30 \end{bmatrix}$, **(b)** $\begin{bmatrix} 10 & -13 \\ -23 & 30 \end{bmatrix}$

31. $B^{-1} = \begin{bmatrix} 1 & -1 \\ -3 & 4 \end{bmatrix}$; $x = -5, y = 18$ **33.** $x = -6, y = -1, z = -10$

35. (a) $(0, 0), (\frac{5}{4}, 0), (\frac{5}{6}, \frac{5}{6})$ **(b)** Maximum $\frac{15}{2}$ when $x = \frac{5}{6}, y = \frac{5}{6}$ **37. (a)** $(0, 2), (1, 1), (3, 5)$,
(b) Minimum 7 when $x = 1, y = 1$ **39.** $\frac{5}{3}$ **41.** For x (number of $5 tickets) and y (number of $3 tickets),
$0 \le x \le 500, 0 \le y \le 1,000$, and $5x + 3y \ge 3,700$ **43.** 14 hrs. and 24 min.   **45.** Minimum cost is
$1,140 when x is 50 and y is 20.

CHAPTER 10

Exercises 10.1

Check Your Understanding   **1.** T   **3.** F   **5.** T   **7.** F   **9.** T

Develop Mastery   **1.** $x + y = 0$ **3.** $x - 3y = -4$ **5.** $(x - 7)^2 + (y - 12)^2 = 80$
7. $(x - 1.5)^2 + (y + 0.5)^2 = 4.5$ **17.** $x^2 + y^2 - 6x - 4y = 0$ **19.** $x^2 + y^2 - 6x - 4y + 4 = 0$
21. Two circles: $(x - 5)^2 + (y - 5)^2 = 25$, $(x - 17)^2 + (y - 17)^2 = 289$ **23.** $(x + 2)^2 + y^2 = 50$
25. $(x - 3)^2 + (y - 6)^2 = 4$ **27.** $x^2 + y^2 - 4x + 2y - 8 = 0$ **29.** $x^2 + y^2 - 4x - 21 = 0$
31. Two lines: $y = -x + 2$ and $y = x - 4$ **33.** Two lines: $y = 1$ and $8x - 15y = 17$
35. Two lines: $y = x - 2$ and $x + 7y = 10$ **37.** (a) $(\frac{2}{\sqrt{13}})x + (\frac{3}{\sqrt{13}})y = \frac{6}{\sqrt{13}}$,   (b) $\frac{6}{\sqrt{13}}$
39. (a) $(\frac{5}{13})x + (\frac{12}{13})y = 2$,   (b) 2   **41.** (b) $56°$ **43.** (b) $162°$ **45.** $\frac{3}{\sqrt{10}}$ **47.** $\sqrt{2}$ **49.** (a) $\frac{2}{\sqrt{5}}$,
(b) 4   **51.** (a) $3\sqrt{2}$,   (b) 12

Exercises 10.2

Check Your Understanding   **1.** F   **3.** F   **5.** T   **7.** b   **9.** a, b

Develop Mastery   **1.** $V(0, 0)$, $F(2, 0)$; $D: x = -2$ **3.** $V(-2, 1)$, $F(-3, 1)$; $D: x = -1$
5. $V(1, 2)$, $F(1, 1.5)$; $D: y = 2.5$ **7.** $V(-1, -3)$, $F(-1, -1.5)$; $D: y = -4.5$ **9.** $y^2 = 8x$. Parabola opens to the
right, vertex at $(0, 0)$.   **11.** $x^2 = -2y$. Parabola opens down, vertex at $(0, 0)$ **13.** $(y + 1)^2 = 4(x - 2)$. Parabola
opens to the right, vertex at $(2, -1)$ **15.** Two parabolas: $(y + 2)^2 = 12.5(x + 1)$, opens to the right, vertex at
$(-1, -2)$; $(x + 1)^2 = 0.8(y + 2)$, opens up, vertex as $(-1, -2)$ **17.** Two parabolas: $(y - 1)^2 = -8(x - 2)$,
opens to the left, vertex at $(2, 1)$; $(x - 2)^2 = -8(y - 1)$, opens down, vertex at $(2, 1)$ **19.** $(y - 1)^2 = 2(x + 1)$.
Parabola opens to the right, vertex at $(-1, 1)$ **21.** $(y - 6)^2 = 8(x - 4)$ **23.** Two parabolas:
$(x - 1)^2 = 4(y - 1)$ and $(x - 1)^2 = -4(y - 3)$ **25.** Two parabolas: $(y + 1)^2 = 4x$ and $(y + 1)^2 = -4(x - 2)$
27. $(x + 0.5)^2 + y^2 = 1$ **29.** $\frac{1}{4}$ in.   **31.** (a) $y = mx + (1 - m)$, (b) $m = 2$

Exercises 10.3

Check Your Understanding   **1.** F   **3.** F   **5.** T   **7.** c   **9.** a

Develop Mastery   **3.** (a) Ellipse; $V_1(-3, 0)$, $V_2(3, 0)$; $F_1(-\sqrt{5}, 0)$, $F_2(\sqrt{5}, 0)$ (b) Major axis 6, minor axis 4
5. (a) Hyperbola; $V_1(-3, 0)$, $V_2(3, 0)$; $F_1(-\sqrt{13}, 0)$, $F_2(\sqrt{13}, 0)$ (b) $y = \pm\frac{2x}{3}$ **7.** (a) Ellipse; $V_1(-\sqrt{5}, 0)$,
$V_2(\sqrt{5}, 0)$; $F_1(-1, 0)$, $F_2(1, 0)$ (b) Major axis $2\sqrt{5}$, minor axis 4.   **9.** (a) Hyperbola; $V_1(-2, 0)$, $V_2(2, 0)$;
$F_1(-3, 0)$, $F_2(3, 0)$,   (b) $y = \pm\sqrt{5}x/2$ **11.** (a) Hyperbola; $V_1(0, -4)$, $V_2(0, 4)$; $F_1(0, -4\sqrt{10})$, $F_2(0, 4\sqrt{10})$
(b) $y = \pm\frac{x}{3}$ **13.** $\frac{x^2}{25} + \frac{y^2}{16} = 1$ **15.** $\frac{x^2}{9} + \frac{y^2}{5} = 1$ **17.** $x^2 + 9y^2 = 25$ **19.** $16x^2 + 11y^2 = 576$
21. $\frac{y^2}{4} - \frac{x^2}{12} = 1$ **23.** $\frac{x^2}{1} - \frac{y^2}{4} = 1$ **25.** $4x^2 - y^2 = 15$ **29.** $(\frac{3}{2}, -1)$ and $(-\frac{9}{14}, \frac{13}{7})$ **31.** $(0.5, 0.5)$,
$(-0.5, 0.5)$, $(0.5, -0.5)$, $(-0.5, -0.5)$ **33.** $y^2 = 0.81(x + 8)$ **37.** 25 ft.

Exercises 10.4

Check Your Understanding   **1.** T   **3.** F   **5.** T   **7.** c   **9.** a, c, e, g

Develop Mastery   **1.** $A[-1, -3]$, $B[-8, -4]$, $C(4, 3)$, $D(1, 6)$ **3.** $X^2 + Y^2 = 5$ **5.** $Y^2 = 8X$
7. Hyperbola with center at $(1, -1)$, vertices $(-1, -1)$ and $(3, -1)$, and asymptotes $y = \frac{3x - 5}{2}$ and $y = \frac{-3x + 1}{2}$
9. Ellipse with center at $(0, 1)$, vertices $(0, -2)$ and $(0, 4)$, and minor axis endpoints $(-2\sqrt{2}, 1)$ and $(2\sqrt{2}, 1)$
11. Ellipse with center at $(-\frac{1}{2}, \frac{3}{2})$, vertices at $(-\frac{9}{2}, \frac{3}{2})$ and $(\frac{7}{2}, \frac{3}{2})$, and minor axis endpoints $(-\frac{1}{2}, \frac{1}{2})$ and $(-\frac{1}{2}, \frac{5}{2})$
13. Parabola with vertex at $(-3, -5)$, opens up   **15.** Ellipse with center at $(1, 0)$, vertices $(1, -3)$ and $(1, 3)$,
minor axis endpoints $(-1, 0)$ and $(3, 0)$ **17.** Circle with center at $(-3, 1)$ and radius 2   **19.** Hyperbola with
center at $(-1, 2)$, vertices $(-3, 2)$ and $(1, 2)$, and asymptotes $y = \frac{x + 5}{2}$ and $y = \frac{-x + 3}{2}$
21. $9(x - 3)^2 + 5y^2 = 45$ **23.** $7(x - 1)^2 + 16(y + 1)^2 = 28$ **25.** $9(x + 3)^2 + 4y^2 = 36$

27. $5(y - 1)^2 - 4(x + 2)^2 = 20$ **29.** $3x^2 - (y - 2)^2 = 12$ **31. (a)** $(x - 3)^2 = y + 5$, **(b)** $X^2 = Y$, **(c)** Parabola with focus at $[0, \frac{1}{4}]$ or $(3, -\frac{19}{4})$ **33. (a)** $\frac{(x - 1)^2}{4} + \frac{(y + 2)^2}{16} = 1$ **(b)** $\frac{X^2}{4} + \frac{Y^2}{16} = 1$ **(c)** Ellipse with foci $[0, 2\sqrt{3}]$ and $[0, -2\sqrt{3}]$ **35. (a)** $(x - 3)^2 + (y + 1)^2 = 4$ **(b)** $X^2 + Y^2 = 4$ **(c)** Circle with center at $[0, 0]$ or $(3, -1)$ **37. (a)** $\frac{(x - 2)^2}{4} - \frac{(y + 3)^2}{4} = 1$ **(b)** $\frac{X^2}{4} - \frac{Y^2}{4} = 1$ **(c)** Hyperbola with foci at $[\pm 2\sqrt{2}, 0]$ or $(2 \pm 2\sqrt{2}, -3)$ **39. (a)** $\cos 2\theta = \frac{3}{5}$, **(b)** $x = \frac{2X - Y}{\sqrt{5}}$, $y = \frac{X + 2Y}{\sqrt{5}}$, **(c)** Graph is a hyperbola. **41. (a)** $\theta = 30°$, **(b)** $x = \frac{\sqrt{3}X - Y}{2}$, $y = \frac{X + \sqrt{3}Y}{2}$, **(c)** $\frac{X^2}{20} + \frac{Y^2}{4} = 1$; Graph an ellipse. **43. (a)** $\cos 2\theta = -\frac{3}{5}$, **(b)** $x = \frac{X - 2Y}{\sqrt{5}}$, $y = \frac{2X + Y}{\sqrt{5}}$, **(c)** $9X^2 - Y^2 = 1$; Graph a hyperbola. **45. (a)** $\cos 2\theta = \frac{4}{5}$ **(b)** $x = \frac{3X - Y}{\sqrt{10}}$, $y = \frac{X + 3Y}{\sqrt{10}}$, **(c)** $\frac{X^2}{9} + \frac{Y^2}{4} = 1$; Graph is an ellipse. **47. (a)** $x = \frac{\sqrt{3}X - Y}{2}$, $y = \frac{X + \sqrt{3}Y}{2}$, **(b)** $[\sqrt{3} + 1, \sqrt{3} - 1]$

Exercises 10.5

Check Your Understanding **1.** T **3.** T **5.** F **7.** g, h **9.** g, h

Develop Mastery **1.** A is $(1, \sqrt{3})$; B is $(-1, -\sqrt{3})$. **3.** A is $[2, -\frac{\pi}{6}]$ or $[2, \frac{11\pi}{6}]$; B is $(\sqrt{2}, -\sqrt{2})$. **5.** P is $[2, \frac{5\pi}{6}]$ or $[-2, -\frac{\pi}{6}]$ or $(-\sqrt{3}, 1)$. Q is $[2, \frac{11\pi}{6}]$ or $[2, -\frac{\pi}{6}]$ or $(\sqrt{3}, -1)$. **7.** A is $(0, \sqrt{3})$ or $[\sqrt{3}, \frac{\pi}{2}]$; B is $(-1, 0)$ or $[1, \pi]$; C is $(1, 0)$ or $[1, 0]$. **9.** $r = 2$ or $r = -2$; Graph is a circle with center at the origin and radius 2. **11.** $r = 3 \sec \theta$; Graph is a vertical line. **13.** $\theta = \tan^{-1} 3$; Graph is a line through the origin. **15.** $r = 2 \cos \theta - 2 \sin \theta$; Graph is a circle with center at $(1, -1)$ and radius $\sqrt{2}$. Pole is given by $[0, \frac{\pi}{4}]$. **17.** $x^2 + y^2 = 4$; Graph is a circle with center at $(0, 0)$ and radius 2. **19.** $x^2 + y^2 + 4x = 0$; Graph is a circle with a hole at the origin. **21.** $x + y = 0$; Graph is a line. **23.** $x^2 + y^2 = 1$; Graph is a circle with center at the origin and radius 1. **25.** $x^2 + y^2 - 2\sqrt{3}x - 2y = 12$; Graph is a circle with center at $(\sqrt{3}, 1)$ and radius 4. **27.** Graph is a three-leafed rose (see the catalog) passing through $[1, 0], [0, \frac{\pi}{6}], [-1, \frac{\pi}{3}], [-1, \frac{2\pi}{3}], [-1, \pi]$. **29.** Graph is a cardioid (see the catalog) passing through $[4, 0], [2, \frac{\pi}{2}], [0, \pi], [2, \frac{3\pi}{2}]$. **31.** $r = \cos 2\theta$; Graph is a four-leafed rose (see the catalog) passing through $[1, 0], [0, \frac{\pi}{4}], [-1, \frac{\pi}{2}], [1, \pi], [-1, \frac{3\pi}{2}]$. **33.** The two graphs are the same. **35.** The first graph is a circle while the second is a cardioid. **37.** The first graph is a cardioid while the second is a limaçon with no loop. **39.** Both graphs are the same spiral. **41.** The graphs are two cardioids intersecting at 3 points: the pole, $[1, \frac{\pi}{2}]$, and $[1, \frac{3\pi}{2}]$. **43.** $\sqrt{3}x - y - 4$; Graph is a line. **45.** Circle with center at $(\frac{a}{2}, \frac{b}{2})$ and radius $\frac{\sqrt{a^2 + b^2}}{2}$

Exercises 10.6

Check Your Understanding **1.** T **3.** F **5.** F **7.** h **9.** c

Develop Mastery **1.** $y = 4 - x^2$; Graph is a parabola that opens down. **3.** $y = \sqrt{4 - x^2}$; Graph is the upper half of a circle with center at $(0, 0)$ and radius 2. **5.** $y = \sqrt{4 - x^2}$ where $x \geq 0$ and $y \geq 0$. Graph is a quarter-circle. **7.** $x + y = 7$; Graph is a line. **9.** $5x + 3y = 11$; Graph is a line. **11.** $(x - 1)^2 + (y - 1)^2 = 1$; Graph is a circle. **13.** $x + y = 0$ where $-1 \leq x \leq 1$; Graph is the line segment with endpoints $(-1, 1)$ and $(1, -1)$. **15.** $x + y = 2$ where $x > 1$; Graph is a half-line from endpoint $(1, 1)$. **17.** $y = x^2 - 1$ where $-1 \leq x \leq 1$; Graph is part of a parabola with endpoints $(-1, 0)$ and $(1, 0)$. **19.** Both graphs are parts of the line $x + y = 0$. **(a)** line segment with endpoints $(-1, 1)$ and $(1, -1)$, **(b)** line segment with endpoints $(0, 0)$ and $(1, -1)$ **21.** Both graphs are parts of the graph of $y = \frac{1}{x}$. **(a)** Graph is the part in the first quadrant. **(b)** Graph is the part in the third quadrant. **23.** Both graphs are parts of the circle $x^2 + y^2 = 1$. **(a)** Graph is the upper half. **(b)** Graph is the right half. **25.** Both graphs are parts of the line $3x + y = 1$. For both (a) and (b) the graph is the line segment with endpoints $(1, -2)$ and $(-1, 4)$. **27.** $(x - 1)^2 + (y - 2)^2 = 1$; graph is a circle. **29.** $x + y = 3$ where $0 \leq x \leq 2$; graph is a line segment. **31.** $\frac{x^2}{16} - \frac{y^2}{25} = 1$; Graph is a hyperbola. **33.** $\frac{(x - 1)^2}{16} - \frac{y^2}{25} = 1$; Graph is a hyperbola. **35.** $x = t - 2, y = 3t + 4$, or $x = t, y = 3t + 10$ **37.** $x = 4t - 3, y = 3t + 4$, or $x = 4t + 1$, $y = 3t + 7$ **41.** $x = 3 \cos \alpha, y = \sin \alpha$ where $0 \leq \alpha \leq \frac{\pi}{2}$; Graph is part of the ellipse $\frac{x^2}{9} + \frac{y^2}{1} = 1$.

43. $x = (4 - a) \cos \alpha$, $y = a \sin \alpha$; Graph is an ellipse, except when $a = 2$—then the graph is a circle.

45. $x = 2t - \frac{t^2}{10}$, $y = \frac{t\sqrt{100 - t^2}}{10}$ for $0 \le t \le 10$; $x = 20 - t$, $y = 0$ for $10 \le t \le 20$.   **47.** $x = a \cos \theta$, $y = b \sin \theta$; path is an ellipse.

Chapter 10 Review

Test Your Understanding   **1.** T   **3.** F   **5.** F   **7.** T   **9.** F   **11.** F   **13.** T   **15.** T   **17.** F   **19.** T   **21.** T   **23.** T   **25.** T   **27.** F   **29.** F

Mastery Review   **1.** Ellipse; $V(0, \pm 5)$, $F(0, \pm 4)$ **3.** Hyperbola; $V(\pm 3, 0)$, $F(\pm\sqrt{34}, 0)$ **5.** Ellipse; $V_1(1, 3)$, $V_2(1, -7)$, $F_1(1, 2)$, $F_2(1, -6)$ **7.** $(x + 2)^2 + (y - 1)^2 = 9$ **9.** $y^2 = 12x$ **11.** $\frac{(x + 1)^2}{12} + \frac{(y - 4)^2}{16} = 1$ **13.** $\frac{(x - 1)^2}{4} - \frac{(y + 1)^2}{5} = 1$ **15.** $(y - 1)^2 = 2(x - 2.5)$ **17.** $(x - 3)^2 = \frac{4(y + 1)}{3}$ **19.** Parabola, opens down, $V(1, 3)$, $F(1, 2.5)$ **21.** Circle, center $(0, 1)$, radius $\sqrt{3}$ **23.** Parabola, opens up, $V(1, -1)$, $F(1, -\frac{3}{4})$ **27.** Graph is a limaçon with no inside loop.   **29.** Graph is a cardioid.   **31.** Points of intersection, pole and $[\sqrt{2}, \frac{\pi}{4}]$ **33.** $y = \sqrt{4 - x^2}$, upper half of a circle   **35.** $y = 2x + 5$; $x = -1$; Graph is a half-line with endpoint $(-1, 3)$.   **37.** Graph is the upper half of the parabola $y^2 = x$ without $(0, 0)$.

Sec. 6.1   Basic identities

$$\tan t = \frac{\sin t}{\cos t} \qquad \cot t = \frac{\cos t}{\sin t}$$

$$\sin(-t) = -\sin t \qquad \cos(-t) = \cos t$$

$$\tan(-t) = -\tan t \qquad \sin^2 t + \cos^2 t = 1$$

$$\tan^2 t + 1 = \sec^2 t \qquad 1 + \cot^2 t = \csc^2 t$$

Sec. 6.2   Sum and difference identities

$$\sin(\alpha \pm \beta) = \sin \alpha \cos \beta \pm \cos \alpha \sin \beta$$
$$\cos(\alpha \pm \beta) = \cos \alpha \cos \beta \mp \sin \alpha \sin \beta$$

$$\tan(\alpha \pm \beta) = \frac{\tan \alpha \pm \tan \beta}{1 \mp \tan \alpha \tan \beta}$$

Double angle identities

$$\sin 2t = 2 \sin t \cos t$$
$$\cos 2t = \cos^2 t - \sin^2 t = 1 - 2 \sin^2 t = 2 \cos^2 t - 1$$
$$\tan 2t = \frac{2 \tan t}{1 - \tan^2 t}$$

Sec. 6.3   Product-sum identities

$$2 \sin \alpha \cos \beta = \sin(\alpha + \beta) + \sin(\alpha - \beta)$$
$$2 \cos \alpha \cos \beta = \cos(\alpha + \beta) + \cos(\alpha - \beta)$$
$$2 \sin \alpha \sin \beta = \cos(\alpha - \beta) - \cos(\alpha + \beta)$$
$$\sin x + \sin y = 2 \sin \frac{x + y}{2} \cos \frac{x - y}{2}$$

$$\sin x - \sin y = 2 \cos \frac{x + y}{2} \sin \frac{x - y}{2}$$

$$\cos x + \cos y = 2 \cos \frac{x + y}{2} \cos \frac{x - y}{2}$$

$$\cos x - \cos y = -2 \sin \frac{x + y}{2} \sin \frac{x - y}{2}$$

Half angle identities

$$\sin \frac{t}{2} = \pm \sqrt{\frac{1 - \cos t}{2}}$$

$$\cos \frac{t}{2} = \pm \sqrt{\frac{1 + \cos t}{2}}$$

$$\tan \frac{t}{2} = \frac{\sin t}{1 + \cos t} = \frac{1 - \cos t}{\sin t}$$

Reduction formulas

$$\sin\left(\frac{\pi}{2} \pm t\right) = \cos t \qquad \sin(\pi \pm t) = \mp \sin t$$
$$\cos(\pi \pm t) = -\cos t$$
$$\cos\left(\frac{\pi}{2} \pm t\right) = \mp \sin t$$

Sec. 7.2   Law of sines

$$\frac{\sin \alpha}{a} = \frac{\sin \beta}{b} = \frac{\sin \gamma}{c}$$

Sec. 7.3   Law of cosines

$$c^2 = a^2 + b^2 - 2ab \cos \gamma$$
$$\cos \gamma = \frac{a^2 + b^2 - c^2}{2ab}$$

Sec. 7.4   Complex numbers

Trigonometric form

$$a + bi = r(\cos \theta + i \sin \theta),$$
$$r = \sqrt{a^2 + b^2}, \ \tan \theta = b/a$$

Powers and roots

$$(a + bi)^n = [r(\cos \theta + i \sin \theta)]^n = r^n(\cos n\theta + i \sin n\theta)$$

The nth roots of $r(\cos \theta + i \sin \theta)$ are given by

$$w_k = r^{1/n}\left[\cos\left(\frac{\theta + k \cdot 360°}{n}\right) + i \sin\left(\frac{\theta + k \cdot 360°}{n}\right)\right],$$

where $k = 0, 1, 2, \ldots, n - 1$.

Sec. 8.2   Arithmetic sequence

First term $a_1 = a$, common difference d, $a_n = a + (n - 1)d$

$$\text{Sum } a_1 + a_2 + \ldots + a_n = n\frac{a_1 + a_n}{2} = n\frac{2a + (n - 1)d}{2}$$

Geometric sequence

First term $a_1 = a$, common ratio r, $a_n = ar^{(n-1)}r$

$$\text{Sum } a_1 + a_2 + \ldots + a_n = \frac{a}{1 - r}(1 - r^n)$$

$$\text{Geometric series } \sum_{n=1}^{\infty} ar^{n-1} = \frac{a}{1 - r}, \text{ if } |r| < 1$$